Kranz/Schmutterer/Koch
Diseases, Pests and Weeds in Tropical Crops

Diseases, Pests and Weeds in Tropical Crops

Edited by
Dr. Jürgen Kranz
Professor, Justus-Liebig-Universität Giessen
Dr. Heinz Schmutterer
Professor, Justus-Liebig-Universität Giessen
Dr. Werner Koch
Professor, Universität Hohenheim

In collaboration with 152 scientists

With 238 figures, 6 tables
and 251 illustrations in colour on 64 plates

JOHN WILEY & SONS
Chichester · New York · Brisbane · Toronto

Copyright © 1977 Verlag Paul Parey, Lindenstrasse 44–47, D-1000 Berlin 61/Spitaler Strasse 12, D-2000 Hamburg 1 (Fed. Rep. Germany).

Published in English by Verlag Paul Parey 1977; first published in Great Britain by John Wiley & Sons Ltd. 1978.

Library of Congress Cataloging in Publication Data:

Main entry under title:

Diseases, pests, and weeds in tropical crops.

    Bibliography: p.
    Includes indexes.
    1. Tropical crops—Diseases and pests.
I. Kranz, Jürgen.   II. Schmutterer, H.   III. Koch, Werner, Schätzungssachverstandiger.

SB608.T8D57 1978   632'.0913   78–6212
ISBN 0 471 99667 X

Blocks and films by Carl Schütte and C. Behling, D-1000 Berlin 42.
Printed in W. Germany by Saladruck Steinkopf & Sohn, D-1000 Berlin 36.

List of contributors

Abo-El-Dahab, M. K., Prof. Dr., Plant Pathology Dept., University of Alexandria, Alexandria (Egypt).

Abul-Nasr, S. E., Prof., Department of Economic Entomology and Insecticides, Cairo University, Giza (Egypt).

Adsuar, J., Dr., Agricultural Exp. Station, Rio Piedras (Puerto Rico).

Agarwal, R. A., Dr., Indian Agricultural Research Institute, New Delhi (India).

Agnihotis, V. P., Dr., Indian Institute of Sugarcane Research, Lucknow (India).

Ampuero, E., Dr., Instituto Nacional de Investigaciones Agropecuaría (INIAP), Quito (Ecuador).

Asare-Nyako, A., Dr., Cocoa Research Institute, Tafo (Ghana).

Assawah, M. W., Prof. Dr., University of Central Delta, Plant Pathology Dept., Alexandria (Egypt).

Baker, Celia, Dr., BASF, Limburgerhof (Fed. Rep. Germany).

Barry, Dean, Dr., Department of Entomology, University of Missouri, Columbia/Missouri (USA).

Bashi, Esther, Dr., Agricultural Research Organization, Bet Dagan (Israel).

Behrendt, S., Dr., BASF, Limburgerhof (Fed. Rep. Germany).

Bess, H. A., Prof. Dr., College of Tropical Agriculture, University of Hawaii, Honolulu (USA).

Bischof, F., Prof. Dr., University of Khartoum, Faculty of Agriculture, Shambat (Democratic Republic of the Sudan).

Bock, K. R., Dr., East African Agricultural & Forestry Research Organization (EAAFRO), Nairobi (Kenya).

Bové, J. M., Dr., INRA, Pont-de-la-Maye (France).

Bradbury, J. F., Dr., Commonwealth Mycological Institute, Kew/Surrey (UK).

Brenière, J., Institut de Recherches Agronomiques Tropicales et des Cultures Vivrières (IRAT), Montpellier (France).

Broodryk, S. W., Dr., Plant Protection Research Institute, Pretoria (South Africa).

Brooks, R. F., Prof., Institute of Food and Agricultural Sciences, University of Florida, Lake Alfred/Florida (USA).

Brun, J., Dr., Institut de Recherches Fruitières et Agrumes (IRFA), Paris (France).

Burckhardt, Fridgard, Dr., Institut für Hackfruchtkrankheiten und Nematodenforschung, Münster/Westf. (Fed. Rep. Germany).

Butani, Dhamo K., Dr., Indian Agricultural Research Institute, New Delhi (India).

Butler, L., Koronivia Research Station, Nausori (Fiji-Islands).

Chagas, C. M., Seccao de Virologia, Instituto Biologico, São Paulo (Brazil).

Chitzanidis, Anna, Dr., Institut Phytopathologique Benaki, Kiphissa/Athens (Greece).

Cornes, M. A., Nigerian Stored Products Research Institute, Lagos (Nigeria).

Coutin, R., Institut National de la Recherche Agronomique (INRA), Versailles (France).

Crowe, T. J., Institute of Agricultural Research, Addis Ababa (Ethiopia).

Dawson, P. S., Dr., Department of Biology, University of South Florida, Tampa/Florida (USA).

Daxl, R., Dr., Food and Agricultural Organization of the United Nations (FAO), Managua (Nicaragua).

Dinther, J. van, Dr., Department of Entomology, Agricultural University, Wageningen (The Netherlands).

Dongo-Denegri, D. S., Prof., Dept. Fitopatologia, Estación Experimental Agrícola, La Molina (Peru).

Dosse, G., Prof. Dr., Institut für Phytomedizin der Universität Hohenheim, Stuttgart-Hohenheim (Fed. Rep. Germany).

Eastop, V. F., Dr., Department of Entomology, British Museum (Natural History), London (UK).

Ekundayo, J. A., Dr., School of Biological Sciences, University of Lagos (Nigeria).

El-Khidir, I., Dr., Faculty of Agriculture, University of Khartoum, Shambat (Sudan).

Entwistle, P. F., Commonwealth Forestry Institute, Unit of Invertebrate Virology, Oxford (UK).

Fassi, B., Dr., Instituto Nazionale Piante da Legno "Giacomo Piccardo", Torino (Italy).

Fewkes, D. W., Dr., Tate & Lyle Ltd., Reading (UK).

Fernando, H. E., Dr., Central Agricultural Research Institute, Gannoruwa, Peradeniya (Sri Lanka).

Frank, Z. R., Dr., Agricultural Research Organization, Bet Dagan (Israel).

Frossard, P., Institut de Recherches Fruitières et Agrumes (IRFA), Section Côte d'Ivoire, Abidjan (Elfenbeinküste).

Gálvez-E., G. E., Dr., Centro Internacional de Agricultura Tropical (CIAT), Cali (Columbia).

Gameel, O. I., Dr., Agricultural Research Corporation, Wad Medani (Sudan).

Gerlach, W., Prof. Dr., Biologische Bundesanstalt, Berlin West (Fed. Rep. Germany).

Gerson, U., The Hebrew University of Jerusalem, Rehovot (Israel).

Gibbons, R. W., Dr., International Crops Research Institute for the Semi-Arid Tropics (ICRISAT), Hyderabad (India).

Gibbs, D. G., Eastwood/Notts. (UK).

Gibson, I.A.S., Dr., Commonwealth Mycological Institute, Kew/Surrey (UK).

Gühne, M., Dr., CELAMERCK, Ingelheim (Fed. Rep. Germany).

Guthrie, E. J., Dr., East African Agricultural & Forestry Research Organization (EAAFRO), Nairobi (Kenya).

Hafez, M., Prof. Dr., Department of Entomology, Cairo University, Giza (Egypt).

Haines, C. P., Dr., Tropical Products Institute, Tropical Stored Products Centre, Slough/Berks. (UK).

Hansen del Orbe, R., Ing. Agrón., Centro Nacional de Investigaciones, Extensión y Capacitación Agropecuarias, San Cristóbal (República Dominicana).

Haramoto, F. H., Prof. Dr., College of Tropical Agriculture, University of Hawaii, Honolulu (USA).

Harris, D. C., Dr., East Malling Research Station, Maidstone (UK).

Heinze, K., Prof. Dr., Biologische Bundesanstalt, Berlin West (Fed. Rep. Germany).

Holliday, P., Dr., Commonwealth Mycological Institute, Kew/Surrey (UK).

Hornby, D., Dr., Rothamsted Experimental Station (Lawes Agricultural Trust), Harpenden/Herts. (UK).

Huger, A. M., Dr., Institut für Biologische Schädlingsbekämpfung, Darmstadt (Fed. Rep. Germany).

Iperti, G., Station de Zoologie et de Lutte Biologique, Antibes (France).

Jago, N. D., Dr., Centre for Overseas Pest Research, London (UK).

Joshi, L. M., Dr., Indian Agricultural Research Institute, New Delhi (India).

Joyce, R. J. V., Agricultural Aviation Research Unit, Cranfield/Bedford (UK).

Jürgens, G., Dr., Centro Nacional de Investigaciones, Extensión y Capacitación Agropecuarias, San Cristóbal (República Dominicana).

Kenneth, Robert, Prof., The Levi Eshkol School of Agriculture, Faculty of Agriculture, Rehovot Campus (Israel).

King, C. E., Prof., Department of Biology, University of South Florida, Tampa/Florida (USA).

King, S. B., Dr., USDA-ARS, Mississippi State/Mississippi (USA).

Kogan, M., Prof. Dr., Illinois Natural History Survey, Urbana/Illinois (USA).

Kouyeas, Hebe, Dr., Institut Phytopathologique Benaki, Kiphissa/Athens (Greece).

Kranz, J., Prof. Dr., Abteilung für Phytopathologie und Angewandte Entomologie, Tropeninstitut, Justus-Liebig-Universität Giessen, 6300 Lahn-Giessen (Fed. Rep. Germany).

Krüger, W., Dr., Institut für Getreide-, Ölfrucht- und Futterpflanzenkrankheiten der Biologischen Bundesanstalt, Kiel-Kitzeberg (Fed. Rep. Germany).

Kurian, Ch., Dr., Central Plantation Crops Research Institute, Krishnapuram, Kerala (India).

Lal, O. P., Dr., Indian Agricultural Research Institute, Katrain/Kulu Valley (India).

Lall, B. S., Dr., Department of Zoology, University of Bihar, Muztaffarpur (India).

Laville, E., Institut de Recherches Fruitières et Agrumes (IRFA), Montpellier (France).

Legg, J. T., Dr., Cocoa Research Institute, Tafo (Ghana).

Le Pelley, R. H., Le Mont Ardaine, St. Peter's/Guernsey (UK).

Leuschner, K., Dr., International Institute of Tropical Agriculture (IITA), Ibadan (Nigeria).
Lewis, T., Dr., Rothamsted Experimental Station, Harpenden/Herts. (UK).
Linden, G., Dr., CELAMERCK, Biologische Station, Schwabenheim (Fed. Rep. Germany).
Litsinger, J. A., Dr., The International Rice Research Institute (IRRI), Los Baños (Philippines).
Manwan, Ibrahim, Dr., Maros Research Institute for Agriculture, South Sulawesi (Indonesia).
McFarlane, I. A., Tropical Stored Products Centre, Slough (UK).
Mehta, R. C., Dr., Ramjas College, Delhi (India).
Metcalfe, J. R., Dr., Commonwealth Institute of Entomology, London (UK).
Meyer, J., Prof. Dr., Laboratoire de Phytopathologie, Univ. Cattolique de Louvain, Louvain-La-Neuve (Belgium).
Morrill, W., Prof., University of Georgia, Department of Entomology, Experiment, Georgia (USA).
Mukherji, S. K., Dr., State Agricultural Research Institute, Calcutta (India).

Nasu, Sâchô, National Institute of Agriculture Sciences, Nishigahora-Tokyo (Japan).
Nomura, Ken'ichi, Faculty of Horticulture, Chiba University, Matsudo (Japan).
Norse, D., Dr., Dept. of the Environment, Univ. London, London (UK).
Odiyo, P. O., Armyworm Division, East African Community, Nairobi (Kenya).
Ou, S. H., Dr., Plant Pathologist, The International Rice Research Institute (IRRI), Los Baños/Laguna (Philippines).
Padmanabhan, S. Y., Dr., Central Rice Research Institute, Cuttack (India).
Palti, J., Dr., Agricultural Research Organization, Bet Dagan (Israel).
Patel, R. C., Dr., Institute of Agriculture, Guajarat Agricultural University, Anand Campus (India).
Peries, O. S., Dr., Rubber Research Institute, Agalawatta (Sri Lanka).
Petzoldt, K., Prof. Dr., Direction de la Recherche Agronomique, Rabat (Morocco).
Piltz, H., Dr., Amtliche Pflanzenbeschau, Institut für Angewandte Botanik, Universität Hamburg, Hamburg (Fed. Rep. Germany).
Pitre, H. N., Prof., College of Agriculture, Mississippi State University, Mississippi (USA).
Prakasa Rao, P. S., Dr., Central Rice Research Institute, Cuttack (India).
Prasad, S. K., Indian Council of Agricultural Research, New Delhi (India).
Quezada, J. R., Dr., Centro Nacional de Tecnología Agropecuaria, Santa Tecla (El Salvador).

Raychaudhuri, S. P., Dr., Indian Agricultural Research Institute, New Delhi (India).
Raddatz, E., Dr., CELAMERCK, Granja Experimental Tropical, Palmira (Colombia).
Reed, W., Dr., Indian Agricultural Research Institute, Coimbatore (India).
Reyes, C. E., Dr., CELAMERCK, Granja Experimental Tropical, Palmira (Colombia).
Rolli, K., Dr., Casablanca (Morocco).
Rose, D. J. W., Dr., Centre for Overseas Pest Research, London (UK).
Rosen, David, Prof. Dr., Faculty of Agriculture, The Hebrew University of Jerusalem, Rehovot (Israel).
Rotem, J., Prof. Dr., Agricultural Research Organization, Bet Dagan (Israel).
Saad, Adid T., Prof., American University of Beirut, Beirut (Lebanon).
Saari, E. E., Dr., The Ford Foundation, Cairo (Egypt).
Saba, F., Dr., Direction de la Recherche Agronomique, Rabat (Morocco).
Sabet, K. A., Dr., FAO Near East Regional Office, Dokki (Egypt).
Salama, H. S., Dr., National Research Centre, Dokki/Cairo (Egypt).
Scheinpflug, H., Dr., BAYER, Sparte Pflanzenschutz, Biol. Forschung, Leverkusen (Fed. Rep. Germany).
Schieber, Eugenio, Dr., Antigua (Guatemala).
Schmutterer, H., Prof. Dr., Institut für Phytopathologie, Justus-Liebig-Universität Giessen, 6300 Lahn-Giessen (Fed. Rep. Germany).
Siddig, S. A., Dr., Horticultural Research Unit, Shambat (Sudan).
Silva, R. L. de, Dr., Tea Research Institute of Ceylon, Talawakelle (Sri Lanka).
Sinclair, J. B., Prof. Dr., Dept. of Plant Pathology, University of Illinois, Urbana (USA).
Singh, Kishan, Dr., Indian Institute of Sugarcane Research, Lucknow (India).
Singh, S. R., Dr., International Institute of Tropical Agriculture (IITA), Ibadan (Nigeria).
Smith, D. H., Dr., Plant Disease Experiment Station, Yoakum/Texas (USA).
Smith, R. I., Plant Protection Ltd., Technical Services & Development, Fernhurst, Haslemere/Surrey (UK).

Sogawa, Kazushige, Tropical Agriculture Centre Kitana-Kazuma, Yatabe, Tsukuba, Maraki (Japan).

Srivastava, A. S., Prof. Dr., University of Agriculture & Technology, Faizabad (India).

Steindl, D. R. L., Dr., Bureau of Sugar Experiment Station, Brisbane/Queensland (Australia).

Sternlicht, M., Prof. Dr., Agricultural Research Organization, Bet Dagan (Israel).

Sturhan, D., Dr., Institut für Hackfruchtkrankheiten und Nematodenforschung, Münster/Westf. (Fed. Rep. Germany).

Talhouk, A. M., Prof. Dr., Faculty of Agricultural Sciences, American University of Beirut, Beirut (Lebanon).

Tunstall, J. P., Makoka Research Station, Thondwe (Malawi).

Turner, P. D., Dr., Harrisons Fleming Advisory Service Limited, London (UK).

Ullstrup, A. J., Dr., Dept. Botany and Plant Pathology, Purdue University, Lafayette/Indiana (USA).

Usua, E. J., Dr., Department of Biological Sciences, University of Lagos, Lagos (Nigeria).

Vicente-L. B. Oliveira, Marly, Dr., Seccao de Virologia, Instituto Biologico, São Paulo (Brazil).

Vogel, R., Station de Recherches Agrumicoles, San Nicolao (France).

Wakimoto, S., Dr., Dept. Plant Pathology, Kyushu University, Faculty of Agriculture, Fukuoka (Japan).

Waller, J. M., Dr., Commonwealth Mycology Institute, Kew/Surrey (UK).

Ward, P., Dr., Centre for Overseas Pest Research, London (UK).

Watson, T. F., Prof., College of Agriculture, University of Arizona, Tucson/Arizona (USA).

Webley, I. J., Tropical Products Institute, Tropical Stored Products Centre, Slough/Berks. (UK).

Weischer, B., Dr., Institut für Hackfruchtkrankheiten und Nematodenforschung, Münster/Westf. (Fed. Rep. Germany).

Weststeijn, G., Dr., Stichting Laboratorium voor Bloembollenonderzoek, Lisse (Netherland).

Wilhelm, S., Prof. Dr., Dept. Plant Pathology, Univ. of California, Berkeley/California (USA).

Williams, J. R., Dr., Mauritius Sugar Industry Research Institute, Reduit (Mauritius).

Yunus, A., Ministry of Agriculture and Fisheries, Kuala Lumpur (Malaysia).

Zaher, M. A., Prof. Dr., Faculty of Agriculture, University of Cairo, Giza (Egypt).

Zentmyer, G. A., Prof. Dr., Dept. Plant Pathology, Univ. of California, Riverside/California (USA).

Introduction

Many books have been written on tropical diseases, pests and weeds. They usually deal with particular aspects such as diseases or pests of a single crop or one group of harmful organisms. Only a few attempt to deal comprehensively with diseases or pests and none covers diseases, pests and weeds in one volume. Most of these books are by a single author who inevitably cannot be an authority on all the diseases, pests or weeds he covers. This work has been written by 152 authors from many countries, all of whom can claim personal experience in their subjects, gained largely in the field.

This book aims to supply background information to those working in crop protection, to extension workers, agronomists and horticulturists in the tropics and subtropics or more generally in warmer climates. It may also well serve as a textbook for students. Although not primarily written for experts we hope that specialized plant pathologists, entomologists and those concerned with the control of weeds may benefit from this book which collates information on the more important diseases, pests and weeds in crops predominantly grown in warmer areas. It is not intended as a textbook on mycology, entomology or weed science. The emphasis is on symptoms, biology, ecology and control of agencies harmful to crops. Special attention has been given to illustrations.

To keep the volume concise the material had to be chosen carefully. Any selection is obviously open to criticism depending on the personal experience of the reader in his particular region. However, we attempted to choose representative examples of the more important diseases, pests and weeds. Each is treated concisely and in a standardized, sometimes slightly modified fashion and brief reference is made to related organisms. Our objective was not to give complete coverage but rather to acquaint the reader with the basic problems of crop protection by means of as many case studies as possible.

Host plants were the first to be selected, with preference given to important field crops grown either exclusively or predominantly in the warmer parts of the world and often not considered in textbooks published in Europe and the United States. The crops omitted include ornamentals, a number of vegetables, and plants yielding drugs and dyes. We have, however, included various crops, such as wheat, barley, and potato, which are most commonly grown in temperate regions, but which also have an increasing importance at the higher altitudes of tropical countries.

The task of selecting harmful organisms and viruses was equally critical. Most of the polyphagous and widely distributed pathogens and pests and weeds were obviously included. With those harmful organisms which possess a more limited range of host and distribution selection sometimes depended on finding authors.

We trust that this procedure does not deprive the reader of essential information about the great diversity of diseases, pests and weeds. The order of presentation within the parts devoted to diseases, pests and weeds is respectively by classes of pathogens and orders or families of pests and weeds. A treatment based on crops would have involved too many tedious repetitions and it would have been too voluminous for a single book. A comprehensive host index guides the reader to the organism affecting a given crop. When writing on a pathogen or pest with a wide host range, authors were asked to dwell on the problems caused to specific crops (see subheadings "Disease" or "Symptoms" in each chapter). In some cases where there are many similarities, we found it appropriate to treat several species or a whole group jointly in one chapter.

Weeds are considered only in botanical families. Diseases are grouped under virus, mycoplasma, bacteria and fungi. The systematics of bacteria and fungi are followed to the level of subdivisions under which pathogens appear alphabetically. Pests are also arranged under orders and families. For nomenclature the usages of the CMI and CIE are adopted. Common names are either those chosen by contributors or those given in the "Lexicon of plant pests and diseases" by Merino-Rodriguez (1966).

CMI and CIE distribution maps, when available, have been quoted, in order to supplement the often abbreviated information on distribution. Symptoms are described in detail for the disease or pest on the main crop but reference is also made to symptoms on other crops where appropriate. Information on control usually reflects the experience of the authors and is obviously subject to change. Therefore, more complete details and recommendations should be obtained from local extension services, research stations, universities or specialists elsewhere. As the contributing authors are considered authorities on their subjects, it has not been thought necessary to support their texts by extensive literature references. The literature cited generally has been limited to that easily obtainable by readers interested in more detail. Some literature of a more general nature is listed after introductory notes on larger taxa of pathogens.

Comprehensive books or monographs relevant to plant protection in the subtropics and tropics are listed at the end of this volume to provide both broader and more detailed sources of information.

It is hoped that this book will be useful to agriculturalists and students throughout the tropics and subtropics and help them to increase food production for a growing world population.

The editors acknowledge the advice of numerous colleagues and in particular the help of Dr. Arroyo, Spain; Mr. D. J. Butt and Dr. D. J. Royle, UK; Dr. G. Jürgens, Dominican Republic and Mr. E. Laville, France. Thanks are also expressed to Lic. phil. (Mrs.) Christa Wiesner for her services as assistant editor as well as to Mr. Rüdiger Kaske and Mr. Arno Wiegand (GTZ) for their initiative and support. Miss Harriet Harth and Miss Inge Kleinschmit prepared the indices. Paul Parey Publishers, Berlin–Hamburg, kindly agreed to publish this book and Mrs. Christel Hoff rendered invaluable help in its production.

The work emanates from a recommendation made by the field staff of the German Agency for Technical Cooperation, Ltd (GTZ). The Federal Ministry for Economic Cooperation in Bonn sponsored the project and provided the funds.

Giessen and Stuttgart-Hohenheim
March 1977

J. Kranz, H. Schmutterer, W. Koch

Contents

Sources of coloured illustrations

(253 illustrations on 64 plates)

Plates 1–16 (Part "Diseases", between pages 112 and 113)

C. J. Baker:	7 a
J. M. Bové:	1 c, 2 a, 2 b
A. Chitzanidis:	5 c, 14 a, 14 c
B. Fassi:	8 b, 8 c
K. Heinze:	2 c, 2 d, 3 a, 3 b
J. Kranz:	3 c, 4 a, 5 a, 7 d, 8 a, 8 d, 9 a, 9 b, 9 c, 10 a, 10 b, 11 d, 13 a, 13 b, 13 c, 13 d, 16 a, 16 b, 16 c, 16 d
E. Laville:	14 b, 14 d
H. Schmutterer:	10 c, 14 a, 14 b, 14 c, 14 d
D. H. Smith:	7 c
D. R. L. Steindl:	6 a
A. J. Ullstrup:	6 b, 6 c, 6 d
R. Vogel:	1 a, 1 b, 1 d
S. Wakimoto:	4 b, 4 c, 4 d, 5 a, 5 b
G. Weststeijn:	15 a, 15 b, 25 c, 15 d

Plates 17–48 (Part "Pests", between pages 320 and 321 as well as pages 448 and 449)

J. Brenière:	42 c
D. K. Butani:	35 a
R. Daxl:	37 c
G. Dean:	17 a
V. Dittrich:	18 a, 18 c, 19 a
G. Dosse:	18 b
F. H. Haramoto:	47 a
A. Huger:	31 a, 31 b
W. L. Morrill:	44 d
I. R. Quezada:	25 b
K. Rolli:	34 c
H. Schmutterer:	17 b, 18 d, 19 b, 19 c, 19 d, 20 a, 20 b, 20 c, 20 d, 21 a, 21 b, 21 c, 21 d, 22 a, 22 b, 22 c, 22 d, 23 a, 23 b, 23 c, 23 d, 24 a, 24 b, 24 c, 24 d, 25 a, 25 c, 25 d, 26 a, 26 b, 26 c, 26 d, 27 a, 27 b, 27 c, 27 d, 28 a, 28 b, 28 c, 28 d, 29 a, 29 b, 29 c, 29 d, 30 a, 30 b, 30 c, 30 d, 31 c, 31 d, 32 a, 32 b, 32 c, 32 d, 33 a, 33 b, 33 c, 33 d, 34 a, 34 d,

	35 b, 35 c, 35 d, 36 a, 36 b, 36 c, 36 d, 37 a, 37 b, 37 d,
	38 b, 38 c, 38 d, 39 a, 39 b, 39 c, 39 d, 40 a, 40 c, 40 d,
	41 a, 41 b, 41 c, 41 d, 42 a, 42 b, 42 d, 43 a, 43 b, 43 c,
	43 d, 44 a, 44 b, 44 c, 45 a, 45 b, 45 c, 45 d, 46 a, 46 b,
	46 c, 46 d, 47 b, 47 c, 47 d, 48 a, 48 b, 48 c, 48 d
A. S. Talhouk:	34 b
J. P. Tunstall:	38 a, 40 b
B. Weischer:	17 c, 17 d

Plates 49–64 (Part "Weeds", between pages 576 and 577)

BASF, Landwirtschaftliche Versuchsstation, Limburgerhof (Fed. Rep. Germany):	58 b, 58 c, 59 c
G. Jürgens:	49 b, 49 c, 50 a, 50 b, 50 c, 50 d, 51 a, 51 b, 51 c, 52 a, 52 b, 52 c, 52 d, 53 b, 53 c, 53 d, 54 a, 54 c, 56 a, 56 b, 56 c, 58 a, 58 d, 59 a, 59 b, 60 a, 60 b, 60 c, 60 d, 61 a, 61 b, 62 c, 62 d, 63 d, 64 a, 64 b, 64 c
W. Koch:	49 a, 49 d, 51 d, 53 a, 54 b, 54 d, 55 a, 55 b, 55 c, 55 d, 56 d, 57 a, 57 d, 59 d, 61 c, 61 d, 62 a, 62 b, 63 a, 63 b, 63 c, 64 d
K. Petzoldt:	57 b, 57 c

Source of figures
(299 text figures, as nos 1–238)

Figures 1–88 (Part "Diseases")

BASF, Ludwigshafen (Fed. Rep. Germany):	69
R. A. Christ:	45
J. Kranz:	17, 18, 19, 21, 25, 29, 34, 48, 49 a, 49 b, 49 c, 52 a, 53, 55, 63, 68, 75
H. Schmutterer:	9

All other figures were provided by the respective authors.

Figures 89–206 (Part "Pests")

Source of these figures is quoted with each figure.

Figures 207–238 (Part "Weeds")

All figures have been drawn by R. Hansen del Orbe and D. Hernandez, San Cristóbal, Dominican Republic.

Diseases in Tropical Crops

Edited by Jürgen Kranz

In collaboration with: M. K. Abo-El-Dahab, J. Adsuar, V. P. Agnihotri, E. Ampuero, A. Asare-Nyako, M. W. Assawah, Celia Baker, Esther Bashi, K. R. Bock, J. M. Bové, J. F. Bradbury, J. Brun, L. Butler, C. M. Chagas, Anna Chitzanidis-Manuelides, D. S. Dongo-D., J. A. Ekundayo, B. Fassi, Z. R. Frank, P. Frossard, G. E. Gálvez-E., W. Gerlach, W. Gibbons, I. A. S. Gibson, E. J. Guthrie, D. C. Harris, K. Heinze, P. Hollyday, D. Hornby, L. M. Joshi, R. Kenneth, S. B. King, Hebe Kouyeas, J. Kranz, W. Krüger, E. Laville, J. T. Legg, J. Meyer, D. Norse, S. H. Ou, S. Y. Padmanabhan, J. Palti, O. S. Peries, S. P. Raychaudhuri, J. Rotem, Adib T. Saad, E. E. Saari, K. A. Sabet, H. Scheinpflug, E. Schieber, R. L. de Silva, J. B. Sinclair, Kishan Singh, D. H. Smith, D. R. L. Steindl, P. D. Turner, A. J. Ullstrup, Marly Vicente-L. B. Oliveira, R. Vogel, S. Wakimoto, J. M. Waller, G. Weststeijn, S. Wilhelm, G. A. Zentmyer

Diseases caused by viruses and viroids

Viruses are pathogenic agents of high molecular weight, composed of proteins and either DNA or RNA, which multiply in living cells of their hosts when introduced. Two main types of virus particles can be shown by means of electronic microscopes vz rod shaped (150–750 nm x 10–30 nm) or sphaerical (25–75 nm) ones.

Nomenclature of virus names is still unregulated. Some authors prefer numbering of viruses whereas others have suggested latin binomials. But most commonly used nowadays are disease name derivatives, often with abreviations in upper cases letters (e. g. Cocoa swollen shoot virus, CSSV). In recent years so-called cryptograms have been proposed by Gibbs et al. as codes of essential features to assess similarities between viruses (s. below). There is also no accepted basis for a virus classification yet. Many viruses form "strains", which may have antigens in common ("Serotypes"). Strains may also be designated on account of different symptoms they cause, or because of differences in pathogenicity.

Cross protection of hosts plants after preinfection with certain strains may indicate a close relationship between this strain and the virus used for preinfection.

Transmission of viruses can take place through plant sap by contact and tools (mechanical transmission), insect vectors, dodder (*Cuscuta spp*) and in a few cases also through seed. Most viruses can be transmitted by grafting. Sucking insects such as aphids, leaf and plant hoppers. Thrips and the white fly dominate amongst the insect vectors. But also mites, biting insects (beetles, grasshoppers), nematodes and fungi may transmit viruses, the latter two in the case of so-called soilborne virus diseases. One vector may transmit one ore many viruses, one virus may have one or more vectors. For non-persistent viruses an insect remains only infective for some short period after feeding on an infected plant. For persistent viruses a vector remains infective over a long period (even for its lifetime) after acquisition of the virus. The infective period depends on various factors, including the stage during which the virus had been acquired. Some leafhoppers even may transmit viruses through their eggs. In the case of persistent viruses there is often a distinct incubation time, during which the virus passes through the animal. Also for the acquisition of the virus during the feeding a more or less distinct period may be required.

The symptoms of diseases caused by virus can be summarized as: necrotic local lesions, slight or severe depressions of growth rate and/or yield, mosaics, mottling, vein clearing, distortion, yellowing and discolorations (including necrosis ring spots and other distinct patterns), flower and fruit variegations, or distortions. Also node length (longer, shorter) can be affected and witches broom may occur. But infected plants may also show no obvious symptoms at all and still carry the multiplying virus.

Identification of virus diseases can be based on these symptoms. However, similar symptoms may be caused by different viruses, or even deficiencies or genetical disorders. Symptoms, therefore, can only be used for diagnoses when the identity of the agent has been ascertained earlier in the region. These include: Grafting, sap inoculation on indicator plants (also useful for the separation of viruses), determination of longevity in juice extracts, dilution end-points, thermal inactivation point (all with subsequent inoculation of indicator or host plants). Serological identification by means of antisera is possible. A standard method for virus identification is electron microscopy.

Control of virus diseases can best be achieved by exclusion of infection and planting virus-free material. A number of approaches will be dealt with. Resistant varieties and, where feasible, insecticides against vectors, cultural methods, and sanitation will help to reduce the spread of viruses in the field.

Viroids

Viroids have been discovered only recently and independently by Diener, Sänger, Semancik, Wheather and Singh. So far only few diseases are known to be caused by this new agent, including Exocortis (p. 14) and Cadang-cadang. Most of them have been known for long as virus diseases. Some other virus-like disease may be due to the same cause. Viroids are single-stranded covalently closed circular RNA molecules existing as highly base-paired rod-like structures with a molecular weight between 107 000 to 127 000 dalton (Sänger et al., 1976). The chain length is of about 250–275 nucleotides, which is about 1/10, 1/20 the size of the nucleic acid of conventional viruses. The viroids themselves are located inside the nucleus. Transmission may take place by pollen, seed, mechanical means, and possibly by insects.

Literatur on Viruses
BENNETT, C. W. (1967): Epidemiology of leafhopper-transmitted viruses. Ann. Rev. Phytopathology **5**, 87–108.
BOS, L. (1963): Symptoms of virus diseases in plants. Pudoc, Wageningen.
DUFFUS, J. E. (1971): Role of weeds in the incidence of virus diseases. Ann. Rev. Phytopathology **9**, 319–340.
FULTON, R. W. (1966): Mechanical transmission of viruses of woody plants. Ann. Rev. Phytopathology **4**, 79–102.
HEINZE, K. (1959): Phytopathogene Viren und ihre Überträger. Duncker & Humblot, Berlin.
HOLLINGS, M. (1965): Disease control through virus-free stock. Ann. Rev. Phytopathology **3**, 367–396.
KENNEDY, J. S., M. F. DAY & V. T. EASTROP (1962): A conspectus of aphids as vectors of plant viruses. Commonwealth Institute of Entomology, London.
KLINKOWSKI, M. (ed.) (1958): Pflanzliche Virologie. Vols 1 & 2. Akademie-Verlag, Berlin.
MARAMAROSCH, K., & H. KOPROWSKI (eds.) (1967–1971): Methods in virology. 5 vols Academic Press, New York and London.
MARTYN, E. B. (ed.) (1968): Plant virus names. Phytopathological papers, No. 9, Commonwealth Mycological Institute, Kew, UK; with Suppl. 1, issued June 1971.
NYLAND, G., & A. C. GOHEEN (1969): Heat therapy of virus diseases of perennial plants. Ann. Rev. Phytopathology **7**, 331–354.
POSNETTE, A. F. (1969): Tolerance of virus infection in plants. Rev. appl. Mycol. **48**, 113–119.
SÄNGER, H. L., G. KLOTZ, D. RIESNER, H. J. GROSS, A. K. KLEINSCHMIDT (1976): Viroids are single-stranded covalently closed circular RNA molecules existing as highly base-paired rod-like structures, Proc. Natl. Acad. Sci USA **73**, (11) in press.
SMITH, K. M. (1973): A textbook of plant virus diseases. 3rd ed. Academic Press, New York & London.
SMITH, K. M. (1974): Plant viruses. 5th ed. Chapman & Hall, London, 211 pp.
SOMMEREYNS, Ghislaine (1967): Les virus des végéteaux. 2nd ed. Maison Rustique, Paris.
SWENSON, K. G. (1968): Role of aphids in the ecology of plant viruses. Ann. Rev. Phytopathology **6**, 351–374.
Further literature is cited with the following diseases.

Cryptograms[1]

The cryptograms given are in a form similar to that suggested by Gibbs, Harrison, Watson, & Wildy (1966, in Nature **45**, 1714). Each consists of four pairs of symbols (for example, R/1: 2/5: E/E: S/* for tobacco mosaic virus) with the following meanings:
1st pair. Type of nucleic acid/strandedness of nucleid acid
   Symbols for type of nucleic acid
   R = RNA
   D = DNA
   Symbols for strandedness
   1 = single-stranded
   2 = double-stranded
2nd pair. Molecular weight of nucleic acid (in millions)/percentage of nucleic acid in infective particles
3rd pair. outline of particle/outline of "nucleocapsid" (the nucleic acide plus the protein most closely in contact with it)

[1] A. J. Gibbs in Martyn (ed.) ibid.

Symbols for both properties

S = essentially spherical
E = elongated with parallel sides, ends not rounded
U = elongated with parallel sides, end(s) rounded
X = complex or none of above
4th pair. Kinds of host infected/Kinds of vector
Symbols for kinds of host
A = Actinomycete
B = Bacterium
F = Fungus
I = Invertebrate
S = Seed plant
V = Vertebrate
Symbols for kind of vector
Ac = Mite and tick (Acarina, Arachnida)
Al = White fly (Aleyrodidae, Hemiptera)
Ap = Aphid (Aphididae, Hemiptera)
Au = Leaf-, plant-, or tree-hopper (Auchenorrhyncha, Hemiptera)
Cc = Mealy-bug (Coccidae, Hemiptera)
Cl = Beetle (Coleoptera)
Di = Fly and mosquito (Diptera)
Fu = Fungus (Chytridiales and Plasmodiophorales)
Gy = Mirid, Piesmid, or Tingid bug (Gymnocerata, Hemiptera)
Ne = Nematode (Nematoda)
Ps = Psyllid (Psyllidae, Hemiptera)
Si = Flea (Siphonaptera)
Th = Thrips (Thysanoptera)
Ve = Vectors known but none of above
Symbols for all pairs
* Property of the virus is not known
( ) Enclosed information is doubtful or unconfirmed.

Banana bunchy top virus (Figs. 1–3)

/:*/*:*/*:S/Ap.

Synonyms: "curly top", "cabbage top" and "strangles";

Disease: Bunchy top virus disease of banana; Büschelkrankheit; bunchy top du bananier; cogollo racimoso del bananero.

Geographical distribution: The disease has been recorded in Australia, Pacific Islands (Fiji, Tonga, Samoa, Wallis and Ellice), New Guinea, Malaysia, Taiwan, Hong Kong, the Philippines, North Borneo, Bangladesch, Sri Lanka, India, Egypt, Zaire (CMI map no 19) and most recently in Vietnam and the Mariana Islands. Bunchy top does not apparently occur in the Americas; but see similarities with other diseases.

Host plants: Only the banana aphid, *Pentalonia nigronervosa* (p. 337), which is specific to *Musa* spp. and universally present wherever bananas are grown, transmits the virus. Possibly due to this fact alone, only various species of *Musa* have thus far been found to be susceptible. Susceptible species include *M. sapientum* (dessert banana), *M. sinensis* (dwarf cavendish), or AA, AAA and AAB, respectively, *M. ensete* (African banana) and *M. textilis* (abaca).

Symptoms: Infection and subsequent symptom development may occur at any stage of plant growth. Although the virus becomes systemic and moves through all organs of the plant, only the leaf is thought directly affected. Decay of roots generally in association with the disease and the occasional occurence of pseudostem heart rot are considered secondary effects.

Symptoms may vary depending upon stage of growth of the plant at time of infection, species, and climatic factors but the most consistent indication of the disease is the presence of interveinal thin dark-green lines broken in varying lengths simulating a "Morse code", dot-dash pattern observed on the underside of the second or third leaf held up to the light (Fig. 1). The dark lines usually continue into the midrib and appear as "hooks" as they follow the flow of veins into the midrib. Broken streaks of these lines are often observed on the back of the petiole. "Hooks" and streaks are often more readily observed than lines in the lamina proper. Occasionally vein-clearing is the first symptom noted and, then, particularly during cool weather.

Fig. 1.

Fig. 2.

Fig. 3.

Plants are inevitably stunted to a degree the more so the earlier the infection (Fig. 2). Leaves increasingly assume an erect and clorotic habit. Young leaves narrow and shorten and become stiff, brittle and corrugated. Margins of such leaves yellow considerably and often become necrotic which in turn gives the plant a rather ragged appearance (Fig. 3). The throat of the pseudostem usually becomes congested with the proliferation of leaves preventing normal throwing of the bunch. Bunches, if they are formed and manage to emerge, are invariably mishapen, small and worthless.

Certain symptoms as chlorosis and stunting may confuse the observer with other virus diseases of banana such as mosaic and infectious chlorosis under certain conditions. However, symptoms must be observed in total rather than compared as individual events. The so-called Roxana disease of bananas in Costa Rica was noted in 1967 to have many characteristics in common with bunchy top but all cases were eradicated before suspicions were verified.

Physiological specialization: Observed "recovery" from bunchy top and relatively low percentages of disease incidence in plants of the Robusta variety has led to theories regarding the existence of a "mild" strain of the virus affording crossprotection and preventing 100 percent disease incidence within any given crop. At least in Fiji where only Robusta is grown there have been no observations to indicate the prevalence of a mild strain although the fact that disease incidence does not usually exceed 30 percent in any one crop lends credence to the explanation.

Epidemiology: The virus is harboured in infected suckers and transmitted by the banana aphid, *P. nigronervosa*. Mechanical transmission by cutting tools and juice has not been demonstrated. Dissemination by planting infected suckers is common and quite unavoidable since infection with latent forms may delay symptom expression indefinitely.

Transmission by *P. nigronervosa* is responsible for intra- and interplantation epidemics due to the ubiquity of the insect and winged forms which may be blown long distances by winds. Aphids become infective by feeding on infected plants for at least 17 hours. Availability of virus, however, decreases with increasing age of the symptomatic plant. As few as 4 viruliferous aphids may, successfully transmit sufficient virus to cause disease within a few to 48 hours after feeding on an infected plant but may retain their infectivity for about 13 days. External leaf symptoms are usually expressed between 23–29 days after infection. Every environmental condition most favorable to the banana plant is also favorable for maximum disease development and maximum increase and dissemination of the vector. Thus, maximum intensity and transmission of disease occurs during periods of warm weather, high rainfall and in plantings grown in soils of high fertility and in sheltered positions.

Control: The only realistic means of control of bunchy top involves several strictly maintained eradication and sanitation procedures. The following recommendations were adapted, from schemes pioneered in Australia, by Graham for Fiji planters:

"1. Select original planting material very carefully. If a nursery is to be established, spray at 10–14 day intervals with Demeton (1 oz./10 gallons water = ~ 6 gs/10 litres) paying particular attention to young suckers.

2. Inspect nurseries and mature plantations regularly, using the "hook" system (s. symptoms) of bunchy top identification.

3. Spray detected plants with Demeton before taking them out, paying close attention to all the suckers.

4. Dig out the plants, making sure that no buds are left to start the disease off again. Dig out all the plants in a mat and cut them into small bits.

5. If a plantation is more than 50 % infected, destroy the lot rather than try to keep up with replants."

The practice of keeping the plantation weed free as much as practicable should also be added to the above procedures.

Considering the formidable nature of bunchy top, where phyto-sanitary schemes as outlined above for local situations and more rigid, sophisticated national schemes involving severe quarantine and eradication measures instituted by legislation as in Australia, successful control has become reality. In New South Wales, Australia, reported incidence fell from 2700 mats/1000 acres in 1936–37 to less than 50 mats/1000 acres/year between 1960 and 1968 after institution of a legislated program, still in effect, in 1935. In Fiji, reduction of disease incidence to at least the 2 percent level has been proven possible.

Literature

STOVER, R. H. (1972): Banana, Plantain and Abaca diseases. Commonwealth Mycological Institute, Kew.

Author: L. Butler

Other virus diseases of bananas
Cucumber mosaic virus

Cacao swollen shoot virus (Figs. 4–5)

/:*/*:U/*:S/Cc

Synonyms: Theobroma virus 1, Marmor theobromae etc.

Disease: Cocoa swollen shoot disease; Afrikanische Sproßschwellung des Kakaobaumes; Swollen shoot du cacaoyer; retoño del cacaotero.

Geographical distribution: The disease is widespread in West Africa (Ghana, Ivory Coast, Nigeria, Togo and Sierra Leone) and also occurs in Sri Lanka, and possibly Sabah.

Host plants: Swollen shoot virus is usually considered to be endemic in the forest trees (Tiliales) although infected cocoa provides a better source of virus. Natural infection has been demonstrated, apart from cocoa in *Ceiba pentandra, Cola chlamydantha, C. gigantea* var. *glabrescens, Adansonia digitata* and *Sterculia traga cantha*. Since other species within the Tiliales are also susceptible to swollen shoot virus, it is likely that they too may carry infection. Symptoms in infected forest trees (leaf deformation, mottling and chlorosis) are often indistinct or localized.

Symptoms: The first recognised symptoms of virus infection in cocoa were shoot swellings, both nodal and internodal (Fig. 4). These result from greater development of both xylem and phloem without necrosis. Swellings also occur on roots especially tap roots and severe virus induces necrosis of fine roots. Some isolates of swollen shoot virus do not produce swellings, but most of them induce leaf symptoms. First a transient red banding of the veins develops. Later chlorotic vein flecking or banding develops and this is more extensive with virulent strains (Fig. 5). The chlorotic areas exhibit non-differentiation of the mesophyll and small poorly developed chloroplasts. Fruits (pods) on infected trees are rounded and may develop light and dark green mottling.
Similarities exist with cocoa mottle leaf viruses found in West-Africa, which are mealybug transmitted but never induce stem swellings.
Furthermore, the red colouration produced in leaves is more diffuse and is replaced by dark green banding of the larger veins; these areas being delimited by chlorotic tissue. Two mealybug transmitted virus have been reported in Trinidad. Strain A or "red mottle" causes red vein banding and yellow flecks while strain B or "vein clearing" causes extensive yellow vein banding, neither virus causes swellings. A virus presumably similar to that reported in Sabah, causes an intermittent yellow reticulate which occasionally is difficult to distinguish from the leaf symptoms caused by swollen shoot.

Fig. 4.   Fig. 5.

With all the viruses referred to, the described symptoms are typical on West African Amelonado cocoa, symptoms in other cocoa types may differ and in Upper Amazon types they are usually less apparent.

Morphology: The bacilliform particles are of about 121–130 x 28 nm.

Physiological specialization: Many varients are known and these are usually named from the locality of their origin. New Juaben, Mampong, Anibil and Kpeve are serologically related strains. Varients can otherwise be classified on virulence, host range, vector specificity and symptomology i. e. (a) severity and presence and type of leaf symptoms and (b) presence of stem swellings.

Epidemiology: The virus is transmitted by members of the Pseudococcoidae (mealybugs); at least fourteen species of which are known to be vectors. Most important species are *Planococcoides njalensis* (p. 346), *Planococcus kenyae* and *P. citri* (p. 350), *Ferrisia virgata* (p. 369). Nymphs of the 1st to 3rd instars and female adults are possible vectors.
With some species of vectors, attendance by ants, particularly *Crematogaster striatular* (p. 347) and *C. luctans* is important. The minimum acquisition period is 20 min. and the optimum 2–4 days: insects may transmit after 15 min. with maximum transmission after 2–10 hrs., virus can be retained for 72 hrs. There is no transmission through the eggs.
Mealybugs mainly move by walking, although there is considerable wind movement of nymphs. This results in new infections predominating at the periphery of outbreaks with some jump spread by wind blown vectors. In infected mature Amelonado cocoa latent periods may last from 6 to 24 months for virulent isolates, the period being longer for the avirulent virus. In Ghana, 5–17 % latent infection has been recorded, 64 % of it occurring within 12 mtrs of the overt infection. In Nigeria, there is usually less latent infection.
The virus is not seed borne neither it is spread mechanically by cultural operations.

Control: Control of swollen shoot disease in West African countries is primarily by removal of infected trees as they are discovered. This demands frequent survey of cocoa areas, treatment of outbreaks, and regular and frequent retreatment of outbreaks areas. Attempts to control vectors by chemicals or biological means have been unsuccessful. The only active chemicals are too expensive and are highly poisonous to man.

Cocoa hybrids tolerant of infection are used in Nigeria in epidemic areas but they are unsatisfactory in Ghana where the cocoa viruses are more virulent. In Ghana, resistance to primary infection has been found among Upper Amazon cocoa especially those from Nanay and Iquitos. Current research is being aimed at producing resistant varieties acceptably to both farmers and consumers.

Literature

BRUNT, A. A., & R. H. KENTEN (1971): Viruses infecting cocoa. Rev. Plant Path. **50**, 591–602.

DALE, W. T. (1962): Diseases and pests of cocoa. Virus diseases. In Agriculture and land use in Ghana. Ed. J. B. Wills, London, Oxford University Press.

KENTEN, R. H., & J. T. LEGG (1971): Varietal resistance of cocoa to swollen shoot disease in West Africa. Pl. Prot. Bull. F. A. O., **19**, 1–12.

LEGG, J. T. (1972): Measures to control spread of cocoa swollen shoot disease in Ghana. PANS **18**, 1. 57–60.

THOROLD, C. A. (1975): Cocoa diseases. Clarendon Oxford.

CMI/AAB Description no 10.

Author: J. T. Legg

Other virus diseases of cacao
Cacao mottle leaf virus.
Cacao necrosis virus.
Cacao yellow mosaic virus, Ref.: CMI/AAB Description no 11.

Cassava mosaic (Figs. 6–8)

Disease: Cassava mosaic disease; Cassava Kräuselkrankheit; mosaique du manioc; mosaíco de la mandioca.

The Pathogen: Although the symptoms of the cassava mosaic diseases of the Old (Africa, Asia) and New Worlds (America) are similar, the diseases are caused by two distinct and unrelated viruses. The cassava mosaic which occurs in Brazil, known as cassava common mosaic virus, is able to infect a comparatively wide range of plant species. No natural vector is known.

The cassava mosaic which occurs in Africa and Asia is transmitted by whitefly (*Bemisia tabaci*, p. 320) and has been transmitted by grafting, but is not sap-transmissible; it is presumed to be caused by a virus.

Geographical distribution: Cassava common mosaic virus has only been reported from Brazil, but probably occurs in other areas of South America.

African cassava mosaic disease is prevalent and common wherever cassava is grown in East, Central and West Africa and Madagascar; in Asia it is widespread in Kerala State, India and in Java. (CMI map no 184). Yield losses may be more than 30 per cent (Brazil) and as high as 95 per cent (Africa).

Host plants: Natural occurence of the Brazilian mosaic apparently is confined to cassava (*Manihot esculenta*); the African mosaic is confined to *M. esculenta* and (in rare instances only) *M. glaziovii*.

Fig. 7.

Fig. 6 (left).

Fig. 8.

Symptoms: Symptoms show wide variation due to varietal reactions to infection; they are also greatly influenced by the stage of growth at which infection occurs and by environment. Symptoms are characteristic of a mosaic disease, where clearly defined areas of the leaf are chlorotic: pale or bright yellow, pale green or nearly white. There is a great variation in the extent of chlorotic areas. They may vary in size from small flecks or spots to chlorosis confined to one leaflet only, or the entire leaf may be affected. Often chlorosis is confined to the base of the leaflet. Leaves may be severely distorted and reduced in size; with severe infection there is a general stunting of the plant (Fig. 6–8).

Morphology: The cassava mosaic in Brazil is caused by a sap-transmissible virus with particles about 495 nm long, the one occurring in Africa has not, as yet, been characterized.

Physiological specialization: Strains of Brazilian cassava common mosaic virus differing in virulence have been recorded.

African cassava mosaic virus occurs in mild and severe forms. In the severe group, chlorosis and distortion of leaves are severe, and the chlorosis is bright yellow or nearly white. Affected areas are large, usually more or less uniformly distributed, but occasionally localised. With the mild group, affected areas are only slightly paler green than normal and are often limited in size. The mild group does not confer cross-protection against the severe group.

Epidemiology: In Tanzania it has been shown that time of planting significantly affects rate of infection, although it may not necessarily affect final incidence.

In East Africa there are other undetermined factors which influence incidence of mosaic, particularly in resistant selections. These may be a direct effect of edaphic and climatic factors on growth or an indirect effect of environment on vector populations and movement. Varieties which show only moderate resistance near the East African coast maintain satisfactory resistance in Uganda. In general, results obtained in resistance trials do not always agree with those obtained in other areas. Such geographic variations in addition to climatic and edaphic factors, may either reflect differences in virus populations or variation in ability to transmit the virus in local populations of the whitefly vector.

Neither the Brazilian nor the African virus is transmitted through seed of *M. esculenta*.

The spread of both viruses in infected cuttings, which give immediate rise to fully diseased plants, is of great significance in the dispersal of the diseases.

In addition, the African virus is transmitted by the whitefly, *Bemisia tabaci*. Whiteflies acquire the virus by feeding on diseased leaves for 4–6 hours; they require another 4 hours to become viruliferous. They can then transmit the virus to healthy plants in a feeding period of 15 minutes, but longer periods give more infections. The virus can only be transmitted by whitefly to immature leaves less than one quarter of their full size; it cannot be transmitted to plants through mature leaves.

Control: The Brazilian cassava common mosaic is of minor importance as it can be controlled easily by selecting healthy cuttings for propagation, and by roguing. Such control is practicable because of the lack of an insect vector.

In Africa, the use of only healthy resistant cuttings for propagation and strict roguing greatly reduces the incidence of cassava mosaic. Because of the insect vector, this recommendation is often only of limited success; if disease control in adjacent plots or farms is not of a high standard there is inevitable spread into clean plots.

In East Africa much effort has been directed towards attempts to breed for resistance. Inter-clonal crossing between local varieties which possessed some degree of resistance resulted in improved but inadequate resistance. Interspecific crosses between cassava selections and *M. glaziovii*, *M. dichotoma*, *M. catingae*, *M. saxicola* or *M. melanobasis* result in hybrids with near-immunity to mosaic, but these are tree-like in form and fibrous-rooted. When these hybrids are repeatedly back-crossed to cassava clones to restore tuberous roots of acceptable quality, some resistance is retained, but much is eroded. Immunity has thus not been achieved in the East African programme; however, clones containing useful levels of resistance exist, particularly those incorporating genes from *M. glaziovii*.

Reasonable control may be achieved by combining the use of resistant varieties with propagation of healthy material only, and the strict roguing of infected plants.

Literature

CHANT, S. R. (1958): Studies on the transmission of cassava mosaic virus by *Bemisia* spp. (Aleyrodidae). Ann. appl. Biol., **46**, 210–215.

JENNINGS, D. L. (1957): Further studies in breeding cassava for virus resistance. E. Afr. agric. For. J., **22**, 213–219.
STOREY, H. H., & R. F. W. NICHOLS (1938): Studies of the mosaic diseases of cassava. Ann. appl. Biol., **25**, 790–806.
CMI/AAB Description no 90.

Author: K. R. Bock, & E. J. Guthrie

Other virus diseases of cassava
Cassava brown streak virus.
Cassava vein mosaic virus.

Citrus cachexia-xyloporosis virus (Plate 1 d)

/:*/*:*/*:S/*

Disease: Cachexia-xyloporose; citrus cachexia-xyloporosis; xiloporosis de los agrios.
Cachexia described by Childs (1950) in Florida on Tangelo Orlando. Xyloporosis described by Reichert and Perlberger (1934) in Palestine on sweet limette (*C. limettioides*). Cachexie and Xyloporosis is believed to be caused by the same virus (Childs et al., 1965).

Geographical distribution: In all the citrus-growing regions (CMI map no 374).

Host plants: Susceptible citrus (symptoms present): – mandarin or tangerine (*C. reticulata, C. deliciosa, C. nobilis*), sweet limette (*C. limettioides*), kumquat (*Fortunella* sp.), tangelo (*C. paradisi* x *C. reticulata*), *C. macrophylla*.
Tolerant citrus (no manifestation of symptoms): – sour or seville orange (*C. aurantium*), sweet orange (*C. sinensis*), grapefruit (*C, paradisi*), pummelo or shaddock (*C. grandis*), lemon (*C. limon*), trifoliate orange (*Poncirus trifoliata*), etc.
Susceptible herbaceous plants: – unknown.

Symptoms: Trees are stunted, the degree of which varies with the virulence of the strain of virus and the susceptibility of the host species. The foliage suffers chlorosis and early leaf-fall. Stem pitting, present on the susceptible part of the tree (rootstock or scion) is evident as pits in the xylem which correspond with peg-like projections from the inner surface of the bark (Plate 1 d). Gum accumulates in the thickness of the bark. In very susceptible species necrotic areas appear on the surface of the bark, often in the shape of "button-holes". According to the species and ecological conditions, the symptoms, do not appear until 3–8 years after planting.
There is no specific symptom on fruit, although crop yields are very much reduced.
Comparison with other disorders:
Cristacortis: in comparison with citrus xyloporosis, the stem pitting of cristacortis is deeper and more localized, and the host range is more important for it includes sweet orange, grapefruit, sour orange, etc.
Scale insects: punctures by *Lepidosaphes beckii* (p. 367) can induce a mild stem pitting of the xylem, but there is no development of gum in the thickness of the bark.

Morphology: The virus of citrus cachexia-xyloporosis has not been isolated yet.

Physiological specialization: Strains seem to differ in virulence, and some result in a greater production of gum.

Epidemiology: Normal transmission: – by grafting scion wood or buds. No vectors are known, and transmission by seed or mechanical means seems impossible.

Experimental transmission: – by grafting buds or pieces of bark, and is also possible with *Cuscuta*. No antiserum has been obtained.

Control: There is no curative treatment. Disease-free lines are sought through indexing and from nucellar selections.

Indexing: – Indicator plant: seed-grown tangelo Orlando aged 12–15 months (or the tangelos Sunshine, Seminole etc.). Methods: 1) graft two buds from the candidate tree, and cut back the top of the indicator plant to above the upper bud to induce growth. 2) inoculation of the indicator plant with inoculum. In both methods use three indicator plants for each candidate tree. Conditions favouring symptom·expression: vigorous indicator plants. Incubation: 6 months to 5 years depending upon the strain and the environmental conditions. It is necessary to do the indexing in the open. Symptoms: stem pitting on the trunk of tangelo, gum formation in the bark, and stunting.

Nucellar selection: – plants raised from seed are free of citrus xyloporosis.

A new quick indexing technique uses the mandarine Parsons Special as indicator plant. One "eye" of this cultivar is inserted in a vigorous rootstock, and two pieces from the candidate tree are inoculated in a vertical line, and as close as possible, one above, one below the piece from Parsons Special. Yellow-brown gummosis develops in the cambium of the Parsons Special in case of infection. Droplets of gum may appear through cracks of the bark. The first symptoms may be seen 7–12 months after inoculation. A temperature near 30 °C is required.

Literature

CHILDS, J. F. L., J. L. EICHHORN, L. E. KOPP & R. E. JOHNSON (1965): Experimental evidence that Cachexia and Xyloporosis are caused by the same virus. In Proc. 3rd Conf. Intern. Org. Citrus Virol.: 61–69.
ROISTACHER, C. N., R. L. BLUE & E. C. CALAVAN (1973): A new test for Citrus Cachexia. Citrograph **58**, 261–262.
VOGEL, R., & J. M. BOVÉ (1968): Cristacortis, a virus disease inducing Stem pitting on sour orange and other Citrus species. Proc. 4th Conf. Intern. Org. Citrus Virol.: 221–228.

Author: R. Vogel

Citrus exocortis (Plate 1 a)

Disease: scaly butt; exocortis

Geographical distribution: All citrus-growing regions (CMI map no 290).

Host plants: Susceptible citrus (scaling of the bark): – trifoliate orange (*Poncirus trifoliata*), Rangpur lime (*C. reticulata var. austera hybrid*), citrange (*C. sinensis* x *P. trifoliata*), sweet limette (*C. limettioides*), citron (*C. medica*), certain lemons (*C. limon*).
Susceptible herbaceous plants: – *Gynura aurantiaca,* petunia hybrids, tomato, potato.
Resistant citrus: – unknown.
Tolerant citrus (no manifestation of scaling bark, but plants can be stunted): – sweet orange (*C. sinensis*), sour orange (*C. aurantium*), grapefruit (*C. paradisi*), pummelo or shaddock (*C. grandis*) mandarin or tangerine (*C. reticulata, C. deliciosa, C. nobilis*) etc.

Symptoms: Stunting of the tree to a degree which varies with the virulence of the infecting strain, and vertical scaling of the bark along the complete length of the susceptible rootstock (*P. trifoliata*, Rangpur lime, citrange etc., plate 1 a). Yellow lesions and cracks develop on the bark of susceptible varieties (citron, certain lemons etc.). Epinasty of the leaves and necrosis of the lower surface of the main vein of certain species (citron Etrog, Rangpur lime etc.). Fruit colour develops early and crop yield is greatly reduced.

Morphology: The pathogenic agent is a viroid (free RNA, without a protein capsid). The RNA is of low molecular weight, approximately 15×10^4 daltons.

Physiological specialization: Strains of differing virulence are distinguished on the basis of the severity and speed of development of the symptoms.

Epidemiology: Normal transmission: – by grafting scion wood or buds. Mechanical transmission is possible, by the blades of contaminated tools and through punctures.
Experimental transmission: – by grafting buds, pieces of bark or portions of leaves, and mechanically through cuts or punctures. It can also be transmitted by *Cuscuta*.
No antiserum has been obtained.
Comparison with other diseases: – Shell Bark: a vertical scaling of the bark of certain lemons and bergamots, but not of *P. trifoliata* or citron Etrog. Scaly Bark: bark scaling of sweet oranges, grapefruits etc., but not of *P. trifoliata* or citron Etrog. Potato Spindle Tuber: caused by the same viroid as exocortis (Semancik and Weathers, 1972).

Control: No curative treatment is known for plantation trees. Tools used during propagation and for the training of trees should be disinfected in concentrated sodium hypochlorite. Research is concerned with the production of disease-free lines by indexing and from nucellar selections.
Indexing: – Indicator plants: citrons Etrog, 60–13 or Arizona 861. Method: first graft a bud of citron onto a vigorous rootstock, and then graft two pieces of bark from the donor tree, one above and one below the citron bud, and on the same vertical line and as near the grafted bud as possible. The indicator plants can be maintained in pots under glass. Conditions favouring symptom development: temperature approximately 30 °C.
Incubation: 1–3 months, according to the virulence of the strain.
Symptoms: leaf epinasty, necrosis of the lower surface of the main veins, and the stunting of plants.
Nucellar selections: – exocortis-free plants are raised from seed. This method is used with all the polyembryonic varieties of citrus.

Literature

CALAVAN, E. C. (1968): Indexing Procedures for 15 Virus Diseases of Citrus Trees. Washington D. C. USDA Agric. Handbook **333.**
FAWCETT, H. S., & L. J. KLOTZ (1948): Exocortis of trifoliate orange. Citrus leaves **28**, (4) 8.
SEMANCIK, J. S., & L. G. WEATHERS (1972): Exocortis disease: evidence for a new species of infectious low molecular weight RNA in plants. Nature **237**, 242–244.

Author: R. Vogel

Citrus psorosis virus (Plate 1 b)

/:*/*:*/*:S/*

Disease: scaly bark; viröse Rindenschuppigkeit; psorose ecailleuse, citrus psorosis; corteza escamosa del naranjo.

Geographical distribution: All citrus-growing regions (CMI map no 65).

Host plants: Susceptible citrus (scaling of the bark): – sweet orange (*C. sinensis*), mandarin or tangerine (*C. reticulata, C. deliciosa*), grapefruit (*C. paradisi*).
Susceptible herbaceous plants: – natural infections unknown.
Resistant citrus: – unknown.

Tolerant citrus (no manifestation of bark scaling, but can show psorosis leaf symptoms): – sour orange (*C. aurantium*), lemon (*C. limon*), trifoliate orange (*Poncirus trifoliata*), citrange (*C. sinensis* x *P. trifoliata*), etc.

Symptoms: Scaling of the outer layer of the bark (Plate 1 b). Beneath the scales the inner bark remains green. The scaling can appear on the trunk and on the main and secondary branches. Deposits of gum are sometimes visible beneath the scales. The scaling spreads laterally and has a tendency to girdle the affected trunk or branch. The branches or the entire tree decline and sometimes the plant dies. Crop yields are greatly reduced. The scaling generally appears from the sixth year.

On trees affected by scaly bark, as well as on those with symptoms of concave gum, blind pocket, crinkle – infectious variegation and cristacortis, two types of symptoms (psorosis) appear on the leaves: "flecking": small, elongated discoloured spots between the secondary veins: "oak-leaf patterns": irregularly shaped discoloured areas on both sides of the main vein. These symptoms only develop on young leaves if the temperature does not exceed ca. 25 °C.

Comparison with other disorders: –

Exocortis: bark scaling of *P. trifoliata* but not sweet orange, mandarin or grapefruit. No appearance of leaf symptoms of the "psorosis" type.

Shell Bark: scaling of certain lemons (*C. limon*) and bergamot (*C. bergamia*), but not sweet orange, mandarin or grapefruit. No appearance of leaf symptoms of the "psorosis" type.

Leprose: scaling of sweet orange, grapefruit etc. in South America and Florida, believed caused by a virus associated with mites. The disorder produces circular spots on the leaves, but not of the "psorosis" type.

Concave Gum – Blind pocket: for a long time these have been considered forms of psorosis because they induce foliar symptoms which resemble those of scaly psorosis. It seems, however, that they are caused by other infectious agents for they produce different symptoms in the cortex, and there is no "shock" reaction (see below) or cross protection.

Crinkle-infectious variegation: also considered for a long time to be a form of psorosis. Leaf symptoms of the "psorosis" type are produced but there are no cortical symptoms, nor any "shock" reaction (see below) or cross protection.

Morphology: The causal agent has not been isolated. Strains differing in virulence are distinguished on the basis of the speed and intensity of symptom development.
No antiserum has been obtained.

Epidemiology: Normal transmission: – by grafting scion wood or buds. Seed transmission seems possible in certain cases, e. g. citrange Carrizo and citrange Troyer. In Argentina an insect vector is believed to transmit scaly bark.

Experimental transmission: –by grafting buds, pieces of bark and leaves, and also by *Cuscuta*. Weathers (1969) may have transmitted the causal agent mechanically, from citrus to citrus and from citrus to herbaceous plants.

Control: No curative treatment is known for plantation trees, although the scraping and disinfection of the damaged bark can prolong the life of the trees by reducing the spread of these areas. Heat therapy is possible for young plants and grafts (Calavan et al., 1972). Disease-free lines are being sought by indexing and from nucellar selections.

Indexing: – Indicator plant: mainly seed-grown sweet oranges aged 12–18 months. Method: grafting two buds or two pieces of bark from the candidate tree, the indicator plant being cut back to encourage new shoots. Conditions favouring symptom development: a temperature of 18–25 °C and vigorous indicators. Incubation: 3 weeks to 3 months. Symptoms: foliar symptoms of the "psorosis" type. If the lime Mexican (*C. aurantifolia*) is used as the indicator plant young shoots which develop after inoculation can suddenly wither; this is described as a "shock" reaction. The inoculation of seed-grown sweet orange by grafting with a piece of scaled bark taken from a tree affected by scaly psorosis results in severe scaling, psorosis B, on the indicator plant. This reaction allows psorosis to be distinguished from other causes of scaling.

Nucellar selection: – This method is used for all polyembryonic varieties of citrus. Plants raised from seed may carry scaly psorosis transmitted in the seed, and must therefore be indexed before multiplication.

Literature

CALAVAN, E. C., C. N. ROISTACHER & D. M. NAUER (1972): Heat treatment of buds for the elimination of Citrus viruses. Plant Dis. Reptr. **56,** 976–980.
FAWCETT, H. S. (1936): Citrus diseases and their control. Mc Graw-Hill Book Co, Inc.
KITAJIMA, E. W., G. W. MÜLLER, A. S. COSTA & W. YUKI (1972) Short, rod like particles associated with Citrus leprosis. Virology **50,** 254–258.
WHEATHERS, L. G. (1969): Mechanical transmission of viruses from Citrus to Citrus and herbaceous plants. Proc. 1. Intern. Citrus Symp. **3,** 1473–1479.

Author: R. Vogel

Citrus tristeza virus (Plate 1 c)

/:*/*:E/E:S/Ap

Disease: Quick Decline or Bud Union Decline; Citrus-Abbau; tristeza; podredumbre de las raicillas.

Geographical distribution: All regions of the world apart from most of the Mediterranean basin (except Spain). Isolated cases of diseased trees have occured in the majority of Mediterranean countries but have been destroyed. (CMI map no 289).

Host plants: Susceptible citrus: – a) Causing death of trees: all species grafted onto sour orange with the exception of lemon (*C. limon*) and possibly bergamot (*C. bergamia*). The citrange Troyer behaves in a similar manner as sour orange in certain areas of California. b) Causing stem pitting and sometimes decline: true lime (*C. aurantifolia*), grapefruit (*C. paradisi*), pummelo or shaddock (*C. grandis*), *C. macrophylla,* etc. c) Causing stem pitting: certain varieties like sweet orange Pera and Rangpur lime (*C. reticulata* var. *austera hybrid*) in Brazil.
Susceptible herbaceous plants: – the virus can multiply in certain *Passiflora* spp.
Resistant citrus: – unknown.
Tolerant citrus: – The following plants, grown from seed or grafted onto a rootstock other than sour orange (and the citrange Troyer in certain areas of California) are considered tolerant to tristeza (except in certain regions of Brazil where almost all the species show stem pitting, plate 1c): sweet orange (*C. sinensis*), mandarin or tangerine (*C. reticulata, C. nobilis, C. deliciosa*), lemon (*C. limon*), trifoliate orange (*Poncirus trifoliata*) etc.

Symptoms: Trees grafted onto sour orange (with the exception of lemon) die due to the destruction of the phloem bundles below the union. "Inverse pitting" (pinholing" or "honeycombing") occurs on sour orange below the union; this symptom is also found in association with stubborn (p. 47). Susceptible varieties are stunted to a degree which depends upon the virulence of the strain of tristeza. Stem pitting appears on certain susceptible varieties (true lime, grapefruit, pummelo, *C. macrophylla* etc.). On some varieties the number and size of leaves is reduced, vein clearing is seen, and the number and quality of fruit can suffer.
Comparison with other diseases: –
Cristacortis: causes stem pitting on numerous species but not on true lime. It does not produce vein clearing. Xyloporosis: causes a less deep stem pitting than tristeza, and no vein clearing. Various "declines": these do not produce the specific reaction of true lime, nor vein clearing.

Morphology: The virus has been isolated and partially purified. It is considered to be a flexuous particle, approximately 10 x 2000 nm.

Epidemiology: According to the severity of the symptoms, strains of differing virulence have been distinguished.

Normal transmission: by grafting scion wood or buds. There are a number of aphid vectors; *Toxoptera citricidus* (p. 343) is the most effective, but *Aphis gossypii* (p. 328), *A. spiraecola* (p. 330), *Toxoptera aurantii* (p. 342) etc. also transmit tristeza. Mechanical and seed transmission have not been demonstrated.

Experimental transmission: by grafting buds, pieces of bark or leaves.

No antiserum has been obtained.

Control: There is no cure for infected plantation trees, but heat therapy of young plants is possible. It is also possible to limit symptoms by protection with a weak strain of tristeza which precludes the expression of more severe symptoms by a more virulent strain. Virus free lines are sought through indexing and from nucellar selections.

Indexing: – Indicator plant: true lime (*C. aurantifolia*) raised from seed, and 12–18 months old. Method: by grafting two buds or two pieces of bark from the candiate tree. Conditions favouring symptom expression: vigorous indicator plants. Incubation: 1–3 months for vein clearing, 6–24 months for stem pitting. Symptoms: vein clearing and stem pitting.

Nucellar selection: – This is a technique whereby apomictic seed produced by polyembryonic varieties is grown to produce clonal, virus-free plants.

Literature

BAR JOSEPH, M., G. LOEBENSTEIN & J. COHEN (1970): Partial purification of virus-like particles associated with the Citrus Tristeza disease. Phytopathology **60,** 75–78.

KITAJIMA, E. W., D. M. SILVA, A. R. OLIVEIRA, G. W. MULLER & A. S. COSTA (1964): Thread-like particles associated with Tristeza disease of Citrus. Nature **201,** 1011–1012.

WALLACE, J. M., & R. J. DRAKE (1972): Progress report on experimentally induced resistance in Tristeza-susceptible Citrus scion rootstock combinaitons. Proc. 6th Conf. Int. Org. Citrus Virol. CMI/AAB Description no 33

Author: J. M. Bové

Other virus diseases of citrus

Citrange stunt

Cristacortis

Gummy bark

Gum pocket

Impietratura

Vein enation – Woody gall

Yellow vein

Leaf curl

Multiple sprouting

Ringspot

Satsuma dwarf

Seedling yellows

Tatter leaf

Groundnut rosette virus (Fig. 9)

/:*/*:S/S:S/Ap

Synonyms: Arachis virus 1 Smith., Marmor arachidis Holmes

Disease: Groundnut Rosette; Kräuselkrankheit der Erdnuß; rosette de l'arachide; roseta del maní.

Geographical distribution: The virus is widespread in Africa south of the Sahara and was first reported from Tanzania in 1907. CMI map no 49 shows rosette to be present in New South Wales, Australia, but the herbarium specimens suggest a witches-broom type of virus. The map also shows rosette as being possibly present in Indonesia but later work showed this was another witches-broom virus transmitted by a leafhopper. Several reports have indicated rosette as being present in India but until they can be substantiated by comparison with rosette isolates from Africa the disease must be considered to be of African origin and distribution.

Host plant: G.R.V. has only been demonstrated to infect the cultivated groundnut *Arachis hypogaea* in nature.

Symptoms: Many different symptoms have been recorded from the cultivated groundnut but they can be broadly grouped into two main types – chlorotic rosette, which predominates in East and Central Africa; and green rosette, which is common in West Africa.
a) Chlorosis: First symptoms are faint indefinite mottling of the younger leaflets and the next leaves to open are predominantly pale yellow, often with the veins remaining green. Later formed leaves bear progressively smaller leaflets which are chlorotic, curled and distorted (Fig. 9). Internodes become shortened and the stems become thickened. The degree of stunting depends on the time of infection. Flowering is decreased but apart from a shortening of the hypanthium the floral parts are normal. Although gynophores may develop in early infected plants few of them form pods. Later infections cause less pronounced effects on yield. In Central and East Africa mosaic symptoms are common and the leaflets are sharply divided into irregular patches of green and yellow. Less stunting occurs in plants with mosaic symptoms.
b) Green rosette: Plants are severely stunted if early infection occurs, but apart from occasional isolated flecks the leaves are a normal green in colour.
Atypical symptoms occur in the Asirya Mwitunde cultivars from East Africa. Field grown plants are only slightly stunted with extreme proliferation and rosetting of secondary shoots. Leaflets are

Fig. 9.

small, cupped, crinkled, malformed and chlorotic. Most annual wild species of *Arachis* show normal symptoms but the perennial species, *A. villosulicarpa* Hoehne, shows chlorotic flecks which tend to fade as the leaves mature.

Morphology: Okusanya and Watson (1966) were the first to isolate the virus. They reported rounded particles with an apparent diameter of 25–28 mμ, but even concentrated extracts only provided five particles per electron microscope field. Infectivity of buffered sap was reduced by one third between 40 and 45 °C, and totally between 50 and 55 °C. Sap from an East African isolate was infective when diluted to 1/100 but not at 1/1000. A West African isolate withstood dilution only to 1/10. The virus particles resemble those of several persistent aphid-transmitted diseases such as pea enation mosaic, barley yellow dwarf and carrot motley dwarf.

Local lesion hosts are *Chenopodium amaranticolor, C. album,* and *C. quinoa.* Systemic infections occur in *Trifolium incarnatum, T. repens, Nicotiana clevelandii, N. rustica, Stylosanthes sundaica, S. guyanensis (S. gracilis)* and *S. mucronata.*

Physiological specialization: Hull and Adams (1968) showed that rosette is a complex of two viruses. One virus, which is manually but not aphid-transmissible, caused the symptoms normally found in rosette infected plants. They named this groundnut rosette virus (GRV). The other virus, which is aphid transmitted, is symptomless in groundnuts and this was named groundnut rosette assistor virus (GRAV), Rochow (1972) used the terms 'dependant' virus for GRV and 'helper' virus for GRAV.

Chlorotic rosette and green rosette are related. Symptom differences are due to differences in the manually transmissible GRV. Differences in transmissibility of green and chlorotic rosette by different races of the vector. *Aphis craccivora,* appear to be due to differences in the relationship between GRV isolates and their vector races.

Epidemiology: a) Survival: Tests from many countries in Africa have shown that naturally occurring alternate hosts of the vector are not sources of the virus. This does not preclude the possibility that such wild hosts do exist and planted pastures containing *Stylosanthes* could be perennial reservoirs of the virus. Dry season carry over of the virus in infected volunteer groundnuts is possible in some areas (East Africa) but not in others (Sudan, Nigeria and Malawi). It is very possible that viruliferous alate aphids travelling on the moving rainfall fronts are responsible for early infections in the groundnut crop (Davies, 1972).

b) Transmission: *Aphis craccivora* (p. 328) is the only important field vector of the disease although under laboratory conditions. *A. gossypii* (p. 324) has been shown to be an inefficient vector. The virus is transmitted in a persistant or circulative manner.

Transmissions from infected plants in the field are by alate or apterous aphids. In Nigeria winged aphids are considered to be responsible for most infections, but in Uganda and Malawi secondary spread by apterous aphids is more important. The virus is not seedborne.

c) Infection: The optimum time for acquisition and test feeds are 96 hours and 10 hours respectively. The shortest acquisition feed recorded is 30 minutes.

Control: a) Sanitation: Destruction of volunteer groundnuts and primary infections in the current crop will reduce spread of the disease.

b) Cultural practices: Early planting and high plant populations have been conclusively shown to help in the control of rosette. In Malawi young plants may be infected with three to five times as many winged aphids as older plants. Winged aphids are more numerous in open than densely planted groundnuts and secondary spread is also slower in dense than open crops.

c) Resistance: High grade resistance, but not immunity, exists in a group of related cultivars from the Ivory Coast, Upper Volta area of West Africa. Many early reports of resistance from other cultivars, e. g. Philippine Pink have been disproved by controlled laboratory tests. The resistant cultivars are small seeded and low yielding but progress is being made in breeding for high yield coupled with resistance (Dhéry and Gillier 1972; Gibbons and Mercer 1972). Resistance is governed by two independent recessive genes designated aabb.

d) Chemical control: For the control of the vector see p. 324.

Literature

DAVIES, J. C. (1972): Studies on the ecology of *Aphis craccivora* Koch. (Hem., Aphididae), the vector of rosette disease of groundnuts, in Uganda. Bull. ent. Res. **62**, 169–181.

DHERY, M., & P. GILLIER (1971): Un nouveau pas dans la lutte contre la rosette de l'arachide. Oléagineux **26**, 243–251.

GIBBONS, R. W., & P. C. MERCER (1972): Peanut disease control in Malawi, Central Africa. Am. Peanut Res. and Educ. J. **4**, 58–66.

HULL, R., & A. N. ADAMS (1968): Groundnut rosette and its assistor virus. Ann. appl. Biol. **62**, 139–145.

OKUSANYA, B. A. M., & M. A. WATSON (1966): Host range and some properties of groundnuts rosette virus. Ann. appl. Biol. **58**, 377–387.

ROCHOW, W. F. (1972): The role of mixed infections in the transmission of plant viruses by aphids. Ann. Rev. Phytopath. **10**, 101–124.

Author: R. W. Gibbons

Other virus diseases of groundnut

Groundnut (peanut) marginal chlorosis virus.

Groundnut mosaic virus.

Groundnut (peanut) mottle virus. Ref.: CMI/AAB Description no 141.

Groundnut ringspot virus.

Peanut stunt virus. Ref.: CMI/AAB Description no 92.

Tomato spotted wilt virus (p. 35).

Maize streak disease virus (Fig. 10)

(R)/1:*/*:S/S:S/Au

Disease: Maize streak disease; Strichelkrankheit des Maises; striure du mais; enfermedad de las rayas del maíz.

Geographical distribution: Maize streak disease occurs throughout Africa south of the Sahara wherever maize is cultivated, and is almost certainly of African origin; it also occurs in Mauritius. A similar disease has been recorded from India, but maize streak has not been reported from Europe or the Americas.

Host plants: The virus infects many species of the Gramineae in Africa, including sugarcane (*Saccharum officinarum*), millet (*Eleusine coracana*) and guinea grass (*Panicum maximum*). Natural infections of streak disease have also been recorded on *Avena sativa, Digitaria* spp. *Eleusine indica, Eragrostis* spp., *Euchlaena mexicana, Panicum* spp., and other.

Symptoms: Streak disease, when fully developed in the maize plant, is characterised by a pronounced chlorosis of the leaves, confined to narrow, broken streaks arranged along the veins. The streaks vary from a few millimetres to several centimetres in length and are individually from 0,5 to 1 millimetre in width, although they frequently fuse laterally. The streaks are nearly evenly distributed over every leaf formed subsequent to infection (Fig. 10).

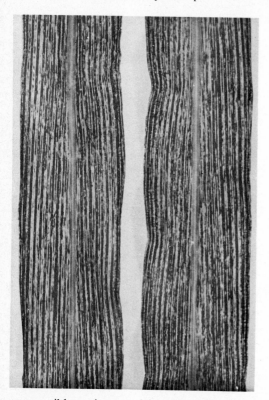

Fig. 10.

Two other similar diseases of maize occur in East Africa, and possibly in other parts, which are caused by different, unrelated viruses. Maize stripe virus induces broad yellow stripes or a yellowing of the entire leaf, acute bending of the shoot apex, and severe stunting. Maize line virus causes unbroken narrow yellow lines along the leaf veins. Experimentally, they are differentiated from maize streak virus by their vector, *Peregrinus maidis*, which does not transmit maize streak.

Morphology: Maize streak disease is caused by a small spherical virus which has paired or bonded particles (30 x 20 nm); single particles are about 20 nm in diameter.

Physiological specialization: Although maize streak has an apparently wide natural host range among the African Gramineae, the virus shows a marked degree of host orientation in many of these species. For example, the maize strain of the virus causes a mild transient streak in sugar cane; infection is not permanent. The sugar cane strain induces a permanent but mild disease in maize; the *Panicum maximum* strain does not infect maize. Many of the host species listed cannot therefore be considered as reservoirs of infection of the disease for economic crops.

Epidemiology: In young seedlings, first symptoms develop 4 to 7 days after infection as rows of chlorotic spots. Infection at this stage may result in total loss; yield depression is directly correlated with age of plant at time of infection.

In East Africa, incidence of the disease is in general much greater in low-altitude areas (sea level to 1500 metres). This is presumably an effect of the distribution of dense populations of the insect vector. However, even at higher altitudes (2100 metres) the incidence may be locally high. This is often a result of continual planting of maize in the same area over prolonged periods.

Maize streak virus is transmitted only by leafhoppers of the genus *Cicadulina* (p. 306). Hoppers may acquire the virus in under 6 hours, and are able to transmit it after a brief latent period of 6 hours; they remain infective for life. There are races of the vector which are unable to transmit the virus. Streak disease is not transmitted through the seed of maize.

Control: The continual planting of maize may result in a build-up of high incidences of streak disease, and the practice should be avoided.

The use of resistant varieties appears to be the only economic method of control. Unfortunately, resistance factors capable of easy incorporation into improved composite and synthetic maize varieties have not, as yet, been found.

The only known resistance in Africa has been found in the varieties Peruvian Yellow and selections of Hickory King. This resistance is apparently governed by a single major gene, but the heterozygote displays a considerable degree of susceptibility. Although this resistance has been used with some success in certain areas, there is a clear need for more effective sources.

Literature

CMI/AAB Description no 133.

Authors: K. R. Bock & E. J. Guthrie

Other virus diseases of maize: see table 1.

Papaya virus diseases

The subject of papaya viruses has been well reviewed by Jensen (1949) and more recently by Frossard (1969) and Cook (1972). Unfortunately, and as pointed out by Cook, "the term 'mosaic' has been used both to describe a type symptom associated with more than one disease as well as the common name for a single disease caused by a distinct, infectious entity". There is no question that the identification of mosaic diseases from symptoms alone is not conducive to the proper characterization of the infectious entities involved since it is a well known fact that similar symptoms are often times induced by different viruses.

Papaw mosaic virus

R/1:22/7:E/E:S/*

Synonym: Papaya mild mosaic virus.

Disease: Papaya Mosaic; mosaique de la papaya; mosaico de la papaya.

Geographical distribution: Florida and Venezuela.

Differential hosts: *Gomphrena globosa* and *Cassia occidentalis* produced localized necrotic lesions when inoculated.

Symptoms: Vein clearing mottling and rugosity. Laminae of leaves reduced and filiform. Petioles, stems and fruits usually do not show symptoms. Latex flows freely.

Epidemiology: Transmission by inoculation of expressed juice. Not transmitted by aphids.

Morphology: Average length of particle 533 nm; inactivated by heat for 10 minutes at 73–78 °C, and at dilution greater than 2×10^{-4}.

Control: Not determined. Development of resistant varieties should be investigated. CMI/AAB Description no 56.

Papaw ring spot virus

/:*/*:E/E:S/Ap

Serologically related to watermelon mosaic virus.

Disease: Papaw ring spot; Ringfleckenkrankheit; tache annulaire; mancha anular.

Geographical distribution: Africa, Australia, Caribbean area, Florida, Hawaii, India and South America.

Table 1. Principal virus diseases affecting maize in tropical areas

Virus	Characteristic symptoms in maize	Differential hosts	Other hosts
Sugarcane mosaic */*:*/*:E/E:S/Ap	chlorotic mottle, mild mosaic	maize, sweet corn, sorghum, sugarcane cvs CP31-294 (for strains A, B, D, E, F) Co281 (for strain C) CP31-588 (for strain A, H)	sugarcane millet sorghum wild grasses
∞**Maize dwarf mosaic** (= strain of sugarcane mosaic)	mosaic; occasionaly reddening and dwarfing	maize, sorghum	*Sorghum halepense* (Johnson grass)
Maize streak */*:*/*:S/S:S/Au	initially yellow spots developing as discontinuous streaks	maize	sugarcane millet wheat barley and several wild and cultivated grasses
Maize stunt	stripes, chlorotic to bronzy; stunted bushy growth	maize	maize teosinte *Tripsacum*
Maize (corn) mosaic */*:*/*:U/*:S,I/Au	yellow spots and narrow stripes; stunting	maize, cvs Sicarigua and line Theobromina Blanco	*Rottboellia exaltata* *Setaria vulpiseta* sorghum
Maize stripe */*:*/*:S/S:S/Au	pale yellow bands 1 cm or more in width	maize	barley sorghum
Maize line */*:*/*:S/S:S/Au	narrow yellow lines, interveinal mottle	maize	unknown
∞**Maize rough dwarf** */*:*/*:S/S:S,I/Au	young leaves dark green, develop enations, plants dwarfed	maize, cvs Laguna Elite, Neve Yaar 22, Wisconsin 641 AA	*Digitaria sanguinialis* *Echinochloa crus-galli*

*1 : 2 : 3
1 = minimum acquisition period of virus by vector
2 = incubation period of virus in vector
3 = time taken for appearance of symptoms after inoculation

∞∞ Important diseases of maize apparently not recorded in the tropics

Authors: K. R. Bock & E. J. Guthrie

Transmission (1: 2: 3*)	Particles	Distribution	References
sap transmissible stylet-borne, nonpersistent *Dactynotus ambrosiae, Hysteroneura setariae, Rhophalosiphum maidis* (p. 338), *Toxoptera graminum* (p. 339), and many others	750 nm filamentous	Africa, India, America, and many parts of the world where susceptiable species are grown	CMI/AAB no 88
as for sugarcane mosaic virus, but seed transmission in maize also reported	750 nm filamentous	USA	
Cicadulina spp., (p. 306), 30 sec: 12 hr: 4-7 days	single particles 19 nm; double or paired particles 19 × 32 nm	Africa, India, Mauritius, Reunion	CMI/AAB no 133
Dalbulus maidis (p. 308), *Graminella nigrifrons* 1 day: 14 days: 26 days	mycoplasma-like bodies associated	Central America, Caribbean, USA	
Peregrinus maidis 1 day: 4-34 days: 4-28 days	bullet shaped or bacilliform 225 × 90 nm	Hawaii, Caribbean, S. America	CMI/AAB no 94
Peregrinus maidis 5 days: ×: 5-35 days	isometric 40 nm	E. Africa, Madagascar	
Peregrinus maidis 8 days: ×: 12-33 days	isometric 34 nm	E. Africa	
Laodelphax striatellus 1 day: 10-15 days: 10-15 days	isometric 70 nm	Europe, Israel	CMI/AAB no 72

Symptoms: Vein clearing, chlorosis and mottling. Green streaks on petioles and stem. Latex flow not interrupted. Ring spots formed on fruit.

Morphology: Average length of particles in 780 nm. Virus inactivated by heat at 55 °C for 10 minutes, by dilution greater than 10^{-3}. Does not resist ageing for more than 8 hours at room temperature.

Epidemiology: Transmitted mechanically and by grafting and also by various aphids among them *Aphis spiraecola* (p. 330) and *A. gossypii* (p. 328).

Control: Spraying with insecticides not successful. Development of resistant varieties is a possibility.
CMI/AAB Description no 84.

Isabela mosaic virus

Disease: Isabela mosaic; Isabela mosaique; mosaico Isabela.

Properties of the Pathogen: Thermal inactivation point 60 °C, dilution end point 1:100, inactivated in about 72 hours at laboratory temperature. Cross protection test demonstrated the Isabela mosaic virus and the Puerto Rican Southern Coast papaw mosaic virus are related.

Geographical distribution: Puerto Rico.

Symptoms: Yellow mottling and slight rugosity of leaves. Oily spots on stem, but no distortion or deformation of leaves observed. Latex flows on wounding plant.

Epidemiology: Transmission by mechanical inoculation of extracted juice. Transmitted by the aphids *Aphis nerii, A. gossypii* (p. 328), *A. spiraecola* (p. 330) and *Myzus periscae* (p. 333); not by seed from infected trees or through the soil.

Control: Not determined. Extensive inoculation trials in Puerto Rico have shown that *Carica candamarcensis* is resistant to Isabela mosaic.

Leaf curl virus

Disease: Kräuselkrankheit der Papaya; frisolée foliaire; arrugamiento de la hoja.

Geographical distribution: India and the Philippines.

Symptoms: Severe distortion due to curling and wrinkleness of the leaves which became leathery and brittle. Twisted petioles and thickened veins. Cessation of growth.

Epidemiology: Transmission by whitefly *Bemisia tabaci* (p. 320) and by grafting; not by mechanical inoculation. The disease has been transmitted to tomato and tobacco (principal host). The transmissibility of papaw leaf curl to tobacco and vice versa, strongly suggests the virus involved to be one of the tobacco leaf curl viruses.

Control: Spraying with insecticides and roguing of infected plants.

Spotted wilt virus

Disease: Bronzefleckenkrankheit; maladie des taches de bronze; enfermedad bronzeada.

Geographical distribution: Hawaii.

Symptoms: Premature defoliation is a typical symptom, followed by necrosis of top leaves. Water-soaked lesions on petioles and stem. Ring spots and necrotic areas are observed on mature fruits. Latex flows freely from wounded tissues.

Epidemiology: The virus is transmitted mechanically and by four species of thrips, among others by *Thrips tabaci* (p. 282).

Control: Spraying with insecticides to combat thrips, and elimination of weeds. Removal of tops from infested papaws has been recommended as a control measure. No resistant papaws known.

Tobacco ringspot virus

Disease: Tabakringfleckenkrankheit; taches annulaires du tabac; manchas en anillo del tabaco.

Geographical distribution: Rio Grande Valley, USA.

Symptoms: Wilt and top necrosis followed by death of young plants.

Transmission: Virus transmitted mechanically and by the nematode *Xiphinema americanum* (p. 256). The virus infects plants belonging to the Cucurbitaceae, Leguminosae and Solanaceae. Virus not transmitted by seed from infected papaw plants.

Control: Application of nematicides before planting and roguing of infected plants as well as weeds around papaw plantations.

Yellow crinkle virus

Disease: Gelbe Kräuselkrankheit; frisolée du tabac; rizadura de la hoja del tabaco.

Geographical distribution: Australia.

Symptoms: Young leaves became yellow and noticeable reduced in size. Translucent areas on leaves drop presenting a "shot hole" effect. Affected plants become defoliated. The petals and other floral structures are converted into rough leaf-like structures. The virus responsible for yellow crinkle is the tomato bigbud virus.

Transmission: The virus has been transmitted from tomato to papaw via dodder, *Cuscuta australis*. The insect vector of this virus is *Orosius argentatus*.

Control: Roguing of infected plants and elimination of dodder.

Diseases of papaya of uncertain etiology

A disease known as "die-back" in Puerto Rico and also reported from Trinidad and Australia is characterized by top necrosis followed by complete defoliation and death of the entire plant. As in bunchy top of papaw, no latex flows when the plant is wounded. The fruit in the process of development fails to grow and falls. The relation of this disease to bunchy top (p. 45) is unknown. There is another disease reported by Da Costa which is also characterized by top necrosis and die-back similar to bunchy top. The disease is usually lethal to young trees, but there is a tendency for adult trees to recover from infection.

In Tanzania a disease which has been named "feather leaf" is characterized by small leaves restricted to the top part of the plant. The leaves are leathery in texture and their laminae distorted. Translucent bands on both sides of the larger veins and angular patches of dark green tissues are typical symptoms of this disease.

Literature

ADSUAR, J. E. (1972): A new virus disease of papaya (*Carica papaya* L.) in Puerto Rico. Journal of Agriculture of the University of Puerto Rico **55**, 397–402.

CONOVER, R. A. (1962): Virus diseases of papaya in Florida. Phytopathology **52**, 6–19.

CONOVER, R. A. (1964): Mild mosaic and faint mottle ringspot. two papaya virus diseases of minor importance in Florida. Proceedings of the Florida State Horticultural Society **77**, 444–448.

COOK, A. A. (1972): Virus diseases of papaya. Florida Agricultural Experiment Station. Technical Bulletin **750**, 3–18.

FROSSARD, P. (1969): Maladies á virus et d'origines inconnue. Fruits **24**, 483–490.

JENSEN, D. D. (1949): Papaya virus diseases with special reference to papaya ring spot. Phytopathology **39**, 191–211

KULKARNI, H. Y. (1970): Decline viruses of papaw (*Carica papaya* L.) in East Africa. Ann. appl. Biol. **66**, 1–9.

LAMBE, R. C. (1963): Terminal necrosis and wilt of papayas. Journal of the Rio Grande Valley Horticultural Society **17**, 128–129.

NARIANA, T. K. (1956): Leaf curl of papayas. Indian Phytopathology **9**, 151–155.

REYES, G. M., MARTINEZ, A. L., and CHINTE, P. T. (1959): Three virus diseases of plants new to the Philippines. FAO Plant Prot. Bull., **7**, 141–143.

STOREY, G. E., & R. S. HALLIWELL (1969): Identification of distortion ring spot virus disease of papaya in the Dominican Repulic. Plant Dis. Rep. **53**, 757–760.

TRUJILLO, E. E., & D. GONSALVEZ (1967): Tomato spotted wilt in papaya. Phytopathology **57, 9**.

WALLACE, G. B., & M. M. WALLACE (1948): Diseases of papaw and their control. E. Afr. agric. For. J. **13**, 240–244.

Author: José Adsuar

Rice hoja blanca virus (Fig. 11)

/:*/*:*/*:S/Au

Disease: Whiteleaf of rice; Hoja blanca des Reises; feuille blanche du riz; hoja blanca del arroz. The disease is also known as chlorosis, cinta blanca (white band), raya (stripe), raya blanca (white stripe), and rayadilla (striped).

Geographical distribution: This disease occurs only in the Western Hemisphere; it has been reported in Argentina, Brazil, British Honduras, Colombia, Costa Rica, Cuba, Dominican Republic, El Salvador, Ecuador, Guatemala, Guyana, Honduras, Mexico, Nicaragua, Panama, Peru, Puerto Rico, Surinam, The United States (Florida, Louisiana, and Mississippi), and Venezuela. (CMI map no 359).

Host plants: It affects the following grasses: *Brachiaria plantaginea, Echinochloa colonum, E. crusgalli, E. walteri, Echinochloa* sp., *Panicum fasciculatum, P. cappillari, Panicum* sp., *Paspalum* sp., *Rottboellia exaltata, Sacciolepsis striata. Avena sativa, Cyperus* sp., *Digitaria horizontalis, Hordeum vulgare, Leptochloa filiformis, Triticum aestivum, T. compactum, T. durum, Secale cereale,* and several *Oryza* spp., including rice, red rice, and black rice.

Symptoms: One or more white stripes may occur on the leaf blade, the entire leaf blade may be white, or the leaves, may be mottled in a typical mosaic pattern (Fig. 11). Diseased plants are reduced in height and in severely affected fields, the panicles of healthy plants are taller than those of diseased plants. The panicles of diseased plants are somewhat reduced in size and often not fully exserted from the sheath. The lemma and palea show a brownish discoloration, dry out rapidly, and are frequently distorted in shape. The floral parts are often absent, or if present are sterile. Panicles of diseased plants contain few or no seeds and remain in an upright position. Infected plants are not killed by the disease, and new tillers of a second or ratoon crop often show no symptoms. Both normal and diseased tillers are frequently observed on the same plant. The symptoms on several hosts are similar to those on rice.

Morphology: Shikata and Gálvez (1969) found in cells of diseased rice and *Echinochloa colonum* leaves, as well as in infective insects, numerous bundles of long, flexuous, threadlike particles. These particles are approximately 8 to 10 nm in diameter and variable in length.
These threadlike particles have been isolated and shown to be infective. The purification procedure described by Gálvez and Martínez (1971).
The infectivity of the preparation is tested by injecting *Sogatodes oryzicola* nymphs at the last instar. The injected insects are then caged on healthy rice seedlings.

Physiological specialization: No strains of the virus, or biotypes of the vector have been identified.

Epidemiology: Hoja blanca virus is transmitted by two species of *Sogatodes* (p. 318): *S. oryzicola* and *S. cubanus. S. oryzicola* is the main vector because it thrives on rice. *S. cubanus* prefers *Echinochloa* spp. and plays an important role in the disease cycle under natural conditions although it cannot live on rice for any length of time. Other species of insects commonly found on rice have not given positive transmission. The virus is not transmitted by mechanical means, through soil, nor through seeds.
The virus not only persists in the vector but is also transmitted through the eggs from infective females to their progeny, and from one stage to the other. Five to 15 per cent of the natural population of *E. oryzicola* are active transmitters. The shortest acquisition feeding period is 15 minutes, and the incubation period of the virus in the insect is from 5 to 36 days. The shortest inoculation feeding period is 30 minutes. The incuba-

Fig. 11.

tion period in the plant varies from 3 or 4 to 45 days according to the seedling age at the time of inoculation and susceptibility of the rice variety.

Virus-free *S. oryzicola* lay three times more eggs, and hatch more nymphs than do viruliferous individuals. The percentage of nymphs reaching the adult stage, the life span, and the weight are also reduced by the presence of the virus.

Control: The only efficient and economic ontrol method is by use of varieties resistant to the hoja blanca virus. The main sources of resistance are Asahi, Colusa, Gulfrose, Lacrose, Pandhori No 4, Missouri R-500, Napal, Mudgo, ICA-3, ICA-10, and PI 215936. The disease is controlled satisfactorily with the use of commercial varieties resistant either to the virus or to the vector.

Resistance to hoja blanca is not necessarily associated with resistance to its insect vector. Some varieties are resistant to the direct damage by the insect as IR-8; some to only the virus, as ICA-3, ICA-10, and Napal; and Mudgo shows resistance to both the insect damage and the virus. The varieties with resistance to the insect can be used successfully in the field, as CICA-4.

Judging from the reaction of single-cross F_1 plants, backcross F_2 plants, and F_3 and F_4 line selections, Beachell and Jennings (1961) concluded that the resistance is dominant and controlled by one major gene pair.

Literature

BEACHELL, H. M., & P. R. JENNINGS (1961): Mode of inheritance of hoja blanca resistance in rice. Rice Techn. Working Group, Proc. 1960, 11–12. Lafayette, Louisiana.

GÁLVEZ-E., G. E. (1969a): Hoja blanca disease of rice, p. 35–49. In: Proceedings of a symposium on the virus diseases of the rice plant, 25–28 April, 1967. Los Baños, Philippines. Johns Hopkins Press, Baltimore.

GÁLVEZ-E., G. E., (1969b): Transmission of hoja blanca virus of rice, p. 155–163. In: Proceedings of a symposium on the virus diseases of the rice plant, 25–28 April, 1967. Los Baños, Philippines. Johns Hopkins Press, Baltimore.

JENNINGS, P. R., & ALICIA PINEDA (1970): Screening rice for resistance to the planthopper, *Sogatodes orizicola* (Muir). Crop Sci. **10**, 687–689.

JENNINGS, P. R., & ALICIA PINEDA (1971): The effect of the hoja blanca virus on its insect vector. Phytopathology **61**, 142–143.

SHIKATA, E., & G. E. GÁLVEZ-E. (1969): Fine flexous threadlike particles in cells of plants and insect hosts infected with rice hoja blanca virus. Virology **39**, 635–641.

Author: G. E. Gálvez-E.

Rice "tungro" virus

/:*/(12):S/S:S/Au

Disease: Tungro; Tungro des Reises; tungro virus du riz; tungro virus del arroz.

Tungro which means degenerated growth, was first observed in the Philippines in 1963 and its viral nature was identified by Rivera and Ou (1965). Synonyms are 'Penyakit Merah' (Red disease) in Malaysia and Mentek' disease of Indonesia (since 1859). Yellow-orange leaf and tungro are similar and the leaf yellowing from India was shown to be the same as tungro virus.

Geographical distribution: Philippines, India, Malaysia, Thailand and Indonesia and Bangladesh. Tungro was reported to cause enormous losses in the Philippines during 1971 and in Indonesia during 1972. Due to the cultivation of resistant varieties in recent years the disease occurs in the pockets where old susceptible varieties are still in practice.

Host plants: Rice, and on some grasses occuring in or near paddy fields such as *Leersia hexandra*, *Rottboellia compressa* and *Cynodon dactylon, Eleusine indica, Echinochloa colonum* and *E. crusgalli.*

Symptoms: Tungro affected rice plants, are stunted with reduced number of tillers. The young emergenced leaves develop interveinal chlorosis leading to discolouration of the leaves, starting from tip downwards. Often the whole leaf is discolored. The leaf discolouration in various shades of yellow is common in Japonica varieties, but in Indica varieties orange colouration is common. Root development is poor.

Plants infected very early, generally die premature but usually they live until maturity. Infected plants take more time for maturity because of delayed flowering. The panicles are often small, sterile and not completely exerted. The grains are often covered with dark brown blotches and are lighter than those of healthy plants.

Morphology: Galvez (1968) reported that the particles are polyhedral and 30–33 nm in diameter. The virus withstands temperatures of 63 °C for 10 minutes and pH value up to 9 without apparent denaturation. The virus can be kept at room temperature (*in vitro*) for more than 24 hours. The sedimentation coefficient ist 175 ± 5 S.

Physiological spezialisation: Antiserum to the tungro virus has been obtained, but it reacts non specifically, i. e. not only to tungro virus but also to orange-leaf, yellow dwarf and grassy stunt. The tungro virus is known to have three strains. Rivera and Ou (1967) reported 'S' and 'M' strains of the virus. Although both the strains produce similar symptoms on varieties like TN-1, IR-8 and Tainan-3, they can be differentiated by their reactions on varieties viz: Acheh, FK-135, Pacita. The 'S' strain in these three varieties produces conspicious interveinal chlorosis, giving an appearance of yellow strips and sometimes irregular chlorotic specks on younger leaves. On the other hand, the 'M' strain produces only mottling. The 'S' strain is widely distributed in the Philippines and also in India. Recently another strain was described from the Philippines and was designated as 'T' strain. The new strain incites narrow leaf blades on Taichung native-1, IR-5, IR-8, IR-22, but produces interveinal stripes on FK-135 which closely resembles with the symptoms produced by 'S' strain. The 'T' strain, however, retards growth much less than that of 'S' strain, even less than does the 'M' strain.

Epidemiology: Seed transmission, soil or mechanical transmission of tungro virus always gave negative results. The virus is, however, transmitted by *Nephotettix impicticeps* (= *N. bipunctatus*) (p. 312). Recently *N. apicalis* and *Recilia (Inazuma) dorsalis* were also found to transmit the virus.

Up to 83 % of *N. impicticeps* in a population are reported as active transmitters. In case of *N. apicalis* 27 % are active transmitters whereas 4 % to 8 % of *Recilia dorsalis* transmit the virus. The shortest acquisition feeding for *N. impicticeps* is 5 minutes, others authors have reported 30 minutes as the optimum. Ling found a very unusual virus-vector interaction, there is no apparent incubation period in the insect, us being the only example of a non-persistent leaf hopper born virus. The incubation period cannot be longer than 2 hours because virus-free *N. impicticeps* can transmit the virus by having acquisition and inoculation feeding of 1 hour each.

The insects, however, do not retain the virus for more than 5 to 6 days. Infective insects usually transmit the virus immediately after their acquisition feeding and continue to transmit every day until they loose their infectivity. Once, they loose their infectivity they remain non-infective for the rest of their lives. The longest retention period for *N. apicalis* is 3 days and for *R. dorsalis* 4 days. Nymphs are as good transmitters as adultes but there is no transstadial passage (passage through moulting) nor transovarial passage. The incubation period in plant varies from 6 days to 15 days.

The virus seems to have no deleterious effect on *N. impicticeps* because of no significant differences in life span, fecundity and rate of hatching rate between viruliferous and non viruliferous insects.

Control: Resistance is the only economical means of control. Based on the results of artificial inoculation the following are some of the varieties resistant to the tungro virus: Kataribogh, Latisail, Tilakkachari, Pankhari 203, Dara, Peta, Badshabogh, T-412, Basmati 37, Bangwan, Fadjar, Indrasail, Gampai, Lantijang M-sung song, Ram Tulasi, Raja Mandal Barain, Seri Raja, Tjeremas, etc. Pankhari 203 is not only resistant to tungro but also to its vectors. Pankhari 203 and Latisail-have been used as resistant doners by breeders at IRRI and AICIP. IR 26 was found to be resistant to tungro in the Philippines.

Literature

LING, K. C. (1972): Rice virus diseases. International Rice Research Institute, Los Baños, Philippines. CMI/AAB Description no 67.

Author: S. P. Raychaudhuri

Key for classifying rice virus diseases[1]

A_1. Plants showing inconspicuous stunting, but reduced tillering
  B_1. Upright growth habit, premature death, orange-colored
   and rolled leaves ....**Orange leaf**
  B_2. Spreading growth habit, oval to oblong faint chlorotic patches
   or fine faint mottling on leaves, brown necrotic lesions
   on basal parts of culms at later stages ....**Necrosis Mosaic**

A_2. Plants showing stunting and reduced tillering
  C_1. Leaves with chlorotic spots and white stripes
   D_1. New leaves not unfolding properly but
     twisted and droopy ....**Stripe**
   D_2. New leaves unfolding normally ....**Hoja Blanca**
  C_2. Leaves with mottling and yellowish streaks,
   crinkling of the first newly formed leaves
   when infected at an early stage of growth ....**Yellow mottle**
  C_3. Leaves with yellow or yellow-orange discoloration
   E_1. Virus particles are bullet-shaped and persist in the vector ....**Transitory yellowing**
   E_2. Virus particles are spherical or polyhedral
     and do not persist in the vector ....**Tungro**
                    (leaf yellowing,
                 penyakit merah, and yellow-orange leaf)
   E_3. Mycoplasma probably the causal organism, transmission unknown .....**Giallume**

A_3. Plants showing severe stunting and excessive tillering
  F_1. Galls on leaves and culms ....**Black-streaked dwarf**
  F_2. No galls
   G_1. Leaves with chlorotic to whitisch specks
     forming interrupted streaks ....**Dwarf**
   G_2. Narrow, stiff, light-green leaves often
     with rusty spots ....**Grassy stunt**
   G_3. Leaves showing general chlorosis ....**Yellow dwarf** (padi jantan)

Literature on principal virus diseases of beans (table 3, p. 40/41)

AGRAWAL, H. O. (1964): Identification of cowpea mosaic virus isolates. Mededel. Landbouwhogeschool Wageningen, **64,** 1–53.
CAPOOR, S. P., & P. M. VARMA (1948): Enation mosaic of *Dolichos lablab*, a new virus disease. Curr. Sci. **17,** 57–58.
CAPOOR, S. P., & P. M. VARMA (1950): A new virus disease of *Dolichos lablab*. Curr. Sci. **19,** 248.
NARIANI, T. K. (1960): Yellow mosaic of mung (*Phaseolus aureus* L.). Indian Phytopath. **13,** 24–29.
NARIANI, T. K., & K. V. PINGALEY (1960): A mosaic disease of soybean (Glycine max (L.) Merr). Indian Phytopath. **13,** 130–136.
NEGI, L. S., & T. K. NARIANI (1970): A mosaic disease of broad bean (*Vicia faba* L.). Proc. 57th Session of Indian Science Congress, Kharagpur, p. 545.
ZAUMEYER, W. J., & H. R. THOMAS (1957): A monographic study of bean diseases and methods of their control. USDA Bull. No 868.

[1] With kind permission by Dr. K. C. Ling from "Rice virus diseases". IRRI 1972

Sugarcane ratoon stunting virus (Fig. 12)

Disease: Ratoon stunting; rabougrissement du canne á sucre; rachitismo de la caña de azucar. Sugarcane ratoon stunting virus (RSD) has also been associated with the so called 'decline' or 'deterioration' of sugarcane. Tolerance to dilution of infectious juices, mode of transmission and association of certain spheroid particles in the affected tissues indicate that the disease is of virus origin. However, recent reports from USA (Gillaspie et al 1973) and Australia (Teakle et al 1974) have indicated an association of coryneform bacterium with disease.

Geographical distribution: Ratoon stunting disease was first recognized in particularly poor ratoon of variety Q 28 in Australia. It has since been reported from almost all important sugarcane growing areas of the world. (CMI map no 318).
RSD is a major deterrent to ratooning of sugarcane, the most profitable part in sugarcane culture. Reduction in yields, varying with variety, disease incidence and agronomic practices, has been reported to be 10 to 15 % in plant cane in Australia, about 20 % in Taiwan and Natal and up to 50 % in USA. The disease does not cause any reduction in the sugar content in juice.

Host plants: RSD can be transmitted to several grasses such as *Chloris gayana, Brachiaria mutica, Cynodon dactylon, Sporobolus capensis, Imperata cylindrica, Panicum maximum, Sorghum verticilliflorum,* etc., through artificial inoculation, though RSD has not so far been observed on any of these plants in nature (Steindl 1961).

Symptoms: The absence of any easily discernible physical symptom makes the diagnosis of the disease very difficult. Diseased plants usually exhibit stunted growth, poor root system, reduced tillering, shortened internodes and thin stalks. Orange red vascular fibres have been seen within the mature nodes of many varieties (Q 28, Co L 9, Co 975, Co 6611) (Fig. 12). However, many varieties are known to behave as symptomless carriers. In such varieties appearance of pink colour in the meristematic tissues at the growing point has been reported to be a patent symptom.

Several chemical tests to detect the disease in sugar cane stalks have been developed. On treating longitudinally sliced nodes with a mixture of hydrogen peroxide and hydrochloric acid, Farrar (1957) observed blue green coloration of the parenchyma around vascular stands of healthy canes, while diseased canes did not develop any such colour. Antoine (1958) reported that sections of nodal tissues when treated with 0,5 % 2,3,5 triphenyl tetrazolium chloride developed red colour. The red colour, extracted with acetone, was more in diseased tissues than in the healthy ones. Recently, Matsuoka (1972) reported that *Pennisetum purpureum* could be used as an indicator plant, wherein 80 to 100 % of the inoculated plants developed well defined nodal symptoms on inoculation with standard inoculum.

Fig. 12.

Epidemiology: The disease spreads through cane harvesting implements. No insect vector is involved in the dissemination of the disease. From Cuba it is reported that RSD is transmitted by rats. Similarly, jackals and foxes are also known to spread infection.

Control: Hot water (2 to $2^1/_2$ hours at 50 °C) and hot air therapy (8 to 9 hrs. at 54 °C) effectively inactivate the virus in canes. The duration of treatment depends largely upon the thickness of the stalks to be treated. Crop raised from heat treated seed cane grows vigorously and gives rise to good ratoons. Bud damage is less on hot air treatment as compared to hot water treatment. Hot air treatment units have been designed to take whole cane. It has recently been observed that by raising the humidity within the hot air chamber, the duration of the treatment could be reduced. Even the so called 'deteriorated' varieties have shown revival of their earlier vigour after heat therapy.

Among disease susceptible varieties some tend to deteriorate at a rate slower than others, while CP 29/116 is highly tolerant. Wismer (1971) report, that clones of H 60–6909 failed to transmit the disease to indicator clones even after repeated inoculations, indicates possibility of breeding for resistance against RSD.

Literature

ANTOINE, R. (1958): A staining technique for detecting ratoon stunting disease in sugarcane. Nature **81**, 276–277.

FARRAR, L. L. (1957): A chemical test for ratoon stunting disease of sugarcane. Phytopathology **47**, 10 (Abs.).

GILLASPIE, A. G. JR., R. E. DAVIS & J. F. WORLEY (1973): Diagnosis of ratoon stunting disease based on the presence of specific microorganism. Plant Dis. Rep. **57**, 987–900.

MARTIN, J. P., E. V. ABBOTT & C. G. HUGHES (1961): Sugarcane diseases of the world. Vol **1**. Elsevier Pub. Company, Amsterdam.

MATSUOKA, S. (1972): Ratoon stunting disease diagnosis with elephant grass as an indicator plant. Sugarcane Pathologists Newsletter **8**, 10–11.

STEINDL, D. R. L. (1961): Ratoon stunting disease. In Sugarcane diseases of the world. Vol 1. Ed. Martin et al. Elsevier Pub. Company, Amsterdam.

TEAKLE, D. S., P. M. SMITH & D. R. L. STEINDL (1974): Association of a Bacterium with R. S. D. Sugarcane Pathologists Newsletter **11/12**, 13.

WISMER, C. A. (1971): A sugarcane clone apparently immune to RSD. Sugarcane Pathologists Newsletter **6**, 46.

Authors: Kishan Singh, & V. P. Agnihotri

Other virus diseases of sugarcane

Sugarcane chlorotic streak virus.
Sugarcane dwarf virus.
Sugarcane Fiji disease virus, Ref. CMI/AAB Description no 119.
Sugarcane mosaic virus, Ref. CMI/AAB Description no 88
  with the following strains:
  Abaca mosaic virus.
  Maize dwarf mosaic virus (Table 1).
  Maize mosaic virus.
  Sorghum concentric ring spot virus.
  Sorghum red stripe disease virus.
Sugarcane sereh disease virus.
Sugarcane streak virus.
Sugarcane striate mosaic virus.
Sugarcane white leaf disease.

Tomato spotted wilt virus (Fig. 13 a–e)

R/*:*/*:S/S:S/Th

Disease: Tomato spotted wilt; Bronzefleckenkrankheit; maladie des taches de bronze de la tomate; peste negra del tomate. For synonyms, see Martyn (1968).

Geographical distribution: Spotted wilt, caused by tomato spotted virus (TSWV), was first reported in Australia in 1919; today the disease occurs world-wide, mainly distributed in temperate and subtropical regions. Under favourable conditions, it may become the most serious tomato disease, causing complete crop losses.

Host plants: The host range includes 181 species within 46 families, including 7 *Monocotyledoneae,* and important crops such as tobacco, potato, peppers, eggplant, groundnut and lettuce. The families *Solanaceae* and *Compositae* contain the largest number of hosts among which the following are a frequent source of the virus: *Nicotiana tabacum, Solanum tuberosum, S. nigrum, S. dulcamara, S. melongena, Lycopersicon esculentum, Datura stramonium, Nicandra physaloides, Physalis peruviana, P. brasiliensis, Capsicum annuum, C. frutescens, Petunia spp., Amaranthus* spp., *Bidens pilosa, Lactuca sativa, Tropaeolum majus* and *Portulaca oleracea.*

Symptoms: The symptoms of spotted wilt may vary according to the virus strain, environmental conditions, host and plant age. The disease affects tomatoes at any age, but particularly younger plants ready for transplanting.
One of the first characteristic symptoms in affected tomato plants is a bronze-colored marking on the upper surface of leaflets, generally followed by a downward curling of the leaves (Fig. 13a).

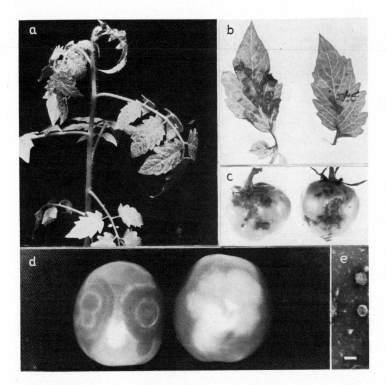

Fig. 13.

Under favourable conditions such bronzing commonly appears as necrotic spots (Fig. 13b); necrosis may continue towards the petioles and stem, reaching the top and causing the plant to die. Occasionally, depending on the strain, diseased plants exhibit an apparent recovery, but in most of these cases a poor yield results.

The young affected plants show stunting and frequently a pale yellowish colouring of the leaves occurs. Although downward curling is more common, some cases of upward curling of leaflets may occur. In developed diseased plants the symptoms are generally less severe; the young leaves may show characteristic symptoms but the plants usually survive.

Green fruits of diseased plants show necrotic, irregular, sometimes circular and depressed spots (Fig. 13c). Ripe fruits show skin discoloration or concentric rings (Fig. 13d). Differential hosts are *Nicotiana glutinosa, Nicotiana tabacum,* and *Petunia hybrida.* Other plants such as *Cucumis sativus, Vinca rosea* and *Tropaeolum majus* are also used as differential hosts. For similarities with other virus diseases of this crop s. table 2.

Morphology: TSWV particles are approximately isometric, with slight variation in shape (Fig. 13e, bar represents 100 nm). The particles range in diameter from 85 nm to 125 nm, and are bounded by a membrane which has protuberances or spikes projecting from the outside surface. TSWV is one of the most unstable plant viruses. The thermal inactivation point (10 min.) varies from 41 °C to 46 °C; dilution end point is between 10^{-4} and 10^{-5} and the longevity in vitro (room temperature) is 2–5 hrs. The virus is not resistant to desiccation.

Physiological specialization: Several strains of TSWV have been reported as causing considerable variation in the symptomatology, but these differences in symptomatology cannot always be attributed to different strains. Norris reported five strains, one of them causing severe tip blight symptoms; Best & Gallus described six strains, referred to as A, B, C_1, C_2, D and E. Strain A, the most severe, has been called "tomato tip blight virus".

Epidemiology: TSWV is naturally transmitted by the following thrips: *Frankliniella schultzei, F. occidentalis, F. fusca,* and *Thrips tabaci* (p. 282). The insects can acquire the virus in the larval stage; if they do not acquire it during this stage, they cannot transmit it at all. The shortest period of virus acquisition was reported as 15 minutes. The incubation period varies according to the thrips species and is between 4 and 18 days. The retention period of TSWV also varies, according to the thrips species between 24 and 43 days. It seems that the infectivity can be retained throughout the life time of the insects, but does not persist through the eggs.

Transmission of TSWV by mechanical means is easy. Reports on seed borne virus are as yet contradictory.

Control: Several factors must be considered regarding the control of spotted wilt, namely:

1. Crop installation – Crop installation near gardens, vegetable – gardens and old crops (chiefly peppers, tomato, tobacco, eggplant and potato), must be avoided because such crops may be source of the virus and colonized by the vector.

2. Crop transplanting time – Transplanting time, whenever possible, must not coincide with wetter and warmer months. This practice is especially advisable in regions where such environmental conditions prevail favouring vector proliferation.

3. Cultural practices – The crop and surrounding areas should be maintained free from possible reservoirs (see host list) of the virus. Plant refuse, from one planting season to the next, as well as volunteer tomato plants, solanaceous and other weeds growing in the neighbouring crop, must be eradicated.

4. Natural barriers – Costa et al. reported that physical barriers of *Crotalaria juncea,* surrounding a tobacco crop, reduced thrips' migration from outside to the crop, thereby reducing the attack of spotted wilt. This practice could also be used for tomato crops.

5. Vector control – As the thrips are the most important means of introduction and propagation of spotted wilt within the crop, their control and the elimination of host plants from which the vector

can spread the virus, are the most efficient measures for reducing the disease. Thrips control is obtained by periodical applications of suitable insecticides, starting in the nursery but mainly after transplanting. At this time, the chemical treatment must be applied more frequently then gradually reduced within 2 months. Thereafter treatment can be stopped because at this age the plants are less susceptible. For foliar sprays, organophosphorus insecticides have been widely used.

6. Resistant varieties – The use of resistant varieties could be one of the most effective means of controlling spotted wilt. However, a completely resistant tomato variety has not yet been obtained. Furthermore, a variety which is resistant in one region may not be so in another, because the resistance is influenced by environmental conditions and depends on the virus strains prevalent in a given area.

Whenever possible, the factors every regarding the control of spotted wilt must be considered simultaneously. If this should be impracticable, satisfactory control can be obtained by using local resistant varieties, combined with the elimination of vectors and virus hosts.

Literature

BEST, R. J., & H. P. GALLUS (1953): Strains of tomato spotted wilt virus. Aust. J. Sci. **15,** 212–214.
COSTA, A. S., A. M. B. CARVALHO, C. L. COSTA & H. NAGAI (1964): Molestias de vírus do tomateire. Boletim do Campo, outubro-novembro, 8–26.
GALLI, F., H. TOKESHI, P. C. T. CARVALHO, E. BALMER, H. KIMATI, C. O. N. CARDOSO & C. L. SALGADO (1968): Doenças do Tomateiro. Manual de Fitopatologia. Bibl. Agr. Ceres, São Paulo, p. 558–611.
KLINKOWSKI, M., & H. A. USCHDRAWEIT (1952): Die Bronzefleckenkrankheit der Tomate eine bisher in Deutschland noch nicht beobachtete Viruskrankheit. Phytopath. Z. **19,** 269–283.
NORRIS, D. O. (1946): The strain complex and symptom variability of tomato spotted wilt virus. C.S.I.R.O. (Australia) Bull. 202.
SMITH, K. M. (1957): Tomato spottet wilt. A textbook of plant virus diseases. Little, Brown and Co., Boston.
CMI/AAB Description no 39.

Authors: C. M. Chagas & Marly Vicente

Other virus diseases of tomato: see table 2.

Virus diseases of hosts not referred to in this chapter:

Avocado pear sunblotch virus.
Black pepper stunt virus.
Bottle gourd mosaic virus.
Chilli (pepper) mosaic virus (Puerto Rico).
Coffee blister spot virus.
Coffee ring spot virus.
Cotton anthocyanosis virus.
Cotton leaf crumple virus.
Cotton leaf curl virus. Ref: Tarr (1964) Misc. publ. no 18, CMI.
Cotton leaf roll virus.
Cowpea s. beans (table 3).
Crotolaria (sunn hemp) phyllody virus.
Crotolaria witches broom virus.
Cucumber green mottle mosaic virus.
Cucumber mosaic virus. Ref.: CMI/AAB Description no 1,
    causing numerous diseases on a variety of host plants (see Martyn p. 4); more important strains are: legume strain, lucerne strain, sunflower strain, spinach strain, tobacco strain.
Cucumber necrosis virus. Ref.: CMI/AAB Description no 82.
Cucumber vein yellowing virus.
Cucumber wild mosaic virus. Ref.: CMI/AAB Description no 105.

Table 2. Differential characteristics of the principal tomato viruses

Virus	Symptoms in Tomato	Physical properties			Natural transmission by	Morphology	References
		Thermal inactivation point (10 min)	Dilution end point	Longevity „in vitro"			
Cucumber mosaic $R/1:1/18:S/S:S/Ap$	light mosaic and much narrowing of leaves (fern leaf symptom)	60–70 °C	10^{-4}	3-4 days (room)	aphids	isometric **c.** 35 nm in diameter	CMI / AAB Descr. no 1
Potato leaf roll $*/*:*/*:S/S:S,I/Ap$	rolling of the leaves that become rigid and leathery; yellowing	70 °C	10^{-4}	4 days (2 °C)	several aphid spp.:*Myzus persicae* (p. 333) efficient	isometric 24 nm in diameter	CMI / AAB Descr. no 36
Potato X $R/1:2.1/6:E/E:S/$ (Fu)	mosaic mottle with some necrosis; faint mottle in in some cases	**c.** 70° C	10^{-5}–10^{-6}	several weeks (20 °C)	contact	flexuous **c.** 515 × 13 nm	CMI / AAB Descr. no 4
Potato Y $*/*:*/*:E/E:S/Ap$	vein-clearing and mottling followed by green banding of the veins; masking of the symptoms may occur	56–60 °C	10^{-1}–10^{-3}	1-2 days (room)	several aphid spp.; *Myzus persicae* the most efficient	flexuous **c.** 730 × 11 nm	CMI / AAB Descr. no 37
Tobacco mosaic $R/1:2/5:E/E:S/*$	mottling with raised dark green areas and some distortion of the youngest leaves; stunting	90–93 °C	$\geqq 10^{-6}$	$\geqq$ 1 month (room)	contact	rod-shaped 300 nm × 15 nm	
Tobacco rattle $R/1:2.3 + 0.6$ to $1.3/5$ $:E/E:S/Ne$	yellow bands in ring and line pattern on leaves; mottling	70–80 °C	10^{-3}	20 days (room)	nematode *Trichodorus* spp. (p. 256)	rod-shaped particles of 2 or 3 predominant lengths, one **c.** 190 nm (L) and the other(s) 45-115 nm (S).	CMI / AAB Descr. no 12

	Symptoms	Thermal inactivation	Dilution end point	Longevity in vitro	Vector	Morphology	CMI/AAB Descr.
Tobacco streak (Brasilian strain) * / * : * / * : S / S : S / *	ring spot of the leaflets; malformation of the leaves and narrowing of the corollas	65 °C	1/30–1/15,625	9-27 hrs (room ?)	thrips Franklinella spp.	isometric 27-29 nm and 34 nm in diameter	CMI / AAB Descr. no 44
Tomato aspermy R / 1 : * / * : S / S : S / Ap	leaf mottle, distortion, dwarfing, sometimes with proliferation of axilary shoots; malformed and seedless fruits	50–55° C	10^{-2}-10^{-3}	2 days (room)	aphids	isometric 30 nm in diameter	CMI / AAB Descr. no 79
Tomato black ring R / * : * / 38 : S / S : S / Ne	black necrotic rings on leaves; dark streak on the undersides of the petioles, slight mottling and distortion of the leaves	62 °C	10^{-2}–10^{-4}	7 days (room)	nematode Longidorus spp. (p. 256)	isometric 30 nm in diameter	CMI / AAB Descr. no 38
Tomato bushy stunt R / 1 : 1.5 / 17 : S / S : S / *	yellowing and purplish coloration of the leaves; mottling; stunting and bush growth	80–90° C	10^{-2}–10^{-6}	4–5 weeks (20 °C)	unknown	isometric 30 nm in diameter	CMI / AAB Descr. no 69
Tomato ring spot R / 1 : 2.3 / 40 : S / S : S / Ne	curling and necrosis of the terminals growing shoots; necrotic rings and sinuous lines on the younger leaves; necrotic streaks and rings on petioles and stems	56 °C	2×10^{-3}	21 hrs (room)	nematode Xiphinema americanum (p. 256)	isometric 28 nm in diameter	CMI / AAB Descr. no 18
Tomato spotted wilt R / * : * / * : S / S : S / Th	bronze-colored marking on the upper surface of leaflets; downward curling of the leaves; stunting; spotted fruits	40–46° C	2×10^{-2} 2×10^{-3}	2-5 hrs (room)	thrips Franklinella spp.,Thrips tabaci (p. 282)	isometric 70–90 nm in diameter	CMI/AAB Descr. no 39
Double streak (TMV + X)	mosaic and necrosis on leaves; streaking of the stem and petioles; leaf shed; fruit malformation; stunting	–	–	–	–	–	

Authors : C. M. Chagas & Marly Vicente

Table 3. Principal virus diseases affecting beans in tropical areas

Virus	Characteristic symptoms	Differential hosts
1. Bean common mosaic */* : */* : E / E : S / Ap	Mottling or chlorosis blistering; stunted bushy growth	Refugee Green
2. Bean yellow mosaic */* : */* E / E : S / Ap	Distinct mottling of yellow-green and dark green areas; plants stunted bushy growth	*Teragonia expensa, Crotalaria spectabilis, Gladiolus*
3. Southern bean mosaic R / 1 : 1.4 / 21 : S / S : S / Cl	Mosaic and mottling, necrotic local lesions, puckering and vein-banding may occur	–
4. Mung bean yellow mosaic */* : */* : */* : S / Al	Bright yellow patches interspersed with green areas	–
5. Dolichos lablab yellow mosaic */* : */* : */* * S / Al	Broad bright yellow patches	–
6. Dolichos enation mosaic */* : */* : */* * S / O	Mosaic and chlorotic streaks; leaves malformed and reduced in size with foliar enations on their under surfaces	–
7. Soybean mosaic */* : */* : E / E : S / Ap	Mosaic, leaves reduced in size and puckered with dark green puffy areas; plants stunted growth	–
8. Broad bean mosaic */* : */* : S / S : S / Ap	Mosaic mottling	*Chenopodium amaranticolor,* Cluster bean, *Dolichos lablab, Vigna cylindrica*
9. Cowpea mosaic (Bean (Asparagus) Mosaic) R / 1 : 1.5 / 24 + 2.5 / 33 : S / S : S / Ce	Irregular yellowish and dark green mottling with blisters	*Canavalia ensiformis*
10. Cowpea aphid-borne mosaic */*:*/*:E/E:S/Ap	Severe mosaic with dark green vein-banding or interveinal chlorosis leaf distortion, blistering and stunting	*Chenopodium amaranticolor,* soybean

* 1 : 2 : 3

1 = minimum acquisition period of virus by vector   [4] for further literature see p. 32
2 = incubation period of virus in vector
3 = time taken for ûppearance of symptoms after inoculation
X = unknown   **Author : S. P. Raychaudhuri**

Other hosts	Transmission (1 : 2 : 3*)	Particles	Distribution	References[4]
1. *Phaseolus mungo, P. aureus, P. lunatus, P. calcaratus, P. lathyroides,* Cluster bean, *Crotalaria sericea,* broad bean	Sap transmissible; vectors: *Aphis craccivora* (p. 324) *A. gossypii* (p. 328), *A. evonymi, Myzus persicae* (p. 333), and many others	long rod 750 nm	22 different countries including India	CMI/AAB Description no 73
2. White sweet clover, broad bean and other leguminous species given as susceptible to BCMV with the exception of *P. lunatus, P. calcaratus*	Sap transmissible; styletborne, non-persistent several species of aphids including *Aphis fabae* (p. 326) and *Myzus persicae* 15 sec : X; Seed transmission in broad bean	flexuous rod 750 × 13 – 14 nm	Brazil, China, Cuba, India, Tanzania, USA, Iran.	CMI/AAB Description no 40
3. Cowpea	Sap transmissible; seedborne; vector bean leaf beetle *Ceratoma trifurcata*	isometric 28 nm	Warm temp. & tropical areas of the Americas and Africa; France	CMI/AAB Description no 57
4. *P. mungo,* pigeon pea, horsegram, soybean, *P. vulgaris* var. Manitov and some weeds	Grafting; *Bemisia tabaci* (p. 320) (Whitefly) 15 min : 4hrs : 12 days		India	
5. Nil	*Bemisia tabaci*	–	India	
6. Many hosts in leguminous plants including *Phaseolus vulgaris,* tobacco var. white Burley	Sap transmissible	–	India	
7. Nil	Sap transmissible; several species of aphids, including *Myzus persicae* and *Macrosiphum pisi* ; Seed transmission	flexuous rod 750 ± 25 nm	India, Russia, South Africa, USA and many parts of the world wherever soybean is grown.	CMI/AAB Description no 93
8. Sunn hemp, pea, sweet pea, chickpea, cowpea and some other leguminous plants	Sap transmissible; *Aphis craccivora , A. gossypii, Myzus persicae , Rhopalosiphum maidis , Acrythosiphon pisum*	spherical 25 nm	India	
9. Many hosts in leguminuous plants; *Gomphrena,* Zinnia	Sap transmissible; *Ceratoma ruficormis* (leaf beetle); seed transmission in asparagus bean	24 to 27 nm	USA, Trinidad, Nigeria and South America	CMI/AAB Description no 47
10. Many spp. of Leguminosa, spp. of Chenopodiaceae, Cucurbitaticeae, Solanaceae, etc.	Seedborne (0-3%) also up to 28%; *Aphis craccivora , A. fabae , A. gossypina, A. medicaginis, Macrosiphum euphorbiae* (p. 331), and *Myzus persicae*	flexuous filamentous particles 750 nm	Africa, Asia Europe	CMI/AAB Description no 134

Cucurbit latent virus.
Dolichos enation mosaic virus.
Dolichos lablab yellow mosaic virus.
Eggplant mosaic virus. Ref.: CMI/AAB Description no 124.
Eggplant mottled dwarf virus. Ref.: CMI/AAB Description no 115.
Fig mosaic virus.
Hibiscus esculentus yellow vein mosaic virus.
Jute leaf mosaic virus.
Melon mosaic virus.
Mulberry mosaic virus.
Mulberry ring spot virus. Ref.: CMI/AAB Description no 142.
Okra mosaic virus. Ref.: CMI/AAB Description no 128.
Olive partial paralysis virus.
Passion fruit woodiness virus. Ref.: CMI/AAB Description no 122.
Pepper veinal mosaic mottle virus. Ref.: CMI/AAB Description no 104.
Sorghum concentric ring blotch virus.
Soybean s. beans (table 3).
Squash mosaic virus. Ref.: CMI/AAB Description no 43.
Sunn hemp mosaic virus. Ref.: CMI/AAB Description no 153.
Sweet potato internal cork virus.
Sweet potato mosaic virus.
Sweet potato ring spot virus.
Sweet potato russet crack virus.
Sweet potato vein-clearing virus.
Sweet potato yellow dwarf virus.
Tea phloem necrosis virus.
Watermelon mosaic virus. Ref.: CMI/AAB Description no 63.

Diseases caused by mycoplasmas

Mycoplasmas, or Mycoplasma-like-organism, as they are somtimes called in plant pathology, are unicellular, procaryotic organisms of pleomorphic structures with no cell wall. In vitro they grow on special media and form "fried egg" shaped colonies. Like viruses they are filtrable but are much bigger. Growth of their cells can be inhibited by specific antisera and by tetracyclines. Transmission is effected by leafhoppers, planthoppers, and also by psyllids as vectors, and by grafting and dodder. Common symptomes so far found associated with mycoplasmas are yellowing combined with stunting, stubborn, witches broom or phyllody. Diseases occuring in the tropics and now ascribed to mycoplasmas are listed below (courtesy Dr. S. P. Raychaudhuri). Control measures are similar to those of virus diseases including heat therapy. Antibiotics (tetracyclines) are effective against the diseases.
Not much is known of the biology of mycoplasmas and the diseases they cause.

General Bibliography

DAVIS, R. E., & R. F. WHITCOMB, (1947): Mycoplasmas, Rickettsiae and Chlamydiae: possible relation to yellow diseases and other disorders of plants and insects. Ann. Rev. Phytopathology **9**, 119–154.

HAMPTON, R. O. (1972): Mycoplasmas as plant pathogens. Perspective and principles. Ann. Rev. Plant Physiol. **23**, 389–418.

HULL, R., (1971): Mycoplasma-like organisms in plants. Rev. Plant Path. **50**, 121–130.

MARAMOROSCH, K., R. R. GRANADOS & H. HIRUMI (1970): Mycoplasma diseases of plants and insects. Adv. Virus Res. **16**, 135–193.

MARAMOROSCH, K. (ed.) (1973): Mycoplasma and Mycoplasma-like agents of human, animal and plant diseases. Ann. New York Acadamy Sci. Vol. **225.**

MARTYN, E. B. (ed.) (1971): Plant virus names. Phytopathological Papers, No 9, Suppl. 1, Commonwealth Mycological Institute, Kew, U. K.

Subcomittee on the taxonomy of Mycoplasmatales (1972): Proposal for minimal standards for descriptions of new species of order mycoplasmatales. Int. J. System. Bacteriology **22**, 184–188.

WHITCOMB, R. F., & R. E. DAVIS (1970): Mycoplasma and phytarborviruses as plant pathogens persistently transmitted by insects. Ann. Rev. Entomology **15**, 405–464.

Plant diseases in tropics and subtropics associated with mycoplasma[1]

Disease	Distribution	Vector (where known)	References
Cassava witches' broom	S. America	–	16
Citrus greening			p. 45
Citrus likubin	Taiwan	–	5
Citrus stubborn			p. 47
Coconut lethal yellowing			p. 48
Corn stunt			Table 1
Cotton virescence	W. Africa	–	6
Cowpea witches' broom	India	–	22
Eggplant (brinjal) little leaf	India	–	21, 27, 28
Mulberry dwarf	Far East	Leafhopper	9
Pawpaw bunchy top	Carribean	Leafhopper	24, p.45
Peanut witches' broom	Indonesia	Leafhopper	25, 26
Pigeon pea witches' broom	Puerto Rico	Leafhopper	26
Potato witches' broom	Europe, Far East, India, N. America	Leafhopper	9, 10
Rice 'enrochat'	Europe	–	1
Rice 'giallume'	Europe	–	2, p.32
Rice grassy stunt	Sri Lanka, Philippines	Leafhopper	23, p. 32
Rice 'padi jantan'	Malaysia	Leafhopper	23, p. 32
Rice yellow dwarf	Far East, India	Leafhopper	19, p. 32
Safflower phyllody	Israel	Leafhopper	13
Sandal spike	India, Far East	Leafhopper	8, 11, 20, 27
Sesamum phyllody	Indonesia	Leafhopper	7
Sugarcane grassy shoot			p. 51
Sugarcane white leaf	Taiwan	Leafhopper	15
Sweet potato little leaf	Far East	–	14
Tomato big bud	Australia, Europe, N. & S. America	Leafhopper	4, 12
Tomato 'mal-azul'	Europe	Leafhopper	3
Tomato 'stolbur'	Europe	Leafhopper	18

[1] Compiled by Dr. S. P. Raychaudhuri

References

1. AMICI, A., R. BALLESTEROS, J. A. BATALLA, & G. BELLI (1970): Corpi riferibili a micoplasmi in piante di Riso spagnolo afetto da 'Enrochat'. Riv. Patol. Veg., Padova **6**, 247–253.
2. BELLI, G. (1969): Mycoplasma – like particles in clarified extracts of diseased rice plants. Riv. Patol. Veg., Padova **5**, 105–113 3.
3. BORGES, M., V. de LOURDES & J. F. DAVID-FERREIRA (1968): Presence of mycoplasma in *Lycopersicon esculentum* Mill. with "Mal Azul" Bol. Soc. Broteriana **42**, 321–333.
4. BOWYER, J. W., J. G. ATHERTON, D. S. TEAKLE & G. A. AHERN (1696): Mycoplasma-like bodies in plants affected by legume little leaf, tomato big bud and lucerne witches'broom diseases. Aust. J. biol. Sci. **22**, 271–274.
5. CHEN, M. H., T. MIYAKAWA & C. MATSUI (1971): Mycoplasma-like bodies associated with Likubin diseased Ponkan citrus. Phytopathology **61**, 598.
6. COUSIN, M. T., P. L. MAILLET & J. P. GOURRET (1969): La virescence du cotonnier (*Gossypium hirsutum* L.) novelle maladie a mycoplasmas. C.r. hebd. Seanc. Acad. Sci. Paris (Sect. D) **268**, 2382–2384.
7. COUSIN, M. T., J. P. MOREAU, T. STARON & A. FAIVERE-AMIOT (1970b): Le deperissement jaune du Lavendin nouvelle maladie a mycoplasmas. Annls Phytopath. **2**, 227–237.
8. DIJKSTRA, J. & T. S. LE (1969): Presence of mycoplasma-like bodies in the phloem of sandal affected with spike disease. Neth. J. Pl. Path. **75**, 374–378.
9. DOI, Y., M. TERANAKA, K. YORA & H. ASUYAMA (1967): Mycoplasma or PLT group-like microorganisms found in the phloem elements of plants infected with mulberry dwarf, potato witches' broom, aster yellows, or Paulownia witches'broom. Ann. Phytopath. Soc. Japan **33**, 259–266.
10. HARRISON, B. D. & I. M. ROBERTS (1969): Association of mycoplasma-like bodies with potato witches'broom disease from Scotland. Ann. appl. Biol. **63**, 347–349.
11. HULL, R., R. W. HORNE & R. M. NAYAR (1969): Mycoplasma – like bodies associated with sandal spike disease. Nature, Lond. **224**, 1121–1122.
12. KITAJIMA, E. W. & A. S. COSTA (1968): Estructuras do tipo mycoplasma no floema de Tomateira afetado pelo calice gigante. Bragentia 27, Nota **23**, 97–99.
13. KLEIN, M. (1970): Safflower phyllody – a mycoplasma disease of *Carthamus tinctorius* in Israel, Plant Dis. Reptr. **54**, 735–738.
14. LAWSON, R. H., R. P. KAHAN, S. HEARSON & F. F. SMITH (1970): The association of mycoplasma-like bodies with sweet potato little leaf (witches'broom) disease. Phytopathology **60**, 1016.
15. LIN, S. C., C. S. LEE & R. J. CHIU (1970): Isolation and cultivation of an innoculation with a mycoplasma causing white leaf disease of sugarcane. Phytopathology **60**, 795–797.
16. MARAMOROSCH, K., R. R. GRANADOS & H. HIRUMI (1970): Mycoplasma diseases of plants and insects. Adv. Virus Res. **16**, 136–193.
17. MARAMOROSCH, K., E. SHIKATA & R. R. GRANADOS (1968): Structures resembling mycoplasma in diseased plants and in insects vectors. Trans. N. Y. Acad. Sci. **30**, 841–855.
18. MARCHOUX, G., J. GIANNOTTI & H. LATERROT (1969): The stolbur P. une nouvelle maladie de type jaunisse chez la tomate. Symptomes et examen cytologique des tissues au microscope electronique. Ann. Phytopath. **1**, 633–640.
19. PLAVSIC-BANJAC, Biljana, K. MARAMOROSCH, V. T. JOHN & S. P. RAYCHAUDHURI (1973): Rice yellow dwarf in India: Mycoplasma-like etiology. FAO Plant Prot. Bull. **21**, 1–4.
20. PLAVSIC-BANJAC, Biljana, K. MARAMOROSCH, S. P. RAYCHAUDHURI, V. V. CHENULU, A. VARMA & S. K. GOSH (1973): Electron microscopy of graft-transmitted sandal spike. FAO Plant Prot. Bull. **21**, 25–26.
21. RAYCHAUDHURI, S. P., A. VARMA, V. V. CHENULU, N. PRAKASH & S. SINGH (1970): Association of mycoplasma-like bodies with little leaf of *Solanum melongena*. X. Int. Cong. Microbiol. 222 (Abst.).
22. SHARMA, S. R. & A. VARMA (1975): Virus and virus-like diseases of cowpea in northern India. Proc. 62nd Indian Sci. Congr. Part III p. 74–75 (Abstr.).
23. SINGH, K. G., Y. SAITO & S. NASU (1970): Mycoplasma-like structures in rice plant infected with 'padi jantan' disease. Malay Agric. J. **47**, 333–337.
24. STOREY, G. E. & R. S. HALLIWELL (1969): Association of a mycoplasma-like organism with the bunchy top disease of Papaya. Phytopathology **59**, 1336–1337.
25. TRIHARSO (1972): Peanut witches'broom associated with mycoplasma like bodies. INSA Symp. Mycoplasma Diseases. p. 38.
26. VAKILI, NADER G. & K. MARAMOROSCH (1974): Witches'Broom disease caused by mycoplasma-like organisms on pigeon peas (*Cajanus cajan*) in Puerto Rico. Plant. Dis. Reptr. **58**, 96.
27. VARMA, A., V. V. CHENULU, S. P. RAYCHAUDHURI, N. PRAKASH & R. S. RAO (1969): Mycoplasma-like bodies in tissues infected with sandal spike and brinjal leaf. Indian Phytopath. **22**, 289–291.
28. VARMA, A., A. SANG, S. K. GHOSH, S. P. RAYCHAUDHURI, V. V. CHENULU & N. PRAKASH (1974): Probable mycoplasmal etiology of broom bush witches'broom. Curr. Sci. **43**, 349–350.

Papaw bunchy top

Disease: Büschelkrankheit der Papaya; Sommet touffu; cogollo racimoso.

Geographical distribiton: Puerto Rico, Cuba, Haiti, Jamaica and Trinidad.

Symptoms: Faint mottling of upper leaves, followed by wrinkleness and yellowing. Internodes progressively shortened, petioles acquiring horizontal position. Complete cessation of apical growth gives the plant a "bunchy top" appearance. The main diagnostic characteristic is failure of latex to flow when the plant is wounded.

Epidemiology: Transmission by grafting and the leafhopper vector *Empoasca papaya;* not by sap or through seeds.

Control: Effective control has been achieved by application of insecticides against the leafhopper vector. Also topping of infected plants below the point of latex exudation followed by protection of new growth with insecticides. Remission of symptoms following soil drenching with chlortetracycline hydrochloride (at 3-day intervals).

Literature

STOREY, G. E. & R. S. HALLIWELL (1969): Association of mycoplasmalike organism with the bunchy top disease of papaya. Phytopathology **59**, 1336–1337.

Author: José Adsuar

Citrus greening (Plate 2 a)

Disease: Yellow branch disease; Vergrünen; le greening; enverdecimiento.

Geographical distribution: Citrus greening disease has been recorded in the southern region of Africa (South Africa, Swaziland, Rhodesia, Madagascar, Réunion etc.) and in south-east Asia (India, Nepal, Pakistan, Thailand, China, Taiwan, the Philippines, Hong Kong, Indonesia etc.). It is sometimes difficult to know whether citrus greening or citrus stubborn is present in certain of these countries.

Host plants: Susceptible citrus: – almost all commercial varieties. The most severe symptoms are to be found on sweet orange (*C. sinensis*), mandarin or tangerine (*C. reticulata, C. deliciosa*), and tangelo (*C. paradisi* x *C. reticulata*).
Susceptible herbaceous plants: – unknown.
Resistant citrus: – unknown.
Tolerant citrus: – trifoliate orange (*P. trifoliata*) and citrange (*C. sinensis* x *P. trifoliata*) are less susceptible than other species but they can show leaf symptoms.

Symptoms: The disease (Plate 2a) causes dwarfing of trees, relatively little foliage and dead shoots. The leaves are often chlorotic or marbled with prominent yellowish veins. Foliar discolourations can resemble symptoms of zinc or magnesium deficiency. A single branch will often be more acutely affected than the rest of the tree.

Fruits are often deformed and grow lop-sided. The side of a fruit facing the sun develops a normal colour whereas the shaded surface has lesions which remain green, a condition which gives rise to the name of the disease. If the fruit skin is pressed, a silvery-white halo appears. The seeds frequently abort and the juice is acid or bitter.

Comparison with other disorders: – Stubborn: a very similar disease, seen especially in the northern hemisphere, which induces less severe symptoms on mandarin than does greening. Fruits with an appearance of acorns are more characteristic of stubborn (see below).

Mineral deficiency: Symptoms not transmissible and can be eliminated by foliar nutrient sprays.

Morphology: Until 1970, greening was believed to be caused by a virus, but Lafleche and Bové (1970a, 1970b) and later Chen et al. (1971) discovered mycoplasma-like microorganisms in the tissues of citrus seeds inoculated with greening. The causal agent has a membrane 200 A° thick, twice the thickness of *Spiroplasma citri*. It has not yet proved possible to culture the microorganism in vitro.

Physiological specialization: Strains of greening are known. Some induce symptoms at 24 °C (southern Africa strain) whereas others (from India and the Philippines) require a temperature of about 30 °C.

Epidemiology: Normal transmission: – by grafting scion wood and buds. Two vectors are known, *Trioza erytreae* (p. 319), the african psyllid from the southern region of Africa, and *Diaphorina citri,* the asian psyllid from southeast Asia.

Experimental transmission: – by grafting buds, pieces, of bark and especially very young leaves, 1–1.5 cm long. Also by psyllids.

No antiserum has been obtained.

Control: The severity of greening can be halved by injecting trees with solutions of tetracyclines at 1000 ppm. Heat treatment of scion wood also reduces the propagation of the disease. Disease-free lines are sought by indexing and from nucellar selections.

Indexing: – Indicator plant: seed-raised sweet orange or tangelo Orlando, aged 12–18 months. Method: grafting each indicator plant with two young leaves from the candida tree. The indicators must be maintained at 24 °C for cases of greening caused by the southern Africa strain, and at 30 °C for the south-east Asia strain. Incubation: 2–6 months. Symptoms: small chlorotic or marbled leaves on stems with short internodes. The plants are stunted in comparison with the controls. A fluorescent compound, gentisic acid glycoside, is found in the bark of sweet orange trees affected by greening and in the pith of their fruits. Although non-specific, this compound is of considerable value in indexing.

Nucellar selection: – seed-grown plants are free of greening and can be protected from subsequent contamination by vectors. This type of selection is possible with all polyembryonic varieties of citrus.

Literature

CHEN, M. H., T. MIYAKAWA & C. MATSUI (1971): Mycoplasmalike bodies associated with Likubin diseased Ponkan Citrus. Phytopathology **61**, 589.

LAFLECHE, D., & J. M. BOVE (1970b): Mycoplasmes dans les agrumes atteints de Greening, de Stubborn ou de maladies similaires. Fruits, **25**, 455–465.

SAGLIO, P., D. LAFLECHE, C. BONISSOL & J. M. BOVÉ (1971): Isolement et culture in vitro des mycoplasmes associés au Stubborn des agrumes et leur observation au microscope électronique. C. R. Acad. Sci. Paris, **272**, 1387–1390.

SCHWARZ, R. E. (1965): A fluorescent substance present in tissues of Greening affected sweet orange. S. Africa J. Agr. Sci **8**, 1177–1180.

Author: J. M. Bové

Citrus stubborn (Plate 2 b)

Disease: Little leaf, acorn disease; Stubborn; stubborn; stubborn.

Geographical distribution: Citrus stubborn occurs in all citrus-growing regions (CMI map no 375). The effects of the disease are mainly seen in the hottest areas (Arizona, California, Morocco etc.).

Host plants: Susceptible citrus (symptoms visible): – almost all commercial varieties. Symptoms are most severe on sweet orange (*C. sinensis*) Washington Navel, grapefruit (*C. paradisi*), tangelo (*C. paradisis* x *C. reticulata*), satsuma (*C. unshiu*), mandarin or tangerine (*C. reticulata, C. deliciosa*) etc.
Susceptible herbaceous plants: – unknown.
Resistant citrus: – unknown.
Tolerant citrus (no visible symptoms): – the citranges Troyer and Curringham, but there have not induced tolerance to scions grafted onto them.

Symptoms: Stunting more or less acute, numerous dead branches, and a bushy appearance of the tree (Plate 2b). Crop yield is very poor or even reduced to nothing. Leaves are small and may be mottled, or discoloured to resemble mineral deficiencies; the central vein is discoloured and often thick. The leaves are frequently cup-shaped and stand well out from the branch. Short internodes give a bushy appearance, and multiple branching produces "witches'brooms". Flowering is irregular so that immature fruits are present at all seasons. Young fruits grow lop-sided with a curved central axis. The rind is thicker on the peduncular half of the fruit than on the distal half, where the epidermis is smoother and glossier. This gives an appearance of oak acorns which is diagnostic of stubborn, although under certain conditions the fruits become cylindrical.
In grapefruit, the pith of the rind can be blue instead of the normal white colour. (This effect can also be produced by 2,4,5-T).
Affected fruits have a weak epidermis and often show dry rots. The seeds are black and aborted, and the juice is acid or bitter. The flesh of "blood" varieties is less coloured than normal. Infected trees may show 'inverse pitting' ('pinholing' or 'honeycombing') near the graft union, but this symptom can also be caused by tristeza. Comparison with similar conditions: Citrus greening: – causes similar symptoms but usually with more defoliation and dead wood. However, on mandarin the damage is more acute with stubborn. Mineral deficiency: – symptoms of zinc, magnesium and boron deficiency resemble certain features of stubborn, but can be distinguished by indexing.

Morphology: Until 1970, stubborn was believed to be a virus disease. However, mycoplasma-like bodies have been found in the phloem tissue of citrus seeds inoculated with stubborn (Igwegbe and Calavan, 1970; Lafleche and Bové, 1970). This micro-organism has been successfully cultured in vitro (Saglio et al. 1971), characterized biologically, biochemically and serologically (Bové and Saglio, 1972), and named *Spiroplasma citri*. It has a single membrane 100 A° thick, compared with 200 A° thick in the case of the microorganism associated with citrus greening.

Physiological specialization: Biological tests have already revealed two strains, from California and Morocco respectively. Others may exist.

Transmission: Normal by grafting infected scion wood or buds. One or more vectors are suspected but not identified. Seed transmission has not been demonstrated.
Experimental by grafting buds, pieces of bark and, in particular, very young leaves 1–1.5 cm long.

Control: No therapeutic treatment in yet available for plantation trees, but antibiotics of the tetracycline type are under trial.

Disease-free lines are sought by indexing, and with the support of the electron microscope and in vitro techniques of culturing *Spiroplasma citri*. Nucellar selections are also used.

Indexing Indicator plant: seed-grown orange Mme Vinous or Hamlin, aged 12–18 months. Method: grafting two young leaves from the candidate tree onto each indicator plant. Conditions favouring symptom development: indicator plants kept at 32 °C during the day and 27 °C at night. Incubation for 2–10 months. Symptoms are mottling, discolouration and size reduction of leaves. Direct examination for *Spiroplasma citri* in growing phloem tissues, using the electron microscope. The in vitro method of Saglio et al (1971) can be used to confirm the results of indexing. Nucellar selection: – Plants raised from seed are free of stubborn. This technique is useful with polyembryonic varieties of citrus if the plants grown from apomictic seeds are protected from vectors.

Literature

BOVÉ, J. M., & SAGLIO (1972): Stubborn 1969–1972. Proc. 6th Conf. Intern. Org. Citrus Virol.
IGWEBGE, E. C. K., & E. C. CALAVAN (1970): Occurence of mycoplasmalike bodies in phloem of Stubborn infected Citrus seedlings. Phytopathology **60**, 1525–1526.
LAFLECHE, D., & J. M. BOVÉ (1970): Mycoplasmas dans les agrumes atteints de Greening, de Stubborn ou de maladies similaires. Fruits, **25**, 455–465.
SAGLIO, P., D. LAFLECHE, C. BONISSOL & J. M. BOVÉ (1971): Culture in vitro des mycoplasmes associés au stubborn des agrumes et leur observation au microscope électronique. C. R. Acad. Sci. Série D. **272**, 1387–1390.

Author: J. M. Bové

Lethal yellowing disease of coconuts (Plates 2 c, d, 3 a, b, c, and fig. 14)

Synonyms: Kaincopé et "Cape St. Paul wilt" du cocotier (plate 3c), Coronie wilt (?)

Disease: Lethal yellowing of coconut caused by mycoplasma-like bodies. Tödliche Vergilbung der Kokospalme; Pudrición del cogollo del cocotero.

Geographical distribution: The disease is widespread in the Caribbean region (Jamaica, Cayman Islands, Cuba, Bahama Islands, the Dominican Republic, Haiti) and extends as far as the southern parts of Florida. A special strain (Coronie wilt) of this disease seems to be present in Surinam. Outside the West Indies, the disease occurs in West Africa in the region of the Gulf of Guinea (Ghana, Togo, Nigeria, Cameroon), where it is known by various names. The somewhat similar Cadang-Cadang disease of Coconut in the Philippines seems to have no connection with Lethal Yellowing. (Rickettsias or viroids suspected to be the cause of the disease.)

Host plants: Lethal Yellowing has so far only been found on Coconut. However, Parthasarathy (1974) has recently found a mycoplasma on some other palm species in Florida.

Symptoms: The mycoplasmosis affects young and old coconut trees of susceptible varieties equally. On young $1^{1}/_{2}$–2 year old trees, disease symptoms show as a yellowing of the oldest fronds, starting mostly at the tip (Plate 2c). The yellowing spreads gradually to other fronds. The pinnae turn brown and dry up, until finally the innermost fronds alone have remained green or yellowish green. Eventually, even these show symptoms of the disease. At the very start of the disease, more or less extensive brown necrotic lesions can be seen on the so-called spear – the lance-like closed up pinnae of the youngest frond pushing through. As the disease progresses, these necrotic lesions extend deeply inwards (Plate 2d), finally killing off the growing point. No necrotic lesions or discolourations can be seen at basal cross sections of the stem through the midrib of fronds. The cut surface is off-white. The young plant dies within 3–6 months after symptoms are first noticed. On nut bearing palms, the disease starts similarly with yellowing of the oldest fronds. In addition, unripe nuts drop prematurely and can be seen heaped around the tree. Necrotic lesions on the spear are not readily distinguished (even with field glasses) owing to the height of the crown, but young inflorescences are visibly blackened (necroses) even before the trusses burst through their enclosing sheath. The disease progresses towards the apical regions of the palm (centre palm in plate 3a), one frond after the other breaks and hangs brown and withered on the stem until it finally drops off. A small tuft of greenish yellow or completely yellow fronds remains for a longer period, but finally succumbs as well. Within half a year, the destruction is complete (Plate 3a). On opening the growing region of a felled, diseased palm which still has some fronds, the inside is seen to be extensively affected by a brown necrosis (much as in plate 2d) and the process is accompanied by an unpleasant smell of anaerobic rot.

Since the symptoms of Lethal Yellowing on palm are easily mistaken for those of bud rot or red ring disease (p. 241), the salient features of these diseases will be briefly described. Bud rot, a rotting of the growing zone, can be caused by *Phytophthora palmivora* (Plate 3b, p. 83) or by bacteria. Typically, the inner core of the young coconut palm dies and rots, without accompanying unpleasant smell. The outermost fronds remain green for months without wilting. Basal cross sections and longitudinal sections through the fronds of bud rot diseased palms show orange coloured areas of varying intensity. These discolourations seem to be absent in the less frequent bacterial bud rot infections. The symptoms of red ring disease (p. 241), greatly resemble Lethal Yellowing on young palms, but there is no necrosis of the spike. The main distinguishing feature of the disease is a red, ring shaped discolouration in the stem, discolouration in the stem, and a red-orange discolouration with brown center in leaf stalks (the last symptom sufficient for diagnosis, no felling necessary).

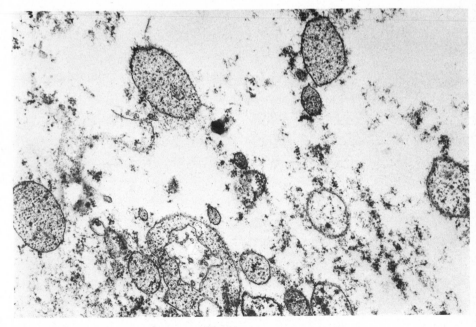

Fig. 14.

Morphology: The presence of mycoplasmas in the phloem of diseased palms has been confirmed repeatedly by electron-microscopy (Fig. 14), and there is little doubt that they are responsible for the Lethal Yellowing of coconut palm. In addition, the disease could be cured, or at least arrested with temporarily diminished symptoms, by means of tetracycline treatment, which also indicates that mycoplasma-like bodies are the pathogen concerned.

Epidemiology: The incubation period for Lethal Yellowing on young palms is about 3–6 months and appears to last up to 10–15 months for bearing trees. Presumably the disease vectors are leaf-hoppers (fulgorids?), since leaf psyllids (suckers) (Psylloidea) were not found on palms in affected regions. Present experience shows, that other insect groups do not transmit mycoplasma. Cage trials have shown that soil borne organisms also do not function as vectors. Despite assertions to the contrary, the disease can not be transmitted mechanically.

Control: Since Lethal Yellowing of coconut results in enormous annual losses (in Jamaica alone about 60 000 palms die every year) and as scenic decor also greatly affects the tourist trade (see plate 3a), great efforts have been made to control the disease. Large-scale insecticide sprays could reduce local attack by half, but are uneconomical, since treatments would have to be carried out at monthly intervals, to be effective. Rogueing of diseased palms is usually too late, owing to the long incubation period during which symptomless or slightly diseased trees may be source of infection. The variety "Malayan Dwarf" is resistant to Lethal Yellowing, but has certain disadvantages (smaller nuts, early ripening low on the stem, greater demands on moisture, fertilizer etc.). In Jamaica, cultivation of coconut has concentrated more on this variety.

Literature

BEAKBANE, B., C. H. W. SLATER & A. F. POSNETTE (1972): Mycoplasmas in the phloem of coconut, *Cocos nucifera,* with lethal yellowing disease. J. hort. Sci. **47,** 265.
GRYLLS, N. E., & P. HUNT (1971): Studies on the aetiology of coconut lethal yellowing in Jamaica by mechanical and bacteria inoculations and by insect vectors. Oléagineux **26,** (8–9), 543–549.
HARRIES, H. C. (1973): Selection and breeding of coconuts for resistance to diseases such as lethal yellowing. Oléagineux **28,** 395–398.
HEINZE, K. G., H. PETZOLD & R. MARWITZ (1972): Beitrag zur Tödlichen Vergilbung der Kokospalme (Lethal Yellowing Disease of Coconut Palm). Phytopath. Z. **74,** 230–237.
HEINZE, K. G., M. SCHUILING & D. ROMNEY (1972): The possible cause of lethal yellowing disease of coconut. FAO Plant Prot. Bull. **20,** 58–68.
McCOY, R. B. (1972): Remission of Lethal Yellowing in Coconut Palm treated with Tetracycline Antibiotics. Plant Dis. Reptr. **56,** 1019–1021.
PARTHASARATHY, M. V. (1974): Mycoplasmalike organisms associated with lethal yellowing disease of palms. Phytopathology **64,** 667–674.
PLAVSIĆ-BANJAC, B., P. HUNT & K. MARAMOROSCH (1972): Mycoplasma-like bodies associated with yellowing disease of coconut palms. Phytopathology **62,** 298–299.
PRICE, W. C., A. P. MARTINEZ & D. A. ROBERTS (1967): Mechanical transmission of coconut lethal yellowing. FAO Plant Prot. Bull. **15,** 105–108.
WHITEHEAD, R. A. (1968): Selection and breeding coconut palms resistant to lethal yellowing disease. Euphytica **17,** 81–101.

Author: Kurt Heinze

Sugarcane grassy shoot (Fig. 15)

Disease: Grassy shoot disease; neue chlorotische Krankheit des Zuckerrohrs; "grassy shoot" de la canne à sucre; mata zacatosa.
'

The pathogen: Till Corbett et al. (1971) demonstrated the presence of mycoplasma-like bodies in the phloem cells of diseased tissues, the disease was considered to be of virus origin.

Geographical distribution: India and Sri Lanka. Depending on the variety and degree of infection in planting material, the disease has been observed to range from 1 to 45 per cent in plant crop and 4 to 85 per cent in the ratoons of commercial crops. The effect of the disease is far more severe when sugarcane is infected in the early stages of its growth.

Host plant: Sugarcane.

Symptoms: Grassy shoot is characterised by the production of numerous small and thin tillers with narrow leaves, with or without varying degrees of albinism. Premature and excessive tillering gives a crowded and grass-like appearance to the clump (Fig. 15). The root system in affected clump gets considerably reduced. GSD affected clumps are usually stunted and in many instances exhibit premature proliferation of buds. Hardly one or two millable canes are produced in a clump raised from a diseased seed piece. The disease exhibits different types of symptoms at various stages of growth and because of this the GSD has been given different names such as – 'bunchy disease', 'yellowing', 'stunting', 'new chlorotic disease' and 'albino' from time to time at different places. Profuse tillering, a common feature to all of them, leaves little doubt that all reported cases, irrespective of the name, refer to GSD. As regards albinism, the condition does not positively confirm the presence of GSD as it could also be due to disturbance in the Fe/Mn ratio in the diseased plants. "White leaf disease" of sugarcane observed in Taiwan is similar to GSD as regards symptomatology but unlike GSD it is transmitted by a hopper, *Epitettix hiroglyphicus*.

Epidemiology: GSD is primarily transmitted through the diseased seed material. On planting diseased seed pieces, 40 to 90 % of the plants can be affected with GSD. Secondary transmission of the disease has been reported through aphids, namely, *Rhopalosiphum maidis* (p. 338), *Melanaphis sacchari* and *M. indosacchari*. It requires an acquisition period of 34 seconds and the test feeding of 30 seconds. However, maximum infection results when the aphids are allowed to feed for 15 minutes.

Fig. 15.

Control: Hot water treatment at 50 °C for 2 to 2^1/$_2$ hours or hot air treatment at 54 °C for 8 hours, effectively eradicates primary infection from the seed piece. However, with better circulation of air in between the cane stalks being treated, hot air treatment units are more efficient, convenient to operate and far cheaper than the hot water equipment of the same capacity. The hot air treatment invariably gives complete freedom from GSD, while in the case of hot water treatment there are always some escapes varying between 6 and 12 per cent, and there is a report that hot water treatment reduced germination from 70–85 % to 30–40 %. Plants from heat treated material develop lush green foliage, thicker and taller canes, with better root system and more number of millable canes per clump as compared to those from untreated seed pieces.

Chemotherapy against the disease has not given encouraging results so far. Tetracycline antibiotics when applied to diseased seed cane at 250 ppm under negative pressure cause remission of symptoms in the emerging plants for about 24 weeks.

The secondary transmission of the disease by vectors in grown up canes can be effectively controlled by repeated foliar applications of 0.1 % malathion at 14-day intervals.

The response of varieties to GSD infection, through vectors under field as well as green house conditions, varies considerably. Varieties showing tolerant to immune reaction can be used in breeding programme, for effective control of the GSD.

Literature

CORBETT, M. K., S. R. MISRA & K. SINGH (1971): Grassy shoot disease of sugarcane IV. Association of mycoplasmalike bodies. Plant Science **3**, 80–82.
SINGH, K., U. S. SHUKLA & N.S.L. SRIVASTAVA (1973): Hot air therapy of sugarcane against grassy shoot and ratoon stunting diseases. Indian Sugar **23**, 43–47.
SINGH, K., U. S. SHUKLA & S. R. MISRA (1970): Grassy shoot disease of sugarcane III. Response of varieties to infection. Indian Phytopathology **23**, 80–83.

Author: Kishan Singh

Bacterial diseases

Bacteria or Schizomycetes are unicellular organisms, still lacking a genuine nucleus, but having cellwalls. Plant pathogenic bacteria are all rod shaped, usually mobile by means of flagellae, and more or less aerobic. They do not form resting spores and reproduce only by means of fission. The rickettsias are submicroscopic, highly modified bacteria with rigid, wavy cellwalls. They are known as parasites of arthropods, mammals and man. In recent years they have been found associated with some plant diseases (Pierce disease and other diseases of grapevine, etc.). Their role as pathogens has not yet been established.

Only few genera are of importance in plant pathology: *Agrobacterium, Erwinia, Pseudomonas,* and *Xanthomonas,* which are all Gram negative, and the Gram positive species of *Corynebacterium* and *Streptomyces.*

Gram negative bacteria are differentiated on the basis of morphology, such as mode of flagellation, and cultural characteristics including carbohydrate metabolismes and growth rate (Bradbury[1]). The most important genera, which comprising by far the majority of plant pathogenic spe-

---

[1] Bradbury, A. C. in: Plant Pathologists Pocketbook, (1968), pp 17–26

cies, are *Pseudomonas* and *Xanthomonas*. They can be distinguished on the number of their polar flagella (one or more in *Pseudomonas,* one in *Xanthomonas*); the former produce a green diffusible, fluorescent pigment on a particular medium, whereas the latter produce a non-difussiable yellow pigment, and they usually form copiously slimy colonies on media containing sufficient glucose or sucrose. For the major characteristic of the other genera we may refer to the literature listed below.

We cannot go into details of classification and their basis either. The above mentioned genera fall into four families: Pseudomonadaceae (*Pseudomonas, Xanthomonas*), Enterobacteriaceae (*Erwinia*), Corynebacteriaceae (*Corynebacterium*) and Rhizobiaceae (*Agrobacterium*). Within both the first genera, however, numerous synonyms still exist.

Plant pathogenic bacteria enter their host through stomata, hydathodes, nectaries, lenticels, and wounds of any kind. Free water on the host's surface is a prerequisite for infection. Transmission takes place on or in seeds, planting material, plant residues, by wind and water (rain in particular), by insects, nematodes, man and his cultural practices. Bacteria may survive in soil, on underground parts of plants and can thus become soil-borne. Spread in fields is often facilitated by rain driven winds. These carry bacterial cells from exsudates on diseased parts to healthy plants. Some bacteria are very specific as pathogens, as *Xanthomonas citri* (p. 62), or nearly all *Corynebacterium* spp., others have a wide host range, as *Agrobacterium tumefasciens, Pseudomonas solanacearum,* and many others. There are quite a few plants being host of several bacterial diseases, like maize, soybean, sugarcane, and tomato. Others have no bacterial disease recorded on them, as cocoa, coffee and rubber.

Though in plant pathology the overall importance of bacterial diseases is far less than that of fungal or even virus diseases, in a number of cases bacteria can be the cause of most severe diseases. Some of the major ones will be treated here.

Bacteria do not only cause soft rots. In the field spots, necroses and blights, stem cankers, vascular wilts and scabs are more important. As bacteria may be transported within the vascular bundles necroses often occur alongside leaf veins.

In the long run the use of resistant varieties has been the most successful control measure. Economic control of bacteria may prove difficult in the absence of resistant cultivars. Cultural practices alone or in combination with resistant varieties and seed disinfection are often highly effective. Production of disease-free seed is on the same lines. Chemical control beyond seed disinfection is not much in use yet. Antibiotics are often effective but their application is restricted. Quarantine against bacterial diseases is more promising than against wind-borne fungal diseases. Appropriate quarantine measures may thus be used to avoid further spread of bacterial diseases. Spectacular and costly eradication campaigns like that against *Xanthomonas citri* in Florida, South Africa and elsewhere, have been successful.

Literature
CROSSE, J. E. (1966): Epidemiological relationships of the pseudomonad pathogens of deciduous fruit trees. Ann. Rev. Phytopathology **11**, 291–310.
DOWSON, W. J. (1957): Plant diseases due to bacteria. Cambridge Univ. Press.
GRAHAM, D. C. (1964): Taxonomy of the soft rot coliform bacteria. Ann. Rev. Phytopathology **2**, 13–42.
OKABE, N., & M. GOTO (1963): Bacteriophages of plant pathogens. Ann. Rev. Phytopathology, **1**, 397–418.
PALLERONI, N. J., & M. DOUDOROFF (1972): Some properties and taxonomic subdivisons of the genus Pseudomonas. Ann. Rev. Phytopathology **10**, 73–100.
PATIL, SURESH, S. (1974): Toxins produced by phytopathogenic bacteria. Ann. Rev. Phytopathology **12**, 254–259.
RANGASWAMI, G. (1962): Bacterial plant diseases in India. Asia Publishing House, London.
SCHNEIDER, H. (1973): Cytological and histological aberrations in woody plants following infection with viruses, mycoplasmas, rickettsias, and flagellates. Ann. Rev. Phytopathology **11**, 119–146.
SCHUSTER, M. L., & D. P. COYNE (1974): Survival mechanisms of phytopathogenic bacteria. Ann. Rev. Phytopathology **12**, 199–221.
STAPP, C. (1961): Bacterial plant pathogens. Oxford Univ. Press.
STARR, MORTIMER P., & ARUN K. CHATTERJEE (1973): The genus Erwinia: Enterobacteria pathogenic to plants and animals. Ann. Rev. Microbiology **26**, 389–426.
STOLP, H., P. MORTIMER STARR & NANCY L. BAIGENT (1965): Problems in speciation of phytopathogenic pseudomonads and Xanthomonads. Ann Rev. Phytopathology **3**, 231–264.

Pseudomonas glycinea Coerper (Figs. 16 a, b)

Schizomycetes, Pseudomonales, Pseudomonadaceae

Disease: Bacterial blight of soybean; Bakteriose der Sojabohne; bactériose du soya; bacteriosis de la soya.

Geographical distribution: The disease is world wide in distribution, found whereever soybeans are grown, usually during cool, damp weather.

Host plant: The soybean (*Glycine max*).

Symptoms: *P. glycinea* can attack all plant parts causing a seed decay, seedling blight (Fig. 16a) and malformation, seedling death as well as a foliage and pod blight. Foliage blight is the most conspicuous field symptom (Fig. 16b). The bacterium enters through stomata or wounds and within 7 days, small angular, water-soaked spots develop which are at first yellow, then turn brown as the tissues die. The brown areas have a water-soaked and yellowish margin. Under conditions of high relative humidity, a cream-colored exudate may form on the underside of affected leaves.

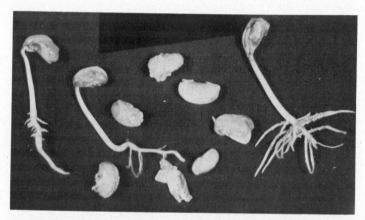

Fig. 16 a.

Fig. 16 b.

Lesions coalesce and dead tissues drop out giving a ragged appearance to the leaves. Leaf veins can become brown. Defoliation can occur under severe infections. Symptoms may be due in part to a toxin associated with *P. glycinea*. The disease can be confused with bacterial pustule (*Xanthomonas phaseoli* (E. F. Sm.) Dows. var. *sojensis* (Hedges) Starr & Burkh. and wildfire (*Pseudomonas tabaci* (Wolf & Foster) F. L. Stevens particularly in early stages.

Physiological spezialization: The bacterium is made up of many races. A group of epiphytic pseudomonads pathogenic to soybeans was described. A partially selective medium for *P. glycinea* was developed.

Epidemiology: *P. glycinea* is seedborne and widespread in commercial seed lots. Detection in seed is best under conditions of high humidity and temperature (35 °C). The bacterium can colonize leaves and buds without showing symptoms. It can residue internally in field-grown plants and survive from season to season in plant parts in or on soil, on sod, or in leaves stored above ground. Seedlings from infected seeds show symptoms on cotyledons, but blight may not develop on unifolialate and trifolialate leaves. The disease is usually observed before flowering, when conditions of cool temperatures and high humidity are prevalent. Wind-blown rains may initiate outbreaks of the disease. Toxemia and severe defoliation can significantly reduce yields.

Control: *P. glycinea* is made up of many races and resistant varieties cannot be considered for control. Planting seed from severely infected fields should be avoided, as well as replanting in the suceeding season in infected fields. *Bdellovibrio bacteriovorus* inhibited the development of *P. glycinea* and the disease.

Literature
CHAMBERLAIN, D. W., & B. R. LIPSCOMB (1967): Bibliography of soybean diseases. U.S. Dept. Agr. CR-50-67.
DAFT, G. C., & C. LEBEN (1972): Bacterial blight of soybeans: epidemiology of blight outbreaks. Phytopathology **57–62.**
DUECK, J., V. B. CARDWELL & B. W. KENNEDY (1972): Physiological characteristica of systemic toximia in soybean. Phytopathology **62,** 964–968.
DUNLEAVY, J. M., D. W. CHAMBERLAIN & J. P. ROSS (1966): Soybean diseases. U.S. Dept. Agr. Handbook No **302.**
LEBEN, C. (1972): The development of a selective medium for *Pseudomonas glycinea*. Phytopathology **62, 674–676.**
MEW, T. W., & B. W. KENNEDY (1971): Epiphytic *Pseudomonas* on soybean in the field. Phytopathology **61,** 903.
NICHOLSON, J. F., & J. B. SINCLAIR (1971): Amsoy soybean seed germination inhibited by *Pseudomonas glycinea*. Phytopathology **61,** 1390–1393.
SCHERFF, R. H. (1971): Inhibition of bacterial blight of soybean by *Bdellovibrio bacteriovorus*. Phytopathology **61,** 1025.

Author: J. B. Sinclair

Other bacterial diseases of soybeans: Brown rot (*Pseudomonas solanacearum* – p. 58)

Pseudomonas lachrymans (Smith & Bryan) Carsner

Schizomycetes, Pseudomonadales, Pseudomonadaceae

Disease: Angular leaf spot of cucumber; eckige Blattfleckenkrankheit der Gurke; taches anguleuses des feuilles du concombre; bacteriosis de los pepinos.

Geographical distribution: Very widespread. The pathogen probably occurs in most countries where cucumber is grown (CMI map no 355).

Host plants: Cucumber (*Cucumis sativus*), gherkin (*Cucumis anguria*), occasionally found on squash (*Cucurbita pepo*), the variety "Black Zucchini" being particularly susceptible. Occurs infrequently on watermelon (*Citrullus vulgaris*) and cantaloupe (*Cucumis melo* var. *cantalupensis*). It can also produce lesions on honeydew melon (*Cucumis melo* var. *inodorus*) in transit after harvest. According to Gorlenko the pathogen exists as two *formae speciales*, one restricted to cucumber (f. sp. *cucumis*), and one to melons (f. sp. *melonis*). Other workers do not seem to have found this specificity.

Symptoms: On leaves small irregular watersoaked spots appear. These enlarge, become more angular in shape where delimited by the veins, and become tan to brown in colour. The tissue of larger spots may dry and shrink, causing holes in the leaves and sometimes a very ragged appearance. On stems and fruits lesions are smaller and more rounded. They are mostly superficial, but detract from the appearance of the fruit and the damage to the epidermis allows entry of other organisms and subsequent rotting. Under damp conditions tear-like drops of bacterial exudate are formed, which suggested the specific name derived from mediaeval latin *lachryma*, a tear. The exudate usually dries to form whitish crusty deposits near the lesions. Symptoms that are often indistinguishable, but restricted to leaves, are caused by the bacterium *Xanthomonas cucurbitae* (Bryan) Dowson. This is mainly a pathogen of squash, but it does occasionally attack cucumber. The only certain method of distinguishing the diseases when leaf spots only are present is by isolation of the pathogen. Lesions of the fungal disease anthracnose (*Colletotrichum lagenarium (Pass.) Ell. & Halst.*) may appear similar on leaves, but on fruit the larger, sunken spots, frequently showing pinkish areas of fungal sporulation are quite distinct.

Morphology: The organism is a Gram-negative rod, about 0.6 x 1–2 μ, motile with 1–5 polar flagella. Colonies on nutrient agar are whitish, translucent, smooth, flat and circular, with an entire margin and a butyrous consistency. On some media (e. g. King's Medium B) greenish fluorescent pigment is produced that diffuses into the medium around the colonies. The organism belongs to Group Ia of the fluorescent plant pathogenic bacteria in the scheme of Lelliott et al. (1966). This group includes many plant pathogens that are all very similar in culture to the well known *Pseudomonas syringae*. *P. lachrymans* is distinguished from most of these by its ability to use L (+) tartrate, but not DL-lactate for growth, and by its ability to produce pitting of sodium polypectate gel at pH 8,5. The final confirmation of the species, however, is still by proof of pathogenicity to cucumber.

Physiological specialization: There are no records of physiologically specialized races, and experiments have usually shown that all varieties of cucumber are susceptible. In Russia two groups of differing virulence were distinguished on a standard selection of cucurbits; isolates from cooler, damper areas were found to be generally more infectious than those from warmer, drier ones.

Epidemiology: The pathogen is seed borne and can also overwinter in plant debris from infected crops. It is splashed from soil to leaves during rain and enters through the open stomata. It is spread from leaf to leaf and plant to plant by rain splash, hands and clothing of workers, and probably also by insects. The optimum conditions for infection are a temperature of 24–27 °C after extended rain has gorged the plant tissues with water and thoroughly dispersed the pathogen. Epidemics may then occur.

Control: Very effective control is usually obtained by a rotation of two or more years between cucurbit crops, coupled with use of disease-free or treated seed. Seed grown under good conditions in arid regions should be free of disease. Treatment with mercuric chloride is effective and still recommended for elimination of the pathogen from seed. The seed should be soaked for 5 minutes in a solution of 1 part mercuric chloride to 1000 of water by weight, followed by thorough washing in running water, drying, and treatment with a combination fungicide/insecticide protectant before planting (e. g. thiram-heptachlor or captan-dieldrin seed protectant).

If the disease occurs in spite of these precautions, care should be taken not to spread it by working among wet plants or by overhead irrigation. Spraying with fixed copper at 3.36 kg/hectare metallic copper is also recommended except for young plants which may be damaged. These may be sprayed with ziram or captan for the first one or two sprays until runners appear and the plants become more vine-like.

Literature

LELLIOTT, R. A., E. BILLING & A. C. HAYWARD (1966): A determinative scheme for the fluorescent plant pathogenic pseudomonads. Journal of Applied Bacteriology **29**, 470–489.
STAPP, C. (1958): Pflanzenpathogene Bakterien, pp. 164–168. Paul Parey, Berlin & Hamburg. English ed. Oxford University Press, 1961.
CMI Description no 124.

Author: J. F. Bradbury

Other bacterial diseases of cucumber and other Cucurbitaceae
Erwinia carotovora (L. R. Jones) Bergey et al. Soft rot.
Erwinia tracheiphila (E. F. Smith) Bergey et al. Wilt. Ref.: CMI Description no 233.
Xanthomonas cucurbitae (Bryan) Dowson. Bacterial spot.

Pseudomonas phaseolicola (Burkholder) Dowson

Schizomycetes, Pseudomonadales, Pseudomononadaceae

Synonyms: *Pseudomonas medicaginis* Sackett = *Pseudomonas medicaginis* Sackett var. *phaseolicola* (Burkholder) Link & Hull

Disease: Halo blight of beans; Fettfleckenkrankheit; maladie de la graisse du haricot; tizón del halo.

Geographical distribution: In nearly all bean-growing areas (CMI map no 85).

Host plants: The major hosts are: *Phaseolus vulgaris, P. coccineus, P. lunatus* var. *macrocarpus, P. multiflorus, Pueraria thunbergiana, P. hirsuta, Glycine max, Pisum sativum, Vigna unguiculata.*

Symptoms: Characteristic symptoms arise on leaves and pods: First symptoms on the leaves are small coffee brown dots, which acquire a chlorotic halo as they enlarge. These spots remain localised or extend across the entire leaf forming dried brown zones.
Elongated, brown streaks form on leaf stalks; affected leaf stalks are thickened at the base, twisted and easily detached from the stems.
Moist reddish zones are first seen on the stems, mostly at a height of the lowermost nodes. Later they are slightly sunken and blackened. Such a lesion can finally encircle the entire stem, which can break off at this point. This happens when pods start to ripen.
On the pods, small moist spots are first formed, surrounded by a coffee brown or reddish ring. Later a bacterial exudate forms at the centre, resembling a drop of grease. Finally the spots dry up and become depressed. The upper joint of the pod is discoloured if infected. If young pods are infected, the hilum of the seed is discoloured, which is particularly noticeable on light coloured beans. On dark beans, it can hardly be seen. All or most of the seed in severely affected pods is small and shrivelled. The symptoms of halo blight greatly resemble those of *X. phaseoli* (p. 68) and of bacterial wilt.
The main distinguishing feature is the yellowish halo around the lesions of halo blight, which is ab-

sent in the other diseases. The exudate of *P. phaseolicola* is cream coloured, that of *X. phaseoli* is yellow.

X. phaseoli requires higher temperatures (25 °C). In other respects the two diseases are similar in distribution and mode of transmission. In the initial stages, the symptoms of bacterial wilt (*Corynebacterium flaccumfaciens* Hedges) and halo blight are almost identical. Later the bacterial wilt spots turn yellow and extend to all tissues.

Morphology: The bacterium is an aerobic, Gram-negative rod, size 1.3–3.4 x 0.5 – 1 μ, with up to 12 flagella. No gas is liberated from saccharose, no acid formed from fructose, lactose and maltose. Nitrate is not reduced and no indole is formed. Acid is first formed from glucose, galactose, saccharose and inulin, but later the fluid turns alkaline. Optimum temperature is in the region of 25–30 °C, thermal death point 49–50 °C.

Physiological specialization: Races 1 and 2 are known, which differ in virulence. Less virulent strains are classed with race 1.

Epidemiology: The bacterium penetrates through the stomata of leaves, stems and pods or through injuries on these organs.

The main source of infection is seed from diseased plants. In the field, the bacterium spreads from plant to plant in rain drops, wind dispersed dew or by means of insects. Rain and moisture and rather cool weather promote spread of the disease and development of the bacterium. Opt. temperature of symptom development is 16–20 °C.

Control: The use of healthy seed and crop rotation are recommended. Healthy seed is best obtained in areas where rainfall does not exceed 255 mm during the vegetative period. Since the bacterium can survive for two years in the soil, crop rotation in severely affected fields is advisable. Numerous fungicides have been tested for their suitability to control the disease. Antibiotics proved the most promising. The cultivation of resistant varieties would be desirable, but every bean species reacts very differently to the various strains of the bacterium. The reaction depends on one or two genetic factors, in turn depending on crossed origins.

Resistance has been found to be greater in beans of the dry bean type, than in those of the green bean or "Vainita" type. Some of the 'dry' beans are resistant to race 1 but susceptible to race 2 or new strains of the bacterium.

Varieties which have been listed as resistant are: Pinto, Great Northern, Red Mexican, Michelite, Canocel, Mecentral, Bayo 159, GN Nebraska sel 27, etc.

Literature:

TAYLOR, C. E. (1972): Field studies on halo blight of beans (*P. phaseolicola*) and its control by foliar sprays. Ann. appl. Biol. **70**, 191–197.
ZAUMEYER, W. J., & H. R. THOMAS (1957): A monographic study of bean diseases and methods for their control. Tech. Bull. U.S. Dep. Agric. **868.**
CMI Description no 45.

Author: S. L. Dongo Denegri

Pseudomonas solanacearum (E. F. Smith) E. F. Smith (Plate 4 a)

Schizomycetes, Pseudomonadales, Pseudomonadaceae

Disease: Bacterial wilt; bakterielle Welke; flétrissement bactérien; marchitez bacteriana and other diseases (s. host range).

Geographical distribution: Widespread in tropical, subtropical and warm temperate parts of Africa, Australasia, Asia, the Americas and West Indies (CMI map no 138).

Host plants: Major economic hosts: banana, plantain (moko disease), tobacco (Granville wilt), potato (wilt, brown rot), tomato, groundnut, pepper (*Capsicum*), eggplant, ginger, castorbean. Other hosts: cassava, sesame, cultivated *Physalis* spp., some legumes, some ornamentals, jute, teak, and many weeds especially in the family Solanaceae.

Symptoms: The pathogen invades xylem elements and the major pathological effects of the disease result from a disruption of the water economy of the host. Characteristic symptoms are wilting, yellowing and stunting (Plate 4a) although the disease syndrome varies according to host and environment. Under suitable conditions susceptible hosts (especially tobacco, potato, tomato and eggplant) wilt rapidly and die in a few days. Under less favourable conditions wilting may be slow or absent and stunting, yellowing and desiccation of leaves are more obvious symptoms. In some hosts (e. g. ginger and groundnut) the latter symptoms may be seen almost exclusively. Epinasty and adventitious roots occur on some hosts when disease development is slow. In pepper the main effect is gradual defoliation. In banana there is a progressive discoloration and collapse of younger leaves; suckers are stunted and blackened; and fruit development may be arrested or fruit rot occur.

On more resistant hosts a chronic disease may be established in which no above-ground symptoms are seen or only partial and reversible wilting occurs. Invaded roots may rot, however.

A vascular discoloration is frequently seen in roots and stems of affected plants and when sectioned transversely bacteria exude from the cut ends of vascular tissues.

Bacterial wilt can be confused with wilt diseases due to fungi such as *Verticillium* and *Fusarium* spp. However the presence or absence of bacteria can be ascertained readily by suspending a longitudinal section of vascular tissue in water. In cases of wilt an unmistakable milky stream of bacteria descends from the tissue. In tomato it may be confused with wilt caused by *Corynebacterium michiganense* (E. F. Smith) Jensen. The latter, however, causes a chlorosis of the leaves, a stem canker and "birds eye" spots on fruits.

Morphology: *P. solanacearum* is an aerobic, Gram negative, rod (0.5 x 1.5 μ), motile with one or several polar flagella, and cells contain massive inclusions of poly-β-hydroxybutyrate which stain blue/black with Sudan Black B. Carbohydrate utilisation varies with strain. All strains reduce nitrate and some produce gas. No strain liquefies gelatin or hydrolyses starch. The optimum temperature for growth varies with strain from 30 to 37 °C. All strains rapidly change in culture from the pathogenic form with mucoid, often fluidal, colonies to an avirulent form with smaller butyrous colonies.

Physiological specialization: There is considerable variation in *P. solanacearum*. This nomenspecies consists of a number of strains of different pathogenic potentials and different geographic distributions. Information on strains and their distributions is incomplete but certain facts are well established. The number of hosts of each strain varies considerably and the host ranges of different strains may overlap to varying degrees. One strain, attacking potato and tomato (race 3), is distinct from other strains and causes disease at lower temperatures. Other strains are divisible into two groups: those attacking triploid bananas (race 2); and those attacking solanaceous and other hosts (race 1). The distinctive potato/tomato strain is worldwide although restricted to the cooler parts of the distribution of the species. Banana strains occur only in Central America, northern South America and the Caribbean, while the strains attacking ginger are known only in Australia, Hawaii, Malaya and Mauritius. Strains are frequently co existing, so that a host may be attacked by one or more strains in the same locality.

Epidemiology: For most crops the soil is the source of primary inoculum but with vegetatively propagated plants such as potato, banana and ginger, the pathogen may be introduced with the seed material. Infection occurs via wounds on the root system (including those made naturaly by the emergence of lateral roots). In susceptible hosts the bacteria multiply in the vascular tissues and rapidly become systemic. Symptoms can appear four days after infection but may take much longer depending on host and conditions. From the early stages of disease and until the host dies large numbers of bacteria are liberated into the soil from diseased roots. Under favourable circumstances these bacteria infect neighbouring plants. Except in very wet conditions the pathogen does not spread far through the soil, but dispersal is facilitated by practices such as furrow irrigation, cultivation, transplanting, cutting and dipping of seed pieces, hydroponics, and pruning. Some strains affecting musaceous hosts are dispersed by insects visiting flowers from which bacteria ooze. The insects transfer bacteria to other inflorescences and new infections occur through abscission scars of the male flower bracts.

Reports on the longevity of *P. solanacearum* in the field in the absence of susceptible crops range from a few months to several years. This probably reflects the different characteristics of different strains. The survival of some strains is considerably enhanced by their ability to attack weed hosts, some of which may show no symptoms. Although no specialised resting structures are formed some strains are evidently able to survive free in soil for long periods. It is not known whether the pathogen is ever truly saprophytic.

Bacterial wilt is favoured by high soil temperatures (21–35 °C) and high soil moisture. Any agency causing root damage such as cultivating implements or root knot nematodes increases the amount of disease. Plants which are in their most active phase of growth are most prone to infection.

Control: The simplest control is to avoid contaminated land. Where this is impossible the level of contamination can be reduced by crop rotation. Because of the diversity of strains and the agroclimatic zones they occupy, the most suitable rotation can only be determined by local experience. Rotations with maize, cotton, soybeans, grasses, *Mimosa invisa,* and rice have been employed in various parts of the world. Rotations generally need to be of several years to be effective, and it is important to exclude weed hosts. However, moko disease is controlled in Central America by weed fallowing for only two years. No satisfactory chemical method of treating field soil is available, although for glasshouse soils methyl bromide fumigation at 3 lb/100 sq. ft. is effective.

Where the pathogen may be propagated with the "seed", a rigorous selection of healthy material is most important for control. If cutting of seed material and pruning of plants are practised tools should be disinfected at frequent intervals. Rogueing diseased plants and the early removal of male buds are also important for control of moko disease.

The most satisfactory method of controlling bacterial wilt is by using resistant cultivars. Resistant types of groundnut, tobacco and eggplant have been available for some years and high resistance is now being introduced to tomato and potato. There is some evidence, however, that the resistance of some of these cultivars is not universally effective. No significant resistance is reported in ginger and banana, although the plantain Pelipita does escape infection by the insect borne strain of moko by virtue of its persistent male flower bracts. Peppers are generally more resistant than other solanaceous crops.

Resistance has also been exploited for control by grafting solanaceous crop plants onto the rootstocks of resistant selections of the same species or onto roots of other resistant solanaceous species.

Antibiotic treatment of tubers and seedlings has given good control of potato and eggplant wilt respectively in trials.

Literature

KELMAN, A. (1953): The bacterial wilt caused by *Pseudomonas solanacearum.* N. Carolina Agr. Expt. Sta. Tech. Bull. **99**
BUDDENHAGEN, I., & A. KELMAN (1964): Biological and physiological aspects of bacterial wilt caused by *Pseudomonas solanacearum.* Ann. Rev. Phytopath. **2**, 203–230.
CMI Description no 15.

Author: D. C. Harris

Other more important Pseudomonas spp. as pathogens on tropical and subtropical crops (Fig. 17–19)

P. alboprecipitans Rosen. Bacterial leaf blight and stalk rot of maize and teosinte. Ref.: CMI Description no 371.

P. andropogonis (E. F. Smith) Stapp. Bacterial stripe of sorghum and leaf blight of legumes. Ref.: CMI Description no 372.

P. mangiferae-indicae Patel, Kulkarni & Moriz. Bacterial leaf spots of mango (Fig. 17).

P. mori (Boyer & Lambert) F. L. Stevens. Bacterial blight of mulberry.

P. rubrilineans (Lee et al.) Stapp. Red stripe disease of sugarcane. Ref.: CMI Description no 127 (Fig. 18).

P. rubrisubalbicans (Christopher & Edgeston) Krasil'nikow. Mottle stripe of sugarcane. Ref.: CMI Description no 128.

P. passiflorae (Reid.) Burkholder. Bacterial spot of passion fruit.

P. savastanoi (E. F. Smith) F. L. Stevens. Canker of olive. CMI map no 135 (Fig. 19).

P. sesami Malkoff. Leaf spot of sesame (s. also p. 74). Ref.: CMI Description no 17.

P. syringae van Hall. Causing stem canker and gum exudation of stone fruits, blossom blight, leaf blight, dieback on a variety of hosts, such as avocado, beans, citrus (p. 64), guar, safflower, sorghum, etc. Ref.: CMI Description no 46.

P. tabaci (Wolf & Foster) Stevens. Wildfire of tabacco, also on capsicum pepper, eggplant, potato, tomato. Probably identical with *P. angulata* (CMI map no 321), though symptoms differ. CMI Description no 129.

Fig. 17 (left above).

Fig. 18 (right).

Fig. 19 (left below).

Xanthomonas citri (Hasse) Dowson (Figs. 20 a, b)

Schizomycetes, Pseudomonadales, Pseudomonadaceae

Disease: Citrus canker; Bakterienkrebs der Zitrusarten; chancre bacterien; cáncer de los agrios.

Geographical distribution: This disease seems to have originated in the Indo-Malay region and has been identified on herbarium specimens dating from 1830 which were collected in India and Java. It is present throughout the tropical zone of the Pacific. It was later introduced into Japan, and reached the Gulf of Mexico about 1910 and then Brazil, Argentina and Uruguay in South America. In Africa it has been confirmed in South Africa and in Mozambique, the Comoro Islands, and the islands of Réunion and Mauritius. It has never been observed in the Mediterranean region (CMI map no 11).

Host plants: *X. citri* infects species of the genus *Citrus* and its hybrids, and numerous species of the Rutaceae. The degree of susceptibility of commercial varieties varies between regions, probably under the influence of climatic conditions. In Florida, grapefruit is the most susceptible species, followed by lime, sweet orange and lemon. Mandarin (tangerine) offers a high degree of resistance, as does citron and pummelo (shaddock). In New Zealand lemon seems to be more susceptible than sweet orange, and in Sri Lanka, grapefruit and lime are classed as very susceptible, then sweet orange Jaffa, lemon and mandarin are very resistant. In South America the problem is complicated by the probable existence of different races of *X. citri*, for in addition to race "A" which attacks the whole citrus group there are races which are species-specific.

Symptoms: The symptoms are very characteristic but vary appreciably with the organ affected. On leaves, the disease begins with the appearance of minute, brilliant yellow flecks, less than 1 mm in diameter and first visible on the lower surface. At a later stage these develop into shiny raised lesions, whitish-pale yellow in wet weather and browner in dry weather (Fig. 20a). These lesions, at first surrounded by a glazed margin with an oily appearance and a yellow halo, eventually become rough and cracked. The diameter of the lesions varies from 2–5 mm on orange and lemon, and from 8–12 mm on grapefruit and pummelo. Each lesion affects both surfaces.
On fruit, the overall picture is rather similar. The yellowish halo is often less evident but the lesions have a characteristic cratered look which is more pronounced than on leaves (Fig. 20b).

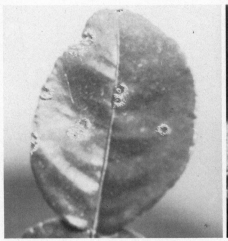

b)   Fig. 20.   a)

These lesions never affect the pulp but they deform the fruit and lead to premature fall.
Lesions are only found on the stems of the most susceptible varieties. On young shoots the symptoms are similar to those on leaves, but on the trunk and branches the cankers can reach a diameter of 5–15 cm.
Cankerous lesions have been reported on exposed roots.
This bacterial canker can easily be confused with citrus scab caused by *Elsinoe fawcetti* (p. 110). The two diseases are distinguished by the fact that each lesion of *Xanthomonas* develops on both surfaces of a leaf; furthermore, citrus canker does not deform the leaves. There is also a similarity with the fruit damage caused by *Colletotrichum gloeosporioides* (p. 119), but corky excrescences are more apparent with the latter pathogen.

Morphology: *X. citri* is a rod 1.5–2 X 0.5 – 0.75 μ, rounded at the ends and with a polar flagellum. Pinpoint colonies at 36–48 hours are shiny; at 4 days they are rounded, yellowish, smooth and shiny. This bacterium liquifies gelatin, coagulates milk and hydrolyses starch. It does not reduce nitrates.

Physiological specialization: It is certain that several races of *X. citri* exist which differ in their degree of pathogenicity and in their host range. In Argentina, for example, the common race "A" co-exists with race "B" which cannot attack grapefruit or sweet orange (see above).

Epidemiology: *X. citri* chiefly survives in the cortical tissues of infected stems, and can also persist in plant debris, and in soil. It is very sensitive to insolation and is killed after a few minutes exposure to direct sunlight.
The bacteria which exudate from wet cankers are effectively dispersed by the flow of rainwater onto leaves and fruits on lower branches. Wind, pruning tools and animals are also excellent agents and vectors. Man has been responsible for the dispersal of the disease in various citrus-growing areas of the world by importing and distributing contaminated plant material.
The optimum temperature for infection is 26.5 °C (20–30 °C) and the disease can develop between 5 and 35 °C. A cloudy and wet climate is very favourable.
The infection of young organs often occurs by entry through stomata, lenticels and accidental wounds.

Control: The control of *X. citri* is possible by several methods which differ between regions. First, strict quarantine is required by countries which have successfully eliminated the disease or have remained disease-free. The export of fruit from countries where the disease is serious to other citrus-growing countries is strictly forbidden.
Complete eradication of the disease has been successfully achieved in the following places: South Africa, New Zealand, Australia, Mozambique, Fiji and parts of the Gulf of Mexico. (It is re-appearing in South Africa). This method requires large financial outlays, the implementation and enforcement of legislation and the absence of wild *Citrus*.
Agronomic control measures rely on the selection of resistant or only slightly susceptible varieties like mandarin, the systematic removal of diseased tissues and certain precautions when irrigating, but these measures are always of limited benefit.
Chemical control is achieved with treatments based on Bordeaux mixture (1 %) applied soon after flowering and repeated in accordance with rainfall. In Réunion, for example, this covers a period of three months. Sodium arsenite mixed with copper sulphate at a rate of 10 g/100 l for each compound is effective, as is a mixture of Dithane and copper sulphate. Streptomycin sulphate (50 g or 100 g/hectolitre) applied every 2 weeks has cleared the disease from certain parts of India. In Japan, a mixture of basic copper, chloromycetin and an organomercurial compound gave good results. It is necessary to record that treatments based on antibiotics are often more onerous than those based on copper salts. Research is being undertaken to study the use of bacteriophages active against *X. citri*.

Literature

BRUN, J. (1971): Le chancre bactérien des Citrus. Fruits, **26**, 535–540.
FAWCETT, H. S. (1936): Citrus diseases and their control. McGraw Hill, New York.
KNORR, L. C., R. F. SUIT & E. P. DUCHARME (1957): Handbook of Citrus diseases in Florida – Bull. 587. University of Florida.
RANGASWAMI, G., R. RAMA RAO & A. R. LAKSHMANAN (1959): Studies on the control of Citrus Canker with streptomycin. Phytopathology **49**, 224–226.
RAO, Y. P. & M. K. HINGORANI (1963): Survival of *X. citri* in leaves and soil. The possible occurence of strains of *X. citri*. Indian Phytopath. **16**, 362–364, 374–375.
CMI Description no 11.

Author: E. Laville

Other bacterial diseases of Citrus
Pseudomonas syringae van Hall. Blast. Ref.: CMI Description no 46.
Erwinia herbicola (Geilinger) Dye. Bacterial spot. Ref.: CMI Description no 232.

Xanthomonas malvacearum (E. F. Smith) Dowson (Fig. 21)

Schizomycetes, Pseudomonadales, Pseudomonadaceae

Disease: Bacterial blight of cotton of angular leafspot, blackarm and boll rot of cotton; Baumwollbakteriose; bactériose du cotonnier; mancha angular de la hoja del algodonero.

Geographical distribution: Bacterial blight disease of cotton has been reported from many areas throughout the world (CMI map no 57). It causes considerable damage to the crop in the warmer, more humid areas of the Americas, Africa and Asia.

Host plants: Bacterial blight is particularly destructive to the long staple, tetraploid cottons of *Gossypium barbadense*. It also attacks the more widely grown tetraploid *Gossypium hirsutum*. The cultivated diploid Asiatic cottons (*G. herbaceum* and *G. arboreum)* and the wild cottons (*Gossypium* spp.) are resistant or immune.

Symptoms: 'Bacterial blight' is a collective term covering the different manifestations of the disease on seedlings (seedling blight), leaves (angular leaf spot), veins (vein blight), stems (blackarm), bolls (boll rot) and bracts (bract spots). Seedling blight is the first phase of the disease to appear on the newly sown crop. Contaminated seeds give rise to infected seedlings whose cotyledons show marginal watersoaked lesions. Infection may run inwards along the veins and reach the terminal bud, causing death of the seedling. A considerable number of seedlings may be killed in this way under wet conditions, and make re-sowing necessary. The angular leaf-spot phase follows. The characteristic leaf spots (Fig. 21) are small, dark-green and watersoaked at first, later becoming angular (being limited by the veinlets) and dark brown in colour. They may coalesce to form large blotches. On young leaves the attack is limited to the tissue on either side of the veins, so as to form narrow, dark-brown areas which extend to, and along, the petioles during prolonged periods of wet weather. Should the weather become drier, the severely attacked leaves fall off, giving the plants a very bare appearance.
Vein blight is a phase of the disease that develops more frequently towards, or after, the end of the rainy or wet season. The first sign is the appearance of watersoaked sections, usually of the main vein of young leaves. The lesion spreads along the vein and its branches, and the adjacent tissues may become watersoaked. Eventually the lesions become brown to black in colour, and large areas of leaf first become flaccid, then lighter green, and dry to a light brown paper texture.
The blackarm phase of the disease may cause more serious damage, than any of the other phases in certain areas of the world. Elongated (some centimeters long), reddish to dark brown lesions

Fig. 21.

appear on the main branches and young shoots. The lesions are sunken and may girdle the stem, causing the part above to shrivel and break. Bacterial exudate dries as yellowish crusts on the lesion surface.

The bolls may be attacked at all stages of development. If young, they drop off; older bolls bear dark green, watersoaked lesions which become brown or black, and shrunken. The lint within infected bolls becomes wet, brown-stained an rotten.

The angular leafspot phase may be confused with leafspot caused by *Alternaria alternata* (Fr.) Keissler = *A. tenuis* and/or *Alternaria macrospora* Zimm. (CMI Description no 246). In the latter disease, however, the spots are roundish, with faint concentric zones, and dry. *Macrophomina phaseoli* (p. 217) may cause stem lesions similar to those of the blackarm phase. Lesions due to *M. phaseoli* are often near the stem base, elongated and dry, and appear at an early stage of plant growth.

Morphology: The bacterium consists of short rods (0.6 x 1.2–2.5 μ), non-sporing, capsulated, motile by means of a single polar flagellum; it is Gram-negative. Colonies on yeast extract + 1 % glucose agar are pale yellow deepening with age, round, convex, slimy, becoming about 7–8 mm in diameter after some days at 30 °C. Aerobic. Optimum temperature 29 °–30 °C, maximum between 33 and 37 °C and minimum about 10 °C.

Physiological specialization: Two races of *X. malvacearum* were recognized in the USA on the basis of reactions of three American Upland differentials. Race 1 attacked Stoneville 2B, and Race 2 Stoneville 2B and Stoneville 2O, whereas neither race attacked Mebane BI. Brinkerhoff described ten new races of the pathogen on the basis of their disease reactions (based on a leaf spot grading system depending on the size and shape of the spots) on eight differential lines of cotton (three *G. barbadense* and five *G. hirsutum*), with different disease-conditioning genes.

Epidemiology: Seeds from infected bolls constitute the most important survival site. Carry-over is mainly on the surface of seed and attached fibers. The organism is very resistant to desiccation and can survice for years in dried, infected leaves and in stems and bolls. Infected bolls may give rise to infected volunteer seedlings. The pathogen may hibernate in soil provided that it is not flooded or waterlogged for a lengthy period.

Dispersal of *X. malvacearum* is mainly by contaminated seeds, winddriven rains, rain splashes and leaf debris carried by high winds. The role played by insects is of little importance and is confined to mechanical transmission of bacterial exudate.

In the infected bolls the bacteria penetrate to the developing seed and form slimy masses around the hairs surrounding the microphyle. In this position, the bacteria can withstand desiccation for a long time, and on germination the seeds give rise to seedlings with cotyledonary lesions. In rainy weather, the leaves and stems are attacked, especially if the rains are heavy and accompanied by strong winds. Many stem lesions are the result of infection spreading from infected leaves via the petioles. Vein lesions (blight) appear towards the end of the rainy season.

Infection takes place through the stomata. The incubation period varies between 5 and 10 days, being shortest when the host tissues contain a sufficient level of water, and the weather is warm (at approx. 28 °C) and humid (at approx. 85 % RH). Young tissues of the host are particularly susceptible and host resistance increases with age. The bacteria are confined to the parenchyma and do not usually invade the vascular system. However, they may attack actively growing tissues(i.e. stem apices and leaf primordia), in which little differentiation has yet taken place. The subsequent growth of these primordia leads to the dispersal of the bacteria into separate masses, some of which attack all the elements of the young leaf while others are confined to the young vascular bundles of the developing shoots.

Control: Field sanitation measures (including pulling out the plants and burning all plant debris after harvest), are scrupulously carried out in the Sudan and many African countries. Volunteer plants and ratoons are destroyed before the new crop is sown. Seed production may be restricted to areas relatively free from the disease. Sowing date may be adjusted so that the period of highest rainfall does not coincide with the critical growth stage of cotton (2–3 weeks old).
Ten genetic factors controlling resistance against bacterial blight have been reported from a range of wild and cultivated cottons. Many resistant Egyptian and American Upland cotton varieties have been evolved in various parts of the world by incorporating resistance genes in commercial parents.
For the Egyptian cotton type (*G. barbadense*), stress has been placed on incorporating genes B_2, B_3 and B_6m, which confer additive resistance. B_2 is a strong, fully dominant gene found in Old World races of American Upland and *G. punctatum* cottons. B_3 is a strong, partially dominant gene found in some punctatum cottons. B_6m is a resistance intensifying gene from *G. arboreum*. It has been found that expression of resistance is often influenced by environmental conditions. By the following method an attempt can be made to disinfect the seeds to reduce primary infection. The seeds are delinted with sulphuric acid and then streeped in 1 % formaldehyde or dressed with mercury compounds. Organic mercury compounds are effectively used as seed dressings. These compounds are very toxic and should be handled with care.

Literature

BRINKERHOFF, L. A. (1963): Variability of *Xanthomonas malvacearum:* The cotton bacterial blight pathogen. Oklahoma Agric. Exper. Sta. Tech. Bul. T-18.
DOWSON, W. J. (1957): Plant Diseases due to Bacteria. Camb. Univ. Press.
SABET, K. A. (1960): Studies in the bacterial diseases of Sudan crops. VI. The production of atypical symptoms by *Xanthomonas malvacearum* E. F. Sm. Dowson and other *Xanthomonas* spp. Ann. appl. Biol. **48**: 529–540.
CMI Description no 12.

Author: K. A. Sabet

Xanthomonas oryzae (Uyeda et Ishiyama) Dowson (Plate 4 b, c, d and fig. 22)

Schizomycetes, Pseudomonadales, Pseudomonadaceae

Disease: Bacterial leaf blight of rice; Weißblättrigkeit des Reises; maladie bactérienne du riz; mancha foliares bacteriana del arroz.

Geographical distribution: Tropical and subtropical Asian countries such as India, Nepal, Bangladesh, Sri Lanka (Ceylon), Thailand, Cambodia, Malaysia, Indonesia, the Philippines, China, Japan and Corea (CMI map no 304).

Host plants: Rice (*Oryza sativa*), mud grass (*Leersia oryzoides*) var. *japonica, L. oryzoides*), water oat (*Zizania latifolia*).

Symptoms: Symptoms develop on the leaf blade (Fig. 85 f.), leaf sheath, and on grains. Bacterial leaf blight is principally a vascular disease; the pathogen invades the vascular bundles of leaf blades through hydathodes or wounds and multiplies inside the tissue in all directions, causing pale yellow or whitish lesions (Plate 4 c). If susceptible varieties are affected with highly virulent strains under favorable conditions, leaf rolling and withering quickly occur but without discoloration. The lesions extend downwards to the sheaths. Bacterial exudate, which emerges from lesions occasionally, is shiny yellow in colour and sticky. (Plate 4d). If the seedlings are heavily contaminated or affected with bacteria before transplanting, withering of the whole plant in the tillering stage results (Plate 4b). This is the so called "kresek symptom", which is rare in northern rice areas, but very common in tropical, warmer areas. The yellowing of leaf blades reported in the Philippines is caused by the same pathogen. When the panicles are affected, a grayish to brownish discoloration appears on the glumes; this symptom is particularly clear in the early stages of ripening. The early infection of panicles of susceptible varieties causes sterility of the grains. If the cut end of a diseased leaf is dipped into water, the bacteria ooze from the vascular bundles. This method is extremely useful for microscopical diagnosis of the disease.

"Kresek" somewhat resembles the injury caused by stem borers (pp. 452, 462), but the leaves withered by bacterial leaf blight cannot be pulled out so easily as those affected by the stem borer. The symptom on the grains is quite similar to rice blast (*Pyricularia oryzae*, p. 223), some other fungus diseases and bacterial grain rot (*Pseudomonas glumae* Kurita & Tabei). Grain infection, however, is always accompanied by obvious symptoms on the leaf blades.

Morphology: The PSA medium (decoction of potato 300 g, $Na_2HPO_4 \cdot 12H_2O$ 2.0 g, $Ca(NO_3)_2$ 0.5 g, peptone 5 g, sucrose 20 g, agar 15 g, pH 7.0) is the best for growing the bacterium. The colonies on this medium are circular, entire in margin, convex, and waxy white to honey yellow colored. The bacterial cells are capsulated, Gram-negative, and rod shaped 1.8–3.0 x 0.5–1.0 μ in size, having a long monotrichous flagellum (Fig. 22).

Physiological specialization: The virulence of the bacteria varies markedly between the isolates. Some isolates cause only slight symptoms in susceptible varieties, but others can produce severe symptoms even in resistant varieties. The highly virulent isolates occur with high frequency in poorly fertilized tropical areas. Isolates also differ in their sensitivity to the phages. In Japan they

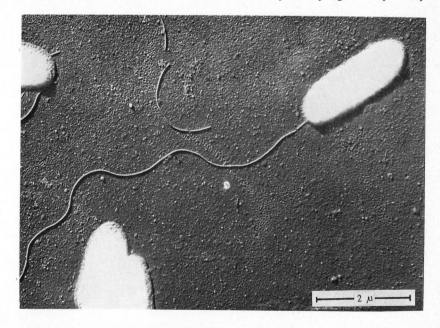

Fig. 22.

were classified into 5 strains (A, B, C, D, and E) according to phage sensitivity. The bacterial isolates distributed in tropical areas are quite different in phage sensitivity from those in Japan. In the tropics, isolates belonging to C and D are predominant whereas in Japan A and B prevail (according to the Japanese criterion for classification). No correlation can be observed between virulence and phage sensitivity.

Epidemiology: The bacteria survive for more than 1 year in sterilized soil and on culture medium covered with mineral oil, whereas they rapidly die in sterilized water. In Japan, natural populations of the bacteria in paddy soil decrease rapidly after the harvesting of rice. They survive winter in the husks of diseased seed grains and straws stored in farm houses, and in the rhizospheres of the intermediate host grasses and ratoon rice. As the temperature increases bacteria surviving in such situations gradually increase in rhizospheres of grasses or at the surface of rice roots. The bacteria then transfer to the aerial parts of rice seedlings to multiply at stomata though without producing any symptoms. These bacteria ooze out on to the surface of the plant and are washed down by the rain, thus increasing the bacterial population in irrigation water. Irrigation water plays an important role in dispersing the pathogen, which is also transmitted by wind and rainfall. The bacteria then invade the upper leaves through hydathodes, wounded leaf edges and roots. Climatic conditions such as high temperature (higher than 25 °C), high humidity, little sunshine, flooding, and strong winds accompanied with rain, favor disease development. Thick morning fog in rice growing seasons also causes severe infection.

Control: Integrated control measures are required to protect rice from the disease. Cultivation of resistant varieties, use of seeds obtained from disease-free fields, raising of seedlings in upland nurseries, controlling the level of irrigation water, and application of fertilizers in suitable amounts, are important cultural practices for controlling the disease.
Burning of diseased straws and eliminating volunteer plants and ratoon rice are also recommended in tropical areas. Several kinds of resistant varieties have been reported, not only in Japan but also in tropical Asian countries, but most are not sufficiently resistant to highly virulent bacterial isolates.
Some effective chemicals such as Sankel (dithiocarbamate-Ni) and Phenazine have been commercially applied in Japan, but 2 or 3 applications are necessary to obtain good results.

Literature

GOTO, M. (1964): "Kresek" and pale yellow leaf, systemic symptom of bacterial leaf blight of rice caused by *Xanthomonas oryzae* (Uyeda & Ishiyama) Dowson. Plant Dis. Reptr. **48**, 858–861.
MIZUKAMI, T., & S. WAKIMOTO (1969): Epidemiology and control of bacterial leaf blight of rice. Ann. Rev. Phytopath. **7**, 51–72.
SRIVASTAVA, D. N. (1972): Bacterial blight of rice. Indian Phytopath. **25**, 1–16.
WAKIMOTO, S. (1960): Classification of strains of *Xanthomonas oryzae* on the basis of their susceptibility to bacteriophages. Ann. Phytopathol. Soc. Japan **25**, 193–198.
CMI Description no 239.

Author: S. Wakimoto

Xanthomonas phaseoli (E. F. Smith) Dowson

Schizomycetes, Pseudomonadales, Pseudomonadaceae

Disease: Bean blight; Bohnenbakteriose; bacteriose du haricot; tizón comun.

Geographical distribution: Worldwide (CMI map no 401).

Host plants: The major hosts of the bacterium are *Phaseolus vulgaris, P. aureus, P. coccineus,*

P. lunatus, P. lunatus var. *macrocarpus, P. mungo. P. acutifolius* var. *latifolius, P. aconitifolius, P. angularis, Pisum sativum, Dolichos lablab, Strophostyles lelvola, Glycine max, Vigna unguiculata, Stizolobium deeringianum, Lupinus polyphyllus, Armoracia rusticana,* and *Lycopersicum esculentum.*

Symptoms: Leaves, stalks, pods and seed of plants are all attacked. The symptoms of this bacteriosis greatly resemble those of halo blight (*Pseudomonas phaseolicola,* p. 57). Leaf spots are usually 1 mm in width and coffee brown. Later the diseased tissue turns yellow, dies off and forms necrotic lesions of varying size. Hyaline spots appear in the leaf axils on the stem, sometimes in form of stripes.
As the disease progresses, the vascular system can discolour a brown colour, if colonised by the bacterium. A brown stem canker can form at the first node, leading to stem breakage. Pod lesions resemble those caused by *P. phaseolicola (p. 57).*
The symptoms of this bacterial bean disease resemble those of halo blight (see above), but a ring (halo) forms around the spots in the latter disease. The disease also resembles bacterial wilt (see p. 57), especially the leaf spots of that disease in the early stages. Later however, they turn yellow and affect the entire leaf tissue. In addition, they require a particular temperature.

Morphology: The bacterium is aerobic, Gram-negative, mobile, with a polar flagellum 0.87 x 1.9 μ in size. It forms acid but no gas from glucose and other mono- and disaccharides, as well as glycerol. The salts of organic acids have an alkaline reaction. Hydrolyses starch, does not reduce nitrate, forms no indole or sulphuric acid, liquifies gelatine. On agar it forms round, yellowish, smooth colonies with whole edges.

Phyisiological specialization: Races of the pathogen are not known, but not every strain can infect every host. Sabet regards the species *X. vignicola, X. alfalfae, X. cassiae, X. tamarindi* and *X. phaseoli* var. *sojensis* as *formae specialis* of *X. phaseoli.*

Epidemiology: The bacterium survives in seed and dead or diseased plant portions and penetrates through stomata of leaves, stems and pods or wounds. It is usually transmitted by diseased seed, but can also be spread by plant remains, blown soil, rain, sprinkling, high relative humidity and temperatures above 22 °C. Insects can also spread the disease.

Control: As for halo blight (p. 58). The variety Great Northern is fairly resistant.

Literature
ARP, G., D. P. COYNE & M. L. SCHUSTER (1971): Disease reaction of bean varieties to *Xanthomonas phaseoli* and *X. phaseoli* var. *fuscans,* using two inoculation methods. Plant Dis. Reptr. **55**, 577–579.
SCHUSTER, M. L. & D. P. COYNE (1971): New virulent strains of *Xanthomonas phaseoli,* Plant Dis. Reptr. **55**, 505–506.
SCHUSTER, M. L., & S. K. PERRY (1972): Seed transmitted bacterial diseases in Michigan Navy (pea) beans. Plant Dis. Reptr. **56**, 378–381.
URQUIJO, P., J. R. SARDIÑA & G. SANTOLALLA (1971): Patología Vegetal Agrícola, Edt. Salvat, Barcelona.
CMI Description no 48.
Author: S. L. Dongo Denegri

Xanthomonas translucens f. sp. **oryzicola** (Fang et al.) Bradbury (Plate 5a, b and fig. 23)

Synonym: *X. oryzicola* Fang et al.
Schizomycetes, Pseudomonadales, Pseudomonadaceae

Disease: Bacterial leaf streak of rice; Bakterielle Blattstreifigkeit des Reises; maladie des stries bactériennes du riz; rayado bacteriano de la hoja del arroz.

Geographical distribution: Tropical Asian countries such as the Philippines, Thailand, Indonesia, China, India, East Pakistan, and West Malaysia (CMI map no 463).

Host plant: Rice (*Oryza sativa*).

Symptoms: Symptoms develop on the leaf blade of rice (Fig. 85d). The bacteria invade leaf tissue through the stomata but spread only within the parenchymatous tissue.

Watersoaked lesions appear and extend in both directions. The veins of the leaf act as barriers for lateral spread of the lesions which are therefore oriented as streaks parallel to the veins (Plate 5a). This symptom is especially clear when the affected leaves are observed against the light. The nature of the bacterial exudate, which is deposited on both leaf surfaces in linear rows, depends on the moisture conditions. In dry condition the bacteria ooze out of the stomata as beads or cirri (Plate 5b), but spread into a flat mass of irregular shape when moistened. When the rice panicles are inoculated between flowering to pre-milk stages, a brown or black discoloration, and death of the ovary, the stamens and the endosperm occur. The blumes also turn brown.

In later stages of the disease, the symptoms of bacterial streak resemble those of bacterial leaf blight (p. 66). The bacterial streak lesion, however, is composed of a group of thin, straight lesions, confined exclusively to the parenchymatous tissue.

Morphology: The colonies grown on nutrient agar are circular, with entire margins, convex, opaque and waxy white to honey yellow in colour. The bacterial cells are capsulated, Gram-negative, rod-shaped, 2.0 x 0.8 μ in average size and have a long monotrichous flagellum (Fig. 23).

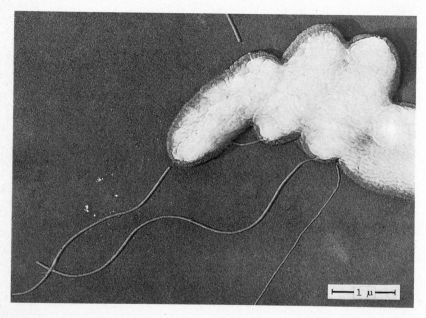

Fig. 23.

Physiological specialization: The bacterial isolates differ greatly in phage sensitivity and in virulence. The isolates collected in Asian countries were classified into 6 groups according to their phage sensitivity. Differentiation of the bacteria in terms of their virulence was reported in India. Based on the reaction on 10 rice variety differentials, 15 isolates of the bacteria collected in India could be assigned to 8 races.

Epidemiology: The bacteria persist in the glumes of the seed, but not in the soil or in infected debris. When the infected seeds germinate, the bacteria invade the coleoptile and leaf sheath through stomata, and cause minute, brownish, small lesions on the first and second leaves. The multiplied bacteria in the host tissues exude from the tissue to cause secondary infection. Thus, the disease extends to the upper leaves as the host plants grow. Young rice leaves are susceptible, but become resistant with age. If rice plants are inoculated at flowering to pre-milk stages, the symptoms appear on glumes, floral parts and endosperms. Only glumes are infected if the inoculation is conducted at post-milk stage, however. Two to three consecutive days with high humidity or dew during the morning hours, are necessary for infection. Enlargement of lesions is promoted by moderate temperatures.

Control: For the control of the disease in endemic areas, the use of disease-free seeds, or of seeds soaked in 0.025 % streptomycin, and hot-water treatment (at 52 °C for 30 min) are recommended. Vitavax spray (0.15–0.3 %) is the best preventive of infection and lesion enlargement. The varieties resistant to some isolates are not necessarily resistent to the others.
According to the results reported from India, only the variety "BJ 1" was resistant (or moderately resistant) to all the bacterial isolate inoculations. All of the others, including Indica and Japonica varieties, were susceptible.

Literature

SHEKHAWAT, G. S., & D. N. SRIVASTAVA (1972): Mode of infection in bacterial leaf streak of rice and histology of the diseased leaf. Phytopathology **74**, 84–90.
SRIVASTAVA, D. N., Y. P. RAO, J. C. DURGAPAL & J. K. JINDAL (1967): Bacterial leaf streak of rice in India. Plant Dis. Reptr. **51**, 928–929.
CMI Description no 240.

Author: S. Wakimoto

Xanthomonas vesicatoria (Doidge) Dowson (Fig. 24)

Synonyms: *Pseudomonas vesicatoria* (Doidge) Stevens, and *Pseudomonas exitiosa* Gardner & Kendrick,
Schizomycetes, Pseudomonadales, Pseudomonadaceae.

Disease: Bacterial spot of tomato; Bakterielle Fleckenkrankheiten der Tomaten; Tache bactérienne de la tomate; Mancha bacteriana del tomate.

Geographical distribution: Very widespread. The pathogen is known to occur in many of the countries where tomatoes are grown, and records are increasing rapidly (CMI map no 269). Recend records, not shown on this map include, Barbados, Colombia, Cuba, Dominica, Egypt, Fiji, Guadeloupe, Martinique, possibly Nigeria, St. Vincent, Seychelles, Trinidad, Tunisia and others.

Host plants: Tomato (*Lycopersicum esculentum*) and peppers (*Capsicum* spp.); also found naturally infecting potato fruit (*Solanum tuberosum*) in Italy, *Nicandra physaloides* in New Zealand, *Physalis peruviana* and *P. virginiana* f. *macrophysa* in Australia.

Symptoms: Lesions may appear on any above ground parts of pepper or tomato. The first symptoms usually are small, dark, greasy-looking spots on leaves and stems of young plants. These enlarge, become drier-looking and greyishbrown, and in severe attacks leaf tissues, especially tips and margins shrivel and die. Bacterial ooze may form and dry to a glistening cream-coloured film. Lesions on stems are elongated, greyish and scab-like. Flowers show dark spots and infected blossoms and young fruits often wither and fall. On fruit, which is attacked only when green, the first symptoms are dark, water-soaked spots. These are sometimes surrounded by a whitish halo, which can cause confusion with the fruit spots of bacterial canker. As the lesions enlarge they become rougher and scabby-looking, and the haloes disappear. They are usually quite small

Fig. 24.

(2–4 mm diam.) and shallow, but they spoil the appearence of the fruit, making it unmarketable (Fig. 24). Bacterial canker (*Corynebacterium michiganense,* p. 73) is distinguished by the haloes and smoother surfaces of the fruit lesions and by the leaves wilting and shrivelling rather than showing discrete spots. Bacterial speck (*Pseudomonas tomato* (Okabe) Alstatt) is usually distinguished by the much tinier spots on both leaves and fruit spots. Under very damp conditions, however, the spots may be identical and the pathogen must be isolated for diagnosis.

Morphology: The organism is a Gram-negative rod, motile, with a single polar flagellum. Colonies on nutrient agar are yellow, smooth, round and butyrous in consistency. Growth is inhibited by 0.02 % triphenyl tetrazolium chloride, and by 5 % sodium chloride. No diffusible pigments are produced. Acid is produced from glucose and various other carbohydrates aerobically but not anaerobically. These and some others are the characteristics of the common yellow species of *Xanthomonas,* which are all very similar. The species should therefore be confirmed by pathogenicity tests.

Physiological specialization: Using 3 bacteriophages, 2 distinct strains of the organism have been detected on tomato and 1 on pepper. Other work suggests that many more phage types occur. Pathotypes, or races, have been distinguished by injecting suspensions of the bacteria into tomato and pepper leaves, which react with either hypersensitive or susceptible reactions. A strain with different pathogenicity has been found infecting turnip, radish and tomato in Brazil and USA. It has been named *X. vesicatoria* var. *raphani. X. physalidis* and *X. physalidicola* have several hosts in common with *X. vesicatoria* and may well be strains of this latter organism.

Epidemiology: The disease is introduced into new areas in seed. Once in an area, the pathogen can overwinter in plant debris and possibly also in the rhizospheres of nonsusceptible plants. It is probable that some solanaceous weeds can act as alternate hosts; several are susceptible. The pathogen spreads from the soil and from plant to plant by rain splash, insects and workers. The optimum temperature for disease development is about 25 °C and infection will not take place above 35 °. A continuous temperature of 38 ° or more for several days is reported to kill the organism. The pathogen enters leaves through stomata. Fruit, which have no stomata, are thought to be infected through minute wounds caused by breaking of hairs, wind-blown sand, insects, and possibly tiny growth fissures. Ripe fruit are immune, probably because of their acidity.

Control: Crop rotation is recommended, and if soil is known to be infected, it should be kept free of susceptible plants, including solanaceous weeds, for at least two years. Under glass, infested soil should be steamed or fumigated. Seed should be treated or known to be disease free. Hot water treatment for 25 minutes at an accurate 50 °C is most effective and cheapest. Soaking in 1 : 3000 mercuric chloride solution for 5 minutes, followed by very thorough rinsing, is often preferred for pepper, which may not stand the hot water. Treated seed should be dried and mixed with a protectant dust such as thiram before planting.

These recommendations, if carefully followed, should control the disease, but if required, sprays of 2 kg per 400 l waters basic copper sulphate or copper oxychloride should reduce the disease. In an infected crop irrigation should not be overhead and work should be done only when plants are dry.

If possible, healthy plants should be worked over before touching diseased ones.

In spite of various reports of promising sources of resistance, there seem to be no satisfactory resistant varieties yet available.

Other bacterial diseases of tomatos and other solanaceous crops:

Corynebacterium michiganense (E. F. Smith) Jensen. Bacterial canker. Ref.: CMI Description no 19.

Erwinia carotovora (Jones) Bergey et al, soft rots of fruits.

Pseudomonas solanacearum. Bacterial wilt (p. 58).

Literature

CHUPP, C., & A. F. SHERF (1960): Vegetable Diseases and their Control. pp. 528–530. New York: Roland Press.
CMI Description no 20.

Author: J. F. Bradbury

Other more important Xanthomonas spp. as pathogens on tropical and subtropical crops (Fig. 25):

X. albilineans (Ashby) Dowson. Leaf scald of sugarcane. Ref.: CMI Description no 18.

X. holcicola (Elliott) Starr & Burkholder. Bacterial leaf streak of *Sorghum* spp. CMI map no 395.

X. manihotis (Arth.-Ber.) Starr. Cassava bacterial blight. Ref.: PANS **20** (1) 31–34, 1974 (Fig. 25).

X. ricini (Yoshi & Takimoto) Dowson. Angular leaf spots of castorbeans. Ref.: CMI Descriptions no 379.

Fig. 25.

X. sesami Sabet & Dowson. Angular leaf spots of sesame. Ref.: CMI Description no 16; Phytopath. Z. **54**, 193–201, 1965.

X. vascularum (Cobb) Dowson. Gumming disease of sugarcane. Ref.: CMI Description no 380.

X. zingiberi (Uyeda) Savulescu. Soft rot of ginger and turmeric.

Erwinia spp. as pathogens on tropical and subtropical crops

E. carotovora (Jones) Holland. Causing soft rots on a wide range of hosts, including: bananas, cucumber, cumin, mango, capsicum, pineapple, potato, etc.

E. herbicola (Geilinger) Dye. A soft rot causing species on a large number of hosts with an extensive synonymy including: *E. cassavae* (Hansf.) Burkholder; *E., citrimaculans* (Doidge) Magrou; E. mangiferae (Doidge) Bergey et al., *Xanthomonas maydis* Rangaswami, Prasad & Eswaran and *X. penniseti* Rajagopalan & Rangaswami. Ref.: CMI Description no 232.

E. stewartii (Smith) Dye. Stewart's disease (a wilt) on maize. Ref.: CMI Description no 123.

E. tracheiphila (Smith) Bergey et al. Bacterial wilt of cucumber. Ref.: CMI Description no 233.

Fungal diseases

Fungi are eucaritic thallophytes that have no chlorophyll, and an undifferentiated thalli. Fungi are heterotrophic, absorbing food from organic material previously photosynthesized by higher plants.

They either live as saprophytes, which is the majority, on dead organic matter, or as parasites on living plants, animals and fungi. Amongst the parasites again most of them have saprophytic and parasitic phases (facultative parasites). Only a few taxonomic groups, such as rusts (Uredinales), powdery mildews (Erysiphales), downy mildews (higher Peronosporales), and some others, are obligate parasites, thus entirely dependend on their living hosts. Practically only parasites can become pathogens of plant diseases.

The thallus of fungi may be plasmodial amoeboid or pseudoplasmodial (Myxomycota), or filamentous and then either unicellular (hyphae, mycelium) and in the latter case non-septate (Mastigomycotina, Zygomycotina) or septate (Ascomycotina, Basidiomycotina, Deuteromycotina). Fungi are typically nonmotile but motile states (e. g. zoospores) may occur. Cell walls are chitinized with the exception of the oomycetes (which have cellulose). Cells may be multinucleate, and the mycelium homo- or heterothallic. Within their life cycles fungi can be haploid, dicaryotic (prominent with basidiomycotina) and – mostly transitionally - diploid. Reproduction occurs either asexual (zoosporangia, conidia, uredospores) or sexual (oospores, ascospores, basidiospores), and in the latter case homo - or heterothallic.

Fungi are no longer considered members of the plant kingdom but as a kingdom of their own. They are nutrionally distinct from the plant kingdom on account of lacking photosynthesis, and from the animal kingdom by the fact that fungi do not ingest but absorb their food. In this respect, as well as in the classification and nomenclature we essentially follow here Ainsworth, Sparrow and Sussman in their book Fungi, vol IV (see below).

The reader will soon understand that fungal classification is still in a state of transition. Many taxonomic groups at present must rather be understood as pigeonholes than part of a natural system of the fungi. However, as this book is on plant pathology we shall not indulge in this subject but leave it alone and utilize the subdivisions of eumycota as headings of phytopathological relevant genera, which then are being treated alphabetically. For details we have to refer to the following books.

Dipersal of fungi takes place by means of spores of various kinds, sclerotia, chlamydospores, rhizomorphs (strands), and mycelium. The transmission can be achived by seed or planting material, wind (the most common vehicle), water (as rain, irrigation water, etc.), insects, animals and man (and his tools) as vectors.

Fungi can pass unfavourable periods with their resting spores (oospores, ascomata, teliospores etc.) or sclerotia, chlamydospores and other vegetative organs. They may do this on or in the soil (from where they attack their hosts), on living or dead host organs, or any dead matter. In this way they also may bridge periods of absence of hosts, or they infect alternate hosts, which for a great number of Uredinales is obligatory.

Infection by fungi in most cases primarily depends on free water on the hosts surface. In addition, temperature, density of inoculum (amount of infections entities on or near the infection court) and actual susceptibility of the host are critical and amount of infection of host are largely determined by these factors. During the infection process fungi may be exposed to fungicides as well as to adverse environmental factors. Efficient barriers against infection are the cuticle and the epidermis. Still, many fungi can overcome these obstacles directly. Others depend on stomata or preexisting fresh wounds of any kind.

Penetration of hosts during pathogenesis by the pathogens is achieved by active growth of hyphae, enzymes, and vivotoxins. Hosts oppose penetration by means of preformed chemical substances, existing barriers (sclerenchyme, lignin etc.) and active host reactions (hypersensitivity, and others). This interaction between pathogen and host determines the amount of disease (number and size of lesion) and duration of the highly variable incubation period. A host is considered susceptible if lesions are more numerous and bigger, and if the incubation period is shorter and sporulation (after the latent period has elapsed) is richer – all under the same environment, of course. Length of latent periods have (amoungst other factors) a decisive influence on the final amount of disease in a crop.

Many fungus species have a very restricted host range. Others can infect many species form various families amongst di- and monocotolydones.

Symptoms caused by fungi are manyfold. They range from soft and dry rots; damping-offs, root and collar rots; scabs, stem necrosis, cankers; various leaf spots, including blights and blasts; rusts and mildews; and wilts or even apoplexias. Fungi may also cause dwarfing, rosetting, galls, witches brooms and many other malformations. Often the same fungus can cause a variety of these symptoms on the some or different hosts, may it be in sequence or simultaneously. Climate and/other environmental factors as well as degree of susceptibility of the host interact often markedly. However, on a given host many pathogens may be responsible for similar symptoms. Therefore, identification of a fungus as a pathogen of a crop on symptoms alone is often risky. For anyone unfamiliar with the diseases in a given region, or for a disease apparently new to that region, the identification of the fungus by its morphology is a must. If necessary, the help of specialists has to be asked.

Fungi cause the majority of plant diseases, many of them are highly destructive, or limiting factors for a crop in a given area. Control of fungal diseases is possible through cultural methods, production of healthy or uncontaminated seeds or planting material, resistant cultivars, seed-dressing and a still increasing number of fungicides. Physical control measures such as soil steaming, heat therapy or simply "cut and burn" can also be highly effective. Also internal and external quarantine may work, although effectiviness is limited in the case of windborne diseases. The following chapters, which deal with a number of selected fungi as pathogens on tropical and subtropical crops, will provide in detail many examples for the brief outlines above on dispersal, overwintering (oversummering), infection, host range, and control methods.

Some general textbooks on mycology

AINSWORTH, G. C. (1971): Dictionary of the fungi. 6th ed. Commonwealth Mycological Institute, Kew, UK.

AINSWORTH, G. C., & A. S. SUSSMAN (1965–1968): The fungi. An advanced treatise, vols I–III. Academic Press, New York and London.

AINSWORTH, G. C., F. K. SPARROW & A. S. SUSSMAN (1973): The fungi. An advanced treatise, vols IV A & B. Academic Press, New York and London.

ALEXOPOULOS, C. J., & E. S. BENEKE (1962): Laboratory manual for introductory mycology. Burgess Publ. Co., Minneapolis.

ARX, J. A. von (1970): The genera of fungi sporulating in pure culture. J. Cramer, Lehre.

BURNETT, J. H. (1968): Fundamentals of mycology. Edward Arnold (Publ.) Ltd., London.

CLEMENTS, F. E., & C. L. SHEAR (1931): The genera of fungi. Wilson, New York.
COCHRANE, V. W. (1963): Physiology of fungi. John Wiley & Sons, New York & London.
GÄUMANN, E. (1964): Die Pilze. Birkhäuser, Basel.
HAWKSWORTH, D. L. (1974): Mycologists handbook. Commonwealth Mycological Institute, Kew, UK.
INGOLD, C. T. (1965): Spore liberation. Clarendon Press, Oxford.
TALBOT, P. H. B. (1971): Principles of fungal taxonomy. MacMillan, London.

Mastigomycotina

This subdivision of zoosporic fungi comprises the classes Chytridiomycetes, Hyphochytridiomycetes and Oomycetes. Amongst these the latter is the most important one for plant pathologists. Only a few genera with species pathogenic to plants belong to the other classes (*Plasmodiophora, Spongospora, Polymyxa, Olpidium, Synchytrium,* etc.).

Nearly all plant pathogenic oomycetes belong to the order Peronosporales with their three families *Pythiaceae, Peronosporaceae,* and *Albuginaceae.*

The Pythiaceae (with *Pythium, Phytophthora, Trachysphaeria, Sclerophthora*) are facultative parasites (with the exception of some *Phytophthora* and all *Sclerophthora* spp.). As pathogens the *Pythium* and some *Phytophthora* spp. cause unspecific rots, damping-off, whereas other *Phytophthora* spp. and *Sclerophthora* spp. are agents of downy mildew as are the Peronosporaceae (*Sclerospora, Plasmopara, Pseudoperonospora, Peronospora, Bremia*).

But whilst Pythiaceae still depend on free water for their zoospores released from zoosporangiae, borne on little differentiated sporangiophores, *Peronosporaceae* have typical sporangiophores and their sporangia (in *Peronospora, Bremia*) have lost the ability to release zoospores, and thus behave like conidia that are wind-borne. This is most pronounced with the white 'rusts' of the Albugineae (*Albugo*). Somewhat parallel with this trend host specificity becomes more pronounced. Peronosporaceae and Albugineae are obligate parasites.

Literature

FITZPATRICK, H. M. (1930): The lower fungi. Phycomycetes. McGraw Hill, New York.
GÄUMANN, E. (1923): Beiträge zu einer Monographie der Gattung *Peronospora.* Beitr. Kryptogamenflora
    Schweiz **5**, 1–360.
See also literature cited above, and in the following texts.

Zygomycotina

From the two classes Zygomycetes and Trichomycetes only the former comprise a few facultative parasites of minor importance as plant pathogens. Some of them are listed below. They all belong to the Mucorales.

Literature

ZYCHA, H., R. SIEPMANN & G. LINNEMANN (1969): Mucorales. J. Cramer, Lehre.

Phytophthora cinnamomi Rands.

Oomycetes, Peronosporales, Pythiaceae

Disease: Phytophthora root rot of avocado; Phytophthora-Wurzelfäule der Avocado; Phytophthora pourriture de racine d'avocat; Phytophthora pudrición de la raíz del avocado.

Geographical distribution: *P. cinnamomi* is widely distributed throughout many of the subtropical and tropical regions of the world, and less commonly in temperate zones (CMI map no 302).

Host plants: This pathogen has an extremely wide host range; over 450 different species of plants in a large number of families have been listed as affected. Affected plants range from primitive Gymnosperms (*Macrozamia*) through monocotyledonous plants (*Xanthorrhea*), to many woody dicots, with particularly large numbers of species in the families Myrtaceae, Proteaceae etc. as well as many conifers. Some of the most important hosts are: *Eucalyptus marginata, Persea americana, Pinus radiata, Ananas sativus* and many ornamental plants.

Symptoms: Leaves of diseased avocado trees are smaller than normal and usually pale or yellow-green instead of dark green. Leaves are often wilted and in advanced stages of disease they fall, giving the tree a sparse appearance. New growth is often absent. In advanced stages of disease, branches die back. Diseased trees often set an abnormally heavy crop of fruit which remain small. Many of the feeder roots are blackened, brittle and dead; in advanced stages it is difficult to find feeder roots. *P. cinnamomi* can also cause trunk cankers on avocado trees; these are characterized by whitish exudation of sugar, occasional cracking and extensive necrosis. No other avocado disease can be confused with *Phytophthora* root rot when the entire symptomatology is considered. *Armillariella* root rot (p. 145) causes somewhat similar top symptoms, but is readily distinguished by the extensive rotting of large roots and occurrence of white mycelial plaques and rhizomorphs. Avocado trees will wilt when affected with *Verticillium* (p. 229), but vascular discoloration is usually obvious and roots are not rotted.

Morphology: This species is forms oogonia and amphigynous antheridia when the two opposite mating or compatibility types (A^1 and A^2) are present; thick-walled oospores are formed within the oogonia following fertilization. The fungus also forms two types of asexual spores: chlamydospores, and sporangia which liberate zoospores under proper temperature and moisture conditions. *P. cinnamomi* forms a characteristic, zonate, camelloid pattern of growth on potato dextrose agar. Sporangia are non-papillate, and are not formed in agar culture; they are most readily formed in soil extract, but are formed in axenic culture following extensive washing of young mycelium and incubation in a salt solution. Chlamydospores are readily formed in culture, especially in V8 broth or on V8 agar.

Physiological specialization: *P. cinnamomi* is heterothallic. The A^2 mating or compatibility type is the common one, with the A^1 much more rare in occurrence. Races have not yet been separated, though there are some obvious differences in pathogenicity between isolates.

Epidemiology: The pathogen can survive for several years (up to 6 years) in moist soil, in the absence of a host, either in the form of chlamydospores or oospores. The pathogen forms abundant sporangia, under proper environmental conditions in the soil; these release zoospores into water in the soil. *P. cinnamomi* also forms chlamydospores and oospores. The motile zoospores can be spread in water. The fungus can also be dispersed in nursery stock, and by any means that moist soil is moved (cultivation equipment, shovels, etc.).

Infection takes place primarily as the result of zoospore infection of young roots; zoospores are attracted to amino acids exuding from the region of elongation, encyst, germinate and infect the root within a few hours. Excess soil moisture, resulting from restricted soil drainage, is necessary for infection.

The pathogen can readily invade many of the small feeder roots under favorable conditions of soil moisture and temperature; large roots are not generally attacked; thus the disease primarily affects uptake of nutrients and of water. Symptoms develop in the top of the tree when active roots are reduced to a low level.

Under irrigated agriculture, soil moisture conditions necessary for production of sporangia, and for zoospore release and infection can occur any time of the year. Most infection takes place in the warmer months of the year, however.

Temperatures from 20 to 30 °C are favorable for the disease; infection drops sharply above 30 °C. Soil pH conditions of from 5 to 7,5 are favorable for disease development, with maximum development at pH 6,5.

Control: Sanitary measures are important in keeping *P. cinnamomi* out of the avocado nursery; this can be acomplished by growing plants in containers, steaming or fumigating the soil, heat treating seed, and taking precautions so that the fungus is not spread into the nursery. To keep the pathogen from invading a healthy grove, use clean nursery stock, and take all possible precautions to prevent movement of the fungus into the grove in soil, on cultivation equipment, by water running over infested areas, or by other means. Soils with good internal drainage should be selected for the avocado planting; the disease develops slowly if at all on well-drained soil.

Careful irrigation so that the excess water does not develop in the soil profile will aid in retarding disease development. Affected trees use much less water than healthy trees because the feeder roots are destroyed. Possibilities for control with soil amendments and modfied nutrition are still under investigation.

Most types of avocado used for rootstocks are susceptible to *P. cinnamomi.* One of the Mexican varieties, the "Duke", has moderate resistance. High resistance is present in small-fruited species of *Persea (P. borbonia, P. caerulea, P. Donnell-Smithii),* but these are not graft compatible with the avocado (*P. americana*).

P. cinnamomi can be killed in soil by high dosages of several fumigants, including methyl bromide, the mixture of dichloropropene and dichloropropane, and sodium methyl dithiocarbamate. Thus it is possible to treat planting sites and obtain good growth of new trees though re-invasion by the fungus usually occurs in 2 to 3 years. Chemicals such as DAS (p-dimethyl aminobenzene diazosodium sulfonate) and Terrazole or Truban show promise in treating diseased trees by applying in irrigation water, but are expensive, and Dexon is no longer registered for use on avocado trees in the United States; residue data have not yet been obtained for Terrazole.

Replanting the infested soil with resistant plants is another way to combat the disease. The fungus has a wide host range but there are many plants that are not susceptible, including citrus, most vegetables, annual flower crops, and fruit trees such as cherimoya, persimmon and fig.

Literature

ZENTMYER, G. A., A. O. PAULUS & R. M. BURNS (1967): Avocado root rot. Calif. Agric. Exp. Station Circular. **511,** 1–16.
CMI Description no 113.

Author: G. A. Zentmyer

Other Phytophthora spp. on Avocado:
P. cactorum (Leb. et Cohn) Schroeter, collar rot. Ref.: CMI Description no 111
P. palmivora (see p. 83)
P. citricola Sawada, canker, root rot. Ref.: Mycology **66,** 830–845, 1974

Phytophthora citrophthora (Smith & Smith) Leonian (Plate 5 c)

Oomycetes, Peronosporales, Phythiaceae.

Disease: Brown rot gummosis or foot rot of citrus; Gummose der Zitrusarten; gommose des citrus; gomosis de los agrios. *Phytophthora nicotianae* B. de Haan var. *parasitica* (Dastur) Waterh., *Phytophthora palmivora.*

Geographical distribution: The disease is present in all countries where citrus trees, are cultivated (CMI map no 35 for *P. citrophthora*).

Host plants: All three pathogens have a wide host range; they may infect fruit trees, vegetables and ornamentals. Among common commercial citrus trees, grown either for fruit or as rootstocks, several can be attacked by these fungi. The different species though, differ in their susceptibility towards the disease. Lemon (*Citrus limon*), citrons (*C. medica*) and several citranges (*Poncirus trifoliata x C. sinensis*), except Troyer and Carrizo are highly susceptible. To a declining degree the following are susceptible: clementine (*C. reticulata*), sweet orange (*C. sinensis*), limes (*C. aurantifolia*), Pummelo (*C. grandis*), rough lemon (*C. jambhiri*) grapefruit (*C. paradisi*), mandarins (*C. reticulata*), Troyer and Carrizo citranges, most selections of trifoliate orange (*P. trifoliata*). Sour orange (*C. aurantium*), some trifoliates (Texas, Barnes, English, Rubidoux and Davis B), Kumquat (*Fortunella* spp.), and Severinia (*S. buxifolia*) are resistant.

Symptoms: Brown rot gummosis attacks the trunk near the soil and the larger main roots. The first symptom to be seen is a profuse gumming on the surface of the affected bark (Plate 5c). When the infection is below ground this gum is absorbed by the soil. The infection extends both upwards and lateraly. When scraped the affected part is brown in colour which contrasts to the green colour of the surrounding healthy tissue. The bark is killed through the wood. Removal of the infected bark will reveal a dark brown staining of the cambial surface. Further inward, the wood is healthy. At a later stage, the dead bark dries, shrinks, and cracks, and sometimes, patches of it become loose and fall off leaving an open canker.

The leaves that correspond to the invaded part of the tree become chlorotic, the yellow colour appearing first in the midrib and spreading to the lamina. Later, the yellow leaves drop and twigs and even branches die back. The leaves of the new shoots are small and fruits are reduced in size and quantity. When the invasion girdles the trunk the tree dies. The decline caused by brown rot gummosis is slow although on a susceptible host and under favorable conditions of temperature and moisture it can be very rapid. The symptoms on the foliage can be seen not only on trees attacked by *Phytophthora*, but also on trees suffering from rootrots, nematods or any other disease in which the movement of water between roots and top is obstructed. Brown rot gummosis can be distinguished from these diseases by the symptoms on the base of the trunks. The symptoms on the affected part of the tree, however, can be confused with advanced stages of psorosis (p. 15). In the latter though, only the outer layers of the bark are destroyed while *Phytophthora* infection kills the entire bark and the cambium.

Yet, the positive diagnosis of the disease can be made only in the laboratory after the pathogen has been isolated. Species of *Phytophthora* can be isolated only from the margin of the infected parts. In cultures on corn meal agar or in water, the above three species produce coenocytic mycelium and the ovoid sporangia which are characteristic of the genus *Phytophthora*. The identification of the species is difficult.

Epidemiology: The fungi causing brown rot gummosis live in the soil. Their spores can be dispersed by irrigation or splashing water. In case of floods or heavy rains they can attack parts of the trunk that lie above ground. For infection to take place, water must be in contact with the bark for at least five hours. Thus the disease is more prevalent in low wet or heavy soils that do not drain easily. The fungi can enter the plant through the uninjured bark but when injuries are present the infection is hastened. Root bark in general is less susceptible than stem bark. Brown rot gummosis shows a very strong seasonal development which depends on the temperature requirements of the species. For instance in temperate zones *P. citrophthora* attacks the trees in spring and autumn while *P. parasitica* during summer.

Control:
1. Dead and badly infected trees must be removed and destroyed. Before using again the tree site it has to be desinfected with one of the following materials: formalin 2 %, methyl bromide, Vapam, chemicals based on chlorinated C_3 hydrocarbons with or without methyl isothiocyanate (D. D., Telone etc.).
2. In districts where the disease is prevalent trees must be inspected at least once a year. The soil

must be removed and the trunk examined down to the first lateral roots. By following the above practice it is possible to detect gummosis at its earliest stages.

3. When gummosis is detected and the affected area does not exceed half of the circumferance of the trunk, the following corrective measures can be taken: the affected bark must be removed with a stripe two cm wide of healthy tissue. It is not necessary to cut the wood. The exposed part of the trunk or roots should be disinfected with either a 1 % solution of potassium permanganate or with Bordeaux paste containing 6 kg of copper sulfate and 12 kg of hydrated lime in 100 l of water. After the cut edges of the bark begin to heal, the exposed wood is painted with asphalt paint or any other suitable sealing. The tops of treated trees must be cut back or thinned.

4. It is advisable to plant trees high with their first roots barely under the soil surface, and paint their trunks from the height of one meter down to the main roots with Bordeaux paste in early spring.

5. Where furrow irrigation is used the water should not come into contact with the trunk. To achieve this the soil is banked up 50 cm away from and around the base of the trunk. On the outside of this barrier a basin is formed to receive the irrigation water. The water for each tree should come directly from the irrigation furrow and not from the basins of other trees. If the disease is detected in the orchard, the irrigation water should be disinfected by placing in the main irrigation canal a sack containing large crystals of copper sulfate. The small quantity of copper sulfate dissolved, as water passes through, is enough to stop the spread of the disease. This procedure must be followed only twice during the irrigation period.

6. Wounding of the trunk and roots must be avoided at all times.

7. The most successful method of preventing the disease is the use of resistant rootstocks budded at least 50 cm above ground. Some stocks, however, very resistant to gummosis, are very susceptible to other diseases. For instance sweet orange on sour orange stock is very resistant to gummosis but very susceptible to tristeza. Other stocks relatively resistant to gummosis are not suitable to the climate or soil in a given locality. Even rootstocks very susceptible to *Phytophthora* can be protected by using the precaution listed above. It is therefore recommended that a stock be chosen primarily for its resistance to tristeza (if tristeza, p. 17), is a serious threat in that locality) and its suitability to local conditions and secondarily for its resistance to gummosis.

Literature

FAWCETT, H. S. (1936): Citrus diseases and their control. McGraw-Hill Book Co., Inc., New York (2nd edition)

KLOTZ, L. J., & E. C. CALAVAN (1969): Gum diseases of Citrus in California. Cal. Agr. Exp. Sta. Ext. Ser. Circular **396** (2nd revision).

CMI Description no 33 for *P. citrophthora*, and no 35 for *P. nicotianae* var. *parasitica*.

Author: Anna Chitzanidis

Other Phytophthora spp. on Citrus spp.:
P. hibernalis Carne. Brown rot of fruit, leaf and twig blight. Ref.: CMI Description no 31.

Phytophthora megasperma Drechs. var. sojae A. A. Hildeb.
(Figs. 26–28)

Oomycetes, Peronosporales, Pythiaceae

Disease: Phytophthora root and stem rot of soybean; *Phytophthora* - Wurzel- und Stengelfäule der Soyabohne; Phytophthora pourriture des tiges et racine de Soya; Phytophthora en podredumbre de raiz y tallo de la soya.

Geographical distribution: The disease is still restricted to the North American continent, reported from soybean-growing states of the USA and providences of Canada.

Fig. 26.

Host plants: Includes *Trifolium subterraneum, Medicago sativa,* and *Lupine* spp. It can subsist on the roots of other legumes.

Symptoms: The fungus attacks soybeans in all stages of growth, causing seed decay, pre- and post-emergence damping-off, and a root and stem rot. The root and stem rot phase results in wilting and death of infected seedlings and mature plants. The first symptoms to appear on older plants are interveinal and marginal yellowing of the leaves, then wilting, followed by a dark brown canker spreading up the stem into the branches (Fig. 26). The diseased roots of infected plants are dark brown and decayed. Root rot may develop without the fungus moving up the stem. Stem cankers may develop without root rot. Seedlings are more susceptible than older plants. Symptoms on young plants may be confused with infection by *Rhizoctonia solani* (p. 178). *Diaporthe phaseolorum,* the pod and stem blight fungus, and *Pythium* spp. and *Fusarium* spp. are often found associated with Phytophthora stem cankers.

Morphology: See Figs. 27 and 28, and text.

Physiological specialization: At least three races of the fungus are known. Varieties known to be susceptible to all three races are: Harosoy, Amsoy, Clark, D55–1492 and Lindarin. Varieties re-

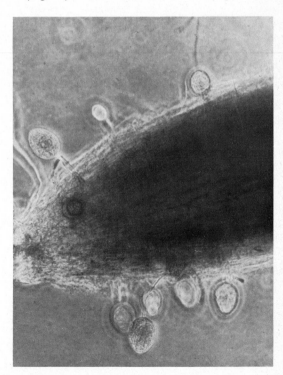

Fig. 27.

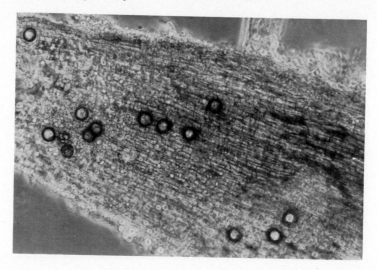

Fig. 28.

sistant to races 1 and 2 are: Amsoy 71, A. K., Beeson, Boone, Calland, Clark 63, Illini, L 66, Lindarin 63, Mukden, and S1-12. Varieties resistant to races 1 and 3 are: Harrell, Nansemond, and Sanga. Varieties resistant to all three races are: Arksoy, Lee 68 nd Higan. Varieties susceptible to races 3 are: Chippewa, Chippewa 64, Hark, Hawkeye, Hawkeye 63, Henry and Monroe, as well as a number of commercial blends and brands. Host resistance is associated with phytoalexin production, the nature of which is not thoroughly understood.

Epidemiology: The disease develops on plants growing in heavy, compacted and light-sandy soils which are in low, poorly drained areas, or on higher ground during rainy seasons. Moisture is more critical than temperature for the spread of the pathogen. Disease development occurs between 22–28 °C. The disease pattern varies, but is usually circular, but it may appear on scattered plants within a field, often at the end of rows. The pathogen survives between growing seasons in plant refuse or as oospores (resting spores) in the soil. After infection takes place, the fungus gives rise to sporangia (fruiting structures) on the root surface (Fig. 27). These in turn, produce motile spores (zoospores) that move through the moisture film in the soil or in irrigation water to the roots of other susceptible plants. The zoospore forms a cyst on the root surface. A germ tub (infection tube) arises from the cyst and penetrates the host tissue. Oospores (Fig. 28) are formed within the host tissues as the result of sexual fusion of unlike sexual spores (gametes). The fungus can infect both susceptible and resistant plants and form oospores in root tissues. The presence of oospores in root tissues are diagnostic. Oospores are released into the soil when the surrounding tissue disintegrates. Optimal temperatures for fungal development and penetration are between 25 and 30 °C.

Control: The control of the disease is through resistant varieties, crop rotation with nonhost species, good drainage, and phytosanitary practices.

Literature

CHAMBERLAIN, D. W., & B. R. LIPSCOMB. (1967): Bibliography of soybean diseases. U.S. Dept. Agr. CR-50-67.
MEYER, W. A., & J. B. SINCLAIR. (1972): Root reduction and stem lesion development on soybeans by *Phytophthora megasperma* var. *sojae*. Phytopathology **62**, 1414–1416.
SCHMITTHENNER, A. F. (1972): Evidence for a new race of *Phytophthora megasperma* var. *sojae* pathogenic to soybean. Plant Dis. Reptr. **56**, 536–539.

Author: J. B. Sinclair

Phytophthora palmivora (Butl.) Butl. (Figs. 29–31)

Oomycetes, Peronosporales, Pythiaceae

Disease: Black pod of cocoa; Braunfäule des Kakaos; pourriture brune des cabosses du cacaoyer; piña negra del cacao.

Geographical distribution: Cosmopolitan in the warmer parts of the world with the possible exception of French Guiana.

Host plants: Over 80 hosts are known. The most important include: Cocoa – (black pod, canker, leaf blight, root rot), coconut (bud rot, Plate 3b, Fig. 29), rubber (p. 86), pepper (root rot, wilt, leaf blight), pineapple (heart rot), oilpalm (rot of terminal leaves), Areca palm (fruit rot), papaya (fruit and stem rots), *Annona* spp. (fruit and seedling rots), durian (patch canker), breadfruit and sapodilla (fruit rot), cashew nut and tung (leaf spot), etc.

Symptoms Roots: In seedlings, infection with *P. palmivora* results in root-rot. Infection can be halted and new roots formed, either replacing the tap root or increasing the number of feeder roots. The plant then appears healthy but still is prone to lodging.
Stem: Stem infections or cankers may be limited to the bark in old plants but in seedlings the mycelia reach the pith through the ray parenchyma cells. The mycelia in old plants may be loose or compacted into black sclerotia-like strands. When the rot girdles the stem, the plant may die. Stem invasion tends to be halted in older plants and in seedlings known to be relatively resistant; the fungal mycelia die and are sloughed off with the rotted bark.
Leaves: Symptoms on leaves range from discrete necrotic spots to a typical blight with the crinkled leaf margins curled (Fig. 30).
Pods: Initial symptoms may be necrotic spots which, in multiple infections, coalesce to give the typical wet, brownish rot (Fig. 31). The mycelia penetrate the husk and reach the beans and placenta within two or three days depending on the pod size. The husk remains rather hard when pressed. Depending on the humidity of the climate, aerial hyphae and sporangia develop, initially from the older infected parts. The white, sporulating mycelium is rather smooth or slippery to the touch. When overrun by secondary invaders, the aerial mycelium may turn a brownish colour.
When old cankered barks peel off vertical cracks result though these do not penetrate to the stele as with the collar crack disease caused by *Armillariella mellea* (p. 145). On leaves, the crinkled curled edge of the necrotic areas is typical but the necrotic spots, if these develop no further, can be mistaken for *Colletotrichum* leaf spot (p. 119). When kept for 24h in a moist chamber however, sporangia of *P. palmivora* are formed.

Fig. 29.

On the pod, *P. palmivora* lesions are not sunken: this distinguishes black pod from *Colletotrichum* infection at the non-fruiting stage. *Botryodiplodia theobromae* pod rots (p. 188) are spongy or springy when pressed and can thus be distinguished from black pod without the blackening typical of the old *Botryodiplodia* infection. The rapid invasion of the inner layers of the pod husk, beans and placenta, distinguishes the black pod lesion from the late brown stage of immature ripening or wilting of young pods (cherelles). When the browning goes no deeper than the small parenchyma cells under the epidermis, then *P. palmivora* is not responsible especially when the entire pod surface is brown. *Trachysphaera fructigena* (p. 99) lesions on pods are generally difficult to distinguish from those of black pod: it must be noted, however, that *T. fructigena* mycelia on the pod tend to turn brownish. The spores of *T. fructigena* are spiny and coarse to the touch which can thus be felt between sensitive fingers. They also tend to occur in clumps which can be recognised by the trained eye. The presence in most *T. fructigena* lesions of wounds on the pod is an additional identifying characteristic.

Morphology: The hyaline hyphae (rarely wider than 5 μ diameter) are aseptate and contain many oil droplets. The characteristic *P. palmivora* sporangia (mostly 50–60 x 31–35 μ) are borne on indeterminate sporangiophores with pedicels 2–10 μ long. The beak or operculum is prominent in ovoid sporangia but is less prominent in more rounded and in secondary sporangia. Secondary sporangia are readily produced in moist conditions *in vivo* and *in vitro*. They are much smaller and more spherical and the operculum is indistinct. Zoospores are biflagellate and number 4–16 per sporangium. Recently Zentmyer has shown that the flagella of the pyriform zoospore are both of

Fig. 30.

Fig. 31.

the tinsel type. In nature chlamydospores occur in infected pod husks and roots. Oogonia average 25–42 μ in diameter. Oospores may be produced from the mating of complementary strains. There are instances where *P. palmivora* appears to be homothallic.

Physiological specialization: The differentation of races is still being worked out but there are so far no agreed standard varieties or clones for this purpose. It is important to note that while *P. palmivora* in Ghana is capable of infecting all parts of the cocoa plant, it apparently does not infect stems and roots in East Cameroun.

Epidemiology: When yearly rainfall is evenly distributed, the vegetative phase of *P. palmivora* can be active all year round. Where these is a dry spell, as in West Africa, *P. palmivora* has been shown to become dormant as mycelia or chlamydospores in various parts of the infected plant remaining in the soil or on the tree.
Zoospore dispersal from infected to healthy plant parts tends to occur actively in water films and passively in water drops. Water splashes from infected soil or plant parts also disperses sporangia and chlamydospores. Tent-building ants – *Crematogaster* spp., *Camponotus* spp., and *Pheidole* spp. – have been implicated in spreading *P. palmivora* inoculum in their tents. Species of Nitidulidae (beetles), snails, caterpillars and millipedes ingest and excrete *P. palmivora* sporangia which

remain viable and capable of infecting cocoa pods. Chlamydospores also remain undamaged after passing through the guts of most of these invertebrates.

Harvesting knives have been shown to be responsible for transmission of inoculum from diseased to infected cushions. Any organism or object which touches infected plant parts may carry spores to other plant parts.

Wind dispersal is suspected but has not been demonstrated. Primary pod infection could be from inoculum in soil or from infected plant parts. Secondary infection may result from rain splash, zoospore migration, contact with infected pods or through insect and human agents.

P. palmivora can infect all parts of the cocoa plant; providing there is adequate moisture and temperature, infection appears to be possible at any time.

On the pod, *P. palmivora* may enter through stomata. Normally necrotic spots become discernible two or three days after infection. Mycelia, which are initially intercellular, become intracellular upon reaching necrotic cells which have been killed in advance. The rot tends to progress faster in the placenta than in the husk. There tends to be one or two peak periods of infection depending on whether one or two maxima of the rainfall cycle occurs.

Resistant plants, with a low percentage of pods infected, exist but no immune plants are known. The cause of the resistance has been variously attributed to inhibitory effects of tannins or polyphenols on the fungus and to small parenchyma cells beneath the epidermis.

High humidity maintains a free water film on pods and other susceptible organs thus enhancing zoospore liberation and dispersal. Zoospore liberation is high at relatively low temperatures, i. e. around 15 °C. High temperatures, i. e. above 32 °C, slow down the growth of the fungus and cause zoospores to encyst and even disintegrate.

Control: Sanitary and cultural practices aim at reducing the humidity and inoculum on the farm. Removal of weeds, pruning of the canopy, wide spacing of plants (2.40 x 2.40 – 3.60 x 3.60 m) and prompt removal of infected pods and other infected plant parts are all to be recommended. Resistant varieties or types are being studied but no immune types are known.

Seed treatment with Cupric hydroxide (a solution of 21 g in 1.0 litre water), Bordeaux Mixture and Perecol (60 g in 1.0 litre water), have been found to reduce root rot and leaf blight of seedlings in nurseries. Aerial spray application: a) Fungicides known to be effective include Bordeaux mixture and other copper fungicides, Fentinhydroxide, Fentinacetate, and Orthodifolatan. b) Spraying schedules should follow the disease cycles. 3-weekly or 2-weekly applications only when the disease is at peak incidence may ensure economical chemical control. There is no need to apply chemicals when the disease is naturally on the decline.

Literature

CHEE, K. H. (1969): Hosts of *Phytophthora palmivora*. Rev. appl. Mycol. **48**, 337–344.
GREGORY, P. H. (Ed.) (1974): Phytophthora Disease of Cocoa. Longman.
THOROLD, C. A. (1975): Cocoa diseases. Clarendon, Oxford.

Author: A. Asare-Nyako

Phytophthora spp. on Hevea brasiliensis (Figs. 32–34)

Phytophthora leaf disease of the para rubber tree, *Hevea brasiliensis,* is caused by different species of *Phytophthora* in different parts of the world: In Sri Lanka it is caused by *P. meadii* MacRae; in Malaysia by *P. botryosa* Chee, *P. heveae* Thompson (CMI map no 428), and *P. palmivora* (Butl.) Butl. (p. 83), and in India by *P. palmivora* (Butl.) Butl.

Disease: Phytophthora disease of rubber; Phytophthora-Krankheit des Kautschukbaumes; pourriture de hévéa; podredumbre del árbol de hevea.

Geographical distribution: This disease has been recorded at varying degrees of severity, in all the rubber growing countries of the world. In Sri Lanka and Malaysia it causes some leaf fall each year but not sufficient to warrant control measures. The intensity of the disease is high in India and South America, causing almost complete defoliation of trees regularly every year, so that control measures have to be adopted in these countries.

Host plants: Apart from *H. brasiliensis,* Cacoa (*Theobroma cacao*), coconut (*Cocos nucifera*), papaw (*Carica papaya*) and many others are attacked by *P. palmivora* (p. 83).

Symptoms: The fungus causes mature leaf fall, die back of green stems, pod rot, bark rot (black thread, patch canker) and root rot of the rubber tree.
Phytophthora leaf disease occurs during the South West Monsoon season – May to August – each year in Sri Lanka; being more prevalent in the wetter rubber growing areas. The disease starts with pod rot, green mature pods form an ideal substrate for the growth and sporulation of the fungus. Pod rot is characterised by a water-soaked, blackened appearance of the pod with the affected areas, usually the bottom ends, being dotted with black coagulated latex. In the later stages of the attack, the pod is encrusted with a white mat, consisting mainly of the sporangia of the fungus. During rainy weather, these sporangia and their zoospores are splashed on to green twigs, stems. leaves and petioles, causing infection of all these organs.

The most conspicuous symptom of the disease, when mature leaves are affected, is the petiole lesion, which appears as a blackening of the leaf stalk, accompanied by the exudation of latex from infected areas (Fig. 32). The infection of the petiole cuts off the transport of water and nutrients to the leaflets and the leaves turn yellow and fall off. Immature leaves when affected turn black and wilt rapidly.

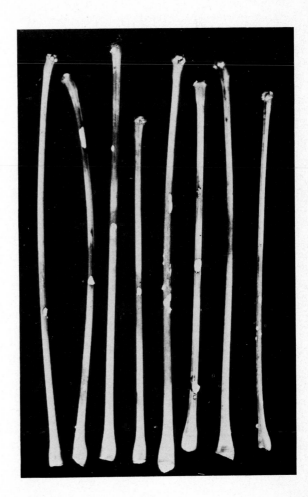

Fig. 32.

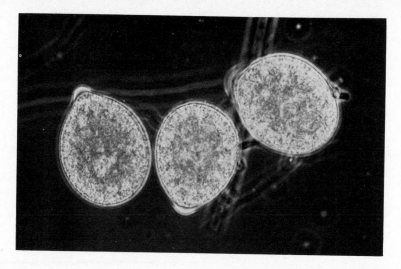

Fig. 33.

Morphology: *P. meadii* produces white aseptate hyphae, which branch at right angles. The fungus grows rapidly on culture media or infected plant organs and produces oval shaped sporangia (Fig. 33) in profusion. Each sporangium, when mature, produces a number of bi-flagellate zoo-spores, which come to rest in contact with a suitable substrate, shed the flagellae and germinate to produce a hypha, which can cause infection of a rubber pod within 6 hr of inoculation. *P. meadii* also produces round oospores (Fig. 34), the fungus being generally homothallic but capable of pairing with other *Phytophthora* spp. too.

Physiological specialization: Studies carried out at the Rubber Research Institute of Sri Lanka, have shown that *P. meadii* produces physiologic races.

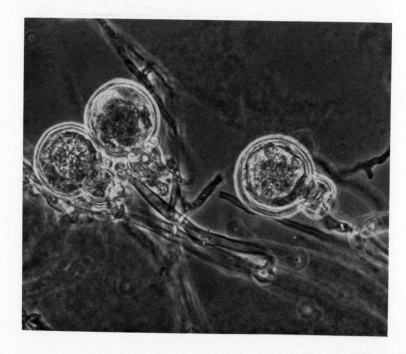

Fig. 34.

Epidemiology: The fungus (*P. meadii*) can live on any of the alternative hosts noted above. The fungus can also survive, in a resting stage, on the *Hevea* tree itself, from season to season in mummified pods, shoots that have died back due to infection and infected bark, and for limited periods in bark debris, infected wood and soil. From these sources the fungus can cause pod infection, when weather conditions become suitable for its propagation; from the pods the disease will then spread to the leaves and other organs.

Phytophthora spp. require free water for the propagation of their zoospores. Consequently, the disease is closely associated with frequent rains, mist, generally cloudy, overcast conditions and temperatures slightly lower than normal for that period of the year – about 25 °C, whereas the normal temperature is 28 ± 2 °C. By contrast bright, sunny, warm weather retards the growth of the fungus and the occurrence of even a single warm sunny day, during a period when the disease is prevalent, would tend to check its spread. These data have made it possible to forecast the occurrence of *Phytophthora* leaf disease successfully in this country.

The fungus is dispersed mainly through water droplets carrying the zoospores of the fungus (Peries, 1972); therefore, the range of spread of the disease is limited unlike *Oidium* leaf disease, which is spread by a windborne spore. The zoospores can cause infection of pods and leaf stalks rapidly, in 6–10 hr.

Control: A certain degree of control of the disease can be caused by picking infected pods and pruning out diseased twigs. However, with a tall tree such as *Hevea* these methods are impracticable. All *Hevea* clones that produce few pods suffer very little leaf fall due to this disease. *Hevea* clones e. g. RRIC 52, which are resistant to *Phytophthora* leaf disease, are known. The resistance of these clones appears to depend on the presence of certain antifungal substances inherently present in them and also on their ability to produce phytoalexins.

Copper based fungicides have been found to be effective for the control of *Phytophthora* leaf disease on *Hevea*. In India the disease is successfully controlled regularly at economic levels, by aerial spraying of copper-in-oil preparations.

Literature

LLOYD, J. H. (1963): The control of abnormal leaf-fall disease *Phytophthora palmivora* of *Hevea* in Ceylon. Bull. Rub. Res. Inst. Cey. **57**.

PERIES, O. S. (1972): Studies on the relationship between weather and incidence of leaf disease of *Hevea*. A Symposium on Plant Diseases in South East Asia. Published by The University of Malaya (in Press).

PERIES, O. S., & D. M. DANTANARAYANA (1965): Compatibility and variation in *Phytophthora* cultures isolated from *Hevea brasiliensis* in Ceylon. Trans. Brit. mycol. Soc. **48**, 631–637.

Author: O. S. Peries

Other more important Phytophthora spp. on tropical and subtropical crops:

Phytophthora arecae (Col.) Perthyb. Zebra leaf spot of sisal agave.

P. capsici Leonian. Blight of capsicum peppers.

P. colocasiae Rac. Blight of taro (dasheen). CMI map no 466.

P. drechsleri Tucker. Root rot of safflower.

P. nicotianae Breda de Haan var. *nicotianae*. Black shank of tobacco. Ref.: CMI Description no 34.

P. nicotianae Breda de Haan var. *parasitica* (Dastur) Waterh. Damping-off of seedlings, root rot, crown rot, stem canker, leaf blight) or fruit rot on a wide range of host plants. These include avocado, betle, castor, citrus, cotton, guava, papaw, pineapple, sesame, tobacco, tomato, etc. Ref.: CMI Description no 35 (= *P. parasitica* Dastur).

Pseudoperonospora cubensis (Berk. et Curt.) Rost. (Plate 5 d)

Oomycetes, Peronosporales, Peronosporaceae

Disease: Downy mildew of cucumber; Falscher Mehltau der Gurke; le mildiou des cucurbitacées; mildíu de las cucurbitaceas.

Geographical distribution: Widely distributed especially on cucumbers and melons in warm and humid zones, including all of Africa (except the driest regions), the southern parts of Asia and Europe, Australia, South, Central and North America. Distribution on watermelons more limited, mostly to hot countries (CMI map no 285).

Host plants: Affects only *Cucurbitaceae,* chiefly causing downy mildew diseases of cultivated species of *Cucumis* (cucumber, melon), *Cucurbita* (squash, marrow, pumpkin) and *Citrullus* (watermelon), less frequently found on some 40 wild and cultivated species of 18 other genera (e. g. *Benincasa, Lagenaria, Luffa, Momordica, Trichosanthes).*

Symptoms: Only leaves, ordinarily affected. Bright yellow spots on upper surface of leaves, with light spots covered by greyish-black down on their lower surface (Plate 5d); spots become necrotic and turn brown from their centre outwards. On cucumbers, spots are angular, clearly limited by leaf veins; on melons and most other hosts, vein delimitation is not so clear. Cotyledons, but not very young true leaves, may be affected. Strongest development on leaves 5–15 days after their formation. Affected leaves dry up, do not shed. Flower parts rarely, fruit and seeds never affected.

Morphology: Mycelium intercellular with haustoria. Sporangiophores 180–400 μ, basally inflated, dichotomously branched, emerge from stomata singly or in groups. Sporangia 20–40 x 14–25 μ produce biciliate zoospores 10–13 μ in diameter. Oospores repeatedly found only in Japan and China.

Physiological specialization: Distinct races reported from *Cucumis sativus* and *Cucurbita moschata* (Iwata, 1942), and from *Cucumis sativus* and *Citrullus vulgaris.* No data available from other countries, but failure of mildew common in cucumber and melon to affect watermelon in many countries, also tends to indicate specialization.

Epidemiology: In warm and humid climates, transmission from older to younger crops all the year round. Where warm and dry summers alternate with cooler and wet winters, year- round survival is possible on summer-irrigated crops and crops grown in winter under cover. Transmission on wild cucurbits not proved. Annual summer invasions from countries with mild to those with cooler winters is likely. Overwintering by oospores held to be possible in the Far East.
Spores formed on lower leaf surface, most commonly at night. Sporulation abundant on plants amply supplied with photosynthesates, on yellow, but not necrotic, lesions. Minimum, optimum and maximum temperatures are 5 °, 15 ° and 30 °C, respectively; at optimal temperatures sporangia appear after 6 hours of leaf wetness.
Dispersal is mostly by wind, as moisture on leaves dries up in the morning. Favoured by moderate atmospheric humidities, but viability of dispersed sporangia diminishes rapidly at high humidities and temperatures and at low humidities, especially in bright light.
Sporangia release zoospores, and these germinate in water only. Optimum temperatures 15 °–20 °C; at other temperatures amount of infection depends on interaction with length of leaf wetness periods and size of inoculum load, e. g. minimum and maximum temperatures 5 ° and 28 °C, respectively, with plentiful inoculum and long wetness periods, but only 12 ° and 25 °C, respectively, with little inoculum and shorter wetness periods.
Infection through stomata, within 5 hours at optimal condition. Incubation period 4–12 days, depending on temperature. Maximum lesion development at cycles of about 25 °C daytime, 15 °C

night temperature and at photoperiods of 18 hours light and 6 hours darkness. Early stages of lesion development favoured by bright, later stages by weaker light.

Control: Avoid immediate neighbourhood of older, infected cucumber or melon crops to younger fields of either crop. Destroy foliage of old crop at once after last picking. In rainless, dew seasons, all measures reducing hours of leaf wetness may limit downy mildew: avoid excessive crop density, shading by hedges etc.; sow parallel to wind direction; overhead sprinkling favours the mildew more than any other form of irrigation, especially when applied before morning dew has dried. Resistance bred into some cucumber, melon, and watermelon varieties, most of which, however, possess some commercially undesirable characteristics.

Many copper and carbamate (zineb, maneb, mancozeb) fungicides effective as dust or sprays, but copper sprays often somewhat phytotoxic. Frequency of applications usually once in 4–10 days, depends on rate of vegetative growth and irrigation intervals. Applications should promptly follow rain or overhead sprinkling, ideally within a few hours. No generally acceptable forecasting schemes available.

Literature

COHEN, Y. & J.R. ROTEM (1971): Field and growth chamber approach to epidemiology of *Pseudoperonospora cubensis* in cucumbers. Phytopathology **61**, 736–737.
IWATA, Y. (1942): Specialisation in *Pseudoperonospora cubensis* (B. et C.) Rostow. II. Comparative studies on the morphologies of the Fungi from *Cucumis sativus* L. and *Cucurbita moschata* Dutch. Ann. Phytopathol. Soc. Japan **XI**, 172–185.
VAN HALTERN, F. (1933): Spraying cantaloups for the control of downy mildew and other diseases. Georgia Exp. Sta. Bull. **175**, 1–53.

Author: J. Palti

Species of the Genera Plasmopara and Peronospora, agents of downy mildews, occur also in tropical and subtropical areas on "temperate" hosts grown there (*Plasmopara viticola* (Berk. et Curt.) Berl. & de Toni, *Peronospora destructor* (Berk.) Casp., *P. halstedii* (Naum.) Syd. (CMI map no 286), *P. parasitica* (Pers.) Fr., *P. tabacina* Adam, etc.). They are thus usually covered by textbooks published in Europa and the USA. Only a few species are confined to hosts of the warmer regions, where they do not attain a high degree of importance. These include: *Peronospora manshurica* (Naum.) Syd. Downy mildew of soybean. CMI map no 268.

Pythium myriotylum Drechsler (Figs. 35–37)[1]

Oomycetes, Peronosporales, Pythiaceae

Disease: Pod-rot of groundnut (*Arachis hypogaea* L.); Hülsenfäule der Erdnuß; pourriture des fruits du arachide; podredumbre de los frutos del cacahuete.

It may cause damping-off of seedlings in warm soil (approximately 30 °C) and is important in causing rot of various fruits which are in contact with moist soil, for instance groundnut pods. It may destroy about 1/3 of the groundnut yield and blemish the shells of an additional high percentage of the pods. Latent (symptomless) root infection of groundnut by *P. myriotylum* may be frequent, and at certain locations even root-rot and extensive wilt of adult plants are recorded.

Geographical distribution: This fungus is known to cause diseases in tropical regions (Australia, India, Indonesia, Sri Lanka, Madagascar, Nigeria, Sierra Leone) and, in summertime, in subtropical regions (Israel, Libya, South Africa, northern Argentinia, some states of the USA).

Host range: The fungus has many natural hosts: groundnut (peanut), cucumber, watermelon, eggplant, rice; and, to a lesser extent, beans (*Phaseolus*), ginger (*Zingiber officinale*), lucerne, tobacco, tomato, papaya, and *Robinia pseudoacacia*.

Symptoms: *P. myriotylum* is a hot-climate Pythium attacking seedlings, underground organs and fruits of various crops and causes a dry rot in the fruit of groundnut (peanut). The pod is invaded when still soft. The first symptoms are small palebrown irregular spots. Later chocolate-

---

[1] Contribution from the Agricultural Research Organization, The Volcani Center, Bet Dagan, Israel, 1973 Series No 185-E.

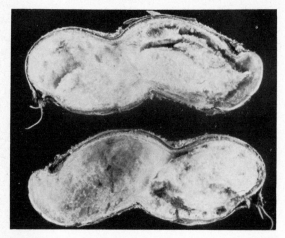

Fig. 35.

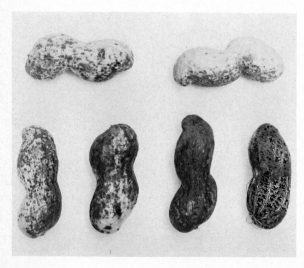

Fig. 36.

brown dots and necrotic areas are noticed (Fig. 35). In a variable proportion of pods the cavity is filled by *Pythium* hyphae (Fig. 36). Later, other fungi replace the *Pythium* hyphae in the cavity, but oospores may still be found there. In a continuously wet soil, when bacteria invade the diseased pod, the rot may be soft; at this stage *Pythium* may not be observed any more.

Occassionally some other *Pythium* spp. are found as causal agents of this rot. Rots caused by *Verticillium* spp., *Cylindrocladium crotolariae* (Loos) Bell & Sobers and *Thielaviopsis basicola* (Berk. & Br.) Ferraris may superficially resemble the *Pythium* pod-rot.

Morphology: Diagnosis of *P. myriotylum* is based on the following characters: Digitate or lobulate sporangia. Zoospores mature at high temperatures, around 30 °C. Oogonia smooth, mostly 23–30 μ. Antheridial branch not winding around oogonial stalk. Antheridia diclinous; a few to 10 per oogonium, clavate, often curved, with both tip and base touching oogonium. Oospore mostly 18 to 24 μ, wall 1.3–1.9 μ thick. Numerous clavate or knob-like appressoria are typical; they can easily be observed (especially on some poor media), by low microscopic magnification, at the bottom of a thin walled petri dish. Optimal temperature for vegetative growth ranges from 27 to 37 °C.

Epidemiology: Pathogenesis by *P. myriotylum* has been shown to be predisposed by a latent infection with *Fusarium solani* (Mart.) App. & Wr., which frequently occurs in shells of apparently healthy, as well as of diseased, pods. In the absence of *F. solani* the infection by *P. myriotylum* will be latent or only very slight symptoms will develop. At a later stage, once *P. myriotylum* has established itself in the pod, *F. solani* functions secondarily, together with a succession of other microorganisms, in the saprophytic disintegration of the diseased pod.

Vegetative growth of the pathogen through soil and its sporangial reproduction, as well as the resulting spread of the disease from pod to pod, are favoured by continuous moisture in well aerated (mostly light) soil. Inoculum is spread from diseased patches of a field by cultivating equipment and by flowing water. Infection occurs as long as the pod-shell is alive.

Disease development and spread are favoured by too-frequent irrigation. The inoculum increases during the fruiting period in the warm season. Oospores, which are left in soil after a rot-affected crop, diminish with time; however, much inoculum remains viable until the next season.

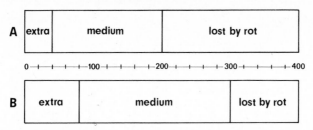

Fig. 37. Effect of irrigation frequency on quality (extra, medium) and yield loss in an infested field, in kg/1000 m² (scaled on central line). A: irrigated weekly with a small amount of water; B: irrigated in intervals of two weeks, with a double amount of water per irrigation (total amount as in A)

Control: Crop rotation with only one groundnut crop in 3 years, decreases inoculum density in the soil. However, when the percentage of rotted pods in the previous groundnut crop was high, the natural decrease alone is not sufficiently effective to reduce losses and should be supplemented by other means. Intervals between irrigations should be extended so that the topsoil, in which the pods are located, dries out between irrigations and pod rot development and spread are retarded (Fig. 37). An eventual water deficit in the crop may be prevented by increasing the amount of water given at each irrigation (in order to reach deeper located roots).

Cultivars with an acceptable level of resistance to internal rot include, among others, the Spanish types Schwarz-21 and Matjan, and the Valencia-type Mwitunde-7. No resistance has been found in Virginia-type cultivars, but susceptible cultivars may escape heavy infection, when fruiting in a shallow, easily drying, soil layer.

Literature

FRANK, Z. R. (1967): Effects of irrigation procedure on *Pythium* rot of groundnut pods. Plant Dis. Reptr. **51**, 414–416.

FRANK, Z. R. (1972): *Pythium myriotylum* and *Fusarium solani* as cofactors in a pod-rot complex of peanut. Phytopathology **62**, 1331–1334.

JACKSON, C. R., & D. K. BELL (1969): Diseases of peanut (groundnut) caused by fungi. Georgia Agr. Exp. Sta. Bull. **56**

PORTER, D. M. (1970): Peanut wilt caused by *Pythium myriotylum*. Phytopathology 60: 393–394.

WATERHOUSE, GRACE M. (1968): The genus *Pythium* Pringsheim Commonwealth Mycological Inst., Mycological Papers no **10**.

CMI Description no 118.

Author: Z. R. Frank

Pythium spp. (Fig. 38)

P. aphanidermatum (Edson) Fitzpatrick, *P. arrhenomones* Drechsler, *P. butleri* Subramaniam, *P. debaryanum* Hesse (CMI map no 208), *P. deliense* Meurs, *P. ultimum* Trow. (CMI map no 207), and others.

Oomycetes, Peronosporales, Pythiaceae

Disease: Damping-off; Keimlings- und Umfallkrankheiten; fonte de semis; enfermedad de los almácigos.

Host plants: *Pythium* spp. are often the cause of a serious seedling disease known as damping-off. Several species of *Pythium* can be associated with the disease and a great variety of plants in seed beds, glasshouses and fields can be affected.

Symptoms: The pre-emergence phase of the disease, i. e. the rotting of the seed or germinating seedling in the ground, often escapes attention and poor stands are frequently erroneously attributed to inferior seed. In the case of post-emergence attacks, the seedling tissues appear water-soaked at soil level and the young plants topple over, often with their leaves still green. Under those conditions favouring the disease, such as high humidity and overcrowding of the plants, the pathogen, having gained a foothold established itself in a single plant, spreads rapidly in widening circles between plants.

Several fungi other than *Pythium* may cause damping-off, e. g. those belonging to the closely related genus *Phytophthora*, *Rhizoctonia solani* (p. 178), *Fusarium* spp. (p. 210) and *Thielaviopsis basicola* (p. 236). The pathogen cannot usually be identified by macroscopic examination of the infected plants. However, accurate diagnosis is essential for the application of appropriate control measures especially in relation to the use of fungicides.

Damping-off can sometimes be confused with a non-parasitic disorder due to high soil salinity. In this case only a browning of the young roots is observed or, when severe, a shrivelling of the roots

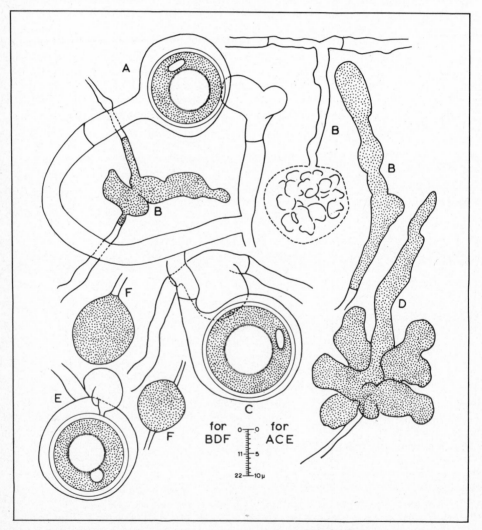

Fig. 38. A–B: *P. deliense*. A: sexual reproductive unit; B: sporangia and zoospore formation. C–D: *P. butleri*. C: sexual unit; D: sporangium. E–F: *P. ultimum*. E: sexual unit; F: sporangia.

and most of the stems resulting in eventual plants death. In addition diseased and healthy tissue cannot be distinguished easily in contrast to damping-off. Another symptom associated with this nonparasitic disorder is uneven growth of seedlings or transplants which have escaped the obvious effects of salinity.

Morphology: Species of *Pythium* form a vegetative mycelium without septa, sexual (oospores) and asexual (sporangia) reproductive bodies. The sporangia of *Pythium* can be either spheroidal or filamentous, depending on the species, and they germinate either by the production of one or more germ tubes, or by zoospores. In the latter case the entire contents of the sporangium flow through an evacuation tube into an evanescent vesicle where differentiation into motile spores (zoospores) takes place.

The reproductive bodies of *Pythium* can be easily observed by placing pieces of infected plant tissue, carefully washed, in a thin layer of tap or distilled water in a shallow dish. After 1–3 days incubation, the structures can be observed under a stereomicroscope (Fig. 38).

The same method can be used for species of *Phytophthora*. Differentiation between these two genera is not always easy but for damping-off not usually necessary, as control measures are the same for both. *Rhizoctonia solani* can usually be detected by inspection of the seedlings with a hand lens, because this fungus spreads over the surface of host tissue by its brown runner hyphae. Also, if the infected plant tissue is placed in water, as previously described, the characteristically septate hyphae of the fungus – hyaline at first then browning with age – can be observed spreading into the water from the infected material.

Epidemiology: *Pythium* is a soil-borne pathogen existing in practically all cultivated soils and generally attacking plants at the seedling stage. Plants can be attacked either before (pre-emergence damping-off) or after (post-emergence-damping-off) emergence, depending on the amount and vigour of the fungus inoculum in the soil and the speed of seedling growth. The plants are susceptible to the disease from the time the seed is sown until emergence and for a few days afterwards depending on the plant species and the prevailing conditions. In some cases older plants can be affected, e. g. cucumbers, very susceptible to *Pythium* attacks. Conditions unfavourable for plant growth, such as poor field drainage or unbalanced nutrition, increase the susceptibility of older plants.

The absence of damping-off does not always imply the absence of causal pathogens. Damping-off results from a disturbance of the fine balance between conditions favouring plant development and those favouring infection by the causal organism. In a given soil, damping-off can be serious under conditions unfavourable for seedling growth and completely absent under those favouring rapid plant development.

Contamination by *Pythium* may arise from infested soil or from compost in which diseased plants have been incorporated. *Pythium* can also be spread by water carrying zoospores, by contaminated soil particles, or by diseased plant fragments.

Control: 1. Use clean soil or soil disinfected by physical means (e. g. steam or preferably a mixture of steam and air) or by chemicals (e. g. formaldehyde, methylbromide or chemicals based on methyl isothiocyanate).

Do not recontaminate treated soil by (a) mixing with untreated soil, (b) using contaminated boxes, pots or tools, (c) transplanting plants from contaminated soil or (d) by allowing water from contaminated soil to flow over it. Do not cultivate treated soil very deeply as untreated soil may thus be brought up from below.

It should be remembered that soil treatment is not meant to sterilise soil, (sterilization is actually undesirable), but only to reduce the inoculum potential of the pathogen to a level below which plant infection does not occur. If the soil is heavily contaminated, soil treatment may prove inadequate as the percentage of fungus propagules remaining may be high enough to start the disease again.

Soil into which transplants are to be placed can be treated against damping-off organisms by incorparating funcicides like thiram (75 %), or captan (50 %), at a rate of 1.5 g per square metre of seed bed and working this thoroughly into the top 8 cm of soil. It is mentioned that thiram can damage the roots and hypocotyl of young plants at temperatures over 26–27 °C.

Boxes, tools and pots can be disinfected by soaking these in a 2 % formalin solution for a few hours.

2. Use seed dressed with a seed protectant such as thiram or captan.

3. Reduce the critical phase of germination and emergence as much as possible by using high quality seed and by planting under optimum conditions for seedling growth.

4. Avoid creating high moisture and bad aeration conditions by overwatering the plants or by overcrowding. Water only when needed, and preferably in the morning, so as to prevent excess moisture on the soil surface and foliage during the night. Seedbeds can be placed on gravel or on a layer of sand for good drainage, and above the surrounding ground to facilitate run-off of excess water. Captan added to the first watering often improves stands.

5. If the disease arises, spray the plants and surrounding soil thoroughly with Cheshunt compound, captan or zineb every 4–5 days. In untreated soil, start spraying as soon as plants emerge and at 7–10 day intervals thereafter.

6. Use clean water. Dirty tanks may contaminate water which can spread the disease. Do not wash plant material or tools in the tanks as these are apt to carry contaminated soil.

7. Do not contaminate compost heaps with infected plants which should always be destroyed, preferably by burning.

8. If infection due to *Pythium* (or *Phytophthora*) starts in irrigated fields, disinfect irrigation water by placing a bag of large copper sulphate crystals in the main irrigation canal. The small quantity of bluestone dissolved during one irrigation, as water passes through, is enough to stop the disease. Do not apply this measure more than 2–3 times as an excess of copper sulphate may damage plants.

Literature

GARRETT, S. D. (1970): Pathogenic Root-Infecting Fungi. Cambridge University Press.
CMI Descriptions nos 36, 37, 38, 39, and 116.

Author: Hebe Kouyeas

Other more important Pythium spp. on tropical and subtropical crops:
Pythium vexans de By. Patch canker of rubber trees, claret canker of Durian (*Durio zibethinus*), etc.
Pythium splendens Braun. Damping-off of black pepper, maize, mottle necrosis of sweet potato; wilt of betel, blast of oil palm seedlings. Ref.: CMI Description no 120.

Sclerospora graminicola (Sacc.) Schroet. (Figs. 39–41)

Synonym: *Sclerospora graminicola* (Sacc.) Schroet. var. *setariae-italicae* Traverso 1902
Oomycetes, Peronosporales, Peronosporaceae

Disease: Graminicola downy mildew or green ear disease (of pearl millet), Falscher Mehltau der Hirse; Maladie de l'epi vert; mildíu de los cereales.

Geographical distribution: Widespread (CMI map no 431). In Fiji it is more likely *S. sacchari*, and the record from northeastern Argentina is more likely another downy mildew fungus, *Sclerophthora macrospora* (Sacc.) Thirum., Shaw. & Naras. (CMI map no 287), as are the records from Bulgaria and the Netherlands.

Host plants: *Perl millet (Pennisetum typhoides, P. glaucum, P. spicatum)*, foxtail millet (*Setaria italica*), maize, teosinte (*Euchlaena mexicana*), barnyard grass (*Echinochloa cursgalli*), broom-corn millet, proso (*Panicum miliaceum*). Reported on the following, but probably *Sclerospora sorghi* Weston & Uppal or *Sclerophthora macrospora: Sorghum halepense, S. sudanense, S. verticilliflorum, S. vulgare.*

Symptoms: Symptoms vary somewhat according to host. In all hosts, systemic infection predominates and in pearl millet and maize is apparently the only form. Chlorosis is evident on leaf blades; on the lowest leaf displaying symptoms, it consists of pallid continuous laciniate areas of stripes extending from base of blade toward apex of normal colour ('half-leaf symptoms'); successive leaves have more extensive chlorosis, until leaves are entirely chlorotic as they unfold. Plants showing symptoms at an early age remain stunted and may die as leaves turn brown.
Those showing symptoms at a later age tend to have short internodes and often display erect leaves. On dewy mornings, a white cast (sporulation) appears over lower surface of leaves, and on erect leaves over both surfaces. On maize, chlorosis tends to appear as a closed system of stripes, sporulation is sparse (mostly at seedling stage), and leaves are thickened, corrugated and brittle; occasionally, grayish mottling of leaves occurs. Eventually, the sexual phase, consisting of resting spores (oospores), form in great number in mesophyll of chlorotic areas between vascular bundles (not grouped around them as in *Sclerophthora macrospora*), giving a tan colour to the leaf, which becomes necrotic. As oospores form, sporulation ceases and in fully chlorotic leaves the oogonia may be present already as leaf unfolds, without sporulation. In maize, oospores are unknown in leaves. In *Setaria* spp., leaves containing oospores shred; in other hosts, shredding is rare.
Teratological changes occur in hosts. Tillering is excessive, and in pearl millet, nodal buds are often stimulated to develop into diseased or healthy lateral shoots. The spike of pearl millet and to a lesser extent, *Setaria* spp., may be transformed entirely or in part into leafy growth (the 'Green ear' phase on pearl millet which can occur even without other symptoms). In pearl millet, the cob might be of normal length but converted into short twisted leaves, or, only the lower part is so infected, or, (Fig. 39) small 'fists' of leafy structures supplant the spike (Fig. 40). These hypertro-

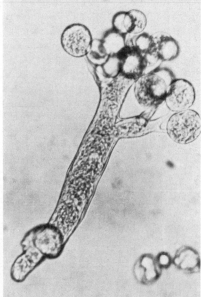

Fig. 39.   Fig. 40.   Fig. 41.

phied malformations may derive from various floral organs. Ears of maize and tassels of teosinte may be deformed. Oospores may appear in distorted tissues. Linear chlorotic local lesions 2–3 cm long may be sometimes found in the wild *S. magna* and *S. verticillata,* and small, spot-like lesions in *S. italica.*

The chlorotic systemic symptoms resemble those of some diseases caused by other *Sclerospora* spp., *Sclerophthora macrospora* and *Maize* dwarf mosaic virus (considered a strain of sugarcane mosaic virus), the last-named at an early stage only.

Morphology: The only species of *Sclerospora* known which produces sporangia rather than conidia. Typically broadly elliptical and widest above mid-spore, with poroid apical papilla of dehiscence. Empty cases denote sporangia from which zoospores (3–8) discharged. Sporangia mostly 16–37 x 12–20.7 μ but are variable among collections; on occasion, from various hosts, giant sporangia, more elongated, 28–57 x 17–26 μ (much narrower than in *Sclerophthora macrospora* on maize, *Setaria,* etc.) can be found.

Ephemeral club-shaped sporangiophores, of variable length, have a well-defined non-septate main axis which near the apex produce short branches of unequal length at irregular intervals, one of which usually is extension of the trunk (Fig. 41). Sterigmata are relatively short, ca. 8 μ. Resting spores consist of smooth, globular oospores, 19–45 μ diam. with thick walls (1.9–2.9 μ), within a retentive, light to reddish brown oogonial wall which is sometimes slightly uneven but not ridged, convoluted or knobbed. Resting spores are 28–60 μ. Grows in axenic culture on special media.

Physiological specialization: Isolates from pearl millets, are usually limited to that host, and rarely to maize, whereas from *Setaria* spp. does not attack pearl millet but passes to various Setarias, teosinte and sometimes to maize and *Panicum miliaceum.* In India and part of China, both kinds of isolates present (in Mysore, a pearl millet isolate was infective to *Setaria*).

Epidemiology: Oospores, the principal means for overseasoning and inducing the systemic primary infection, are longlived in field (3–8 years according to conditions), and may survive freezing and passage through digestive tract of cattle. They may be infective during the same season in which they form. They may blow to distance, may adhere to seeds or be in bits of plant debris together with seeds. Dormant hyphae in seed from infected spikes is claimed. Oospores claimed to germinate variously – by germ tube or by formation of sporangia. Sown in oospore infested soil, seedlings become systemically infected, with symptom expression (chlorosis) first appearing on first leaf or as late as emergence of inflorescence (latent-like). In maize, infection may occur from time testa is broken until emergence of plumule from soil, and seedling susceptibility decreases with age; 15–16 °C soil temp. reported to favor infection more than 15–30 °C. In *Setaria* spp., penetration is through coleorhiza, and also mesocotyl, coleoptile and roots; in pearl millet, through roots; in *S. italica,* infection until 7–8 days, with min. temp. for infection 12–13 °C, opt. 20–21 ° C, max. 30 °C, with highest infection (in Japan) if sown in April and none if sown in June. In pearl millet, in Israel, no infection if sown in early spring (cool weather).

Sporangial infection: In pearl millet, by artificial inoculation, infective on plants till 5-leaf stage, and young plants might become infected in the field if wet for long periods. In arid Rajasthan (India), sporangia are not formed, yet 'green ear' is particularly destructive there. In young maize and *Setaria,* zoospores can induce systemic infection and in older *Setaria,* sometimes local lesions. Sporulation from 10–28 °C, with optimum on pearl millet al 25 °C. Produced at night shortly after dew forms, usually from near midnight till 0300–0400 and zoospores are immediately released and germinate at once at ca 24 °C. Sporangia die within minutes under dry conditions and normally don't cause infection at any distance.

Control: Rogue living stricken plants and volunteers before oospores form. Destroy straw before oospores released. Do not sow susceptible crop in infected soil for a number of years. Clean seed of bits of oospore-containing plant debris. Treat infested seed with organo-mercurial fungicides.

Lack of K or P claimed to predispose *Setaria* to the disease. There is no agreement whether sowing in relatively dry soils or wet soils reduces or enhances disease incidence. No dependable sources of resistance released for pearl millet; the variety 'Starr' is very susceptible. Inbreds are usually more susceptible than open-pollinated varieties.

Literature

Anonymuos (1975): Proc. Symposium on Downy Mildew of Maize. TARC/IACP, Tokyo. Trop. Agric. Res. Ser. **8**.
WATERHOUSE, Grace M. (1964): CMI Miscelleneous publ. no **17**. Commonwealth Mycol. Inst. Kew.
NENE, Y. L., & S. D. SINGH (1975): Downy mildew and ergot of pearl millet. ICRISAT, 47 p.
CMI Description no 453.

Author: R. Kenneth

Other Sclerospora spp. on tropical and subtropical crops:

S. maydis (Racib.) Butl. Downy mildew of maize and teosinte.
S. oryzae Brizi = *Sclerophthora macrospora*.
S. philippenensis Weston. Downy mildew of maize, sorghum and teosinte of great importance in the Philippines. CMI map no 497; CMI Description no 454.
S. sacchari Miyake. Downy mildew of sugarcane, sorghum and teosinte. Ref.: CMI Description no 453.
S. sorghi (Kulk.) Weston & Uppal. Downy mildew of sorghum, maize and some wild *Sorghum* spp (CMI map no 179). Ref.: CMI Description no 451.

Other more important Oomycetes as pathogens:

Trachysphaeria fructigena Tabor & Bunting. Mealy pod of cacao, fruit rot of coffee and bananas (cigar-end rot). Ref.: CMI Description no 229
Bremia lactucae Regel. Downy mildew of compositae. CMI map no 86.

Some more important pathogens from the Zygomycotina:

Choanephora cucurbitarum (Berk. & Rav.) Thaxt. Blossom blight of cotton, cucumber, capsicum pepper, squash, sweet potato. A subsequent fruit rot develops in cucumber and squash.
Rhizopus arrhizus Fisch. Involved in boll rot of cotton.
R. oryzae Went & Geer. Soft rot of sweet potato, preemergence damping-off of groundnut etc. Ref.: CMI Description no 109.
R. stolonifer (Ehrenberg ex Fr.) Lind. Soft fruit rot of breadfruit, papaw, sweet potato etc., boll rot of cotton. Ref.: CMI Description no 110.

Ascomycotina

This is the largest subdivision of fungi with great morphological variation and the only feature in common are the asci with (mostly 8) ascospores. Their hyphae are septate and the majority forms fruit bodies, e. g. ascocarps like cleistothecia, perithecia and apothecia. No motile structures exist. From the classes recognized by the authors of Fungi, vol. IV B (p. 75), the Hemiascomycetes (except some Spermophthoraceae, Protomycetales and Taphrinales), Plectomycetes and Laboulbeniomycetes are of little interest to tropical plant pathologists. The remainder, e. g. Loculoascomycetes (with bitunicate asci), Pyrenomycetes (unitunicate and inoperculate asci, perithecia as fruit bodies) and Discomycetes (unitunicate but operculate asci, apothecia as fruit bodies), comprise numerous plant pathogens.

Ascomycetes tend to have pleomorphic life cycles (sexual or perfect, as well as asexual or imperfect states). This is reflected in the two names for one fungus if both states are known. If existing, the imperfect or conidial state (see also p. 182) is usually more frequent. The perfect or ascigerous state can often be extremely rare in nature. As conidia usually propagate the fungi during the vegetation period of their hosts plant pathologists thus are more familiar with the conidial state of an ascomycete and their names (e. g. *Cercospora arachidicola* instead of *Mycosphaerella arachidis*, p. 129). We however, shall file a fungus under the name of its perfect state, whenever this has been ascertained. For details of classifications nomenclature, and life cycles we have to refer to the following literature and that on pp. 75 and 76. Talbot (1971) can be recommended to students in particular.

Literature

ARX, J. A. VON, & E. MÜLLER (1954): Die Gattungen der amerosporen Pyrenomyceten. Beitr. Krypto-
    gamenflora Schweiz **2**, 1–434.
LUTTRELL, E. S. (1951): Taxonomy of pyrenomycetes. Univ. Missouri Stud. **24**, (3), 1–20.
MOREAU, F. (1953): Les champignons. Vol. 2, Chevalier, Paris.
MÜLLER, E. (1971): Imperfect-perfect connections in ascomycetes. In "Taxonomy of Fungi Imperfecti"
    (ed. W. B. KENDRICK) Univ. Toronto Press, Toronto.
MÜLLER, E., & J. A. VON ARX. (1962): Die Gattungen der didymosporen Pyrenomyceten. Beitr. Kryp-
    togamenflora Schweiz **2**, 1–922.
RAPER, K. B., & D. I. FENNEL (1965): The genus Aspergillus. Williams & Wilkins, Baltimore.
RAPER, K. B., & C. THOM (1949): A manual of the Penicillia. Williams & Wilkins, Baltimore.
VIEGAS, J. H. (1944): Alguns fungos do Brazil. II. Ascomicitos. Bragantia **4**, 5–392.

Ceratocystis fimbriata Ell. et Halst. (Figs. 42–43)

Synonyms: *Ceratostomella fimbriata* (Ell. & Halst.) Elliot = *Ophiostoma fimbriata* (Ell. & Halst.) Nannfeldt
Pyrenomycetes, Sphaeriales, Ophiotomataceae

Disease: Cacao canker; Kakaokrebs; pourriture du cacao; cáncer del cacao.

Geographical distribution: World-wide. On cocoa it was reported in 1918 from Ecuador, in 1952 and 1956 from Venezuela and later on from Mexico, Colombia, Trinidad, Guatemala, and Dominican Republic. (CMI map no 91).

Host plants: *Ceratocystis fimbriata* has many hosts other than cocoa, among these are sweet potatoes (*Ipomoea batatas*) causing a black rot, coffee (*Coffea arabica*), mango (*Mangifera indica*) coconut (*Cocos nucifera*), rubber (*Hevea brasiliensis*) causing a mouldy rot, tobacco (*Nicotiana tabacum*), some Leguminoseae and other hosts.

Symptoms: In adult trees, symptoms are localized as stem and branch canker on the above tree hosts in the stem appear and branches of the plant. Diseased areas in the trunk and branches on the surface as dark zones, sometimes sunken into the bark. These affected zones may also crack. Affected wood shows the typical zonal spots of grey to violet coloration, and sometimes even a deep red or purple color (Fig. 43).
Symptoms are characteristic at the bifurcation (junction) of branches and give the impression that the disease has been stopped (Fig. 42).

Fig. 42.   Fig. 43.

Leaves show first a typical wilting, then dry out completely, but remain hanging on the affected tree. In some countries a "dieback" effect is observed in terminal branches, however this can also be due to factors other than *C. fimbriata*. Severely affected trees die.

Morphology: Isolations of the pathogen from these affected tissues produce long-necked perithecia and conidia; the conidia are produced endogenously. The perithecia are superficial, brown to black, globose, 140–220 μ diam., the necks are long and black. Ascospores are elliptical, with a ringlike sheath giving a hat-shaped appearance, hyaline, non septate, smooth and 4.5–8 x 2.6– 5.5 μ. The conidiophores are slender, septate, phialidic, hyaline to very pale brown, up to 160 μ long, usually tapering towards the tip and producing a succession of conidia through the open end. The conidia are cylindrical, hyaline, smoothwalled and 11–25 (15) x 4–5.5 μ. The chlamydospores are borne terminally in chains, obovoid to oval, thick walled, brown and 9–18 x 6–13 μ.

Physiological specialization: Cross inoculation experiments have shown much variation in the pathogenicity of strains from different hosts. Isolates from cocoa have been shown to be more pathogenic to this host than to coffee and similarly isolates from coffee are more pathogenic to coffee than to cocoa.

Epidemiology: The disease is spread from one plant to the other during pruning of the trees with the "machete" or knife. This is why, in Latin America, the disease is also known as "Mal de Machete". In certain regions, the disease is also spread by insects of the genus *Xyleborus* (p. 418). These insects produce galeries in the diseased wood, spreading the fungus from there to healthy trees. The fungus needs high temperatures and high humidity for infection and disease development. In drier regions the disease is not severe.

Control:
1. Chemical control: If pruning is necessary, the knife has to be disinfected, or the wound has to be protected with a cupric fungicide. A thick mixture of this fungicide, dissolved in some water, has to be painted on every wound made during pruning.
2. Resistance: Sources of resistance have been found in Ecuador, for example, clones "S-62" and "S-46". In Venezuela, resistance has been found in "Pound 12", some "Panaquiritos" clones, "Santa Cruz", and "IMC-67". In Costa Rica, the IICA in Turrialba has found resistance in the clones "SPA-9", "IMC-67", "Pound 12" and "PA-121".
3. Cultural practices: Pruning and burning of old affected trees is important to avoid the preservation and dissemination of the pathogen. Shade trees have to be regulated to allow good aeration in the plantation and to avoid high humidity. Very dense planting favors disease establishment and development.

Literature

DELGADO, J. C., & E. ECHANDI (1965): Evaluación de la resistencia de especies y clones de cacao al mal de machete provocado por *Ceratocystis fimbriata*. Turrialba **15**, 286–289.
CMI Description no 141.

Autor: E. Schieber

Ceratocystis paradoxa (Dade) Moreau (Plate 6 a)

Synonyms: *Ceratostomella paradoxa* Dade = *Ophiostoma paradoxa* (Dade) Nannfeldt
Pyrenomycetes, Sphaeriales, Ophiostomataceae,
Conidial state: *Thielaviopsis paradoxa* (de Seynes) v. Höhn.
Hyphomycetes (H,2. A2.ph).

Disease: Pineapple disease of sugarcane; Schwarzfäule des Zuckerrohrs; maladie de l'ananas; enfermedad del corazón negro de la caña.

Geographical distribution: The fungus was first studied in France in 1886 on sugarcane. It was reported in 1893 by Wakker and Went from Java and Massee, from the West-Indies. Since then the disease has been recorded from practically all sugar cane growing countries of the world, as well as in a number of countries where other hosts are grown. Countries where serious losses can be caused by the pineapple disease include Australia, Brazil, Hawaii, India, Indonesia, Mauritius, the Philippines, Puerto Rico, South Africa, Taiwan and the West Indies. A complete list of countries where it has been recorded on sugarcane appears in "Sugar-Cane Diseases and their Word Distribution" (Egan et al., 1971) (CMI map no 142).

Host plants: Apart from sugarcane, which is the most important host, *C. paradoxa* has been reported on a wide variety of plants. Those on which serious damage can occur include pineapple (base rot and soft rot or water blister), banana and plantain (stem-end rot), coconut (bud rot and bleeding disease), potatoes (wet rot). Other plants on which it has been recorded include: cocoa, coffee, *Cucurbita moschata*, maize, mango, papaya and various palms.

Symptoms: The disease is mainly one of newly planted sugarcane cuttings or setts, often resulting in very poor germinations, which necessitate costly replanting. The fungus enters the cuttings through the ends from the soil, spreading rapidly through the parenchymatous tissues. The more dense nodal tissues slow the progress of the fungus, but this check is only temporary. Internally the affected tissue at first becomes reddened and water soaked, but remains firm for a time, then the parenchyma breaks down and the cuttings become hollow and sooty black in colour (Plate 6a). The fibrovascular bundles remain intact and can be seen as a mass of lighter coloured strands. During the early stages of disease development, an odour is usually produced which resembles that of over-ripe pineapples.

A disease resembling pineapple disease is black rot, caused by *Ceratocystis adiposa* (Butler) C. Moreau. It attacks sugarcane cuttings in a similar manner to pineapple disease; however, during the early stages of rotting the tissues are purplish, rather than red. It also produces an odour of fermenting pineapples. This disease is less common and less destructive than pineapple disease.

Morphology: The imperfect form, *T. paradoxa* is normally the only one to occur in cane and on artificial media. It produces two spore types in great abundance. Microspores are the first to be produced, giving the fungal mass a greyish white colour. They are at first hyaline, then become almost black, thin walled and cylindriform measuring 10.0–15.0 x 3.5–5.0 μ. They are produced endogenously, being pushed out of the conidiophores in chains by the spores developing behind them. Macrospores are produced later; they are generally elliptical in shape, but may be truncate, pyriform or spherical. They are produced on short lateral conidiophores and are usually in chains of up to 20 spores. Colour of the macrospores changes from hyaline to an olive green to greenish black, giving the sooty colour to the fungus. Measurements are 16–19 x 10–12 μ. The mycelium is colourless to brown, the hyphae being 3.5–7 μ in diameter. The ascigerous perfect stage is seldom seen, and consequently is of little importance in diagnosing the disease.

Physiological specialization: Little work has been done on races or strains of *C. paradoxa* attacking sugarcane; however, light coloured and dark coloured forms have been recorded. Strains attacking hosts other than sugarcane are usually less virulent on sugarcane, and vice versa. In Australia, the strains attacking sugarcane and pineapples will not attack bananas.

Epidemiology: Both micro- and macrospores persist in the soil and will infect sugarcane cuttings when they are planted. If cane is replanted immediately after a germination failure, the fungus may pass directly from the rotting cuttings to the newly planted ones. Standing cane is occasionally infected by wind-blown spores which enter the stalks through rat, insect or mechanical injuries. Macrospores remain viable in the soil for a longer period, and under more adverse conditions than do the microspores.

Low soil temperatures at planting time, combined with excessively wet or dry conditions, and planting too deeply, adversely affect germination, and under these conditions the pineapple disease organism can completely destroy the cuttings before the shoots become established, unless they are adequately protected by fungicides. On all host plants, the fungus depends on some form of wounding for entry into the cuttings or plants.

Control: Cuttings planted when conditions are ideal for germination will quickly produce healthy shoots, and are seldom destroyed by the disease. However, because of various factors including the availability of planting material, and general farm routines necessary to produce a maximum crop at a suitable season for harvesting, it is necessary to plant in autumn or early winter when adverse conditions are likely to occur. Since nodal tissues temporarily arrest the growth of the fungus, cuttings of not less than three nodes should be used to give the centre buds additional time to become established. However, to give maximum protection against the disease, cuttings should be treated with a suitable fungicide at planting time.

By far the most effective materials available during the past 25 years have been the organic mercurial compounds. Cuttings are either dipped or sprayed with a solution containing approximately 0,015 per cent mercury, or they are soaked in a solution containing 0,002 to 0,004 per cent mercury at 50 or 52 °C for 30 or 20 minutes respectively (see also p. 34). A number of devices for dipping or spraying the cuttings are incorporated in many modern planting machines. The hot soak is used mainly in Hawaii where bins of cuttings are treated in large concrete tanks holding up to 14 000 gallons of solution. Under more primitive conditions the cuttings may be dipped in small bundles by hand. As well as controlling pineapple disease, these treatments protect the cuttings from other minor soil organisms and generally stimulate germination. During more recent years, there has been a growing concern about the pollution dangers of mercurial compounds; consequently, efforts to find a non-mercurial substitute have been intensified. Benomyl has proved to be equal to the mercurials in both Hawaii and Australia, and is to be used as the standard treatment in the former country where mercurials are to be banned. It is used at the rate of 1 part in 1600 parts of water for cold dipping or spraying, or half this concentration as a hot water soak.

Literature

EGAN, B. T., et al (1971): Sugarcane diseases and their world distribution. Prepared by the 1968–1971 I.S.S.C.T. standing committee on sugarcane diseases. International Society of Sugar Cane Technologists, Proc. 14th Cong. New Orleans La. p. 1662. Franklin Press Inc. Baton Rouge La, U.S.A.
HILTON, H. W., C. A. WISMER & N. S. NOMURA (1971): Benomyl seedpiece treatment for sugarcane, and its analysis. Hawaiian Planters Record, 58, 12, (1971) (from Hawaiian Sugar Planters Association Experiment Station, Honolulu, Hawaii, USA).
WISMER, C. A. (1961): Pineapple disease. In: Sugar-Cane Diseases of the World, Vol. **I.** Spanish summary. By J. P. MARTIN, E. V. ABBOTT & C. G. HUGHES (eds.) Elsevier Publishing Co., Amsterdam. CMI Description no 143.

Author: D. R. L. Steindl

Cochliobolus heterostrophus (Drechsler) Drechsler (Plate 6 b, c and fig. 44)

Loculoascomycetes, Pleosporales, Pleosporaceae
The sexual stage has not been found under field conditions. By appropriate pairings of mating types the perfect stage can be produced in vitro. The naturally occurring conidial stage is *Drechslera maydis* (Nisikado) Subram. et Jain (= *Helminthosporium maydis* Nisikado)
Hyphomycetes (H,2.C2.po)

Disease: Southern corn leaf blight; Blattflecken des Maises; helminthosporiose; añublo de la hoja del maiz.

Geographical distribution: Southern corn leaf blight is widely distributed over the world particularly in tropical and warm-temperate regions (CMI map no 346).

Host plants: The host range of the pathogen includes corn, sorghum and teosinte (*Euchlaena mexicana*). Corn is by far the most important host; sorghum is seldom if ever severely infected and there are few reports of the disease of this host.

Symptoms: Lesions caused by Race 0 of *D. maydis* (see discussion of races below) are tan to straw-colored, ranging up to 4–8 x 25–45 mm in size and tend to be parallel sided. Genotype of the host may affect size and shape of the lesions. The greater the number of lesions on a leaf the smaller their size. Lesions incited by Race T of the pathogen on corn with Texas male-sterile cytoplasm (Tcms) have some tendency to be slightly spindle-shaped (Plate 6 c).
Race T attacks all tissues and organs of the host with Tcms; leaf sheaths, husks and ears are readily invaded. Infected ears are deep slate gray to black owing to the dark mycelial growth on and between the kernels (Plate 6 b). Such infected ears are oftern indistinguishable from the ear rots incited by Race I or Race II of *C. carbonus* Nelson (= *Drechslera* state, = *Helminthosporium carbonum* Ullstrup), or by a new, and as yet unnamed, species of *Helminthosporium*. Race 0 may attack ears but does so only rarely.
Leaf symptoms incited by Race T on corn with normal cytoplasm are generally small, benign lesions that vary in size, shape and color depending on the genotype of the host. These lesions are rarely conspicuous under conditions of natural infection. Leaf lesions caused by either race may be confused with those of yellow leaf blight (*Phyllosticta maydis*), Helminthosporium leaf spot (*C. carbonus,* Race I) or, more rarely, with anthracnose (*Colletotrichum graminicola* (Ces.) Wils.).

Morphology: Conidia of *D. maydis* are pale-smoky to olivebrown in color, have 3–13 septa, average 15 x 90 μ in size and show more curvature than any of the other species of this genus attacking corn (Fig. 44). Perithecia are black 0.4–0.6 mm in diameter and beaked. Asci are long, cylindrical measure 24 x 28 x 100–180 μ and contain up to 8, but more often 4, ascospores. Ascospores are pale smoky colored, 6–7 x 130 – 340 μ, bear 5–9 septa and are arranged in a helicoid manner.

Physiological specialization: It was observed that Tcms corn was extremely susceptible while near-isogenic, normal-cytoplasm corn was resistant. Later it was demonstrated that two physiologic races were present within the species. Isolates from Tcms corn were highly virulent on corn with this type of cytoplasm, but caused only mild symptoms on corn with normal cytoplasm. Such isolates were designated as Race T. Isolates from corn with normal cytoplasm did not show this differential virulence when inoculated on Tcms and normal-cytoplasm corn of the same genotype. This race, which is the one on which the original description was based, and which has been encountered for many years, was designated as Race 0.

Epidemiology: Both races survive the rigorous winters of the central Corn Belt, as well as in the sub-tropical regions of the United States. Both races are nearly world-wide in distribution.
Race T sporulates prolifically of Tcms corn and spores are readily air-borne. Infection may take place in 4 to 6 hours when a film of water is present on the leaf surface and the temperature 28–32 °C. The latent period can be completed within 10–14 days under favorable conditions. Dry, cool weather (10–20 °C) is unfavorable for disease development.

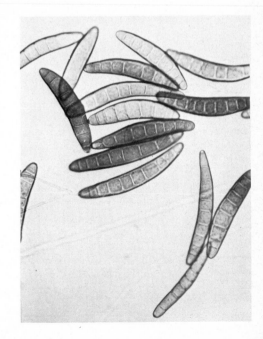

Fig. 44.

Control: Control of the disease incited by Race T is effected through use of normal-cytoplasm corn. The rapid change-over from Tcms corn to corn with normal cytoplasm was the means by which this devastating disease was controlled in the United States in 1972. Resistance to Race 0 is determined generally by a number of genes and is not affected by the type of cytoplasm as in the case of resistance to Race T. A source of resistance to Race 0, from Africa, has been shown to be controlled by a single dominant gene.

Since the pathogen can survive in infected debris, clean plowing to bury the source of inoculum is helpful in delaying onset of the disease.

Foliar application of fungicides have been used to control Race T of *D. maydis,* but the use of normal-cytoplasm corn has supplanted chemical control.

Literature

DRECHSLER, C. (1934): Phytopathological and taxonomic aspects of *Ophiobolus, Pyrenophora, Helminthosporium* and a new genus, *Cochliobolus. Phytopathology* **24,** 953–983.

NELSON, R. R. (1957): Heterothallism in *Helminthosporium maydis*. Phytopatholoy **47,** 191–192.

SMITH, D. R., A. L. HOOKER & S. M. LIM (1970): Physiologic races of *Helminthosporium maydis*. Plant Dis. Reptr. **54,** 819–822.

ULLSTRUP, A. J. (1972): The impact of the southern corn leaf blight epidemics of 1970–1971. Ann. Rev. Phytopathology **10,** 37–50.

CMI Description no 301.

Author: A. J. Ullstrup

Cochliobolus miyabeanus (Ito & Kuribayashi) Drechsler ex Dastur

Synonym: *Ophiobolus miyabeanus* Ito & Kuribayashi
Loculoascomycetes Pleosporales, Pleosporaceae
Conidial state: *Drechslera oryzae* (Breda de Haan) Subram. & Jain. (= *Helminthosporium oryzae* Breda de Haan.)
Hyphomycetes (H,2.C2.po)

Disease: Helminthosporium disease, Brown-spot; Helminthosporium-Blattflecken; Helmithosporiose; helmintosporiosis del arroz.

Geographical distribution: Helminthosporium disease of rice has been reported from all the rice growing regions of the world (CMI map no 92). It is endemic in certain areas which have characteristic soil abnormalities.

Host plants: Rice, *Leersia hexandra* and *Echinochloa colona.*

Symptoms: *Drechslera oryzae* infects rice in all stages of growth, from germination to maturity. Small spots may appear on the coleoptile, leaf sheaths and leaves; the seedlings may die (when the spots are numerous). Seedling death may also occur without the appearance of spots due to infection at the collar region (seedling blight).

Leaf spots on adult leaves are small, reddish brown in colour, irregular to oval in shape and about 3 x 0.5 mm in size; they may be larger, (up to 1 cm in length) in susceptible varieties. "Neck" infection or "rotten neck" (at the principal node below the rachis), has a characteristic water-soaked appearance and occurs at flowering; grains are spotted and in severe attacks become shrivelled.

Leaf spots are fairly distinct from those caused by other fungi. In the case of "rotten neck" the brown colouration and water-soaked appearance distinguish the disease from blast (p. 223, Fig. 85b) in which greyish to blackish velvetty rotten necks occur.

Morphology: The conidia are usually curved either to one side or straight. They are broadest at the middle or a little below, and taper into blunt ends; when the distal end is curved, it may be somewhat pointed. The spore walls are mostly thick, but in the terminal cells generally thinner. A wide variation in spore size and septation has been recorded. They range from 15–170 μ in length and 7–26 μ in breadth.

Physiological specialization: The performance of a common set of varieties in different test locations in India indicates the possible existence of physiologic specialization.

Epidemiology: The fungus is viable in the seed from harvest until sowing of the next crop. The spores of the pathogen are also windborne and could be caught in sporetraps throughout the year though in very low numbers from April to August. Under sub-tropical conditions survival is in plant parts and debris preserved in snow.

Spores are released during the daytime, reaching a peak a round 14–15 hours. Spore release is favoured by cloudy conditions during the daytime, slight drizzle, and a low range of daily temperature (16–32 °C). Under laboratory conditions conidia are formed between 5–38 °C. Conidia are presumably dispersed by wind and air currents.

Rice increases in susceptibility with age, and it is most susceptible to infection at flowering and when mature; older leaves of a plant are more susceptible than younger ones.

Both deficiency and an excess of N favours the establishment of infection; phosphates have an ameliorating effect. Infection is greather under particularly low and high levels of K_2O, under leached conditions, and when N alone instead of N + P and P and K is added after leaching. It is also enhanced by Zn deficiency, and with H_2S toxicity – generally, under any abnormal soil conditions requiring amelioration.

Infection takes place over the range 16–38 °C; the optimum range is reported to be 20–25 °C with some isolates, and 25–30 °C with others. Free water on the leaf surface is necessary for infection. Shading (or cloudy conditions) favours infection. At the optimum temperature (25 °C) germination takes about 3 hours, the formation of appressoria and penetration 6 hours, and the establishment of infection through infection hyphae 12 hours. But also 3–4 days may elapse from germination of conidia to penetration of viable spores.

The fungus produces a toxin, ophiobolin, which, amongst others leads to accumulation of phenolic substances in host cells which are oxidized to quinones which in turn are polymerised into brown pigment which delimit the spread of the pathogen. The behaviour of the phenolic substances after penetration may be related to resistance phenomenon.

When a second crop of rice is grown the infection from the first spreads to be second crop, generally through seed-bed infections.

Certain abnormal trends in weather conditions have always been associated with severe outbreaks of Helminthosporium disease. Heavy rainfall, accompanied by an uniformly favourable temperature range of 25–30 °C throughout the day, as well as by continuous cloudy weather (and consequently low solar radiation) can be associated with epidemic outbreaks. It was precisely under these conditions that abnormally large numbers of spores have been recorded on slides exposed in a sporetrops.

Continuous rainfall, however, interferes with spore dispersal and deposition. Prolonged dry weather without the dew formation required for spore germination, a vigorous tillering phase of the host, and balanced nutrition represent unfavourable conditions for the disease.

Control: Removal of stubble, and secondary tillers arising from stubbles which carry the infection; destruction of collateral hosts like *Leersia hexandra* and *Echinochloa colona* in the rice fields through herbicidal spray. Also soil amendment to restore deficiencies and abnormalities, may help in keeping the disease at a low level.

Several resistant varieties have been reported, eg. *CH* 13, *CH* 45, *CI* 9515 etc. Resistance in *CH* 13 and *CI* 9515 is governed by three recessive genens.

Seed treatment by organo-mercuricals containing 0.1 per cent Hg at 1/400 by weight of seed, copper fungicides at 0.5 per cent and other fungicides appeared to give good control. Spraying in the fields may be cone after cessation of rains. Three fortnightly treatments with Cu fungicides (0.5 kg/100 l) between tillering and flowering stages of rice are recommended. Also organomercurical dust (1 % Hg) may be applied at 20 kg/ha.

Low sunshine hours (continuous cloudy weather) at susceptible stages of crop growth (i. e. towards flowering and maturity) accompanied by slight drizzles occurring over a number of days may serve as warning for epidemic outbreak.

Literature

ELLIS, M. B. (1971): Dematious Hyphomycetes. Commonwealth Mycological Institute, Kew (A general taxonomic account on conidial states of *Cochliobolus*).
HASHIOKA, Y. (1970): Rice Diseases in the world – VII (Fungal diseases – 4). Riso **XIX**, 309–338.
OU, S. H. (1972): Rice Diseases. Commonwealth Mycological Institute, Kew.
PADMANABHAN, S. Y. (1973): Great Bengal Famine. Ann. Rev. Phytopathology. **11**, 11–26.
CMI Description no 302.

Author: S. Y. Padmanabhan

Other important Cochliobolus spp. on tropical and subtropical crops:
C. carbonum (p. 105). Ref.: CMI Description no 349.
Cochliobolus nodulosus Luttrell with a *Drechslera* state. Seedling blight, foot rot and leaf blight of finger millet (*Eleusine coracana*). Ref.: CMI Description no 341.

Diaporthe medusaea Nits. (Fig. 45)

Synonym: *Diaporthe citri Wolf*
Pyrenomycetes, Sphaeriales, Diaporthaceae
Conidial state *Phomopsis cytosporella* Penz. & Sacc. = *Phomopsis citri* Fawcett.
Coelomycetes (C,1.A1.ph)

Disease: Melanose; Stielendfäule der Zitrusarten; melanose of citrus; melanosis del fruto de los agrios.

Geographical distribution: This species, observed in Florida by Swingle and Weber as early as 1892, is present nearly everywhere in the world, notably in the citrus-growing regions of North America, Mexico, South America (Brazil, Argentina), the West Indies, the Mediterranean, Africa (Nigeria), New Zealand, Australia, the Philippines, Indonesia, Japan, China, etc. (CMI map no 126).

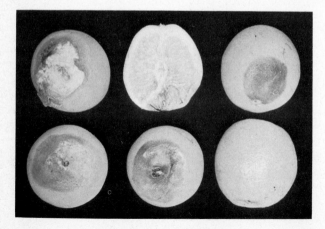

Host plants: This parasite is common on nearly all varieties of wild and cultivated citrus; grapefruit, orange, lemon, lime, mandarin, tangelo, pummelo, kumquat, but it is also found on avocado, cocoa, mango, pawpaw (papaya), apple, walnut etc.

Symptoms: The disease is seen on leaves, branches and fruits. On fruits it appears in two forms, the melanose and the *Phomopsis* peduncle rot (Fig. 45).

Fig. 45.

The first symptoms show with the appearance of very small round spots, the size of a pinhead, which enlarge, blacken at the centre and slowly sink, and are encircled by a yellowish halo. Later this halo disappears and the spots become dark brown and acquire a rough surface like glass paper. These symptoms occur on both faces of the leaves. The spots can be aggregated or dispersed. In cases of severe attack the leaves fall prematurely.

On branches the symptoms are identical to those on the leaves, although the small corky pustules project further from the surface. In the case of severe attack the branches die. The symptoms on fruit are:

a) Melanose: These symptoms are very similar to those observed on leaves. The small circular spots are at first light brown, then raised and red, brown and black. To the touch they also feel like glass paper, which distinguishes them from mite damage (p. 268) and anthracnose (p. 119).

On the fruits these spots are either arranged in patterns which result from the spores being dispersed by dew and raindrops, or are confluent, which induces the formation of wound scab tissue sometimes streaked with a network of small cracks resembling dried mud. Fruits which are severely attacked at an early stage die stunted and fall prematurely.

b) Phomopsis peduncle rot: The symptoms, observed either in the orchard or the store, are very similar.

First, a zone of light chamois-brown colour develops, generally around the point of attachment of the peduncle, but sometimes around the stylar scar if the fruits touch the ground. To the touch this zone is tender, as if cooked. When the fruit is half invaded the colour of the necrosed zone becomes a deeper brown, more especially if the disease develops in the orchard; then the fruit falls. Upon opening an attacked fruit one notes a more rapid invasion of the central column than the epidermis, and a preferential localisation of the fungus in the albedo.

The symptoms of melanose on leaves and on fruits can sometimes be confused with those caused by *Colletotrichum gloeosporioides* (anthracnose, p. 119) or by *Guignardia citricarpa* Kiely (black spot). The symptoms of *Phomopsis* peduncle rot are very similar to those caused by attacks of the peduncle due to *Diplodia natalensis* (p. 133).

Morphology: *D. medusaea* produces two types of spores. Bicellular, elliptical ascospores $(11.5 \times 3.2\,\mu)$ in groups of eight develop in asci within bottleshaped perithecia ($155\,\mu$) which have a long neck ($200–800\,\mu$). Usually the perithecia develop on wood and dead branches which have fallen to the ground. Asexual spores are produced in pycnidia ($200 \times 500\,\mu$) which look something like perithecia, and are often localized on dead twigs. The pycnidia contain two types of spores: unicellular conidia, hyaline and ovoid (alpha conidia) $(5–9 \times 2.4 – 4\,\mu)$ whose production is favoured by light and temperatures from 15 to 25 °C, and filiform conidia, curved at their upper end (beta conidia) $(20–30 \times 0.75–1.5\,\mu)$.

Physiological specialization: With respect to different clones of citrus, variations in aggressiveness has been observed among about twenty different races of *D. medusaea*.

Epidemiology: Spores produced by either pycnidia or perithecia are present throughout the year in more or less large numbers, depending upon the season. Essentially they are produced on dead wood and dried branches whether or not fallen to the ground, and are disseminated by waterdrops and dew.

Leaves and young growths are susceptible for 2–3 weeks after their emergence, and fruits from petal-fall until their diameter reaches 2–3 cm, according to variety. Infection is established in 24–48 hours on young fruits and in 3–4 days on mature fruits, and the first symptoms appear 5–7 days later, if the temperature is about 25 °C. At 10 °C incubation can last 8 days.

The most favourable conditions are when warm, humid and cloudy weather coincides with the start of shoot growth and the setting of the young fruits.

Control: In orchards, the control of this disease consists of a careful and systematic removal of centres of infection by cutting out dried branches and the disposal of dead wood and rotten fruits, together with the application of fungicides. In general, copper sprays containing 90 g of metal copper/100 litres of water are recommended, with a first application one week after flowering, followed by a second five weeks later. In certain areas a single treatment three weeks after flowering is adequate.

Copper sprays are clearly more effective than organic fungicides such as dithiocarbamates in cases of severe attack. These products (ferbam for example) can be used, however, at doses of about 180 g/100 litres when there is a risk of damage due to the phytotoxicity of copper.

Spraying also reduces the incidence of peduncle infections on fruits before harvest.

After harvest, treatments usually applied for the control of *Penicillium* rots are also active against the peduncle rots. These post-harvest treatments are of warm water (5 minutes at 53 °C.) and fungicide dips such as Sodium orthophenylphenate (2–3 %), and 4 g of Diphenyl (Biphenyl) to impregnate the cardboard sheets of each 15 kilo case, equal to 4.7 g/4–5 bushel), and Thiabendazole (0.2 %), and Benomyl (0.1 %).

Literature

ROGER, L. (1954): Phytopathologie des pays chauds. Vol 1–3. Paul Lechevalier Paris.
KNORR, L. C., R. F. SUIT & E. P. DUCHARME (1957): Handbook of Citrus Diseases in Florida. Univ. of Florida Bull. 587, Gainesville Florida USA.
FAWCETT, H. S. (1936): Citrus diseases and their control. McGraw-Hill Book Cy. New York & London. CMI Description no 396.

Author: E. Laville

Other Diaporthe spp. on tropical and subtropical crops:

D. batatis Harter & Field. Dry rot of sweet potato.
D. phaseolorum (Cke & Ell.) Sacc. var. *soyae* (Lehman) Wehm. Pod and stem blight of soybean.
D. vexans (Sacc. & Syd.) Gratz = *Phomopsis vexans* (Sacc. & Syd.) Harter.
Stem and leaf blight, and other symptoms on eggplants (*Solanum melongena*). Ref.: CMI Description no 338.

Literature

WEHMEYER, L. E. (1933): The genus Diaporthe Nitschke and its segregates. Ann Arbor.

Elsinoe fawcetti Jenkins (Fig. 46)

Loculoascomycetes, Myriangiales
Conidial state *Sphaceloma fawcetti* Jenkins
Elsinoe australis Bitanc. & Jenkins
Conidial state *Sphaceloma fawcetti* var. *viscosa* Jenkins;
Sphaceloma fawcetti var. *scabiosa* (McAlpine & Tryon) Jenkins, perfect state unknown (Australian scab)
Coelomycetes (C,2. A1)

Disease: Citrus scab; Schorf der Zitrusfrüchte; Scab des agrumes; roña de los agrios.

Geographical distribution: Citrus scab is known in most of the countries where citrus is grown, except in the driest areas. It is not present in California or in Arizona, nor it seems in the Mediterranean basin (CMI map no 125). *E. australis* is only known in South America (CMI map no 55). *S. fawcetti* var. *scabiosa* is only present in Australia and New Zealand, but in the Comoro Islands and Madagascar a form with very similar pathogenic characteristics has been observed.

Host plants: This problem is particularly complex since it relates the full range of citrus varieties and the three different pathogens, the behaviour of which can vary according to climatic conditions. With respect to *E. fawcetti,* the following range of hosts can be listed:

Very susceptible: sour orange, rough lemon, lemon (Calamandin, Combava), tangelo.

Average susceptibility: tangor (King orange), satsuma, tangerine or mandarin, grapefruit (except Royal & Triumph), *Poncirus trifoliata,* the citranges in general, sweet lemon, Rangpur lime, lime (Kusaie).
Resistant: certain oranges, oval kumquat, lime (Tahiti), shaddock or pummelo.
Apparently immune: citrons, lime (Mexican), certain oranges, mandarin (Cleopatra), satsuma (Wase).
In the case of *E. australis* (orange scab), the orange, together with lemon are most susceptible, but it is also seen on tangerine, lime (Combava), kumquat, grapefruit, satsuma and tangelo.
Regarding Australian scab, lemon seem to be the most susceptible, together with rough lemon.

Symptoms: The disease occurs on fruits, leaves and branches, the severity varying with the species. It is characterized by the appearance of more or less raised lesions in the form of scabs or corky warts.
On young leaves the first symptoms are small, translucent spots which rapidly become pustular, 2–3 mm in diameter, sometimes coalescent, pale rose and glossy then turning chamois-beige in colour. Each lesion develops on only one side of the leaf. On branches the warts are often larger and can completely girdle the stem. On fruits the development of young lesions (Fig. 46) is identical to that on leaves; they result in serious deformities and the premature fall of affected fruits. Scab is often confused with citrus canker caused by *Xanthomonas citri* (p. 62). However, the latter can be distinguished by the fact that individual corky lesions on the leaves are not limited to one surface.

Morphology: The perfect state *E. fawcetti* Jenkins is characterized by a diffuse stroma mixed with the host tissues, with fructifications (38–106 x 36–80 μ) which enclose one to twenty globular ovoid asci (12–16 μ in diameter) containing hyaline ascospores with 1–3 septae, and which are oblong – elliptical (10 x 5 μ).
The conidial state *Sphaceloma fawcetti* has sub-circular acervulae less than 1 mm in diameter. Conidiophores, standing perpendicular to the stroma, are cylindrical with a tapering tip. They measure 12–22 x 3–4 μ and have 1–3 cells. The conidia are hyaline, oblong, elliptical (5–10 x 2–5 μ) and frequently have two minute droplets at their ends. In pure culture the pathogen grows slowly.
E. australis and its conidial state *S. fawcetti var. viscosa* have features different from *S. fawcetti,* and are subject to considerable morphological variations.

Physiological specialization: A better knowledge of the citrus species which are affected by each species of scab should allow the selection of a range of representative hosts and offer a clearer differentation of the three scab species, taking into account the influence of climate on their pathogencity.

Fig. 46.

Epidemiology: The disease is spread mainly by rain, dew and wind which carry the spores to young organs. Certain insects (notably mites) also contribute to dissemination. The attacks are most frequent on the lower leaf surface.

Fawcett believes that in the presence of inoculum at least four conditions are necessary if infection is to occur: The presence of a susceptible variety, very young tissue, sufficient humidity, and favourable temperatures.

Very young tissue is an indispensable requirement because adult leaves seem to be almost immune.

At temperatures between 13–30 °C incubation lasts 4–5 days; beyond 30 °C the rate of development is reduced and the fungus is killed in a few minutes if exposed to temperatures near 45 °C. In tropical and subtropical regions drought is definitely the most important factor limiting the progress of this disease.

Control: The two most important methods are the use of resistant varieties and the destruction of old, contaminated leaves, fruits and branches before the appearance of new vegetative growth. However, the application of fungicides is also recommended in the majority of cases.

Bordeaux mixture (1 %) can be used, repeating the applications before and after vegetative growth. The dithiocarbamates ferbam and zineb also offer good results at doses varying from 180–240 g/100 l when applied twice with a 7-day interval. Difolatan is recommended at 125 g/hectolitre, two or more sprays being applied at 7 or 14-day intervals according to climatic conditions.

Literature

BITANCOURT, A. A., & ANNA E. JENKINS (1957): *Elsinoe fawcetti* the perfect stage of the citrus scab fungi. Phytopathology, **26**, 393–395.
BRUN, J. (1971): Les "Scab" des agrumes. Fruits, **26**, 759–767.
FAWCETT, H. S. (1936): Citrus diseases and their control. Mc Graw-Hill Book Cy., New York and London.
FISHER, F. E. (1970): Scab can be controlled. Citrus Veg. Mag., **33**, 8–13.
CMI Descriptions nos 438, 440 & 437.

Author: J. Brun

Other more important Elsinoe spp. on tropical and subtropical crops
(see also *Sphaceloma* p. 227).
E. batatas Jenkins & Viégas Scab of sweet potato. CMI map no 447.
E. chinchonae Jenkins. Scab of *Chinchona* sp.
E. dolichi Jenkins, Bitanc. & Cheo. Scab of *Lablab niger*.
E. mangiferae Bitanc. & Jenkins. Scab of mango.
E. phaseoli Jenkins. Scab of lunabean (*Phaseolus lunatus*). Ref.: CMI Description no 314.
E. sacchari (Lo) Bitanc. & Jenkins. Spot anthracnose of sugarcane.
E. theae Bitanc. & Jenkins. Scab of tea. CMI map no 154.

Gaeumannomyces graminis (Sacc.) Arx & Olivier

Synonym: *Ophiobolus graminis* (Sacc.) Sacc.
Pyrenomycetes, Sphaeriales, Diaporthaceae
Conidial state *Phialophora-like*
Hyphomycetes (H,2.A2.ph)

Disease: Take-all; Schwarzbeinigkeit; piétin échaudage; mal de pie.

Plate 1

a Exocortis on lime Rangpur
b Psorosis on orange Valencia late
c Tristeza – Stem pitting on real lime
d Cachexie – Xyloporose on mandarin Setubal

Plate 2

a Greening – In front two trees attacked
b Stubborn – Severely attacked tree
c Lethal Yellowing Disease of coconut palm (early stage)
d Lethal Yellowing – Necrotic lesions on the spike of a young tree

Plate 3

a Lethal Yellowing – Devastated plantation at the north coast of Jamaica
b Bud rot on stalks of fronds of 'Malayan dwarf' (Jamaica)
c Kainkope disease of coconut palms in Togo

Plate 4

a *Pseudomonas solanacearum* – Wilting potatoes
b *Xanthomonas oryzae* – Withering of the whole plants
c *Xanthomonas oryzae* – Lesions on rice leaves
d *Xanthomonas oryzae* – Bacterial exudate on a leaf of rice

Plate 5

a *Xanthomonas translucens* f. sp. *oryzicola* – Lesions as streaks parallel to the veins
b *Xanthomonas translucens* f. sp. *oryzicola* – Bacteria oozed out of the stomata
c *Phytophthora citrophthora* – Brown rot gummosis (1-healthy tissue, 2-affected tissue, 3-gum exudation)
d *Pseudoperonospora cubensis* – Downy mildew of cucurbits (upper and lower leaf surfaces)

Plate 6

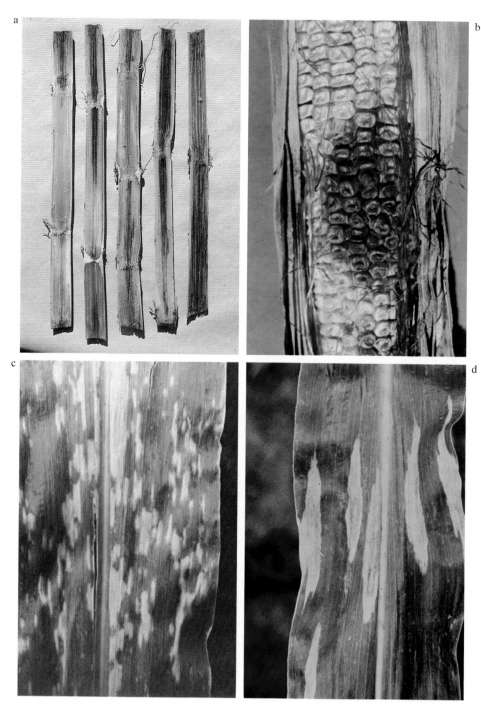

a *Ceratocystis paradoxa* – Pineapple disease. Sugarcane cuttings in various stages of rotting; right: healthy stalk
b *Cochliobolus heterostrophus* – Southern corn leaf blight. Mycelial growth on and between the kernels
c *idem* – Lesions on leaves
d *Setosphaeria turcica* – Northern corn leaf blight. Lesions on leaves

Plate 7

a *Fusarium solani* – Purple discolouration in Arabica-coffee trees
b *Leveillula taurica* – Leaf symptoms on *Capsicum*
c *Mycosphaerella arachidis* and *M. berkeleyii* – Light and dark leaf spots, respectively
d *Mycosphaerella musicola* – Old leaf spots

Plate 8

a *Mycosphaerella musicola* – Fruit symptoms; left: from severely affected plant; right: from healthy plant
b *Armillariella mellea* – Root rot of coffee
c *Armillariella mellea* – Fruiting bodies
d *Ganoderma* root rot of tea

Plate 9

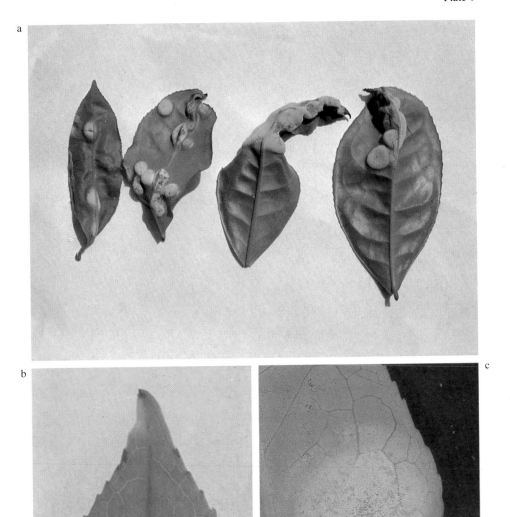

a *Exobasidium vexans* – Symptoms on leaves
b *Exobasidium vexans* – Blisters on leaves seen from above
c *Exobasidium vexans* – Blisters on leaves seen from below

Plate 10

a Three root rot pathogens on roots of Hevea brasiliensis; left: *R. lignosus;* centre: *G. pseudofer-reum;* right: *P. noxius* (from a preparation of the Rubber Res. Inst. Malaysia)
b *Ganoderma* spp. – Fructifications on oil palm tree
c *Hemileia vastatrix* – Symptoms of coffee leaf rust

Plate 11

a *Puccinia graminis tritici* – Stem rust of wheat (urediosori)
b *Puccinia recondita* and *P. striiformis* – Leaf (right) and stripe (left) rust of wheat (urediosori)
c *Puccinia hordei* – Urediosori of barley leaf rust
d *Puccinia sorghi* – Maize rust urediosori

Plate 12

a *Sphacelotheca sorghi* – Covered smut of sorghum
b *Sphacelotheca cruenta* – Loose smut of sorghum
c *Sphacelotheca reiliana* – Head smut of sorghum
d *Tolyposporium penicillariae* – Long smut of pearl millet

Plate 13

a *Cercospora coffeicola* – Brown eye spot of coffee
b *Colletotrichum coffeanum* – Coffee berry disease (green cherries) and brown blight (red cherries)
c *Colletotrichum gloeosporioides* – Anthracnose of mango
d *Colletotrichum musae* – Anthracnose of ripe bananas

Plate 14

a *Deuterophoma tracheiphila* – Defoliated branches of citrus
b *Fusarium oxysporum* f. sp. *cubense* – Wilting banana plant
c *Deuterophoma tracheiphila* – Cross sections of the affected parts of the wood; above: from healthy tree
d *Fusarium oxysporum* f. sp. *cubense* – Internal symptom

Plate 15

a *Fusarium oxysporum* f. sp. *lycopersici* – Leaf yellowing and wilt symptoms on tomato
b *Fusarium oxysporum* f. sp. *lycopersici* – Typical yellowing of leaves and stem cortex
c *Fusarium oxysporum* f. sp. *lycopersici* – Brown discoloration of vascular bundles
d *Fusarium oxysporum* f. sp. *lycopersici* – Final stage of wilt

Plate 16

a *Verticillium dahliae* – Wilting cacao tree
b *Ascochyta tarda* – Leaf blight of Arabica coffee
c *Oidium* sp. – Powdery mildew on citrus
d *Oidium mangiferae* – Powdery mildew on flowers of mango

Geographical distribution: In temperate regions take-all is widespread and relatively well-documented, but in most tropical and subtropical countries, where wheat is grown at high elevations or at lower altitudes in the cooler part of the year, there is a lack of information (CMI map no 334).

Host plants: Serious infections occur only in the Gramineae and the disease is most damaging on wheat, barley, oats, and rye (only after recent liming). The fungus causes a minor disease of rice (crown, black or brown sheath rot; Arkansas foot rot) and attacks maize, but with little damage. Pasture and turf grasses can be seriously affected (*Ophiobolus* patch disease) and many weed grasses are important as carriers.

Symptoms: Severely-infected wheat plants have extensively blackened roots, stunted aerial growth, chlorotic foliage and frequently occur in patches in the crop. Those that survive until ripening, die prematurely and become very conspicuous as blanched plants, which in wet weather are blackened by mould growth. These plants, called 'whiteheads', are easily pulled and contain little or no grain. Less severe infections adversely affect grain size and appearance, but even without aboveground symptoms yield is frequently reduced. Other diagnostic aids are dark brown 'runner' hyphae growing along roots; plate or sheath mycelium coating the stem beneath the sheaths of the lowermost leaves, particularly at the whiteheads stage; and lignitubers in invaded tissues. Whiteheads can be caused by brown foot rot, eyespot, frost, insects or, indeed, anything depleting the root system and causing water shortage. Root discoloration resulting from brown foot rot, common root rot, browning root rot or drought can at times be confused with take-all and root symptoms may be difficult to diagnose on ripe plants. Several cereal root fungi produce runner hyphae.

Morphology: Perithecia form beneath the basal leaf sheaths of maturing plants, or on stubble after harvest. They are black spherical bodies (up to 0.6 mm diam.) with elongated necks that protrude through the sheaths and eject or extrude spores in wet or humid weather. In culture many isolates develop sterile, fast-growing colonies, the leading hyphae of which curl back on themselves at the margin. Mycelium is appressed or woolly, colourless to dark olive-gray and sometimes differentiated into coarse (runner) and fine hyaline hyphae. If microconidia develop, they are usually sickle-shaped (4–8 x 1.5–2 μ). A few isolates will produce perthecia, containing unitunicate asci, each with a conspicuous apical ring. The ascospores are linear curved or vermiculate, hyaline and septate and in isolates from wheat range from 60–118 (mostly 70–85) x 3–5 μ.

Physiological specialization: Three varieties of *G. graminis* are recognised: var. *graminis* (brown sheath rot of rice) = *Ophiobolus oryzinus* Sacc., var. *tritici* (wheat take-all fungus) and var. *avenae* (oat take-all fungus). Var. *graminis* has lobed hyphodia; the others have simple hyphodia. Var. *avenae* is most reliably identified by its ability to cause take-all of oats. Within varietal categories there are biotypes differing in morphology physiology and pathogenicity, but these are not classified formally.

Epidemiology: *G. graminis* competes poorly for dead substrates and declines as a saprophyte in soil, but may persist in stubble and root residues for more than a year. Depletion of available nitrogen, medium-high temperatures, adequate moisture and good aeration aid the loss of inoculum, but the fungus can survive on self-sown cereals and weed grasses. Ascospores and microconidia seem to be unimportant in the epidemiology of take-all in established arable land, where spread is mostly by growth of the fungus along living roots.

The epidermis of primary and secondary roots can be penetrated at any stage of their growth. Infection hyphae grow through the cortex into the stele, causing disorganization of the phloem, occlusion of sieve tubes and rupture of their walls. Hyphae also grow into xylem vessels, which may become plugged. The lesion eventually prevents the downward movement of assimilates and the transport of ions from below the lesion, root elongation ceases and an enhanced movement of carbohydrates to the uninfected part of the root promotes the growth of adventitious roots.

In temperate climates there is little infection until the soil warms up in the spring and then disease increases extensively until harvest. It is often stated that take-all is favoured by a wet growing season and loose-textured, well aerated soils of alkaline reaction. High water potential, poor drainage and high temperatures in soil, root damage (mechanical, drought, insects or nematodes), frost damage and late sowing also favour the disease. That most of these statements are generalities is demonstrated by many exceptions described in the literature. There is, however, agreement that balanced nutrition of the host discourages take-all.

Control: As no resistant varieties or practical and economical fungicides are known, the key to avoiding take-all problems is good husbandry, particularly crop rotation, adequate use of fertilizers (especially nitrogen) and weed control. The disease is increased by frequent cropping of susceptible plants, but in sequences of wheat or barley crops it often subsides after progressing to a maximum in the first few crops and recurs in subsequent years at a level that allows profitable crops. The beneficial effects of this 'take-all decline' are partly or wholly lost by short breaks in a susceptible crop sequence and the whole process of disease increase and decline will begin again. Some control of take-all was achieved by direct-drilling winter wheat, possibly because spread of the fungus was limited in undisturbed soil. Green manuring by undersowing cereals with ryegrass-trefoil mixture has also improved yields, but whether this arises from disease control or nitrogen availability is unresolved.

Literature

DOMSCH, K. H., & W. GAMS (1970): Pilze aus Agrarböden. Gustav Fischer Verlag, Stuttgart.
GAIR, R., J. E. E. JENKINS & E. LESTER (1972): Cereal pests and diseases. Farming Press Ltd. Ipswich.
GERLAGH, M. (1968): Introduction of *Ophiobotus graminis* into new Polders and its decline. Maded. Lab. Fytopathologie, Wageningen, no 241.
NILSSON, H. E., (1969): Studies of root and foot rot diseases of cereals and grasses. I. On resistance to *Ophiobolus graminis* Sacc. Lantbr-Högsk. Annlr. **35**, 275–807.
SALLANS, B. J. (1965): Root rots of cereals. III. Bot. Rev. **31**, 505–536.
WALKER, J. (1972): Type studies on *Gaeumannomyces graminis* and related fungi. Trans. Brit. mycol. Soc. **58**, 427–457.
WALKER, J. (1975): Take-all diseases of Graminae. A review of recent work. Rev. Plant Path. **54,** 113–144.
CMI Descriptions nos 381, 382, 383.

Author: D. Hornby

Gibberella stilboides Gordon ex Booth (Fig. 47)

Pyrenomycetes, Sphaeriales, Hypocreaceae
Conidial state *Fusarium stilboides* Wr.
Hyphomycetes (H,4.C1.ph)

Disease: Fusarium bark disease of coffee; Rindenkrankheit des Kaffees; psorosis de caféièr; psoriasis del cafeto.

Geographical distribution: Ethiopia, Kenya, Tanzania, Malawi, Southern India, Rhodesia, West Indies and possibly Malagasy Republic. On citrus in Ghana, Zambia, India, New Guinea, South Africa and Rhodesia.

Host plants: *Coffea arabica, C. liberica, C. canephora, Citrus* and *Brachiaria* spp.

Fig. 47.

Symptoms: On *C. arabica* the fungus affects the stems, the disease taking three possible forms:
1) Storey's Bark Disease: Bases of young suckers are attacked, a brown lesion, often with a chlorotic yellow margin, developing at the junction with the main stem. Ultimately a constriction or "bottle neck" results as the sucker matures and the sucker may thus be ring-barked and die off, or may become weak and break understress (Fig. 47).
Young branches may also be affected in a similar manner. Usually it is a secondary which is attacked at the base while still green, a brown lesion develops, the leaves turn black and dieback occurs.
2) Scaly Bark: The fungus may spread beneath the bark of a mature stem causing it to flake off; this can happen at the base of an infected sucker or may arise independently of other symptoms. It is uncertain just how damaging the condition alone is, and it has formerly been described as non-pathogenic in nature.
3) Collar rot: When the fungus girdles the stem at soil level this is known as collar rot. This symptom may be confused with root rots due to other fungi such as *F. solani* (p. 210) and the stem pitting condition. It has not been observed in Kenya but is reported to be common in Malawi, particularly on young replanted trees in infected areas.
F. stilboides has in addition been found on both ripe coffee berries and leaves in E. Africa where it appears to maintain a saprophytic existence. In Trinidad it has been reported attacking immature berries of *C. liberica* but this damage appears to be of little importance.

Morphology: On potato sucrose agar pH 6.5 mycelial growth is flat and white, somewhat felty in appearance and with a deep carmine to port-wine colour developing on the underside of the colony. On 2 % malt agar the colony underside is deep carmine, peach or lemon yellow depending upon pH.
Microconidia and chlamydospores are absent. macroconidia are long, narrow, cylindrical to fusiform, straight to falcate, often beaked at the apex, normally 6–9 septate, 20–35 x 3–4 μ to 45–82 x 4–5 μ. (See also p. 215).

Physiological specialization: Not known.

Epidemiology: Reports of the survival of *F. stilboides* in soil are unsubstantiated. The fungus is common in all aerial parts of coffee but is normally non-parasitic, it sporulates freely under humid conditions on infected tissue and sporodochia can frequently be seen on the brown lesions of Storey's bark disease or emerging from cracks in the bark of infected wood.
The spores are possibly insect-transmitted; in Kenya there is a close association between this disease and the occurence of the Yellow Headed Borer, *Dirphya nigricornis*, dispersed in water

films and transmitted on pruning tools. Infection frequently occurs through wounds such as pruning cuts or enters the young wood of suckers as they arise from the stem. The growth of suckers close to ground level, mulching too close to the stem, and dense weed cover encourage this type of infection.

The optimum season for attack by the agent of Storey's bark disease is during and after the rains when new suckers are produced in abundance, and the fungus has been found to have its maximum pathogenicity at this time.

Spread of the fungus beneath the bark to produce scaly bark symptoms may occur at any time. Unfavourable cultural conditions and poor husbandry greatly encourage the spread and development of *F. stilboides*. Weakening due to the wind and insect damage and poor nutritional status of the soil may all predispose coffee trees to infection. Prolific weed growth, excessive mulch and irregular de-suckering and pruning enhance the micro-climatic conditions necessary for infection.

Control: Principle control methods are by sanitation and improved cultural practices. Pruning tools should be sterilized with methylated spirit between each tree and diseased wood should be excised and destroyed by burning. In cases of Storey's bark disease complete uprooting and destruction of infected plants is considered a drastic remedy since new, healthy suckers can often be brought up once the diseased areas have been excised. Trees with severe trunk infection or collar rot should, however, be uprooted and burnt. Pruning off branches affected by scaly bark may prevent spread of the fungus and remove a source of infection for the two other symptoms. In all cases where this surgery is practiced it is recommended that the scars be dressed with a fungicidal paint prepared by mixing 1 teaspoonful of Captan 50 in 125 ml tung or linseed oil. This paint should also be used in routine desuckering and major pruning of infected trees. Reduction in the acidity of the soil by using alkaline fertilizer such as C.A.N. instead of A.S.N. with the possible addition of lime in extreme cases, is recommended both to improve the nutritional status of the trees and to inhibit fungal development which may result in collar rot. Sisal waste mulch may also be used for this purpose but care should be taken to avoid spreading it too close to the bases of the trees. Although extensive research has been undertaken in Malawi, as yet no truly resistant variety of *Coffea arabica* has been found. In addition to the above sanitation measures chemical treatment is therefore recommended where this is economically feasible. Spraying of suckers kept for conversion with 0,4 % captan or captafol (40 gms/10 l) at fortnightly intervals from their emergence to bark maturation will effectively prevent Storey's bark disease.

Gibberella xylarioides Heim & Saccas

Conidial state *Fusarium xylarioides* Stey.

This fungus causes a severe tracheomycosis of coffee in Central-, West- and East Africa, notably Zaire, Central African Republic, Guinea and the Ivory Coast. *Coffea canephora, C. liberica* and *C. arabica* are affected and some resistant varieties of the former have been reported.

On potato sucrose agar colonies are pale to beige with sparse white mycelium, a purple discolouration develops later with dark bluish-black stromata in which perithecia are embedded. Macroconidia fusoid, falcate, 2–3 septate, 20–25 x 4–5 μ. A male strain exists in which conidia are longer and straighter, 5–7 septate, 62–100 x 3.5–4–5 μ. Chlamydospores, oval to globose, smooth or roughened, 10–15 x 8–10 μ, these are rare but may occur in male conidia.

Perithecia violaceous, globose, with a flattened base, occuring in groups, 230–350 μ in diameter. Asci cylindrical to clavate. 70–110 x 7–10 μ containing 6–8 fusoid, hyaline to straw coloured, 1 septate ascospores, 15–20 x 5–6.5 μ.

Spread of disease is essentially similar to that of *F. stilboides* with invasion occurring in addition through soil. Control is also at present only by santitation, infected trees being uprooted and burnt. Use of resistant varieties is the best means of control.

Fusarium spp. pathogenic to coffee but of minor importance are *F. lateritium* (Nees.) which has been found attacking trees and berries in Malagasy Republik, W. Indies and Kenya, *F. javanicum* Koorders causing a root infection and wilt of adult coffee trees in India, *F. oxysporum* Schlect causing a foot rot and wilt of nursery seedlings in Kenya and *F. bulbigenum* Cke. et. Mass v. *coffeae* causing a root rot and wilt of adult trees in Puerto Rico. This latter species is considered synonymus with *F. oxysporum* Schl. f. sp. *coffeae* Garcia.

Literature

ALVAREZ GARCIA, LUIS A. (1945: Studies on Coffee Root disease in Puerto Rico. I. A coffee *Fusarium* wilt. J. Agric. Univ. of Puerto Rico. **29** (1) 1–29.
BAKER, CELIA J. (1970): Coffee bark Disease in Kenya. Kenya Coff. **35** (414), 226–228.
SIDDIQI, M. A., & D.G.M. CORBETT (1963): Coffee bark diseases in Nyasaland. I. Pathogenicity, description and identity of the causal organism. Trans. Br. mycol. Soc. **46** (1), 91–101.
SIDDIQI, M. A., & D.G.M. CORBETT (1968): Coffee bark diseases in Nyasaland. II. Properties of the causal organism. Trans., Br., mycol., Soc. **51** (1), 129–135.
CMI Descriptions nos 24, 29, 30.

Author: Celia J. Baker

Gibberella zeae (Schw.) Petch (Fig. 48)

Synonyms: *G. roseum* f. sp. *cerealis* (Cke.) Snyd. & Hansen = *G. saubinettii* (Mont.) Sacc.

Pyrenomycetes, Sphaeriales, Hypocreaceae
Condidial state *Fusarium graminearum* Schw. = *F. roseum* f. sp. *cerealis* "*Graminearum*" Hyphomycetes (H,4.C1.ph)

Disease: Gibberella stalk and ear rot; Kolbenfäule und Ährenfäule; flétrissement des plantules des céréales; añublo blanco del trigo.

Geographical distribution: Worldwide.

Host plants: Maize, oats, wheat, barley, rice, sorghum and many other Gramineae.

Symptoms: *G. zeae* and the other fungi mentioned herein cause seedling rots, damping off, stalk rots and ear rots. We, however, concentrate here on ear rots. Red discolouration mainly at the tip of the ears spreading downwards. The mycelium covers the kernels and is invading them, killing the embryo. The red colour is more due to the discoloured kernels than to the mycelium (Fig. 48, left & right). When the infection takes place early, the inner husks also become reddish and the husks adhere to the ears. Spores of the fungus are seldom found on the ears, but more often on the husks and shanks.

Fig. 48.

Many *Fusarium* species are causing ear rots. The effect on the seed is the same, but the discolouration of the ears is different. Some of them have a whitish, other a slight to deep pink colour. Most of the *Fusarium* species produce spores so that the species can be determined (p. 210). Three other fungi are furthermore causing ear rot: *Diplodia maydis (Berk.) Sacc.* is by far dominating, the other species are *Nigrospora oryzae* (Berk. & Br.) Petch and *Physalospora zeae* Stout. *Diplodia maydis* may easily be distinguished by the numerous pycnidia produced in the affected ears and husks. The colour of the mycelium is whitish. The spores are 2-celled and brown. Ears severely infected by *Nigrospora oryzae* are very light in weight. There is usually no mycelium to be seen between the rows of the kernels or on the kernels. The infection rather starts more from the bottom than at the tip of the ear. The disease may easily be identified by the numerous dark spores formed in dots around the central axis of the ears and also at the tip of the kernels. *Physalospora* kernel rot is similar to early stages of the *Diplodia* rot. Later, the husks adhere strongly to the ear and the ears are very low in weight. Later in autumn the fungus develops many small sclerotia which can be seen by the naked eye with the aid of a 10x magnifier, they are found to be irregular in shape. There are some more ear rots of minor importance.

Morphology: The fungus forms bluish-black spherical superficially born perithecia mainly on the stalks. They are much less numerous than the pycnidia of *D. maydis*. The asci contain 8 fusiform, 3 celled spores arranged in one row.

Physiological specialization: From Australia and the USA two separate races are known on maize and wheat and some Gramineae, respectively. In the USA (Pennsylvania) two races were detected in inbred lines and hybrids .

Epidemiology: *G. zeae* survives in the crop residues. Two years after infection, the fungus could be isolated from cereal residues. Chlamydospores are not formed, but persistent cells are present in the mycelium and the conidia. Perithecia and conidia are produced on crop residues, where they are formed preferably during warm and moist weather. In culture, *G. zeae* does not sporulate freely.
Mature ascospores extrude from the perithecia and are carried by wind to ears and stalks. Macroconidia are formed on old crop residues lying on the surface of the soil help to increase inoculum to infect the ears. On the residues conidia are also formed in the soil. The infection of the ears takes place after silking. But the fungus may penetrate any time up to the harvest, depending on the weather condition, entering through the tip of the ears. There seems to be no correlation between the percentage of infection and the coverage of the tips of the ears by the husks.
The occurence of *G. zeae* is fluctuating from year to year. Moist and rainy weather after pollination favours infection. The temperature needs not to be as high as with *Diplodia maydis*.

Control: As *G. zeae* is common on many crops, the chance to reduce inoculum by crop rotation is, therefore, small. To avoid spore dispersal from crop residues lying on the ground deep ploughing may be advantageous, also for *D. maydis*. Breeding for resistance against stalk rot does not necessarily include resistance against ear rot as well. But it can be assumed that inoculum is less when hybrids are used which are resistant against stalk rot. Seed treatment is obligatory in many countries to reduce soil-borne infection. Infected seed is usually intercepted by seed inspection, and such batches are not certified. Seed treatment in this case would be of little use because most seeds are no longer viable anyway.
No chemical control is recommended in the field.
Infected ears are highly toxic to man, swine and dogs and animals with a similar digestive system. Care should therefore be taken even when using slightly infected material.

Literature

CHRISTENSEN, J. J., & R. D. WILCOXSON (1966): Stalk rot of corn. Monograph no **3**, Am. Phytopath. Soc. 1–59.
KOEHLER, B. (1969): Corn ear rots in Illinois. Bull. **639**, Univ. Ill. Agric. Exp. Sta., 1–87.
KRÜGER, W. (1973): Maiskrankheiten, eine Broschüre für den Berater und Praktiker. Saaten Union, Hannover.
CMI Description no 384, and no 84 for *Diplodia maydis* (= *D. zeae* (Schw.) Lév.).

Author: W. Krüger

Other more important Gibberella spp. and tropical and subtropical crops:
Gibberella fujikuroi (Saw.) Wr. Conidial state *Fusarium moniliforme* Sheld. Ear rot on maize, foot rot and Bakanaë disease of rice. The *Fusarium* state is occuring widely on a large number of hosts and substrates. Ref.: CMI Description no 22.
G. fujikuroi (Saw.) Wr. var. *subglutinans* Edwards. Seedling blight, foot, stalk and kernel rot of maize and sorghum (foot and stem rot), stem and top rot ("pokkah boeng") of sugarcane. Also on many other important hosts like pineapple (fruit rot).

Glomerella cingulata (Stonem.) Spauld. et Schrenk (Figs. 49 a–c and plate 13 c)

Pyrenomycetes, Sphaeriales, Polystigmataceae
Conidial state *Colletotrichum gloeosporioides* Penz.
Coelomycetes (C,2.A1)

Disease: Black spot or anthracnose; Anthraknose; antracnosis; l'anthracnose.

Geographical distribution: A species which is very polyphagous and ubiquitous, this fungus is mainly present in warm and wet regions of the tropics and sub-tropics. It causes, for instance, a major disease of avocado in Israel, and of citrus in Zanzibar.

Host plants: *C. gloeosporioides* and its perfect state *Glomerella cingulata* have been recorded on a great variety of hosts such as citrus (anthracnose, wither-tip) *Annona* spp., avocado, mango, pawpaw, banana, rubber, tea, tomato etc.

Symptoms: A flesh rot affects the unripe fruits on the tree or after harvest, in association with Cercospora spot (p. 192), scab (p. 227), or other types of lesion.
At the approach of fruit maturity black spots appear, nearly circular, and 5–10 mm or more in diameter (Fig. 49a on Citrus, fruit and leaf symptoms). The centre of the spots is slightly sunken and in humid conditions small, rose-coloured masses of spores appear. The surface of the largest spots is often cracked and split. Beneath the skin the flesh is transformed and separates very easily from the healthy part. At first this blackish-brown zone is soft but later becomes firm and hard. The rot spreads rapidly towards the centre of the fruit. These spots accelerate fruit maturation and bring about a premature abscission. One or two spots are sufficient to result in the rapid invasion of nearly all the flesh. The soft flesh of the ripe avocado is an excellent substrate for the pathogen (Fig. 49b).

Fig. 49 a.   Fig. 49 b.

Fig. 49 c.

On young branches and twigs a drying of the tips is seen (dieback) accompanied by a blackening of the affected zones.
On leaves, round, rust-brown spots appear and rapidly spread, often resulting in leaf-fall.

On the panicles of mango flowers the parasite produces black spots which rapidly enlarge and lead to a desiccation of the inflorescences. On the unripe mangos the disease can appear from the time of fruit set until harvest. Very small brown or black spots form which are non-developing (latent form), and either isolated or grouped in a pattern (tear-stains) which is evidence of the distribution of spores in dew drops (Fig. 49c). On ripe fruits in the warehouse, large brown, nearly black spots develop on the epidermis from these latent infections, and coalesce. The rot, superficial at first, reaches the pulp below which browns and softens.

This is one of the most serious post-harvest diseases of mangos (Plate 13c).

There are resemblances to other diseases. On avocado and mango a drying of twigs is sometimes noticed which is of physiological origin, but resembles attacks of *C. gloeosporioides*. *Diplodia mangiferae* Koord. and *D. perseana* Delacr. are also responsible for a similar drying of the branch tips of mango and avocado, respectively.

Morphology: The conidial state *C. gloeosporioides* is extremely polymorphic and unstable. Generally the young mycelium is septate and hyaline, but light brown in older cultures. The conidia, individually colourless, are salmon red in mass, single-celled and oblong ($12–16$ x $4–5\,\mu$). They are grouped within acervulae ($90–270\,\mu$ diameter) which sometimes have sterile bristles.

The perithecia ($125–250\,\mu$) of the perfect state *G. cingulata* are spherical, brown, and isolated or grouped. The oblong asci ($50–70$ x $9–10\,\mu$) contain 8 curved, unicellular ascospores ($12–22$ x $4–5\,\mu$).

Physiological specialization: *C. gloeosporioides* comprises many races, more or less specialized according to host, and within any one race there are differences in pathogeneity. However, no precise classification has been made and the races are often very unstable in pure culture. It is also noticeable how, on mango, susceptibility to the disease varies according to variety.

Epidemiology: Fructifications of the fungus can be found on numerous organs of the avocado where the fungus lives saprophytically: dried twigs, dead areas of weak leaves, the surface of rotted fallen fruits. Sporulation occurs in wet weather and water disperses the conidia. *C. gloeosporioides* cannot penetrate an undamaged epidermis and infections on fruits approaching maturity occur through cracks (see Fig. 49 b) in the skin caused by fungi (*Cercospora, Sphaceloma*) or mechanical damage (wind rubbing).
Recently, Binyamini and Schiffmann-Nadel (1972) demonstrated the role of latent infections. In Israel, anthracnose spots appear as the fruits soften, and apparently without the presence of wounds. After depositing spores on fruits at all stages of development these workers observed rapid spore germination and the formation of appressoria on the wax layer covering the cuticle. At the time the fruits matured fine hyphae grew from the appressoria, passed through the cuticle and invaded the flesh. According to these authors no infection developed whilst the fruits were on the tree.

Control: It is recommended to cut out dead wood and frequently remove dried branches. Beyond this, no special treatment is necessary for the control of anthracnose when Cercospora spot or scab are already being treated. If these latter treatments are properly applied a large proportion of fruits are harvested without spots and they store and ripen well. However, the smallest wound or crack can rapidly result in an anthracnose rot when the fruit softens.
Systemic fungicides (thiabendazole, benomyl) applied after harvest have no effect on anthracnose of avocado, but the control of this disease on mango is effective with these products.
To control anthracnose of twigs and leaves regular sprays of maneb, zineb or mancozeb (0.2 kg/100 litres) are recommended. For the protection of flowers these same treatments must commence between the appearance of the flowers and blossoming. Depending upon climatic conditions the treatments must be repeated every 10 or 25 days.
Against attacks on unripe fruits copper sprays can be used in addition to the dithiocarbamates mentioned above. The oxychloride and oxide of copper, at rates of 0.2 to 0.3 kg/100 litres, are used with an added wetter and applied at a frequency which depends upon climatic conditions. Mango fruits can be given a post-harvest dip in water at 55 °C for 3–5 minutes, with or without the addition of fungicide (benomyl at 50 g/100 l). Storage is recommended at 10–12 °C according to the variety.

Literature

BINYAMINI, N., & MINA SCHIFFMANN-NADEL (1972): Latent infection in avocado fruit due to *Colletotrichum gloeosporioides*. Phytopathology **62**, 592–594.
CMI Description no 315.

Author: P. Frossard

Glomerella tucumanensis (Speg.) Arx & Müller

Synonym: *Physalospora tucumanensis* Speg.
Pyrenomycetes, Sphaeriales, Polystigmataceae
Conidial state *Colletotrichum falcatum* Went
Coelomycetes (C,2.A1)

Disease: Red rot of sugarcane; Rotfäule des Zuckerrohrs; pourriture rouge de cane à sucre; podredumbre roja de la caña de azúcar.

Geographical distribution: The disease has been reported from all sugarcane growing countries (CMI map no 186). It is one of the serious diseases in continental United States, Hawaii, Taiwan, Bangla Desh, India, Pakistan and Queensland (Australia).

Most serious effect of this disease is that it damages the buds of the seed cane. This gives a poor stand and consequently low yields. Sucrose content in the juice of diseased canes is considerably reduced. The disease also hampers juice extraction, lowes the purity and induces deleterious chemical changes.

Symptoms: The fungus infects both stalks and foliage. In India, it is mainly a problem of standing canes, while in Louisiana (USA) of the seed cane. In early stages, it is difficult to recognise the disease in the field. It is usually seen when the plant growth virtually stops and sucrose accumulation starts. The first external symptom is that the upper fully mature leaves of the plant wither at the tip and along the margins. Later on, the whole crown may wither and dry up. Typical symptoms of red rot are seen in stalks by splitting them longitudinally. These include reddening of internal tissues with white spots, specific to the disease, usually elongated at right angles to the long axis of the stalk. In the later stages, stalk becomes hollow and the fungus grows and sporulates abundantly in the lumen. At this stage, the rind shrinks and becomes longitudinally wrinkled with fruiting bodies of the fungus protruding out of the rind. Such canes are lighter in weight and break easily. The spread of red rot within the stalk depends on the resistance of the sugarcane variety and virulence of the pathogen. In susceptible varieties all internodes are affected, while in the resistant ones only some show the disease.

On the leaves, red rot fungus produces elongated reddish spots on the midribs where the pathogen produces abundant tiny carbonaceous fruiting bodies, the acervuli.

Morphology: The fungus grows and sporulates luxuriantly on oat-meal-agar. The hyphae are branched and septate. Numerous acervuli are produced on the surface of the medium. The conidia are hyaline, falcate or sickle shaped, single celled and 15 to 40 μ in length. The conidium usually possesses a large oil globule in the centre. Conidia develop in a mucilagenous matrix and spore masses are usually pink coloured. The acervuli are covered with brown to black, 3 to 4 septate setae, 100 to 200 μ long, with slightly bulbous base. The perfect stage occurs only rarely in the field.

Epidemiology: The annual recurrence of the disease is primarily through infected cane seed and secondary spread of the inoculum through rain, irrigation or flood water. Fungus can survive in soil on cane stubbles or trash only for a short period of time. Most common sites of infection of a stalk are the root primordia and leaf scars. On occasions initial infection has been traced to buds, growth rings and borer holes. When the fungus comes in contact with root primordia, leaf scars or buds under favourable weather conditions it enters into the host, spreads within the tissues to produce typical disease symptoms of rotting and drying of the affected stalk. However, if the infection occurs late in the season, the infection confines to a few millimetre depth in the nodal region, generally over root primordia or in the leaf scars. It is not easily discernible unless the rind is lightly scraped off.

Cut ends do not give any indication of this kind of infection. It is generally known as latent or incipient infection and is likely to be missed in case of seed selection except when one is vigilant. On planting, as the bud sprouts, the incipient infection is also activated and the pathogen spreads into the newly emerged shoot, to cause the disease..

Physiological specialization: Two types of races or strains, differing in colour and pathogenicity are usually encountered in nature. The light coloured race consists of virulent types. In nature probably new races are produced through mutations because the fungus is known to produce mutants in culture.

Control: Once the disease has appeared, it is almost impossible to control it even with fungicides, though infection on the leaf can be considerably reduced by spraying 1.0 % solution of copper oxychloride (50 % Cu) and cuprous oxide (50 % Cu).

However, red rot fungus can be eliminated from the seed material by the hot air treatment. The disease incidence can be reduced by taking precautions such as, (a) use of healthy seed. Any set showing reddening at the cut ends or at the nodal region should be discarded, (b) systematic roguing of diseased clumps throughout the season, (c) avoidance of planting of crop in fields where diseased crop stood previously, (d) discouraging ratooning of diseased crop, and (e) practicing two to three year crop rotation.

Literature

MARTIN, J. P., E. V. ABBOTT & G. H. HUGHES (1961): Sugarcane diseases of the world. Vol 1. Elsevier Pub. Company, Amsterdam.
SINGH, K. (1973): Hot air therapy against red rot. Plant Dis. Reptr. **27,** 220–222.
STEIB, R. J., & S. J. P. CHILTON (1951): Infection of sugarcane stalks by the red rot fungus *Physalospora tucumanensis* Speg. Phytopathology **41,** 522–528.
CMI Description no 133.

Author: Kishan Singh

Other more important Glomerella spp. on tropical and subtropicals crops:
Glomerella gossypii Edg. Conidial state *Colletotrichum.* Anthracnose on all above ground parts of cotton, including bolls. CMI map no 317.

Leveillula taurica (Lév.) Arn. (Plate 7 b)

Pyrenomycetes, Erysiphales, Erysiphaceae
Conidial state *Oidiopsis taurica* (Lév.) Salm.
Hyphomycetes (H,2.A1)

Disease: Powdery mildew; echter Mehltau; Oidiopsis blanc; Oidio.

Geographical distribution: Distribution differs widely on various hosts. Most widely distributed on *Capsicum annuum,* in temperate, semi-arid and tropical zones. Centres of distribution are the drier regions of Central and Western Asia and of the Mediterranean area. Epidemic outbreaks on major hosts (tomatoes, eggplants, cucurbits, cotton) are largely restricted to these regions (CMI map no 217).

Host plants: Host range comprises about 700 species in almost 60 families, mostly herbaceous plants, but olive and some woody perennials are also affected. Hosts most numerous in the Compositae (149 hosts) and Leguminosae (112), but economically most important hosts occur in the Solanaceae (pepper, tomato, eggplant), and Malvaceae (cotton, okra). Among monocotyledons, some species of *Allium,* but not Gramineae, are sometimes affected.

Symptoms: Chiefly affects leaf blades, less frequent on petioles, stalks, flower parts and pods. On leaf blades, most common symptom more or less brightly yellow spots on the upper leaf surface, and a powdery covering of these spots on the lower leaf surface (Plate 7 b).
On some hosts, among them pepper, brownish grainy discolorations on tissue underlying the powdery covering on lower leaf surfaces.
Shedding of affected leaves prominent only in pepper, occurs also in olive. On other hosts, affected leaves usually dry up and persist on the plants. On artichokes, white, indeterminate flecks on lower leaf surfaces. Older leaves show symptoms first.

Morphology: Mycelium mostly endophytic, and then intercellular in mesophyll of ventral leaf tissue. When growth is ectophytic, appressoria and whitish to yellowish mycelial mats formed on one or both leaf sides.

Multicellular conidiophores, 50–70 μ long, growing out of stomata or superficial mycelium.

Cylindrical or ellipsoid conidia of the Oidiopsis type, borne singly, more rarely in short chains; hyaline, greatly varying in size, most common measurements 40–80 x 12–18 μ. Cleistothecia, rare on many hosts, mostly on ventral side of the leaves; at first globose, later concave, most frequently 160–200 μ in diameter. Numerous short, hyaline appendages, densely interwoven. Number of asci highly variable (6–40); mostly contain two ellipsoid ascospores measuring 20–40 x 15–20 μ.

Physiological specialization: Specialization of individual isolates of *L. taurica* is far from uniform in various countries. Can pass freely from one solanaoeaus host to another, from malvaceous crops to tomato. Transmission from Compositae to Solanaceae apparently rare. No generally accepted distinctions between well-defined *formae speciales* or races so far available.

Epidemiology: Basic aspects of outbreaks of *L. taurica:*

a) Many of the major host crops grow in all or most seasons of the year. b) Infection mounts as crop matures. c) Extremely wide host range of many isolates. Therefore sources of infection usually ample and not a limiting factor. Infection predominantly by aerial dispersal of conidia. Many crops affected both under dry and humid conditions (pepper, eggplant, sesame), but on many others outbreaks linked with dry conditions (tomato, lucerne, guar, cotton). Conidia are capable of germinating at extremely low humidities, but germinate much better at high humidities. However, spread of conidia in some instances known to be favoured by dry conditions. At temperatures most favourable for germination of conidia (about 15–25 °C), incubation periods are 10 to 12 days.

Control: Only few varieties resistant to *L. taurica* so far available. Early artichoke varieties with almost entire leaf blades and no spines more resistant than late varieties with lobate leaves. Among tomato varieties, VF groups of canning tomatoes extremely susceptible. Eggplant varieties also differing greatly in susceptibility.

Proximity of young solanaceous or malvaceous crops to older crops of the same family should be avoided. Overhead sprinkling preferable to other types of irrigation on crops more severely attacked under dry conditions (tomatoes).

Control treatments not usually required before initial third of growing period completed.

Sulphur dusts and sprays are effective, but tend to scorch foliage and fruit under warm and dry conditions. Numerous systemic fungicides now being tsted, with promising results.

Literature

BLUMER, S. (1967): Echte Mehltaupilze (Erysiphaceae). VEB Gustav Fischer Verlag, Jena.

CICCARONE, A. (1953): La "nebbia" del Carciofo (*Cynara scolymus* L.) e del Cardo (*Cynara cardunculus* L.). Boll. Staz. Patol. Veg., Roma, ser. **3**, 9, 163–204.

HIRATA, K. (1966): Host range and geographical distribution of the powdery mildews. Fac. Agric. Niigata Univ.

NOUR, M. A. (1959): Studies on the specialization of *Sphaerotheca fuliginea* (Schlecht.) Poll. and other powdery mildews. Trans. Brit. mycol. Soc., **42**, 90–94.

PALTI, J. (1971): Biological characteristics, distribution and control of *Leveillula taurica* (Lév.). Arn. Phytopathologia Mediterranea, **10**, 139–153.

REUVENI, R., & J. ROTEM (1973): Epidemics of Leveillula taurica on tomatoes and peppers as affected by the conditions of humidity. Phytopath. Z., **76**, 153–157.

CMI Description no 182.

Author: J. Palti

Microcyclus ulei (P. Henn.) v. Arx (Figs. 50–51)

Synonym: *Dothidella ulei* P. Henn.
Loculoascomycetes, Dothideales, Dothideaceae.
Conidial state *Fusicladium macrosporum* Kuyper
Hyphomycetes (H,4.B2.sy)

Disease: South American leaf blight of rubber; Südamerikanische Blattkrankheit des Kautschukbaums; Flétrissure sudaméricaine des feuilles de l'hévéa; Enfermedad sudamericana de hojas del cauchero.

Geographical distribution: This most serious disease occurs only in tropical America: Bolivia, Brazil, Columbia, Costa Rica, French Guiana, Guatemala, Guyana, Honduras, Mexico, Nicaragua, Panama, Peru, Surinam, Trinidad and Venezuela (CMI map no 27).

Host plants: The pathogen is restricted to the genus *Hevea* and the only economic host is the Para rubber tree (*Hevea brasiliensis*). It can be found on three wild *Hevea* spp. in the primary forests of the Amazon and Orinoco river basins. The disease is an ever present threat to the important natural rubber growing industries of S.E. Asia and W. Africa.

Symptoms: The symptoms are most conspicuous on the leaves. On young, red pigmented ones, almost black powdery conidial lesions are formed and the leaves fall. On older, pale green leaves these lesions are dull olive-green (Fig. 50) and the dry conidia are easily dislodged from them. Later, if the leaves do not fall, dark stromatic, pustular masses of the ascospore stage develop, mainly on the lower leaf surface; they often form in rings and round the edges of a shothole. All these fructifications also occur on green stems, inflorescences and young fruit. Severe infection leads to stem dieback and death of both young and mature trees. The fructification symptoms are characteristic and need not be confused with any other rubber leaf disease.

Morphology: The conidia are particularly distinctive (Fig. 51). They are mostly 2-celled, greyish, ellipsoidal, 23–63 x 5–10 μ; the proximal cell is broader, with a thickened truncate end and an extremely distinctive single twist, giving the conidium a bent appearance in flat view. The ascospores

Fig. 50.

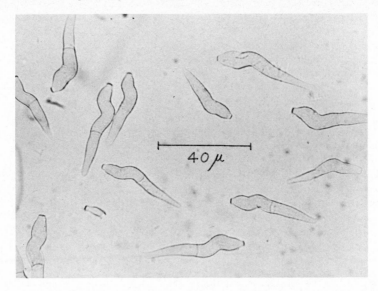

Fig. 51.

are 2-celled, hyaline, ellipsoidal, 12–20 x 2–5 μ, with the longer cell (with a more acute apex) lying towards the base of the ascus. Conidia are also formed, before the perithecial stage.

Physiological specialization: Four physiologic races have been described but they are insufficiently characterized. All commercial rubber based on Asian clones grown outside the Americas is known to be highly susceptible to the common or wild type race. It is not known whether the fungus is heterothallic.

Epidemiology: The disease is spread through the dry, air-dispersed conidia but the epidemiological role of the ascospore, which can cause infection, is unknown. The conidia have a diurnal periodicity (most marked on dry days) with a maximum concentration at 10,00 hours, and low numbers in the evening, night and early morning. Rain causes large, transient increases in numbers of dispersed conidia, especially in the forenoon and early afternoon. Short periods of comparatively low temperatures (13–16 °C) are apparently necessary for triggering ascospore release. Conidial germination is complete in 3–4 hours at saturation and an optimum temperature of 24 °C. Leaf penetration of the host is via the cuticle by the conidia which are viable for 2–4 days at very low light intensities. Leaves more than 8–10 days old become increasingly resistant to infection. The leaf lesions which result begin to form conidia within a week of infection and the perfect or ascospore stage is mature about 8 weeks later. The diurnal periodicity of the ascospore has now been described (K. H. Chee, in press). The maximum concentration is at about 06.00 hours. The concentration falls after dawn on sunny days but on overcast ones it can remain high for most of the day.

Since the pathogen infects young leaves it causes the phenomenon known in rubber as secondary leaf fall which can also be caused by other fungi and other factors. This abnormal leaf fall needs to be distinguished from the natural wintering of the trees. The disease can also be serious on young trees which are not yet wintering and it can completely destroy rubber nurseries. Where rainfall is less than 3–4 mm per day conidial sporulation is very low or absent; with a rainfall twice this amount it is very high and the disease is severe. A dry season of 4 consecutive months with less than 70–80 mm rainfall per month limits the disease on mature trees. Where no such dry season exists incidence is extremely severe where the annual rainfall is about 2000 mm or more.

Control: Failure to control South American leaf blight in Central and S. America has been one of the main factors which has prevented the establishment of an extensive and viable natural rubber industry in this part of the world. In certain regions where there is a long dry season (notably in parts of Central America) the high yielding but extremely susceptible clones from Asia can be grown, provided that they are not severely infected as young trees. Chemical control has been used only in nurseries where weekly applications, in wet periods, of formulations containing zinc ethylene bisdithiocarbamate are effective. But generally, resistant material must always be used. High resistance from wild populations of *H. brasiliensis, H. pauciflora* and *H. benthamiana* (especially from the Ford clone 4542 of the last species) has been bred into some of the older Asian commercial clones. Many clones of varying resistance are now available but their yields are low and only the first generation has been adequately tested for yield and other characteristics. Nothing is known of the inheritance of resistance; it appears to be governed by dominant genes in the immune Ford 4542. One control method (used with some success) is to bud a resistant crown on to a high yielding (Asian) but susceptible, panel or trunk clone. Although the method has some disadvantages in terms of both labour and cost it could reduce the time required to produce an adequately resistant tree which also has a yield comparable to present day commercial clones which have been selected in Asia. Selection, testing and breeding against South American leaf blight is continuing in Brazil, Guatemala, Liberia, Malaysia and Sri Lanka. Strict quarantine measures against the disease are in force to protect rubber grown in the Old World.

Literature

HOLLIDAY, P. (1970): South American Leaf Blight (*Microcyclus ulei*) of *Hevea brasiliensis*. Phytopathology Pap. **13**, CMI.
CMI Description no 225.

Author: Paul Holliday

Mycosphaerella arachidis Deighton (Plate 7 c)

Synonym: *Mycosphaerella arachidicola* W. A. Jenkins
Conidial state *Cercospora arachidicola* Hori

Disease: Early leafspot; Braunfleckigkeit; taches brunes des feuilles; manchas pardas de las hojas.

Mycosphaerella berkeleyii W. A. Jenkins

Conidial state *Cercosporidium personatum* (Berk. & Curt.) Deighton = *Cercospora personata* Berk. & Curt.
Loculoascomycetes, Dothideales, Dothideaceae (for the perfect states)
Hyphomycetes (H,2.E2.sy and H,2.C2.ph, respectively).

Disease: Late leafspot; Schwarzfleckigkeit; taches noires des feuilles; manchas negras de las hojas.

Geographical distribution: *Cercospora* leafspots occur wherever groundnuts occur. The distribution of *Cercospora* leafspots is presented in CMI maps nos 152 and 166.

Host plants: *Arachis hypogaea* L. is the principal host of economic importance. Several other *Arachis* species are natural hosts.

Symptoms: The most conspicuous symptoms occur on leaves, but symptoms are commonly present on petioles, stipules, stems and pegs. Juvenile lesions are first apparent as slightly pale spots on adaxial leaf surfaces. Mature lesions, 1 to 10 mm or more in diameter, are characterized by a necrotic center, surrounded by a yellow halo of varying intensity. The most consistently dependable diagnostic characteristic for macroscopic identification of *Cercospora arachidicola* and *Cercosporidium personatum* is the color or the lesion on the abaxial leaf surface (Plate 7 c). *C. arachidicola* lesions are dark brown, and *C. personatum* lesions are black.

Although groundnuts are susceptible to a number of foliar disease organisms, it is unlikely that one would confuse *Cercospora* leafspot with any other fungal disease of groundnuts. However, certain chemical phytotoxicity symptoms, particularly those caused by some organophosphorus compounds, are nearly identical to *Cercospora* leafspot symptoms.

Morphology: Rapid identification is accomplished by studying the conidial size, shape, color, and number of septa. Conidia of *C. arachidicola* are colorless to slightly olivaceous, obclavate to clavate, often curved, 35 –108 x 2 –5.4 μ, and 4 to 12 septate. Conidia of *C. personatum* are somewhat obclavate but more generally cylindrical with somewhat attenuated tips, pale brown to dilutely olivaceous, 18 –60 x 5 –11 μ and one to eight septate. Conidia of *C. arachidicola* are usually produced on the adaxial surface of leaves, and *C. personatum* conidia are usually produced on the abaxial leaf surface.

Physiological specialization: Specialization on the basis of pathogenicity has not been reported.

Epidemiology: Both fungi are capable of surviving in crop residue from season to season. Although the perfect state has been described for both fungi, it has been observed only occasionally. *C. arachidicola* and *C. personatum* both produce chlamydospores, and this is probably a means of survival. Additionally, the production of secondary conidia by *C. arachidicola* is a potential survival mechanism.

The first macroscopically visible symptoms do not usually appear until approximately a month after planting. Frequently the appearance of initial symptoms coincides with the onset of flowering. There is a paucity of knowledge about the primary source of inoculum. Although it has been proven that ascospores constitute one source of primary inoculum, it is probable that there are other more significant sources.

After the onset of the disease, conidia are produced on necrotic lesions and disseminated principally by wind, splashing rain, and insects. Peak spore dispersal periods are associated with the end of the dew period in the morning and with the onset of rainfall. Penetration occurs primarily through stomata on the adaxial leaf surface.

The incubation period varies depending on various factors, but it usually ranges from 8–14 days. Subsequent sporulation is enhanced by long periods of high relative humidity.

Control: Epidemic progress is delayed by crop rotation and deep burial of crop residue. A considerable amount of research effort has been devoted to a search for disease resistance. However, at the present time all commercially acceptable varieties are highly susceptible to *C. arachidicola* and *C. personatum*.

The principal method of disease control is based on the systematic application of fungicidal dusts and sprays at intervals ranging from 7–21 days. In some groundnut areas disease control is accomplished with dusts containing sulfur or a combination of copper and sulfur, Benomyl and chlorothalonil are two of the most effective sprayable fungicides in current use. The effectiveness of benomyl is often enhanced by the addition of a non-phytotoxic oil. Unfortunately the future of benomyl as an effective leafspot fungicide is in doubt because of the recent appearance of benomyl tolerant strains of *C. arachidicola*.

A leafspot spray advisory based on daily temperature und relative humidity has been developed by scientists in Georgia (USA) in an effort to obtain effective control with a minimum number of fungicide applications.

Literature

DEIGHTON, F. C. (1967): Studies on Cercospora and allied genera. II. *Passalora, Cercosporidium,* and some species of *Fusicladium* on *Euphorbia.* CMI Paper No. **112.**
DEIGHTON, F. C. (1967): New names in Mycosphaerella (*M. arachidis* and *M. pruni-persici*) and validation of *M. rosicola.* Trans. Brit. mycol. Soc. **50,** 328–329.
GARREN, K. H., & C. R. JACKSON (1973): Peanut diseases, p. 429–494. In APREA. Peanuts-culture and uses. Stone Printing Company, Roanoke, Virginia. USA.
JENSEN, R. E., & L. W. BOYLE (1966): A technique for forecasting leafspot on peanuts. Plant. Dis. Reptr. **50,** 810–814.
SMITH, D. H., & F. L. CROSBY (1973): Aerobiology of two peanut leafspot fungi. Phytopathology **63,** 703-707.
CMI Descriptions nos 411 & 412.

Author: D. H. Smith

Mycosphaerella musicola Leach (Plates 7 d, 8 a)

Loculoascomycetes, Dothideales, Dothideaceae
Conidial state *Cercospora musae* Zimm.
Hyphomycetes (H,2.E2.sy)

Disease: Banana leaf spot; Sigatoka-Krankheit der Banane; Cercosporiose du bananier; la Sigatoka de la platanera.

Geographical distribution: Observed and described for the first time in 1902 in Java, the Sigatoka disease spread from Indo-Malaysia to the Pacific area (Fiji 1912, Australia 1924), and has been in America since 1933 and in Africa since 1938. In 1973 leaf spot is present throughout the tropics where the banana is cultivated, and is absent only from Egypt, Israel and the Canary Islands (CMI map no 7).

Host plants: *Musa* spp.

Symptoms: Leaf spot, also known as Sigatoka, is a foliar disease characterized by well-defined, necrotic, and generally elongated spots (Plate 7 d). The lesions pass through the following successive stages: I. Small, yellowish-green flecks, 1 mm across, and scarcely visible to the eye. II. These flecks elongate to become yellow streaks, 3–4 x 1 mm. III. The streak-like lesions enlarge to become elongated spots of a rusty brown colour. IV. The spots reach full size, 12–15 x 2–5 mm, with a deep brown to black centre and a yellow halo which appears water-soaked. V. The central area dries, collapses, turns grey, and is surrounded by a black ring and often a yellow halo. This fully-developed spot persists after the leaf desiccates.
On normal, non-flowering plants in commercial plantations, the ,,cigar'' (the rolled heart leaf) and the two or three youngest unrolled leaves look healthy, the first streaks are visible in the region of the fourth to sixth leaf, and necrotic spots are present on the sixth to the eighth leaf. This distribution is for unsprayed plants in periods which favour the disease, but it can vary greatly with season, plant vigour and the efficiency of spray programmes.
The location of spots on individual leaves is important because it provides a means of identifying the origin of the infections. It is possible, for example, to distinguish attacks at the tip of a leaf (,,tip-spotting'') caused by ascospore infections from attacks arranged in lines (,,line-spotting'') which result from conidial infections. When the number of spots is too many for the area of the leaf they become confluent, resulting in necrotic areas not surrounded by black rings.
Serious attacks cause a premature drying of the leaves, and the reduction of photosynthetic area leads to a loss of weight of harvested bunches of fruit. Also the interval from flowering to harvest is

extended. Much more serious is the effect on fruit quality; in the severest cases the pulp of the fruit acquires an abnormal salmon-yellow colour (Plate 8 a). The fruits ripen prematurely, either on the standing crop, or a few hours after cutting or during refrigerated transportation.

Morphology: The fructifications of the pathogen appear as small black dots in the middle of the spots. The conidial state *Cercospora musae* Zimm. is characterized by the production of small, hyaline, pluricellular, rod-like spores 20–80 μ long, which emerge through stomata and are grouped in sporodochia on the leaf surface. The perfect form *Mycosphaerella musicola* Leach was not described until 1941. Ascospores are produced in flask-shaped perithecia embedded in the necrotic tissues of the spots. The neck of the perithecium emerges at the level of the stomata. The hyaline, bicellular ascospores are approximately 12–15 μ long.
(See also *M. fijiensis, p. 132*).

Epidemiology: Under natural conditions conidia can survive 3–4 weeks on the leaf surface and ascospores 8 weeks within the perithecia, if rain does not release them.
The conidia form on both surfaces of spots which have reached or passed stage III (brown spots); sporulation is maximal at stage IV (black spots). The spots can produce several crops of spores during 20–30 days if conditions are favourable. Moisture is a major factor: conidia form rapidly and in large numbers when the leaves are covered with a film of water, but they can be produced on dry leaves if the humidity exceeds 98 % R.H. The optimum temperature lies between 24 and 30 °C. Sporulation is much reduced below 20 °C but does not cease, and in northern Queensland (Australia) conidia form at night at temperatures in the range 11–16 °C.
Perithecia are normally found in the dried areas of the leaves where there is a concentration of spots; very few perithecia develop on isolated, well-spaced spots. Important seasonal variations in the formation of perithecia have been observed in Jamaica, Guinea and Central America, with a maximum production in warm and wet periods and a minimum in cool, dry seasons. According to Stover the number of perithecia is greatly diminished, irrespective of the rainfall, when the minimum temperature is below 21 °C.
Rain and dew play major roles in the release and dispersal of conidia. When mature, these spores are easily liberated by water. Transmission is chiefly from the diseased leaves on large plants to the young, healthy leaves on smaller plants below them. Ripe ascospores are released when leaves are wet, rain being much more effective than dew. Their ejection commences about half an hour after rain begins and continues for several hours. The ascospores are caught in air currents which can carry them great distances. The conidia are, however, more abundant than the ascospores. Water which is charged with conidia flows along the leaves and between the folds of the „cigar" (see above) where many spores are deposited in water retained by capillarity in vertical lines in the folds. This results in the characteristic pattern of conidial infections in lines parallel to the border of the leaf on the left lamina, and oblique, with respect to the central vein, on the right side. This type of infection, "line-spotting", is common on small plants growing under older diseased plants. Ascospores caught in air currents are deposited on the lower surface of unrolled young leaves, more abundantly at the tip of the leaf than at the base, and more abundantly near the borders than near the main vein. The result is "tip-spotting". The "cigars" can also be infected by ascospores. It is believed that the two youngest leaves constitute the main centre of infection although infections are possible on older leaves. The infections can arise on both faces of the leaves but penetration is more frequent on the lower surface where there is a greater number of stomata. Conidia require a film of water on the leaf for germination whereas ascospores germinate at 95 % R. H. and above. The optimum temperature is from 25 to 29 °C; germination fails below 12 and above 35 °C. Ascospores (2–3 hours) germinate faster than conidia (6 hours). The growth of germ tubes is arrested by dry conditions but recovers when the leaves are re-wetted by dew, rain, or irrigation water. Four to six days elapse before the germ tube produces a terminal appressorium above a stomata. An infection hypha develops from the appressorium and passes through the stomatal aperture, the slight gradient in humidity attracting germ tubes to the stomata. In the absence of

dew penetration is impossible. The incubation time varies widely, from 15 to 70 days; it is shortest when both temperature and humidity are high, when infection has been intense, and when the plants are growing rapidly. It seems that a high humidity which allows the leaves to remain wet for a long time, and temperatures between 23 and 28 °C, are particularly favourable conditions for the establishment and progress of banana leaf spot.

Control: Sanitation methods: The removal and destruction of diseased leaves, as advised in the past, does not seem to reduce leaf spot when the disease is widespread.

Cultural practices: Measures to encourage plant growth and reduce humidity in the banana gardens (improvement of drainage, use of fertilizers, reduced density of plants and suckers) are ineffective in the face of attacks in periods favourable to the disease.

Resistance: All commercial varieties of dessert banana in the triploid group AAA are very susceptible to leaf spot. Resistance varies among the plantains: it is considerable in group ABB and generally average in group AAB. The seed bananas *Musa balbisiana, M. acuminata* and *M. textilis* are immune. In the search for hybrids resistant to Panama disease, work in Jamaica since 1930 has produced two tetraploids (AAAA), 1C2 and Bodles Altafort, which are much more resistant to banana leaf spot than commercial varieties.

Unfortunately, certain serious faults make their further exploitation impossible.

Chemical control: Since 1950 the work of the IFAC has resulted in the development of a new method to replace the application of Bordeaux mixture, which was inefficient against ascospore attacks. On small areas applications of 15–20 l/ha of pure mineral oil applied with knapsack mist sprayers have been very effective. On large areas applications of 10–14 l/ha are applied by aeroplanes fitted with Micronair atomizers. Aerial application is better because the diameter of the droplets is very uniform, as is the cover achieved on the young leaves.

Mineral oil used alone has curative properties. It is not a fungicide but acts fungistatically, penetrating to the interior of the leaves and impeding the development of the fungus without killing it. Applied during incubation it delays or prevents the appearance of symptoms. The yellow streaks at stage II are virtually prevented from further development if sprayed with oil, and therefore an attack which is already in progress can be stopped, which was impossible with Bordeaux mixture. The oil has no or very little antisporulant action against the conidiophores, but its protective role is not negligible for it slows down and diminishes various stages of infection (germination, penetration).

The addition of a fungicide (copper, maneb) to the oil can improve antisporulant activity, but this is not always an economical proposition.

The use of atomized oil is not without problems. In particular this technique is attributed with responsibility for severe phytotoxicity which results in the scorching of leaves and fruits, accelerated senescence of foliage and loss of crop weight. Such damage is often associated with avoidable operating conditions: too frequent application of excessive quantities, low-quality oil, treatment in hot, dry, sunny weather.

Other techniques have been adopted in Central America where a mixture of water, fungicide and emulsified oil, the proportions of which vary with local conditions, is atomized at 20–50 l/ha. The dose of oil is increased when the disease is severe; in the dry season, when there is a risk of phytotoxicity, the quantity of oil is reduced and supplemented by fungicide (dithiocarbamate). The amount of oil ranges from 5.6 to 11.7 l/ha, and the emulsifying agent Triton X45 is added to the oil at a rate of 0.75–1 % by volume of oil. The fungicides maneb, Dithane M45 or Metiram are used at 2–4 kg/ha. Aerial spraying by plane or helicopter is usually repeated at intervals of 21 days but this can be reduced to 14 days in cases of severe outbreaks.

Suspensions of Benonyl in pure oil (300 g/14 l/ha) have, when applied by air, given a large curative effect which has allowed the spray interval to be extended to 3–4 weeks. However, the Benomyl formulation is difficult to suspend in the oil and so Peltis is preferred (40 % oil suspension of thiophanate-methyl) at 800 g/ha. Cypendazol, Carbendazim and Tecto-flow are equally promising, but their cost is high.

Mycosphaerella fijiensis Morelet

Loculoascomycetes, Dothideales, Dothideaceae

Disease: Black leaf streak; Schwarzstreifigkeit; Maladies des raies noires; rayado negro del platanero.

Geographical distribution: It was as recently as 1963 that this "new disease" was identified by Rhodes on banana in Fiji where it has since completely superseded Sigatoka disease (banana leaf spot). It is now present in Hawaii, Polynesia (Tahiti, Samoa, Tonga), Melanesia (New Caledonia, New Guinea), the Philippines, Malaysia, Taiwan and Singapore. It has not yet been found in Australia, Africa or America.

Symptoms: The first symptoms appear on the lower surface of the third and fourth leaves as small streaks, 20 x 2 mm, deep brown-red to black. Only rarely are yellow streaks seen which resemble those of leaf spot (Sigatoka). When there are few lesions they develop into elliptical, necrotic streaks with a grey centre, bordered with a thin black ring around which is a yellow halo. Usually the streaks are very numerous on the left side and at the tip of a leaf, and if sufficiently dense the entire leaf blackens, dries and is dead 3–4 weeks after the symptoms appeared. The damage is identical to that of leaf spot, namely, serious defoliation and premature maturation of the fruit.

Morphology: The perfect state *Mycosphaerella fijiensis* is almost identical to *M. musicola*. The conidial (imperfect) state *Cercospora* sp. can be differentiated from *C. musae* by microscopic features which are distinguishable by a mycologist. The main difference visible with the aid of a magnifying glass is that whereas the conidiophores of *C. musae* are grouped in dense clusters produced from a dark stroma, those of the *Cercospora* causing black leaf streak are isolated or in groups of 2–8, emerging from stomata rather than a stroma.

Epidemiology: The biological data, still rather fragmentary, shows that the stages of lesion development are like those of leaf spot disease. However, sporulation occurs sooner and perithecia are more abundant, and secondary infections occur on old leaves more frequently than with leaf spot. Ascospores are the main source of infection and are released when the humidity is high, especially in rainy weather. Their production is seasonal, reaching a peak in the period November-December-January in Fiji and Hawaii.

Control: Sanitation: As with leaf spot the destruction of affected leaves is advised, with the object of eliminating sources of ascospores.
Resistance: It has been shown that many varieties of banana are either susceptible or very susceptible to black leaf streak; this is particularly true of all commercial varieties (Gros Michel, the Cavendish group, Cocos etc.). The pathogen is more virulent and attacks more genotypes than *M. musicola*. The tetraploid 'IC2' is almost immune to leaf spot but is susceptible to black leaf streak, just as are numerous plantains (Silk, Pome). Even *M. balbisiana* has been found with lesions on its lower leaves.
Chemical control: Methods used against leaf spot (oil alone, oil-fungicide emulsions) have also been used against black leaf streak, but the latter disease is more difficult to control at an acceptable level. It has proved necessary to increase the dose and shorten the interval between sprays. The following Table compares recommendations, against black leaf streak in the Philippines and against leaf spot in Central America, for aerial application of fungicides in oil emulsions. These recommendations provide better control in Central America.

Comparison of recommendations against leaf spot (Central America) and leaf streak (Philippines) diseases of banana

Treatments	Central America	Philippines
Fungicide[1] (kg/ha)	1.7–2.0	2.2 – 3.4
Oil (l/ha)	7.0–9.4	14.0–16.4
Total volume (l/ha)	23.4	28 –47
Width of sprayed swath (m)	24 –30	18
Time between applications (days)	16 –23	8 10

[1]Dithane M45, Metiram M or Maneb

Benomyl at 150–300 g/ha has given interesting results and could provide improvements in control.

Literature

MELIN, P. (1970): Nouvelles perspectives de lutte contre la cercosporiose du bananier. Fruits **25,** 141–145.
MELIN, P. (1973): Etude de nouveaux fongicides sur la cercosporiose du bananier. Fruits **28,** 429–431.
MEREDITH, M. A. (1970): Banana leaf spot disease (Sigatoka) caused by *Mycosphaerella musicola* Leach. Phytopathological Papers no **11**
STOVER, R. H. (1971): Banana leaf spot caused by *Mycosphaerella musicola* contrasting features of Sigatoka and Black leaf streak control. Plant. Dis. Rept. **55,** 437–439.
STOVER, R. H. (1972): Banana, Plantain and Abaca diseases. See p. 8.
WARDLAW, C. W. (1972): Banana disease including Plantain and Abaca. Longman London.
CMI Descriptions nos 414 & 413.

Author: P. Frossard

Other more important species of the extensive genus Mycosphaerella on tropical and subtropical crops:

Mycosphaerella bolleana Higg. Conidial state *Cercospora bolleana* (Thüm.) Speg. Angular leaf spot of fig.

Mycosphaerella caricae Syd. Conidial state *Fusicladium caricae* (Speg.) Sacc. Leaf and fruit spots of papaw.

M. caryophyllata Bour. & Heim. Leaf spots of clove trees.

M. colocasiae Hara. Leaf spot of taro.

M. gossypina (Atk.) Earle. Conidial state *Cercospora gossypina* Cke. Leaf spot of cotton.

M. melonis (Pass.) Chiu & Walker. Conidial state *Phyllosticta citrullina* Chester. Gummy stem blight of cucumber and other Cucurbitaceae.

M. mori (Fuckel) Wolf. Conidial state *Cylindrosporium mori* (Lév.) Berl. (CM.E). Leaf spot of mulberry. Some more *Mycosphaerella* spp. are listed on this host.

Physalospora rhodina (Berk. & Curt.) Cke.

Pyrenomycetes, Sphaeriales, Polystigmataceae (or Amphisphaeriaceae)
Conidial state: *Diplodia natalensis* Evans (this fungus is now considered a synonym of *Botryodiplodia theobromae* Pat., p. 188).

Disease: stem end rot; Stielendfäule; pourriture pédonculaire; podredumbre peduncular.

Geographical distribution: Worldwide in warm regions.

Host plants: Avocado, breadfruit, *Citrus* spp., mango, tung, sugar beet.

Symptoms: Stem end rots are post-harvest diseases, which become apparent with the ripening process. The first symptom is a browning of the peel at the stem end, in form of a clearly defined, dark brown little cap. Within two or three days, the whole fruit is affected. The greatly altered, softened fruit flesh is of a pale brown colour, which gradually darkens. After 8–10 days, the firm and pliable peel is covered by the pycnidia of the pathogen. Eventually, the fruit mummifies. *D. natalensis* Evans, *Phomopsis* spp. and *Dothiorella* sp. can all cause stem end rot on avocado, breadfruit, *Citrus* spp., mango etc. There is a close resemblance between all of them, so that one description suffices.

Epidemiology: Stem end rots are of major importance if the fruit is stored in tropical climates. The optimum temperature for *D. natalensis* is 30 °C.

Control: Harvested, uninfected avocado fruit which has been treated against Cercosporiosis, will ripen and keep well without any special measures, if placed immediately in cold storage.

Author: P. Frossard

Other Physalospora spp. on tropical and subtropical crops:
P. psidii Stev. & Pierce. Conidial state *Diplodia* sp. Dieback of guava.
P. zeae Stout. Conidial state *Macrophoma zeae* Tehon & Daniel. Gray ear rot of maize.
P. zeicola Ell & Ev. Conidial state *Diplodia frumenti* Ell. & Ev. Stalk rot of maize.

Rosellinia arcuata Petch

Pyrenomycetes, Sphaeriales, Xylariaceae

Disease: Black root rot of Tea; Schwarzer Wurzelschimmel des Tees; pourridié noir du théier; podredumbre negra del té.

Geographical distribution: Africa (Central African Republic, Zaire, Kenya), Asia (India, Hong Kong, Sri Lanka), Indonesia (Java and Sumatra) and Papua/New Guinea.

Host plants: The most important host is tea. Other hosts include camphor, *Cinchona*, coffee, *Crotalaria anagyroides, Grevillea* spp., and *Tephrosia* spp.

Symptoms: Death of part or all of the host. In young tea death may occur suddenly leaving the leaves attached to the plant for some time afterwards. The base of the stem and roots are covered with mycelial sheets, white at the margin, shading to black in the older parts. A black network of hyphal strands then develops on the roots, giving a wooly appearance, and white star shaped mycelial patches spread in these regions between bark and wood.

Morphology: Brownish black or black perithecia occur in groups embedded in a mat of brown hyphae on the host. Ellipsoid or ovoid, single celled, hyaline to pale brown, conidia (4–6 x 2–3 μ) are formed on synnemata 2–5 mm high x 50–100 μ thick, either in association with perithecia or independently. Hyphae do not show septal swellings characteristic of *R. necatrix* (p. 137).

Physiological specialization: None known.

Epidemiology: Infections arise from infected plant debris in and on the soil; the distribution of the disease in the field is therefore patchy. Spread is favoured by moist and warm conditions. The role of air borne spores in transmission of the disease is not understood. In tea, vigorous plants are readily attacked.

Control: By crop sanitation, in removing all plant debris from the soil that might harbour the pathogen. In Sri Lanka soil fumigation with chloropicrin, methyl bromide, D-D, formaldehyde and vapam will eradicate inoculum from the soil.

Literature

ROGER, L. (1953): Phytopathologie des Pays Chauds, vol II. Paul Lechevalier Paris.
CMI Description no 353.

Author: I.A.S. Gibson

Rosellinia bunodes (Berk. & Br.) Sacc.

Pyrenomycetes, Sphaeriales, Xylariaceae

Disease: Black root rot; Schwarzer Wurzelschimmel; Pourridié noir; Llaga radicular negra.

Geographical distribution: Central America and West Indies, Brazil and Uruguay, Central Africa (Zaire and Central African Republic), India, Sri Lanka, West Malaysia, Indonesia (Java and Sumatra) and Philippines (CMI map no 358).

Host plants: Mainly tropical woody hosts: Arrowroot, *Artocarpus integer,* avocado, banana, cacao, camphor, cassava, *Centrosema pubescens, Cinchona, Citrus,* coffee, dasheen (*Colocasia antiquorum*), *Crotalaria, Erythrina,* ginger, black pepper, pigeon pea, rubber; Sea Island cotton, *Schleichera trijuga,* tea, *Tephrosia,* yams, *Zea mays.* Mango, sugarcane and coconut are among important crop species that are resistant.

Symptoms: Wilting and death of part or all of the host accompanied by a sheet of mycelium at the collar, at first white then turning purplish black, extending above the soil surface under damp conditions. The roots are covered with firm textured black branching strands, thickened into coarse irregular knots. At later stages these strands may fill in to form a dense layer growing into the outer layers of bark. The strands also penetrate the wood of the root and appear as black dots and radial lines when this is cut. This invasion of the wood takes place much earlier in *R. bunodes* than in infection by *R. pepo* (p. 137). Further, where mycelium of *R. pepo* has invaded the root wood of the host it appears as long zig zag lines formed by cutting through a continuous black mycelial layer. In herbaceous plants the distinction between the yellow-white strands of *R. pepo* and black strands of *R. bunodes* is quite clear.

Morphology: Perithecia are formed readily at the base of the stem and on the surface of exposed roots of infected plants, as well as on dead woody debris in the soil. Ellipsoid to obovoid, hyaline to pale brown conidia (4–10 x 2–5 μ) are borne on synnemata 1.7–3 mm high and 30–100μ thick. They are not readily distinguished from those of *R. pepo.*

Physiological specialization: None known.

Epidemiology: Transmission is mainly through infected plant debris in the soil. Ascospores and conidia appear to play little part in spread of the disease. Field distribution is thus characteristically patchy. *R. bunodes* has been shown to be more virulent than *R. pepo* and to be most favoured by a soil pH of 5.2 and moisture content of 50–50 % M.H.C. Host mortality increases with inoculum size.

Control: Mainly by sanitation. Removal and treatment of infected plants and cleaning sites of debris likely to harbour the pathogen. Spraying of early infection in young coffee trees with quintozene or 0.25 % copper fungicide has been recommended in Guatemala. Older infected trees should be removed and the hole treated with the same fungicides. These measures are aimed at control of dispersal of the pathogen by air borne spores as well as the eradication of inoculum on site.

Literature

FERNANDEZ-BORRERO, O., & S. LOPEZ (1964): Llagas radiculares negras (*Rosellinia bunodes*) y estrelladas (*Rosellinia pepo*) del Cafeto. I. Patogenicidad e influencia de la clase de inoculo en la infección. Cenicafe **15**, 126–144.
LOPEZ-DUQUE, S., & O. FERNANDEZ-BORRERO (1966): Llages radiculares negras (*Rosellinia bunodes*) y estrelladas (*Rosellinia pepo*) del Cafeto. II. Efecto de la humedad y pH del suelo en el desarrollo micelial e infección. Cenicafe **17**, 61–69.
CMI Description no 351.

Author: I.A.S. Gibson

Rosellinia necatrix Prill.

Pyrenomycetes, Sphaeriales, Xylariaceae

Disease: White Root Rot; Weißer Wurzelschimmel; Pourridié laineux; podredumbre de las raices de los frutales.

Geographical distribution: Widely distributed in temperate and tropical regions including central and southern Africa (and possibly Madagascar), India, Korea, Japan and the Philippines, Colombia, Brazil, Argentina, Uruguay, Mexico and parts of the USA, New Zealand but not Australia and the Pacific Islands (CMI map no 306).

Host plants: Almond, *Annona,* apples, apricot, artichoke, avocado pear, barley, bean, beet, *Citrus,* coffee, currants, fig, lucerne, maize, mulberry, oak, olive, peach, pear, pepper (black), pistachio, plum, potato, quince, sorghum, tea, vine, wheat.

Symptoms: First signs of infection appear as a yellowing of the foliage with premature leaf cast. In fruit trees this may be accompanied by heavy blossom and fruit set. Die-back follows but the complete death of large trees may not occur until two or three years after the first foliage symptoms appear.
Infected trees have scanty fibrous roots and the main roots are covered with white mycelium which turns greenish grey or black later on. After the death of the tree the mycelial weft disappears and may be replaced by small black sclerotia. However, in New Zealand this does not occur and conidiophores may be produced instead on the host at ground level. These appear as dark rough patches on the bark where the synnematous conidiophores can be seen as spikes under a lens. Distinguished from other root pathogens by absence of well defined rhizomorphs.

Morphology: The fungus forms densely aggregated, globose, black shortly pedicellate perithecia which are embedded in a mat of brown septate hyphae. These, and conidia, are rarely found on host tissues (with the exception noted above) and the fungis is most readily recognised by the swellings that often occur at one end of the cells of mature hyphae. Synnemata are up to 1.5 mm high, 40–300 μ thick bearing ellipsoid to obvoid conidia, hyaline to pale brown, -1celled, 3–4.5 x 2–2.5 μ.

Physiological specialization: None known.

Epidemiology: The fungus spreads from infected plant debris or sclerotia in the soil. Infection takes place from diffuse active mycelium permeating the soil which attacks the fine roots, producing a rot. It does not kill the host by destruction of the cambium and girdling, as in other root pathogens such as *Armillariella mellea* (Fr.) Karst. (p. 145). Ascospores and conidia do not readily germinate *in vitro* and appear to play little part in the distribution of the pathogen. The fungus may survive in the soil for several years, according to soil type and succeeding crops. The disease is favoured by moist conditions and temperatures below 20 °C.

Control: By removal of infected debris from the previous crop where there is a history of the disease and trenching around centres where early symptoms have appeared. By the use of legume cover crops for several years on infected sites and by soil sterilants where the values of the crop and risk of attack warrants this. Chloropicrin has been used with some success and organomercurial compounds.
Early attack of young fruit trees may be checked by lifting the plants, trimming the finer roots and replanting.

Literature

ATKINSON, J. D. (1971): Diseases of Tree Fruits in New Zealand. Govt. Printer, Wellington, New Zealand.
WORMALD, H. (1955): Diseases of Fruit and Hops. 3rd. Ed. Crosby Lockwood, London.
CMI Description no 352.

Author: I.A.S. Gibson

Rosellinia pepo Pat.

Pyrenomycetes, Sphaeriales, Xylariaceae

Disease: Black root rot; Schwarzer Wurzelschimmel; pourridié noir; Llaga radicular negra.

Geographical distribution: Central America, West Indies and West Africa (CMI map no 298).

Host plants: Avocado, bread fruit, banana, cacao, cassava, coffee, dasheen (*Colocasia antiquorum*), *Artocarpus integer, Erythrina,* lime, nutmeg, pigeon pea, horse bean. Mango, sugarcane, coconut are among important crop plants which are resistant.

Symptoms: Wilting and death of part or all of the host. A broad mycelial fan encircling the stem at ground level, with a light grey margin shading to brown or purplish-black with olive-green tint. On roots loose cobweb-like strands, at first grey, then black, coalesce later into a mass with a woolly felt like surface. This is associated with white star-like fans of mycelium under the bark and black mycelial layers penetrating the wood. The latter develop at a much later stage of the disease than the black strand of *R. bunodes* (p. 135).

Morphology: Perithecia are formed much less freely than in *R. bunodes.* They occur on woody substrates singly or in groups on or partially in a subiculum of brown to black mycelium. Conidia, not readily distinguished from those of *R. bunodes,* are single-celled, hyaline, oblong to ovoid (4–6 x 2 μ), borne on synnomata 1–2 mm high and 30–70 μ thick. These develop abundantly on infected plant material on the soil surface and exposed roots and stem base of the host.

Physiological specialization: None known.

Epidemiology: The fungus spreads from infected woody debris in the soil causing patches of dead plants in the crop. The role of ascospores and conidia in spread of the disease is not known but appears to be of limited importance. *R. pepo* has been shown to be less virulent than *R. bunodes* but like the latter, is favoured by a soil pH of 5.2 and soil moisture in the region of 50–70 % M.H.C. Host mortality due to the fungus increases with size of inoculum (Fernandez-Borrero & Lopez 1964; Lopez-Duque & Fernandez-Borrero 1966).

Control: By efficient sanitary measures to reduce soil inoculum to a minimum.

Literature

FERNANDEZ-BORRERO, O., & S. LOPEZ (1964): Llagas radiculares negras (*Rosellinia bunodes*) y estrelladas (*Rosellinia pepo*) del Cafeto. I. Patogenicidad e influencia de la clase de inoculo en la infección. Cenicafe **15**, 126–144.
LOPEZ-DUQUE, S., & O. FERNANDEZ-BORRERO (1966): Llagas radiculares negras (*Rosellinia bunodes*) y estrelladas (*Rosellinia pepo*) del Cafeto. II. Efecto de la humedad y pH del suelo en el desarollo micelial e infección. Cenicafe **17**, 61–69.
CMI Description no 354.

Author: I. A. S. Gibson

Sclerotinia sclerotiorum (Lib.) de By (Figs. 52–53)

Discomycetes, Helotiales, Helotiaceae

Disease: Cottony rot; Sclerotiniafäule; maladie de sclérotes; mal del esclerocio de las plantas cultivadas.

Geographical distribution: Worldwide occurrence in cool, moderately warm and warm regions. In tropical zones mostly restricted to higher elevations. In semi-arid zones largely limited to rainy seasons.

Host plants: Affects about 300 hosts in 55 families of dicotyledons and about 20 hosts in 4 families of monocotyledons. Hosts are most numerous in *Compositae* (60), *Leguminosae* (35) and *Cruciferae* (30). Most widespread on *Helianthus annuus* (sunflower), *Lactuca sativa* (lettuce), *Cynara scolymus* (globe artichoke) *Brassicae, Cucumis sativus* (cucumber), *Glycine max* (soybean), *Phaseolus vulgaris* (bean), *Lycopersicum esculentum* (tomato), *Solanum tuberosum* (potato), *Apium graveolens* (celery), *Daucus carota* (carrot).

Symptoms: a) Soft, watery, odourless decay of fruits, leaf bases, corns, stems and other fleshy or succulent plant organs, especially at or just above soil level or in storage. Affected parts progressively covered with white, cottony growth (Fig. 52 and 52a) in which black sclerotia are imbedded (Fig. 53). b) Dry rot of collar and branches, at or considerably above soil level; affected parts light-coloured, often hollow, with sclerotia and white growth in the cavities. c) Damping off in crowded stands of seedlings. Roots affected only where protruding above soil level (carrots), or in storage.

Morphology: Hyaline, septate hyphae, 3–12 μ wide. Microconidia are formed on short branches

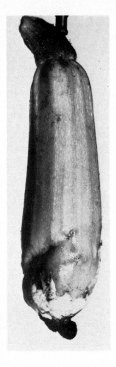

Fig. 52 (left).

Fig. 52 a (right).

Fig. 53 (below).

of mycelium. Sclerotia are oblong, length 2–12 mm or more, and give rise to flat, brown, 2–10 mm wide apothecia, on cylindrical stipes up to 2,5 cm long. Asci are hyaline, cylindrical, 125–190 x 4.3–12.4 μ, with 8 ellipsoid ascospores, 9.0–16.8, x 4.2–8,4 μ.

Physiological specialization: Isolates differ in growth made in culture under various environmental conditions, but specialization with regard to hosts is not proved.

Epidemiology: Infection may stem from seed bearing mycelium, sclerotia mixed with seed, mycelial growth from sclerotia in soil, but most frequently (under moderately warm conditions) from windborne ascospores. With its wide host range and ability for survival on decaying plant matter the pathogen does not lack substrates for formation of sclerotia wherever dicotyledonous crops or weeds grow under humid conditions. Sclerotia persist in upmost soil layers, rarely below 20 cm depth, can remain viable for several years. Apothecia form only on soil surface or in top 5 cm of soil, between 10 and 23 °C at high humidities. Ascospores germinate best at 10–15 °C, cannot penetrate the uninjured cuticle; but mycelium can do so, especially when it proceeds from an adequate food base (dead flowers, senescent leaves) to attack healthy tissue. After penetration, growth intercellular in living, intracellular in dead tissues. Infection possible between 2–3 °C to 28–30 °C, optimal at 15–25 °C, requires 95–100 % humidity.
Epidemics particularly severe in dense or weed-infested crops where root collar, stem basis and basal leaves permanently shaded. Outbreaks are aided by crop injury due to climatic factors, particularly frost, hail. Crops grown in mild winters under glass or plastic cover are extremely vulnerable (tomato, pepper, cucurbits).
Storage rot: Prevalent in storage, including cold storage (above 3 °C) on many vegetables, especially bean, pea, carrot, celery, lettuce, squash, Brassicae, (but not potato, onion, beet). May affect citrus, banana, strawberry, apricots and occasionally other fruit.

Control: Use disease-free seed, especially of sunflowers, clover, soybean, Brassicae, flax. Sclerotia may persist in manure and composts.

Avoid excessively dense stands by spacing crops properly, keeping weeds down, applying nitrogen sparingly. Ventilate covered crops at every opportunity.

Varietal differences in susceptibility known to exist in sunflowers, artichokes, lettuce, possibly in carrots, not in Solanaceae and Brassicae.

Residues of crops affected should be burnt or buried at least 30 cm deep. Flooding kills sclerotia after 3 weeks. Rotation of susceptible crops with cereals over 2–3 years reduces sclerotial population, if fields kept free from dicotyledonous weeds. Danger of ascospore infection from other fields makes control a regional problem to be dealt with by regional sanitation.

Occurrence may be expected in a) temperate regions, where adequate rain coincides with temperatures of 15–25 °C; b) semi-arid regions, where in the rainy season temperatures do not greatly exceed 15–25 °C, especially in covered crops; c) hot and humid regions, where heat is somewhat reduced by altitude or microclimatical factors.

Literature

MOORE, W. D., R. A. CONOVER & D. L. STODDARD (1949): The *Sclerotinia* disease of vegetables in Florida. Univ. Florida Agr. Exp. Sta. Bull. **457**.

PARTYKA, R. E., & W. F. MAI (1962): Effects of environment and some chemicals on *Sclerotinia sclerotiorum* in laboratory and potato field. Phytopathology **52**, 766–770.

RAMSEY, G. B. (1925): *Sclerotinia* species causing decay of vegetables under transit and market conditions. Jour. Agr. Res. **31**, 597–632.

REICHERT, J., & J. PALTI (1967): Prediction of plant disease occurrence. A patho-geographical approach. Mycopathol. et Mycol. Appl. **32**, 337–55.

Author: J. Palti

Other Sclerotinia spp. on tropical and subtropical crops:

Sclerotinia ricini Godfr. Conidial state *Botrytis ricini* Godfr.(H,2.A1.bo). Graymold of castorbean.

Setosphaerica turcica (Luttrell) Leonard & Sugg (Plate 6 d and fig. 54)

Synonym: *Trichometasphaerica turcica* Luttrell

Loculoascomycetes, Pleosporales, Pleosporaceae

The sexual stage of the pathogen was first discovered in 1958 when appropriate pairings of mating types were grown in petri dishes. This stage of the pathogen has not been seen in the field.

Conidial state *Drechslera turcica* (Pass.) Subram. et Jain = *Helminthosporium turcicum* Pass. Hyphomycetes (H,2.C2.po)

Disease: Northern corn leaf blight; Blattfleckenkrankheit des Maises; brûlure des feuilles du mais; niebla del maiz.

Geographical distribution: Northern corn leaf blight is world-wide in distribution but most prevalent in the cooler, more humid areas of the word. In tropical regions it is found in the higher altitudes where cool, humid conditions prevail. It does occur in tropical lowlands, but then in the cooler seasons of the year (CMI map no 257).

Host plants: Under natural conditions in the field the pathogen, in addition to infecting corn, incites disease on several species of *Sorghum,* including *S. bicolor, S. sudanensis* and *S. halipense.* Teosinte (*Euchlaena mexicana*) is also susceptible.

Symptoms: Northern corn leaf blight is essentially a leaf disease. Even under the most severe epidemics infection of kernels has not been observed but lesions may occur also on leaf sheaths and

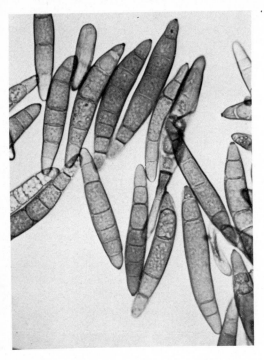

husks. Fully developed symptoms are characterized by long, elliptical lesions ranging up to 25–40 x 150–170 mm in size (Plate 6 d). Lesions, which are oriented parallel to the long axis of the leaf, are gray to tan and within each a concentric, zonate pattern is often observed.

Symptoms may sometimes be confused with lesions of the "leaf blight phase" of bacterial wilt (*Erwinia stewartii*) that develop after silking. The latter, however, are generally longer, narrower, irregular in width and show translucent margins when held to the light.

Morphology: Conidia are elongate, spindle-shaped, slightly curved, olivaceous-gray and average about 20–105 μ in size (Fig. 54). Septations range from 1 in the shortest spores to 9 in the longest. A conspicuous feature of the conidia that distinguishes it from other of the more common species of *Drechslera* attacking corn is the protruding hilum.

Fig. 54.

Physiological specialization: Physiologic specialization is present within the species. The race that attacks Johnsongrass does not attack corn; likewise isolates from sorghum and sudangrass do not infect corn.

Recently a second physiologic race of *D. turcica,* capable of attacking in genotype with the Ht gene, has been identified in Hawaii.

A new source of resistance to *D. turcica* has been identified in Africa. Reaction appears to be conditioned by a single dominant gene which protects the host until after silking at which time lesions begin to enlarge.

Epidemiology: Penetration of the host takes place within 6 to 12 hours after inoculation in the presence of free water on the leaf surface and at temperatures of 25–30 °C. Small chlorotic flecks appear within 48–72 hours after infection. Within 8 to 10 days small, flaccid, grayish-green lesions become evident. These enlarge into fully developed necrotic lesions within 10 to 14 days. Sporulation is abundant on the lower surface of the mature lesions during damp weather when the necrotic tissue is wet. Dry weather is unfavorable for development of the pathogen. Spores and mycelium within infected plant debris can overwinter on the surface of the soil under the continental climate of the Corn Belt of the United States.

Control: Control of northern corn leaf blight is most effectively accomplished through resistance. Both polygenic and monogenic types of resistance are found in corn germplasm. Polygenic resistance appears to govern numbers of lesions; monogenic resistance, determined by a single dominant gene (Ht), appears to control lesion size. The latter is typified by a small necrotic lesion about 3–8 x 15–40 mm in size surrounded by a chlorotic halo. Little sporulation occurs in these small lesions.

Crop sanitation, i. e. clean plowing may delay onset of the disease, since the pathogen can survive in trash on the soil surface.

Foliar applications of fungicides have been used in areas where the disease is severe and where the crop is of high value such as sweet corn for winter market, or seed corn. This practice is not generally economical for use on field corn. Seed treatment has no effect in control of the disease.

Literature

BERQUIST, R. R., & O. R. MASAIS (1974): Physiological specialization in *Trichometasphaerica turcica* f. sp. *zeae* and *T. turcica* f. sp. *sorghi* in Hawaii. Phytopathology **64**, 45–649.
GEVERS, H. O. (1975): A new major gene for resistance to *Helminthosporium turcium* leaf blight of maize. Plant Dis. Reptr. **59**, 296–299.
LIM, S. M., J. G. KINSEY & A. L. HOOKER (1974): Inheritance of virulence in *Helminthosporium turcicum* to monogenic resistant corn. Phytopathology **74**, 1150–1151.
ROBERT, ALICE L. (1960): Physiologic specialization in *Helminthosporium turcicum*. Phytopathology **50**, 217–220.
RODRIGUEZ, A. E., & A. J. ULLSTRUP (1962): Pathogenicity of single ascospore isolates of *Helminthosporium turcicum*. Phytopathology **52**, 599–601.
ULLSTRUP, A. J. (1970): A comparison of monogenic and polygenic resistance to *Helminthosporium turcicum* in corn. Phytopathology **60**, 1597–1599.
CMI Description no 304.

Author: A. J. Ullstrup

Sphaerotheca fuliginea (Schlecht. ex Fr.) Poll. (Fig. 55)

Pyrenomycetes, Erysiphales, Erysiphaceae

Disease: Powdery mildew; Echter Mehltau; Oidium blanc; Oídio blanco.

Geographical distribution: Specially adapted to cool regions, including arctic and subarctic, but most frequent in Europe, N. America, Continental Asia and the Mediterranean region. Exact distribution in hot climates undefined, since perithecia there form more rarely, and on some hosts, not at all (e.g. some cucurbits). Distribution varies with host species: In cool and moderately warm climates Compositae much affected everywhere, Scrophulariaceae chiefly in Europe, Leguminosae in the Far East and Australia. Cucurbitaceae affected in Far East, Australia, Central Asia, Mediterranean and probably many more warm regions and in N. America.

Host plants: Recorded on about 630 mostly herbaceous species in 34 dicotyledonous families, but probably affects additional hosts on which perithecia are absent. Hosts most numerous in Compositae (330), Scrophulariaceae (125), Cucurbitaceae (20). Commercially important hosts: cucurbits, *Helianthus annuus, Hibiscus esculentus,* composite flower crops (Dahlia, Calendula, Gerbera, Zinnia).

Symptoms: Whitish, powdery spots on upper and lower side of leaf blade, and on petioles and green stems (Fig. 55). Infection progresses from older to younger leaves. On cucurbits, infected leaves dry up. Symptoms practically indistinguishable from those of powdery mildews caused by *Erysiphe cichoracearum* DC.

Morphology: Mycelium hyaline, occasionally brownish when old. Conidia in chains, often with distinct fibrosin bodies, ellipsoid to barrel-shaped, 25–37 x 14–25 μ. Conidial germ tubes mostly forked. Perithecia round, 66–98 μ in diameter, with various numbers of mostly tortuous appendages. Ascus broadly elliptic, 50–80 x 30–60 μ; eight ellipsoid ascospores, 17–22 x 12–20 μ.

Physiological specialization: Degrees of specialization of populations differs from country to country. Transmission between Cucurbitaceae and Leguminosae proved in most countries, be-

Fig. 55.

tween Cucurbitaceae and Compositae in Mediterranean region (but not in Japan). Many populations likely to comprise two or more strains.

Epidemiology: In warmer climates chiefly in the conidial stage on weeds and successions of crops, especially cucurbits. In cold climates survival predominantly in the sexual stage. The ectophytic mycelium bears its conidial chains on short hyphae. Perithecia embedded in mycelium.
Conidia dispersed by wind, preferably at lower atmospheric humidity. Infection by formation of appresoria favoured by continued high atmospheric humidity. Overall disease development best at lower humidities, at approximately 25 °C.

Control: Avoid sowing in proximity to older crops affected by Oidium mildews, especially Compositae and Cucurbitaceae. Ensure vigorous growth.
Resistant varieties of cucumbers, melons and watermelons have been bred, but resistance tends to break down rapidly. Sulphur, Dimocap, Chinomethionate, and many systemic fungicides, are effective. Sulphur often scorches leaves, and resistant mildew populations tend to emerge after continued use of systemic fungicides on cucurbits.
Fungicide applications to cucurbits usually required from early fruiting stage onwards, rarely before.

Literature

BLUMER, S. (1967): Echte Mehltaupilze (Erysiphaceae). VEB Gustav Fischer Verlag, Jena.
HIRATA, K. (1966): Host range and geographical distribution of the powdery mildews. Niigata Univ., Niigata.
CMI Description no 159.

Author: J. Palti

Other important Erysiphales on tropical and subtropical crops:
Powdery mildews are common throughout the world and often coexistant with their hosts. See above references. *Leveillula* (p. 123) and *Oidium* (p. 222):
Phyllactinia moricola Saw. Powdery mildew of mulberry.

Ascomycotina as more important pathogens on tropical and subtropical crops from genera not covered in this book:

Asterina camelliae Syd. & Butl. Black blight of tea.

Asterina and *Meliola* spp. are typically tropical, and common on a large number of hosts. Their importance as pathogens has hardly been evaluated. Ref.: Hansford, C. G. (1946): The foliicolous ascomycetes, their parasites and associated fungi. Mycol. Papers, No. 15; Commonwealth Mycological Institute, Kew, UK.

Theisen, F. (1913): Die Gattung Asterina in systematischer Darstellung. Reprint 1968 J. Cramer 3301 Lehre; W. Germany.

Botryosphaeria ribis Gross. & Dug. Conidial state *Dothiorella gregaria* Sacc. (C,1.A1). Dothiorella rot of citrus fruit; dieback of tung, surface rot of avocado, etc.

Calonectria rigidiuscula (Berk. & Br.) Sacc. Conidial state *Fusarium decemcellulare* Brick (H, 4.Cl.ph). Branch canker, dieback, pod rot and 'green point' cushion galls of cacao, panel decay of rubber, etc. Ref.: CMI Description no 21.

C. theae (Petch) Loos. Conidial state *Cercosporella theae* Petch (H,2.E1.an). Leaf spots on tea. Ref.: CMI Description no 424.

Claviceps gigantea Fuentes, Isla, Ullstrup & Rodrig. Ergot of maize.

C. paspali Stev. & Hall. Conidial state *Sphacelia* (H, 4.A1). Ergot on a variety of grasses, toxic to cattle and other animals. Also *Sphacelia oryzae* Massee and *S. sorghi* McRae, the latter on *Pennisetum* spp. should be mentioned here. CMI map no 90.

Endothia eugeniae (Nutman & Roberts) Reid & Booth. Acute dieback of clove. Ref.: CMI Description no 363.

Gnomonia iliau Lyon. Conidial state *Melanconium iliau* Lyon (C,2 A2.an). Causing a disease of sugarcane called iliau. CMI map no 158.

Guignardia camelliae (Cke) Butl. Conidial state *Phoma camelliae* Cke. (C,1.A1.ph). Copper blight of tea.

G. citricarpa (Mc.Alp.) Kiehly. Conidial state *Phoma citricarpa* McAlp. (C,1.A1.ph). Black spot of citrus fruits.

G. heveae Syd. Rim blight of leaves of rubber.

G. yersini Vincens. Leaf spot of *Cinchona* spp.

Khuskia oryzae Hudson. Conidial state *Nigrospora oryzae* (Berk. & Br.) Petch (H,2.A2.al/bl). Stem and grain infection of maize, rice, sorghum and many others; largely saprophytic. Ref.: CMI Description no 311.

Leptosphaeria bondari Bitanc. & Jenkins. Areolate leaf spot of citrus.

L. cinnamomi Shirai & Hara. Leaf spot cinnamom.

L. elaeidis Booth & Robertson. Conidial state *Pestalotiopsis* sp. (C,2.C2,an). Anthracnose of oilpalm.

L. michotii (West.) Sacc. Conidial state *Coniothyrium scirpi* Trail (C,1.A2). Leaf spot or blast of surgarcane and other gramineae. Ref.: CMI Description no 144.

L. sacchari Breda de Haan. Conidial state *Phyllosticta* sp. (C,1.A1). Ring spot of sugarcane. Ref.: CMI Description no 145.

L. salvinii Catt. Conidial state *Nakataea* (*Helminthosporium*) *sigmoideum* Cav. (H,2.C2.po). Stem rot of rice. Ref.: CMI Description no 344.

Meliola ipomoeae Earle. Black mildew of sweet potato.

M. mangiferae Earle. Black mildew of mango and many others. See *Asterina* and Hansford, C. G. (1961): The Meliolineae. A monograph. II. Beiheft Sydowia, Verlag Ferdinand Berger, Horn, Austria. Hansford, C. G. (1963): Iconographia Meliolinearum. V. Beiheft Sydowia, ibid.

Nectria tjibodensis Penz. & Sacc. Brown spot of vanilla. There are numerous *Nectria* spp. recorded, particularly so on cacao, many of them seem to be rather saprophytic.

Phyllachora gratissima Rehm. Tar spot of avocado. *Phyllachora* spp. predonderably occur in the tropics causing tar spots on numerous hosts, damage is mostly regarded negligeable.

Pleospora herbarum s. *Stemphylium botryosum* (p. 228) and CMI Description no 150.

Sphaerostilbe repens Berk. & Br. Violet root rot of cacao, root rot of papaw, stinking root disease of rubber, red root disease of tea. Ref.: CMI Description no 391.

Ustulina deusta (Hoffm. ex Fr.) Lind. = *U. zonata* (Lév.) Sacc. Causing decay of stumps, butts and dead roots of oilpalm, rubber (charcoal rot, collar rot), tea (root disease) and many other species of trees and shrubs. Ref.: CMI Description no 360.

Basidiomycotina

The Basidiomycotina are characterized by basidia on which 2–4 basidiospores are formed. Another very common feature is the often extensive septate mycelium with its dicaryotic cells tending to form clamp connexions. Hyphal strands and rhizomorphs are often found. Otherwise basidiomycetes can be rather diverse in morphology (various kinds of stoadstools, rust, smut etc.).

Most important from point of view of a plant pathologist is the class Teliomycetes which comprises the rust (Uredinales) and the smut fungi (Ustilaginales). But also a few species of the Hymenomycetes (with the Phragmobasidiomycetidae and Holobasidiomycetidae) are known as plant pathogens. None seems to be reported from the class Gasteromycetes.

Though we cannot go into details of life cycles of basidiomycetes here some mention should be made of that of rusts. From the about 4000 species of rust fungi, belonging to about 100 genera roughly half of them are heterooecious (obliged to change host after the aecial and telial stage), the other complete their life cycles on one host. A full life cycle of rusts consists of a complex of five states: (O = pycnia, I = aecia, II = uredinia, III = telia, IV = basidia, with subdivisions in I and II). But this life cycle often is reduced, most drasticycally in microcyclic species where O, I and II are eliminated. Apart from macro- and microcyclic ones species there are brachycyclic, demicyclic and endocyclic ones (see Laundon in Fungi IV A, p. 252).

The teliospores of Ustilaginales are unicellular and single (*Ustilago*), though they may aggregate into sori. These may be covered by a membrane of hyphae (*Sphacelotheca*) or these hyphae may internally unite to a columella (*Cintractia*).

They are usually coloured, thickwalled and often ornamented. They germinate with a promycelium which produces sporidia of different kind that give rise to haploid primary hyphae which after fusion with a mating partner becomes dicarytic and infective. There is, however, some variation in this stage. This secondary mycelium later achieves infection, penetration of the host and is later rounding off to a teliospore, which eventually becomes diploid.

For details on classification, nomenclature, life cycles, and biology we must refer again to the literature cited on pp. 75, 76, 171 and 182.

Armillariella mellea (Vahl.) Pat. (Plate 8 b–c)

Synonym: *Armillaria mellea* (Fr.) Quél.
Hymenomycetes, Agaricales, Agaricaceae

Disease: Armillaria root rot; Hallimasch; Pourridié à Armillaire; podredumbre blanca de las raices.

Geographical distribution: *A. mellea* has been recorded in all the temperate regions of the globe. In tropical countries *Armillariella* is confined to altitude zones, as in the Far East where it remains above 1000 metres and consequently the rubber plantations escape the attack of this parasite. In West and Central Africa this parasite descends into the lowlands. *Armillaria* has not been recorded in tropical America (CMI map no 143).

Host plants: *A. mellea* is a polyphagous fungus which attacks nearly all species of trees and shrubs, and some herbaceous plants. In tropical regions *A. mellea* is a parasite on a large number of cultivated species: tung, citrus, avocado, banana, cocoa, coffee, coconut palm, kola, rubber, mango, cassava, oilpalms, pepper, cinchona, tea, and several species of forest trees.

Symptoms: The external symptoms of *Armillariella* only become visible in the top of the tree at a stage when the disease has already attacked a significant portion of the root system; at this stage the leaves develop yellow or sometimes copper-red tints, and then wither and fall. These symptoms in the canopy can be due to causes other than *Armillariella* (see *Rigidoporus lignosus* p. 171). In the case of advanced infection one can find, however, at the collar of rubber trees or on the trunk, characteristic signs of the pathogen. At the collar this disease manifests itself either by splits which affect the cortex, with or without a flow of latex ("collar crack"), or more often by a thick cushion of rubber which can cover a large part of the circumference of the tree. Raising this skin exposes thin, white, mycelial plates, characteristic of *Armillariella*. On the roots the infection can appear in two very different ways. The first, very characteristic, shows itself by the presence of a sleeve of coagulated rubber mixed with soil which encircles the root in advance of the infection; under the action of the mycelial plates the bark splits in the healthy zone ahead of the infection and allows latex to ooze in abundance. The sleeve and the underlying skin are black and often emit a nauseating odour. In contrast, tissues directly invaded (see below) by *Armillariella* emits a penetrating but rather agreeable smell of fresh mushroom. Lifting the sleeve reveals a rooted bark, on the surface of which are white mycelial formations characteristic of *Armillariella*.
The second type of appearance on roots lacks the formation of a sleeve and is characterized at the start by a bluish-black colouration of the affected bark and by a more or less accentuated hypertrophy of the cortical tissues which can feel spongy when pressed. Deep longitudinal cracks eventually appear on the infected areas. Black cords of sclerotial origin are lodged in these splits and are clearly seen as cushions which protrude onto the surface of the root.
In addition to the mycelial formations visible at all depths of the cortex, a continuous sheet, particularly thick and resistant, more or less completely envelops the woody cylinder (Plate 8 b) and can even colonize it, especially by progressing through the medullary rays. The enlargement of lenticels and the formation of additional lenticels are also very important identification characters. Stellar lenticels develop on the infection sites and are hidden by the sleeve, but others, very large and supernumerary, appear on both sides of the infection site for distances up to 50–60 cm. This symptom is particularly useful because it is evidence of the disease on parts of the root which might be hidden.

Morphology: The mycelial sheets can be smooth or perforated and are often luminescent. The fructifications of *A. mellea* appear sporadically on rubber and other hosts in wet tropical forests; they develop in clusters with the pileus honey-coloured and with a typical ring around the stipe or foot (Plate 8 c).
This latter feature differentiates *A. mellea* from *Clitocybe tabescens* (Scop.ex.Fr.) Bres., another rotting agent with a very similar syndrome, but whose fructifications lack the ring. Furthermore, *C. tabescens* has never been recorded on rubber.

Physiological specialization: It does not seem that *A. mellea* possesses sub-species or physiological races which are host-specific. Strains of the pathogen in hot tropical zones do not produce rhizomorphs.

Epidemiology: *A. mellea* is exclusively a root-inhabiting fungus. It does not remain viable and develop in soil unless supported by vegetation. It is also limited in its development by competition with other lignicoles because it does not successfully utilize plant tissues already invaded by other fungi. The propagation of *A. mellea* is normally through vegetative channels. The spores do not have any parasitic capacity but they can function in the saprophytic propagation of the fungus. The infection of rubber by *A. mellea* occurs when developing healthy roots come into contact with infected roots. Rhizomorphic cushions attach themselves to healthy bark by a mucilaginous substance and grow one or several branches which penetrate perpendicularly into the bark. In rubber plantations *A. mellea* does not form rhizomorphs which penetrate the soil. The fungus can spread rapidly along the length of a root from the point of infection, join the tap root and pass onto the collar. From the tap root the infection can reach the other main roots.

In a natural population of forest or savanna, the foci of *Armillariella* are generally dispersed and limited in their number and importance. With the establishment of a plantation the cutting of trunks results in the multiplication of the foci. In fact, the roots of the stumps provide an environment which is particularly favourable to the spread of *Armillariella*. These roots, once invaded, form new foci which can result in the infection of healthy, vigorous trees. Although the disease is able to spread afterwards, from rubber tree to rubber tree, the infectious wave tends to decline and even to disappear by the exhaustion of primary foci (forest stumps). Indeed, the secondary foci (colonised rubber trees) are not always capable of contaminating all their neighbours which have acquired, meanwhile, a bigger root mass and accordingly, a greater resistance. The secondary foci often exhaust themselves without resulting in further infections.

The disease persists in the form of small dispersed foci, as in natural and balanced populations. In rubber plantations in Africa *A. mellea* occurs with the fungus *R. lignosus,* the latter being by far the more abundant and more damaging, especially in young plantations. At an age which seems to lie between 8 and 10 years, *Armillariella* often remains the only danger.

Control methods: Control is based upon the ringing of forest species before the establishment of plantations. The purpose of this operation is partly to speed up the exhaustion of carbohydrates in the stumps, which could be utilized by the parasitic fungi, and partly to encourage a rapid colonisation of the stumps by weak parasitic fungi and saprophytic competitors of the root pathogens[1]. When the rubber plants follow food crops or plantations of palm or coffee less susceptible to the rot fungi, infection is so reduced that sanitary treatments are not needed. It is necessary to determine the healthy status of old trees by exposing roots. To replant, seed, preferable germinated, is sown densely (759–1000 rubber plants/ha); this will later permit a rapid identification of infectious stumps which exist. Thinning the densely-planted trees is undertaken between the second and fifth years, depending upon the health and vigour of the trees. From the time tapping begins thinning is based on the health and productivity of the plantation.

The classical method of control against rots in general and *Armillariella* in particular rests on the following principles (see also *R. lignosus*):

The periodical inspection of the root system of every tree in a plantation. Surgical treatment and the application of a wound-treating product to the affected parts of contaminated or infected rubber trees. Continual exposure to the air of the cleaned root system. The first inspection must take place early, when the plantation is between 2 and 3 years old. The inspection rounds must be continued at 4-month intervals until the age of 6–8 years, depending upon the infection rate. The frequency can then be reduced to 6 months until the plantation is 10 years old. At the time, and to the extent hat the recommendations have been followed, the rate of infection is reduced to a value so low that control is generally superfluous, although annual rounds of inspection will give reassurance.

[1]The most efficient ringing technique is known as a double slash or notch. For this the tree is slashed with a sharp axe, cuts being directed towards its base. A second slash 8–10 cm lower removes a piece of wood, resulting in a notch 5–7 cm deep, around the circumference of the trunk. The notch should be deep but must not completely remove the sap wood for in that case the upper part of the tree dies rapidly instead of slowly declining. The ringing operation can also be done with a specially adapted power saw. It is sufficient to make two holes in the guide of the saw's blade, and to fix there, by two bolts and nuts, a sheet of wood 7–8 mm thick, the outer edge of which will be at the required distance from the level of the cutting teeth.

Literature

FASSI, B. (1962): Maladies cryptogamiques de l'hévéa-Précis des maladies et des insectes nuisibles rencontrés sur les plantes cultivées au Congo. Sous la direction de E.J.E. BUYCKX. Publication INEAC, Hors série.

GARRETT, S. D. (1956): Biology of root-infecting fungi. Cambridge, University Press.

LEACH, R. (1939): Biological control and ecology of Armillaria mellea. Trans. Brit. myc. Soc. **23**, 320–29.

RISHBETH, J. (1971): The role of basidiospores in stump infection by Armillaria mellea. Root diseases and soil borne pathogens. T. A. Tousoun, R. V. Bega and P.E. Nelson, Edts. Berkeley, Univ. California Press. CMI-Description no 321.

Author: B. Fassi

Corticium rolfsii (Sacc.) Curzi (Figs. 56–57)

Synonyms: Pellicularia rolfsii (Curzi) West. = Botryobasidium rolfsii (Sacc.) Venkat.
Hymenomycetes, Aphyllophorales, Corticiaceae
Conidial state *Sclerotium rolfsii* Sacc. (H,1)

Disease: Seedling blight; Sämlings- und Fußfäule; pourriture des capsules; mal del esclerocio.

Geographical distribution: The fungus is widely distributed in the warm climates of the world acting as a virulent parasite of many plants (CMI map no 311).

Host plants: Beans, cabbage, clover, cotton, groundnut, maize, peas, black pepper, sweet potato, soybean, sugarcane, tobacco, tomato, wheat, and others.

Symptoms: *C. rolfsii* causes damping-off of seedlings and collar or stem rot of older hosts (Fig. 56 A). When young plants are attacked they die quickly, but when older plants are attacked the shoots turn yellow, wilt and then die. The affected parts of the stem and root at soil level rot and subsequently become covered with white, mycelial strands in which white to brown sclerotia are embedded. Rots similar to that caused by *C. rolfsii* (Fig. 56 A) can be produced also by *Macrophomina phaseoli* (Fig. 56B, p. 217), and by *Sclerotinia sclerotiorum* (Fig. 56C, p. 138).

Morphology: In artificial culture the fungus produces abundant white mycelium with clamp-connexions at the septa (Fig. 57A), and small sclerotia, about the size of mustard seed which are white at first but then brown (Fig. 57B). The basidial stage grows as a spreading white hymenium on the surface of the host. In the hymenium basidia usually bearing four hyaline unicellular basidiospores, are produced (Fig. 57C).

Physiological specialization: There are no distinct physiologic strains or races of the fungus, isolates from one host being able to attack any of the other hosts.

Epidemiology: The sclerotia of *C. rolfsii* retain their viability for long periods on crop residues on the soil surface. Such surviving sclerotia act as excellent inoculum sources, either for primary infections at the beginning of a new season, or for secondary infections occurring in the same season. Germination is by the formation of mycelial strands which attack the host, usually near ground level. Uninjured tissues are readily invaded by the mycelium, though injuries by soil nematodes and insects facilitate such invasion. The parasite has been found to be most destructive in light, sandy soils well provided with moisture.

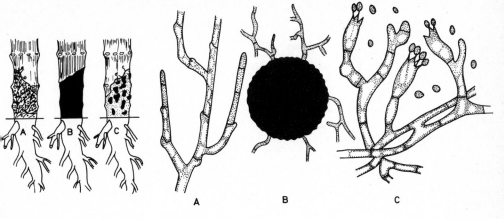

Fig. 56.   Fig. 57.

It has been demonstrated that oxalic acid production and the secretion of pectic enzymes are involved in the pathogenesis of *C. rolfsii,* and that the action of these two compounds together is more effective in destroying plant tissues than of either one alone.

Control: Control of the diseases caused by *C. rolfsii* depends largely upon good crop management. Removal of plants as they become diseased, avoidance of cultivation of crops in contaminated areas and proper disposal of plant refuse which harbours the pathogen, are cultural practices which are often recommended. Crop rotation is of little value in controlling the disease, but ploughing-in of the contaminated top soil has been found to decrease stem rots due to *C. rolfsii,* since deeply-buried sclerotia do not germinate. It seems that the retarded germination of sclerotia is due to the accumulation of carbon dioxide in non-aerated soil.

Seed treatment tests at the rate of 5 g/kilogram seed, showed that Thiram followed by organic mercury compounds and MAS could control root rot and damping-off of sunflower seedlings grown in pots.

Literature

DICKSON, J. G. (1966): Diseases of field crops. 2nd Ed. McGrawHill Inc., New York.
KINCAID, R. R. (1960): Crop rotation and fallowing in relation to tobacco disease control. Bot. Rev. **26,**
    261–276.
WEST, E. (1961): *Sclerotium rolfsii,* history, taxonomy, host range and distribution. Phytopathology **51,**
    108–109.
CMI Description no 410.

Author: M.W. Assawah

Corticium sasakii (Shirai) Matsumoto (Fig. 58)

Synonyms: *Pellicularia sasakii* (Shirai) Ito, *Pellicularia filamentosa* (Pat.) Rogers f. sasakii Exner = ? *Tanatephorus sasakii* (Shirai) Donk.

Hymenomycetes, Aphyllophorales, Corticiaceae
Conidial state: It is still disputed if the fungus belongs to the *Rhizoctonia solani* group (p. 178)
Mycelia sterilia (H,1)

Disease: Sheath blight; Blattscheidendürre; nécrose des gaines du riz; Necrosis de las vainas foliares del arroz.

Geographical distribution: *C. sasakii* is found in all rice growing countries in Asia: Japan, Taiwan, the Philippines, China, Vietnam, Sri Lanka, India. In recent times, the disease has also been reported in Brazil, Surinam, Venezuela and Madagascar. According to Hashioka et al. (1969). *C. sasakii* could also be isolated from samples collected in Louisiana and Texas, but the fungus occurs less frequently in those regions than *Rhizoctonia oryzae,* with which it can be confused.

Host plant: Kozaka (1965) found that 188 plant species from 32 families could be infected with *C. sasakii.* Apart from rice, these included sugar cane, maize, peanut, soybean, beans (Phaseolus and Vicia), wheat, flax and camphor tree. The strains of *C. sasakii* isolated from various host plants are sometimes regarded as separate strains.

Symptoms: On rice, the first spots usually appear on the leaf sheaths, at the irrigation water level. These spots are elliptical, initially about 1 cm long and green-grey. Later they extend to about 2–4 cm. The spots on the leaf sheaths turn grey-white at the centre, with a definite brown, irregular edge. The fungus can penetrate the leaf sheaths and kill off individual stems or whole clusters. If the relative humidity in the crop is high, the fungus extends to leaf blades and produces leaf spots or kills affected leaves.
White mycelium which later turns brown and semicircular sclerotia up to 5 mm diameter (Fig. 58) can be seen near affected areas. Sclerotia can also form on the inside of leaf sheaths.
Several other pathogens can produce symptoms on rice resembling those known to be due to an attack by *C. sasakii.* Since these fungi also belong to the genera *Corticium* (*Pellicularia*) vz *Rhizoctonia,* many mistakes have been made. This has been sorted out by Hashioka and Makino (1968) for *C. sasakii; Rhizoctonia oryzae* (see below); *R. solani* Kühn; *R. zeae* Voorhees; *Corticium microsclerotia* Weber; *C. rolfsii* Curzi; *C. gramineum* Ikata et Matsuura (all isolated from rice).
C. sasakii and *Rhizoctonia oryzae* Ryker et Gooch are very easily confused. Table 4 shows the distinguishing features.

Table 4.

	Corticium sasakii	*Rhizoctonia oryzae*
Climatic zone	occurs also in climatic zones with temperatures below 0°C	does not occur in climatic zones where temperatures may drop below 0°C.
Symptoms	initially spots at the level of the water surface, later spread on leaf blade	spots formed below the water surface. Later blackened leaf sheaths
Sclerotia	numerous sclerotia on the plant, size up to 5 mm	few or no sclerotia on the plant, size up to 1 mm
Number of nuclei per mycelial cell	6 − 8 nuclei	4 nuclei
Synthetic culture	white-brown fungus colonies	pink-reddish-fungus colonies

Morphology: *C. sasakii* grows easily on many nutrient media. Young hyphae are colourless, old ones yellow to brown. Hyphae have a diameter of 8–12 μ, which is generally greater in culture than on host plants. Septation is regular but scant. Short, swollen, branched hyphae can develop on host plants or in culture and are regarded as precursors of the basidiospore stage. Similar cell formations have also been observed before infection on the leaf. Sclerotia form both on the plant and in artificial culture and their formation is greatly influenced by the type of nutrient medium provided. Young sclerotia are white and turn brown later, they are spherical in shape or flattened spheroid. They reach a diameter of up to 5 mm. The perfect stage is not always formed on the host plant, but has been described by various authors. The size of basidia is 10–15 x 7–9 μ. The size of sterigmata is 4.5–7 x 2–3 μ. Basidiospores per basidium number 2–4 and they measure 8–11 x 5–6.5 μ.

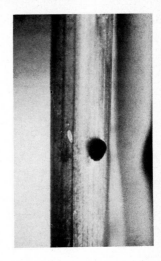

Fig. 58.

Physiological specialization: Several races of *C. sasakii* are known. In Taiwan, 6 physiological races have been distinguished obtained from a test sample of 16 rice varieties and to establish agreement with some strains showing distinctive behaviour in culture. These strains could also be differentiated on deficient nutrient media, and differed distinctly in pathogenicity.

Epidemiology: Sclerotia play the most important part in the survival of the fungus at times when no host plants are available. The fungus can persist for some time in mycelial form. A viability up to 21 months has been observed for sclerotia. Sclerotia could last longer in irrigated soils than in dry and moist soils.
The fungus spreads primarily by means of sclerotia and fungus-carrying plant parts. It can be dispersed with the irrigation water and in the course of cultural practices, such as levelling or mechanical weed control. Basidiospores are formed relatively rarely and play a minor role in the spread of the fungus. If organs of fungus, e. g. sclerotia, come into contact with rice plants, they begin to germinate and form mycelium which quickly grows up the plant. Infection usually spreads from inoculum present on the water surface.
Infection takes place at temperatures of 23–35 °C. Optimum conditions obtain at 30–32 °C and a relative humidity of 96–97 %. At such temperatures, the infection occurs within only 18 hours. Under favourable conditions for the fungus, the incubation period in the field is 7–10 days.
The fungus can gain entry through stomatal openings, but can also penetrate directly through the cuticle into the leaf tissue. It has been shown that leaf sheaths of rice plants are particularly susceptible at the stage of rapid growth, while younger plants are more resistant. This can be explained to some extent by the fact that leaf sheaths separate from the stem as they shoot up, so that infection can occur on the inside of leaf sheaths. Leaf blades are particularly susceptible at the stage of panicle formation. The disease spreads easily in densely planted crops and is more severe if there is a high supply of fertiliser, particularly nitrogen.

Control: Little has so far been achieved with attempts to suppress the occurrence and progress of the disease with hygiene measures and other cultural practices, because sclerotia are not eliminated in such ways. The control of susceptible weeds such as water hyacinth, the destruction of infected crop trash and the avoidance of trash susceptible vegetables, for instance beans planted in rotation with rice, can keep down sources of infection, but cannot provide lasting control.
It has so far not been found possible to breed rice varieties which are resistant to *C. sasakii*. True resistance is evidently hard to find. Rice varieties of the Indica type are less susceptible than Japo-

nica types, but since this work was carried out in Japan, it can be assumed that this only applies to races which were isolated and used for the tests in Japan. If attack is severe, especially in regions where fertiliser is used intensively and yields are high, the disease is best controlled with fungicides. The most important fungicides which are used to control this disease, belong to the group of organic arsenical fungicides. Two antibiotics have also been in use for a number of years. Same organophosphates used primarily to control *Pyricularia oryzae* (p. 223), also have a note worthy side effect against C. sasakii.

All products used to control *C. sasakii,* are applied as dusts or sprays. Seed treatment would be useless. Table 5 gives details of the formulations and doses of the major fungicides:

Table 5.

Common name	Constitution	Amounts used
Mixture of: 40% TMTD, 20% Ziram. 20% Urbazide = Methyl-arsenic-bis-dimethyl- dithiocarbamate	80% Wettable Powder 2,25% dust	0,4 kg/ha 30 − 40 kg/ha
Neo-Asozin = Methyl-arsenic acid iron-and ammonium salt	6,5% liquid form 0,4% dust	0,5 l/ha 30 − 40 kg/ha
Ediphenphos	30% liquid form 2,5% dust	1 − 1,5 l/ha 30 − 40 kg/ha
Validamycin A	30% liquid form 0,3% dust	1 − 1,5 l/ha 30 − 40 kg/ha

The fungicides are applied after completion of tillerings during elongation, one or two applications being mode depending on degree of attack. From the heading stage onwards, organic arsenical compounds should no longer be used, to avoid possible phytotoxic effects. Ediphenphos is suitable for control at later stages, and is used to control *P. oryzae* after the heading stage.

Polyoxin preparations and Validamycin A are antibiotics which effectively control *C. sasakii.* Polyoxin is apparently inadequate with severe attack, but Validamycin has proved highly satisfactory in tests carried out so far.

Literature

ANONYMOUS (1970): Pest control in rice. Pans Manual Nr. 3, Ministry of Overseas Development.
CHIEN, C. C., & S. C. CHUNG (1963): Physiologic races of Pellicularia sasakii in Taiwan. Agric. Res., Taiwan **12** (2), p. 1–6.
HASHIOKA, Y., & M. MAKINO (1968): Rhizoctonia group causing the rice sheath spot in the temperate and tropical regions, with special reference to Pellicularia sasakii and Rhizoctonia oryzae. Res. Bull. Fac. Agr. Cifu Univ. (Japan) **28**, p. 51–63.
KOZAKA, T. (1965): Ecology of Pellicularia sheath blight of rice plant and its chemical control. Ann. phytopath. Soc. Japan **31**, p. 179–185.
OU, S. H. (1972): Rice diseases. Commonwealth Mycological Institute, Kew, Surrey, England.
TU, J. C. (1968): Physiological specialization of strains of Pellicularia sasakii isolated from rice plants. Plant Dis. Reptr. **52**, 323–326.
CMI Description no 409 (*Rhizoctonia oryzae-sativae*).

Author: H. Scheinpflug

Other more important Corticium spp. on tropical and subtropical crops:
C. invisum Petch. Thread blight of cocao, coffee, and tea.

C. koleroga (Cke.) v. Höhnel = *Ceratobasidium stevensii* (Burt.) Venkat. Thread blight of cacao, citrus, coffee, fig, guava, mango, mangosteen, nutmeg, tea, tung, etc. CMI map no 64.
C. (Botryobasidium) microsclerotia Weber. Web blight of beans, fig, kenaf, soybean, tung, etc.
C. penicillatum Petch. Thread blight of coconut.
C. (Botryobasidium) salmonicolor Berk. & Br. Pink disease of branches and stems of cacao, cinchona, citrus, coffee, fig, mango, nutmeg, rubber, tea, etc. CMI map no 122.
C. theae Petch. Thread blight of tea.

Crinipellis perniciosus (Stahel) Singer (Fig. 59)

Synonym: *Marasmius perniciosus* Stahel
Hymenomycetes, Agaricales, Agaricaceae

Disease: Witches' Broom of Cocoa; Hexenbesen des Kakaos; balai de sorcière; escoba de bruja.

Geographical distribution: The disease originated in the Amazonas Basin. To-date it has spread to Ecuador, Colombia, Venezuela, Bolivia, Peru, Brazil, Guiana, Surinam, Trinidad and Grenada. Witches' Broom has not been found in Central America or in any other part of the world (CMI map no 37).

Host plant: Under natural conditions the fungus only attacks *Theobroma spp.* and *Herrania* spp.

Symptoms: The pathogen attacks meristematic tissue in the buds of branches, fruit and flower pads. The characteristic symptom of this disease is a proliferation of adventitious buds on 1st. and 2nd. order branches, leading to fan-shaped hypertrophied vegetative shoots (Fig. 59). The fruit can be infected at any age. The fruit retains its rounded shape while young, but on ripening assumes carrot shape or is otherwise distorted. Such distortion can be accompanied by irregular, coffee-brown blotches. On opening the fruit, the contents and seed are seen to be destroyed. If flower pads are affected, over-developed, broom-shaped shoots are formed. The size and appearance of the brooms depends on the size of the tree and the type and age of the affected tissue. Under favourable moist conditions, the fungus forms fruiting bodies or sporophores on the surface of the diseased tissue. All this weakens the entire tree and leads to high losses in yield. The symptoms of witches' broom disease are very characteristic, but early symptoms in fruit before ripening can be mistaken for those of *Monilia* (p. 219) or *Phytophthora* (p. 83).

Fig. 59.

Physiological specialization: No physiological races of the fungus have so far been found, but aggressive races of the fungus apparently occur in Ecuador.

Morphology: The surface of the fructification of the fungus is red, dark red at the centre. It is initially rounded until the stipe appears, which is 10 mm long. The pileus usually has a width of 10–25 mm. The spores are white and measure 5–10 μ.

Epidemiology: The pathogen survives in affected tissues. Under suitable conditions of high relative humidity (90 %) and temperature (27 °C), sporophores of the fungus develop during the rainy season on withered brooms, but never on green ones. The basidiospores are discharged at night at low temperatures (16–27 °C). The spores are wind-dispersed to the meristem of vegetative buds, flower buds and fruit initials. The pathogen enters through the stomata to penetrate the tissue. The incubation period varies, but visible symptoms appear after 6 weeks The witches' brooms develop within a period of 5 to 10 weeks and dry up. Sporophores are produced on them after 5 or 6 months. Depending on temperature and humidity, the brooms can periodically produce sporophores for two years, not producing them during the dry season. The formation of witches' brooms depends on the periodicity of buds, preponderance of basidiospores and favourable environmental conditions. Most witches' brooms form in the first 3 or 4 months of the year. In Trinidad sporophores are formed in June with the onset of the wet season and reaches its maximum in December.

Control: If the number of witches' brooms is small, the inoculum can be reduced by destroying green brooms. In countries in which the fungus has not developed very aggressive races, it is best controlled by growing resistant varieties, such as the clones SCA 6 and SCA 6 12, SILECIA 1 and 55 EE T 399 and 400. These clones are not resistant in Ecuador. Fungicides have so far not been very effective.

Literature

BAKER, R. & P. HOLLIDAY (1957): Witches' broom disease of cocoa. (*Marasmius perniciosus*) Stahel, Phytopathological Paper no **2**, CMI.
THOROLD, C. A. (1975): Cocoa diseases. Clarendon Oxford.
WELLMANN, F. L. (1972): Tropical American Plant Disease. The Scarecrow Press, Inc.
CMI Description no 223.

Author: E. Ampuero

Exobasidium vexans Massee (Plate 9 a–c and fig. 60)

Holobasidiomycetidae, Exobasidiales, Exobasidiaceae

Disease: Blister blight of tea; Blasenkrankheit des Tees; cloque du théier; agallas de las hojas del té.

Geographical distribution: North-East India, South India, Sri Lanka (Ceylon), Vietnam, Malaysia, Indonesia, Taiwan, Japan, China. Not present in Africa and the Americas (CMI map no 45).

Host plants: The pathogen is an obligate parasite only on the tea plant, *Camellia sinensis.*

Symptoms: Young succulent leaves and stems of tea plants are susceptible to attack. Older leaves and stems which have become leathery are resistant. The characteristic blisters on leaves appear as light yellow translucent spots (Plate 9b). They later develop into concave blisters which become white as spore production takes place (Plate 9c). Spores are produced on the lower surface of the leaves. In extremely rare instances they may appear on the upper surface. Blisters are always circular. The upper surface of the leaf blister is light yellowish green and concave but never white (Plate 9a). When the spore production phase is complete, necrosis of the diseased area begins from the centre and proceeds outwards. Necrotic areas are black in colour.

On young stems, the spore production phase is shortlived and necrosis quickly occurs, leading to the dieback of shoots, at the point of infection. Infected stems become distorted. The green outer case of tea fruits has been known to bear lesions but seeds are not infected.

Morphology: *E. vexans* produces two-celled basidiospores (Fig. 60, 1–6) borne on basidia (Fig. 60, 7–8), which are borne on a hymenium (Fig. 60, 9). Basidia are longer than the surrounding cells and bear two, three or four sterigmata in the form of minute spikes. After the release of the basidiospores from the sterigmata the basidia collapse.

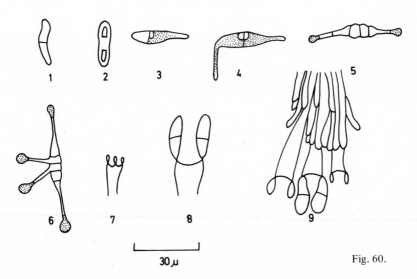

30 μ   Fig. 60.

Physiological specialization: Several generations are produced each year. Different tea clones vary considerably in their resistance to *E. vexans* but in some cases, clones known to be highly resistant ten years ago are now extremely susceptible. It is clear that new, more virulent races have been produced.

Epidemiology: The fungus survives in the form of spores in shaded tea bushes. Spores are readily killed by exposure to direct sunlight but may remain viable for longer periods under shade. When moist humid atmospheric conditions ensue in the tropical monsoons, infections and spore production are profuse. Spores are disseminated by wind. Infection takes place only on young shoots and stems, under moist shady conditions. Infection occurs only from the upper surfaces of leaves from basidiospores which produce appressoria which penetrate leaves in 14 to 16 hours after spore germination begins. The latent period varies between 11 and 21 days. Sporulation begins in 11 days, reaches a peak in 15 days and declines in 21 days under average conditions. Spore liberation follows a diurnal pattern, with maximum spore discharge taking place at night. Bushes which have been recently pruned (in a 2–6 years rotation) and have recovered, have large blisters on their shoots, but as time goes on, the intensity of attack as measured by the size and number of blisters per unit area of tissue gets progressively less until the end of the pruning cycle. The physiological condition of the tea leaves varies with age from pruning. This condition also affects disease severity. The presence of shade trees in which the foliage is left unlopped during the monsoons, increases blister blight infection, and also the period of susceptibility. This becomes more important at the beginning and end of the monsoon season. Where shade trees are lopped, the disease is not aggravated at the time of lopping but can be affected as new foliage develops.

Control: Sanitational methods are not feasible for the control of the disease because of the rapid process of reinfection. For the same reason the use of resistant varieties is not possible because resistance may break down with the formation of new races of the pathogen. The only sure method of control is by the use of fungicides. Cuprous oxide and cuprous oxychloride are the most effective fungicides available. Nickel chloride and Nickel sulphate although less effective, can also be used. Cuprous oxides and oxychlorides protect leaves from infection and do not penetrate the host tissues. Nickel salts being soluble, penetrate into the tissue having some eradicant effect, but they have the disadvantage of being easily washed off from the leaf surface because of their solubility and therefore have little protective effect. A suspension of 100 to 170 g/hectare of copper fungicide WP formulations containing 50 % w/w metallic copper suspended in 10 to 12 litres of water are used for controlling the disease on tea in its first year from pruning. Smaller doses, 30 to 100 g/hectare are used on tea in its second year from pruning.

Nickel chloride hexahydrate is not recommended for use on tea which has been pruned less than one year previously. This is because of the risk of leaf scorch. On tea older than one year from pruning it is recommended at the rate of 100 to 125 g dissolved in 20 to 25 litres of water per hectare, used in mistblowers. More water is used than with copper fungicides because the risk of leaf scorch is minimized. On tea older than two years after pruning, less fungicide is applied and often spraying can be discontinued altogether. Spray are applied in monsoon weather, immediately following harvesting so that the chance of contamination of the harvested shoots is minimized. Sprays rounds are applied every 7 to 10 days depending on weather conditions and the duration of plucking rounds. New fungicides also have shown promising results.

As sunlight has a fungicidal effect, considerable savings in costs of control of blister blight can be achieved if this factor is taken into consideration. Several schemes or modifications thereof may be practised depending on variations in weather conditions on different tea plantations. A useful guide would be that if there has been an average of 4 hours or more of bright sunshine per day for a 4 day period immediately preceding a day when a spraying round is due, spraying can be omitted. Many plantations have used this scheme with advantage.

Author: R.L. de Silva

Ganoderma spp. (Plates 8 d, 10 a–b)

Numerous species of *Ganoderma* have been associated with basal stem rot, including *G. applanatum* (Pers. ex Wallr.) Pat., *G. australe* (Fr.) Pat., *G. boninense* Pat., *G. chalceum* (Cooke) Stey., etc.

Disease: Basal stem rot of palms; Stammendfäule der Palmen; pourriture basal du tronc de la palmier à huile; podredumbre de la base del tronco de la palma de aceite.

Distribution: The disease has been recorded from all countries where oil palm is grown but has been of particular importance in Indonesia and Malaysia, where losses of 50 % or more have frequently been caused. It is of potential economic importance elsewhere if close attention is not given to control.

Host plants: *Ganoderma spp.* are characteristically saprophytes of dead jungle timbers. Their economic importance is derived from their ability to colonise dead trunks and stumps of coconut and oil palm, but also tea (Plate 8 d) rubber (Plate 10 a) and various other plantation crops.

Symptoms: Normally, the first symptoms of basal stem rot are those of wilting and malnutrition. Initially, many new fronds remain unopened, i.e. in the spear stage, and the diseased palm is usually a paler green colour than its healthy neighbours. The oldest fronds then wither, with necrosis beginning distally; such fronds droop down around the trunk. At a variable stage of disease development, usually when fronds begin to wither, sporophores are formed at the trunk base (Plate 10 b). Affected roots are very brittle. Internally, the lesion is light brown in colour and marked with irregular dark bands. Bright yellow zones occur between the lesion and healthy tissue. Small lacunae are present in the lesion and these contain the white mycelium of the pathogen, which is readily visible.

The appearance of numerous spears is not absolutely diagnostic of basal stem rot since this can be brought about by any factor causing a water deficit in the palm. Symptoms of malnutrition and wilt will also be similar wherever there is interference with the conduction of water and nutrients, so the disease has some resemblance to upper stem rot (p. 162) and vascular wilt (p. 204).

Morphology: Sporophores first appear as white buttons of mycelium, rapidly developing into a bracket form. Shape of fructifications is variable, ranging from sessile brackets to brackets arising from a stipe. Typically, the upper surface is light to dark brown in colour, zoned, has a white border, and has a shiny lacquered appearance, especially when young. The underside is dull white and bruises readily when handled.

Physiological specialization: Nothing is known of the comparative pathogenic ability of the various species. It seems that many, if not all, of the species recorded can become severe pathogens, with palms usually dying within 6–12 months of the appearance of foliar symptoms.

Epidemiology: *Ganoderma* is primarily a saprophyte or weak parasite, surviving in dead or moribund tissues. The significance of sporulation in oil palm cultivation is in reaching potential infection foci, especially dead coconut and oil palm tissues after these have been felled, with the stumps left in the ground, or poisoned and left to rot in situ. Coconut tissues are colonised virtually to the exclusion of other fungi, and old oil palm tissues to a variable degree. A minimum inoculum size is required to initiate infection, estimated to be at least 750 cm^3, and the great amounts of tissue colonised seem to impart a massive inoculum potential to the pathogen. Infection takes place through root contact of the new palm stand with colonised tissue, the pathogen moving through the interior of the root to the base of the trunk. Active growth in the soil does not occur. The course of infection at first is very slow, although a young palm may be killed rapidly. Normally it seems that initial growth within the affected palm is slow, with the period of greatest frequency of symptom appearance being when palms are 10–15 years old. When palms reach 30 years old or more, senescence seems to permit infection in the absence of large inoculum sources.

A number of environmental conditions have been cited as favouring the disease. Dry weather primarily accentuates the severity of wilting symptoms. Other factors, such as poor drainage, flooding, poor maintenance leading to heavy weed growth, and nutritional disorders have all been cited as predisposing palms to infection. However, these appear to be of negligible importance when compared with the presence of large infection foci.

Control: For long-term control in the absence of resistant material, the only safe procedure when replanting from oil palm or coconut is to ensure that all potential infection sources are removed. Clean-clearing is essential for this. For both oil palm and coconut the important tissues to be removed are those of the bole and the thick crust of roots immediately surrounding it. Whilst the other, smaller roots may be infected by the pathogen, they are not infective. Clean-clearing is usually done mechanically, after first poisoning the old stand with sodium arsenite. When the palms are pushed over, this usually uproots the bole. Old diseased palms tend to snap off and the boles then require to be treated individually. After clearing, a final plough using deep tines brings to the surface any large pieces of tissue. For preference, the old stand should be burned. When this is not possible, the old tissues are pushed into the new interrows, with the heaps having as low a profile as possible to enable a rapid legume cover overgrowth as a protection against rhinoceros beetle. Trunks should be cut into three or four sections, using chainsaws. No attempt should ever be made to dispose of oil palm or coconut tissues by burial in the planting area. Cultural treatments such as mounding earth around the stem base, sporophore collection and trenching have given no control. If a palm is not too badly diseased, i.e. the colour of the foliage still appears quite good and necrosis of the oldest fronds has not begun, surgery has given some success. All diseased tissues are excised, with care being taken to preserve as much of the outer stem tissue as possible. After excision, the cut surface is painted with protectant, such as coal tar. Since it is difficult to remove every piece of diseased tissue, especially at ground level, inspection is necessary for re-treatment at 3-month intervals. Any retreatment is usually not extensive and is quickly done. Palms too badly diseased for attempted surgery need to be excavated. This should be done as soon as possible to avoid infectious spread and the formation of large disease patches. Palms are first poisoned to accelerate later decay, taking care to place the poison in an uninfected part of the trunk. About 2 weeks later they are felled and a pit 60–90 cm square and deep dug at the planting point to remove all bole tissues and the thick root crust. Felled palms can be trimmed and left in the interrow to rot. In badly affected areas, inspection and treatment rounds at intervals of 3–4 months are needed, but a lower frequency of 6–12 months is adequate for areas of low disease incidence.

Literature

TURNER, P. D., & R. A. GILLBANKS (1974): Oil Palm Cultivation and Management. Kuala Lumpur: Incorporated Society of Planters.
CMI Descriptions nos 443, 444, 445, 446 & 448.

Author: P. D. Turner

Hemileia vastatrix Berk. & Br. (Plate 10 c)

Teliomycetes, Uredinales

Disease: Coffee leaf rust; Kaffeerost; rouille du caféier; roya del cafeto.
Of less importance so far is *H. coffeicola* Maubl. & Roger.

Geographical distribution: *H. vastatrix* has spread since 1868 in Africa, Aisa, Australia (not Papua), Brazil, Paraguay and Argentine (CMI map no 5). *H. coffeicola* is known since 1932 in the Cameroons, Northern Nigeria, Sao Tomé and Principe Islands and Uganda.

Host plants: *Coffea arabica, C. canephora, C. liberica* and other cultivated as well as wild *Coffea* and *Gardenia* spp. No host of the aecidial stage has yet been found for this rust.

Symptoms: *H. vastatrix* produces orange-yellow, circular lesions (sori) on the undersurface of leaves. They vary in size and have a powdery cover (the urediospores) (Plate 10 c). These lesions can confluence and cover entire leaves. Older lesions turn first white, from the centre outwards, and then necrotic. These rust sori can be seen through the upper leaf surface as "oil spots". Affected leaves eventually turn increasingly necrotic and finally drop prematurely. This is followed by dieback of branches, with weakening and finally death of the whole plant. Young shoots and fruit are usually free from attack. *H. coffeicola* does not produce lesions, but a more or less uniformly orange-coloured coating on the leaf undersurface, nor does it produce "oil spots" on the upper surface of leaves. If leaves are attacked, the rusts are unmistakable.

Morphology of the pathogens: Both fungi are, in practice, found only with their very characteristic urediospores: Kidney-shaped, 28–36 x 18–28 μ (*H. vastatrix*) and 34–40 x 20–28 μ (*H. coffeicola*) in size, with definite spines on the convex side, hyaline but with orange-coloured inclusions. The two species can also be differentiated by smaller and more numerous spines on urediospores of *H. vastatrix*.

Physiological specialization: Up to 1972, 26 races of *H. vastatrix* were identified in Oeiras, Portugal, most of which attacked only *C. arabica,* while the rest affected only *C. canephora* or other *Coffea* spp.
Race II is the most widely distributed, followed by I, III and, rather less than the others, XV. Other races have only local significance.

Epidemiology: Coffee leaf rust survives drought periods on affected organs. The attack increases with the start of the rainy season and continues to spread throughout the rainy period.
Leaves are increasingly infected after the rain ceases. The urediospores are dispersed through the crop by wind, water droplets and insects. Wind dispersal also spreads the disease further afield, and such spread presumably also takes place by means of transport of infected seedlings. The viability of spores varies from 7 to 28 days, depending on environmental conditions. *H. vastatrix* infects through stomatal openings on the leaf undersurface, if the leaf stays moist for 3.5–12 hrs. The temperature optimum lies between 21 and 25 °C. Younger leaves are about twice as susceptible as older ones. The incubation period varies and is, for instance 12–16 (Sri Lanka), 15–16 (Southern India), 27–40 days (Kenya highlands). The extent to which the incidence of coffee leaf rust increases in the rainy period, depends on the amount of disease at the first shower of at least 7.5 mm, on density of the foliage and on the intensity and distribution of rainfall in the early phase of the epidemic. The disease incidence decreases with increasing altitude. *H. coffeicola* on the other hand, has only been found at heights of 500 m or more, in regions which have had unusually long rainy periods or show a high relative humidity.

Control: Prophylactic measures include everything enabling the coffee plant to withstand a rust attack without lasting damage and everything reducing rust spots to a minimum.
"Hybride de Timor" is resistant to all races as well as its hybrides like Catimor (Caturra x Timor), and the variety Geisha and its progeny. Some varieties have sufficient resistance in *C. arabica* to some strains of *H. vastatrix,* (e. g. K7), but are of little commercial value. All Bourbon varieties are susceptible to all races except XIX and XX. Varieties of *C. canephora* are much more resistant than *C. arabica.* No resistance has ever been found in *C. arabica* to *H. coffeicola.*
The most effective fungicides are still copper preparations. Spray dates and spray successions vary from region to region. An application within three weeks before the first rainfalls is essential. Copper must thereafter be sprayed at intervals of 3–4 weeks. Total rounds of spray application will depend on the duration of the rainy period. Recommendations in Kenya are:
6.6–7.5 kg/ha or a 0.7 % preparation of a 50 % copper fungicide should be sprayed during the rainy season at 14–21 day intervals, depending on the amount of rainfall. For spray applications, 250 gm of the chemical should be used in 20 l water/50 trees, for low volume sprays 500 gm/20 l water/100 trees.
Recently also recommended are Fentinhydroxide (2.5 kg/ha), Dithianon 75 % WP (3.3 kg/ha) and Pyracarbolid 15 % O.D. (4 l/ha). Maneb is being recommended in Brazil, where other fungicides also have given promising results.

Literature

NUTMAN, F. J., & F. M. ROBERTS (1970): Coffee leaf rust. Pans **16,** 606–624.
SACCAS, A. M. (1971): La rouille des caféiers due à *Hemileia vastatrix* B. & Br. IFCC Bull. **10,** Paris, 1–123.
SACCAS, A. M. (1972): La rouille "farineuse" des caféiers due à *Hemileia coffeicola* Maub. & Rog. IFCC Bull. **11,** Paris, 1–68.
CMI Description nos 1 & 2.

Author: J. Kranz

Mycena citricolor (Berk. & Curt.) Sacc. (Figs. 61–62)

Synonym: *Omphalia flavida* Maubl. & Rangel
Hymenomycete, Agaricales, Tricholomataceae
Conidial state *Stilbum flavidum* Cke.
Hyphomycetes (H,3.A1.ph)

Disease: American leafspot disease of coffee; Amerikanische Blattkrankheit des Kaffees; champignon maculicole du caféir; ojo de gallo del café.

Geographical distribution: This disease is found in all coffee-producing countries in Latin America (from Brazil to Mexico) and in the Caribbean islands. Recently Schieber (1971) has identified it in Hawaii, outside the American continent.

Host plants: Apart from coffee, cacao, cinchona, citrus and some 500 species from other genera.

Symptoms: The pathogen *Mycena citricolor* mainly attacks the coffee leaves, causing inactivation of auxins and consequent defoliation of the tree. In some regions of Latin America the pathogen also attacks the coffee berries. Defoliation causes reduction in yields that, in some regions, reaches 20–30 %. In some microregions of the American continent it reduces the yield by 50 %. The spots caused by *Mycena* have well-defined margins and have no halo, as with *Cercospora* disease (*C. coffeicola,* p. 190). Spots have also a pale brown (straw) color, in contrast to the red-brown color of *Cercospora* leaf-spot. The spots produced by *M. citricolor* are round to oblong (Fig. 61) and are 5–15 mm in diameter. Mature spots turn lighter and show the typical fruiting bodies, gemmae (gemmifers) or cabecitas. These are the true infection bodies. The spots on the leaves are so characteristic that they cannot be confused with other common diseases found in the western hemisphere.

Fig. 61 (left).

Fig. 62 (below).

Morphology: The fruiting bodies, gemmae or cabecitas, are produced in 6–10 days depending on humidity, and the age of the leaf spots. The gemmae are of a citrus-yellow color (see latin name) with stalks up to 3 mm in height (Fig. 62) and heads up to 1 mm in diameter. The fruiting body of the perfect stage (the agaric stage) is occasionally produced in very humid areas of the American neotropics. This stage is characteristically a small agaric with a peaked pileus, 5–8 mm in diameter, and of a sulfur-yellow colour. The mycelium of this fungus is luminescent at night.

Physiological specialization: Work on the identification of races has not been carried out; however variation in the virulence of the pathogen must exist.

Epidemiology: The gemmae of *M. citricolor* are spread by rain water and rain splash carries these infection bodies between leaves of the same plant, and between plants. The amount and intensity of the rain must therefore play an important role in the spread of this disease. At the plantation level, *M. citricolor* spreads in foci, not evenly, over a coffee plantation. These foci or discrete areas are defined according to the microecology and topography of the plantation. In addition, plantations have an incidence and spread of the disease according to the intensity of their shade.

The American leaf-spot disease of coffee is encountered throughout Latin America where heavy rainfall is common; in drier areas the disease does not develop. Although it is believed that its severity increases in warmer areas, it is also found in the cooler high altitude plantations of Colombia, Mexico and Central America.

Control: Bordeaux Mixture was first recommended for chemical control of the disease, and later the use of copper fungicides. The number of applications was however high and expensive. In Central America certain organic-mercuries were found to stop gemmae formation, only few applications eradicating the disease. However it was soon found that mercurials could not be used as a spray on coffee, since residual mercury was found in coffee beans.

Before 1957 some coffee farmers in Colombia applied lead arsenate to coffee plantings, and by accident found that "Ojo de Gallo" was being eradicated. Further experiments carried out in Costa Rica indicated that lead arsenate was the most effective chemical to control the American leaf-spot disease.

It is of interest that farmers in Colombia, Central America and Mexico soon eradicated the disease in many plantations by the systematic use of basic lead arsenate.

Three applications of basic lead arsenate at a concentration of 3.64g per liter of water (and an added sticker) are recommended in Central America. In addition, some applications of Zinc (Nu-Z) at the rate of 3.64 per liter of water, have to be made to correct phytotoxic effects of the arsenic.

New fungicides, including Tridemorph and others, are presently being tested in Central America. Some observation have been carried out in relation to resistance to the American leaf-spot disease, but no definite and confirmed results are available.

As coffee under heavy shade suffers more from the disease, it is recommended that shade be reduced regularly to minimize disease severity.

Since sunlight and aeration are important factors in blocking the pathogen, the distance in and between rows in the plantation plays an important role in disease control. Also pruning of the coffee plant is a factor to be considered in a control program.

Literature

ECHANDI, E., & R. H. SEGALL (1958): The effectiveness of certain eradicant fungicides on inhibition of gemmae of *Mycena citricolor* Phytopathology **48**, 11–14.

SCHIEBER, E. (1970): Report on coffee diseases in Hawaii. Unpublished report to the chairman Department of Plant Pathology, University of Hawaii, Honolulu-Hawaii.

WELLMAN, F. L. (1972): Tropical American plant disease. The Scarecrow Press, Inc., Metuchen, N. J., USA.

Author: E. Schieber

Some Marasmius spp. as pathogens on tropical and subtropical crops:

M. pulcher (Berk. & Br.) Petch. Thread blight of nutmeg.

M. sacchari Wakk. Root rot of sugarcane.

M. scandens Mass. White thread of cacao, cola, black pepper, etc.

M. semiustes Berk. & Curt. Stem rot of banana and abaca.

Phellinus noxius (Corner) G. H. Cunn. (Plate 10 a and fig. 63)

Synonym: *Fomes noxius* Corner
Hymenomycetes, Aphyllosphorales, Hymenochaetaceae

Disease: Upper stem rot of oil palms; Stammfäule der Ölpalme; pourriture du tronc de la palmier à huile; podredumbre del tronco de la palma de aceite.

Geographical distribution: Indonesia and Malaysia; a similar disease has been recorded for West Africa. The same pathogen also causes a basal trunk infection in Malaysia and New Guinea (CMI map no 104).

Host plants: Numerous alternative hosts in countries where oil palm is grown, including avocado pear, cocoa, coffee, *Hevea* rubber (Plate 10a), kapok, mandarin, mangosteen, orange, ramie fibre, rambutan, tea, *Tephrosia vogelii,* and decaying stumps of numerous forest tree species.

Fig. 63.

Symptoms: Lesions develop at any height on the trunk, usually in palms 10 years old or more. Frequently, the first obvious symptom is trunk collapse (Fig. 63). A variable amount of chlorosis may be shown by the foliage before collapse and older fronds may wilt and hang down around the trunk. Internally, the lesion is darker brown in colour than that caused by *Ganoderma* (p. 156); the zonations are also darker and the lacunae contain dark-coloured mycelium. Sometimes more than one lesion may occur on the stem.

Wilting fronds and chlorosis resemble symptoms of basal stem rot (p. 156). The diseases can be distinguished by sporophores and the type and location of the lesions.

Morphology: Fructifications of *P. noxius* may or may not be produced. The sporophores are usually resupinate grey-brown crusts, although the upper margin may grow outwards to form a bracket type of fructification. The simultaneous appearance of sporophores of *Ganoderma* in some instances is thought to be through later invasion of tissues initially colonised by *P. noxius.*

Epidemiology: Lesions height indicate infection by airborne spores derived either from an alternative host or an infected palm. Frond bases left on the palm after pruning are colonised but the disease remains superficial on the trunk until a large area has been infected. Disease then penetrates deeper but it is 1–3 years before the palm is killed. At the time of trunk collapse, the lesion usually occupies about 60–80 % of the stem is cross section. Palms may be predisposed to infection by poor soil conditions and a low potassium nutrient status.

Control: Successful control depends on early detection and surgery. This is done by a sonic method in which a wooden pole is run upwards over the leaf bases on two or three sides of the palm. When a dull sound is heard, the stem is inspected for disease. Surgery of diseased areas entails removal of all infected tissue and the exposed area then treated with a dressing such as coal tar. Given early treatment, a high success rate has been obtained. Disease survey usually need only be carried out annually. Palms which have collapsed should be excavated.

Literature

TURNER, P. D., & R. A. GILLBANKS (1974): Oil Palm Cultivation and Management. Kuala Lumpur. Incorporated Society of Planters.
CMI Description no 195.

Author: P. D. Turner

Puccinia erianthi Padwick & Khan
Puccinia kuehnii (Krüg.) Butler

Teliomycetes, Uredinales

Disease: Rust of sugarcane; Zuckerrohrrost; rouille de la cane à sucre; roya de la caña de azúcar.

Geographical distribution: The rust is restricted to eastern hemisphere only. A couple of severe out-breaks of the disease have been reported from India on variety Co. 475 and Co. S. 510.

Host plants: In India, *Erianthus fulvus* and *Saccharum spontaneum* are collateral hosts of *P. erianthi;* while *P. kuehnii* has been reported to occur on *Saccharum spontaneum, S. officinarum* and other hybrids (*Spontaneum officinarum robustum*) in Indonesia and Australia.

Symptoms: The rust pustules are formed on both surfaces of the leaves. On young leaves these appear as minute, elongated, yellowish spots, usually 2 to 10 mm in length and 1 to 3 mm in width. These turn brown on maturity. In case of epidemics, rust pustules appear on leaf sheaths also and the leaves look brownish from a distance.

Morphology: *Puccinia erianthi* and *P. kuehnii* occur on sugarcane. Urediospores of *P. kuehnii* have distinct apical thickening, while urediospores of *P. erianthi* have walls more or less uniformly thickened all around. Urediospores of *P. erianthi* are hypophyllous, sometimes amphigenous, ovoid to pear shaped 29–57 μ long, finaly echinulate with 3 to 5 equitorially placed germ pores. Paraphyses which are hyaline to golden in colour are club shaped and are usually in abundance at the margins of the urediosori or mixed with spores.

Physiological specialization: The presence of parasitic races of the sugarcane rust pathogen has been reported.

Epidemiology: The spread of rust is usually rapid at 30 °C with humidity between 70 and 90 %. Besides these factors, cloudiness of weather and wind velocity help development of rust pustules and dissemination of the fungal spores.
These remain viable up to 5 weeks at room temperatures (18 to 28 °C) but rapidly lose their viability during hot weather at temperatures above 35 °C. Urediospores germinate readily in water from 16 to 29 °C, optimum temperature being 20–25 °C.
Teliosori are produced abundantly on the under surface of the leaf, sometimes on the upper surface also. Teliospores are oblong to club shaped, two celled, smooth walled, slightly constricted at the septum and measure 25 to 40μ x 10 to 18 μ in diameter.
Rust usually appears in November in India. The spores remain viable till the middle of April. Later on viable spores are rarely met with in nature. In north Indian plains, the disease passes summer as tiny uredo pustules on the foliage of young sugarcane tillers in autumn planted or ratoons.

11*

Comparatively lower temperatures and higher humidity near the ground level facilitate rust development. At the level of leaf canopy, urediospores do not remain viable beyond a few hours due to high temperature and low humidity.

Control: Though high degree of resistance to rust has been observed in several cultivars and their parents, breeding of rust resistant varieties has not so far been attempted.
Ferbam (ferric dimethyl dithiocarbamate) and Ziram (Zinc dimethyl dithiocarbamate) were reported effective against sugarcane rust. Spraying with a mixture of Ferbam (0.75 %) and nickel sulphate (0.5 %) at three week intervals between November and March effectively controls the disease under field conditions.

Literature

HUGHES, C. G., E. V. ABBOTT & C. A. WISMER (1964): Sugarcane diseases of the world. Vol 2. Elsevier Pub. Company, Amsterdam.
SAHNI, M. L., & B. L. CHONA (1965): Studies on sugarcane rust in India. Indian Phytopathology **28**, 191–203.
CMI Description nos 9 & 10.

Authors: Kishan Singh and V. P. Agnihotri

Puccinia sorghi Schw. (Plate 11 d and fig. 64 a–c)
Puccinia polysora Underwood
Physopella zeae (Mains) Cummins & Ramachar

Teliomycetes, Uredinales

Disease: Maize rusts; Maisroste; rouilles du maize; royas del maiz.

Geographical distribution: *Puccinia sorghi* is found in all regions of the world where maize is grown (CMI map no 279), in contrast *Physopella zeae* is restricted to the region from Mexico down to Venezuela, including the Caribbean islands. The Polysora rust (*Puccinia polysora*) is found in all tropical regions of the Americas and Asia (CMI map no 237); Schieber (1970) has recently found this rust in Hawaii. First reported from the USA in 1891, and from the Caribbean in 1940, *Puccinia polysora* reached Africa (Sierra Leone) in 1949. After spreading through West Africa it crossed the continent, reaching Tanzania, Kenya and Zanzibar in 1952. Later, in 1953, it was also reported from Malawi, Zambia, Mozambique, South Africa and was spreading towards Mauritius. The disease reached the Philippines in 1955, and the same year was also found in Thailand.

Host plants: The uredial stage of *Puccinia polysora* is restricted mainly to *Euchlaena mexicana, Tripsacum dactyloides, T. lanceolatum, T. laxum, T. pilosum, Zea mays,* and *Erianthus alopecuroides. P. polysora* does not infect *Oxalis* species as does *P. sorghi* (Schieber and Dickson 1963). Hosts of the latter fungus are *Euchlaena mexicana* and *Zea mays.* Hosts of *Physopella zeae* are *Euchlaena mexicana, E. perennis* and *Zea mays.*

Symptoms: The three rusts produce distinctly different symptoms on corns. The symptoms relate to the uredio-pustules produced on the maize host.
Puccinia polysora produces uredio-pustules that are round to oblong in shape. In the field, the epidermis is sometimes retained covering the pustules until maturity. However occasionally the epidermis breaks and spore-masses in abundance become visible. When open urediosori are cha-

racteristically orange to deep-orange in color. Numerous pustules are formed on the leaves and some-times also on the leaf-sheaths; they cause the upper leaf surface to be rough. In advanced stages of the disease, the rust completely "burns" parts of the leaves.

Puccinia sorghi produces long or oblong urediosori on the leaves. The epidermis partly ruptures and masses of spores are released which give the pustule a brown or deep brown color (Plate 11d); this differentiates *P. sorghi* from *P. polysora*. Mature pustules turn from brown to black when teliospores are formed.

Physopella zeae produces urediosori scattered on the leaf surface and frequently also on the leaf sheath. Masses of cream-colored spores are found on the leaf surface. Sometimes, the uredio-pustulus, when mature, give a purple color to the epidermis; this reaction has not been yet studied in detail.

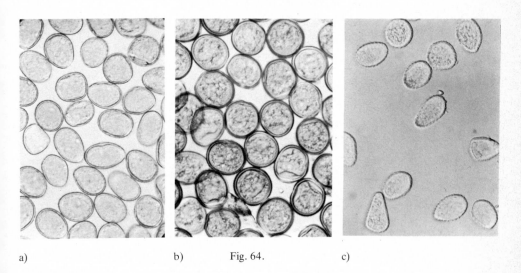

a)   b)   Fig. 64.   c)

Morphology: Since the telial stage of these rusts is seldom found naturally, identification depends on the characteristics of the uredial stage. The urediospores of *P. polysora* (Fig. 64a) and *P. sorghi* (Fig. 64b) were reported are different in size and shape, with the length-breadth ratio as the major difference. The thin-walled urediospores of *P. sorghi* are spherical to globoid and in contrast, those of *P. polysora* are clearly oval to ovoid and thickwalled. In addition the urediospores of *P. polysora* are a golden color, rather than the reddish brown of *P. sorghi*. Urediospores of *P. polysora* are covered sparingly with fine echinulations. The germ pores are more equatorial in position in *P. polysora* than in *P. sorghi*. The urediospores of *Physopella zeae* (Fig. 64c) are yellow, ellipsoid and distinctly echinulate and with obscure pores.

Physiological specialization: Two races of *P. polysora* are designated as WA1 (West African 1) and WA2 (West African 2). In East Africa three more races (EA 1–3) have been defined. One race (EA 2) was detected in greenhouses but has not been found in the field.

Epidemiology: The rust fungus *P. polysora* is spread by wind as are the other cereal rusts, and wind plays an important role in its rapid dissemination. It has been stated in the literature that in contrast to *P. sorghi* Polysora rust is found in warmer regions but Schieber has found *P. polysora* in the cool regions of Latin America at elevations of 1.800 m above sea level.

Control: The only control measure against *Puccinia polysora* rust is by utilizing resistance. In West Africa, Stanton and Cammack reported the discovery of a gene which they designated as

Rpp 2, derived from the Mexican corn varieties San Luis Potosi and Coahuila 8 and covering resistance to races EA 1 (East African 1) and WA 1 (West African 1) of the pathogen.
Storey's genetic studies in East Africa, revealed two genes determining resistance; gene Rpp1, fully dominant for resistance to Race 1, and gene Rpp 2, not completely dominant and subject to modifying genes that give a range of resistant reactions to races 1 and 2 in East Africa.
In Africa resistance was found mainly in genotypes from Latin America.

Literature

CAMMACK, R. H. (1958): Studies on *Puccinia polysora* Underw. I. The world distribution of forms of *P. polysora*. Trans. Brit. mycol. Soc. **41**, 189–94.
SCHIEBER, E., & J. G. DICKSON (1963): Comparative pathology of three tropical corn rusts. Phytopathology, **53**, 517–521.
SCHIEBER, E. (1971): Distribution of *Puccinia polysora* and *P. sorghi* in Africa and their pathogenicity on Latin American maize germ plasm. FAO Plant Prot. Bull. **19**, 25–31.
STANTON, W. R., & R. H. CAMMACK (1953): Resistance to the maize rust *Puccinia polysora* Underw. Nature, Lond., **172**, 505–506.
WOOD, J. T., & R. LIPSCOMB (1956): Spread of *Puccinia polysora* with a bibliography on the three rusts on *Zea mays*. Spec. Publ. Agr. Res. Serv. U.S. Dept. Agr. **9**
CMI Description no 3, 4 and 5.

Author: E. Schieber

Puccinia spp. on wheat and barley (Plate 11 a–c and fig. 65)

(1) *Puccinia graminis* Pers. (f. sp. *tritici* and *secalis*),
(2) *Puccinia striiformis* Westend (f. sp. *tritici* and *hordei*),
(3) *Puccinia recondita* Rob ex Desm. f. sp. *tritici*,
(4) *Puccinia hordei* Otth.
Teliomycetes, Uredinales

Disease:
(1) Stem rust or black rust of wheat and barley; Schwarzrost des Weizens und der Gerste; Rouille noire ou rouille linéaire des céréales (blé et orge); Roya negra de los cereales o roya del tallo del trigo y cebada.
(2) Stripe rust or yellow rust of wheat and barley; Gelbroste des Weizens und der Gerste; Rouille jaune ou rouille des glumes des céréales (blé et orge), Roya de las glumas o roya amarilla de los cereales.
(3) Leaf rust or brown rust of wheat; Weizenbraunrost; Rouille brune de blé; Roya parda del trigo.
(4) Leaf rust of barley or dwarf leaf rust; Gerstenzwergrost; Rouille naine de l'orge; Roya de las hojas de cebada.

Geographical distribution:
1. Stem rust is generally found where wheat and barley is grown commercially. The disease is favored by warm temperate climates where moisture is not limiting.
2. Stripe rust is widely distributed and favored by cooler temperate climates or higher elevations. It does not occur in Oceania and South Africa (CMI map no 97).
3. Leaf rust of wheat is probably the most widespread disease of wheat. It is often found with either stem or stripe rust. The disease development is favored in temperate climates (CMI map no 226).
4. Leaf rust of barley is reported to exist in most barley growing regions of the world. Disease development is favored in coastal climates, like that of the Mediterranean area.

Host plants:
1. Stem rust attacks species of *Triticum* and a number of grass hosts in nature. The most common species attacked are: *Aegilops, Agropyron, Avena, Elmyus, Hordeum* and *Secale*. Physiological specialization is pronounced and confirmation is required to determine if the rust found on grasses can attack wheat and barley.
2. Stripe rust of wheat and barley attacks a number of grasses in nature but physiologic specialization is complicated. The forms attacking wheat often do not attack barley and the converse is also true. Confirmation is required of the relationship between the wheat, barley and grass forms.
3. Leaf rust of wheat has been reported to attack a limited number of grasses in nature. The physiologic specialization is more specific than with stem and stripe rust.
4. Leaf rust of barley is reported to attack a limited number of related grasses.

Symptoms:
1. Stem rust can attack all aerial portions of the plant. It is commonly found on the stem, leaf sheath, peduncle and spike. The uredial stage produces reddish-brown to cinnamon-brown colored urediospores. Stem rust infections on the leaf usually erupt from both the upper and lower surface. The teliospores are formed at senscence or under unfavorable conditions, are black-brown in color (Plate 11a).
2. Stripe rust attacks all aerial portions of the plant. The color of the urediosori is varying shades of yellow, most often an orange or golden yellow. The pustule are usually in a linear series, vary in size and form a striping pattern (Plate 11b, left).
Teliospores are blackish and form below the epidermis. This stage is often confused with the teliospore stage of leaf rust but the striping pattern usually distinguishes between the two rusts.
3. Leaf rust of wheat usually is confined to the leaves and leaf sheaths. The pustules are small, nearly round and red-brown in color (Plate 11b right).
Teliospores are black in color and are formed under the epidermis.
4. Leaf rust of barley is very similar to leaf rust of wheat but it attacks only barley. The uredia are small, round and pale brown in color, and develop on the leaves and leaf sheaths.
Teliospores are blackish in color and form under the epidermal surface (Plate 11c).
Host specialization for each species is highly developed and often complicated. Many of the rust fungi of cereals and grasses are characterized by having a specific alternate host. *Puccinia striiformis* does not have a known alternate host.
The complete life cycle of *P. graminis, P. recondita* and *P. hordei* is complex. There are five spore stages and two of the spore stages occur on a dicotyledonous alternate host species (Fig. 65).

The alternate host species for the fungi are:

Fungus	Alternate host	
	Primary	Others
1. *P. graminis*	*Berberis* spp.	*Mahonia* spp.
2. *P. striiformis*	Unknown	
3. *P. recondita*	*Thalictrum* spp.	Species of the
	Isopyrum spp.	Boraginaceae, Hydrophylaceae and Balsaminaceae.
4. *P. hordei*	*Ornithogalum* spp.	
		Also Allium and Sedium spp.

Morphology: The morphological features of the teliospore are used for classification (family and genus) of the rust fungi. Species are distinguished by urediospore characters and their host specialization. The urediospore and teliospore characters of the rusts of wheat and barley can be used to dinstinguish the species involved. The main characters are:

	Urediospores	Teliospores
1. *P. graminis*	Single celled oval 26-40 x 16-22 μ light brown	two celled, oblong tapered tip 40-60 x 16-23 μ brown black
2. *P. recondita*	single celled rounded 25-30 x 20-24 μ pale yellow	two celled, oblong flattened tip 40-60 x 17-23 μ brown black
3. *P. striiformis*	single celled rounded 24-32 x 20-25 μ light brown	two celled, oblong rounded tip 40-60 x 15-22 μ brown black
4. *P. hordei*	single celled oval 21-30 x 38-25 μ yellowish brown	one to 3 cells, oblong rounded tip 45-63 x 19-25 μ brown black

Physiological specialization: Physiological specialization in *Puccinia* spp. is highly developed. The cereal rusts are classified beyond the species level to *forma specialis,* and physiological races are recognized within each *forma specialis.* Physiologic races for each rust are determined by a set of differential varieties. The standard international set for *P. graminis, P. striiformis* and *P. recondita* is 12, 13 and 8 varieties respectively. For *P. hordei,* 13 varieties of barley are used. Based on the reaction of these varieties to each rust culture a physiological race number is assigned. Because of the continuous variation possible with each rust culture, depending upon available genes for resistance in the host, most areas of the world use supplemental varieties for further classification of races.

Epidemiology: All four rust species are capable of surviving through the asexual cycle of the urediospore as long as the cereal or grass host is available for infection. In the case of *P. striiformis* this is the only known means of survival. In areas of the world, where the alternate host is present, *P. graminis, P. recondita* and *P. hordei* may survive adverse periods in the teliospore stage. Upon the initiation of favorable conditions the teliospores germinate to infect the alternate host which results in the production of aeciospores which in turn infect wheat and initiate the urediospore cycle again.

Each urediospore that infects wheat may result in a pustule. It is estimated that each infection is capable of producing from 50,000 to 250,000 new spores. Urediospores move by air movements. Because of their size and ability to withstand desiccation, urediospores may be transported long distances by wind. Spore movements of 1,000 to 2,000 kilometers have been documented. If free water is available for a period of six or more hours, germination will occur. The majority of the infections occur within 12 to 18 hours.

Depending upon temperature, a pustule is produced in 8 to 30 days. Under favorable conditions the pustule usually appears 10–14 days after infection.

The response of the host to rust infections is governed genetically. If a race can attack a variety, high fertility conditions favor disease development. Good nutrition of the host alters the microclimate to one more suitable for these fungi.

GENERALIZED LIFE CYCLE OF THE CEREAL RUSTS

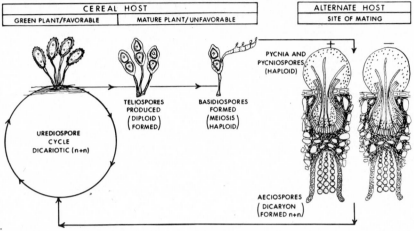

Fig. 65.

The complete life cycle of the rust fungi as (Fig. 65) functions in those areas of the world where the alternate host is near to the cereal crop. In other areas the rusts must maintain themselves on the cereal or grass hosts by the urediospore cycle. In these cases, the rust may survive in the immediate area on volunteer or self-sown plants. Where the crop does not survive from season to season, the rust must be reintroduced from a distant area.

In India, for example, *P. graminis* survives throughout the year in the southern hills at higher elevations. This reservoir of inoculum initiates the infection in the plains each year. In other areas a difference in elevation occurs in a short distance and wheat and rust can be found at the different elevations depending upon the stage of crop development.

The cereal rusts are limited in time and place by moisture and temperature. If moisture is available for the infection process, cool temperatures favor *P. striiformis* (optimum 10–14 °C). With the advent of higher temperatures stripe rust is restricted and rusts such as *P. recondita* and *P. hordei* dominate (optimum 16–20 °C).

Stem rust is favored by slightly warmer temperatures (optimum 18–21 °C).

Control: The principal method for controlling cereal rusts has been through resistant varieties. The resistance of a variety is never permanent. The change that occurs is not in the host but in the new races of the rust that arise by mutation, the sexual cycle or by some variation of the sexual cycle.

A new race which has the ability to attack a previously resistant variety has the potential to create an epidemic if a variety occupies a large acreage and weather is favorable for rust development. It is estimated that the race specific (vertical) resistance of a variety will be of value for four to five years on the average. As a result, control through the development of resistant varieties is a continuous process, often discouraging and subject to some criticism. In spite of the fact that new races readily evolve, notable progress has been achieved through resistance breeding. The frequency and magnitude of epidemics has been reduced considerably on a global basis. An even more effective and lasting control might evolve from the breeding of race nonspecific (horizontal) resistant varieties.

A number of chemical control procedures have been under evaluation and have found limited application. In most cases the irregularity of rust development from year to year and the economic value of treatment has limited the extensive use of chemical control. The most effective chemicals available on a commercial basis are the dithiocarbamates. These chemicals act as protectants and their application requires high degree of technical and management skills. This has limited their value and use commercially.

Some promising systemic fungicides are now appearing on an experimental basis. They have the advantage of requiring less precision and have an extended period of effectiveness. The systemic fungicides as potential control agents of the cereal rusts still need to be evaluated economically and the clearance for human and animal consumption of treated plants needs to be resolved. Several cultural practices can influence the development of cereal rusts because of their effect on epidemiology. The elimination of volunteer or self-sown plants through cultural practices can reduce the possibilities of early infection. Similarly, removal of the alternate host or avoiding the sowing of wheat within 100 m considerably reduces early infection.

In general early sown crops are subject to less damage by rust attack. This is an escape mechanism and applies mostly to stem and leaf rust. The maturing of the crop at an earlier date means that one or two cycles of the rust epidemic are avoided. This can mean a substantial difference in the severity of attack and the damage caused by rust can be minimized.

In some areas of the world primary inoculum arrives from a distant area early in the season. A major shift in the general meteorological pattern may exclude a region at a later date. In such cases the late sown crop may escape either the arrival of the early inoculum, or local weather conditions may change sufficiently to be unfavorable for the establishment of the disease. This type of escape is not common.

Literature

CHESTER, K. S. (1946): The Nature and Prevention of the Cereal Rusts as Exemplified in the Leaf Rust of Wheat. Chronica Botanica Co. Waltham Mass., USA.
CUMMINS, G. B. (1971): The Rust Fungi of Cereals, Grasses and Bamboos. Springer-Verlag, New York.
HOOKER, A. L. (1967): The genetics and expression of resistance in plants to rusts of the genus *Puccinia*. Ann. Rev. Phytopathology **5**, 163–182.
JOHNSON, T., G. J. GREEN & D. J. SAMBORSKI (1967): The world situation of the cereal rusts. Ann. Rev. Phytopathology **5**, 183–200.
ROWELL, J. B. (1968). Chemical control of the cereal rusts. Ann. Rev. Phytopathology **6**, 243–262.
CMI Description no 291.

Authors: E. E. Saari and L. M. Joshi

Other more important or common rusts on tropical and subtropical crops:

(O, I = aecidial state, II, III = uredial and/or telial state)

Cerotelium fici (Butl.) Arth. Fig rust (II, III). Ref.: CMI Description no 284.

Coleosporium ipomoeae (Schw.) Burrill. Orange rust of sweet potato (O, I). Ref.: CMI Description no 282.

Goplana dioscoreae (Berk. & Br.) Ansun. Rust of yams.

Melampsora ricini Noronha. Rust of castorbean (II, III). Ref.: CMI Description no 171.

Phakopsora gossypii (Arth.) Hirat. = *Cerotelium desmium* (Berk. & Br.) Arth. Cotton rust (II, III). Ref.: CMI Description no 172.

P. pachyrhizi Syd. Rust of soybean.

Puccinia arachidis Speg. Rust of groundnut (II, III). Ref.: CMI Description no 53.

P. carthami Cda. Rust of safflower (II, III). Ref.: CMI Description no 174.

P. helianthi Schw. Sunflower rust (II, III). Ref.: CMI Description no 55.

P. penicillariae Speg. Rust on *Pennisetum* spp. (II, III) and *Solanum* spp. (O, I), including eggplant. Ref.: CMI Description no 6.

P. pittieriana P. Henn. Rust of potato and tomato (III). Ref.: CMI Description no 286.

P. psidii Wint. Rust of guava and *Eugenia* spp. etc. (II, III). Ref.: CMI Description no 56.

P. purpurea Cke. Leaf rust of sorghum (II, III). Ref.: CMI Description no 8.

P. schedonardi Kell. & Swing. and *P. stakmanii* Presley = *P. cacabata* Arth. & Holw. Cotton rusts (O, I). Ref.: CMI Description no 293.

Uromyces cicer-arietini Jacz. Chickpea rust (II, III). Ref.: CMI Description no 178.

U. decoratus Syd. Rust of sunn hemp. (*Crotolaria* spp.) (II, III). Ref.: CMI Description no 179.

U. dolicholi Arth. Rust of pigeon pea (II, III). CMI map no 236.

U. joffrini Del. Rust of vanilla (II, III).

U. manihotis P. Henn. Rust of cassava (II, III).

U. mucunae Rabenh. Velvet bean rust (*Mucuna* spp.) (O, I, II, III). Ref.: CMI Description no 290.

U. musae P. Henn. Rust of *Musa* spp. (II, III). Ref.: CMI Description no 295.

U. vignae Barcl. Rust of cowpea (II, III).

Uredo cajani Syd. Rust of pigeon pea (II).

U. erythroxilionis Graz. Rust of cacao (II).

U. ficina Juel Rust of Ficus (II). Ref.: CMI Description no 289.

U. mori Barcl. Rust of mulberry (II).

U. musae Cumm. Rust of *Musa* spp. (II). Ref.: CMI Description no 295.

General literature on rust fungi:

ARTHUR, J. C. (1934): Manual of the rusts in United States and Canada, Lafayette, Indiana.
BLUMER, S. (1963): Rost- und Brandpilze auf Kulturpflanzen. Gustav Fischer, Jena.
CUMMINS, G. B. (1959): Illustrated Genera of rust fungi. Burgess Publ., Minneapolis, USA.
CUMMINS, G. B. (1971): The rust fungi of cereals grasses and bamboos. Springer-Verlag, Berlin-Heidelberg-New York.
GÄUMANN, E. (1959): Die Rostpilze Mitteleuropas. Beitr. Kyptogamenfl. Schweiz. Vol XII.
GUYOT, A. L. (1939–1957): Les Uredinées, Lechevalier, Paris.
LAUNDON, G. F. (1965): The generic names of Uredinales. Mycol. papers no 99. Commonwealth Mycological Institute, Kew, UK.
SYDOW, P. (1902–1924): Monographia Uredinearium, Berlin, 4 vols.
VIEGAS, A. P. (1945): Alguns fungos do Brasil – IV. Uredinales. Bragantia **5**, 1–144.

Rigidoporus lignosus (Klotzsch) Imazeki (Plate 10 a and figs. 66–67)

Synonym: *Fomes lignosus* Klotzsch
Hymenomycetes, Aphyllophorales, Polyporaceae

Disease: White root disease of *Hevea;* weiße Wurzelfäule des Kautschukbaumes; pourriture blanche des racines; podredumbre blanca de las raices.

Geographical distribution: This disease has been recorded in all the countries where *Hevea* is grown as a commercial crop (CMI map no 176).

Host plants: *R. lignosus* in addition attacks a wide range of economically important tropical crops such as coconut (*Cocos nucifera*) cocoa (*Theobroma cacao*), jak or breadfruit (*Artocarpus indicus*) papaw (*Carica papaya*), and tea (*Camellia sinensis*). In fact, given suitable conditions, this fungus will infect almost any tropical plant.

Symptoms: The fungus generally affects the lateral roots first and grows along those roots to the main or tap root. Affected roots are conspicuous because of the white epiphytic mycelium, which is a diagnostic feature of the fungus (Plate 10a, fig. 66). It is characteristic of *R. lignosus* to grow superficially on the roots to a considerable distance, about 0.5 m, before it establishes an infection at the point of original contact with the root. Infection proceeds in this manner, with the epiphytic mycelium always growing ahead of the infected area of the root. The fungus does not spread laterally inside the root.
Affected roots become discoloured and lose their latex, the internal bark tissue becoming brown and crumbly. The woody portion of the roots when affected by the fungus turns white, loses texture and becomes soft and friable.

Leaf symptoms are seen on affected trees, generally, only when the base of the tap root is infected. Leaves turn pale green, lose their lustre and curl inwards, finally turning yellow and falling off.

The above ground symptoms are similar whichever root disease affects *Hevea;* as all root disease pathogens cause a disorganisation of the water-conducting tissue, giving rise to drought symptoms on the leaves. Therefore, the root system must be examined to identify the disease.

Morphology: *R. lignosus* produces fine white hyphae with conspicuous clamp connections, which are characteristic of the basidiomycetes. The hyphae aggregate to produce thick white rhizomorphs which can grow through the soil or over rocks for considerable distances away from infected wood. The fructifications of the fungus grow in tiers and are conspicuous. They are large, bracket shaped, yellow to brick red in colour and have characteristic concentric rings on the upper surface (Fig. 67) and minute pores on the lower surface.

Fig. 66.

Fig. 67.

Physiological specialization: There is no record of physiological specialization in this fungus and it is doubtful whether this occurs; because the fungus is readily transferable between different orders of plants and between dicotyledons and monocotyledons.

Epidemiology: *R. lignosus* is a facultative saprophyte and generally lives on dead organic matter, from where it obtains the necessary energy to infect a living host. It is a weak parasite; therefore, it requires a fairly large outside source of energy, a food base, from which to obtain its nutrients before it can infect a living root. The fungus sporulates profusely, producing millions of tiny spores from the bracket-shaped fructifications. The spores are wind dispersed and there is a diurnal periodicity in spore release with a definite peak shortly after midnight. The fungus has very limited competitive saprophytic ability; therefore, it does not usually cause new infections by means of spores. However, it has been proved that *R. lignosus* spores can cause stump infection, if they fall on freshly cut *Hevea* wood, where it does not have to compete with other fungi.

Infection of living hosts is usually caused by the fungus, on dead organic matter, making contact with the host roots (Fig. 66). The locus of infection is usually a lateral root, and the fungus has to be in contact with the host for 2–3 weeks before infection occurs. The causal fungus has no annual cycle of infection. It requires moist soil for survival and grows best in slightly acid soils at a pH of about 5.6–6.

Control: *R. lignosus* being a weak parasite and requiring a food base for survival and infection of a living host, sanitation is the key to the control of the disease. If infected plant parts are removed from the soil at the time of planting a new crop, the chances of spore infection being negligible, there is every prospect of growing the fresh crop without losses through *Rigidoporus* infection. When the root system of the *Hevea* tree is identified, by foliar symptoms as infected by *Rigidoporus,* the root system is uncovered, the external food base is traced and eradicated, the infected parts of the root system excised and the superficial mycelium on the healthy roots brushed off. The root system is then covered over with soil and allowed to regenerate.

Varieties of *Hevea* resistant to *Rigidoporus* infection are not known. Chemicals do not play any part in the control of the disease. The most important factor in controlling the disease being the eradication of the food base. Following this the tree recovers; as the fungus is a weak parasite and cannot cause infection even if small pieces of it are left behind in the soil. Therefore, chemical treatment of infected trees, treated surgically, is redundant.

Literature

PERIES, O. S., T. M. FERNANDO & S. K. SAMARAWEERA (1965): Control of White Root Disease (*Fomes lignosus*) of *Hevea brasiliensis*. Rub. Res. Inst. Ceylon Quart J., **41,** 81–89.
PERIES, O. S., & Z. E. IRUGALBANDARA (1973). Histology of *Hevea* roots infected by *Fomes lignosus*. Ann. appl. Biol. **73,** 1–7.
SATCHUTHANANTHAVALE, V. (1971): Sulphur in the control of White Root disease. Rub. Res. Inst. Ceylon Quart. J., **48,** 82–91.
CMI Description no 198.

Author: O. S. Peries

Sphacelotheca and Tolyposporum spp. on Sorghum (Plate 12 a–d)

Teliomycetes, Ustilaginales

Four smut diseases commonly occur on sorghum (*Sorghum vulgare*). These are caused by closely related fungi, among three of which interspecific hybrids can be produced with relative ease. Negligible damage occurs to the vegetative parts of the plant, and symptoms are not evident until head exsertion or early seed development. Individual florets or entire panicles are converted to light-colored structures (sori) that contain dark-colored, diploid spores (teliospores). Symptoms of each disease are usually distinct, but sometimes may be difficult to differentiate. A chart of differential characteristics is presented to aid in identification (table 6).

Teliospores become seed- or soil-borne and germinate to form haploid spores (basidiospores). Basidiospores with complementary sex factors fuse before invading the host. Environmental conditions such as soil moisture and temperature influence the incidence of infection, but the relation-ship of these factors to infection is not always clearly understood.

1. *Sphacelotheca sorghi* (Link) Clint.

Disease: Covered smut, kernel smut or grain smut; gedeckter Brand; charbon couvert du millet; carbón cubierto del mijo.

Geographical distribution: Covered smut is almost co-extensive with the culture of sorghum and the most important smut of this crop, having been reported in Africa, Asia, Australasia, Europe, and North and South America. Yield losses, particularly in Africa and Asia, may average 5 to 10 percent annually, with localized losses of 60 percent or more (CMI map no 220).

Host plants: Hosts of *S. sorghi*, other than *Sorghum bicolor*, are *Sorghum sudanense* and *S. hale-pense*.

Symptoms: see table 6 and plate 12a.

Morphology: see table 6.

Physiological specialization: Nine physiologic races of *S. sorghi* have been reported; however, it seems likely that more races exist. Crosses, which are able to infect and cause disease, have been obtained in the laboratory between races of *S. sorghi* and among isolates of *S. sorghi*, *S. cruenta*, and *S. reiliana*. Resistance to various races has been identified and is controlled as single factor pairs for 3 of the races.

·Epidemiology: Covered smut persists between crop seasons as seed-borne teliospores, which contaminate grain primarily during threshing. Teliospores germinate under favorable environmental conditions and infect very young seedlings, thereafter growing undetected within the apical meristematic tissues of the host. Ultimately the fungus grows in the ovary, producing a sorus consisting of a dark mass of teliospores enclosed in a host-fungal membrane (periderm).
Sori develop in individual florets and generally remain intact, until they rupture during harvest or threshing. They may vary considerably in size, shape, and color, as well as in number and distribution of smutted florets within the panicle. Depending on the pattern of early infection, all panicles of an infected plant may become smutted, or only one or more tiller panicles.

Control: Several seed treatments, including captan and thiram, give excellent control of covered smut. The efficacy of seed treatment for control of covered smut and the apparent potential of the pathogen for physiologic specialization suggest that seed dressing is a more practical approach to control of covered smut than development of resistant varieties.

2. *Sphacelotheca cruenta* (Kühn) Potter

Disease: Loose Smut; Flugbrand der Sorghum-Hirse, charbon nu du sorgho, tizón del sorgo.

Geographical distribution: The geographical distribution of loose smut is apparently less extensive than that of covered smut, but it has been reported in Africa, Asia, Europe, and North and

Table 6. Differential morphological characteristics of the pathogens causing sorghum smuts

Smuts	S. sorghi covered smut	S. cruenta loose smut	S. reiliana head smut	T. ehrenbergii long smut
	2-15 mm long / 2-4 mm diameter	4-18 mm long / 2-4 mm diameter	50-150 mm long / 15-50 mm diameter	8-35 mm long / 2-5 mm diameter
	near globose to conical	generally conical	irregularly oval	cylindrical, often bent near apex
Sori	relatively permanent	ruptures easily	ruptures easily	relatively permanent
	single filament columella	single filament columella	mass of long filaments	6 to 12 filament columella
	single florets	single florets	entire panicle	single florets
Teliospores	4-9 µ diameter, average 6-7 µ olive-brown	5-10 µ diameter, average 7-8 µ olive-brown	7-16 µ diameter average 9-13 µ dark-brown	9-17 µ diameter, average 11-4 µ dark-brown
	single at maturity	single at maturity	single at maturity	in clusters (spore balls)
	high % germination	high % germination	very low % germination	low % germination
Host	not stunted	frequently stunted	not stunted	not stunted
	normal tillering normal heading	generally more tillering premature heading	normal tillering, generally normal heading	normal tillering normal heading
	normal glumes	usually longer glumes	glumes absent	normal glumes
	up to 100% florets smutted, usually 20-90% smutted	usually 100% florets smutted	entire panicle converted to single sorus	scattered florets smutted, rarely exceeding 10%

South America (CMI map no 408). Although this disease is as destructive or more destructive than is covered smut to individual plants, the overall incidence is usually less and rarely affects more than 10 percent of the crop.

Symptoms: Many aspects of loose smut are identical or very similar to those described for covered smut. See table 6, and plate 12b.

Morphology: See table 6. Differentiation between loose smut and covered smut and their respective pathogens is not always clear. They may simply represent the two extremes in a series of variations rather than two distinct species and diseases.

Physiological specialization: Two distinct physiologic races of *S. cruenta* have been reported, and others probably exist. A third race, which is often referred to as a separate species (*S. holci* Jackson), is especially pathogenic to *S. halepense* and *S. sudanense*. *S. cruenta* has also been reported on *Saccharum officinarum*.

Epidemiology: Primary infection occurs during early seedling development from seed-borne teliospores, although under certain circumstances soil-borne teliospores may also provide a source of primary inoculum. There is evidence for secondary infection of florets and auxillary buds by airborne spores, but this is not clearly understood and is probably of little economic significance. The peridium generally ruptures either before or shortly after head exsertion, and teliospores are released well before harvest. Long, slender, curved structures (columellae) generally become apparent in florets after teliospore release, although infected tillers may show little or no evidence of these structures. All florets of infected panicles are generally smutted, and sori may develop on the rachis and its branches or other plant parts. Loose smut infected plants generally head slightly earlier, tiller more profusely, and are somewhat more stunted than healthy or covered smut infected plants.

Control: Resistant varieties have been identified; however, seed dressings are an effective control against primary infection.

3. *Sphacelotheca reiliana* (Kühn) Clint.

Disease: Head Smut; Kopfbrand der Sorghum-Hirse; charbon des inflorescences du sorgho; tizón de la panoja.

Geographical distribution: Head smut has as wide a geographical distribution as covered smut. The incidence of head smut is often sporadic, with small areas sometimes having as much as 50 percent infection. Usually, however, relatively few plants become infected, and widespread serious losses are not encountered. Exceptions to this have occurred in certain years in South Texas, USA (CMI map no 69).

Host plants: *S. reiliana* has a relatively wide host range including several species of *Sorghum* and *Andropogon*, as well as *Cleistachne sorghoides*, *Euchlaena mexicana*, and *Zea mays*.

Symptoms: see table 6 and plate 12 c.

Morphology: see table 6.

Physiological specialization: Physiologic specialization occurs in *S. reiliana*, and at least 2 distinct forms are found: one affecting sorghum and the other affecting maize. The form found on sorghum does not attack maize, and vice versa. Up to 5 physiologic races have been reported on sorghum and several others are likely to exist.

Epidemiology: *S. reiliana* persists as soil-borne teliospores from one crop to the next. Primary infection occurs during the seedling stage, but, unlike covered smut, head smut infection is not limited to the very early stage of seedling development. The fungus becomes established in apical meristematic tissue and remains undetected until heading.

A single large sours usually develops in place of the entire panicle. The peridium ruptures during head exsertion or slightly before, and dark teliospores are released, leaving a mass of long, dark-colored filaments representing the vascular bundles of the affected panicle. A wide range of abnormal panicle symptoms can occur which may involve partial smutting accompanied by sterility, proliferation of individual florets, or blasting with complete absence of a sorus.

Control: Resistant varieties are known, particularly in the USA, and are essential for headsmut control, since seed dressings are virtually ineffective. Crop rotation gives partial control, and collection and destruction of sori may be effective where small plot culture is important.

Other more important Sphacelotheca spp. on tropical and subtropical crops:

S. destruens (Schlecht.) Stevensen & H.G. Johnson. Head smut of common millet (*Panicum miliaceum*). Ref.: CMI Description no 72

S. sacchari (Rabenh.) Cif. Smut of sugarcane, CMI map no 409.

4. *Tolyposporium ehrenbergii* (Kühn) Pat.

Disease: Long Smut; Beulenbrand der Sorghum-Hirse; charbon des sorghos; carbón del sorgo. *T. penicillariae* Bref. causes the pearl millet smut (*Pennisetum typhoides*).

Geographical distribution: This disease is apparently limited to Africa and Asia, where it generally occurs in the dryer areas of sorghum culture. Yield loss from long smut is usually light, although more severe outbreaks resulting in losses of 10 percent do occur locally. Infection is generally limited to scattered florets and rarely exceeds 10 percent on any given panicle (CMI map no 377).

Host plants: *Sorghum versicolor* and *S. purpureosericeum* also are known hosts of *T. ehrenbergii*.

Symptoms: Symptoms of long smut are sometimes confused with those of covered smut. However, long smut sori are generally longer, larger in diameter, more scattered over the panicle, and fewer in number than covered smut sori (Plate 12 d).

Morphology: see table 6.

Physiological specialization: Physiologic specialization has not been demonstrated in *T. ehrenbergii* and relatively little is known about resistance to long smut.

Epidemiology: Compared with the other sorghum smuts, relatively little is known about the life history of *T. ehrenbergii*. The fungus persists in the soil from one crop to the next as teliospores. It seems certain that most infection results from air-borne spores that invade florets before or immediately after head exsertion. Other modes of infection similar to those reported for the other smuts of sorghum may also occur, but these have not been fully documented.

Sori rupture near the tip and split irregularly open from the apex downward, releasing some teliospores before harvest.

Also, the peridium of long smut is thicker and the columella is composed of several fibrous strands, rather than the single structure found in covered smut sori. Even at maturity, teliospores of long smut remain grouped in clusters called "spore balls", which feel somewhat rough when rubbed between two fingers. This is in contrast to teliospores of the other 3 smuts, which feel smooth and powdery.

178   Diseases in tropical crops

Control: Control with seed dressings has not been demonstrated.

Literature

DICKSON, J. G. (1956): Diseases of field crops. McGraw-Hill Book Co. Inc., New York.
FISCHER, G.W., & C. S. HOLTON. (1957): Biology and control of the smut fungi. The Ronald Press Co., New York.
LEUKEL, R. W., J. H. MARTIN & C. L. LEFEBVRE. (1951): Sorghum diseases and their control. USDA Farmers' Bull. No 1959.
RAMAKRISHNAN, T. S. (1963): Diseases of millets. Indian Council of Agri. Res. New Delhi.
TARR, S. A. J. (1962): Diseases of sorghum, sudan grass, and broomcorn. The Commonwealth Mycol. Inst., Kew, Surrey.
CMI Description nos 71, 73, 74 and 76.

Author: Stanley B. King

Other Tolyposporium spp. on tropical and subtropical crops:
Tolyposporium penicillariae Bref. Smut of pearl millet (*Pennisetum typhoides*). Ref.: CMI Description no 77.

Thanatephorus cucumeris (Frank) Donk (Fig. 68)

Synonyms: *Corticium solani* (Prill. & Delacr.) Bourd. & Galz. = *Pellicularia filamentosa* (Pat.) Rogers
Holobasidiomycetidae, Tulasnellales, Ceratobasidiaceae
Imperfect state *Rhizoctonia solani* Kühn. (H,1)

Disease: Rhizoctonia disease; Wurzeltöter und Fußvermorschung; rhizoctone noir; rizoctonosis de la patata.

Geographical distribution: The pathogen is widely spread in almost all areas of the world. As soil inhabitant, it can successfully compete with other soil saprophytes for space and nutrition.

Host plants and symptoms: The pathogen has a relatively wide host range. It infects most of the cultivated crops in their early stages of growth. *T. cucumeris* usually attacks all underground parts causing varying degrees of rots on roots, crowns and/or basal parts of stems. It particularly affects seedlings and young plants causing pre- and post-emergence damping-off or root rots resulting in leaf blight and defoliation. Under certain conditions it also infects leaves of adult plants. Brown hyphae visible to the naked eye, are fairly typical on lesions caused by this fungus.

The following is a list of some of the more economically important hosts of *T. cucumeris* and the diseases it causes on each: cotton (sore-shin and leaf blight); wheat, barley, rye and oats (root rot and crown discoloration); flax (seed decay, damping-off and root rot); potato (damping-off, Fig. 68), black scurf and tuber rot); soybeans (root rot and seedling blight); alfalfa (foliage blight, crown rot and root canker); grain sorghum (stalk rot); peanuts (dry rot and seedling blight); tomato (damping-off and fruit rot); lima beans (root rot); dry

Fig. 68.

and snap beans (root rot); lettuce (seedling decay and blight); squash (seed decay and seedling blight); sunflower (seed decay and seedling blight); Crotolaria (foliage blight); and many others. Several soil-borne fungi other than *T. cucumeris* are capable of causing root rots: (*Fusarium* spp.), preemergence damping-off (*Pythium* spp. p. 93, *Phytophthora* spp.), and basal stem rots (*Corticium rolfsii* p. 148). There are also some soil-borne bacteria that are capable of causing rots of the basal parts of stems (*Erwinia atroseptica* (van Hall) Jennison), and soft rots (*Erwinia caro-tovora* (L. R. Jones) Holland). However most of these soil-borne pathogens are less aggressive than *T. cucumeris*.

Morphology: On artifical media, the fungus produces a dense white mycelium that changes gradually with age to a brown color; sectoring is frequent. Asexual fruit bodies and spores are lakking; small sclerotia are formed among, and are connected by mycelial threads.
Sclerotia are brown to black and variable in form. Hyphae are brown in color, with long cells, and branches from the main hypha have obvious constrictions at their bases. The basidia of the perfect state measure 18–23 x 8–11 μ. The hyaline, 1 celled basidiospores measure 7–13 x 4–7 μ.

Physiological specialization: *T. cucumeris* comprises numerous physiological races. According to Stakman and Christensen, the only criterion on which strains of this fungus should be differentiated is the cultural and pathological behaviour. Parmeter et al. (1969) showed that *T. cucumeris* (or *Rhizoctonia solani* as it has been historically known), is not a single species but is composed of at least four groups which can be separated on the ability of field isolates to anastomosis. Anastomosis occurs between isolates from the same group but not between isolates from different groups. Talbot (1970) disagrees with Parmeter, and considers the four anastomising groups to be *T. cucumeris* (Frank) Donk, even though they comprise four nonbreeding populations. The four groups also differ in their pathological behaviour. Groups 1 & 4 infect many different host plants, Group 2 is pathogenic mainly on crucifers and isolates of Group 3 infect only potato.

Epidemiology: *T. cucumeris* can persist in different types of soils for many years, since it is capable of producing sclerotia which can survive under adverse soil conditions, unfavorable to vegetative growth.
Basidiospores as well as sclerotia and mycelial fragments may help in transmitting the fungus inocula from one place to another. Inocula are dispersed by splashing, wind, irrigation water and by movement of soil by man or animals. The development of the disease on various host plants depends on the prevailing climatic conditions at the time of infection. In the case of sore-shin disease of cotton, for instance, low soil temperature and high moisture content favour the establishment of infection and hence the development of disease symptoms. Such conditions prevail in Egypt when sown early before the formation of true leaves on plants. It was also noticed that poor growth of seedlings due to lack of nitrogen or thrips attack predisposes cotton seedlings to sore-shin infection. Lack of micronutrients also appears to predispose cereal plants to infection with *T. cucumeris*.
Soil infestation with nematodes *Meliodogyne* spp. and *Aphelenchoides* spp. was found to predispose cotton seedlings to infection with sore-shin disease.
It has been shown that isolates of *T. cucumeris*, from stems and roots, usually penetrate host plant tissues through uninjured epidermal cells by dome-shaped infection cushions, whereas isolates from leaves, penetrate host leaves by lobate apressoria through stomata.
The fungus is capable of producing both cellulolytic and pectinolytic enzymes; this makes the pathogen more versatile than other pathogens which can produce only pectinolytic enzymes with respect to the age of attacked plants.

Control: Sanitation measures should be undertaken to minimize the build-up of inoculum in soil. These are achieved by removal of diseased plant residues from infested fields. Special cultural practices may also help in protecting plants from infection e.g. a good soil drainage system.

Aeration of ploughed soil before planting, avoidance of deep planting and maintenance of proper crop rotation to discourage the development of more virulent strains of the fungus.

As *T. cucumeris* is a soil-borne pathogen and has a wide host range, development of resistant varieties may offer a partial means of control. However, plant breeders have found little natural resistance among the many varieties of the hosts of this organism. More thorough research along this line is needed.

Seed treatment with different fungicides has shown some promise in the control of damping-off, root rot and sore-shin symptoms, especially when pelleted seeds incorporate the fungicide. Of the large number of fungicides tested, appreciable control was obtained with organic mercury dusts, ethylmercury chloride, ethylmercury phosphate, and ethylmercury p-toluene sulfonanilide. Another material, Zinc trichlorophenate, gave good control for pre- and post-emergence damping-off. Chemicals can also be applied by the slurry method which has given emergence values of seedlings comparable to the dust treatments.

Biological control: Antagonism of soil-inhabiting fungi or bacteria toward plant pathogens has been proved experimentally with *T. cucumeris*. It has been found that this fungus is destroyed in soil by *Trichoderma viride* Pers. ex. Fr. Certain antibiotics, namely gliotoxin and viridin, can he isolated from cultures of this antagonistic fungus. In unpublished work the writer has obtained a strain of *Bacillus subtilis* which has strong antagonistic action on *T. cucumeris*.

Literature

BARKER, K. R., & J. C. WALKER (1962): Factors affecting the pathogenicity of *Pellicularia filamentosa*. Phytopathology, 52, 2.
LeCLERG, E. L. (1941): Pathogenicity studies with isolates of *Rhizoctonia solani* from potato and sugar beet. Phytopathology, **31**, 49–61.
PARMETER, J. R., R. T. SHERWOOD & W. D. PLATT (1969): Anastomosis grouping among isolates of *Thanatephorus cucumeris*. Phytopathology **59**, 1270–1278.
TALBOT, P. H. B. (1970): Taxonomy and Nomenclature of the perfect state of *Rhizoctonia solani*. In J. R. Parmeter, Jr. (ed.): *Rhizoctonia solani:* biology and pathology. Univ. Calif. Press, Berkeley.
CMI Description no 406.

Author: M. K. Abo-El Dahab

Ustilago scitaminea Sydow (Fig. 69)

Teliomycetes, Ustilaginales

Disease: Smut of sugarcane; Zuckerrohrbrand; charbon de la canne à sucre; carbón de la caña de azúcar.

Geographical distribution: Smut of sugarcane, is generally widespread in sugarcane growing areas of the world (CMI map no 179), especially those situated between 20 °N and 20 °S of the equator. However, countries like mainland U.S.A. and Cuba are yet free from it. Losses in yield depend upon the incidence of the disease, the intensity of which is governed by the variety, factors affecting dissemination of spores and their germination. In plant and ratoon crops of variety Co 312, *Chona* observed 20 % and 70 % losses in yield, respectively. Another estimate puts it at 39 to 56 % in plant crop of Co 419 as compared to 52 to 73 % in the ratoon crop.

Host plants: Sugarcane, *Saccharum barberi*, *S. spontaneum*, *Imperata arundinacea*, *Erianthus saccharoides*.

Symptoms: Patent symptom of the disease is production of a black whip-like structure from the central core of the meristematic apex (Fig. 69). These range from small straight structures to irregularly curved 90 cm or more long whips. The whips which are modified inflorescences, usually 0.5 cm in diameter, are unbranched and consist of a fairly hard core of parenchymatous cells and fibro-vascular elements. This core is surrounded by a dense layer of chlamydospores (teliospores of the pathogen). In early stages, an off-white thin membrance covers the entire whip, which later ruptures liberating the spores which are wind disseminated. The whip is produced, on primary infection from a diseased seed piece, when the plants are 3 to 5 months old. In several instances, a smut whip has been seen to emerge out of the ground from an infected set.

On clipping this off, side buds sprout and each sprout bears a smut whip indicating systemic infection and necessitating removal of the whole clump during roguing operations. In exceptional cases, smut galls are seen on young leaves with an off-white membranous covering which on rupturing exposes smut spores.

Fig. 69.

Diseased plants can be spotted even before the appearance of the smut whip through their narrow leaves that remain stiff at an acute angle. Other morphological abnormalities associated with the disease include reduction in the size of the cane, deepening of the bud groove, reduction in the size of filaments and lack of differentiation of anther lobes, development of six bilobed feathery stigma and occasional formation of two ovaries in one flower. In general, the diseased plants are stunted and bear thin stalks.

Morphology: The pathogen *Ustilago scitaminea* was studied in some detail by Mundkur who subdivided *U. scitaminea* into *U. scitaminea* var. *sacchari-officinarum* and *U. scitaminea* var. *sacchari-barberi* on the basis of the size, colour and pattern of the spore wall. Spores are spherical, smooth walled, or slightly papillate, light brown and 8 to $10\,\mu$ in diameter.

The fungus can be cultured on asparagin-yeast extract agar medium, at pH 5.6.

Physiological specialization: Differences in virulence of various collections, though suspected, have not been demonstrated as yet.

Epidemiology: A peculiar feature in the epidemiology in north Indian plains is the occurrence of two flushes of the disease in a year, the first during May and June (primary infection) and the other one during October-November (secondary infection).

The smut spores have no dormancy and germinate readily over a wide range of temperatures (5 ° to 40 °C), optimum being 25 ° and 30 °C and 100 per cent humidity. It has been observed that bud diffusates stimulate their germination. The smut spores remain viable for about 3 years under dry conditions but readily germinate and deteriorate within three weeks under high humidity.

Smut spores are dessiminated through air currents, germinate and cause infection under humid atmosphere. Spores germinate to produce four septate promycelium which may or may not produce sporidia and these fuse to give rise to dikaryotic mycelium. Bipolar sexuality in the fungus has been demonstrated.

The mycelium of *U. scitaminea* in the host is intercellular and feeds through haustoria. It is usually detected in the meristematic region where young smut spores can be observed on sectioning.

Control: No effective control measure has been developed so far. However, the disease incidence can be minimized by adopting one or more of the following measures: (a) planting of healthy setts; (b) removal of smutted whips – the affected clumps should be removed before the emergence of the whip. In case the whips have emerged, these should be covered with a gunny bag and then removed; (c) discouraging ratooning of diseased crop; (d) planting only disease resistant varietis – sugarcane varieties having compact bud scales usually escape infection; and (e) disinfection of setts with organomercurials before planting help eradicate superficial smut inoculum.

Literature

MARTIN, J. P., E. V. ABBOTT & C. G. HUGHES (1961): Sugarcane diseases of the world. Vol 1. Elsevier Pub. Company, Amsterdam.
CMI Description no 80.

Authors: Kishan Singh and V. P. Agnihotri

Other more important fungi causing smut or bunt of tropical and subtropical crops:
Entyloma oryzae H. & P. Syd. Leaf smut of rice. CMI map no 451; fig. 85e.
Tilletia barclayana (Bref.) Sacc. & Syd. = *Tilletia horrida* Takahashi = *Neovossia horrida* (Tak.) Padwick & Azmatullah Khan. Kernel smut of rice. Ref.: CMI Description no 75.
Ustilago crameri Körnike. Head smut of foxtail millet. Ref.: CMI Description no 78.

All smuts and bunts known on cereals and maize occur worldwide, though they may be absent locally.

General literature on smut fungi:

BLUMER, S. (1963): Rost- und Brandpilze auf Kulturpflanzen. Gustav Fischer, Jena.
DURAN, R., & G. W. FISHER (1961): The genus *Tilletia*. Washington State Univ.
FISCHER, G. W. (1951): The smut fungi. Ronald Press, New York.
FISCHER, G. W., & C. S. HOLTON (1957): Biology and control of the smut fungi. Ronald Press, New York.
MUNDKUR, B. B., & M. J. THIRUMALACHAR (1952): *Ustilaginales* of India. Commonwealth Mycological Institute, Kew, UK.
ZAMBETTAKIS, CH. (1971): Les Ustilaginales des Plantes d'Afrique. Lab. de Cryptogamie, Muséum Nat. d'histoire nat. Paris.
ZUNDEL, G. L. (1953): The Ustilaginales of the world. Contr. no 176, Dept. Botany, Penn. State University.

Deuteromycotina

The subdivison Deuteromycotina is no natural classification. Fungi with conidial states (the majority of which are haploid ascomycetes) that are alike in morphological characters such as: conidiophores, septation, colour and form of conidia etc. are assigned to a so-called form-genus. Such a genus must not be correlated with a particular sexual state and its phylogeny, though this exists (e. g. *Diaporthe – Phomopsis*). Very often no ascigerous state is known or does not seem to exist. The conventional classification of the Deuteromycotina is largely that of Saccardo (s. Barnett &

Hunter 1972). Today there is a tendency amongst mycologists to accept two form-classes of sporulating fungi imperfects: Hyphomycetes (with the form-families Moniliaceae, Dematiaceae, Stilbellaceae, Tuberculariaceae) and Coelomycetes (with the form-orders Sphaeropsidales and Melanconiales). In recent years the mode of spore formation has gained more weight in the determination of genera. The combination of the latter approach and that of Saccardo is reflected in the codings taken from Ainsworth "Dictionary of fungi 6th ed. (1971), and used below. The abbreviations stand for:

C = Coelomycetes, sporulation in acervuli = Melanconiales, or pycnidia = Sphaeropsidales
C,1 = Order Sphaeropsidales, sporulation in pycnidia
C,2 = Order Melanconiales, sporulation in acervuli
H = Hyphomycetes, sporulation on conidiophores or on hyphae
H,1 = Mycelia sterilia
H,2 = Order Hyphomycetales (Monilaceae, Dematiaceae) with free conidiophores
H,3 = Fam. Stilbellaceae; Conidiophores aggregated in synnemata
H,4 = Fam. Tuberculariaceae, conidiophores aggregated as sporodochia

Septation and form of conidia as:
A = Conidia 1 celled
B = 2 celled
C = 2 or more celled
D = muriform
E = filiform
F = spirally coiled
G = star-like

Colouration: figures 1 & 2 following one of the above letters stand for hyaline conidia and coloured conidia, respectively.

Conidial formation as
b1 = Blastospore
bo = Botryose blastospore
sy = Sympodioconidium
al = Aleuriospore
an = Annellospore
ph = Phiallospore
mb = Meristem blastospore
po = Porospore
ma = Meristem arthrospore

Note: Fungi not refered to under Deuteromycotina may be found under Ascomycotina.

Literature

BARNETT, H. L., & B. B. HUNTER (1972): Illustrated genera of imperfect fungi. 3rd. ed. Burgess Publ. Co. Minneapolis.
BARRON, G. L. (1968): The genera of hyphomycetes from soil. Williams & Williams, Baltimore.
ELLIS, M. B. (1971): Dematiaceous hyphomycetes. Commonwealth Mycological Institute, Kew.
GROVE, W. B. (1935, 1937): British stem and leaf-fungi (Coelomycetes) vol I & II, Cambridge Univ. Press., Cambridge.
KENDRICK, W. B. ed. (1971): Taxonomy of fungi imperfecti. Univ. Toronto, Toronto.
SUBRAMANIAN, G. V. (1971): Hyphomycetes. ICAR, New Delhi.
See also literature cited on pp. 75/76 & 100 and with the following genera.

Alternaria longipes (Ell. & Ev.) Mason (Fig. 70)

Synonyms: *Alternaria alternata* (Fries) Keissler, which is the neotype of *Alternaria tenuis* Nees. = *Alternaria tabacina* (Ell. & Ev.) Hori = *Macrosporium longipes* Ell. & Ev.
Hyphomycetes (H,2.D2.po)

Disease: Brown spot; Braunfleckigkeit; Alternariose; Mancha parda.

Geographical distribution: World wide (CMI map no 63). It is a disease of major economic importance in N. America and Central Africa.

Host plants: Tobacco. It is considered that alternative hosts do not play an important part in the epidemiology of this disease, but the fungus may occur as a saprophyte on other hosts.

Symptoms: *A. longipes* is primarily a leaf disease, but sunken stem lesions may occur, particularly late in the season. Lesions first appear on the lower, older leaves as small (circa 1 mm diameter) palish, or more commonly dark brown spots. These enlarge to form distinct brown, approximately circular lesions 1–3 cm. in diameter, commonly with concentric rings or zonations in the dead tissue, and the centres of these lesions may fade to a buff or whitish colour with age. On mature or almost mature leaves the lesions are generally surrounded by a band of bright yellow tissue (the halo), the band width being widest on the more susceptible varieties, and this yellowing may rapidly spread to involve large areas of the leaf which consequently dies prematurely. Following prolonged periods of rain or high humidity one can usually see a dark brown to blackish mass of conidiophores and conidia growing on the lesions.
Under favourable conditions the spots on mature leaves enlarge rapidly, coalesce, and kill the leaf, often progressively from the tip backwards.
Old spots or those on thin, lightly fertilized leaves may be whitish, irregularly shaped, and lack concentric markings, and therefore may be confused with similar spots formed by frogeye (*Cercospora nicotianae,* p. 191), but the latter are not surrounded by a band of yellow tissue. These fungi both produced clusters of conidiophores which project from either leaf surface, but the conidia are morphologically different.

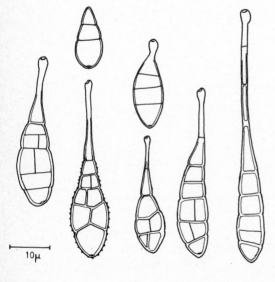

10μ

Fig. 70.

Morphology: The brown conidia of *A. longipes* are variable in size and shape, but on the host they are usually club shaped when mature, being 8–21 μ thick in the broadest part, tapering gradually into a beak which is usually 1/3 to 1/2 the total length of the spore, giving an overall length of 21–110 μ. Mature conidia commonly have both transverse and longitudinal cell walls. *A. longipes* conidia are sometimes solitary, but are usually formed in chains of 3 to 8 (Fig. 70).

Physiological specialization: Different races are not considered to occur, but single conidium isolates vary in their aggressiveness from non-pathogenic to highly pathogenic.

Epidemiology: *A. longipes* can survive from one season to the next on tobacco stalks or leaf debris, although survival is limited if conditions are wet and/or the debris is not on the soil surface. Sporulation occurs readily during periods of high humidity, and lesions may continue to sporulate for several weeks. The conidia are released by hygroscopic twisting movements developing at high saturation deficits, or by mechanical shock. Dispersal is largely by wind or rain splash. Spread by infected seed or seedlings is rare. Germination and germ tube growth is optimal in standing water at 22.5 °C, but occurs over the range 4–37 °C, and at humidities≧ 80 %. Germination can occur within one hour, and penetration may be completed within 8 hours. The conidia usually penetrate directly through the epidermis, but they can enter through stomata. Seedlings are not readily infected. Young leaves may be infected but visible lesion development does not normally occur until the leaves have almost finished expanding, thus the incubation period on young leaves may be as long as 35 days, but on mature susceptible leaves minute spots may develop within 2 days of inoculation. Hyphal growth is intercellular, and living cells are not penetrated. The cells are thought to be killed by the combined action of chlorosis inducing metabolites, and pectic enzymes. It is considered that the lower leaves of young plants are infected by inoculum produced on the debris of previous tobacco crops. Disease development is restricted on such leaves, and does not become destructive until the crop is well advanced and near flowering. Rapid disease development is favoured by moderately high temperature (20–25 °C) and frequent rain which promotes both the production of susceptible tissue by the host, and penetration and sporulation of the fungus. Heavy nitrogen applications result in greater leaf damage, whereas balanced potassium and phosphorus fertilization cause a slight decrease in leaf susceptibility. Tobacco plants are predisposed to infection by brown spot by root knot nematode (*Meliodogyne* spp.) attack, and this predisposition is even greater if *Fusarium oxysporum f. sp. nicotianae* (J. Johnson) Snyder & Hansen is associated with the nematode.

Control: When harvesting is complete tobacco stalks should be ploughed in or removed and burnt or buried. Crops should be rotated so that there is a gap of at least one year between tobacco plantings, and tobacco should not be planted adjacent to where tobacco was grown in the previous year.

Control nematodes and use a balanced fertilizer – particularly avoid over-fertilization with nitrogen. Prime or harvest infected leaves as soon as possible.

There are no resistant commercial varieties, but tolerant varieties can be used, for example, Beinhart 1000-1, N.C. 95, Speight G28 and Florida 22.

Chemically disinfect seed by soaking in 0.1 % silver nitrate for 15 minutes – then wash and dry. Chemical control is generally not economic. Weekly sprays of Zinochlor or maneb at about 300 g/hl from the beginning of flowering onwards give some control, but must not be used later than 7 days before harvest. Polyoxin B or piomycin when applied weekly 3–4 times after topping, have recently been reported to give good control of brown spot in Japan. The incidence is reduced when maleic hydrazide (MH-30) is applied for sucker control.

Literature

LUCAS, G. B. (1975): Diseases of Tobacco. 3rd ed. Biological Consulting Associates, Raleigh, NC.
NORSE, D. (1971): Lesion and epidemic development of *Alternaria longipes* on tobacco. Ann. appl. Biol. **69**, 105–123.
NORSE, D. (1973): Some factors influencing spore germination and penetration of *Alternaria longipes*. Ann. appl. Biol. **74**, 297–306.
STAVELY, J. R., G. W. PITTARELLI & G. B. LUCAS (1971): Reaction of Nicotiana species to *Alternaria alternata*. Phytopathology **61**, 541–545.
CMI Description no 245.

Author: D. Norse

Alternaria solani Sorauer (Fig. 71)

Hyphomycetes (H,2.D2.po)

Disease: Alternaria blight of potato and tomato; Dürrfleckenkrankheit der Kartoffel und Tomate; maladie des taches brunes de la pomme de terre et de la tomate; alternariosis de la patata y del tomate.

Geograɔhical distribution: Worldwide (CMI map no 89). Important particularly in warm regions. Especially adapted to semi-arid areas with dry days, dew nights and occasional sand storms.

Host plants: Potatoes, tomatoes and eggplants; sometimes also hot pepper and a variety of wild Solanaceae.
In potatoes, it infects foliage and sometimes tubers in tomatoes, foliage, fruits and collars.

Symptoms: On leaves, dark brown to black, and often angular lesions, usually with concentric ridges. Minute lesions may merge in a large necrotic area (Fig. 71). On tomato seedlings lesions appear on the base of stems, at the soil surface or slightly above it. In tomato fruits lesions cover the basal end, while in potato tubers they form minute spots.
Early blight lesions sometimes resemble those of late blight (*Phytophthora infestans* (Mont.) de By), but the latter are large, darker and never form concentric ridges. Young lesions resemble those caused by *A. tomato* (Cke) Weber, the *Stemphylium complex* (p. 228), and *Xanthomonas vesicatoria* (p. 71).

Morphology: Mycelium septate, branched and dark when old. Multicellular conidia are beaked, dark, and borne singly on conidiophores. Conidia size variable, averaging 110–190 x 14–20 μ. In culture many isolates produce a yellow, brown or red pigment which diffuses into the substrate.

Physiological specialization: Considerable variation occurs in morphological, physiological and virulence properties. Sometimes attributed to occurence of physiological races, these are more likely to derive from extreme variability of individual isolates.

Epidemiology: Overwinters or oversummers in infected debris or on volunteer plants. Extremely resistant to hot and dry conditions.
Debris in dry, uncultivated soil constitutes source for infection after eight month, but survival is impaired by cultivation, and especially by irrigation. May be also introduced by infected seeds. Sporulation in culture follows induction by irradiation and in plants by alternating conditions of wetness and dryness. Sporulation potential increases when the infected tissue is approaching death. Factors adversely affecting photosynthesis increase the sporulation potential of the pathogen.

Fig. 71.

Conidia are dispersed chiefly by wind. Liberation of conidia is enhanced by low air humidity. With exception of the collar rot phase in tomatoes, predisposition of the host to disease increases with age, and reaches its highest with production of fruits (tomatoes) and tubers (potatoes). Germination of conidia needs water. Duration of leaf wetness needed for infection depends on temperature, e. g. 12 hrs at 10 °C and 4 hrs at the optimum temperature of 25–30 °C. Lesions appear within 1–3 days. The pathogen excretes toxins which add to extent of damage.

In tomatoes seedbeds collar rot may appear almost simultaneously on many plants, indicating contamination of seeds or soil. On adult plants the first leaf lesions appear on the oldest leaves. Heavy infection of foliage may decrease total yield by more than 50 % especially in tomatoes where fruits are affected also.

In some but not all areas, disease has been enhanced by overhead irrigation.

Control: No genetic sources for resistance are known, except for the collar rot phase in tomatoes. To minimize the danger of disease, early removal of plant debris is recommended. It is also recommended to avoid planting of new plots alongside the old ones which, owing to their increased susceptibility, may form a source of inoculum. Plots in which tomatoes or potatoes have been grown should be planted as soon as possible with other plants to decrease survival of the inoculum in plant debris. It is recommended to use clean and preferably disinfected seeds.

Fungicides are often only partially effective. Mostly carbamates and Daconil® are employed, at the time of appearance of the first symptoms.

Literature

KLAUS, H. (1940): Untersuchungen über *Alternaria solani* Jones et Grout, insbesondere über seine Pathogenität an Kartoffelknollen in Abhängigkeit von den Außenfaktoren. Phytopathology Z. **23**, 126–195.

ROTEM, J., & S. FELDMAN (1965): The relation between the ratio of yield to foliage and the incidence of early blight in potato and tomato. Israel J. Agric. Res. **15**, 115–122.

ROTEM, J., & I. REICHERT (1964): Dew – a principal moisture factor enabling early blight epidemics in a semi-arid region of Israel. Plant. Dis. Reptr. **48**, 211–215.

Author: J. Rotem

Other more important Alternaria spp. on tropical and subtropical crops with no ascigerous state:
Alternaria carthami Chowdhury. Leaf spot of safflower. Ref.: CMI Description no. 241.

A. citri Ell & Pierce apud Pierce. Black rot of oranges and fruit rots of other Citrus spp., also on leaves. Ref.: CMI Description no 242.

A. gossypina (Thüm.) Hopkins. Leaf spot of cotton.

A. padwickii (Ganguly) M. B. Ellis = *Trichocornis padwickii* Ganguly. Stackburn, seedling blight and leaf spot of rice. Ref.: CMI Description no 345. Fig. 85 g.

A. macrospora Zimm. Leaf spot of cotton. Ref.: CMI Description no 246.

A. passiflorae Simmonds. Brown spot of passion fruit. Ref.: CMI Description no 247.

A. ricini (Yoshii) Hansf. Leaf spot, seedling blight, inflorescences and pod rot of castorbean. Ref.: CMI Description no 249.

A. sesami (Kawamura) Mohanti & Behari. Damping-off, leaf, stem and pod rot of sesame. Ref.: CMI Description no 250.

A. triticina Prasada & Prabhu. Leaf blight of wheat in India.

General Literature

ELLIS, M. B. (1971): Dematiaceous hyphomycetes. Commonwealth Mycological Institute, Kew, UK.

JOLY, P. (1964): Le genre Alternaria. Lechevalier, Paris.

Botryodiplodia theobromae Pat. (Figs. 72–73)

Synonym: *Lasiodiplodia theobromae* (Pat.) Griff. et Maubl.
Coelomycetes (C,1.B2.al)

Diseases: Rots of sweet potato (*Ipomoea batatas*), cassava and yams; Fäule der Batate etc.; pourriture etc., podredumbre de *Ipomoea batatas, Manihotis utilissima* and *Dioscorea* spp.

Geographical distribution: Occurs commonly in tropical areas.

Host plants: This is a rather polyphagous pathogen on a wide range of hosts, where it often colonizes senescent tissue. Amongst the more important hosts are: bananas (post harvest decay of fruits), cacao (black rot of pods), coconut (leaf necroses), oilpalm (dieback), rubber (dieback) and the above ones.

Symptoms: Rot starts from wounded areas of the tuber. The diseased tissue is initially soft and dirty white in colour. It later turns to a dark brown mass which remains soft in texture and finally

Fig. 72.

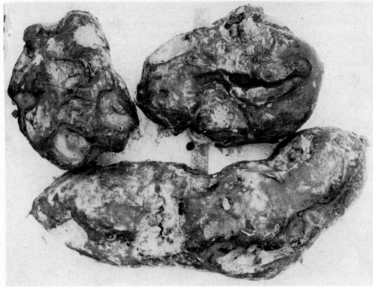

Fig. 73.

becomes black. At this stage loss of moisture results in the tissue becoming hardened, the bark peeling off in flakes in some areas and exposed cells fall off (Figs. 72 and 73).

The microbial rot of sweet potato has also been associated with several pathogens: *Ceratocystis* sp. causes black rot, *Fusarium oxysporum* causes surface rot. Other organisms associated with soft rot of sweet potato are *Rhizopus* spp., *Gibberella zeae*[1], *Trichoderma koningi* Oud., *Botrytis cinerea* Pers. ex Fr., *Penicillium* spp., *Mucor racemosus* Fres., *Alternaria* sp., *Epicoccum* sp. and *Sclerotia* sp.

B. theobromae also causes a moist rot of cassava tubers both before and after harvesting. Here the tubers usually appear to be healthy. Rot generally starts from wounded surfaces, especially from the scar remaining from the attachment of the tuber to the stem and gradually spreads. If an infected tuber is cut through, the cortical tissue appears as a moist, dark-brown pulp (c.f. fermented grated cassava) with green, grey-dirty brown or faint yellow patches depending on the type of pathogen causing the rot. In cases of advanced rot, the whole of the internal tissues, apart from the central vascular strand, becomes a watery mush though the outermost corky layer representing the bark remains intact. Other organisms that may be associated with cassava tuber rot are: *Corticium rolfsii*[2], *Aspergillus niger* v. Tieghem, *A. flavus* Link, *Cylindrocarpon candidum* (Link) Wollenw. and *Trichoderma harzianum* Rifai.

Rotting of yam tubers commences at a wound. Early symptoms include soft, dark spots which are roughly circular or irregular in outline, but with edges that tend to break away from the healthy tissue. Lesions contain dark brown masses of soft, moist tissue which rapidly loses water in a dry atmosphere by evaporation. After cutting through a cavity, the diseased tissue adjacent to uninfected tissue appears as a brownish pink layer of suberized tissue, fading to pinkish, with dark-brown moist cells. Rotted tissues have a characteristic offensive odour.

An *Erwinia* sp. causes a watery rot of yams tubers. In this type of decay, the internal tissues of the tubers become a water-soaked, dirty-white pulp. The bark usually shows no symptom of disease but on applying pressure ruptures to release the internal tissues. The disease is more commonly observed in tubers dug from wet, heavy, poorly-drained soils.

Morphology: When exposed to light, pycnidia of *B. theobromae* brown form on tubers of cassava within three days. They discharge non-septate, white and two-celled brown pycnidiospores.

Epidemiology: Infection of tubers occurs in the soil or, later, during transport and in storage. It takes place through lacerations of wounds on the tubers. Infection always commences at some wound or through natural openings on the tuber surface. The hyphae of the fungus form a thick white mat on the surface of the tuber and later penetrate the tissue inter- and intra-cellularly. As a result of polygalacturonase, cellulase and amyloglucosidase enzyme production by the fungus, the cell walls of the host tissue are broken down and the normally numerous starch grains are depleted. High relative humidities (90–100 %) and temperatures of 25–35 °C favour rot.

The remains of rotten tubers serve as a source of inoculum for further infection.

Control: It is suggested that tubers of these crops for storage should be carefully handled during harvesting and transportation to avoid any mechanical damage to the tissues.

Benomyl and Thiabendazol prevent rot of tubers have little been used so far. Simple control measures include painting of cut surfaces with limewash or Bordeaux mixture and coating with a suspension of wood ashes. In the U.S.A., Japan and India curing of sweet potato tubers is recommended. Curing at 30 °C and 85–90 % R.H. is popular, but storage temperature should be lowered to 12.5–15 °C and a relative humidity of 85–90 %. Storage chambers should be properly ventilated, to avoid accumulation of carbon dioxide, while at the same time keeping the proper storage temperature. In Nigeria work is in progress on breeding varieties resistant to some of the most common diseases of sweet potatoes.

[1] See p. 117.   [2] See p. 148.

Preliminary investigations have shown that low temperature storage of cassava tubers at about 5 °C prevents rot. Incubation at 35 °C prevents establishment of the organisms whereas the tubers still retain their usual texture. Complete control of the fungus is difficult because it is capable of infecting many other crops on a plot and it therefore has many alternative hosts.

No control measures have yet been worked out for the preharvest soft rot.

Literature

AVINZE, A. E., S. H. Z. NAQUI & J. A. EKUNDAYO (1975): Storage rot of sweet potato (*Ipomoea batatas*) and effect of fungicides. Intn. Biodetn. Bull. **11**, 41–47.

CHUPP, C., & A. F. SHERF (1960): Vegetable diseases and their control. The Ronald Press Co.

EKUNDAYO, J. A., & T. M. DANIEL (1973): Studies on cassava rot and its control. Trans. Br. mycol. Soc. **61**, 27–32.

EKUNDAYO, J. A., & S. H. Z. NAQVI (1972): Preharvest microbial rotting of yams (*Dioscorea* spp.) in Nigeria. Trans. Br. mycol. Soc. **58**, 15–18.

OKAFOR, N. (1966): Microbial rotting of stored yams (*Dioscorea* spp.) in Nigeria. Expl. Agric. **2**, 179–182.

OGUNDANA, S. K., S. H. Z. NAQVI & J. A. EKUNDAYO (1970): Fungi associated with soft rot of yams (*Dioscorea* spp.) in storage in Nigeria. Trans. Br. mycol. Soc. **54**, 445–451.

Author: J. A. Ekundayo

Cercospora coffeicola Berk. & Cooke (Plate 13 a)

Hyphomycetes (H,2.E2.sy)

Disease: Brown eye spot of coffee; Braunfleckenkrankheit; maladie des yeux bruns; mancha de hierro.

Geographical distribution: The disease occurs throughout Africa, Central and South America, the Caribbean, S. E. Asia and Oceania. (CMI map no 59).

Host plants: The pathogen can infect most *Coffea* spp., although marked variation in susceptibility exists. There is some evidence that certain common weeds in coffee plantations can act as alternative hosts.

Symptoms: The pathogen can infect both leaves and berries. On leaves, the disease is initially seen as a small chlorotic spot. This expands to produce a central grey area, usually bearing dark tufts of conidiosphores, surrounded by a brown necrotic zone with a outermost chlorotic halo. Lesions are circular to oval, 5–15 mm in diameter (Plate 13a). On berries, the disease appears as oval, brown sunken lesions, up to 5 mm long, with a grey centre. The disease causes shedding of foliage when severe and infected berries are difficult to process because the pulp sticks to the bean. The characteristic zonate "eye spot" symptom distinguishes this disease from other leaf pathogens. On berries, also, the brown colour with a greyish centre distinguishes eye spot from *Colletotrichum* lesions (Coffee Berry Disease, p. 195) which are much darker.

Morphology: *C. coffeicola* sporulates on the upper leaf surface, producing groups of more or less erect midbrown, septate conidiophores arising from a basal stroma. These produce long multiseptate hyaline conidia. Dimensions of the conidia vary greatly between isolates and on different growth media (Siddiqi 1970). The fungus can be isolated with care and grows slowly on Potato Dextrose Agar or PCA (opt. 25 °C).

Physiological specialization: No physiological specialization has been reported, although some variation in lesion size, produced by different isolates, is known.

Epidemiology: Conidia can survive for periods up to 7 weeks, but the main means of survival appears to be fallen leaves in which the pathogen can remain viable for 9 months under dry conditions. Generally, this is not critical, as the disease is present on the tree throughout the whole year. The fungus sporulates readily under conditions of high humidity and spores are dispersed mainly by wind, although rain-splash may be effective as well. Spores deposited on leaves or berries germinate in the presence of liquid water and high temperatures (opt. 30 °C) and infect leaves through stomata within a few hours. Small chlorotic spots are visible after four weeks and complete symptom expression with sporulation by the pathogen, after seven weeks.

On berries these periods are much shorter, being as little as four and seventeen days respectively. Under field conditions the disease usually develops most rapidly during the rainy season, when high humidity favours both sporulation and infection. Exposed, unshaded trees are most susceptible; water stress and nutrient deficiencies also predispose the host to infection. Berries are most susceptible four months after flowering, and sun-scorch damage predisposes them to infection.

Control: Generally, brown eye spot is not a serious disease and control usually consists of adequate cultural practices, such as proper fertilization, irrigation, providing shade trees, etc. The disease can be more severe under nursery conditions. Spraying of plantations is only warranted if the disease is causing much defoliation or berry damage. Copper-based sprays applied every 1–3 months are effective. Dithiocarbamates, such as Fermate, Ziram and Zineb have also been shown to give good control on a similar schedule. Recently, benomyl has been shown to be very effective. Genetic resistance in coffee varieties has not been exploited.

Literature

ECHANDI, E. (1959): La chasparria de los cafetos causada por el hongo *Cercospora coffeicola* Berk. & Cooke. Turrialba **9**, 54–67.
SIDDIQI, M. A. (1970): Incidence, development and symptoms of Cercospora disease of coffee in Malawi. Trans. Br. mycol. Soc. **54**, 415–421.
SUBRAMANIAN, S., & T. S. SRIDHAR (1966): Studies on brown eye spot of coffee I–IV. Riv. Patol. Veg., Pavia. Serie IV, **2**, 127–149.
WELLMAN, F. L. (1955): Coffee. World Crops Series. Pub. Leonard Hill.
CMI Description no 415.

Author: J. M. Waller

Cercospora nicotianae Ell. & Ev. (Fig. 74)

Synonym: *Cercospora apii* Fres.
Hyphomycetes (H,2.E2.sy)

Disease: Frogeye and Barn spot or Green spot; Froschaugenkrankheit; Cercosporiose ou Yeux de grenouille; ojo de rana.

Geographical distribution: World wide (CMI map no 172)

Host plants: Tobacco is the main natural host.

Symptoms: *C. nicotianae* causes two different diseases, Frogeye and barn or green spot. Frogeye spots can be formed on leaves of all ages, but they are primarily produced on the older leaves when they are almost ready for priming or harvest. The first symptoms are small brown circular or irregularly shaped spots, which later enlarge to 1.0–1.5 cm in diameter, and become pale brown or whitish. Barn spot or green spots develop during curing on flue cured and dark fired Western tobacco, respectively. These spots are small, varying in size from 0.1–5 mm, and can be very numerous. Barn spots are blackish, whilst those of green spot are dark green.

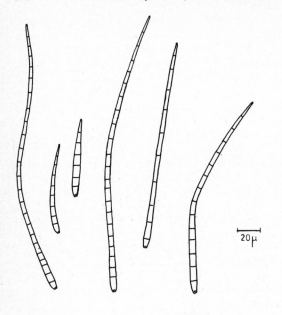

Fig. 74.

Confusion with brown spot symptoms is discussed in the section of that disease. Frogeye may also be confused with the white spots formed by tobacco mosaic virus, but the latter are usually much smaller, and more 'irregularly' shaped.

Morphology: The long hyaline, filiform conidia are produced on clusters of conidiophores, which usually emerge through the stomata. The conidia are commonly 2–4 μ thick near the truncate base, and taper over a length of 40–170 μ to 1–2 μ at the apex. There are 9–17 transverse cell walls, and the conidia are straight or slightly curved (Fig. 74).

Epidemiology: Primary infection generally occurs in the seedbed as a result of the use of infected seed or from inoculum produced on infected overwintering tobacco plants or debris; the latter may also infect transplants. Spore dispersal is by wind or rainsplash, and lesions are visible 8–10 days after penetration. Rapid diseased development is favoured by high humidity, temperatures close to 28–30 °C, and by a deficiency of or over fertilization with nitrogen.

Control: Rotate seed beds or sterilize them; ensure that they are well drained and are not adjacent to previous tobacco seedbeds or crops. Sow seed beds as early as practicable, using chemically disinfected seed (soak in 0.1 % silver nitrate solution for 15 minutes, wash well and dry). Prime infected leaves as soon as possible.

From the time the seedling leaves are 1 cm in diameter spray with Bordeaux mixture, maneb or zineb (preferably Dithane M-45 or mancozeb) at 5–10 day intervals depending on the growth rate and rainfall, or with benomyl (0.1–0.2 g/l) every 7–21 days. The same fungicides are suitable for field application. Barn spot can be controlled by maintaining the temperature and relative humidity as close as possible to 38 °C and 100 % respectively during the initial colouring stage.

Literature

HOPKINS, J. C. F. (1956): Tobacco diseases. Commonwealth Mycological Institute, Kew.
JAILLOUX, F., & J. BULIT (1970): Essais de lutte chemique à l'égard de la cercosporiose du tabac à la Guadeloupe. Phytiat. Phytopharm. **19**, 107–111.
LUCAS, G. B. (1975): Diseases of tobacco. 3rd ed. Biolog. Consulting Associates, Raleigh, NC.
CMI Description no 416.

Author: D. Norse

Cercospora purpurea Cke.

Hyphomycetes (H,2.E2.sy)

Disease: Cercospora spot or blotch of avocado; Avocado-Blattfleckenkrankheit; Cercosporiose; Cercosporiosis del avocado.

Geographical distribution: Observed for the first time in Georgia (U.S.A.) in 1878, this disease has since been recorded in America in the following countries: Bolivia, Brazil, Costa Rica, Guatemala, Martinique, Nicaragua, Peru, Puerto Rico, Venezuela and in the states of Florida and Mississippi (U.S.A.). In Africa it exists in the Cameroons, Ivory Coast, Zaire and Guinea. This disease seems to be absent from several important areas of cultivation: California, Israel, Australia, South Africa, New Zealand.

Host plants: The pathogen is specific to the genus *Persea* (Lauraceae); the chief host is the avocado (*Persea americana*) but it can be found on *P. carolinensis* (*P. pubescens*) and *P. palustris*.

Symptoms: *Cercospora* spot attacks the leaves and fruits of practically all varieties. On adult leaves small, sunken, purple, angular spots appear, visible on both sides of the leaves and measuring 1–2 mm on average. Very often they are ringed by a yellow halo. On fruits the first symptoms are small, slightly raised flecks, pale green to almost white, which become small irregular spots, slightly sunken, 1–2 mm diameter and of a chestnut colour. Finally the spots, often grouped, form dead and tough tissue which is nearly always cracked. Although superficial, these cracks serve as the points of entry for secondary parasites, in particular *Colletotrichum gloeosporioides* (p. 199), the agent of anthracnose.

Morphology: The spores are small, multicellular rods, 20–100 μ long, coloured light olive-brown. With a magnifying glass they are easily seen grouped in clusters on much of the lower surface of the leaf spots and on the fruits.

Epidemiology: Survival: The pathogen survives in avocado leaves. The conidia can resist desiccation for at least three months.
Spore production is maximal after 24 hours in a saturated humidity at 30 °C, is possible at 98 % R. H. (relative humidity), but ceases at 95 % R.H. and below. The optimum temperature is 30 °C, but considerable sporulation is possible from 20 ° to 25 °C; it is very feeble at 15 °C and 35 °C. Light does not seem to have any effect. The conidia are readily dispersed by water. Indeed, they are not detached from leaves by dry winds. Rain and dew therefore play important roles in dissemination, as do the wet winds which very often accompany rain. Another factor is important in dispersal: arthropods (thrips, mites etc.) move around on the fructifying lesions and carry spores to the healthy areas of foliage and fruits.
Conidia deposited on a susceptible surface germinate rapidly in water, and equally well above 92 % R.H. An alternation of drying and wetting does not prevent germination. The cardinal temperatures for germination and growth are 15 °, 25 ° ± 2 °, and between 30 ° and 35 °C. Penetration of leaves takes place through the stomata on the lower surface. Young leaves which have not completely developed are resistant, but are susceptible when they reach full size. It seems that adult leaves become resistant after several months. Penetration of fruits occurs through lenticels. The fruits are particularly susceptible when they measure a quarter to three quarters of their full size, but at the approach of maturity they regain their resistance. From the deposition of spores and the start of germination, direct penetration is achieved after 48 hours. Incubation lasts about fifteen days in leaves, and twenty days in fruits. Sporulation can start two weeks after the appearance of symptoms and may continue for several months.
Favourable conditions: As an example, in the lower part of the Ivory Coast conditions are favourable throughout the year; the minimum temperature rarely falls below 20 °C and even in the dry season the relative humidity has a high average (85 %), and reaches saturation every night with the deposition of dew. Furthermore, flushes of vegetative growth and flowerings are numerous. Throughout the year, therefore, tissues are present (leaves and fruits) which are susceptible to infection. The mediterranean-type climates of California and Israel would seem to be unsatisfactory for the development of Cercospora spot if this disease should ever be introduced.

Control: The spotted fruits are of very poor quality for marketing and furthermore, the smallest lesion can be a source for an anthracnose to develop before, and above all, after maturation. It is absolutely necessary to control this disease if marketable avocados are to be harvested.

All known varieties are susceptible and none seem even highly resistant.

However, the indispensable fungicide treatments have a considerable effectiveness which varies between varieties. Thus the proportion of marketable fruits is larger with Lula, Collinson, Hickson and Booth 7 than with Peterson, Booth 8 and Hall. The sprays are applied if, during the period of fruit susceptibility, the weather is warm and humid.

In Florida copper sprays are recommended at a rate of 50 litre/tree (6 meters high): Bordeaux mixture (0.8–1 %), Kocide 101 (0.24 %), basic copper sulphate (0.36 %), cuprous oxide (0.2 %). The spray calendar calls for two applications a month apart, commencing the first fortnight in May. A third spray is necessary on late varieties in July, and a fourth in September. The addition of a wetter such as Triton B 1956 (0.3 %) is strongly recommended.

It was quickly realized that this spray calendar is far from satisfactory in the West Indies, Guinea, the Ivory Coast and the Cameroons, doubtless because of the rapid removal of spray deposits by heavy tropical rains. In the Cameroons sprays are advised every 10 days in the wet season and every fortnight in the dry season for the duration of fructification, from October to May, giving a total of 15–20 treatments a year. Applications are either hydraulic sprays (700–1000 l/ha, 7–10 l/tree), or atomized (360 l/ha), and sprayed in two directions across the plantation. The fungicides in use are: Bordeaux mixture 10 kg/ha (this spray is too thick for atomization), Carbane 1000 (5 kg/ha), oil formulation of copper fungicides Benomyl (300 g/ha). It is important to ensure that the uppermost parts of the trees are reached by the sprays.

It would be advantageous to establish plantations in much drier regions where the number of spray treatments could be much reduced.

Literature

GAILLARD, J. P. (1971): Lutte contre le Cercospora de l'avocatier au Cameroun. Fruits **26**, 225–230.
RONDON GARNIER, A. (1973): Etude sur la Cercosporiose de l'avocatier en Côte d'Ivoire. Fruits **28**, 279–284.
ZENTMYER, G. A., A. O. PAULUS, C. D. GUSTAFSON, J. M. WALLACE & R. M. BURNS (1965): Avocado diseases. Cal. Agrc. Expt. St. Serv. Circ. **534**, 1–11.

Author: P. Frossard

Some other more important Cercospora spp. on tropical and subtropical crops with no ascigerous state known:

Cercospora abelmoschii Ell. et Ev. Effuse black sooty patches on lower leaf surfaces of okra, kenaf, and rosella.

C. aleuritidis Miyake. Leaf spot of tung.

C. artocarpi H. & P. Syd. Leaf spot on breadfruit.

C. canescens Ellis & Mad. Leaf spot and spots on other above-ground parts of *Dolichos, Phaseolus, Vigna* spp. and other leguminosae. Ref.: CMI Description no 462.

C. capsici Heald. Definite circular leaf spot on *Capsicum* spp. CMI map no 248.

C. caribaea Cif. Gray leaf spot of cassava.

C. cladosporioides Sacc. Leaf spot of olive. CMI map no 415.

C. colocasiae (Höhn.) Chupp. Leaf spot of taro.

C. concors (Casp.) Sacc. Leaf blotch of potato. CMI map no 112.

C. cruenta Sacc. Leaf spot on *Dolichos, Glycine, Phaseolus & Vigna* spp. Ref.: CMI Description no 463.

C. elaeidis Stey. Leaf spot of oilpalm. CMI map no 487. Ref.: CMI Description no 464.

C. henningsii Allesch. Brown leaf spot of cassava.

C. kikuchii (T. Matsu & Tomoyasu) Gardner. Purple stain of soybean and guar (*Cyamopsis tetragonoloba*). Ref.: CMI Description no 466.

C. koepkei Krüger. Yellow spot of sugarcane. CMI Description no 417.
C. longipes Butl. Brown spot of sugarcane. CMI Description no 418.
C. melongenae Welles. Circular leaf spot of eggplant; irregular leaf spots are caused by *C. deightonii* Chupp.
C. oryzae Miyake. Narrow brown leaf spot of rice. CMI Description no 420; Fig. 85 c.
C. ricinella Sacc & Berl. Leaf spot of castorbean.
C. sesami Zimm. Circular gray leaf spot of sesame.
C. sorghi Ell. et Everh. Leaf spot of sorghum and maize. CMI Description no 419.
C. stizolobii Syd. Leaf spot of velvet bean.
C. theae Breda de Haan. Leaf spot of tea. CMI map no 247.
C. unamunoi Castell. Indefinite leaf spot and yellowing of leaves of *Capsicum* spp.
C. vaginae Krüger. Red sheath spot of sugarcane. CMI map no 251.

Cercospora sensu Chupp is a vast genus with a high degree of prevalence in warm climates. Practically every crop there has at least one *Cercospora* sp. as pathogen. Rearrangements of *Cercospora* spp. into different genera can be anticipated in the near future (s. Deighton below).

Literature

CHUPP, C. (1953): A monograph of the fungus genus Cercospora. Ithaca, New York.
DEIGHTON, F. C. (1967, 1971): Studies of Cercospora and allied genera. Mycol. papers nos 112, 124 and 133. Commonwealth Mycological Institute Kew, UK.

Colletotrichum coffeanum Noack (Plate 13 b and fig. 75)

Coelomycetes (M.A1)

This species morphologically greatly resembles *C. gloeosporioides* Penz., the conidial state of *Glomerella cingulata* (Stonem.) Spauld. et Schrenk. *C. gloeosporioides (p. 119) may cause brown blight.*

Disease: Coffee Berry Disease (CBD) and brown blight; Kaffeekirschen-Krankheit und Braun-fäule; l'anthracnose des baies du caféier; antracnosis del cafeto.

Geographical distribution: Tanzania, the Cameroons, Angola, Ruanda, Zaire, Central African Republic (CAR), Ethiopia, Uganda, and particularly in Kenya.

Host plants: *Coffea arabica;* in CAR also *C. canephora* (Robusta) and *C. excelsa.*

Symptoms: The pathogen produces brown, slightly sunken lesions of 1–10 mm diameter on green berries (Fig. 75 and plate 13b). These may drop prematurely or dry up and turn black on the branches (mummies). This shrivelling is the result of brown blight infection on ripening berries. Brown blight can also occur in the absence of coffee berry disease, and is then caused by *C. gloeosporioides*. The punctate acervuli of the sporulating fungus on the lesions can be seen with the naked eye. The fungus also kills off the flowers and colonises the yellow to dark brown bark of branches with numerous

Fig. 75.

spots. The disease may be mistaken for an attack on the fruit by *Cercospora coffeicola* (p. 190), and *Hemileia vastatrix* (p. 158).

Morphology: Small, rod-shaped, unicellular, colourless conidia are formed on short conidiophores in acervuli with or without setae (bristles). They measure $13 \pm 0.6 \times 3.8 \pm 0.2\,\mu$. They germinate with dark, irregularly oval appressoria. As *C. coffeanum* does not differ markedly in its morphological features from other *Colletotrichum* species found on coffee, it can only be identified for certain in culture on malt agar (at 22 °C, in the dark), where it produces a blackish substrate mycelium.

Physiological specialization: No races are known, but isolates vary in aggressiveness.

Epidemiology: The fungus survives in still smooth, brown parts of the bark on branches, in mummified berries and in lesions on affected berries from previous fruiting cycles. It sporulates in the presence of dew or rain at temperatures between 10 and 30 °C. Conidial spread in tree and plantation apparently takes place entirely by means of water droplets. Spread across greater distances is chiefly in infected juvenile plants and in diseased portions of the coffee tree. Green berries are most susceptible at the stage of rapid growth and after a phase of very high resistance, susceptibility again increases as the fruit turns yellow (brown blight). Infection can take place through the undamaged epidermis at temperatures between 12 and 26 °C, in the presence of moisture. At 22 °C, infection is completed after 5 hrs. The incubation period varies from 7 to 24 days.

The disease advances with the season and the rainy period which also triggers flowering. In Kenya, the maximum degree of infection is reached towards the end of the long rainy period (March–June), by about May/June.

Long rainy periods with much rainfall are thought to be particularly suitable conditions for the development of the disease.

Control: Prophylactic cultivation methods are not known. Resistant varieties to date are: Blue Mountain (moderately resistant), Rume Sudan, Timor, Geisha 10 and K7. Only the first one is suitable for cultivation on a commercial scale.

Fungicides which have been found to be effective are copper preparations, Orthodifolatan, Benomyl, Chlorothalonil, Dithianon, Carbendazim and Cypendazol. Orthodifolatan and Benomyl have practically no effect on coffee leaf rust. In Kenya, the following spray recommendations are in force: Starting in early February, 11 kg/ha copper fungicide (about 50 %) every three weeks, or 4.4 kg/ha Orthodifolatan or 1.1 kg/ha Benomyl in 1,100 l/ha water, sprayed every four weeks. For the newer fungicides the following rates are recommended (at 4 weeks intervals) by the Coffee Res. Station of Kenya: Carbendazim (50 % a. i.) 1 kg/ha, (20 % a. i.) 4 l/ha; Chlorothalonil 4.4 kg/ha, Cypendazol 1.1 kg/ha and Diathianon 3.3 kg/ha. The spray programme ends about early July, at the end of the rainy season. Another 1–2 sprays, depending on disease incidence and rainfall, are recommended in the short rainy period (Oct./Nov.), especially to control brown blight.

Author: J. Kranz

Colletotrichum musae (Berk. & Curt.) v. Arx (Plate 13 d)

Synonym: *Gloeosporium musarum* Cooke & Massee
Coelomycetes (C,2.A1).

Disease: Anthracnose (finger stalk rot and crown rot); Anthraknose der Banane; Anthracnose de la banane (pourriture des pédicelles des coussinets); antracnosis del platanero.

Geographical distribution: Anthracnose, finger stalk and crown rot of banana are distributed in all areas of bananas cultivation throughout the world.

Host plants: In natural conditions the fungus only occurs on *Musa* spp. (banana) and *M. textilis.*

Symptoms: *C. musae* is responsible for various post-harvest fruit rots during refrigerated transport and maturation. Numerous other fungi are associated with these rots: *Botryodiplodia theobromae* (p. 188), *Ceratocystis paradoxa* (p. 102), *Fusarium roseum*, etc., but *C. musae* is by far the most important.
a) Crown rot: This rot has become important with the adoption of the practice of packing the fruit as hands cut from the main stalk. A blackening and a progressive softening of the crown tissues progresses from the cut made to separate the hand from the main stalk. Seriously affected hands ripen prematurely, during transport. During ripening this rot spreads and individual fruits are easily separated from each other.
b) Finger stalk rot: These rots follow wounds, very often resulting from the flexing of the pedicels at the time of packing. The tissues appear water-soaked at the position where the flexing occurred, and then blacken in a few days at ambient temperature (25 °C). The rot can reach the crown and the tips of the fruits.
c) Skin antracnose: Skin wounds which result from the rubbing together of unripe fruits can be infected by *C. musae*. Sunken black spots develop, oval in shape and orientated along the long axis of the finger. The pulp underneath is not usually attacked. These spots are often situated on the ridges of the fingers.
d) Latent anthracnose: This only appears during maturation. As apparently healthy fingers turn yellow diffuse brown flat patches appear which enlarge (Plate 13 d). The sunken skin darkens rapidly. Generally the pulp is not affected except when the fruits are at an advanced stage of maturity.
In all the above cases small yellow-orange masses less than a millimeter in diameter can appear on the surface of the black, necrosed tissues. These fructifications form when the humidity is high.

Morphology: *C. musae* is characterized by the formation of small yellow-orange cushions (masses) which appear through small cracks in the skin. These are the acervulae containing unicellular, hyaline, oval conidia measuring $10 - 15 \times 3 - 5 \mu$. This is the asexual state of *C. musae*, of which no perfect form is known. The appressoria are dark brown bodies, more or less rounded, with a diameter of $8-16 \mu$.

Epidemiology: In the field the fungus is present in leaves, petioles and bracts in the process of decomposition. The conidia, formed in wet weather, remain viable in the acervulae for several months. When liberated by rain-splash they are caught in air currents and deposited on unripe fruits. They germinate in water in a few hours and form characteristic superficial appressoria which are resistant to both unfavourable environmental conditions and the usual fungicides. From the appressoria an infection hyphae grows which pierces the cuticle and then remains in a dormant state. Following the wounding or bruising of the skin or pedicels after harvest, anthracnose develops from these hyphae and appressoria. Otherwise *C. musae* stays latent until the fruits mature. Another source of infection is the water of the washing tank. This water, charged with spores, can penetrate deeply (3–4 cm) into the tissues wounded when the hands of bananas are cut.
Temperature plays a major role in the establishment and development of wound anthracnose. At tropical temperatures (25–30 °C) it appears 4–5 days after wounding and progresses rapidly. At 12–13 °C (the temperature in banana boats) the progress is considerably slower. A humidity of 80–95 % RH is indispensable for the preservation of the fruits, but favours the development of anthracnose.
Fruit susceptibility varies according to the season. In the Ivory Coast bananas are particularly susceptible in June–July, the time of heavy monsoon rains.

Control: As these are essentially diseases of wounds it is evident that the latter must be reduced to the minimum. The fruits must be handled with care to avoid flexing the fingers. On placing the hands or bunches into the cartons sheets of Kraft paper or polyethylene are laid between them to avoid their rubbing together. Finally, the interval between harvest and placing in the refrigerated holds of ships is reduced to a minimum.

Chemical control: Numerous chemical products have been tested for the eradication of anthracnose, but the employment of thiabendazole (TBZ) has revolutionised the problem of disinfecting bananas. This product penetrates the skin where it can destroy existing infections (curative action) and protest against future infections (protective action). It is shown below that Benomyl is even more efficient. These two products are not phytotoxic, their toxicity is almost non-existent, and they are at present the only ones tolerated by legislation in the U.S.A. and the Common Market. They can be used as a dip (TBZ 500 ppm a.i., Benomyl 200 ppm) for at least one minute, or as sprays. The dips are more effective but pose problems which arise from the need to re-adjust the continual dilution of the fungicide in the tank. Spraying is simpler to operate in a chain of pakking operations. Both fungicides, but more especially Benomyl, have the further advantage over previous products of considerably reducing the development of latent infections.

Other fungicides, Thiophanate-methyl, Carbendazin, and Cypendazol, tested in the laboratory or in commercial situations, have shown considerable promise in the range 200–500 ppm a.i., but are not approved for use. Steeping in hot water for 2 minutes at 55 °C prevents anthracnose of wounds and latent infections but this method of disinfection has not been adopted into current practice.

A certain danger exists owing to the possible emergence of strains of *C. musae* tolerant to these two fungicides, particularly in areas (Cameroons, West Indies) where Benomyl and Pelt are used against Sigatoka disease. This possibility has recently been demonstrated at St. Lucia where Griffee obtained a Benomyl-tolerant strain of *C. musae*.

Literature

FROSSARD, P., E. LAVILLE & J. MOTILLON (1973): Etude des traitements fongicides appliqués aux bananes après récolte. I. Action des thiophanate et méthylthiophanate. Fruits **28,** 195–202.

GRIFFEE, P. J. (1973): Resistance to benomyl and related fungicides in *Colletotrichum musae*. Trans. Brit. mycol. Soc. **60,** 433–439.

MEREDITH, D. S. (1971): Transport and storage diseases of Bananas: Biology and Control: Trop. Agr. (Trinidad) **48,** 35–50.

STOVER, R. H. (1972): Banana, Plantain and Abaca diseases. CMI, Kew, Surrey, UK.

WARDLAW, C. W. (1972): Banana diseases including Plantains and Abaca. Longman Ed. London. CMI Description no 222.

Author: P. Frossard

Other more important Colletotrichum spp. on tropical and subtropical crops:

C. capsici (Syd.) Butl. & Bisby. Anthracnose of fruit, and various other symptoms on other organs of capsicum pepper. Ref.: CMI Description no 317.

C. coccodes (Wallr.) Hughes. Black dot of potato and tomato, anthracnose of fruit of tomato, capsicum pepper, and squash. Ref.: CMI Description no 131.

Literature

ARX, J. A. von (1970): A revision of the fungi classified as Gloeosporium. J. Cramer, 3301 Lehrte, W.-Germany.

Deuterophoma tracheiphila Petri (Plate 14 a, c)

Synonym: *Phoma tracheiphila* (Petri) Kanciaveli & Thikasvili
Coelomycetes (C,1.A1.ph)

Disease: Mal secco of citrus; "mal secco"; dessèchement des agrumes; mal seco del limonero.

Geographical distribution: The disease which was first observed in Greece, is endemic in the Mediterranean area – except Spain, Portugal, and Morocco – and in the lemon orchards of the Caucasus (CMI map no 155).

Host plants: The pathogen attacks only plants of the genus *Citrus;* lemon (*C. limon*), citron (*C. medica*), sour-orange (*C. aurantia*), and rough lemon (*C. jambhiri*) are very susceptible to it. Lime (*C. aurantifolia*) shows some resistance. Orange (*C. sinensis*), mandarine (*C. reticulata*), grape fruit (*C. paradisi*), and bergamot (*C. bergamia*) are highly resistant.

Symptoms: Mal secco is a typical wilt disease (hadromycosis); the pathogen establishes itself in the xylem vessels of the host plant, and only when the affected part is dead, it invades other tissues and sporulates on the surface of the host.
The leaves of infected twigs and branches become chlorotic and fall off. The defoliated branches (Plate 14a) remain green for a while and die back later, turning light brown in colour. After a few months these dead branches turn silver-grey and are covered with minute black dot-looking fruiting bodies (pycnidia) of the fungus. In cross sections the wood of the affected parts of the tree shows a light orange or salmon discoloration which appears before the branches die (Plate 14c). The above symptoms are most conspicuous on suckers.
The disease appears first on one side of the tree. Usually it advances rapidly downwards from twigs and smaller branches to the main branches and trunk. After one or two years, the whole tree dies. In severe attacks a tree might die suddenly (apoplexy). In such cases the leaves wilt and remain on the branches.
The shedding of leaves and dying-back of branches are not sufficient to identify the disease; similar symptoms may be produced by root-rots, brown rot (p. 78), nematodes, frost, drought, and strong winds. The silver-grey dead twigs may also be confused with the disease caused by *Glomerella cingulata* (p. 119) which is a fungus attacking trees already weakened by other causes. However, the orange discoloration of the affected wood distinguishes mal secco from all other diseases and is enough to identify the disease in the orchard.

Morphology: There is, however, a non-chromogenic strain of the fungus, which does not produce the orange discoloration. In such a case the disease can be identified only by microscopic examination. The fruiting bodies on the dead branches are black pycnidia with a short beak containing minute hyaline spores ($2–3 \times 0.8 – 1 \mu$), that show brownian movement and look like masses of bacteria.
The fungus can be easily isolated in culture. On potato dextrose agar it forms pycnidia with the characteristic bacteria-sized spores.

Physiological specialization: unknown.

Epidemiology: The fungus can survive and sporulate for at least four years on dead twigs and branches. Pycnidia with viable spores can be found all year round. The pycnospores are liberated and dispersed from tree to tree by rain. Long distance dispersal is achieved by planting of infested propagation material. Magpies (*Pica pica*) sometimes use infected dead twigs to build their nests thus serving as carriers of the disease. The fungus can infect any part of the tree, like leaves, twigs, branches, trunk, and even roots. The pathogen enters the tree only through wounds. These can be produced by frost, hail, strong winds, agricultural tools etc.

The infection period starts in autumn and lasts through spring, its peak occuring in January and February. The incubation period is very long lasting 3 to 6 months for autumn and winter infections and 1.5 to 3 months for spring infections.

Rain and high humidity are prerequisite factors for the infection to take place. The fungus can grow and form pycnidia at any temperature between 10 ° and 28 ° with an optimum at 20 °. Below 10 ° its growth is very slow and above 30 ° it stops. Although the fungus thrives at 20 ° the most numerous instances of the infections occur during winter when temperatures are lower. This might indicate an increased susceptibility of the hosts during the dormant period.

The intensity of the disease depends among other factors on the susceptibility of the variety and also on the part of the tree through which the pathogen enters; when the infection is through the roots or the trunk the disease is more serious and usually the tree dies suddenly.

Control:

1. All dead twigs and branches must be removed together with a healthy section 15 cm in length, and then burned. This removal must be carried out with extreme care as soon as such dead twigs appear, regardless of the season.

2. Pruning should start late in spring, i. e. after the end of the rainy season. The wounds thus created must be covered with asphalt paint or any other suitable sealing.

3. The trees must be protected by wind breakers and one should avoid wounding their trunk and roots during cultivation.

4. The sites of dead infected trees must not be used for planting trees susceptible to the disease.

5. Nurseries must be set up in areas where the disease is not prevalent. The young trees should be protected by regular sprays with bordeaux mixture or fixed coppers.

6. The trees in the orchard must be sprayed three times during winter with bordeaux mixture containing 1 kg of copper sulfate and 1 kg of hydrated lime in 100 l of water or with copper oxychloride 0.5 % at monthly intervals. The first spraying must take place in October.

7. In areas where the disease is endemic the use of resistant varieties is the best means of controling the disease. In Italy the lemon varieties "Interdonato", "Monachello" and "Santa Teresa" have proven tolerant to mal secco.

Literature

GOIDANICH, G. (1964): *Deuterophoma tracheiphila* Petri. In: Manuale di Patologia Vegetale. Edizioni Agricole, Bologna. Vol **2**, 902–911.
CMI Description no 399.

Author: Anna Chitzanidis

Fusarium oxysporum Schlecht. f. sp. **albedinis** (Killian & Maire) Gordon (Fig. 76)

Hyphomycetes (H,4.C1.ph)

Disease: Bayoud disease; Bayoud Krankheit; bayoud; Bayoud.

Geographical distribution: (see attached map, Fig. 76). Bayoud disease of date palms was studied for the first time by Sergent & Beguet in 1921 in the Figuid oasis, Morocco. It is thought that this disease existed many decades before and originated in the Draa valley. From this centre the disease spread, first to all the oases and plantations in Morocco, often following the river valleys, and then towards the east where it reached the main plantations of western Algeria at Saoura and Gourara, and at Tidikelt in the central Sahara. It is present at Metlili and in some plantations near M'Zab. It threatens the palms of Zibans, of L'Oued Rhir and of Souf. It has never been recorded in other date-growing areas of the world.

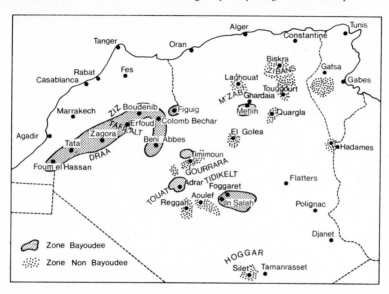

Fig. 76.

Host plants: Essentially, *Phoenix dactylifera*. In diseased plantations *Fusarium oxysporum* f. sp. *albedinis* can be isolated as easily from soil in the vicinity of the roots of resistant trees as from the neighbourhood of susceptible ones. It is present in the roots, stem (stipe) and fronds of susceptible varieties. it has been isolated from the roots of *Lawsonia inermis* (henna).

Symptoms: Symptoms usually appear first on a frond of the middle crown. This frond develops a leaden, dull green tint, and the leaflets on one of its sides bend back against the rachis and whiten. (The arabic word bayoud means white.) The leaflets on the other side of the rachis behave in the same way and the entirely dried frond gradually hangs downwards, against the stem. Later, similar symptoms appear on the other fronds of the middle crown until there remain only a few young green leaves at the summit. Eventually these last leaves also wither and the tree dies several months after the first appearance of the symptoms. Long brown streaks are to be seen along the rachis of each dried frond.

A careful study of grubbed trees reveals the roots where primary infection took place, and allows the path of the pathogen in the stem to be traced. The fibro-vascular bundles which are invaded acquire a yellow-red tint which becomes red-black. In a tree which is badly affected many of the bundles in the terminal bud are discoloured, as are the vascular branches to the vessels of the frond stalks. The vascular symptoms are therefore continuous from the roots to the extremities of the fronds. Infections at the base of the stem which are caused by *Ceratocystis paradoxa* (p. 102) also produce a withering of the foliar crown, but the drying of the fronds is not accompanied by the reddish colouration of the fibro-vascular bundles. Foliar attacks by *Diplodia phoenicum* (Sacc.) Fawcett & Klotz induce a yellowing along the sides of the rachis, but only the parenchymatous tissues are invaded.

Morphology: In pure culture the mycelium of this fungus is often a very pale rose-salmon colour, or tinted violet. Hyaline microconidia, globular or elliptical ($3–15 \times 3 – 5\,\mu$), are abundant and form on bottle-shaped microphialides. The spindle-shaped macroconidia (3–5 septae), tapered at both ends, are less abundant than the microconidia in young cultures. Their size ($20–35 \times 3–4.5\,\mu$) varies with the medium and other conditions. In older cultures globular intercalary chlamydospores are found ($6–20\,\mu$), isolated or in short chains.

Strains of *F. oxysporum* f. sp. *albedinis* cannot be morphologically distinguished from saprophytic strains of *F. oxysporum* (*sensu* Snyder & Hansen).

Physiological specialization: It has been possible to isolate strains of differing pathogenicity from diseased palm trees, but no classification has been established for want of rapid inoculation tests and accurate knowledge of the genetic parentage of the differential hosts.

Epidemiology: This pathogen is a permanent soil inhabitant capable of alternating between parasitic and saprophytic phases, and it can survive for years in the total absence of host plants. Chlamydospores ensure its survival even in a very dry soil. There have not been many studies of the factors which control the spread of this disease. It is known that undercropping the palms with lucerne and vegetables accelerates the passage of the pathogen in the vessels of the stem because of the frequent irrigation demanded by the ground crops. Dispersal of the disease is ensured by the travelling caravans which carry dried but diseased palm fronds used for making everyday objects such as camel packs. Irrigation water plays a very important role in contaminating a plantation after the appearance of a new focus of infection, but wind is not excluded as a possible agent of dispersal.

Control: Apart from some unsuccessful trials of fungicides injected into stems, and of foliar and soil applications of systemic fungicides, no method of chemical control has been adopted.
This is essentially for economic reasons because the cultivation of dates in the affected areas cannot support the cost of treatments.
Therefore research has been concentrated on prophylactic measures to avoid the contamination of new plantations (prohibition of imports of suckers), and towards resistant varieties.
Following surveys in plantations in Morocco and Algeria, varieties can be grouped into four classes:
a) Very resistant – Bou Stammi, Taadmant, Takerboucht, etc.
b) Fairly resistant – Bou Sliken, Azigzao
c) Susceptible – Jihel, Hafs, Assian
d) Very susceptible – Bou Feggous, Ahrdane, Mehjour, Deglet Nour, etc.

Unfortunately, the group of varieties which give crops of good quality and the best yields are the most susceptible, whereas varieties classed as resistant are of mediocre quality. However, Pere-au-Leroy noted that there is no linkage between resistance and any factor determining mediocrity and so the finding and breeding of varieties which possess both quality and disease resistance should be possible. Difficulties arise, partly from the fact that this species is dioecious, and partly because it has a very long vegetative cycle.
Research which it is hoped will produce good quality hybrids resistant to bayoud disease must be orientated from the start towards horizontal (non-specific) resistance. This is important because the date palm is generally grown as a monoculture, the disease is transmitted in the soil, and the pathogen changes easily whereas the breeding of new varieties is a long and difficult challenge.

Literature

BULIT, J., J. LOUVET & D. BOUHOT (1967): Recherches sur les Fusarioses: I. Travaux sur le Bayoud, fusariose du palmier dattier en AFN. Ann. Epiphyties **18**, 213–39.
LAVILLE, E., & P. LOSSOIS (1963): Methode de van der Plank et mode de propagation de Bayoud. Fruits **18**, 249–53.
MUNIER, P. (1974): Le Palmier Dattier. Maisonneuve et Larose Edt. Paris.
NIXON, R. W. (1950): Observations on the Bayoud disease of date palm in Morocco, Plant Dis. Reptr. **34**, 3.

Author: E. Laville

Fusarium oxysporum Schlecht. f. sp. cubense (E. F. Smith) Snyder & Hansen (Plate 14 b, d)

Hyphomycetes (H,4.C1.ph)

Disease: Panama disease; Panamakrankheit; Maladie de Panama; enfermedad del Panama.

Geographical distribution: This pathogen, recorded for the first time in 1876 in Australia by Bancroft, then observed at Panama in 1890 and in plantations of Gros Michel in 1904, is very widely spread in the banana-growing regions of Africa, Asia, Australia, the South Pacific area, Central America, the West Indies and the Caribbean, South America and Mexico. Originating from the Indo-Malaysia region, this parasite has been dispersed by man throughout the world as banana cultivation has extended (CMI map no 214).

Host plants: *Fusarium oxysporum f. sp. cubense* occurs on many species of the *Musaceae*. It is very common on susceptible species belonging to the triploid groups (AAA, AAB and ABB) – Gros Michel, Silk and Fluggoe, on the fibre species *M. textilis,* as well as on more tolerant species of the diploid group (AA) – *M. acuminata.* It can be isolated from wild grasses like *Paspalum fasciculatum, Panicum purpurescens* and local species of the *Musaceae* like *Ravenala* and *Heliconia.* The pathogen is also a component of the root mycoflora of resistant species.

Symptoms: The first visible symptoms show with the appearance of yellowish spots or stripes at the base of one or two old leaves. Next, and on the variety Gros Michel, two types of development are possible. In the first, the laminae of the oldest leaves turn yellow, and younger leaves are similarly affected in 1–2 weeks; the very youngest leaves remain green (Plate 14b). The yellowed leaves break at the point where the peduncle is attached and hang down against the pseudostem ('trunk'). In the second type the yellowing is confined to the petioles and the laminae stay green but, as above, the leaves break in succession and hang.
In cases of severe attack on young plants the pseudostem splits at the base and the sheaths break apart.
On the inside face of the sheaths or in a transverse section of the trunk broken yellow lines are visible, which in specimens infected for a long time are reddish-brown or nearly black (Plate 14d). The discolourations are always in the vascular bundles. A transverse or longitudinal cut through the corm exposes the same yellow or deep red-brown streaks, again confined to the vessels.
The suckers borne from the corm may show the same symptoms or may temporally escape. In the latter case they may wrongly be chosen as resistant material, and are often used for replanting, thereby contributing to the spread of the disease.
On varieties of Abacá or Manila Hemp (*M. textilis*), the internal symptoms are as described for Gros Michel. On the other hand the visible symptoms are appreciably different; the young leaves have a strong tendency to dry without yellowing.
This disease can easily be confused with another vascular infection of banana, Moko disease, caused by a bacterium (*Pseudomonas solanacearum*, p. 58). The visible symptoms are almost identical and if the pseudostem is cut the discontinuous yellow or red-brown lines in the vessels can be seen. However, abundant latex oozes from the cut surface.

Morphology: In pure culture the mycelium is white or tinted rose, peach and violet. Ovoid microconidia (5–12 x 2.2–3.5 μ) are usually plentiful and are borne on simple phialides or branched conidiophores. Macroconidia with 3–4 septae (27–66 x 3.5 μ) develop on the conidiophores or on the surface of sporodochial cushions. The spores are spindle-shaped, tapered at each end. Terminal or intercalary chlamydospores frequently form in old cultures, either isolated or in chains.
Strains of *F. oxysporum f. sp. cubense* pathogenic to banana cannot be distinguished morphologically from saprophytic strains of *F. oxysporum.*

Physiological specialization: The strains can be assigned to two major groups, designated "odour-forming" or "non" colour-forming according to their capacity to emit a fruity smell when grown in pure culture. These two groups correspond to the two types of symptom seen on Gros Michel ("non odour-forming" related to the yellowing, and "odour-forming" to the withering without previous yellowing type).

Three races of this pathogen are known. Race 1 is present in all banana-growing regions of the world and attacks triploids AAA such as Gros Michel, and Abaca (*M. textilis*). Race 2, endemic to Central America, is pathogenic to certain hybrids ABB (Bluggoe). A race 3 has been isolated which is capable of attacking resistant varieties of the Cavendish type (Poyo, Robusta).

Epidemiology: The parasite, being a permanent soil resident capable of alternating between parasitic and saprophytic phases, can survive many years in the absence of host plants. Chlamydospores assure its survival even in dry and air-less soils.

Every factor which encourages or reduces the spread of this disease has been carefully studied for more than 50 years but none has proved sufficiently effective to be used as an economic means of control. It has been recognised that acid soils (pH6 and below) are more favourable to the disease than those which are basic or neutral. Light soils allow rapid spread of the disease, as does poor drainage.

The disease is dispersed mainly by propagating with infected (but apparently healthy) vegetative material, by burying dead banana leaves, by irrigation water and by the carrying of plant debris and soil from one area to area. The wind is not excluded as another possible agent of dispersal.

Control: Various control methods have been tried: the inundation of infested soils to asphyxiate the pathogen, the use of fungicides, cultural methods (follows), quarantine etc. None have been retained as a valuable and economic solution of the problem.

Consequently, research has been directed towards the use of resistant varieties. First, there is the utilization of naturally resistant varieties which have the advantage of possessing attractive commercial features (yield/hectare, transport, maturation, etc.), as with the cultivars Dwarf Cavendish ('Nain'), Giant Cavendish ("Grande Naine"), Poyo and Latacan. Second, there is the creation of new varieties by controlled hydridization.

This last research began several decades ago and is still being followed, but there are numerous difficulties. The banana is difficult to hybridize, is often grown in monoculture, and the disease is easily transmitted in the soil and in plant material. For these reasons vertical resistance (oligogenic) must not be sought, but rather horizontal (polygenic) resistance.

Literature

WARDLAW, C. W. (1972): Banana diseases including plantains and abaca. 2nd edition, Longman, London.
STOVER, R. H. (1972): Fusarial Wilt (Panama Disease) of bananas and other *Musa* species. Phytopathological Paper **4**, Commonwealth Mycological Institute, Kew, UK.
CMI Description no 214.

Author: E. Laville

Fusarium oxysporum Schlecht. f. sp. **elaeidis** Toovey

Hyphomycetes (H,4.C1.ph)

Disease: Vascular wilt disease of oil palm; Welkekrankheit der Ölpalme; fusariose du palmier à huile; fusariosis de la palma africana.

Geographical distribution: The disease was first recorded in Zaire. Now it is present in Nigeria, the Cameroons, the Ivory Coast, Dahomey, the Congo and in Columbia (CMI map no 471).

Host plants: *Elaeis guineensis., E. madagascariensis, E. melanococca.*

Symptoms: On seedlings and young oil palms the disease shows as a stunting and yellowing of the central fronds whilst the outer ones develop normally; the result is a plant with a flat-topped aspect.

On adult plants several appearances are possible depending upon the speed at which the disease develops. The first sign is often a wilting of several fronds at the base of the crown or in an intermediate position. These leaves are normally erect or semi-erect, but they collapse onto the fronds below, turn yellow, dry and break. The collapsed leaves form a cover which envelops the top of the trunk. The symptoms progress towards the centre of the crown. The last five or six normal fronds of the crown are replaced by new ones which are smaller. Eventually these too turn yellow, and the whole crown dies and is liable to be blown down in a tornado. Disease development can, in contrast, be very rapid and cause a severe withering of the fronds which usually remain in their normal position for a long time.

The typical symptom is due to a change, within the vascular system, which can be seen in the roots as well as in the stem and the rachis of the leaves. In nurseries and young plantations a cut into the base (bulb) of the stem of attacked plants will reveal bundles, discoloured brown, leaving the base of the bulb. In adult trees, a cut in the trunk will reveal a flecking which, depending upon the height in the trunk and the age of the attack, is more or less dark coloured and distributed over the exposed surface. There is no need to confuse these coloured vessels with the fibres which are often brown and grouped in a horse-shoe shape around each vessel. The pathogen is easy to isolate from bundles at the base of the petiole and more especially from those below the terminal bud.

Armillariella mellea (p. 145) causes a similar drooping of palm leaves, but the internal symptoms described above and especially the isolation of *Fusarium* will reveal the true cause of the wilt.

Morphology: Culture colonies are completely typical of *Fusarium oxysporum,* with an abundant white aerial mycelium with tints of rose or purplish-blue. Blue-green to blackish sclerotia of varying size can appear after ten days; later, sporodochia coloured salmonrose and pinnotes form. Micro- and macroconidia as well as chlamydospores are abundant in laboratory cultures.

Physiological specialization: No races have been identified.

Epidemiology: *F. oxysporum* f. sp. *elaeidis* is a soil fungus, or more specifically a rhizosphere fungus. It is apparently seed transmitted (Locke & Colhoun, 1973). Entry into the vascular system of the roots necessitates wounds but an association with nematodes has not been demonstrated. In plantations the disease can appear as early as the fourth year, but more commonly between the sixth and tenth years. It is possible that this relationship with age is associated with the physiological condition of the trees at the time they are approaching the production of large crops. The incubation period in plantation trees is not known. On average, a tree which is obviously affected dies 5–6 months after the appearance of symptoms, although some trees will continue to grow for several years. When seedlings are treated with a concentrated inoculum the incubation period lasts 2–8 months depending upon the inoculation technique and the age of the plants. Sandy soils definitely favour the disease, probably due to a deficiency of potassium and to a lesser extent, magnesium. Several trials have shown that in such cases a dressing of potash can check the spread of the disease.

Control: No curative treatment is known. In established plantations it is important to ensure that mineral nutrition is satisfactory, particularly the availability of potassium.

When establishing or replanting oil palms the seed must either be disinfected or obtained from disease-free areas, and should be collected from parents carrying resistance. At the present time there is no plant material which is immune, but the cross Dura resistant (type Deli) x Pisifera resistant gives a high percentage of lines whose seedling-resistance persists well in the field.

Literature

LOCKE, I., & J. COLHOUN (1973): *Fusarium osysporum f.* sp. *elaeidis* as a seed-borne pathogen. Trans. Brit. mycol. Soc. **60**, 594–595.
CMI Description no 216.

Author: J. A. Meyer

Fusarium oxysporum Schlecht f. sp. **lycopersici** (Sacc.) Snyder & Hansen (Plate 15 a–d)

Hyphomycetes (H,4.C1.ph)

Disease: Fusarium wilt of tomatoes; Fusarium-Welke der Tomate; Fusariose de la tomate; Fusariosis del tomate.

Geographical distribution: Fusarium wilt in tomatoes has been found in many countries on all continents. The fungus has an optimal temperature for mycelial growth of 27–28 °C which explains, why the disease can be found in tomatoes growing both in the open in tropical and subtropical climates and in greenhouses in the temperate zones. At temperatures below 16 °C and above 34 °C disease symptoms hardly ever develop.

Host plants: This pathogen can infect *Lycopersicum* spp. only.

Symptoms: The fungus survives in the soil and usually enters the tomato plants through the roots causing browning and blockage of the vascular tissues (Plate 15c). The infection and, consequently, the brown discolouration progresses quickly upwards. Due to the blockage caused by the fungus, the water supply from the roots to the leaves is seriously hampered, resulting in a desiccation of the pith tissue of the stem, followed by an irreversible wilting of the leaves (Plate 15a, b). The fungus also produces toxins which are transported to the leaves. These toxins cause the leaves to turn yellow, sometimes orange-yellow. The yellowing starts at the lowest leaves and can often be unilateral initially, i. e. when one vascular bundle only is infected, symtoms are shown by the leaves – or parts thereof – supplied by that bandle.
Sometimes, the cortex adjacent to the discoloured vascular bundles turns conspicuously yellow. Infected plants initially show reduced growth and premature ripening of fruits. The wilt progresses gradually upwards resulting in the death of the plant (Plate 15d). The speed of this process greatly depends on environmental conditions influencing the growth of the pathogen and the transpiration of the host plant.
Wilt symptoms are also caused by the fungi *Verticillium albo-atrum*, and *V. dahliae* (p. 229) which colonize plants more slowly, however. Initially such plants may recover during cool periods such as at night. Moreover, the discolouration of the vascular bundles is more grey-brown, not tanbrown as with *Fusarium,* and the discolouration of the leaves is for some time restricted to the leaf tips. The *Verticillium* spp. are active at lower ambient temperatures than *Fusarium,* so that *Verticillium* wilt occurs predominantly only in temperate and subtropical regions. Unlike *Fusarium, Verticillium* spp. are often more prevalent in crops on badly structured soils.

Morphologie: In humid conditions whitish aerial mycelium may be formed on infected and decaying tissues, followed by a layer of macrospores which are pink-orange in colour and typically banana-shaped. Such conditions occur, for instance, near the soil surface or in very dense stands (weeds).

Physiological specialization: At present, two physiologic races are known with certainty, of which race 2 is less pathogenic than race 1 and has only been found so far in a few states of the U.S.A., Southern France, Morocco and Brazil.

Epidemiology: The pathogen is able to survive saprophytically in the soil, probably as chlamydospores. Some research workers have observed a period of survival, in the absence of the host plant, of more than 10 years. The disease tends to develop more quickly in plants deficient in calcium; this occurs also when calcium ions are immobilized by high concentrations of magnesium and phosphate ions.

Vigorously growing plants usually show wilt symptoms more quickly than poorly growing ones, because they require more water for transpiration and thus will suffer more quickly from water shortage. Under environmental conditions favourable for disease development, i. e. high soil and air temperatures and low relative humidity of the air, the incubation time may be as short as 7–10 days. When, however, air temperatures are around 15 °C this period may be up to three months.

Macrospores of the fungus, produced on the host plant tissues, may be transmitted mechanically by rain drops, by tools and machinery, by men, etc. Secondary infections usually take place through the roots, though infections can also occur through wounded aerial parts of the plant. The much smaller microspores may be formed on the surface of as well as within the host plant. They may even be transported by the sap stream in the vascular bundles.

Transfer of the disease to neighbouring plants is also possible by direct contact between an infected plant and a healthy one, as, for instance, between roots. The pathogen may occur in and on seeds, so that seed transmission of the disease is possible.

Control: In view of the period of survival mentioned above, crop rotation does not offer good prospects for effective control of this disease. Therefore, it is of utmost importance that the crop is planted on disease-free soil or that the soil is disinfested before use. Disinfestation is possible by means of steam, methylbromide, chloropicrin, Metham-sodium and similar rather unselective soil disinfectants. These treatments, however, are usually so costly that they are only applicable when the crop is potentially of high value.

Reinfestation of the soil should be prevented by sowing healthy seeds and by growing the young plants in a nursery in disease-free soil, preferably in soilless compost.

Reinfestation may also take place when infested soil is transported to the disinfested or disease-free fields, for instance by machines, tools, shoes of men, or when remains of infected tomato plants are introduced. Therefore, such items, which may carry fungal propagules, must be cleaned thoroughly before use in healthy crops: for smooth surfaces washing and ample rinsing may be sufficient, but for coarse surfaces disinfestation with 5 % formaldehyde is required. In brief: hygiene is of great importance. Prevention of root infection by application of fungicides has usually been of little use, though in recent years the use of fungicides based on benzimidazoles and some related compounds has given some promising results, provided the application was started before infection had taken place.

At present the best method of control is by resistance which is available in quite a large number of commercial varieties against race 1 and in a small number against race 2, or against both physiologic races of the pathogen. Though the development of new races has been very slow so far, it remains a menacing threat. The use of resistance has been complicated by the finding that damage by root-knot nematodes (*Meloidogyne* spp.) reduces resistance, so that such varieties should be planted on nematode-free soils. Under these restrictions, however, the resistant varieties offer the most economic means to control this disease.

Literature

WALKER, J. C. (1971): Fusarium wilt of tomato. Monograph no 6, Am. Phyt. Soc. St. Paul, Minn.

Author: G. Weststeijn

Fusarium oxysporum Schlecht. f. sp. vasinfectum (Atk.) Snyder & Hansen

Hyphomycetes (H,4.C1,ph)

Disease: Fusarium wilt of cotton; Welkekrankheit der Baumwolle; la fusariose du cotonnier; el marchitamiento del algodonero.

Geographical distribution: The disease is present in all cotton-growing regions: Africa, Asia, Europe and America (CMI map no 362).

Host plants: Various species of *Gossypium*.

Symptoms: In the case of early attacks of cotton wilt, seedlings wilt and their cotyledonary leaves become yellowish, droop and fall. With older plants which are growing actively the most typical first symptom in the field is a loss of turgescence at the tip of one or several leaves during the hot hours of the day; sometimes the entire leaf may wilt. At first there is recovery at night, but later the symptoms persist and extend. The first leaves to be affected become progressively yellow between the veins, then droop and necrose. They are easily detachable, and when removed black specks show on the exposed surface of their petioles. Finally, the canopy sheds its leaves more or less rapidly. In cases where leaf-fall is slow the plants tend to be stunted, and sometimes grow one or more new shoots. No symptoms are visible on the root system.
Longitudinal tangential cuts through affected stems reveal brown or blackish lines, most evident at the base of the stem but which can extend to the branches and often as far as the bolls.
Almost identical symptoms can be produced by *Verticillium dahliae* (p. 229), but isolation of the pathogen from the brown vessels will identify the true cause. Moreover, in plants attacked by *Verticillium* the marginal and inter-veinal yellowing is very accentuated, more widespread, and sharply defined against the green tissue; these chlorotic areas rapidly necrose and the general effect of *Verticillium* is very severe marbling or mottling.

Morphology: Descriptions of cultures of *F. oxysporum* f. sp. *vasinfectum* vary according to authors, and given the diversity of media used comparisons are difficult to make. In general, fresh isolates rapidly form sclerotia and sporodochia, with a clear dominance of 3-septate macroconidia. Microconidia are numerous. The fungus forms an abundant aerial mycelium tinted purplish-blue; the medium is rarely coloured. Chlamydospores are intercalary or terminal.

Physiological specialization: Using a selection of cotton varieties derived from various species of *Gossypium,* 4 races of *F. oxysporum* f. sp. *vasinfectum* have been differentiated (Armstrong & Armstrong 1966, Ibrahim 1966), which correspond, moreover, to their region of origin: Egypt (race 3), India (race 4), Sudan (race 5), and the United States. Regarding the American race, Armstrong & Armstrong (1960) infact distinguish 2 races (race 1 and race 2) on the basis of behaviour on soya and tobacco, which are attacked by race 2 but not by race 1. The differentiation of races is only valid if the differential hosts represent more than one species, because some varieties of the main species of *Gossypium* are susceptible to all the races.
All commercial varieties of *G. hirsutum* are resistant to races 3, 4 & 5. Within each race there often exists a considerable variation in virulence and in the morphology of the colonies.

Epidemiology: *F. oxysporum* f. sp. *vasinfectum* is a soil fungus. It can survive for many years in the absence of cotton as a saprophyte on plant debris, or in the rhizosphere of non-host plants, or in alternative and tolerant (symptom-free) hosts, or as chlamydospores. Its dispersal seems to be assured by water and especially by seed transmission.
Infection can take place at all stages of plant growth. The incubation period is rather variable, depending upon the soil and the climate.

The establishment and development of the disease is affected by the texture, mineral content and biology of the soil and it is generally more severe on light soils. A deficiency of potassium or an excess of nitrogen is particularly conducive to Fusarium wilt. In the range 4.6–8.4 pH has no influence, but a higher acidity brings about a big increase in disease severity. Nematodes are often associated with the initiation of the disease. Their role is to wound the roots, thereby increasing the chances for the fungus to gain entry; also, nematodes have exercised a biochemical action which has reduced the resistance of varieties considered to be resistant. Among the nematodes which are most important and frequently cited are *Meloidogyne incognita* and *M. incognita* var. *acrita* (Martin, 1956, Minton and Minton, 1966); in many regions Fusarium wilt is closely associated with the presence of root-knot eelworms (p. 251).

Control: Given the importance of seeds to the distribution of the disease, the control of seed health and especially the enforcement of quarantine measures are justified for impeding if not preventing its spread. Delinting with sulphuric acid considerably reduces the proportion of contaminated seed, but the effect of this treatment is entirely external. In "disease-free" areas it is essential to locate the initial foci which may appear. These can be eliminated if the affected plants are grubbed and the debris is burnt, and if the ground is left fallow for some time. A sensible rotation must be established to reduce nematode populations and to ensure a balanced nutrient status. There may be occasions when there is reason to apply additional potassium. Soil sterilization has been considered but in general is too costly.

The selection of resistant varieties remains the only possibility for the efficient control of Fusarium wilt, but the use of resistance is made difficult by the involvement of nematodes. Large populations of these are encouraged by rotating susceptible cotton with other plant species susceptible to nematodes, principally root-knot eelworms, as with crops of *Vicia* spp. and *Vigna* spp. Among the wild varieties of cotton *G. thurberi* is practically immune to *F. oxysporum* f. sp. *vasinfectum*. Resistance to *Fusarium* is generally attributed to a pair of major genes and one or more pairs of modifying genes; additional genes provide resistance to nematodes.

Literature

CMI Description no 28

Author: J. A. Meyer

Other more important formae speciales of Fusarium oxysporum on tropical and subtropical crops:

f. sp. *batatas* (Wollenw.) Snyder & Hansen. Wilt of sweet potato, mainly in the USA. CMI Description no 212.

f. sp. *ciceris* (Pdw.) Matuo & Sato. Wilt of chickpea.

f. sp. *coffeae* (Garcia) Wellman. Wilt of coffee.

f. sp. *coriandrii* Nanila & Joshi. Wilt of coriander.

f. sp. *cucumerinum* Owen. Wilt of cucumber, confined to temperate and subtropical regions. CMI Description no 215.

f. sp. *cumini* Prasad & Patel. Wilt of cumin (*Cuminum cyminum*).

f. sp. *glycines* Armstrong & Armstrong. Wilt of soybean.

f. sp. *lentis* (Vasudeva & Srinivasan) Gordon. Wilt of lentils.

f. sp. *melongenae* Matuo & Ishigami. Wilt of eggplant.

f. sp. *melonis* Snyder & Hansen. Wilt of muskmelon and *Cucumis melo*. CMI Description no 218.

f. sp. *passiflorae* Gordon apud Purss. Wilt of passion fruit.

f. sp. *psidii* Prasad, Mehta & Lal. Wilt of guava.

f. sp. *ricini* (Wollenw.) Gordon. Wilt of castorbean.

f. sp. *vanillae* (Tucker) Gordon. Wilt of vanilla.

f. sp. *zingiberi* Trujillo. Wilt of ginger.

Fusarium solani (Mart.) Sacc. (Plate 7 a)

Disease: Root rot and wilt of coffee. The fungus causes many diseases, mainly root rots, on a wide range of hosts (s. Booth 1971, p. 216, & below).

This was first described causing a root rot and wilt of adult *C. arabica* trees in Kenya in 1972, where investigations have shown that it is widespread in occurrence but not severe. It is also reported as a pathogen in Zambia and in India. *F. solani* var. *minus* haves been described as causing a foot rot of young plants. *F. solani* attacks trees weakened and in poor cultural condition causing a purple discolouration in the wood (Plate 7a) and resulting in wilting and death. The form attakking coffee appears to be distinct and therefore its designation as *F. solani* (Mart.) Sacc. f. sp. *coffeae* Baker is proposed.

Colonies on 2 % malt extract agar are variable, pale to beige with sparse aerial mycelium, a bluish to bluish-brown colouration developing in the agar. Conidia are produced abundantly in beige to bluish masses. Microconidia are abundant, allantoid to oval, 9–16 x 2.5–3 μ. Macroconidia, cylindrical to falcate with a marked foot cell, variable in length 35–100 x 4.5–8 μ.

The fungus occurs in soil from which infection occurs through wounds in the roots. Control is at present only by removing and burning infected trees as completely as possible. Soil sterilization of affected areas before replanting, using dazomet, has tentatively been recommended.

Literature

BAKER, CELIA, J. (1972): *Fusarium solani* associated with a wilt of *Coffea arabica* in Kenya. E. Afr. agric. For. J. **37**, 137–140.

Author: Celia J. Baker

Fusarium species
inciting plant diseases in the tropics (Figs. 77–79)

Hyphomycetes (H,4.C1.ph)

Fungi of the genus *Fusarium* are abundant in nature and widely distributed. Many of them cause plant diseases; some are numbered among the most harmful of all pathogenic fungi. Practically all organs of cultivated and wild plants can be attacked. The symptoms which can be produced are manifold. Some Fusaria, e. g. *F. avenaceum*, *F. culmorum* and *F. moniliforme* have a wide range of hosts. The pathogenicity of others is more or less strictly confined to particular species, genera or families of higher plants, e. g. *F. coeruleum*, *F. eumartii* and *F. sambucinum* f. 6 on potato, *F. buharicum* on cotton and *Hibiscus cannabinus* (Soviet Union and Iran), *F. udum* on *Cajanus* and *Crotalaria* (India) and *F. xylarioides* on coffee (Africa). An extensive specialization of pathogenic types which cannot be morphologically distinguished, occurs with *F. solani*, *F. lateritium*, *F. udum* and above all *F. oxysporum*. In this last named, most important plant pathological *Fusarium* species, about 80 so-called specialized forms are so far known, many of which have been further differentiated into "races" (see Armstrong and Armstrong, 1968; Booth, 1971). They are almost exclusively vascular parasites and usually produce tracheomycoses, mostly leading to wilt diseases, associated with yellowing ("*Fusarium*-wilt", "*Fusarium*-yellows"). Tropical crops affected seriously by diseases of this kind include banana, cotton, date palm, sweet potato and tomato.

The perfect stage of a whole series of Fusaria is known (see Booth, 1971). Invariably it belongs to the ascomycetes in the family of *Hypocreaceae*. In the Fusaria under discussion, this assigns *F. eumartii*, *F. javanicum* and *F. solani* to the genus *Nectria*, *F. acuminatum*, *F. avenaceum*,

F. equiseti, F. graminearum, F. lateritium, F. moniliforme, F. moniliforme var. *subglutinans, F. sambucinum* f. 6, *F. stilboides* and *F. xylarioides* to *Gibberella* and *F. decemcellulare* to *Calonectria*. Most perfect stages are relatively rare in nature, but under certain conditions, some of them are formed more frequently and in greater numbers (e. g. with *F. graminearum, F. moniliforme* and *F. xylarioides*). Their significance in the disease cycle varies and is often obscure.

Opinions vary about the demarcation of species within the genus *Fusarium,* and hence about the number of types which can be differentiated morphologically. The classification proposed by Wollenweber (1916–1935, 1931, 1943) and Wollenweber and Reinking (1935) which differentiated more than 100 species and varieties was accepted by many authors, or at least retained in its basic principles (see Doidge, 1938; Bugnicourt, 1939; Raillo, 1950; Subramanian, 1952, 1954; Bilai, 1955). Other authors accept a system with no more than 9 species which is undoubtedly far too simplified (Matuo, 1961, 1972; Messiaen and Cassini, 1968; Toussoun and Nelson, 1968). However, at least 50 to 60 Fusaria (and probably far more) can definitely be differentiated from one another (Gerlach, 1970; Booth, 1971).

Obviously, the number of Fusaria which can here be selected from the entire literature for description must be strictly, if sensibly limited. Apart from publications which are essential for a survey of the taxonomy of this genus and for purposes of identification, others providing special reference for tropical regions as a whole (Reinking and Wollenweber, 1927; Gordon, 1960) or for particular regions: India (Subramanian, 1952, 1954), Iran (Gerlach and Ershad, 1970), Israel (Joffe and Palti, 1972), Japan (Matuo, 1961, 1972), South Africa (Doidge, 1938), South East Asia (Bugnicourt, 1939), Trinidad (Gordon, 1956), have been taken into consideration, as well as the publication by Sherbakoff (1915) with many illustrations and detailed descriptions of Fusaria occurring on potato.

The identification of Fusaria is no more difficult than that of many other genera of imperfect fungi. True, this is only exceptionally possible with some degree of reliability on the sole basis of natural material. It is really only possible in conjunction with definite, known symptoms of *Fusarium* infection on a particular host species, if the fungus sporulates freely and adequate experience has been gained. Even then, microscopic confirmation is essential for reliable identification. In general, isolation, pure culture and careful determination of macro- and microscopic features and their full range of variability are unavoidable. In *Fusarium* species with morphologically indistinguishable pathogenic forms, the conclusive proof that an isolated *Fusarium* is in fact the organism responsible for the observed symptoms of disease may have to rest on inoculation trials.

All Fusaria can be grown without much trouble in pure culture on nutrient agar media and sterilized plant portions. Experience has shown that most Fusaria show their typical features most readily if they have been freshly isolated and kept in daylight at about 25 °C. Some species do so after a few days, others take many weeks. The features suitable for differentiation are manifold and their permanence and importance must be assessed differently from one case to the next. Features which can carry considerable weight for identification purposes without optical aid are: Rate of growth, type of colony, amount and kind of aerial mycelium, colour tints, type of spore layers (flat slimes or pustulate), shape and colour of sclerotial formations and odours (some isolates of *F. oxysporum*). Important microscopic distinguishing features are: Structure of conidiophores, above all, type of spore forming cell (formation in one place = simple phialide, in several = polyphialide), type of macroconidia (length, width, curvature, cross walls, shape of basal and apical cell, thickness of wall), occurrence of microconidia (in chains or false heads) and their size and shape, presence of thick-walled, spherical spores (chlamydospores) – in conidia and hyphae, single, in chains or clusters, smooth walled or rough to verrucose. In many cases a mixed sample of spores from mucilaginous layers and aerial mycelium can give a definite indication of the *Fusarium* species in question. In others, additional features must be examined, in order to differentiate between similar types.

It seemed only common sense that some of the Fusaria which are mainly of plant pathological significance in temperate regions, should be included in the list of Fusaria which attack cultivated plants in tropical and sub-tropical regions. The *Fusarium* species listed below, are given the same numbers as in the greatly simplified key and in the illustrations of Figs. 77 to 79.

1. *F. oxysporum* Schlecht. ex. Fr.
2. *F. moniliforme* Sheld.
3. *F. moniliforme* Sheld. var. *subglutinans* Wollenw. et Reink.
4. *F. solani* (Mart.) Sacc.
5. *F. javanicum* Koord.
6. *F. coeruleum* Lib. ex Sacc.
7. *F. eumartii* Carpenter
8. *F. udum* Butler
9. *F. xylarioides* Steyaert

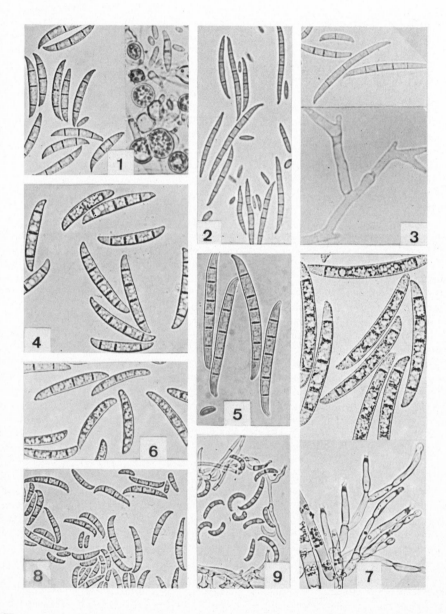

Fig. 77.

10. *F. graminum* Corda
11. *F. acuminatum* Ell. et Ev.
12. *F. equiseti* (Corda) Sacc. sensu Gordon
13. *F. semitectum* Berk. et Rav.
14. *F. lateritium* Nees ex Fr.
15. *F. avenaceum* (Corda ex Fr.) Sacc.

16. *F. stilboides* Wollenw.
17. *F. sambucinum* Fuckel f. 6 Wollenw.
18. *F. buharicum* Jaczewski
19. *F. culmorum* (W. G. Smith) Sacc.
20. *F. graminearum* Schwabe
21. *F. decemcellulare* Brick

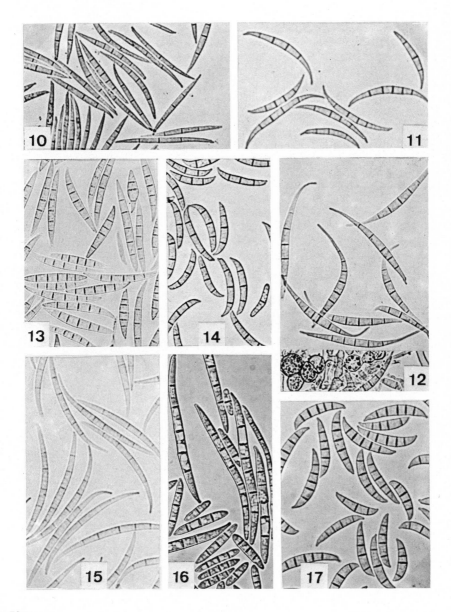

Fig. 78.

An attempt has been made to provide a simple key for the Fusaria listed, based on characteristic which are rapidly and easily determined, to facilitate identification for those who use this book The natural habitat of the pathogens is mentioned, as well as their morphological features. Obviously, the simplified key can only serve as a rough guide and could not satisfy specialists in every respect.

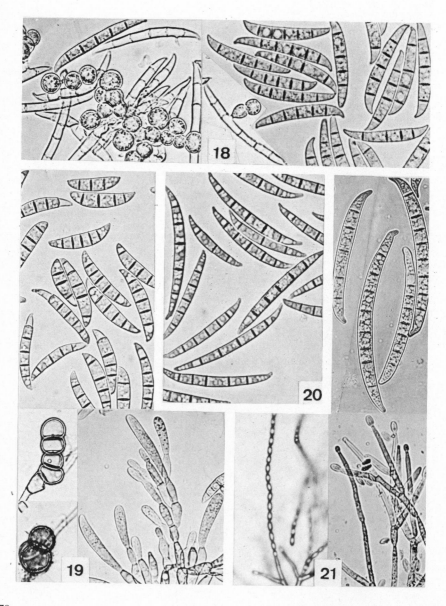

Fig. 79.

Simplified Analytical Key

Fungus characteristics
(Fresh isolated cultures, kept at about 25 °C in daylight)

Macroscopic

Diameter of colony (on PD agar in petri dishes after 4 days)
above 8 cm 19, 20
above 6 cm 13, 17
above 4 cm 1,2,3,8,10,11,12,15,18
above 3 cm .... 4,5,6,7,16,21,(9)
under 3 cm .... 9,14,(16)

Aerial mycelium
mostly luxuriant, tall, matted and felted .... 13,19,20,(10,12)
mostly rich, delicate, loose 1,2,3,4,5,6,7,11,12,16
often fibrous, tufted, powdery .... 2,10,17,18,21,(9,13,14,16)
soon smeared with spore masses .... 4,5,7(6,18)
mostly sparse and low .... 8,9,14,16,17,18(1,12)
later changes colour like the substrate .... 6,8,16,19,20,(1,2,3,11,12)

Colour of stroma and substrate
always, or for long periods, pale .... 4,5,7,10,18,(1,2,3,9,12,13)
yellowish, orange, light–dark brown 4,5,7,12,13,14,16,17,18
pink, violet 1,2,3,11,21
crimson, wine, purple .... 11,15,19,20,21,(16)
red-brown .... 16,(1,9,19)
blue-violet 2,3,6,8,9
in part verdigris to blue-green .... 4,6,(1)

Sclerotial plectochyma
frequent, well developed, mostly raised .... 1,9,15,17,(16)
not infrequent, mostly smaller .... 1,8,14,16,18,21,(11,12)
usually or always absent 2,3,4,5,6,7,10,11,12,13,19,20
pale, cream, buff, amber colour 1,9,10,11,12,13,14,15,17,18
dark, blue-violet, blue-black 1,2,3,4,6,8,9,11,14,16,18
sometimes also verdigris 1,4,6,18

Spore layers
often flat exudate (pionnotal) .... 4,5,6,7,8,10,11,15,16,17,18,19,20,(1,2,3,14)
often pustulate (sporodochial) .... 1,2,3,10,11,14,15,16,17,18,19,20,21,(8,12)
deep salmon, orange, cinnamon colour 1,2,3,8,10,11,12,14,15,16,17,18,19,20
off-white, cream, amber colour .... 4,5,6,7,21,(1,2,3,18)
sometimes verdigris, blue-violet .... 4,6,(8,18)
sometimes or always absent .... 9,13,(1,2,3,11,12,20)

Odour

fruity, aromatic ....some isolates of 1

Microscopic

spore forming cells
also frequently with several openings 3,13

Microconidia
typical ones usually predominate in the aerial mycelium 1,2,3,4,5,6,7,8,21
never in chains 1,3,4,5,6,7,8
also in chains 2,21
usually narrowing towards the base 2
usually slightly curved, kidney-shaped 8
other small conidia not infrequent 9,14
mostly hook-shaped 9
practically absent 10,11,12,13,15,16,17,18,19,20

Macroconidia
thick, mostly 4,5μ and more, thick walled
usually at least 5 septae and 50 μ in length 5,7,12,16,18,20,21
often fewer septae and shorter 4,6,13,17,19
more slender, mostly 3–4, 5μ thick, thin walled
often 5 septae and about 50 μ long .... 15,(1,2,3)
largely 3(–5) septae and shorter 1,2,3,10,11,14
mostly 1–3 septae and up to 30 μ long 8,9
at least dorsal portion usually curved 1,8,11,12,14,15,17,19,21
usually hook-shaped 9
usually straight, approximately cylindrical 4,5,6,7,16,18,20
usually subulate or spindel shaped 10,13
Apical cell
usually long 2,3,10,11,12,15,16
also flagellate 12
usually short and fairly blunt 4,5,6,7
usually short and pointed at one end 1,13,17,18,19,20,21
usually short and hook-like .... 8,9,14,(17)
Basal cell
usually not well marked 4,5,6,7,9,10,13,16
usually well marked 1,2,3,8,14,15,17,19
usually conspicuous 11,12,18,20,21

Chlamydospores ....
soon formed and numerous, conspicuous 11,12,18
not infrequent in older cultures 1,4,5,6,7,8,17,19,20
scant, even in older cultures 9,13,14,16
absent 2,3,10,15,21

Occurrence and disease symptoms

On many plant species
rot on aerial or subterranean organs 1,2,3,4,5,11,12,13,15,19
vascular wilt .... many forms of 1

On woody plants
bark rot, dieback 14,16,21
proliferations (galls, witches broom) 21

On coffee
bark rot (base of stem), wilt 9

On gramineae
rot on roots, haulm and fruiting head 2,3,15,19,20
orange coating on fruiting head (spike) 10,15,19,20

On cotton and *Hibiscus cannabinus*
root and foot rot (base of shoot) 18

On *Cajanus* and *Crotalaria*
root and foot rot (base of stem), wilt 8

On potato
tuber rot .... 6,17,(7,15)
foot rot (base of stem), wilt 7

Literature

ARMSTRONG, G. M., & J. K. ARMSTRONG (1968): Formae speciales and races of *Fusarium oxysporum* causing a tracheomycosis in the syndrome of disease. Phytopathology **58**, 1242–1246.
BILAI, V. I. (1955): Fusarii (The Fusaria). Akad. Nauk UkrSSR. Kiev.
BOOTH, C. (1971): The genus *Fusarium*. CMI, Kew.
BUGNICOURT, F. (1939): Les *Fusarium* et *Cylindrocarpon* de l'Indochine. Encycl. Mycol., Paris, **XI**.
DOIDGE, E. M. (1938): Some South African Fusaria. Bothalia **3**, 331–483.
GERLACH, W. (1970): Suggestions to an acceptable modern *Fusarium* system. Ann. Acad. Sci. fenn. A, IV Biologia **168,** 37–49.

GERLACH, W., & D. ERSHAD (1970): Beitrag zur Kenntnis der *Fusarium-* und *Cylindrocarpon*-Arten in Iran. Nova Hedwigia **20**, 725–784.
GORDON, W. L. (1956): The taxonomy and habitats of the *Fusarium* species in Trinidad, B.W.I. Can. J. Bot. **34**, 847–864.
GORDON, W. L. (1960): The taxonomy and habitats of *Fusarium* species from tropical and temperate regions. Can. J. Bot. **38**, 643–658.
JOFFE, A. Z., & J. PALTI (1972): *Fusarium* species of the *Martiella* section in Israel. Phytopath. Z. **73**, 123–148.
MATUO, T. (1961): On the classification of Japanese Fusaria. Ann. Phytopathology Soc. Japan **26**, 43–47.
MATUO, T. (1972): Taxonomic studies of phytopathogenic Fusaria in Japan. Rev. Plant Prot. Res., Tokyo, **5**, 34–45.
MESSIAEN, C. M., & R. CASSINI (1968): Recherches sur les fusarioses. IV. La systématique des *Fusarium*. Annls Épiphyt. **19**, 387–454.
RAILLO, A. (1950): Griby iz roda *Fusarium*. Moskow.
REINKING, O. A. & H. W. WOLLENWEBER (1927): Tropical Fusaria. Philipp. J. Sci. **32**, 103–253.
SHERBAKOFF, C. D. (1915): Fusaria of potatoes. Mem. Cornell Univ. agric. Exp. Stn. **6**, 85–270.
SUBRAMANIAN, C. V. (1952): Studies on South Indian Fusaria. II. Fusaria isolated from black cotton soils. Proc. natn. Inst. Sci. India **18**, 557–584.
SUBRAMANIAN, C. V. (1954): Studies on South Indian Fusaria. III. Fusaria isolated from some crop plants. J. Madras Univ., B, **24**, 21–46.
TOUSSOUN, T. A., & P. E. NELSON (1968): A pictorial guide to the identification of *Fusarium* species according to the taxonomic system of Snyder and Hansen. The Pennsylvania State University Press, 51 pp.
WOLLENWEBER, H. W. (1916–1935): Fusaria autographice delineata. Selbstverlag, Berlin, 1200 Tafeln.
WOLLENWEBER, H. W. (1931): *Fusarium*-Monographie. Fungi parasitici et saprophytici. Z. Parasit-Kde **3**, 269–516.
WOLLENWEBER, H. W. (1943): *Fusarium*-Monographie. II. Fungi parasitici et saprophytici. Zentbl. Bakt. ParasitKde Abt. II **106**, 104–202.
WOLLENWEBER, H. W., & O. A. REINKING (1935): Die Fusarien, ihre Beschreibung, Schadwirkung und Bekämpfung. Paul Parey, Berlin-Hamburg.

Author: W. Gerlach

Macrophomina phaseolina (Tassi) Goid. (Figs. 80–81)

Synonyms: *Rhizoctonia bataticola* (Taub.) Butler = *Sclerotium bataticolae* Taub., and others

Coelomycetes (C,1.A1)

Disease: Charcoal rot and ashy stem decay; Schwarzbeinigkeit und aschige Stengelfäule; pourriture cendré; podredumbre carbonosa.
The pathogen causes other diseases known as brown stem and root rot; stalk rot; hollow stem; dry rot of bulbs, roots and tubers; blight and wilt of seedlings.

Geographical distribution: The disease is world wide in distribution, notably in the tropics and subtropics, and reported on a wide variety of herbaceous and woody crops. It has been reported on various legumes in temperate regions.

Symptoms: *M. phaseolina* causes a root and lower stem rot, damping-off of seedlings and the early death of maturing plants. The disease is called charcoal rot because infected roots and stems become greyish-black or black (Fig. 80) and is associated with a crust-like accumulation of minute black sclerotia. Wilting may be due to a combination of vascular plugging by sclerotia and enzymatic action. The fungus is often involved in a root or stem decay complex involving other fungi and nematodes.

Morphology: The dark brown, ostiolated pycnidia are often produced on host tissue (Fig. 80). Pycnidia vary in size depending upon the host. Pycniospores are elliptical, thinwalled, single-cel-

Fig. 80.

led, hyaline and measure about $10–24 \times 1–10 \mu$ (Fig. 81) and may remain viable for several months. The fungus is extremely variable, with isolates differing from various parts of the same plant.

Epidemiology: The fungus is a soil- and seed-borne facultative parasite. Temperatures greater than 55 °C are lethal to mycelium, but not sclerotia. It invades directly the host tissues of any age, permeating both inter- and intracellularly. Host plants under water stress are more susceptible than those that are not. Selective media have been developed. Pycnidia development is influenced by temperature, light and ability of the isolate to produce them. Sclerotia and pycniospores can be airborne or spread by irrigation water, tools and implements, and other cultural operations.

Control: Control is difficult because of the wide host range and extreme variability of the fungus. Crop rotation and field sanitation can reduce inoculum potential. Soil fumigation with 365 kg/ha of 57 % methyl bromide plus 43 % chloropicrin controlled the disease on fir seedlings for at least 2 years.

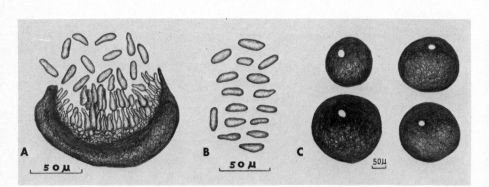

Fig. 81.

Literature

AMMON, V., & T. D. WYLLIE (1972): Penetration and host-parasite relationships of *Macrophomina phaseolina* on *Glycine max*. Phytopathology **62,** 743–744.

DHINGRA, O. D., & J. B. SINCLAIR (1973): Variations among isolates of *Macrophomina phaseoli* (*Rhizoctonia bataticola*) from different regions. Phytopath. Z. **76,** 200–204.

ILYAS, M. B., & J. B. SINCLAIR (1974): Effects of plant age upon development of necrosis and occurrence of intraxylem sclerotia in soybean infected with *Macrophomina phaseolina*. Phytopathology **64,** 156–157.

MEYER, W. A., J. B. SINCLAIR & M. N. KHARE (1973): Biology of *Macrophomina phaseoli* in soil studied with selective media. Phytopathology **63,** 613–620.

WATANABE, T., R. S. SMITH, Jr., & W. C. SNYDER (1970): Populations of *Macrophomina phaseoli* in soil as affected by fumigation and cropping. Phytopathology **60,** 1717–1719.

CMI Description no 275.

Author: J. B. Sinclair

Monilia roreri Cif. & Par. (Fig. 82)

Hyphomycetes (H,2.A.2)

Disease: Monilia Pod Rot (watery disease) of cocoa; Monilia-Fäule des Kakaos; Monilia pourriture; podredumbre acuosa.

Geographical distribution: The disease was first discovered in Ecuador in 1914 and spread from there to Colombia, Peru, Venezuela and South Panama (CMI map no 13). It occurs extensively in Ecuador and Colombia and leads to 15–80 % losses in yield.

Host plants: *Theobroma* spp.

Symptoms: The pathogen only attacks the fruit, especially young fruit; susceptibility diminishes with age. The first sign of attack is the appearance of small, pale spots on the surface of the fruit, which may give the impression that the fruit ripened prematurely. The spots enlarge, turn to a coffee brown colour and are surrounded by a yellowish halo, which may cover some part or the entire surface of the fruit. If the humidity is high, the lesions are covered by a mycelial layer, which has a creamy salmon colour and produces spores profusely (Fig. 82). This is the characteristic symptom picture in the field. Some fruit shows no external symptoms, although the contents of the fruit may be completely destroyed. On opening the fruit, a watery rot is nearly always found. In the final stage of the disease, the fruit is mummified. In the initial stages, the disease can be mistaken for black fruit rot (*Phytophthora palmivora*, p. 83) or witches' broom (*Crinipellis perniciosus*, p. 153), although the fruit is distorted in the latter disease. Identification is by means of the mycelial layer and sporulation.

Morphology: The fungus hyphae are hyaline, slightly septate and 4–5 μ in diameter. The conidia vary from spherical to elliptical, are hyaline and form in chains. They measure 7–10 x 9 – 14 μ.

Epidemiology: The fungus survives with its conidia in affected fruit left hanging on the tree or among crop residues. It is also believed to survive in the soil, although this has not so far been confirmed. Under suitable conditions of temperature and humidity during the rainy period many spores are formed in chains, which are easily separated and spread by wind and rain. Research workers in Colombia ascribe some importance to insect damage as a factor facilitating spread of the disease, but it has been proved that infection can take place without prior injury. The pathogen can penetrate directly through the epidermis of the fruit, especially at the base of glandular hairs. After penetration, it spreads rapidly through the inside of the young, susceptible fruit.

Fig. 82.

There is a close correlation between the amount of rainfall in the period of young fruit formation and the occurrence of *Monilia*. The average temperature in this period is 18 °C. During the dry period, conditions are not very suitable for infection. Attack is believed to take place during flowering or in the first phase of fruit formation, but there is insufficient evidence to support that view. Since affected pods can be found throughout the entire year, several secondary infections are presumed to occur during the rainy period.

Control: Affected fruit should be consistently destroyed, in order to reduce the foci of infection. Pericarps must be burnt far from the plantation. Young fruit should be treated with fungicides during the rainy period. Zineb, Maneb and copper preparations (3 kg/ha) are effective fungicides and must be misted or sprayed every 2–4 weeks. Control measures with fungicides are only profitable in high yield plantations. Little has so far been done to find resistant varieties. The clones EET 233 and SCA 12 were only slightly attacked in pathogenicity tests in Ecuador. It could also be observed that plantations escaped attack, if their crop developed in a period which was unsuitable for the disease.

Literature

AMPUERO, E. (1967): Monilia pod Rot of Cocoa, Cocoa Growers Bulletin **9**, 15–18.
DESROSIERS, R., A. BUCHWALD & C. W. von BOLANOS (1955): Effect rainfall in the incidence of Monilia pod rot in Ecuador. F.A.O. Plant Prot. Bull. **3**, 161–164.
JORGENSEN, H. (1970): Monilia pod rot of cocoa in Ecuador. Cacao (Costa Rica) **15**, 4–13.
THOROLD, C. A. (1975): Cocoa diseases. Clarendon, Oxford.
CMI Description no 226.

Author: E. Ampuero

Oidium heveae Steinm. (Figs. 83–84)

The perfect stage of this fungus belonging to the Erysiphaceae has not yet been recorded. Hyphomycetes (H,2.A1)

Disease: Oidium leaf disease of hevea; Echter Mehltau des Kautschukbaumes; Oidium de caoutchouc; oídio del cauchero.

Geographical distribution: This disease had been observed in all the rubber growing countries of the world, except South America by 1945. (CMI map no 4). Later Rosetti (1958) recorded it in Sao Paulo, Brazil.

Host plants: *Hevea brasiliensis.*

Symptoms: *Oidium* is essentially a disease of young leaves, mature leaves where the cuticle has hardened are immune, as the causal fungus cannot penetrate the fully developed cuticle. Leaves are susceptible as soon as they break out of the buds, when they are copper brown in colour, until they reach the light green stage of development, just before they become fully mature and dark green. At first the disease appears as white spots on the leaf (Fig. 83). Later the fungus spreads, covering a major part of the leaf surface. The leaves being still tender, and the cuticle not yet hardened, they tend to shrivel, lose lustre and get blown down by light winds.
When semi-mature leaves are infected, discrete white circular colonies are produced, as the fungus cannot spread over a wide area because the leaf cuticle is partially developed. Such leaves do not fall, but remain on the tree. The mycelium on these lesions disintegrates after some time, leaving translucent spots, which later turn brown, and these necrotic spots persist through the life of the leaflet.

Fig. 83.

Flower buds and flowers are also susceptible to infection by the fungus, and fruit set is significantly reduced when *Oidium* infection occurs in epidemic proportions. The effect of the disease on young leaves is similar to that of *Colletotrichum* leaf disease of *Hevea*, caused by the fungus *Colletotrichum gloeosporioides* (p. 119). In both cases the leaves shrivel and fall.

Fig. 84.

Morphology: *O. heveae* is an obligate parasite which grows on the surface of the host producing fine white cobweb-like hyphal threads. These branch profusely and send down haustoria into the epidermal cells, through which the fungus absorbs its nutrients. The fungus produces fine white barrel shaped conidia (av: 28 x 17 μ) from hyphal branches acting as conidiophores.

Physiological specialization: There is no indication that physiologic species of the fungus exist; and little work has been done on this subject.

Epidemiology: *O. heveae* does not have an alternate host, it apparently does not produce a persistant spore form and it does not survive in buds; however, *Oidium*-infected leaves are found in nurseries and new shoots of trees in young plantations right through the year. These and infected leaves, on the lower branches of mature trees, help the survival of the fungus from one disease season to the next. The fungus is propagated by conidia, which are carried off by the wind to distant places. A diurnal periodicity, with a peak in the early afternoon, has been observed in the dissemination of spores.

Infection can occur on both surfaces of young leaves. Unlike the majority of fungi, the powdery mildews do not require free water to cause infection. However, like many fungi, it prefers a high humidity, temperatures slightly lower than the normal and cloudy overcast conditions, to effect rapid infection. Given these conditions, the conidia germinate in 4–6 hr, effect leaf infection in 16–20 hr and produce fresh conidia in about 4 days. The disease occurs throughout the year on young leaves but causes economic damage only during the refoliation period, February to April each year, after wintering (leaf fall), while the bulk of the leaves are young and susceptible to infection.

The severity of the disease on susceptible clones is dependent on weather conditions at the time of refoliation. *O. heveae* develops best during the driest but coolest period of the year. But epidemics of the disease during an otherwise dry season are closely associated with infrequent showers of short duration, with high humidity and excess of dew in the nights and early mornings. The weather conditions at high elevations are usually conducive to the propagation of the fungus throughout the year, so that rubber is not planted at high elevations due to the depredations of this disease. Heavy rains of long duration, which maintain leaf surface wetness for prolonged periods and bright, sunny, hot weather are unfavourable to the fungus. Severe attacks of *Oidium* resulting in extensive defoliation can reduce latex yields and successive attacks increase this effect. Repeated defoliation also leads to retardation of growth. This can result in dieback of twigs and branches. Secondary parasites, mainly *Botryodiplodia theobromae* (p. 188) can aggravate this situation and even cause the death of the tree. The causal fungus infects only immature leaves; therefore, *Hevea* clones which winter evenly and have quick maturing foliage are more tolerant to the disease than others. Late wintering clones are generally more severely affected than early winterers, because weather conditions become more favourable for the fungus and the disease inoculum also builds up late in the refoliation season.

The resistance of *Hevea* clones to *Oidium* leaf disease is mainly dependant on the thickness and rate of development of the cuticle. Clones such as LCB 870 which have a thick cuticle are resistant to disease, whereas clones like PB 86 in which the cuticle, although not as thick as in LCB 870 matures rapidly, can escape infection altogether in years when wintering occurs early, before the build up of disease inoculum.

Control: Sulphur dust has been found to be the most effective and economical fungicide for the control of *Oidium* leaf disease. Organic fungicides have proved to be less effective or more expensive than sulphur preparations, which have the further advantage of being practically non-toxic to mammals.

Nine kilos of sulphur dust per hectare per round is the rate recommended by the Rubber Research Institute of Sri Lanka. Three to four rounds of dusting, commencing at the time when about 10 % of the trees in a particular area show signs of refoliation, generally suffice for tolerant clones. Sulphur dusting is carried out with a light portable power driven machine, with a verticle range of 20–30 meters and an effective dust feed regulator (Fig. 84). For maximum effectiveness, it is important that dusting be carried out when the leaves are wet with dew and there is no wind. The best time of the day for dusting is between 2 a.m. and 7 a.m. Each day's dusting should generally be completed by 7 a.m., as it becomes too windy after that, also dew evaporates at about this time, and adhesion of sulphur to dry leaves is poor.

Literature

FERNANDO, T. M. (1970): *Oidium* leaf disease – the effect of environment and control measures on incidence of disease and atmospheric contamination. Quart J. Rub. Res. Inst. Ceylon, **48**, 100–111.
PERIES, O. S. (1970): A handbook of rubber culture and processing. H.W. Cave & Co. Ltd., Colombo.
POPULER, C. (1972): Les épidémies de l'oidium de l'hévéa et la phénologie de son hôte dans le monde. Publications de l'I.N.E.A.C., Série Scientifique No **115**.
ROSETTI, V.O. (1958): The Oidium of rubber. O Biologico, **24**, 260–267.

Author: O.S. Peries

Other more important Oidium spp. on tropical and subtropical crops with no ascigerous state known (Plate 16c, d):
Oidium caricae Noack. Powdery mildew of papaya.
O. mangiferae Berth. Powdery mildew of mango (Plate 16d).
Oidium spp. also occur on avocado and *Citrus* spp. (Plate 16c).
Oidium states of *Erysiphe* and *Sphaerotheca* spp. are widespread and often severe in warm climates particularly during dry periods. Perfect states can be rare in many regions.

Pyricularia oryzae Cavara (Fig. 85)

Hyphomycetes (H,2.C1.sy)
Morphologically, *P. oryzae* is hardly distinguishable from *P. grisea* on several grasses. *P. grisea* is the older name. Similar fungi on various hosts may be considered as special forms of *P. grisea* such as *P. grisea* f. *brachiariae* on *Brachiaria* sp.

Disease: Rice blast disease; Brusone-Krankheit; brunissure du riz; añublo del arroz.

Geographical distribution: It occurs almost in all rice-growing areas of the world (CMI map no 51).

Host plants: Morphologically similar fungi occur on many members of the grass family (*Dactylis, Digitaria, Echinochloa, Eleusine, Leersia, Panicum, Setaria* etc. including a few cereals (*Oryza, Avena, Hordeum, Triticum, Zea*) and members of Zingiberaceae, Cannaceae, and Musaceae. Many cross-inoculation experiments have yielded controversial results. Recent knowledge on the specialization and great variation in pathogenicity of fungus partly explain the controversy. The exact host range of blast fungus needs further study.

Symptoms: The disease attacks all above-ground parts of the rice plant. The most common symptoms of the disease are elliptical leaf spots with more or less pointed ends. The spots usually have a grey or whitish center and a brown or reddish brown margin (Fig. 85a). Their shape and size vary, depending upon environmental conditions, stage of development, and varietal resistance. The spots usually begin as small, water-soaked, whitish, greyish, or bluish circular dots. On susceptible varieties, they enlarge quickly under moist conditions and remain greyish for sometime. Fully developed spots reach 1 to 1.5 cm long and 0.3 to 0.5 cm wide, and usually develop brown margins. On highly resistant varieties, only minute brown specks appear. Varieties with intermediate resistance show small round or short, elliptical spots, a few millimeters wide, with brown borders. When many spots occur, the leaves die. When the node is infected, the sheath pulvillus rots and turns black and often breaks off, remaining connected by the nodal septum only.

Any part of panicle, the grains, and the primary and secondary branches, may be infected and produce brown lesions. Infection near the panicle base often causes "rotten neck" or "neck rot", and the panicles fall over.

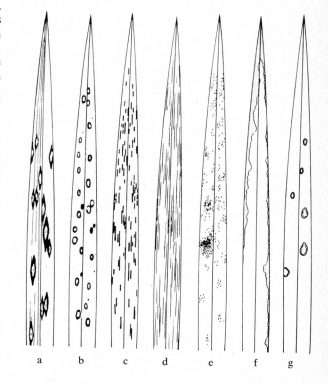

Fig. 85. Sketches of some typical symptoms of common leaf-spot diseases of rice (from OU, Rice diseases): a) blast, b) brown spot, c) Cercospora leaf spot, d) bacterial leaf streak, e) leaf smut, f) bacterial leaf blight, g) Stackburn disease

a   b   c   d   e   f   g

Leaf spot symptoms of the disease are sometimes confused with symptoms of other diseases particularly the brown spot caused by *Cochliobolus miyabeanus* (p. 106). Figure 85 shows typical lesions of common leaf-spot diseases of rice in comparison with other foliar disease of rice.

Morphology: Pear-shaped, three celled conidia are borne on a simple conidiophore. They vary in size from about $20-25 \times 8-9 \mu$.

Physiological specialization: The physiological specialization of the fungus was noticed in Japan as early as 1922. Since 1950 more extensive studies were carried out independently in different countries. In the Philippines, 219 races have been identified by 12 Philippine differential varieties. In 1967 a set of eight varieties was developed as international differentials. Recent studies have also shown that among conidia produced on the same lesion and as well as among conidia from a single conidial pure culture consisted of many races and continuously changed into other races in each conidial generation. The phenomenon of physiological races in *P. oryzae* is therefore only temporary and transitory.

Epidemiology: In the temperate regions, the fungus survives the winter on infected grains and straws. In the tropics, the airborne conidia may be founded throughout the year though the population is low in the dry season and high in the rainy season. Rice is grown throughout the year in the tropics, though much less of it is grown in the dry season.
A typical leaf spot of blast produces 2,000 to 6,000 conidia each night for about 2 weeks. A spot of intermediate type produces 50 to 300 conidia each night for about 1 week. Tremendous numbers of conidia are present in a blast nursery or in a diseased field. Normally conidia are released at night, the highest numbers from 1 to 3 o'clock. Conidia break off from the conidiophores at the small joining cells by hydraulic pressure after absorbing sufficient water – dew or rain – and are released to the air. On a rainy day, conidia are released immediately after the rain begins.
In the temperate region, the air-borne conidia population is high only for about 1 month, while in the tropics, high populations are present during the entire rainy season, which lasts for 6 month or more. Conidia germinate within 4 hours in water. They penetrate the host tissue in 6 to 8 hours after inoculation at favorable temperatures of 24 to 28 °C. The fungus enters the tissue directly through the cuticle or through stomata. The cycle, from inoculation to conidia production, is completed in 6 to 7 days.
Moisture is the most important factor which influences the development of the disease in the tropics. In the temperate regions, temperature also affects disease development. A high level of nitrogen also favors the disease. Rice grown in upland condition suffers more than rice grown in flooded condition.

Control: In Japan, chemicals have been used extensively for controlling blast. Until recently organic mercury compounds have been the major chemicals used. Many effective compounds have been developed in recent years: Kasumycin (an antibiotic), EDDP, EBP, Benomyl, Methylthiophanate, etc. Extensive chemical control such as in Japan is not feasible in tropical countries because of technical, economic and social reasons. However, if the field is heavily infected, two or three weekly applications of fungicide starting shortly before heading stage is recommended to prevent heavy loss due "neck blast". Most of the chemicals mentioned above are effective.
Recent studies on blast emphasize varietal resistance. An international blast nurseries program was started in 1963. More than 50 stations in 26 countries have participated. During the past 9 years several varieties have been identified which serve as excellent sources of resistance through this program. The resistance has been transferred to the new semidwarf new plant type of rice. The resistance is not broken down by any new pathogenic races.

Literature

OU, S. H. (1972): Rice diseases. Commonwealth Mycological Institute, Kew, Surrey, UK. CMI Description no 169.

Author: S. H. Ou

Septoria tritici Rob. apud Desm.

Coelomycetes (C,1.E1)

Disease: Speckled leaf blotch of wheat; Blattfleckenkrankheit des Weizens; nuile de céréales; seca de las hojas del trigo.

Geographical distribution: The disease is worldwide in distribution and has been reported from over 50 countries in Southern and Western Africa, Asia, Australasia, Europe, and North, Central and Southern America (CMI map no 397).

Host plants: *S. tritici* has been recorded on wheat, rye, brome grass and 12 other genera of grasses. However, several workers have demonstrated that the pathogen has several specialized forms and physiological races, therefore not all of these plants can act as alternate hosts for the form on wheat. It is an economically important disease and under suitable conditions the losses may be substantial. It can reduce the yield by 20–65 %, and also grain quality.

Symptoms: The disease is most conspicuous in spring, and its symptoms appear first on the leaves as interveinal, light green, chlorotic areas which develop into elongated, light brown, irregular blotches. The lesions eventually coalesce and may cover most of the leaf area. Abundant pycnidia are produced in the necrotic brown tissue, giving the blotches a speckled appearance. Lesions develop also on the culms, floral bracts and glumes, but are smaller in size and less conspicuous, with sparse pycnidial development. The disease progresses from the lower leaves, which show symptoms first and provide the secondary inoculum, to the upper leaves and head. The glume blotch disease of wheat (*Leptosphaeria nodorum* Müller = *Septoria nodorum* (*Berk.*) *Berk.*) is strikingly similar to the speckled leaf blotch disease, except that *S. tritici* does not produce the darker brown, blotch effect.

Morphology: The pycnidia are subepidermal, usually substomatal, brown, smooth walled, ostiolate, subglobose and measure 60–200 μ (mostly 100–150 μ). Two types of pycnidial spores are produced:
1. the macroconidia are slender with rounded ends, variously curved, hyaline, 3–7 septate, and measure 35 – 98 x 1.4 – 2.8 μ. They are frequently longer than 50 μ.
2. the microconidia, which arise with the macroconidia or alone during periods of low temperature, are curved, hyaline, aseptate, and measure 5–9 x 0.3–1 μ. On potato dextrose agar, colonies of *S. tritici* are mucose, light brown at first then darker brown or black, and cottony.
The conidia of *S. nodorum* are bacillar with rounded ends, hyaline, 0 to 3-septate, and measure 15–32 x 2–4 μ. They are seldom more than 30 μ in length.

Physiological specialization: Besides the *Septoria tritici* on wheat, rye and brome grass, there are at least three other specialized forms of the pathogen, namely: *S. tritici* f. sp. *avenae* occurring on *Avena* sp.; *S. tritici* f. sp. *holci* on *Holcus;* and *S. tritici* f. sp. *lolicola* on *Lolium* species. Physiological races have not yet been identified. Physiological specialization has also not been demonstrated for *S. nodorum.*

Epidemiology: The pathogen survives on volunteer wheat, rye and brome grass as well as on wheat plant debris in the field. The fungus continues to grow and produce additional pycnidia in the infected straw. Conidia can overwinter in the infected straw for 8–18 months with no loss in viability.
The conidia are released from pycnidia only under wet or high humidity conditions. Wind-blown infected debris aids in the dispersal of inoculum. The conidia are also dispersed by wind and splashing rain.
All parts of the wheat plant are susceptible to infection. Wheat plants growing in poor soils or at-

tacked by other diseases become more susceptible to infection by *S. tritici*. Conidia at host surfaces germinate in drops of water in 4–36 hours and penetrate directly or through stomata within 24 hours after germination. The infection hyphae enlarge slightly after penetration and grow intercellularly in all directions; no haustoria are produced. Wet weather is necessary for infection. A temperature of 16–21 °C is favorable for infection, and at 16–27 °C disease development proceeds well. Low light or darkness for 72 hours following inoculation is detrimental to infection. The course of the glume blotch disease is similar to that of the speckled leaf blotch except that *S. nodorum* is seed-borne and may give rise to severe seedling infections. At temperatures below 12 °C the biological balance shifts in favor of *S. nodorum* and favors infection of wheat coleoptiles.

The incubation period ranges from 6–36 days, when light green, chlorotic areas appear on the leaves and develop into elongated, yellowish to light brown, necrotic lesions. Wet weather is also essential for spore release. The occurrence of humid conditions for several days is necessary for severe infections.

Control: 1. Cultural practices. Several cultural practices are recommended to reduce disease incidence and severity. These include: crop rotation for about 3 years; burning stubbles or deep ploughing to destroy inoculum in plant debris; weed and volunteer wheat control; sowing in isolated fields; providing a balanced nutrition; care in the use of stalk shortening agents and the use of early or late maturing varieties to avoid peaks of infections.

2. Resistant varieties. These are likely to be the most effective means of controlling the disease in areas where cropping is intensive, rotations few and environmental conditions favorable. Varieties such as Sterling, Bulgaria 88, Nabob, Lerma 50 and P14 have shown themselves to be good sources of resistance to *S. tritici*.

3. Chemical control. Two to four cover sprays with copper oxychloride, maneb or benomyl after the disease first appears, were reported to be effective though may be uneconomical. Besides the other control measures listed for *S. tritici* seed treatment with organic mercurials, dichlone or chloranil is recommended for the control of *S. nodorum*.

Literature

DICKSON, J. G. (1956): Diseases of Field Crops. 2nd ed. McGraw-Hill Book Co., Inc., New York.
SHIPTON, W. A., W. R. J. BOYD, A. A. ROSIELLE & B. L. SHEARER (1971): The Common Septoria Diseases of Wheat. Bot. Rev. **37**, 231–262.
CMI Description nos 90 and 86 (for *Leptosphaeria nodorum*).

Author: Adib T. Saad

Other more important Septoria spp. on tropical and subtropical crops with no ascigerous state known:

S. bataticola Taub. Leaf spot of sweet potato.

S. cannabis (Lasch.) Sacc. Leaf spot of hemp. CMI map no 477.

S. citri Pass. Fruit pit of citrus.

S. glycines Hemmi. Brown spot of soybean. Ref.: CMI Description no 339.

S. helianthi Ell. & Kell. Leaf spot of sunflower. CMI map no 468.

S. lycopersici Spez. Leaf spot of tomato. CMI map no 108.

S. oryzae Catt. Speckled blotch of rice (Fig. 85c). Also *S. miyakei*. Sacc. & Trav., and other *Septoria* spp. on rice. See Ou, Rice diseases p. 311/12 for a key.

S. passiflorae Louw. Leaf spot of passion fruit.

S. pertusa Heald & Wolf. Leaf stripe of sorghum.

Sphaceloma perseae Jenkins

Coelomycetes (C,2.A1)

Disease: Scab of avocado; Avocadoschorf; le scab; sarna del aguacate.

Geographical distribution: Observed for the first time in Florida (USA) in 1918, this disease is known in Latin America and in several African countries (CMI map no 232).

Host plants: The fungus only attacks avocado.

Symptoms: Among commercial varieties Lula and Duke are especially susceptible. Scab shows as discrete spots on leaves, very often on the lower side of the veins which become deformed, and on branches and fruits. The spots are circular to irregular, sometimes star-like coloured purple-brown to deep brown. The middle is of dry and dead tissues which can drop out to give a shot-hole appearance. In comparison, with lesions of Cercospora spot those of scab are a little bigger, rounded, never angular, and often on the veins. On the petioles and the green wood of shoots the young spots have some resemblance to the shields of scale insects.

On young fruits are found the same type of oval spots as on the branches, but they enlarge and as the fruits approach maturity the lesions can measure 10–20 mm in diameter with their middle part a polished, brilliant deep brown, surrounded by a rough, greyish ring. The lesions can coalesce and the fruit become partly or totally rough. Cracks and crevices provide entry points for secondary invaders which can result in flesh rots (anthracnose, p. 119).

Epidemiology: In contrast to *Cercospora purpurea* (p. 192), *Sphaceloma perseae* is a parasite of young tissues. Only tender leaves during their first month of development are susceptible and they become resistant as soon as they are hardened. The first symptoms, small translucent flecks, appear 8–10 days after infection and rapidly acquire, in several days, the characteristic appearance of scab spots.

Fruits are susceptible over a longer period which extends from petal-fall until the fruits reach one third to one half of their full size. Scab can also develop on the peduncles at flowering, thereby providing very effective sources of infection for the young fruits. If the weather is dry and warm during flowering and fruit set very little scab appears on the fruits, even when the leaves carry numerous old lesions.

Control: Varieties differ greatly in susceptibility. The Mexican group of varieties is generally highly resistant. Likewise Booth 1, Pollock, Collinson, Ruehle, Waldin, Collins and Gottfried. The following are listed in order of increasing susceptibility: McDonald, Eagle Rock, Trapp, Nabal, Taylor, Fuerte, Duke, Taft and Winslowson. Among the most susceptible are Lula, Hall and certain seedlings from the West Indies. Applications of fungicide are often necessary, especially in orchards of var. Lula. The spray calendar developed in Florida is as follows: 1. an application of Bordeaux mixture (0.7 %) when flower buds appear at the end of January; 2. an application at the end of flowering when the majority of fruits have set, towards mid-February; 3. an application 3 to 4 weeks later.

If the weather is wet and cool, a fourth spray can be anticipated a month later. Subsequently the period favourable to Cercospora spot begins, and Bordeaux mixture is replaced by other products based on copper: Kocide 101 (0.24 %), basic copper sulphate (0.36 %) and Ferbam (0.36 %).

Author: P. Frossard

Other more important Sphaceloma spp. on tropical and subtropical crops with no ascigerous state (see p. 112) known:
Sphaceloma arachidis Bitanc. & Jenkins. Scab of groundnut. CMI map no 231.
S. ricini Jenkins & Cheo. Scab of castorbean.

Stemphylium spp. in tomatoes (Fig. 86)

1. *Stemphylium solani* Weber; 2. *S. floridanum* Hannon & Weber; 3. *S. botryosum* Wallr. f. sp. *lycopersici* Rotem, Cohen & Wahl
Hyphomycetes (H,2.D2.po)

Disease: Gray leaf spot, *Stemphylium* blight of tomato; *Stemphylium*-Komplex der Tomate; *Stemphylium* complex dans la tomate; Complejo *Stemphylium* en tomate.

Geographical distribution: Hard to define because of similarity to other diseases, and difficulty in distinguishing among the three species. Probably more prevalent in moderately warm and humid areas. CMI map no 333 for *S. solani*.

Host plants: Chiefly in tomatoes in which leaves, sometimes petioles and occasionally stems are infected. No infection occurs on the fruit, but they may suffer from sun stroke when heavy defoliation occurs. Infection by *S. solani* has been also observed in lupin, eggplants and peppers; and by *S. floridanum* in Chrysanthemum and carnation.

Symptoms: Symptoms produced by the three fungi are indistinguishable in the field. More than one species may be present in the same field, plant or even leaf. Most lesions 1 to 10 mm in diameter, irregular but sometimes circular in outline, light to dark brown or grayish, slightly depressed and occasionally surrounded by a chlorotic halo (Fig. 86). Old lesions may crack at the centre; they coalesce infrequently even at the final stage of development, when the foliage wilts rapidly. Lesions caused by the *Stemphylium* complex resemble those caused by *Alternaria tomato* (Cke) Weber, *Xanthomonas vesicatoria* (p. 71), and young lesions of *A. solani* (p. 186).

Fig. 86.

Morphology: In all three species the mycelium is septate, branched and dark when old. Multicellular conidia are dark and borne singly on conidiophores. Conidia of *S. solani* average 37–48 μ long and 18–22 μ wide, are smooth when young and slightly reticulate when mature. They are constricted by a median septum and have rounded or somewhat pointed apices. Nodular swellings are present in the conidiophores. Perfect stage not known.
Conidia of *S. floridanum* average 36–38 μ by 12–18 μ, are often echinulate and constricted by up to six septa. Conidiophores have nodular swellings and bulbous apices. Perfect stage not known.
Conidia of *S. botryosum* f. sp. *lycopersici* average 22–35 μ by 13–20 μ, are echinulate, constricted by one median septum, with round apices. Conidiophores without swellings but with bulbous apices. The perfect stage is *Pleospora herbarum* (Fr.) Rabenh. (Ascomycetes), perithecia of which may appear in some isolates in culture but are never found on plants.

Physiological specialization: Unknown, but individual isolates vary considerably in their aggressiveness, especially after being cultured for some time.

Epidemiology: Age of the leaf or plant seems to have little effect on its susceptibility. Increase of disease incidence in the field as hosts mature is probably connected with the increasing amounts of inoculum. Spread occurs by air-borne conidia quite resistant to adverse environmental conditions. Conidial germination occurs only in the presence of water. Germ tubes penetrate mostly through stomata, but occasionally through the cuticle.

Minimum, optimum and maximum temperatures for infection are about 10, 26 and 28 °C, respectively, for *S. solani;* unknown for *S. floridanum;* and 10, 25 and 33 °C, respectively, for *S. botryosum* f. sp. *lycopersici.*

S. solani can penetrate at optimum temperature after only 3 h of wetness; *S. floridanum* after 12 h; *S. botryosum* f. sp. *lycopersici* needs at least 24 h of wetness which can, however, be interrupted by temporary periods of dryness.

All three species sporulate on leaves. Sporulation on leaf debris is the chief means of transferring *S. floridanum.*

Sporulation of *S. botryosum* f. sp. *lycopersici* is favored by alternating periods of wetness and dryness. The latter disease and possibly the others also is favored by overhead irrigation. Conditions of wetness rather than temperatures dominate the epidemic patterns.

Control: Use of resistant cultivars is the best and cheapest means of control. However, such cultivars have been developed mostly in the USA and may not suit the agricultural specifications of other areas. Therefore sensitive cultivars are still used, and the control should be exerted by cultural and chemical means. Cultural means involve avoidance of overhead irrigation (when possible) and early removal of debris. The best fungicides are Daconil® and Propineb, but the techniques of application are often of greater importance than the specific material in use. Both the cultural and chemical means of control can reduce the extent of the disease but cannot prevent it entirely. Tomato cultivars resistant to *Stemphylium* blight were originally developed against *S. solani* (e. g. Anahu, Walter, Tropic). However, the same cultivars are also resistant to *S. floridanum* and *S. botryosum* f. sp. *lycopersici.* The resistance is due to a single dominant gene derived from some wild species. Even higher levels of resistance have been found in individual plants belonging to *Lycopersicum hirsutum* var. *glabratum, L. peruvianum* and *L. pimpinellifolium.*

Literature

BASHI, ESTHER, M. PILOWSKY & J. ROTEM (1973): Resistance in tomatoes to *Stemphylium floridanum* and *S. botryosum* f. sp. *lycopersici.* Phytopathology. **63**, 1542–1544.
BASHI, ESTHER, J. ROTEM & J. PUTTER (1973): The effect of wetting duration, and of other environmental factors on the development of *Stemphylium botryosum* f. sp. *lycopersici* in tomatoes. Phytoparasitica. **1**, 87–94.
HANNON, C. I., & G. F. WEBER (1955): A leaf spot of tomato caused by *Stemphylium floridanum* sp. nov. Phytopathology **45**, 11–16.
PAULUS, A. O., & G. S. POUND (1955): Effect of air temperature on initiation and development of gray leaf spot and nailhead spot of tomato. Phytopathology **45**, 168–174.
ROTEM, J., & Y. COHEN (1966): The relationship between mode of irrigation and severity of tomato foliage diseases in Israel. Plant Dis. Reptr. **50**, 635–639.
CMI Descriptions nos 471 & 472.

Authors: J. Rotem & Esther Bashi

Verticillium albo-atrum Rke. & Berth. (Plate 16a and figs. 87a–e, 88a–c)

Some authorities consider *V. albo-atrum, V. dahliae* Kleb. and *V. tricorpus* Isaac to constitute one large, variable species.
Hyphomycetes (H,2.A1.ph)

Disease: Verticillium wilt; Verticillium-Welke; verticilliose; marchitez.

Geographical distribution: Africa: Kenya, Madagascar, Morocco, Mozambique, Rhodesia, Tanzania, Tunesia, Uganda, Zaire. Asia: China, Iran, Israel, Japan, Pakistan, Syria, USSR (Uzbekistan, Central Asia). Australasia: Australia, New Zealand. All of Europe. North America: Canada, Mexico, United States. South America: Argentina, Brazil, Chile, Columbia, Ecuador, Peru, Uruguay, Venezuela (CMI maps nos 365 & 366).

Host plants: The total host range includes more than 300 plant species; the following is a partial list. Field crops: *Arachis hypogaea* (peanut), *Cannabis sativa* (hemp), *Carthamus tinctorius* (safflower), *Gossypium spp.* (cotton), *Helianthus spp.* (sunflower), *Medicago sativa* (alfalfa), *Nico-*

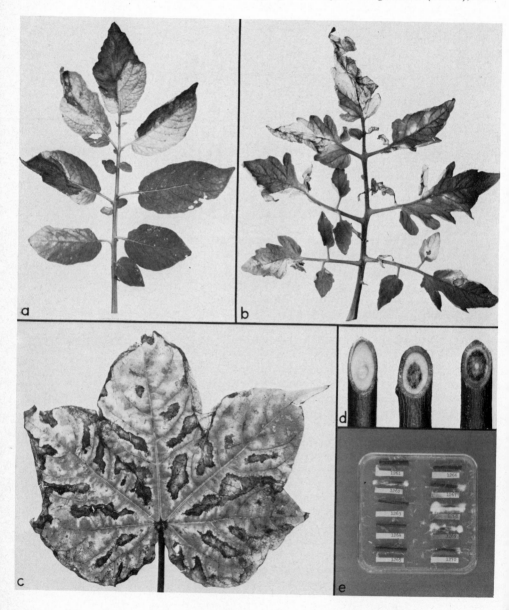

Fig. 87.

tiana spp. (tobacco), *Sesamum orientale* (sesame), *Vigna sinensis* (cowpea). Fruit crops: *Pistacia vera* (pistachio), *Prunus spp.* (almond, apricot, cherry, peach, plum, prune), *Coffea arabica* (coffee), *Olea europea* (olive), *Persea americana* (avocado), *Theobroma cacao* (cocoa, plate 16a). *Vitis vinifera* (European grape). Vegetable crops: *Brassica oleracea* (Brussels sprouts, cabbage, cauliflower), *Capsicum spp.* (green pepper), *Citrullus vulgaris* (watermelon), *Cucumis melo* (musk melon), *Cucumis sativus* (cucumber), *Hibiscus esculentus* (okra), *Lycopersicum esculentum* (tomato), *Solanum melongena* (eggplant), *Solanum tuberosum* (potato).

Symptoms: In herbaceous plants, *Verticillium* wilt typically causes stunting of growth due to shortening of internodes and development of small leaves, and wilting and death of plant parts. First symptoms are often epinasty of leaves and development of darker than normal green color. Ultimately leaves develop interveinal and marginal yellowing, followed by necrosis of the affected areas (Fig. 87a–c), and dehiscence. Symptoms, unless the onset of disease is extremely rapid, develop acropetally. In woody plants and trees, symptoms tend to be localized in certain branches; these often die. In most hosts, the infected portions of the vascular cylinder of root and shoot systems become brown or black. The discoloration may be intense throughout the cylinder or streaked (Fig. 87d). A few hosts, for instance olives, develop only slight or no vascular discoloration. Weeds, which usually do not develop foliage symptoms, may show vascular discoloration. *Verticillium* wilt may be confused with *Fusarium* wilt (p. 206, 208), especially since some crops are susceptible to both diseases, and both diseases may occur in the same geographical area. Compared to *Verticillium* wilt, *Fusarium* wilt usually has a more limited or localized distribution in an area and even within a particular field, higher temperature optima for maximum expression of disease, and develops more intense yellowing of leaves and darker vascular discoloration. In general, *Fusarium* wilt prefers light, sandy soil types and is dependent partially on root knot nematodes for successful penetration, i. e. infection of vascular elements of roots. *Verticillium* wilt, on the other hand, occurs in a great variety of soil types, preferring heavy soils, and is generally independent of nematodes for successful root penetration and infection of vascular tissues. Though *Verticillium* wilt produces rather characteristic symptoms in its numerous hosts, it is always advisable to confirm a field diagnosis by laboratory isolation and identification of the causal fungus. In certain crops, such as tomatoes and cotton, individual plants may be infected by both *Verticillium* and *Fusarium* at the same time.

Morphology: From most hosts, the *Verticillium* fungus grows readily in laboratory culture when discolored vascular tissues are plated on a suitable medium of low nutrient content, such as 2 % plain water agar containing bits of sterilized barley straw (Fig. 87e), or sterile, moist filter paper. Usually within a few days, conidiophores appear on the cultured piece. The conidiophores bear one whorl of phialides or several arranged one above the other; these hold glistening droplets (heads) of liquid, which in turn contain the conidia (Fig. 88a). Hyaline mycelium grows over the agar substrate and sporulates abundantly on the verticillately branched or simple conidiophores. Resting structures, commonly called microsclerotia (Fig. 88b), appear as black, discrete bodies. In culture at laboratory temperatures below 20 °C microsclerotia may coalesce into a tough, black tissue resembling stroma. Colony growth on laboratory media is white at first and later becomes black; this characteristic is the basis for the specific name *albo-atrum* (Fig. 88c).

Physiological specialization: An individual isolate of the *Verticillium* fungus may show either a wide or a narrow host range. Isolates attacking a wide host range may show high virulence to some crops and weeds and low virulence to others. In the author's experience, isolates attacking tomatoes and cotton also attack deciduous stone fruit trees, pistachio, olives, strawberries, roses, chrysanthemums and other ornamentals, but many cotton isolates do not attack tomatoes. In contrast, isolates attacking peppers, mints and the cruciferae (garden stock, radish, cabbage, cauliflower, Brussels sprouts) in general are host-specific.
The capacity of *Verticillium* to infect a host does not necessarily effect pathogenesis and symptom development, though it may be an avenue through which host-specific virulence is eventually ac-

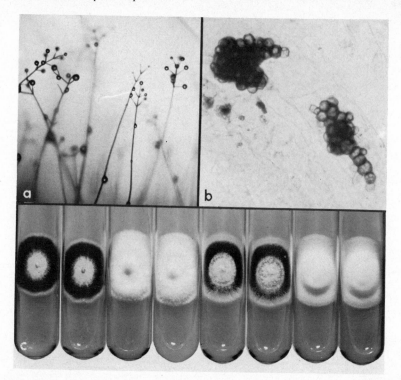

Fig. 88.

quired or selected. Of the many hosts, none is as susceptible to a wide variety of different isolates of *Verticillium* as eggplant, *Solanum melongena.*

Except for a recent report in onion, *Allium cepa,* and for reports of increase in the rhizosphere of various cereals and grasses, monocotyledons are not hosts of *Verticillium* and may be grown successfully on infested lands. In the end, they usually help reduce the inoculum of *Verticillium* in the soil.

Epidemiology: The epidemiology of *Verticillium* wilt follows one of two general patterns. Initial outbreaks in a crop typically are mild and local. Subsequently they either become severe and widespread and threaten the crop, or they localize and disappear. Severe outbreaks are brought on by strains of the fungus that are more virulent than the original, or by a greater inoculum potential (number of infective propagules per unit of soil), or by both. Disappearance of the disease or its failure to intensify, possibly only temporary, have occured after severe outbreaks in sugar beets, spinach, sweet pea seed fields, tobacco in the USA, and grapes.

The *Verticillium* fungus completes its life cycle within the plant. The microsclerotia, which are capable of long persistence in soil, germinate in response to alternate wetting and drying, and produce conidia, which in turn effect the penetration of roots. Subsequently the xylem tissues of certain hosts are invaded and the fungus becomes established as a vascular parasite, spreading by means of mycelial growth and conidia to all plant organs: main stem and branches, petioles, leaf veins, peduncles, ovules and fruit. The fungus interferes with the translocation of water and other vital functions, producing in the xylem elements, in addition to mycelium, gums, toxins and enzymes, which all endanger the life of the plant. Infected xylem vessels form tyloses, which further impede the transportation of water. Spores produced within vessels move rapidly with the transpiration stream, spreading the infection to the leaves. Under climatic conditions of sustained high humidity, the fungus may sporulate on the surface of dying plant parts. Dark mycelium or microsclerotia, or both, subsequently develop in xylem vessels, root tissue, cortex of stems, and leaves, in fact, virtually in any, but not necessarily every invaded tissue.

The amount of disease in a crop and its severity in the individual plant, other factors being equal, depend on the number of infective propagules per unit of soil. In cotton, the presence of 50 to 100 microsclerotia per gram of surface soil results in 100 % infected plants.

The *Verticillium* fungus is spread by contaminated cotton seed (not acid-delinted), within one-seeded dry fruits, such as of sunflower and safflower, by fruits of weeds, such as *Xanthium,* by seed of spinach, by cuttings of rose, *Chrysanthemum* and *Pelargonium,* and tubers of potatoes, by scions and buds of rose, by wind, surface ground water, and by soil itself. Potato, through its tubers, and cotton, through non-acid-delinted seed, probably have been the primary vehicles of spread and establishment of the *Verticillium* fungus throughout the world.

Susceptibility of hosts to *Verticillium* is conditioned by the environment. Low soil and air temperatures, such as commonly occur during the spring, favor infection and vascular systemic invasion of hosts. As the season progresses and temperatures rise, symptoms develop, with severity depending on the state of growth of the host. Crops that fruit during spring and early summer, such as strawberries, collapse from wilt during the transition from spring to high summer temperatures; branches of young stone fruit trees, and olive trees of all ages, also begin to collapse during this period.

Sustained high temperatures (approximately 30 °C and above) during the period of vegetative growth of late-maturing crops, such as cotton and tomato, prevent the development of severe wilt symptoms and the systemic infection of leaves of cotton, and subsequently eventually effect recovery of the infected plant. In climatic areas where sustained high temperatures begin early in the season, it is possible to cultivate successfully certain crops which mature late, such as cotton, safflower, and tomato, though they may be infected by the *Verticillium* pathogen.

Control: Control must include first achieving either *Verticillium*-free planting stocks of vegetatively reproduced crops, which carry the fungus in plant parts, or *Verticillium*-free seed of seed-planted crops. Second, it must include a soil management system that reduces inoculum in the soil to low levels or eliminates it nearly entirely.

The thermal death point of *Verticillium* in water is approximately 50 °C for 10 minutes. Thermal treatment of seeds, using a steam-air mixture, could be developed to eliminate internal seed infection. Acid-delinting of cotton seed with concentrated sulfuric acid, a standard practice, eliminates *Verticillium* inoculum adhering to the lint. *Verticillium* does not occur internally in cotton seed.

Soil fumigation with a 1 : 1 mixture of methyl bromide and chloropicrin, applied 15 cm deep by tractor-mounted chisels that are spaced 30 cm apart on the tool bar, achieves excellent control of *Verticillium* wilt for crops such as strawberries, fresh-market tomatoes, and for rose and other wilt-susceptible nursery crops. Simultaneously with application of the chemical, the soil is covered with thin polyethylene sheeting and remains covered for 48 hours. Depending primarily on soil type and temperature, the rate of fumigant varies from 300 to 450 kg/ha.

Deep, invert plowing that buries the upper 30 cm of soil may achieve a measure of control if the inversion is complete and is accomplished without creating heavy dust. For tree crops, such as olives, sod culture both reduces the severity of wilt in affected trees and slows spread of the disease in the grove.

Rotating *Verticillium* wilt-susceptible annual crops, such as cotton, safflower, and tomato, with grains helps to control the disease. Establishing a rotation sequence before the disease becomes severe is a more effective control than establishing one after land has become heavily infested. Plowing land in mid-summer or early fall or immediately after harvest of a wilt-susceptible annual crop and leaving it rough so that it dries thoroughly, aids in the reduction of *Verticillium* inoculum. Plowing should be planned to maximize the drying.

Resistance: In the major field and vegetable crops, resistance to *Verticillium* wilt is both difficult to achieve and difficult to maintain. Strains of the fungus that have the capacity to attack previously resistant cultivars may be counted on to appear. nevertheless, significant progress has been made in some crops. In cotton, resistance has been derived from cultivars of the species *Gossypium barbadense* and from wild forms of *G. hirsutum,* notably *G. hirsutum* spp. *mexicanum.* In canning tomatoes, the VF-145 series of varieties, with resistance derived from the cultivar Loran Blood (originally from *Lycopersicum pimpinellifolium*), culminated years of research. But new strains of *Verticillium* capable of destroying the VF-145 lines have now appeared. Mexican avocado rootstocks, such as the cultivar Topa-Topa, are more resistant than the Guatemalan. Highly resistant olive clones, potentially valuable as rootstocks, have also been identified.

The stone fruit trees generally resist the disease once they are several years old. Plum rootstocks are more resistant than those of almond, apricot or peach. There are screening programs searching for resistance in peanuts, safflower, alfalfa, sunflower and tobacco; many have had a measure of success, but the efforts should not be allowed to relent.

Literature

ENGELHARD, A. W. (1957): Host index of *Verticillium albo-atrum* Reinke and Berth. (including *Verticillium dahliae Kleb.*). *Plant Dis. Reptr. Suppl.* **244,** 23–49.
EVANS, G. (1971): Influence of weed hosts on the ecology of *Verticillium dahliae* in newly cultivated areas of the Namoi Valley, New South Wales. Ann. appl. Biol. **67,** 169–175.
Verticillium Wilt of Cotton (1973): Proceedings of a Work Conference; National Cotton Pathology Research Laboratory, College Station, Texas, Aug. 30 to Sept. 1, 1971. Agricultural Research Service, U. S. Department of Agriculture.
CMI Descriptions nos 255 and 256.

Author: S. Wilhelm

Other Verticillium spp. on tropical and subtropical crops:

Verticillium theobromae (Turc.) Mason. Syn. *Stachylidium theobromae* Turc. Cigar end rot of banana; black pitting and spotting of pods of cacao. Ref.: CMI Description no 259.

Other more important Deuteromycotina (with no ascigerous state known) from genera not yet covered (Plate 16 b):

(C,1.S.B1) *Ascochyta abelmoschii* Harter. Pod spot of okra.
A. caricae Pat. Black fruit spot of papaya.
A. gossypii Woron. Circular or irregular leaf spots of cotton. Ref.: CMI Description no 271.
A. heveae Petch. Rim blight of rubber.
A. hortorum (Speg.) C.O.Sm. Fruit spot of eggplant.
A. oleae Scalia. Leaf spot of olive.
A. rabiei (Pass.) Labr. Blight of chickpeas. Ref.: CMI Description no 337.
A. sorghi Sacc. Leaf spot of sorghum, Sudan grass and wheat.
A. sorghina Sacc. Rough spot of sorghum.
A. tarda Stewart. Leaf blight of coffee (plate 16b).
(H,2.B2) *Asperisporium caricae* (Speg.) Maubl. Black spot, blight or rust on older leaves, and fruits of papaya. Ref.: CMI Description no 347.
(H,2.B1.ph) *Cephalosporium acremonium* Cda. Black bundle of maize.
C. diospyri Crandall. Wilt of persimmon (kaki) tree.
C. gregatum Allington & Chamberlain. Brown stem rot of soybean.
C. sacchari Butt. Wilt of sugarcane. CMI map no 250.
C. maydis Samra, Sabet & Hingorani. Late wilt disease of maize.
Literature
GAMS, W. (1971): Cephalosporium-artige Schimmelpilze (Hyphomycetes). Gustav Fischer-Verlag, Stuttgart.

(H,2.B2.b1) *Cladosporium colocasiae* Saw. Leaf spot of taro (dasheen).
C. cucumerinum Ellis & Arth. Gummosis or scab of Cucurbitaceae.
C. musae Mason. Large elliptical brown spot of banana.

Literature
see ELLIS, M. B. (p. 183).

(H,2.A1.ph) *Chloridium musae* Stahel. Leaf speckle of banana.
(H,2.B2.Sy) *Cordana musae* (Zimm.) Höhnel. Leaf blotch of banana. Ref.: CMI Description no 350.
(H,2.A2) *Corynespora cassicola* (Berk. & Curt.) Wei. Polyphagous, amongst others: Leaf spots of cotton, rubber and tomato, target spot of sesame and soybean. Ref.: CMI Description no 303.
(C,2.C2) *Coryneum mori* Homuri. Blight of mulberry.
C. myristicae Stein. Nut rot of nutmeg.
(H,2.C2.po/sy) *Curvularia eragrostidis* (P. Henn.) A. Meyer. Seedling blight of oilpalm, leaf spot on pineapple, and on many other hosts.
C. penniseti (Mitra) Boed. Brown spot on leaves of pearl millet.
Literature
ELLIS, M. B. (1966): Dematiaceous Hyphomycetes. VII: Curvularia, Brachysporium etc. Mycol. Papers, no 106, Commonwealth Mycological Institute, Kew, UK.

(H,2.B2) *Cycloconium oleaginum* Cast. Leaf (peacock) spot of olives. CMI map no 183.
(C.2.E.) *Cylindrosporium olivae* Petri. Fruit spot of olive.
C. sesami Hansf. Angular leaf spot of sesame.
Literature
see SCHMUTTERER & KRANZ, Phytopath. Z. (1965) **54**, 193–201.

(H,2.B/C2,an) *Deightoniella papuana* Shaw. Veneer blotch on leaves of sugarcane.
D. torulosa (Syd.) M. B. Ellis. Fruit spot (speckle) and leaf spot of banana. Ref.: CMI Description no 165.
(C,1.B2) *Diplodia macrospora* Earle. Dry rot of ears and stalks of maize. Ref.: CMI Description no 83.
(H,2.C2.po) *Drechslera heveae* (Petch) M.B. Ellis. Bird's eye spot of rubber. Ref.: CMI Description no 343.
D. incurvata (CH. Bernhard) M. B. Ellis. Leaf spot of young coconut. Ref.: CMI Description no 342.
D. musae-sapientum (Hansf.) M. B. Ellis. Leaf spot of *Musa* spp.
D. rostrata (Drechsler) Richardson & Fraser. Leaf spot of sorghum.
D. sacchari (Butl.) Subram. & Jain. Eye spot and seedling blight of sugarcane. Ref.: CMI Description no 305.
D. sorghicola (Lefebvre & Sherwin) Richardson & Fraser. Target spot of sorghum.
D. stenospila (Drechsler) Subram. & Jain. Brown stripe of sugarcane. Ref.: CMI Description no 306.
Literature
see ELLIS, M. B. (p. 183).

(H,4.C1) *Gloeocercospora sorghi* Bain & Edgerton. Zonate leaf spot of sorghum, pearl millet, maize, sugarcane etc. Ref.: CMI Description no 300.
(H,2.A2.b1) *Haplobasidion musae* M. B. Ellis. Malayan leaf spot of banana. CMI map no 474.
Literature
ELLIS, M. B., Mycol. Papers no 67.

(H,2.C2.po) *Helminthosporium* s. Drechslera
(S,1.B/C2) *Hendersonula toruloidea* Nattrass. Branch wilt, dieback or canker of numerous plants, including citrus, and mulberry. Ref.: CMI Description no 274.
(H,3.C2.sy) *Isariopsis griseola* Sacc. Leaf spot of bean. CMI map no 328.
(H,2.A2.ar) *Mauginiella scaettae* Cav. (*Mauginiella* = *Sporendonema* fide Ciferri). Flower blight of date palm. CMI map no 245.
(H,2.A2) *Monilochaetes infuscans* (Ell. & Hals) Harter, Scurf of sweet potato. CMI map no 246.
(H,4.A2.ph) *Myrothecium roridum* Tode ex Tr. Necrotic spot or shot hole on numerous economic

hosts, canker of cotton stem, dry rots on fruits of tomato and cantaloupe. Ref.: CMI Description no 253.

(H,2.A1.ph) *Penicillium digitatum* Sacc. Green mold of citrus fruit. Ref.: CMI Description no 96.
P. italicum Wehmer. Blue mold of citrus fruits. Ref.: CMI Description no 99.

(H,2.A2.bl) *Periconia circinata* (Mangin) Sacc. Milo disease of sorghum and wheat. Ref.: CMI Description no 167.
P. manihoticola (Vincens) Viégas. Blight of leaves, petioles and twigs of cassava and rubber.
Literature
see ELLIS, M. B. (p. 183).

(C,2.C2.an) *Pestalotiopsis guepini* (Desm.) Stey. Gray leaf spot, dieback, stem canker and petal rot of tea. Ref.: CMI Description no 320.
P. palmarum (Cke) Stey. Leaf spot of various cultivated palms. Ref.: CMI Description no 319.
P. theae (Saw.) Stey. Gray blight of tea, blight of mango, palms and cotton. Ref.: CMI Description no 318.
Literature
GUBA, E. F. (1961): Monograph of Monochaetia and Pestalotia. Harvard University Press, Cambridge, Mass., USA.

(C,1.1.A1.ph) *Phoma costaricensis* Echandi. Brown leaf spot of coffee.
P. insidiosa Tassi = Phyllosticta sorghina Sacc. Leaf spot of sorghum, but also on rice and sugar-cane. Ref.: CMI Description no 333.
Literature
see GROVE (p. 183).

(C,1.1.A1.ph) *Phomopsis theae* Petch. Collar and branch canker of tea. Ref.: CMI Description no 330.
P. vexans (Sacc. & Syd.) Harter. Blight and canker of various aerial parts of eggplant. Ref.: CMI Description no 338.
Literature
see GROVE (p. 183).

(C,1.1.A1) *Phyllosticta batatas* (Thüm.) Cke. Leaf spot of sweet potato.
P. zingiberi Ramak. Leaf spot of ginger.
Literature
see GROVE (p. 183).

(C,1.1.A1.ph) *Phyllostictina musarum* (Cke.) Petrak = *Macrophoma musae* Cke. Freckles of leaf and fruit of banana. Ref.: CMI Description no 467 as *Gruignardia musae* Racib.).
(H,3.C1.sy) *Ramularia areola* Atk. White angular leaf spot of cotton. CMI map no 260.
R. bellunensis Speg. Blight of pyrethrum. CMI map no 292.
R. phaseoli (Drummond) Deighton. Leaf spot of bean. CMI map no 436.
R. carthami Zaprom. Leaf spot of safflower.
(H,4) *Ramulispora sorghi* (Ell. & Ev.) Olive & Lefebvre. Sooty stripe of sorghum, Sudan grass and other *Sorghum* spp.
R. sorghicola Harris. Elliptical leaf spot of sorghum.
Literature
see TARR (p. 178).

(H,2.B1) *Rhynchosporium oryzae* Hashioka & Yokogi. Leaf scald of rice. CMI map no 492.
(H,2.2.an) *Spilocaea eriobotryae* (CAV.) Hughes. Leaf spot of loquat. CMI map no 435.
(C,1.1.C1) *Stagonospora sacchari* Lo & Sing. Leaf scorch of sugarcane. CMI map no 418.
(H2.A2.ph) *Thielaviopsis basicola* (Berk. & Br.) Ferraris. Black root rot of cowpea, bean, groundnut, soybean, sunn hemp, and tobacco. Ref.: CMI Description no 170.
(H2.A2) *Ustilaginoidea virens* (Cke.) Takahashi. False smut of rice, also on maize. Ref.: CMI Description no 299.

Pests in Tropical Crops

Edited by Heinz Schmutterer

In collaboration with: S. E. Abul-Nasr, R. A. Agarwal, D. Barry, H. A. Bess, J. Brenière, S. W. Broodryk, R. F. Brooks, Fridgard Burckhardt, Dhamo K. Butani, M. A. Cornes, R. Coutin, T. J. Crowe, P. S. Dawson, R. Daxl, J. van Dinther, G. Dosse, V. F. Eastop, I. El-Khidir, P. F. Entwistle, D. W. Fewkes, H. E. Fernando, O. I. Gameel, U. Gerson, D. G. Gibbs, M. Hafez, C. P. Haines, F. H. Haramoto, K. Heinze, A. M. Huger, G. Iperti, N. D. Jago, R. J. V. Joyce, Kazushige Sōgawa, C. E. King, Ch. Kurian, M. Kogan, O. P. Lal, B. S. Lall, R. H. Le Pelley, K. Leuschner, T. Lewis, J. A. Litsinger, Ibrahim Manwan, I. A. McFarlane, R. C. Mehta, J. R. Metcalfe, W. Morrill, Sôchô Nasu, Ken'ichi Nomura, P. O. Odiyo, R. C. Patel, H. Piltz, H. N. Pitre, P. S. Prakasa Rao, S. K. Prasad, J. R. Quezada, W. Reed, K. Rolli, D. J. W. Rose, D. Rosen, F. Saba, H. S. Salama, H. Schmutterer, S. A. Siddig, S. R. Singh, R. I. Smith, A. S. Srivastava, M. Sternlicht, D. Sturhan, A. M. Talhouk, J. P. Tunstall, E. J. Usua, P. Ward, T. F. Watson, I. J. Webley, B. Weischer, J. R. Williams, A. Yunus, M. A. Zaher

Nematodes, Eelworms; Nematoden, Fadenwürmer; Nématodes; Nemátodos

Phylum: Nematoda

Class: Secernentea + Adenophorea

Order: Tylenchida + Dorylaimida

General features: Nematodes, with their long, threadlike body, are the most abundant multicellular organisms in the soil. 100 ml arable soil usually contains several thousand nematodes. There are at present roughly 17,000 described species, but the actual number of species is probably very much higher. Most of them live on microorganisms or as predators, some thousand species are parasites of man and animal and several hundred of described species are economically significant plant pests. Most plant pathogenic species are about 1 mm long. All have a buccal stylet, which is used to pierce plant cells and suck out their contents. Depending on the part of the plant parasitised, they are differentiated into root nematodes, stem nematodes and leaf nematodes. Root nematodes are the group representing the greatest number of species. Ectoparasitic species remain in the soil and attack only the outermost cell layers of roots, while endoparasites enter the root and only reproduce inside it. Ectoparasites and some endoparasites retain their slim shape and their mobility throughout life. They can leave an affected region at any time and seek out another root. In many endoparasites only second stage larvae and males are able to migrate. The other larval stages and the females are immobile. They swell up and can no longer leave the area attacked. Plant damage is sustained in several ways. First of all, the plant is weakened by direct withdrawal of food. In addition, tissue function is disturbed by mechanical damage, affected roots cannot absorb as much water and nutrient material as healthy ones and affected leaves assimilate less well. Many nematode species also liberate very active enzymes into the plant tissues during feeding, which give rise to far reaching physiological and histological changes. All these effects together lead to poor growth, low yields and impaired quality. Some nematodes have the additional ability to transmit other pathogens such as viruses, bacteria and fungi, and this is often of greater economic significance than the direct feeding activity.

Plant parasitic nematodes occur wherever higher plants are growing, in original habitats or on cultivated soil, in cold climates and tropical regions. There is usually no real damage until population density has greatly increased as a result of repeated cultivation of suitable host plants. Susceptible crops can however be severely damaged by existing nematodes even in the first year after clearing virgin land. In regions without vegetative rest period, for instance in the tropics, in which crops are grown all the year round, a high degree of infestation and extensive damage can result. Reliable data on the extent of harmful effects due to nematodes are so far only available from the USA. On the basis of observations carried out over a period of seven years, the damage was there assessed to be 10 % for peanut, 15 % for citrus, grapevine and tomato, 6 % for rice and sugar cane and 5 % for cotton, coffee, tobacco and pineapple. The losses in yield in 1968 amounted to roughly 310 Mio. US $. Presumably, the losses in regions with less advanced agricultural techniques are even higher.

B. Weischer

Family: Aphelenchoididae

Aphelenchoides besseyi Christie (Fig. 89)

Synonym: *A. oryzae*

Common names: Rice leaf nematode, White tip nematode; Reisblättälchen.

Geographical distribution: Worldwide in tropical and subtropical rice growing regions, also a strawberry pest in Florida and North Carolina.

Host plants: Over 30 host plants, among them rice *(Oryza sativa)*, millet *(Setaria, Digitaria, Pennisetum)*, maize *(Zea mays)* , soybean *(Glycine max)*, strawberry *(Fragaria chiloensis)* and various fungi (e. g. *Alternaria, Fusarium, Helminthosporium*).

Symptoms: *A. besseyi* is the cause of "white tip disease" of rice. At the time of bud emergence, leaf tips turn white or yellow; later brown or black necroses result. The tips can be twisted or curled; severely infested plants are stunted. The panicles are shorter, the ears reduced and in part sterile. The grains are smaller than normal and often deformed. Maturation of infested panicles is retarded. The nematodes can be distributed with infested seed and plant residues, less frequently by flood water.

Economic importance: *A. besseyi* can do much damage in rice fields. Yield losses can amount to 20–60 %.

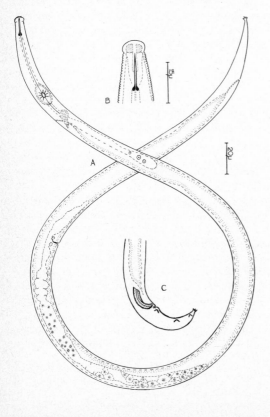

Morphology (Fig. 89): Adults slender, 0.4–0.9 mm long; buccal stylet about 10 μ long, with distinct knobs; tip region slightly enlarged; excretory pore anterior to nerve ring; 4 lateral lines; postvulval uterine sac 2–4 body widths long but less than 1/3 distance from vulva to anus, not containing sperms; 3–4 pointed processes on tail terminus; tail of male curved to about 180 °.

Fig. 89. *Aphelenchoides besseyi*. A = female; B = anterior end of body with stylet; C = posterior end of body of male (drawings F. Burckhardt)

Life cycle and ecology: Optimum temperature for development 21–25 °C; no reproduction below 13 °C. The development of one generation requires a cumulative temperature of 80 °C (cumulative daily mean temperatures above 13 °C). At 25 °C, the life-cycle takes 7 days.

A. besseyi lives as an ectoparasite inside the leaf sheaths of rice seedlings and in the heading stage on the young panicles between inner and outer glumes. At harvest the eelworms become quiescent in the seeds. The nematodes survive up to three years on dry stored grain and up to nine months in the soil.

Infestation starts from infested seed. Grasses in rice fields can be attacked, but this plays an insignificant part in the spread of the pest.

Control: Hot-water treatment of rice seeds, either 16–20 hours at below 20 °C, then 7 min at 50 to 52 °C, or 10–15 min at 56–57 °C without pre-soaking. Hot water treatment can be carried out 60 days before sowing. The seed must be dried rapidly at 43 °C.

Attack is less severe in crops from seed broadcast in flooded land than on dry land subsequently flooded. Seed treatment with methyl bromide leads to seedling damage, if the moisture content of grains exceeds 14 %. Seed treatment trials with organic mercury compounds gave good results in Japan.

Susceptibility of rice varieties varies. Some American and Japanese varieties are practically resistant. Resistance breeding is promising.

Literature

BARAT, H., M. DELASSUS & HUU-HAI-VUONG (1969): The geographical distribution of white tip disease of rice in tropical Africa and Madagascar. In "Nematodes of tropical crops" (J. E. Peachey ed.). Techn. Com. No **40**, Com. Bur. Helminth. St. Albans, 269–273.
CHRISTIE, J. R. (1959): Plant nematodes, their bionomics and control. Agric. Exp. Sta. Univ. Florida, Gainesville, 256 pp.
FORTUNER, R., & J. R. HARRIS (1969): Revue de la litterature sur *Aphelenchoides besseyi* Christie, 1942, cause de la maladie "white tip" du riz. Com. Bur. Helminth. St. Albans, 27 pp.
HASHIOKA, Y. (1964): Nematode diseases of rice in the world. Riso **13**, 139–148.
ICHINOHE, M. (1972): Nematode diseases of rice. In "Economic Nematology" (J.M. Webster ed.). Academic Press, London-New York, 127–143.

Author: F. Burckhardt

Rhadinaphelenchus cocophilus (Cobb) (Fig. 90 and plate 17a)

Synonym: *Aphelenchus cocophilus*

Common names: Coconut-palm nematode; Kokosnußälchen.

Geographical distribution: Central and South America, Caribbean Islands. Spread continues.

Host plants: Coconut palm *(Cocos nucifera)*, oil palm *(Elaeis guineensis)* and other palm species.

Symptoms: *R. cocophilus* causes red ring disease of coconut palm. The symptoms are: First yellowing of lower fronds from the tip down, then golden yellow discolouration, browning and death and spread to other leaves. Inside the stem, 2–3 cm below the surface, an orange red to red ring about 3 cm in width, which extends through the entire stem from the roots to the leaf stalks. Nematodes are present in the discoloured tissue, notably larvae.

Attack leads to the formation of phyto-toxins, plugging of xylem bundles and destruction of root cortex. The tree can die 3–4 months after the first symptoms have appeared.

The most susceptible stage is from 2 years *before* until 2 years *after* fruit production. Younger and older palms are rarely attacked.

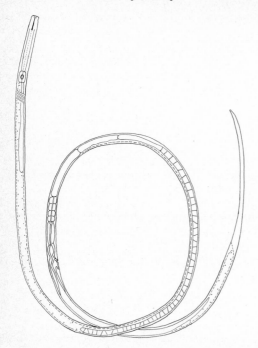

Fig. 90. Female of *Rhadinaphelenchus cocophilus* (drawing B. Weischer)

Economic importance: Infested coconut plantations can be destroyed within a few months.

Morphology: Adults about 1 mm long, very slender (body diameter 10 μm or less); buccal stylet delicate (length 12 μm); Vulva in 66 %; males with small bursa at the tail end.

Life cycle and ecology: Endoparasite, especially in roots and stem. Developmental period about 10 days per generation. Attack host plants by entering from the soil into roots or through injuries on the stem, particularly in the region of the crown at the base of leaves. Spread by wandering from diseased to healthy trees where roots are in contact, but chiefly dispersed, even across larger distances, by palm weevils *(Rhynchophorus palmarum;* see p. 423), which fly from diseased to healthy trees. Also spread with infected plant material.

Control (see also p. 424): Reliable direct control of these nematodes is not yet possible. The most effective measure is the immediate killing of affected trees by the injection of arsenical preparations (e. g. sodium arsenite), since the palm weevils avoid such trees and the nematodes die within 2–3 months. Felling and burning of diseased palm trees is cumbersome and not very effective, since affected tissue residues (e. g. wood shavings) represent continued sources of infection. Direct chemical control of palm weevils by means of monthly application of insecticides to prevent the transmission of nematodes is possible, but expensive and time consuming; there is, moreover, a risk of toxic residues in the fruit.
Indications of differences in varietal resistance exist, but so far without practical significance.

Literature

BLAIR, G. P. (1969): The problem of control of red ring disease. In "Nematodes of tropical crops" (J. E. Peachey ed.). Com. Agric. Bur. Techn. Com. No. **40,** Farnham Royal, 99–108.
FENWICK, D. W. (1963): On the distribution of *Rhadinaphelenchus cocophilus* (Cobb 1919) Goodey 1960 in coconut palms suffering from red ring disease. J. Helminth. **37,** 15–20.
FENWICK, D. W. (1969): Red ring disease of the coconut palm. In "Nematodes of tropical crops" (J.E. Peachey ed.). Com. Agric. Bur. Techn. Com. No. **40,** Farnham Royal, 89–98.
FRANCO, E. (1964): Estudo sôbre o anel vermelho do coqueiro. Pub. No 6, Min. Agric., Sergipe/Brasil, 236 pp.
HAGLEY, E. A. (1965): The mechanism of transmission of *Rhadinaphelenchus cocophilus* by the palm weevil, *Rhynchophorus palmarum.* Phytopathology **55,** 117–118.

Author: B. Weischer

Family: Tylenchidae

Anguina tritici (Steinb.) (Figs. 91–92)

Synonyms: *Anguillula tritici, Tylenchus tritici*

Common names: Wheat gall nematode; Weizenälchen; Anguillule du blé niellé; Nemátodo del trigo.

Geographical distribution: World wide in all wheat growing regions with inadequate seed dressing and in the absence of crop rotation.

Host plants: Wheat *(Triticum aestivum)*, less frequently bearded wheat *(Triticum speltum)* and rye *(Secale cereale).*

Symptoms: *A. tritici* is the cause of 'ear cockles' on wheat. The feeding activity of nematodes on vegetative cones produces wavy and crinkled leaf edges as well as stunted and twisted leaves. Base of shoot slightly thickened, internodes shortened, affected ears shorter than healthy ones and remain green for longer. Glumes erect, so that galls are easily visible; galls still green when wheat grains turn yellow; galls later brown, thick walled, containing thousands of larvae. Depending on degree of infestation, over 60 galls per ear.

Economic importance: *A. tritici* is a major pest of wheat in parts of Asia, Africa and Southern Europe. Yield losses amount to between 30–60 %. *Anguina tritici* attack is often accompanied by infection with *Corynebacterium tritici, Tilletia tritici* or *Dilophospora alopecuri;* intensified damage and different symptoms can result.

Morphology (Fig. 91): ♀ 3–5 mm long; width 0.1–0.2 mm, plump. Vulva far back (V = 90–95 %), ovary large, prodelphic, anterior part reflexed. Stylet very small (10 μm); glandular bulb swollen irregularly.
♂ 2–2.6 mm long, a little more slender than ♀; spicula broad, ♀♀ rolled spirally, ♂♂ and larvae not rolled.
Larva II (infective stage) 0.5 mm long, glandular bulb smooth.

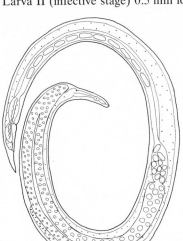

Fig. 92.   Left: healthy wheat grains; right: galls containing wheat gall nematodes (phot. B. Weischer)

Fig. 91.   Female of *Anguina tritici* (drawing B. Weischer)

Life cycle and ecology: Larvae leave the galls which have dropped to the ground and migrate from the soil first into the leaf axils of young plants and later towards the vegetative cone. Main infestation takes place in the spring. Cool, damp weather predisposes to attack. In the course of plant growth, the nematodes are passively raised upwards and enter flower initials in the heading stage. Affected flowers form galls in place of normal grains, in which the nematodes reach sexual maturity. Oviposition follows mating (several thousand eggs per female). After hatching from the egg the larvae turn dormant (anabiosis) and remain infective for years. Spread is by means of galls with the seed, straw, chaff, machines etc.

Control: Crop rotation with 2–3 year cultivation of non-hosts, seed dressing and change of seed.

Literature

GUPTA, P., & G. SWARUP (1968): On the ear-cockle and yellow ear rot diseases of wheat I. Symptoms and histopathology. Indian Phytopath. **21**, 318–323.
LEUKEL, R.W. (1957): Nematode diseases of wheat and rye. Farmers Bull. U.S. Dept. Agric. No 1607, 16 pp.
MIDHA, S. K., M. S. CHATRATH & G. SWARUP (1971): On the feeding of *Anguina tritici* on growing point of wheat seedlings. Indian J. Nematol. **1**, 93–94.
SWARUP, G., & N. J. SINGH (1962): A note on the nematode-bacterium complex in tundu disease complex of wheat. Indian Phytopath. **15**, 294–295.
SWARUP, G., & P. GUPTA (1971): On the ear-cockle and tundo diseases of wheat II. Studies on *Anguina tritici* (Steinbuch 1799) Filipjev 1936 and *Corynebacterium tritici* (Hutch.) Burkh. Indian Phytopath. **24**, 359–365.

Author: B. Weischer

Ditylenchus angustus (Butl.) (Fig. 93)

Common names: Rice stem nematode; Reisstengelälchen.

Geographical distribution: Rice growing regions of Asia and Africa (India, Bangladesh, Burma, Malaysia, Thailand, Philippines, Egypt, Madagascar).

Host plants: Several *Oryza* species, also the wild rice *Leersia hexandra*. Propagation is also possible on various fungi.

Symptoms: *D. angustus* is the cause of "Ufra" disease of rice. The first symptom on rice seedlings is a chlorosis or striping of the uppermost leaves, which later often turn a whitish green colour, with a yellowish midrib which is sometimes thickened. The leaves can be twisted and deformed and frequently have a wavy leaf margin. In severe attack, the panicle may remain enclosed inside the leaf sheath, while the stalk shows a tendency to branch in the affected regions ("swollen ufra"), or the panicles are distorted, have a dark brown discoloured peduncle and only form normal seed at the apex, while the rest of the seed is twisted and sterile ("ripe ufra"). Heavily infested seedlings may show retarded growth and wilted leaves.

Economic importance: The loss in yield resulting from *D. angustus* can be considerable and amount to as much as 90 % of the crop.

Morphology (Fig. 93): Body length 0.6 to 1.2 mm, slender. Lip region flattened, sclerotization weak, stylet 9–10 μ long. Oesophagus with median bulb and long terminal bulb. Vulva at 75–80 %, length of postuterine sac almost $^2/_3$ of vulva – anus distance, spermatheca very long. Tail elongate-conoid, pointed, often with digitate process. Bursa almost reaching to tip of tail.

Fig. 93. *Ditylenchus angustus*. A = anterior end of body; B = posterior end of body of female; C = tail of female; D = tail of male (drawings D. Sturhan)

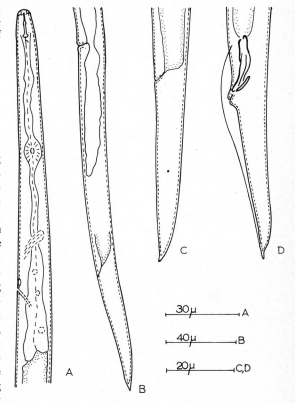

Life cycle and ecology: Rice stem nematodes live as ectoparasites on the young tissues of rice plants. In moist periods they migrate from the soil along the stem of young plants and penetrate into the growing point. Later they are found chiefly in leaf sheaths and stalks, on young stem portions immediately above the uppermost node, in peduncles, panicles and young seed. Under dry conditions, the nematodes coil up on ripening plants and become inactive. If moistened, they soon regain their full mobility. Towards the end of the growing period, cottony masses are formed by nematodes in a state of anabiosis on the ripening and drying plants. Some of these remain on the stubble after harvesting and can survive drought for at least six months. The main sources of infection in the field are stubble, sprouting roots and straw residues. The nematodes are spread by irrigation and rain. Seed transmission seems of little significance. Optimum temperatures for attack of rice plants lie between 28 to 30 °C. *D. angustus* therefore flourishes in tropical regions with high relative humidity and high temperatures – usually all the year round – and is a major rice pest under such conditions.

Control: The most effective control measure was found to consist of burning of stubble and other plant residues, removal of young suckers and ploughing up of fields in the dry period. The nematodes do not tolerate prolonged drought or flooding. Affected seedlings which show symptoms must be destroyed on transplanting from seed beds. Transmission with rice straw and irrigation water must be prevented. If possible, crop rotation should be practised which, since *D. angustus* is strictly host specific, is very advantageous. Resistant rice varieties are not yet known, but many grown varieties escape attack, because they are planted at a time when weather and soil conditions are unsuitable for infestation.

Literature

BUTLER, E. J. (1919): The rice worm *(Tylenchus angustus)* and its control. Mem. Dep. Agric. India **10**, bot. ser., 1–37.
HASHIOKA, Y. (1963): The rice stem nematode *Ditylenchus angustus* in Thailand. Pl. Prot. Bull. F.A.O. **11**, 97–102.
VUONG, H. H. (1969): The occurrence in Madagascar of the rice nematodes *Aphelenchoides besseyi* and *Ditylenchus angustus*. In: Nematodes of Tropical Crops (J. E. Peachey ed.). Commonw. agric. Bur., Farnham Royal, Bucks., pp. 274–288.

Author: D. Sturhan

Family: Hoplolaimidae

Hirschmanniella spp. (Fig. 94)

Common names: Rice root nematodes; Reisnematoden; Nématodes du riz; Nemátodos del arroz.

Important species and geographical distribution: *H. oryzae* (esp. in Asia), *H. spinicaudata* (esp. in Africa).

Host plants: Rice is the main host plant, but other cultivated plants are also attacked, primarily monocotyledons such as maize and sugar cane.
Common weeds in rice crops, such as *Echinochloa* spp., *Cyperus* spp., *Fimbristylis* spp., *Panicum crus-galli* and *Monochloria raginalis* are important hosts which maintain infestation.

Symptoms: Affected rice plants show retarded growth, fewer and shorter haulms, lowered dry weight and discolouration of older leaves. Roots show a yellow to brown discolouration of the cortex, extensive necrosis and large cavities. If attack is not too severe, aerial symptoms can gradually be less pronounced in the course of the vegetative period, if the rate of growth, i. e. regeneration of the root system, exceeds the rate of reproduction of nematodes.

Economic importance: Depending on degree of infestation, losses of up to 38 % have been observed. The extent of damage is also affected by environmental conditions, especially moisture content, structure and chemical composition of the soil.

Morphology: Males and females 1–2 mm long, slender (a = 60). Vulva of female about half way down the body; oesophageal bulb three-lobed, elongated, usually overlapping the gut ventrally.

Life cycle and ecology: *Hirschmanniella* species are migratory endoparasites. Larvae and adults enter from the soil into thicker roots, which contain air ducts. Apical, undifferentiated root portions and fine fibrous roots are avoided. They spread across the air spaces in the root parenchyma and can advance as far as the base of the coleoptile. Leaf sheaths are not affected. The females start oviposition a few days after entry. Development from egg to adult takes at least four weeks. The rate of increase per generation can be more than tenfold. Depending on nematode species, there may be 1 or 2 generations per period of cultivation. Adults and larvae can remain active in the soil without feeding for several weeks. *H. spinicaudata* survives in parched soil for months without difficulty.

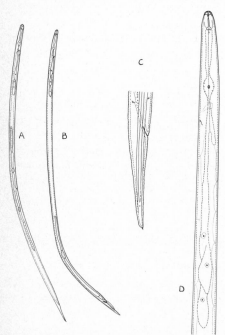

Fig. 94. *Hirschmanniella oryzae*. A = female; B = male; C = tail of female; D = anterior end of body of female (drawings B. Weischer)

Control: Crop rotation and drying up of soil for longer periods generally leads to a marked reduction in population of most species. The control of weeds which are known hosts is also an important protective measure. Rice varieties resistant to *Hirschmanniella* spp. are not yet known. Good results have been obtained in trials with the nematicides ethylenedibromide, 1.3-dichloropropene and dibromochloropropane. The best time for such soil treatment is immediately before transplanting seedling plants.

Literature

ICHINOHE, M. (1972): Nematode diseases of rice. In "Economic Nematology" (Webster, J. M. ed.). Acad. Press London-New York, 127–143.

KUWAHARA, M., & K. IYATOMI (1970): (Studies on the bionomics of the rice-root nematodes, *Hirschmaniella imamuri* Sher and *Hirschmanniella oryzae* (Soltwedel) Luc & Goodey, with special reference to its mode of life and population dynamics). Jap. J. Ent. Zool. **14**, 117–121.

MERNY, G. (1972): Les nématodes phytoparasites des rizières inondées de Côte d'Ivoire III. Etudes sur la dynamique des populations de deux endoparasites: *Hirschmanniella spinicaudata* et *Heterodera oryzae*. Cah. ORSTOM No **16**, 31–88.

SHER, S. A. (1968): Revision of the genus *Hirschmanniella* Luc & Goodey, 1963 (Nematoda: Tylenchoidea). Nematologica **14**, 243–275.

TAYLOR, A. L., T. KAOSIRI, T. SITTAICHI & D. BUANGSUWON (1966): Experiments on the effects of nematodes on the growth and yield of rice in Thailand. Plant Prot. Bull. F.A.O. **14**, 17–23.

Author: B. Weischer

Radopholus similis (Cobb) (Fig. 95)

Common name: Burrowing nematode.

Geographical distribution: Widely distributed in tropical and subtropical region. In Europe not outdoors. Original habitat presumable Australian region. A pest on banana in Central and South America, on the Caribbean islands, in parts of Africa, South and South East Asia, on the Pacific islands and in Australia.

Host plants: Over 250 host plants of *R. similis* are known, among them citrus, black pepper, sugar cane, tea, coffee, avocado, vegetables, maize, ornamentals, trees, wild grasses and weeds. There are however several biological races with varying, sometimes limited host range. The banana strain seems confined to *Musa* spp. and possibly few other plants, such as *Ipomoea batatas* and *Pueraria phaseoloides javanica.* These hosts include many cultivated stocks bred from *Musa acuminata* and *M. balbisiana,* as well as *M. textilis* (abaca) and other *Musa* species. The more polyphagous citrus strain also attacks banana in Florida.

Symptoms: *R. similis* causes "banana root rot" on banana. This disease has also been called "blackhead" or "blackhead toppling disease". Larvae and females of *R. similis* penetrate through wounds made with their buccal stylet into the banana root, where they live intercellularly and produce large cavities and tunnels in the cortical parenchyma by feeding on cell contents. Characteristic reddish brown lesions arise in the root cortex, which later also usually shows deep fissures. The nematodes do not penetrate the endodermis, but fungus invaders extend the necrosis as far as the central cylinder, which can cause distal root portions to die off. The entire root system can be reduced to a few short stubs in that way. *R. similis* can also penetrate to the rhizome along the roots and produce a diffuse black necrosis in the rhizome cortex around the roots.

The most obvious symptom is the toppling of entire banana plants, particularly fruiting ones, owing to the greatly reduced root system. In addition there is stunted growth, premature leaf drop and diminution in bunch weights, in size and number of leaves, in sucker formation and an increased susceptibility to water deficiency.

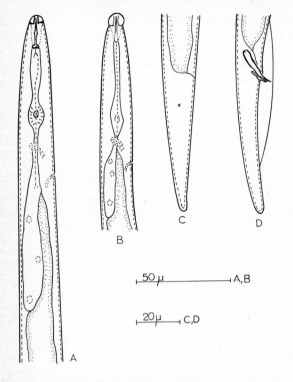

Fig. 95. *Radopholus similis*. A = anterior end of body of female; B = anterior end of body of male; C = tail of female; D = tail of male (drawings D. Sturhan)

Panama wilt disease due to *Fusarium oxysporum* f. sp. *cubense* (see p. 203) is intensified by *R. similis* attack, and the wilt symptoms arise more rapidly. The fungus can enter the roots through wounds made by nematodes.

Economic importance: *R. similis* can produce considerable losses in yield. In the absence of control measures against nematodes, annual replanting may be necessary.

Morphology (Fig. 95): Females: Body 0.5–0.9 mm long, straight or slightly curved. Lateral field with 4 incisures. Anterior end rounded, with strong head skeleton. Length of stylet 17–20 μ, basal knobs well developed. Oesophagus with well developed median bulb and glands overlapping the intestine dorsally. Vulva a little behind middle of body, spermathecae rounded, generally filled with sperms. Tail elongate-conoid, narrowly rounded at the end or with a fine tip. Males: Oesophagus and stylet degenerated. Lip region high and round, offset by constriction, with weak head skeleton. Bursa enveloping about 2/3 of tail.

Life cycle and ecology: *R. similis* is a migratory root nematode and all developmental stages can be found in the root region of affected plants. It generally lives as an endoparasite in the roots and also deposits its eggs there, but can return to the soil in unfavourable conditions. All larval stages and the females can attack plants; the males are probably not parasitic. At temperatures between 24 and 32 °C, the developmental cycle from egg to egg is completed in 20 to 25 days.

Free-living stages and eggs do not seem to survive in fallow soil or in plastic bags for longer than about 12 weeks. In banana plantations, *R. similis* did not survive for more than 6 months, after all stools, rhizomes and roots had been completely removed and destroyed. The spread of the nematode species in the soil is facilitated by the presence of host roots and by transport in water in the soil or on drenching. Spread with soil particles and especially with infected plant material, plays an important part.

Control: Since the banana race of *R. similis* evidently has a restricted host range and survives for only a limited period without feeding, crop rotation with non-host plants (e. g. sugar cane) is feasible, as is a fallow period, provided all roots and rhizomes are removed or killed with herbicide injection. Additional flooding of the soil for 5–6 months also helps to eliminate the nematodes. In soil treatments with nematicides, best results were obtained with DBCP (Nemagon).

The spread of nematodes with sets can be prevented if the rhizome is pared and all discoloured tissue is carefully removed. Additional dipping with a DBCP solution is also advantageous, though plant damage can occur. Hot water treatment at 55 °C for 20 minutes kills the nematodes inside sets. Immersion treatment is enhanced by paring.

Genetical resistance to *R. similis* within the genus *Musa* is known. Attempts are under way, to introduce resistant genes into the genome of new hybrids.

Literature

BLAKE, C. D. (1969): Nematode parasites of banana and their control. In: Nematodes of tropical crops (J. E. Peachey ed.). Commonw. agric Bur., Farnham Royal, Bucks, 109–132.
BLAKE, C. D. (1972): Nematode diseases of banana plantations. In: Economic Nematology (J. M. Webster ed.). London & New York, 245–267.
LOOS, C. A. (1961): Eradication of the burrowing nematode, *Radopholus similis,* from bananas. Plant Dis. Reptr. **45**, 457–461.
LOOS, C. A. (1962): Studies on the life-history and habits of the burrowing nematode, *Radopholus similis,* the cause of black-head disease of banana. Proc. helminth. Soc. Wash. **29**, 43–52.
LUC, M., & A. VILARDEBO (1961): Les nématodes associés aux bananiers cultivés dans l'Ouest Africain. II. Fruits **16**, 261–279.
VILARDEBO, A., & J. ROBIN (1969): Nematicidal treatment of banana planting material. In: Nematodes of tropical crops (J. E. Peachey ed.). Commonw. agric. Bur., Farnham Royal, Bucks., 133–141.

Author: D. Sturhan

Family: Tylenchulidae

Tylenchulus semipenetrans Cobb (Fig. 96)

Common names: Citrus nematode; Citrusnematode; Nemátodo del naranjo.

Geographical distribution: World wide in nearly all citrus growing regions.

Host plants: Presumably all *Citrus* species and hybrids; some species of related Rutaceae genera, e. g. *Fortunella japonica* and several varieties of *Poncirus trifoliata.* Few hosts from other families, among them grapevine *(Vitis vinifera),* olive *(Olea europaea)* and lilac *(Syringa vulgaris).* Many non-citrus species only attacked by particular biological races of the nematodes.

Symptoms: *T. semipenetrans* causes "slow decline" of citrus. Growth vitality gradually decreases while the general – not very specific – symptoms gradually increase. The symptom expression is similar to that due to drought and nutrient deficiency: Stunted growth, leaf chlorosis, leaf drop, twig dieback, early wilt with water deficiency, in-rolling of leaves, small fruit, fewer fruit setts. Roots with extensive blackish necroses (frequently secondary infection with fungi and bacteria), lateral roots generally a little shortened and thickened, with rough surface, root hairs often completely suppressed. Often no symptoms apparent under optimum growth conditions. Symptom expression varies in different hosts.

Economic importance: Reduction in yield can exceed 50 %. Symptoms usually only arise in older citrus plantations. In new plantations on virgin soil, damage is often not apparent until 12–17 years later. Critical threshold 40 000 nematodes/10 gm fibrous roots, but depends greatly on soil type, methods of cultivation and host plant.

Morphology (Fig. 96): Females up to 0,5 mm long, hind part swollen, elongate-saccate (except for tip of tail and anterior part embedded in the roots). Males with small stylet and reduced oesophagus, tail fairly long with blunted end, without bursa. Young larvae slender, buccal stylet 12–14 μ long with knobs, tail pointed, excretory pore – as in adults – posterior to middle of body (!), oesophagus with median and terminal bulb.

Life cycle and ecology: Second-stage larvae hatch from eggs in the soil, penetrate the outermost root cell layers of host plants with their anterior end, and develop into swelling, sessile, semi-endoparasitic females. On average, 30 to 40 eggs are deposited in a gelatinous matrix, which covers almost the entire part of the female protruding from the roots (frequently studded with soil particles, which makes the females hard to recognize). Female second-stage larvae can survive in the soil

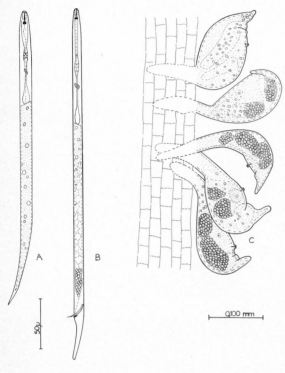

Fig. 96. *Tylenchulus semipenetrans.*
A = female; B = male; C = mature females
on a rootlet (drawings B. Weischer)

for several years without feeding. At 24–26 °C, the life cycle is completed within 6–8 weeks. Optimum reproduction at soil temperatures of 28–31 °C. Can develop in a wide range of soil types (pure sandy soil to heavy clay), does particularly well in 10–15 % clay at pH 6.0–7.5. In fine textured soil, drought promotes reproduction. Citrus roots are invaded up to a depth of 4 m soil.

Control: Improved methods of cultivation can balance parasitic potential of citrus nematodes. Prevention of spread: Establishment of seed beds on virgin or fumigated soil, remote from citrus orchards. Inspection of young plants intended for citrus plantations (plus soil sampling of seed beds), if need be immersion treatment of roots (hot water 25 min. at 45 °C. or aqueous emulsions of systemic organic phosphor compounds). Cleaning of farm implements etc., no recycling of drainage water for watering in citrus plantations.

Soil treatment before (new) planting with various soil fumigants is possible. Under sub-tropical climatic conditions, treatment in late summer or autumn is advisable, followed by planting in the next spring or early summer. Since infestation of soil cannot generally be eradicated, control relies on the protection of young citrus trees. Critical population levels are usually once more exceeded after 4–7 years.

In existing crops, DBCP (Nemagon) and other systemic nematicides tolerated by the plants, can be used. Amount (10–67 l/ha Nemagon) and method of application (e. g. mixed with water supply, soil injection) depends on local conditions. Nemagon can on occasion be phytotoxic, particularly when used in fine grained soils. Treatment should generally be repeated every 4–5 years. A start has been made with breeding resistant varieties (by cross breeding with certain *Poncirus trifoliata* lines).

Literature

BAINES, R. C., T. MIYAKAWA, J. W. CAMERON & R. H. SMALL (1969): Infectivity of two biotypes of the citrus nematode on citrus and on some other hosts. J. Nematol. **1**, 150–159.
COHN, E. (1972): Nematode diseases of citrus. In: Economic Nematology (J. M. Webster ed.). London & New York, 215–244.
DUCHARME, E. P. (1969): Nematode problems of citrus. In: Nematodes of tropical crops (J.E. Peachey ed.). Commonw. agric. Bur., Farnham Royal, Bucks., 225–237.
VAN GUNDY, S. D. (1958): The life history of the citrus nematode *Tylenchulus semipenetrans* Cobb. Nematologica **3**, 283–294.
VILARDEBO, A., & M. LUC (1961): Le "slow decline" des citrus dû au nématode *Tylenchulus semipenetrans* Cobb. Fruits **16**, 445–454.

Author: D. Sturhan

Family: Heteroderidae

Meloidogyne spp. (Figs. 97–98 and plate 17 b)

Common names: Root-knot nematodes; Wurzelgallenälchen; Nématodes à galles; Nemátodos de nódulos.

Important species and geographical distribution: _M. javanica_ occurs in worldwide distribution, especially in tropical and subtropical regions, also at high altitudes up to 3000 m. In temperate climates it is a glasshouse pest. – _M. incognita_ s. l. is economically the most important root-knot nematode, causing much damage outdoors in hot climates and in glasshouses in temperate zones. – _M. arenaria_ is widely distributed in hot climates. – _M. exigua_ is confined to warm, humid regions. – _M. hapla_ has a worldwide distribution particularly in temperate climates. In the tropics it occurs only at high altitudes.

Host plants: _M. javanica:_ Over 700 host plants are known, among them tea, tobacco, potato, grapevine, tomato, numerous vegetables, fruit trees, cereal, ornamentals. Not affected are: _Gossypium barbadense, Capsicum annuum,_ some varieties of oat and barley and some _Nicotiana_ and _Crotolaria_ species. – _M. incognita_ s. l.: More than 700 hosts are known, among them sugar cane, potato, tomato, cotton, tobacco, beet, cereal, beans, peas, carrot, cucumber, grapevine, _Prunus_ spp. and many ornamentals. Not affected are: peanut, millet _(Panicum_ and _Sorghum), Lycopersicum peruvianum_ and strawberry. – _M. arenaria:_ Host plants include peanut, celery, oats, barley, beet, banana, tobacco, tomato, potato, grapevine and maize. Not affected are: strawberry, some _Gossypium_ (cotton) species and some species of _Nicotiana_ and _Crotolaria._ – _M. exigua:_ A destructive pest on _Coffea arabica_ in the coffee growing regions of Central and South America and Southern India. Affected coffee shrubs can die within 1–2 weeks and 7–10 year old shrubs are particularly susceptible. Banana _(Musa cavendishii), Citrus aurantium,_ tea and some Cucurbitaceae can also be affected. Species which are not attacked include _Coffea canephora, C. congensis_ and _C. eugenoides._ – _M. hapla:_ Over 550 hosts are known, including carrot, celery, beet, tomato, strawberry, potato, peanut, soybean. Not generally attacked are grasses, cereals, cotton, onion, and _Asparagus_ spp.

Symptoms: Irregular swellings (galls) on the roots, resulting from hypertrophy of root cortex and the formation of giant cells in the region of the pericycle. If heavily infested, the entire root system is deformed. The shape of galls varies, depending on nematode and plant species. The galls formed by _M. hapla_ are generally small and round with many lateral roots, those of _M. incognita_ are large and span the whole root. The giant cells disrupt vascular bundles and interfere with their function. This leads to poor growth and increased susceptibility to water deficiency, plus visible, if not very specific, symptoms on the aerial portions of the plant.

The host-parasite relationship can be drastically altered in the presence of other pathogens (viruses, bacteria, fungi). Synergistic interrelations are common and can lead to intensified damage. In some cases, attack by _Meloidogyne_ can abolish the resistance of a plant to fungi. _M. incognita_ for instance, abolishes the _Fusarium_ resistance of the tomato variety "Chesapeake". Attack by _Meloidogyne_ can also render plants susceptible to fungi which are normally not very pathogenic or do not attack such plants at all. These fungi include various species of the genera _Aspergillus, Botrytis, Curvularia_ and _Trichoderma._

The intensification of symptoms and increased susceptibility of affected plants is not due to mechanical damage in the root caused by nematodes, but to physiological changes in the root tissue induced by the root knot nematodes. The increased susceptibility is therefore only apparent some time after the entry of nematodes.

Economic importance: Owing to its pathogenicity and the wide range of host plants. _Meloidogyne_ is the most important genus of plant parasitic nematodes. Several hundred hosts are known for

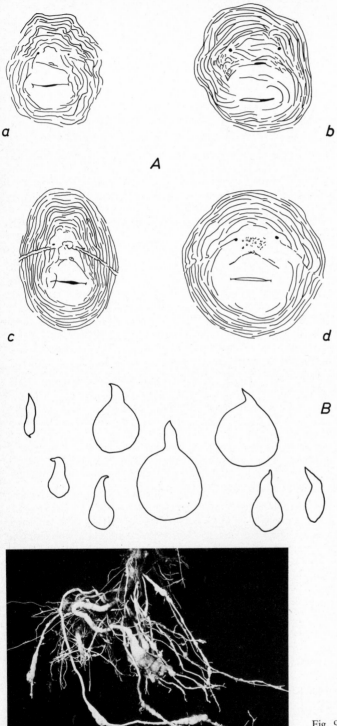

Fig. 97. A = cuticular pattern at the posterior end around anus and vulva: a = *Meloidogyne incognita;* b = *M. arenaria;* c = *M. javanica;* d = *M. hapla.* B = females of *Meloidogyne* spp. in various stages of maturity (drawings B. Weischer)

Fig. 98. Roots of tomato plant with numerous galls of *Meloidogyne* sp. (phot. H. Schmutterer)

some of the species, and there is hardly a cultivated plant which cannot be attacked and damaged by root knot nematodes. As well as poor growth and lowered yield, the quality of the crop may also be greatly diminished.

Morphology: Mature females spherical, with clearly demarcated front portion. Body length about 700 μm, diameter of swollen body portion about 500 μm. Slender stylet about 15 μm in length. Cuticle clearly annulated at the anterior end only. It remains soft and colourless. Typical cuticular pattern at the posterior end around anus and vulva, which is used for species identification. Male slender, body length 1–2 mm. Stylet more robust than in the female. Cuticle clearly annulated. Tail rounded, cloaca almost at end of body.
Larvae II slim, body length about 400 μm; stylet about 12 μm, slender.
Over 40 species have so far been described. They are not easily distinguished and the distinction rests chiefly on the cuticular pattern at the posterior end of the female. This varies greatly in most species. Patterns of different "species" can occur among the progeny of single females. The well known and widely distributed species *M. incognita* is therefore nowadays regarded as a complex of several related species. The identification of a species can therefore not rely solely on the features of the female. Males and larvae must also be examined. In recent years, chromosomes have also been used successfully for species identification. Such identification is of no great significance for practical control purposes, since the most pathogenic species are widely distributed, affect most cultivated plants and are largely controlled by similar means. Moreover, mixed populations are more common on arable land than single species.

Life cycle and ecology: Second-stage larvae (L II) hatch from the eggs in search of a root. They usually settle in the vicinity of a vascular bundle. They lose their mobility within 1–3 days and remain where they are. In the soil they can remain active for 30–60 days. After that, their energy reserves are exhausted and their infective capacity is much reduced. Once inside the host, the L II induce the formation of multinucleate giant cells around their anterior end and suck on them. The next two moults take place in quick succession, and neither L III nor L IV leave the cuticle of the L II. They have no stylet and do not feed. Only the young females begin to feed again, gradually swelling up in pouchlike fashion. The females secrete a gelatinous sac, in which several hundred eggs are deposited. It can be larger than the female herself and often bursts through the rhizodermis, so that it is visible from outside. It hardens in contact with air and provides a protective cover for the eggs. The duration of the life cycle depends on temperature and varies with the species. On average, 4–6 weeks are required for development from egg to egg if conditions are favourable. In temperate climates, only 1–2 generations usually form in the open. In hot regions and glasshouses reproduction can take place throughout the year in the presence of suitable hosts. Up to 10 generations have been observed in a year. In most species, development and reproduction practically ceases at temperatures below 20 °C.
In resistant plants, penetrating L II are rapidly encapsulated by necrotic cells which form as a result of a hypersensitive reaction by root cortex and endodermis. Giant cells are not formed and the larvae cannot develop.

Control:
Crop rotation: Owing to the extraordinary range of host plants, the possibilities are very limited. The occurrence of strains with altered host range and the prevalence of mixed populations of 2–3 *Meloidogyne* species restricts the feasibility of crop rotation even more. The grass *Eragrostis curvula* has effectively reduced *M. javanica* infestation on many occasions. *M. incognita* infestation can be decreased by growing certain *Crotolaria* species. Repeated cultivation of Gramineae lowers the incidence of *M. hapla,* potato crops grown for 1–2 years that of *M. naasi.*
Resistant varieties: The use of *Meloidogyne*-resistant varieties of cultivated plants is probably the most efficient mode of control and has frequently led to good or very good results.
It has to be borne in mind when using resistant varieties, that in some species populations which can break the resistance have been observed. In addition, the resistance is often only effective

within a certain range of temperature. For instance the resistance to *Meloidogyne* by *Phaseolus vulgaris* and *Lycopersicum peruvianum* is lost at temperatures above 30 °C.

Addition of organic substances: Cakes of *Ricinus communis, Arachis hypogea,* peanut or *Azadirachta indica* in amounts of roughly 1800 kg/ha can greatly reduce *Meloidogyne* populations, thereby increasing the yields of subsequently grown crops.

Hot water treatment: Has been used with success, for instance on rose against *M. hapla* (60 min. at 45 °) and on potato tubers against *M. javanica* (120 min. at 46–47.5 °C).

Heat treatment of soil: Steaming or electrical heating is a useful method for cleaning up smaller areas or batches of soil. The entire amount of soil to be treated must be heated to at least 65 °C and maintained at that temperature for several hours.

Drying out the soil for several weeks by repeated deep ploughing, so that the nematodes are exposed to the sun and the hot dry air, can be used as a control measure in very arid regions. Since however a high percentage of eggs survive, the population is generally rapidly restored when susceptible crops are grown. Repeated deep ploughing also damages the soil structure.

Flooding or water logging of the soil for several weeks or months also leads to much reduced infestation. Larvae and adults are killed relatively rapidly and easily, but the eggs are again much more resistant.

Chemical control: Since *Meloidogyne* species serve almost everywhere as test organisms for the development and testing of nematicides, commercial nematicides are all effective against these nematodes. This applies as much for the so-called soil disinfectants such as ethylenedibromide, methylisothiocyanate, methylbromide, 1.3-dichloropropene etc., as for non-phytotoxic nematicides such as aldicarb, carbofuran, oxamyl, phenamiphos etc. The choice of suitable preparation, amount required and mode of application depends on environmental factors such as soil, climate, plant, on economic consideration and on possible risks to man and animal from residues in the crops. It is generally uneconomical to use greater amounts of nematicide for one year crops, than is necessary to ensure adequate yields. For seed and young plant beds and for intensive crops (e. g. under glass), more thorough control measures could be profitable. In crops with more than 60 cm spacing between rows, it often suffices to treat the rows. Compared with whole surface treatment, this could reduce the costs up to 50 %. Greater amounts are required for perennial crops such as fruit or grapevine, since these are more deeply rooted and effective treatment has to include nematodes living at greater depths of soil.

Literature

BIRD, A. F., & H. R. WALLACE (1965): The influence of temperature on *Meloidogyne hapla* and *M. javanica*. Nematologica **11,** 581–589.

CAYROL, J.-C. (1973): Relations entre les nématodes du genre *Meloidogyne* et les autres organismes pathogènes de la rhizosphère. EPPO Bull. **3,** 49–54.

DAVIDE, R. G., & A. C. TRIANTAPHYLLOU (1967): Influence of the environment on development and sex differentiation of root-knot nematodes I. Effect of infection density, age of the host plant and soil temperature. Nematologica **13,** 102–110.

DROPKIN, V. H. (1972): Pathology of *Meloidogyne* – galling, giant cell formation, effects on host physiology. EPPO Bull. **2,** 23–32.

FRANKLIN, M. T., & D. J. HOOPER (1959): Plants recorded as resistant to rootknot nematodes *(Meloidogyne* spp.). Techn. Com. No 31, Com. Bur. Helminth. St. Albans, 33 pp.

GUIRAN de, G. & C. NETSCHER (1970): Les nématodes du genre *Meloidogyne,* parasites de cultures tropicales. Cah. ORSTOM No. **11,** 151–185.

GOODEY, J. B., M. T. FRANKLIN & D. J. HOOPER (1965): T. Goodeys The nematode parasites of plants catalogued under their hosts. 3 rd edn. Farnham Royal, 214 pp.

KINLOCH, R. A., & M. W. ALLEN (1972): Interaction of *Meloidogyne hapla* and *M. javanica* infecting tomato. J. Nematol. **4,** 7–16.

LAMBERTI, F. (1973): Yield response in relation to chemical control of root-knot nematodes in Southern Italy. EPPO Bull. **3,** 55–66.

NETSCHER, C., & J. C. MAUBOUSSIN (1973): Resultats d'un essai concernant l'efficacité comparée d'une variété de tomate résistante et de certains nématicides contre *Meloidogyne javanica.* Cah. ORSTOM, No **21,** 97–102.

NIRULA, K. K., C. L. KUSHU & B. T. RAJ (1969): Resistance in tuber bearing Solanum species to rootknot nematode, *Meloidogyne incognita.* Amer. Potato J. **46,** 251–253.

SASSER, J. N. (1972): Physiological variation in the genus *Meloidogyne* as determined by differential hosts. EPPO Bull. **2**, 41–48.

WHITEHEAD, A. G. (1968): Taxonomy of *Meloidogyne* (Nematodes: Heteroderidae) with descriptions of four new species. Trans. Zool. Soc. London **31**, 263–401.

Author: B. Weischer

Other injurious nematodes (Figs. 99–101 and plate 17 c, d):

1. Migratory root nematodes

Pratylenchus spp. (Root lesion nematodes) are about 0,8 mm long, thickset, with flat lip region, sturdy stylet about 18 μm in length and rounded tail. The vulva lies at 80 %. All developmental stages can both penetrate and leave the roots. Reproduction takes place in the tissues of the root. Necrotic areas arise in affected regions and extensive root rot can result from the action of rot-producing invaders. Several *Pratylenchus* species form synergistic complexes with wilt fungi such as *Rhizoctonia solani, Fusarium* spp. and *Verticillium* spp. The following are major pests on tropical and subtropical crops: *P. brachyurus* (Godfr.) (Fig. 99) on peanut, rice, sugar cane, tobacco, cotton, *Citrus,* coffee, tea, peach, pineapple and some vegetables. *P. coffeae* (Zimm.) on coffee, banana, sugar cane, *Citrus* and potato. *P. loosi* Loof on tea (Plate 17 c). *P. vulnus* All. & Jens. on walnut, peach, grapevine, olive and rose. *P. zeae* Graham on maize, sugar cane, fruit trees and vegetables.

Helicotylenchus spp. (Spiral nematodes) are predominantly ectoparasites about 1 mm in length. They have a conical lip region and a strong stylet about 30 μm long. The vulva lies at about 60 %, the body annulation is clearly visible, the tail is rounded, often with asymmetric tip. At rest, the animals are spirally rolled. The following species are major pests:
H. dihystera (Cobb) on banana, rice, peanut, sugar cane and tea. *H. multicinctus* (Cobb) on rice, banana, pineapple, cocoa and cassava.

Hoplolaimus galeatus (Cobb) (Lance nematode) is about 1.5 mm long and has a well offset, areolated lip region, a robust stylet 45 μm in length and a blunt, rounded tail. The vulva lies at 55 %. Affected crops include lucerne, cotton, wheat and maize. The nematodes live partly as ecto- and partly as endoparasites on the roots. Affected roots have swellings and brown discolourations.

Scutellonema bradys (Steiner & Lettew) resembles *Hoplolaimus galeatus* in life cycle and appearance. It is a destructive pest on yam *(Dioscorea* spp.) in India, West Africa, Brazil and on the Carribean islands. Necrotic lesions first form in the outermost cell layers of affected tubers, which rapidly enlarge with secondary invasion by bacteria, fungi, mites etc., until the entire tuber may be rotted. The nematode has also been found on pineapple, coconut palm and oil palm, banana, cassava and cotton.

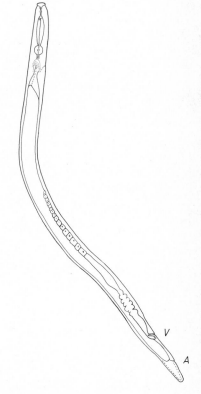

V

A

Fig. 99. *Pratylenchus brachyurus.* V = vulva; A = anus (drawings B. Weischer)

Tylenchorhynchus spp. (Stunt nematodes) are about 1 mm long, slender, with distinct stylet. The vulva is situated roughly half way down the body, i. e. at 50 %. Males abound in most species. The nematodes are predominantly ectoparasites. *T. claytoni* Steiner is a major pest on tobacco and cotton, *T. martini* on rice and sugar cane.

Xiphinema spp. (Dagger nematodes) are slender, ectoparasitic nematodes, several mm long and with a buccal stylet 100–300 µm in length. Their distribution is worldwide, the largest number of species is found in the African tropics. Economically the most important species is *X. index* Thorne & All., which occurs in almost all vine growing regions of the world and not only causes direct feeding damage but also leads indirectly to large losses in yield by transmitting grapevine fanleaf virus. Other widely distributed and polyphagous species are *X. americanum* Cobb, *X. mediterraneum* Mart. & Lamb. and *X. basiri* Sidd.

Longidorus spp. (Needle nematodes), closely related to *Xiphinema,* are also ectoparasites, 2–12 mm long, very slender, with long, needle-shaped stylet. *L. africanus* Merny is a widely distributed pest in hot climates on sugar cane, grapevine, fig and various kinds of vegetable, e. g. egg plant. Affected root tips swell up and cease to grow. A number of *Longidorus* species can transmit plant viruses.

Paratrichodorus minor (Colbran) (= *Trichodorus christiei*), (Stubby root nematode) is a plump nematode, 0.6 mm long, with thick cuticle and round posterior end. The stylet is curved, the vulva lies at 53 %. The nematodes attack mainly the root tips and destroy the growing point. This leads to a stunted root system with very short lateral roots. Severe damage has been observed on maize, tomato, soybean, sugar cane, cotton and *Citrus. P. minor* and some related species are vectors of the widespread tobacco rattle virus.

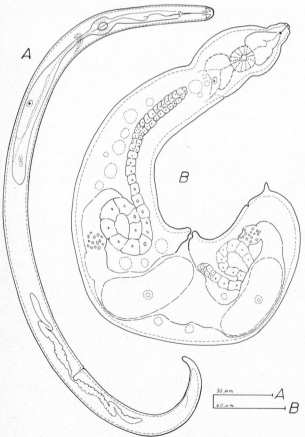

A thorough control of the migratory nematode species mentioned requires the use of nematicides. Both the so-called soil disinfectants and non-phytotoxic preparations have proved suitable (for details see *Meloidogyne*). In case of slight infestation, damage due to nematodes can be prevented by crop rotation. Resistant or tolerant varieties are few at present, for instance of grapevine against *Xiphinema index,* of sugar cane against *Heliocotylenchus dihystera* and *Tylenchorhynchus martini,* and of tea against *Pratylenchus loosi.*

30 µm ——— A
60 µm ——— B

Fig. 100. *Rotylenchus reniformis.* A = young, mobile female; B = mature, sessil female (drawings B. Weischer)

2. Sedentary root nematodes

Rotylenchulus reniformis Linf. & Oliv. (Reniform nematode) (Fig. 100) has a worldwide distribution in hot climates and a wide host range. Habit and life cycle resemble those in *Tylenchulus semipenetrans*. The entire larval development takes place in the soil without feeding, until the young, immature females penetrate into the root tissue from the soil. There they settle and immediately begin to feed. Shortly afterwards their body swells unevenly and oviposition starts. Affected plants have a very poorly developed, scruffy root system with few fibrous roots. Severe damage occurs on pineapple, banana, cotton, tea, papaya, coffee (not *Coffea canephora*) and many vegetables.

Heterodera spp. (Cyst nematodes) (Fig. 101 and plate 17 d) are endoparasites in which, much as in *Meloidogyne,* only the second stage larvae (L II) and males can actively migrate. The L II penetrate suitable host roots from the soil and settle in the vicinity of the vascular tissue. Developing females swell up into spherical or lemon shape and burst through the root cortex with their posterior end, so that they can be seen from the outside with the naked eye. They are at that time about 0,5 mm in size, first white and later brown. The cuticle hardens and the females die to form so-called cysts, which contain several hundred eggs. Larvae inside the cysts remain infective for years. Widely distributed pathogenic species in hot climates are *H. oryzae* Luc & Berd. on rice. *H. sacchari* Luc & Merny on sugar cane, *H. glycines* Ichinohe on soybean, *H. latipons* Franklin and *H. avenae* Woll. on cereals. Potato cyst nematodes, *H. rostochiensis* Woll. (golden potato cyst nematode) and *H. pallida* Stone (white potato cyst nematode) are of special significance. Although they are essentially pests in temperate climates, they have recently also reached tropical and subtropical regions in potato consignments and become established at high altitudes or in coastal regions. They not only lead to high losses in yield, but also exert an effect on political trade agreements. All countries have strict quarantine regulations to prevent the import of infested potato plants and tubers, and statutory laws which prohibit the cultivation of potato on infested land. The commercial losses which result can be considerable. Other host plants are tomato, egg plant and some weeds belonging to the family of Solanaceae. Effective control of potato nematodes is difficult and costly, owing to the longevity of larvae and high rate of reproduction. Losses in yield can largely be avoided, if crop rotation is practised at sufficiently long intervals (5–7 years). Chemical control with soil disinfectants and non-phytotoxic chemicals is possible, but the degree of infestation rises again rapidly as soon as susceptible varieties are grown, since only reduction and not eradication can be achieved. Excellent results have been obtained in recent years in breeding for resistant potato varieties, but the occurrence of resistance-breaking races, so-called pathotypes, leads to difficulties. Pathotypes of *H. rostochiensis* and *H. pallida* are known. The most effective control consists of a combination of methods employing crop rotation, nematicides and resistant varieties. The choice of components must depend on prevailing local conditions.

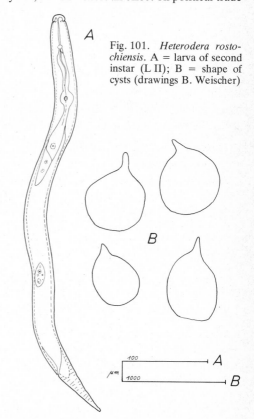

Fig. 101. *Heterodera rostochiensis*. A = larva of second instar (L II); B = shape of cysts (drawings B. Weischer)

B. Weischer

Mites; Milben; Acariens; Acaros

Phylum: Arthropoda

Order: Acari (= Acarida)

General features: Mite pests in tropical and subtropical regions belong mainly to three large families. The most important are the Tetranychidae or "true" spider mites, followed by the Tenuippalpidae (Phytoptipalpidae) or "false spider mites" and finally the Eriophyidae or gall mites. Mites are soft skinned organisms with a chitinous skeleton. They rarely exceed a size of 0.5 mm. Unlike insects, the two first named groups have four pairs of legs and no body portion differentiated into a head. Their colour varies from green to red. They often construct extensive cobwebs, under which they live.

Complete development includes metamorphosis with several moults. The larva hatching from the egg transforms into the first nymph after a short quiescent period, followed by second nymph and finally adult. Development is greatly enhanced by dry, warm weather. Heavy rainfall reduces mite populations in quite a short time. The colour of the various developmental instars relates to nutrition.

Many parasitic mite species prefer the undersurface of plant portions. There are however some, which colonise mainly the upper surface of leaves and the fruit can also be attacked. Severe damage results from their suction activity. They cause leaf discolourations, premature leaf and fruit drop and the crop may fail completely. Gall mites can produce malformations on leaves, shoots and fruit.

The true spider mites, the Tetranychidae, comprise on the whole the largest number of pathogenic species. Their shape is oval, their back arched. They are very lively and extremely quick. They occur in hot and temperate regions. In countries with a proper winter they pass through a state of diapause, which is absent in tropical and subtropical regions, where mites reproduce throughout the year and can give rise to a considerable number of generations.

The Tenuipalpidae or false spider mites are not quite as thin skinned as the Tetranychidae and their body is flattened and not as spherical. They are much slower and more sluggish than members of the first group. Their developmental rhythm is also slow and halting even under suitable climatic conditions, so that the number of generations per year is less than that in Tetranychidae, where it is not infrequently 10–12.

The members of the family Eriophyidae are unusually small and vermiform. They are first a whitish tinge and later tend to assume a brown colour. Their body consists of a greater or lesser number of rings which are studded with microtubercles, a characteristic feature of these species. Unlike Tetranychidae and Tenuipalpidae they have only two pairs of legs.

The eggs are minute, spherical, with a smooth surface and of whitish to slightly yellowish shade. Life cycle of adults and oviposition depends greatly on surrounding temperatures. Under tropical climatic conditions, more than 20 generations can be formed in a year.

Tetranychidae and Tenuipalpidae are generally controlled with acaricides. Care must be taken that the same acaricide is not used too often in succession, in order to avoid a build-up of resistant forms in the population. For the control of Eriophyidae, several sulphur spray preparations have proved most effective.

A start with biological control has been made in California and Hawaii. Two predatory mite species are used, i. e. *Phytoseiulus persimilis* and *P. macropilis*. The former has been used with good results to control Tetranychidae in the strawberry growing regions of California, making chemical control unnecessary. The second species was used in trials carried out in Hawaii, which showed that it is as effective as *P. persimilis*.

G. Dosse

Family: Tetranychidae

Tetranychus cinnabarinus (Boisd.) (Fig. 102A and plate 18 a, b, d)

Synonyms: *Tetranychus telarius, T. cucurbitacearum*

Common names: Carmine spider mite; Rote Spinne; Aragne rouge; Arañita roja.

Geographical distribution: *T. cinnabarinus* is found outside in warmer climates, but only in greenhouses in temperate climates. It is a cosmopolitan species reported from numerous countries in all continents.

Host plants: This polyphagous spider mite is known to infest well over 100 plant species including cotton, apple, bean, peanut, eggplant, citrus, squash, cucumber, ornamentals, and alfalfa. A large number of weeds, mainly dicotyledons, are also hosts of *T. cinnabarinus*.

Symptoms: Citrus leaves show yellow blotches, cotton leaves a reddish-bronze discolouration, and foliage of other hosts shows at first a white specking and then turns pallid or bronzed as the infestation becomes heavy.

Economic importance: In well-managed orchards or in fields with intensively grown crops, especially during dry and warm seasons, losses may be very severe due to premature leaf fall and diminished fruit quality and/or quantity.

Morphology: The female is brownish-red with several dark spots of various sizes (Plate 18 a). It lays pinkish eggs. The males are yellowish-green, in a few cases, with a pinkish hue, and bear small dark spots. The male aedeagus may vary in size and form from the standard shown in fig. 102A. Except for the colour of the female and egg, confusion with *T. urticae* may occur.

Life cycle: *T. cinnabarinus* is an obligate phytophagous mite. On leaves or more seldom on fruits a female may lay over 100 eggs during its life span. Three post-embryonic and three quiescent stages lie between egg and adult. One generation is completed in 9.5d at 30 ° or in 22d at 18 °C. No form of diapause has yet been proved.

Natural enemies: A number of predacious mites and insects are known to feed on this spider mite. The more efficient ones are: *Phytoseiulus persimilis, Phytoseius plumifer, P. corniger, Zetzelia mali, Agistemus fanari, Euseius vivax, Iphiseius degenerans* (Acari); *Stethorus gilvifrons, S. punctillum, S. utilis* (Coleoptera); *Chrysopa carnea, Oligota oviformis* (Neuroptera); *Scolothrips sexmaculatus* (Thysanoptera). The fungus *Entomophthora fresenii* also attacks the spider mite.

Control: The following acaricides are recommended: binapacryl, chinomethionate, chlorphenamidine, dicofol, tetradifon. In cotton, fruit or vegetables an insecticide with acaricidal properties e.g. azinphosethyl, dimethoate, omethoate, monocrotophos, demeton, triazophos is often incorporated in spray programs if heavy infestations do not occur. In crops where mildew and spider mites occur regularly, a spray programm may include chinomethionate at a low dosage of 0.035 % and with repeated treatments at intervals of 7–10 days. From some countries resistance has been reported to a number of organophosphates, dicofol and tetradifon.

Literature

SABA, F. (1975): Comparative studies of species forming two Tetranychid complexes in Morocco. Ann. Entomol. Soc. Am. **68**, 797–800.

Author: F. Saba

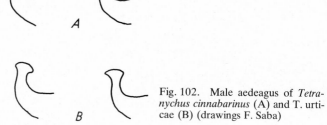

Fig. 102. Male aedeagus of *Tetranychus cinnabarinus* (A) and T. urticae (B) (drawings F. Saba)

Tetranychus urticae Koch (Fig. 102 B and plate 18 c)

Synonyms: *Tetranychus telarius, T. bimaculatus, T. altheae*

Common names: Two-spotted spider mite; Gemeine Spinnmilbe; Acarien jaune commun; Arañita roja.

Geographical distribution: *T. urticae* is found practically in all climates where agriculture is practised. It is a cosmopolitan species reported from most countries in all continents.

Host plants: The pest is polyphagous and known to infest over 100 plant species: cotton, peanut, bean, eggplant, squash, cucumber, apple, peach, citrus, hop, strawberry, castor bean, papaya, sweet corn, ornamental plants and a large number of dicotyledonous weeds.

Symptoms: Citrus leaves show yellow blotches, cotton and castor bean reddish-bronze discolouration, and other foliage at first show specking then turn pallid or bronzed due to heavy infestation.

Economic importance: Usually found in well-managed orchards or in intensive crops where losses may be very severe due to premature leaf drop and diminished fruit quality or quantity.

Morphology: The female is yellowish-green with 2 large dark spots dorso-laterally which, in older females, may extend backwards up to the end of the abdomen; they lay white-hyaline translucent eggs. Males are also yellowish-green of various hues with numerous small dark spots, and their aedeagi (Fig. 102 B) are hardly distinguishable from those of *T. cinnabarinus*. Apart from the colour of the female and egg, confusion with the latter species may occur. Diapausing females are of an orange colour without any dark spots.

Life cycle: *T. urticae* is an obligate phytophagous mite. A female may oviposit over 100 eggs/life-span on leaves or fruits. 3 postembryonic stages and 3 quiescent ones lie between egg and adult stages. 1 generation is completed in 9.5d at 30 °C or in 22d at 18 °C. A high percentage of spider mites go into a female diapause if light and temperature conditions turn unfavourable.

Natural enemies: A number of predacious mites and insects have been reported: (Acari) *Phytoseiulus persimilis, Phytoseius plumifer, P. corniger, Zetzelia mali, Agistemus fanari, Euseius vivax, Iphiseius degenerans;* (Coleoptera) *Stethorus gilvifrons, S. bifidus, S. utilis, S. punctillum;* (Neuroptera) *Chrysopa carnea, Oligota oviformis;* (Thysanoptera) *Scolothrips sexmaculatus.* Moreover, the fungus *Entomophthora fresenii* also attacks *T. urticae.*

Control: Biological or integrated control programmes have not been reported so far.
The following specific acaricides are recommended: binapacryl, chinomethionate, chlorphenamidin, dicofol, tetradifon. In cotton, fruit or vegetables, insecticides with acaricidal properties are often incorporated in spray-programmes: azinphosethyl, dimethoate, omethoate, demeton, monocrotophos, triazophos.
In crops where mildew and spider mites occur at the same time, a spray program may include chinomethionat at a low dosage of 0.035 % c.i. with repeated treatments at 7–10d intervals. Resistance to some pesticides has been reported from some areas; the compounds concerned are mainly organophosphate insecticides and to a lesser extent dicofol and tetradifon.

Literature

GASSER, R. (1951): Zur Kenntnis der gemeinen Spinnmilbe *Tetranychus urticae* Koch. Mitt. Schweiz. Ent. Ges. **24,** 217–262.
SABA, F. (1975): Comperative studies of species forming two Tetranychid complexes in Marocco. Ann. Entomol. Soc. Am. **68,** 797–800.

Author: F. Saba

Panonychus citri (McGreg.) (Fig. 103 and plate 19a, b)

Synonyms: *Metatetranychus citri, Paratetranychus citri*

Common names: Citrus red mite; Rote Citrusspinnmilbe, Arañita roja de los cítricos.

Geographical distribution: North America, South America, parts of Asia, Africa and New Zealand. CIE Map no 192.

Host plants: The citrus tree is the favourite host. Peas, peach, apple, loquat and others are also known as host plants.

Symptoms: The pest produces white, speckled patches on leaves by extracting the chlorophyll. In heavy infestations leaves turn yellow and fall.

Economic importance: The mite is recognized to be one of the most serious pests of citrus. It is of particular importance in several major citrus producing countries, notably North America (central California), Japan and South Africa.

Morphology: The adult is oval and velvety red or purplish in colour with about 20 red bristles on the tubercles. The body length is 0.4–0.5 mm (♀), or 0.3 (♂). The egg is globular, 0.13–0.15 mm in diameter and light red in colour, with a slender mast on the top (Fig. 103).

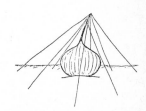

Similarities to other pests: The species resembles the European red mite, *Panonychus ulmi,* from which it is distinguished by its red tubercles.

Fig. 103. Egg of *Panonychus citri* (after Ehara)

Life cycle and ecology: The species can occur at all seasons throughout most tropical and temperate zones. In the lower temperature zones, however, dormant forms appear in the cold season and the winter is spent in this stage. In citrus growing areas, the mite produces more than 10 generations each year. One generation may be completed in 3 to 5 weeks. The mite usually develops best on (1) lemons, (2) navel oranges, and then (3) Valencia oranges and grapefruit. The optimum conditions are considered to be: 25–26 °C and 60–75 % R. H.

Development period of female mite (in days) (after Shinkaji)

Temperature	Larva	Protonymph	Deutonymph	Preoviposition	Total
20 °C	3.6	3.3	3.9	3.4	14.2
22	3.7	2.9	3.0	2.6	11.8
25	2.7	2.3	2.4	2.0	9.4
28	2.1	2.2	1.9	2.1	8.3
30	2.1	2.1	1.4	1.3	7.0
32	1.6	1.1	1.4	1.3	5.7

Natural enemies: Some predators such as lady beetles (Coccinellidae) and predacious mites (Phytoseiidae) are known to be important.

Control:

Chemical control. Control using acaricides or insecticides is considered as the most important and useful method. As acaricides, petroleum oil may control not only the mites but also scale insects injurious to citrus trees. Some other acaricides, e. g. DCPM (Neotran), Aramite, tetradifon (Tedion), dicofol (Kelthane), chlorophenamidine (Galecron), demeton, dimethoate, are also available for mite control.

Resistance. Mite resistance to certain acaricides has been reported chiefly in North America and Japan. Main examples of acaricides or insecticides to which mite resistance has developed are as follows: tetradifon, chlorfenson (Ovotran), DCPM (Neotran), parathion, demeton, phenkapton, dimethoate and some other organic phosphorus chemicals. In addition, some notes on resistance to dicofol, binapacryl (Acricid) and benzomate have also been published.

Literature

EBELING, W. (1959): Subtropical fruit pests. Univ. of California, 435 pp.
FUKUDA, J. (1961): Kaju-Gaichu-Hen (Textbook of Insect Pests injurious to Fruit Trees) (In Japanese). Tokyo.
JEPPSON, L. R., & G. E. CARMAN (1960): Citrus insects and mites. Ann. Rev. Ent. **5**, p. 353–378.
JEPPSON, L. R., H. H. KEIFER & E. W. BAKER (1975): Mites Injurious to Economic Plants. Univ. California Press. 614 pp.

Author: Ken'ichi Nomura

Family: Tenuipalpidae (= Phytoptipalpidae)

Brevipalpus phoenicis (Geijsk.) (Fig. 104)

Synonyms: *Tenuipalpus phoenicis, Brevipalpus yothersi, B. papayensis, B. pseudocuneatus*

Common name: False spider mite.

Geographical distribution: This mite is widely distributed in tropical and subtropical zones. It has been recorded from Trinidad, Florida, Cuba, Hawaii, Malaysia, Sri Lanka, India, Zaire, Kenya, Sudan, Egypt and other parts of North Africa.

Host plants: Citrus, guava, quince, peach, grape, papaya, date palm, sweet potato, *Hibiscus, Duranta, Buddleia* and *Acalypha* sp.

Symptoms of damage and economic importance: *B. phoenicis* infests leaves, twigs, buds and fruits. It prefers the lower leaf surface around the midrib or any places which are protected such as around the pedicel and floral apex of citrus fruits. By sucking the plant sap, the injured areas become pale then change to rusty brown. When infestation is heavy, the leaves become dry and fall off and brownish areas appear on the fruits of citrus.

Morphology: Female. Body oval with a reddish appearance, about 260 μ long and 125 μ wide. Rostrum surpasses middle of femur I, tarsus II with two sensory rods, femora I and II each with a dorsal broadly serrate seta. Propodosoma with three pairs of relatively long lanceolate serrate setae. Hysterosoma with five pairs of dorsolateral lanceolate serrate setae, decreasing in length posteriorly and with three pairs of dorsocentrals. A pair of humerals occurs between propodosoma and hysterosoma.
Male. Body triangular, smaller than female and about 230 μ long and 120 μ wide. It resembles the female in dorsal chaetotaxy.

Life cycle and ecology: After hatching, the mite passes through moving and quiescent larva, protonymph and deutonymph before reaching the adult stage.
This species is thelytokous, nevertheless males are rarely found and mating sometimes occurs. Reddish elliptical eggs are laid singly on the lower leaf surface around the midrib or in concave areas of fruits. The female deposits an average of 12 eggs in winter and 17 eggs in summer, but the numbers range from 3 to 35 eggs. Under the natural climatic conditions of Egypt, when the average temperature ranges from 14 °C in winter to 28 °C in summer, ten generations may develop during a year. Incubation, immature stages and the development period for one generation (from egg to egg) last for an average of 6, 11 and 20 days in summer and 25, 63 and 96 days in winter, re-

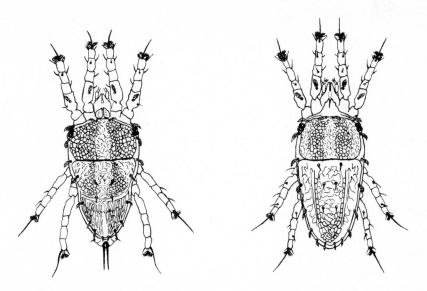

Fig. 104.   *Brevipalpus phoenicis.* Left: male; right: female (dorsal view) (drawings M. A. Zaher)

spectively. About five generations occur during the four hot months (May–August) at an average temperature of 26–28 °C. The longest generation lasts for about 14 weeks during the cold months from mid November to mid February. No diapause occurs during winter.

Natural enemies: Predacious mites such as the phytoseiids *Amblyseius gossipi* and *Typhlodromus pyri,* the stigmaeid *Agistemus exsertus* and cheyletid *Cheletogenes ornatus* have been noticed to feed on different stages of this acarine pest.

Control measures: Chemical control may be carried out by spraying of plants with acaricides such as dicofol, chlordimeform, monocrotophos, formothion and phosalone, though dicofol gives the best and most persistent effects. Therefore, it is advisable to spray infested plants with dicofol 18.5 % E. C. or dicofol SE.C. at the rate of 0.2 % during the rise of the mite population before reaching an economically serious injury level. Sprays can be repeated two or three times at three weeks intervals to suppress the population.

Literature

BAKER, E. W. & A. E. PRITCHARD (1960): The tetranychoid mites of Africa. Hilgardia **2**, 455–574.
ZAHER, M. A., A. K. WAFA & A. A. YOUSEF (1970): Biology of *Brevipalpus phoenicis* (Geijskes) in Egypt (Acarina – Tenuipalpidae). Bull. Soc. ent. Egypte **54**, 177–183.

Author: M. A. Zaher

Family: Eriophyidae

Eriophyes sheldoni Ewing (Fig. 105)

Synonym: *Aceria sheldoni*

Common names: Citrus bud mite; Citrusknospenmilbe; Acarien du bourgeon des citrus.

Geographical distribution: The citrus bud mite is found throughout most of the citrus belt, which extends around the world following the equator and spreading to approximately 35 °N to 35 °S lat. The mite has been recorded from the USA, especially in California and Florida; from around the Mediterranean areas: Algeria, Cyprus, Egypt, Greece, Iran, Israel, Italy, Lebanon, Morocco, Portugal, Spain, Syria, Tunisia, Turkey, U.S.S.R., Yugoslavia; and from the southern hemisphere: Australia, Central and South Africa, and Southern Rhodesia. CIE Map no 127.

Host plants: The mite prefers all lemon varieties *(Citrus limon),* citron *(C. medica),* sweet lemon *(C. limetta),* grapefruit *(C. paradisi)* pummelo *(C. grandis),* all varieties of sweet orange *(C. sinensis),* lime (*C. aurantifolia*), trifoliate orange (*Poncirus trifoliata*), mandarin (*C. reticulata*), bitter orange (*C. aurantium*), and kumquat (*Fortunella* spp.), in that order.

Symptoms: Both the injury incurred by the mite, and its salivary secretion during the feeding process, subsequently results in different forms of damage, such as browning or complete destruction of the bud bracts, deformation of the flowers, fruits, leaves and twigs, and even malformation of the entire tree.

Economic importance: If the buds destroyed by the mite are generative, there is a decrease in the fruit yield; if vegetative, the infested tree twigs and branches are underdeveloped.

Fig. 105. Shoots of Jaffa orange, attacked and malformed by *Aceria sheldoni* (phot. M. Sternlicht)

Morphology: The mite is minute, 110–180 μ long, 27–42 μ wide, worm-like, whitish-yellow to orange in color. Two pairs of legs with a 5-rayed featherclaw. Abdomen with 65–70, 2 μ wide microtuberculated, rings. A second variety of the citrus bud mite first described from Orange County (California), differs slightly from the common species; it is known also from the Upper Jordan Valley, on grapefruit trees.

Life cycle: The mite generation from egg to egg is completed within 7–10 days on buds and within 13–19 days on fruits, at 24–25 °C. Incubation of the egg lasts 3–5 days. The highest proportion of egg hatching (74 %) occurs at 25 °C and the lowest (1.9 %) at 38 °C. The threshold for embryonic development is 9 °C. Newly laid eggs are spherical, 20–30 μ in diameter, but after 1–2 days become elliptical, 35–65 μ long and 25–40 μ wide following imbibition of water from their surroundings. The postembryonic stages of this mite consist of the larva, nymphochrysalis, nymph, imagochrysalis and adult. The nymphochrysalis and imagochrysalis are resting stages, while the others are active stages. The threshold for postembryonic development from larva to adult is 12.5 °C. The mite is arrhenotokous, the unfertilized female produces eggs parthenogenetically, all of them hatching into males. Mature males, 1–5 days old, deposit spermatophores; the virgin females are attracted by the pheromone, move towards the spermatophores; and engulf the sperm mass from the spermatophore's head into their genital aperture. Fertilized females lay eggs of both sexes, the proportion of males varying between 7 % and 25 %. The proportion of males is higher during spring when the mites are migrating from old to new buds and shoots; it remains high with increasing plant growth and drops in winter.

Ecology: The monthly fluctuation in mite populations in untreated groves is similar in all citrus varieties. The population trend for each variety is very conspicuous; the peaks almost always occur between spring and summer, and the troughs in winter. There are several biotic and abiotic factors which influence these fluctuations: a) climatic conditions: seasonal low temperatures of 6–8 °C or less, cause a drop in the population; low relative humidity (below 30 % RH) combined with a hot (39 °C) wind lasting for one or more hours have a lethal effect on the mite and its reproduction; b) plant growth cycles, especially the new growth of most citrus varieties during early spring and early autumn, are accompanied by mite reproduction, an increase in population, the mites' dispersion and subsequent bud infestation by them; c) predators.

Natural enemies: Thripids, Coccinellids, and Ptinids, and predacious mites of the Phytoseiid, Stigmaeid, Eupelopsid and Cheyletid families have been recorded.

Control: The natural enemies bring about good control by diminishing the citrus bud mite populations throughout the year but especially during spring, early summer and early autumn.
The presence of mites in buds may be recognised superficially by the occurrence of deformation in the new tree growth. More specifically it can be recognised by collecting a number of 5–10 cm long twigs from several (6–10) trees, dissecting the terminal buds under a stereomicroscope, and examining for possible infestation.
In order to implement integrated control of this pest, the number of sprays of pesticides each year should be the minimum and selective, so as not to harm the beneficial arthropods. The use of pe-

sticides can be minimized if we take into account that almost all the insecticides commonly used in citrus groves, such as oils, chlorinated hydrocarbons, and phosphorous esters, are also very good acaricides. Hence, a spray applied against an insect pest automatically excludes the need for a separate spray against the citrus bud mite. However, if a separate miticide treatment is needed to control the citrus bud mite, it must be selective and, as far as possible, harmless to the predacious mites. Chemical applications should be made in spring, at the beginning of the mite population increase, and in autumn, before and during the natural population decrease. Application at other times is to be avoided, because of (a) the rapid repopulation of mites (7–10 days per generation) during summer, (b) the comparatively low persistence of the chemicals – which decompose in warm and dry weather, and (c) the low mite population during winter, when the remaining mites are hidden deep beneath the bud bracts – where the chemicals cannot penetrate. The chemicals can be applied from the ground at a high volume (with a power sprayer, at a pressure of 400–600 lb/sq in) when each tree, approx. 8–15 years old, is drenched with 15–20 l of liquid; at a medium volume of about 300 l/1000 m^2 (with a "Speadet" sprayer); or at low volume of 40–70 l/1000 m^2 (with a "Conomist" "RSN"); or from the air. For controlling the citrus bud mite, one application at low-volume is inferior to one at high volume, and two repeated low-volume applications, at an interval of 30–75 days, are superior to one high-volume application.

Literature

BOYCE, A. M., & R. B. KORSMEIER (1941): The citrus bud mite *Eriophyes sheldoni* Ewing. J. econ. Ent. **34**, 745–756.
STERNLICHT, M. (1969): Further trials in the control of the citrus bud mite *Aceria sheldoni* (Ewing) (Eriophydae, Acarina). Z. angew. Ent. **64**, 137–151.
STERNLICHT, M. (1969): A study of fluctuation in the citrus bud mite population. Ann. Zool. Ecol. anim. **1**, 127–147.
STERNLICHT, M. (1970): Contribution to the biology of the citrus bud mite, *Aceria sheldoni* (Ewing) (Acarina: Eriophyidae). Ann. appl. Biol. **65**, 221–230.
TOUZEAU, J. (1960): Un danger pour l'agrumiculture tunisienne: L'acarien du bourgeon des citrus. Tunis agric. **4** et **5**, 59–68, 70–76.

Author: M. Sternlicht

Phyllocoptruta oleivora (Ashm.)

Common names: Citrus rust mite; Citrusgallmilbe.

Geographical distribution: Europe: Italy, Yugoslavia. Asia: China, Japan, Philippines, Vietnam, India, Middle East, Cyprus, Iran. U.S.S.R.: Black Sea coast. Africa: Most countries south of the Sahara. North America: California, Texas, Florida, Arizona. Latin America: Mexico, Guatemala, West Indies, Argentine, Brazil, Columbia, Ecuador, Peru, Uruguay, Venezuela. Australia: Cook Is., Fiji, Hawaii. CIE map no 78.

Host plants: Citrus: lemon, lime, citron, grapefruit, orange, sour orange, tangerine, *Swinglea glutinosa, Fortunella* spp.

Symptoms: Fruits, leaves and green twigs are attacked. Mites pierce, wound and kill epidermal cells of the host plant. In orange, grapefruit and mandarin fruits the affected areas become rustlike; in lemons, they turn silvery. The fruit surface becomes russetted, rough and scaly; peels of young fruits lose their elasticity and shrivel. Darkish spots appear on the leaves which lose their gloss and curl up a little. The lower leaf surface later becomes rust-like. Dark spots also appear on infested green twigs.

Economic importance: The citrus rust mite is considered to be a major pest of citrus, as it may affect 70–100 % of the fruits. Leaves and green twigs may also be severely affected.

Morphology: The citrus rust mite is of a phyllocoptine body aspect, with 31 tergites and 58 sternites. Dorsal shield setae are short and do not point backwards over ringed opisthosoma, featherclaw is 5-rayed.

Similarities to other pests: The citrus rust mite can be confused only with the pink citrus rust mite, *Aculus pelekassi,* as both have a phyllocoptine body. Despite its name, the pink citrus rust mite may be yellowish, just like the citrus rust mite. *A. pelekassi* may, however, be separated from *P. oleivora* by having dorsal shield setae which point backwards over ringed opisthosoma, and by having a 4-rayed featherclaw.

Life cycle: The citrus rust mite lives on citrus the whole year round. Its average fecundity is 8–11 eggs/female. The egg is followed by three postembryonal stages: larva, one nymph and adults. During summer the entire cycle may take as little as 1 week, but in winter 6–10 weeks may be required. There is no diapause. Reproduction is by arrhenotoky, females being inseminated by spermatophores. Males produce 16–30 spermatophores daily.

Ecology: Optimal temperatures are 24–25 °C, the lower temperature threshold being 9 °C. The citrus rust mite is rather resistant to freezing temperatures and requires high humidities in order to survive and develop. On the other hand, the mite is quite susceptible to warm and dry winds. Consequently its populations peak during autumn and winter and decline in the summer.

Natural enemies: Several phytoseiid mites and gall midge (Cecidomyiidae) larvae are known to prey on the citrus rust mite. Of more consequence is the fungus *Hirsutella thompsonii,* which appears to control some field populations of the mite in Florida, and has been employed there for control purposes.

Control:
Resistance of crops. Although some citrus varieties and species appear to be less susceptible to mite attack than others, none are actually resistant.
Biological control. The fungus *H. thompsonii* has been mass-produced in the laboratory and disseminated, as fragmented mycelia, in Florida orange groves. Mites then decreased within one week, the pest populations remaining low for 10–14 weeks after treatment.
Chemical control. Acaricides in common usage are: Sulfur (dust), zineb, maneb, chlorobenzilate, bromopropylate (Neoron) and quinomethionate.
Spraying schemes and prognoses. Numbers of mites per unit area of plant which constitute the economic threshold level differ according to citrus species and varieties, season and geographical area affected. Acaricides should often be applied as soon as pests are found on trees, due to the pest's rapid development and the fact that injury becomes evident only at a later date.
Resistance to pesticides. Some field resistance to zineb was reported from Florida, Cyprus and Israel. The exact nature of this apparent resistance is not yet determined.

Literature

AVIDOV, Z., & I. HARPAZ (1969): Plant Pests of Israel. Israel Universities Press, 549 pp.
DENMARK, H. A. (1963): Eriophyid mites found on Florida citrus. Florida Dept. Agr., Entomol. Circ. 17.
HOBZA, R. F., & L. R. JEPPSON (1974): A temperature and humidity study of citrus rust mite employing a constant humidity air-flow technique. Environ. Entomol. **3**, 813–823.
McCOY, C. W., A. G. SELHIME, R. F. KANAVEL & A. J. HILL (1971): Suppression of citrus rust mite populations with application of fragmented mycelia of *Hirsutella thompsonii.* J. Invert. Pathol. **17**, 270–276.
SWIRSKI, E., M. KEHAT, S. GRUENBERG, N. DORZIA & S. AMITAI (1967): Trials for the control of the citrus rust mite *(Phyllocoptruta oleivora* Ashm.). Israel. J. Agric. Res. **17**, 121–126.

Author: U. Gerson

Other injurious mites (Fig. 106):

Eutetranychus orientalis (Klein), Oriental spider mite (Orientalische Spinnmilbe). Occurs in North-, Central-, North East and East Africa as well as in the Near East. Attacks chiefly the upper surface of young citrus leaves, but also occurs on the leaves of papaya, okra, date palm, cotton, castor bean, eggplant and ornamentals such as frangipani. The closely related species *E. banksi* (McG.) is a pest of citrus in Central and South America.

Oligonychus afrasiaticus (McG.), Date spider mite (Dattelpalmenmilbe). Feeds on leaves and young fruit of date palms in N- and NE-Africa, as well as on the Arabian Peninsula and in Iran.

Oligonychus coffeae (Nietn.), Tea red spider mite (Rote Teemilbe). Widely distributed in Africa and Asia (CIE Map no 165). Attacks tea, coffee and other crops. Control in North India by complete defoliation of tea shrubs by hand in winter. Effective acaricides are tetradifon, dicofol, binapacryl and others.

Aceria spp.. Various species of this genus attack important fruit trees in some tropical countries. They include: *A. ficus* (Cotte) on fig (worldwide distribution), *A. mangiferae* Sayed on mango (India, Brazil etc.), *A. litchii* (Keif.) on litchi (Taiwan), *A. guerreronis* Keif. on coconut (South America, West Africa) (Fig. 106) and *A. oleae* Nal. on olive (mediterranean region). *A. ficus* can transmit fig mosaic virus, while *A. mangiferae* has been associated with "Mango malformation" disease of mango trees.

Fig. 106.   Damage of *Aceria guerreronis* on coconuts (phot. H. Schmutterer)

Aculus lycopersici (Massee) (= *Vasates lycopersici),* Tomato russet mite (Tomatenmilbe). Found in the mediterranean and Black Sea region, in South Africa, Sri Lanka, Australia, North America and Brazil (CIE Map no 164). Attacks all aerial parts of tomato, but also eggplants and potato. Chemical control by application of sulphur, chlorobenzilate or dicofol.

Calacarus carinatus (Green), Purple tea mite (Purpurmilbe). Attacks tea leaves in southern India. Chemical control with dicofol, chlorobenzilate or binapacryl. *Acaphylla theae* (Watt), the Pink mite (Rosafarbene Teegallmilbe) attacks tea in Taiwan.

Brevipalpus spp.. *B. californicus* (Banks) (= *B. australis*), the Scarlet tea mite (Scharlachrote Teemilbe), occurs in southern India and Sri Lanka, *B. obovatus* Donn. in Sri Lanka, Indonesia and Japan. Both species do also attack citrus, as well as many ornamentals and wild plants (CIE Map for *B. californicus*: no 107).

Polyphagotarsonemus latus (Banks) (= *Hemitarsonemus latus)*. Yellow tea mite, Broad mite (Gelbe Teemilbe, Breitmilbe). Very widely distributed in tropical and subtropical regions and can also exist in climatically suitable regions outside these zones (CIE Map no 191). Damages tea, citrus, cotton, jute, potato, sesame, castor bean, rubber etc. Chemical control by application of dicofol and other acaricides.

H. Sch.

Grasshoppers, Locusts, Crickets, Mole crickets; Heuschrecken, Grillen, Maulwurfsgrillen; Sauterelles (criquets), Sauteriaux, Grillons; Langostas, Langostas migratorias, Grillos, Chicharras

Order: Saltatoria

General features: The Orthoptera are medium sized to large insects of very different colouration, but green or brown species are the most common. In tropical savannah regions, they are often the dominating group of insects. Much damage is done on cultivated plants in these areas, particularly by swarming migratory locusts, but also by solitary species. With their powerful chewing-biting mouth parts they can devour soft, as well as harder plant portions.

The short-horned grasshoppers, which include the locusts, are by far the most important group of Orthoptera in the tropics. Among the crickets and mole crickets, which live predominantly in the soil, there are only a few pests attacking roots and other subterranean plant portions.

Owing to their incomplete (hemimetabolic) metamorphosis, the nymphs of Orthoptera live much like the adults.

H. Sch.

Superfamily: Acridoidea

Family: **Acrididae**[1] (Fig. 107 and plates 19 c, d and 20 a, b)

Common names: Grasshoppers and locusts; Feld- und Wanderheuschrecken; Sauterelles (Criquets) et Sauteriaux; Langostas, Langostas migratorias.

Introductionary note: Some 500 spp. of Acridoidea (other than species universally recognised as 'locusts') are recorded as agricultural pests. Pest species occur in a wide spectrum of subfamilies. Few tropical countries are without recorded grasshopper pest species. No generalisations are possible except that attack is usually not by one species but by a varied combination of species. The dominant species will vary from area to area, season to season and year to year.

Important species and their geographical distribution[2]**:** *Tropidacris* spp., *Tropinotus* spp., *Zoniopoda* spp., *Rhammatocerus* spp., *Scyllinops* spp., *Dichroplus* spp. – S. and C. America; *Oxya* spp., *Hieroglyphus* spp. – S. E. Asia; *Acorypha* spp., *Calliptamus* spp., *Aiolopus simulatrix* (Wlk.), *Hieroglyphus* spp. – India; *Austracris guttulosa* Wlk., *Chortoicetes terminifera* Wlk., *Oedalus senegalensis* (Krauss), *Cyrtacanthacris tatarica* (L.) – S. Arabia and S. Iran; *Zonocerus variegatus* (L.), *Z. elegans* (Thnb.), *Cataloipus* spp., *Eyprepocnemis* spp., *Amphiprosopia* spp., *Acorypha*

[1] Since we know more about the habits of Acridoidea it becomes impossible to make a scientific distinction between 'grasshoppers' and 'locusts'. All the Acrididae are grasshoppers in the sense of the English word. We may define the various types of grasshoppers as follows:
Locusts – usually large species, with marked migratory behaviour and very marked phase change both physiological, behavioural and morphological.
Swarming migratory grasshoppers – smaller species, showing some migration but with less marked phase change characteristics, these usually being behavioural and physiological rather than morphological.
Swarming grasshoppers – small to large species showing little or no long distance dispersal, with phase change characteristics, e. g. melanic colour, fewer instars in life cycle, gregarisation etc., weakly developed or absent.
[2] *Schistocerca gregaria* and *Lucusta migratoria* ssp. are considered in separate chapters.

spp., *Catantops axillaris* (Thnb.), *Orthochtha* spp., *Aiolopus* spp., *Oedalus* spp., *Hieroglyphus daganensis* Krauss, *Faureia* spp., *Pnorisa squalus* Stål, *Kraussaria angulifera* Krauss, *Cyrtacanthacris tatarica, C. aeruginosa* (Stoll) ssp., *Acanthacris ruficornis* (F.) – Africa (mainly S. of Sahara).

Host plants: Range of species attacked very wide. Damage usually involves defoliation, but attacking of grain in the milky stage is also common, e. g. millet by *Oedalus* spp. and Sorghum by *Aiolopus.* In lowland moist forest belts long lived cash crops like coffee and cocoa may be defoliated, e. g. by *Zonocerus* in Africa, while forestry of exotic conifers has recently suffered at the hands of lentulid and eumastacid grasshoppers in Malawi.

Symptoms: Damage caused by grasshoppers falls into various categories:
a) complete destruction of seedling plants, e. g. maize, sorghum; b) breakage of stems by nibbling. This may occur when large infestations are walking through unpalatable crops looking for food, e. g. graminivorous species in cotton; c) shaving of grain on the cob or seed head; d) breakage by weight of insects resting on plants.
A very noticeable feature of attack by species with limited mobility is the 'edge effect', e. g. in *Kraussaria* attacking ground nuts; *Cataloipus* spp. attacking maize. In such cases the crop is often adjacent to fallow or uncultivated natural plant associations (the shelter habitat) from which the insects emerge to feed each day. Such movement may be very clear and follow a diurnal routine involving return to roosts at night in the shelter habitat.

Economic importance: Difficult to assess because losses are often incurred by subsistence farmers and records are not kept with loss assessment in mind. Lossed due to *A. simulatrix* in East-Central Sudan on irrigated sorghum have been almost total over large areas. Loss is often on the scale cited under *Locusta* and causes considerable local if not widespread hardship.

Fig. 107.   Adult of *Zonocerus variegatus* (phot. H. Schmutterer)

Biology and ecology: Some species, e. g. *Chortoicetes, Orthochtha* and *Oedaleus* are specifically graminivorous. Others are specifically herbivorous, e. g. *Calliptamus* which has been known to eat only weeds in a wheat crop, leaving the wheat intact (indirectly therefore beneficial). Three major if rather arbitrary groupings of species may be observed:
a) Habitually mobile species, e. g. *O. senegalensis, A. simulatrix* (both distributed from Senegal to India); *C. axillaris* (Africa); *Anacridium* spp. (Africa and Near East); *Dichroplus* spp. (S. America); *Schistocerca* spp. (South America).
b) Species showing ability to move principally under dry season conditions or in exceptionally dry years. These forms therefore have long-winged or short-winged polymorphs in one or both sexes, e. g. *Hieroglyphus* (attacking rice), *Amphiprosopia* (attacking maize, sorghum, cotton etc. in Africa).
c) More or less immobile species, presumably highly tolerant of adverse conditions or feeding on wild plants favoured by dry conditions, or living in areas where conditions are always humid during the rainy season, e. g. *Poekilocerus* (a pyrgomorph) feeding on *Calotropis* – locally a problem on irrigated vegetables, e. g. in S. Arabia; *Cataloipus* spp. (on maize); *Plagiotriptus* spp. (C. & E. Africa) (on conifers); *Kraussaria* (on groundnuts).
Two major differences in biology are noteworthy: a) those only existing in the egg stage over the dry season – e. g. *O. senegalensis* (Oedipodinae); *K. angulifera* (Cyrtacanthacridinae); *Acorypha onerosa* (Calliptaminae); *E. noxius* (Eyprepocnemidinae). b) those capable of surviving the dry season in arrested sexual development as adults, e. g. *A. simulatrix* (Acridinae).

A good example of the first is *O. senegalensis.* Absent as adults during the dry season it shows prolonged staggered emergence during the course of the early rains. Consequently attack of sorghum on dry sandy soils starts with hopper damage to young plants. Adults show mass departure following the ITCZ (inter tropical convergence zone) and lay in sandy areas occupying the limits of the seasonal rainfall belt. Later generations follow the ITCZ southwards laying eggs in southern regions of the Sudan savannah belt. The second type is typified by *A. simulatrix,* which occupies the same tropical belt as *O. senegalensis* (Senegal to India). Unlike *Oedalus,* however, it attacks plants growing on clay soils. Adults hide down the cracks created by dry season shrinkage in heavy soils. With the first rains seedlings are attacked by the adults. Laying follows with rapid production of a first hopper generation and mobile adults. These follow the ITCZ northwards and produce one or two further generations. The exact migratory patterns of these species are still not understood.

Control: Chemicals effective against *Locusta* are those generally applicable here also (see p. 279). Hopper stages should be treated rather than adults.

If we examine the ecology of the species the highly mobile migratory forms must be treated like locusts. Since populations of sedentary species attacking crops usually originate in adjacent natural plant associations and since they walk into the crop for feeding even as adults, effective control might be achieved by clearing an open area between bush and crop, augmenting the effect of this unprotected open zone with persistent insecticide incorporated into a bran bait. Hoppers would be particularly likely to pick up poison as they walked through the barrier. This technique has not been tried on any scale and would involve a great deal of physical effort if done manually by individual farmers.

Literature

DIRSH, V. M. (1965): The African genera of Acridoidea. Cambridge. 1–579, 452 figs.
JOYCE, R. J. V. (1952): The ecology of grasshoppers in East Central Sudan. Anti Locust Bull. **11**, 99 pp., 34 figs.
LIEBERMANN, J. & R. SCHIUMA (1946): Las "Fucuras" más perjudiciales de nuestra agricultura y ganadería. Publ. Min. Ag. Argentina, B. **2** (7), 62 pp.
ROFFEY, et al. (in preparation): Annotated list of pest grasshoppers of tropical S. E. Asia. C.O.P.R. publication.
SJÖSTEDT, Y. (1921): Acridoidea Australia. Kungl. Svenska Vetensk. akad. Handl. **62** (3), 1–318, 18 pls., 18 figs.
WILLEMSE, C. (1955): Synopsis of the Acridoidea of the Indo-Malayan and adjacent regions (Insecta, Orthoptera) II. Acrididae, Catantopinae. Publ. nat. Genoots. in Limburg **8**, 1–225, figs.
WILLEMSE, C. (1957): Ibid. II. Acrididae, Catantopinae (part 2) Ibid. **10**, 227–500, 15 pls. index.

Author: N. D. Jago

Schistocerca gregaria (Forsk.)[1] (Fig. 108 and plate 20 c)

Common names: Desert locust; Wüstenheuschrecke; Criquet pèlerin.

Geographical distribution: Swarms of the Desert Locust have been recorded within a total area of 35 million square kilometers (Distribution Region) namely over one-fifth of the earth's surface, affecting 10 % of the world's population. Territories liable to invasion are Afar Essa, Afghanistan, Algeria, Armenia (USSR), Bahrein, Bangladesh, Burundi, Cameroon, Canary Islands, Cape Verde Islands, Central African Republic, Chad, Cyprus, Benin, Egypt, Ethiopia, Gambia, Ghana, Guinea, Ifni, India, Iran, Iraq, Israel, Ivory Coast, Jordan, Kenya, Kuwait, Lebanon, Libya, Madeira, Mali, Mauretania, Morocco, Nepal, Nigeria, Niger, Oman, Pakistan, Portugal,

[1]DIRSH (1974) considers *S. gregaria* now as a subspecies called *S. americana gregaria.*

Guinea-Bissao, Qatar, Rwanda, Saudi Arabia, Senegal, Sierre Leone, Socotra, Somali Republic, Spain, Spanish Sahara, Sudan, Syria, Tadzhikstan (USSR), Tanzania, Togo, Tunisia, Turkey, Turkmenistan (USSR), Uganda, United Arab Emirates, Voltaie Republic, Uzbekistan (USSR), the Yemen Republics, Zaire.

Host plants: Desert Locusts are polyphagous particularly when in swarms. Of the 50 most important crops, constituting over 98 % of the total area cultivated in the Distribution Region, all can be damaged by this species. These include Wheat, Barley, Maize, Sorghum, Pennisetum, Rice, Finger Millet (*Eleusine coracana*), Hungry Rice (*Digitaria exilis*), Teff (*Eragrostis abyssinica*), Oats, Small Millets (*Panicum & Echinochloa* spp.), Sugar Cane, Cassava, Potato, Sweet Potato (*Impomoea batatas*), Yam, Pulses (chick pea, cow pea, broad bean, lentils etc), Grape Vine, Citrus, Date Palm, Banana, Ensete (*Musa ensete*), Olive, Groundnuts, Linseed, Rape and Mustard, Sesame, Coffee, Tobacco and Cotton.

Symptoms: Damage includes complete destruction (e. g. young cereals, pulses etc), defoliation (e.g. citrus), selective destruction of milky grain, bark, fruit, flowers, seed growing points, mechanical damage by weight, and fouling by excreta.

Economic importance: An active Desert Locust adult eats each day its own weight in fresh vegetation. Swarms may consist of 50×10^6 individuals per km^2, each weighing about 2 gms, and invading swarms may cover 1000 km^2 or more. Thus, during the period of swarm invasion a territory may lose to locusts 100 000 tons of fresh vegetation daily. Such invasions tend to occur at times

Fig. 108.   Part of a large swarm of Desert locust over Hargeisa airport, Somalia in August 1960. Partly visible is one of the aircrafts which sprayed the swarm, killing some 20,000 tons of locusts (phot. A. J. Wood)

when crops and grazing pastures are present. Invading populations maintain high densities, so damage is concentrated and therefore devastating to those farms or areas attacked. Examples of losses to Desert Locusts include 7 million grape-vines (Libya 1944), 6000 tons of oranges (Guinea 1957), and 167 000 tons of grain (Ethiopia 1958), these having been reliably estimated. Of comparable importance, but so far not reliably measured, is loss, of grazing, particularly in ranching and nomad areas.

Analysis of sample records shows that about 8 % of damage records are of hoppers (immature stages), 69 % of immature adults and 23 % of mature swarms.

The economic importance of Desert Locusts in countries liable to invasion is compounded by the unpredictability, not of the chances of invasion which can be anticipated by a reliable international information service, but of the damage which invading swarms may cause or generate. This may be negligible or so catastrophic as to call for special famine relief measures. The scale of such catastrophes is such that even small probability of their occurrence causes Governments in the Invasion Region to allocate a priority to Desert Locust control sometimes second only to Defence (as in the Middle East during World War II).

Morphology: The Desert Locust is a polymorphic species and is commonly described existing as two distinct types, the extreme **gregarious** and **solitarious** phases, together with an unprecise **transiens** phase. There is evidence that the morphological differences between the phases reflects the previous history of the individual rather than its current behaviour. The extreme phases are commonly distinguished by the E/F ratio (E = lenght of elytra, F = lenght of femur). In gregaria form E/F ratios are 2.2–2.3 whilst in solitaria form E/F is about 2.0.

Similarities other pests: The Desert Locust has the distinction of being amongst the oldest of crop pests known to man, references to its depredations being found in the Bible and Koran and carved pictures in sixth dynasty tombs in Saqqara, Egypt. Other Acridids of similar size, distribution and feeding habits, and often locally more numerous, are not pests. The Desert Locust's economic status derives not only from its numbers, which are not exceptionally large in the realm of insects, but from the mobility and coherence of its populations. It is rare for gregarious Desert Locusts to breed less than 500 kilometers from their birthplace and populations may traverse thousands of kilometers during the long life of the adult ($2^1/_2$–5 months). Solitary living Desert Locusts have similar longevity and are probably equally mobile. Other pest species which are strong flyers and make use of similar wind transport systems, because of their shorter adult life, are less able to exploit the range of breeding opportunities available to the Desert Locust over its Distribution Region. Thus the extent and regularity of seasonal movements of Desert Locust populations from, for example, spring breeding in Saudi Arabia, to summer breeding in a belt across the desert areas of Africa south of the Sahara from Sudan to Mauritania, to winter breeding along the north African littoral from Algeria to Libya are, as far as is known, unparalled by other insect pest species. This mobility also results in some countries remaining free from Desert Locust swarms for many consecutive years. When swarms are present in only a few or no countries Desert Locusts are said to be in Recession. When large numbers of countries are invaded there is said to be a Desert Locust Outbreak or Plague.

Unlike other Locusts, such as *Locusta migratoria migratoriodes* and *Nomadacris septemfasciata* which, during periods of plague recession, appear to have restricted and well defined permanent breeding areas, where phase change from solitaria to gregaria can regularly occur (Outbreak Centres), the Desert Locust can become behaviourly, if not morphometrically, gregarious as a result of even short duration contacts with its fellows and this appears to occur at least equally as a result of concentration of airborne adults by windfields as by the habits of hoppers in response to patterns of vegetation. No permanent localised outbreak areas of Desert Locusts have been discovered nor does it seem necessary to postulate their existence.

A further characteristic of Desert Locusts in which they differ from most pests but which they share with other locusts is the synchrony with which adults of high density populations become sexually mature and with which their progeny complete their development. This synchronisation of development is possibly the basis of gregariousness and is certainly a major cause of the economic status of the species.

Life cycle: The life cycle comprises 3 stages, egg, hopper (with five instars) and adult. Eggs are laid in moist soil, preferably sand, and are bound together with a secretion to form a pod which may contain 20–120 eggs. The pod is 3–4 cm long and is placed so that the bottom is about 10 cm below the soil surface. The pod is closed by a foam plug. Though females in the laboratory may lay an average of 11 pods, the first oviposition by swarms in the field can be expected to account for about half the progeny that survive. Eggs need to absorb about their own weight of water for development. This may be taken in during the first five days, or if not all available at once, in two periods of availability. There is no diapause and eggs cannot survive dessication lasting several weeks. Under warm conditions incubation may be completed in as little as 10 days, but may be prolonged to 70 days in the cold winters of North Africa or the Middle East. Egg pod densities may exceed 50 000/ha, egg fields thus being capable of generating 10 million hoppers per hectare.

The dense populations generated by these egg-fields form marching bands of hoppers which pass through five instars typically as follows:

1st instar – 5 days, 2nd instar – 6days, 3rd instar – 7 days,
4th instar 8 days, 5th instar – 12 days. Total: 38 days.

During this development hoppers increase in size from 7 mm in length weighing 30–40 mg in the first instar to 50 mm in length weighing 1000–1200 mg in the fifth instar. Wing buds are easily recognised from the third instar.

Hopper bands commonly retain their cohesion though numerical density decreases as the hoppers grow larger from about 800/m^2 in the first instar to about 25/m^2 in the fifth. Hopper bands are classified as small (0.10 ha), medium (3.5 ha), large (15 ha), very large (70 ha), (in brackets being recorded mean sizes for these categories as classified in standard field report forms). During daytime they march and at night they roost. Their direction of march is often downwind, and during the course of their life they may travel over 10 km. from their birthplace. Flowers and seeds of grasses and herbs are often eaten in preference to leaves and bark. Half the daily food intake is during marching.

Newly fledged adults do not fly for several hours and young fledglings remain in the area where they were born for 5–7 days whilst their wing musculature is strengthening, showing a growing tendency for gregarious behaviour and spontaneous flight. Swarms of Desert Locusts seem rarely to be produced within the area where they developed as hoppers and are first recorded many kilometers downwind some weeks after fledging, often in a different country.

Sexually immature adults are capable of 20 hours continuous flight using their fat body as fuel, this being replaced during daily feeding. Despite differences in orientation between groups of locusts within swarms, particularly near the ground, swarm displacement is downwind normally at less than wind-speed, such populations travelling typically 50–100 km. per day in steady wind conditions. Single sustained flights across the sea of up to 2500 km have been recorded.

The downwind displacement of swarms, which usually results in transporting populations some thousands of kilometers from their birthplace, tends to lead to the accumulation of Desert Locusts in zones of low level wind convergence, which are areas where the first requirement for rain is present – namely, rising air. Since fresh vegetation and moist soil for development are essential for survival of the species, downwind displacement of Desert Locust populations may be considered as an adaptive behaviour established because of its survival value to the species.

Natural enemies: One Hymenopteran, 9 Dipteran and 5 Coleopteran egg predators have been recorded amongst which probably *Systoechus* spp. (Bombyliidae) is probably the most important. Hoppers are eaten by many general insect predators and almost all birds, reptiles and mammals (including lions and man) have been recorded feeding on hoppers and adults. The combined effect of parasites, predators and weather which favours fungal, virus, bacterial and protozoan pathogens have often been shown to have been responsible for the elimination of small populations, particularly in areas such as the Red Sea littoral, where frequency of breeding is high. More often the size of a population immigrant to an area is sufficient to overwhelm any local concentrations of parasites and predators.

Control: Locusts have been killed in many ways including trapping in trenches, poisoning with baits, by insecticidal dusts and sprays. A valuable body of accurate data are available on the absolute toxicity of insecticides to the species. Amongst these dieldrin, diazinon, and gamma BHC with LD 50 s (applied to the abdomen as a single drop) of 6–9 μg/g have proved particularly useful as sprays applied at ultra-low-volume rates from aircraft and the ground to flying and settled swarms (diazinon, dieldrin and gamma BHC) or to vegetation as a stomach poison for killing hoppers (dieldrin). The availability of suitable insecticides satisfies the first requirement of control. Because of the large numbers constituting swarms, and their great mobility, cohesion and density, protection of crops cannot be achieved after crops are invaded. Normal crop spraying procedures are therefore valueless. Crop protection must be directed towards preventing the development of potentially damaging numbers particularly in areas which are the source of swarms which threaten crops. This requirement has led to the study of swarm movements from the Breeding Region, which is largely in deserts or areas of light seasonal rain (usually less than 350 mm) to the rest of the Invasion Region where crops are located (frequently higher rainfall areas). It is rare for the source of a damaging population to be located in the same country as the threatened crops, so that international co-operation is the second requirement for successful Desert Locust control.

The third requirement is measurement of the scale of the required control operation. It is necessary to know the parts of the Breeding Region where infestations are currently present and the threat which these represent to crop areas. This information, provided by survey, both from the ground and air, by national and international teams, is transmitted to Regional Centres for mapping and analysis, these having now taken over the responsibility for the former Desert Locust Information Service located in London.

The fourth requirement is the availability of methods of applying insecticides which match the scale of the problem. The part of the Breeding Region located in Sudan, for example, occupies 300,000 km^2 and study of the distribution of hopper bands between 1950–1958 showed that in order to locate 95 % of those recorded it was necessary to search 200,000 km^2 in the 5 weeks of each year when infestations were present. Survey and control have been inadequately conducted in the past by ground-based teams, but aerial survey can be so conducted that a search rate of up to 2500 km^2 per day per aircraft can be achieved. The theory of barrier spraying is constructed using knowledge of the LD 50 (as a stomach poison) of a persistent and cumulative insecticide, the rate of food intake of marching hopper bands and the expected velocity of displacement, to calculate the amount of active ingredient to be placed on the food plants to enable the hopper to accumulate a toxic dose during its feeding over a number of days. It has been found that the required contamination can be achieved by an application rate of about 100 ml of 20 % dieldrin per ha applied by drift spraying over a swath of a least 150 m as spray barriers, successive lines being separated by 3–5 km. In this way a single aircraft can treat about 2000 km^2 infested area per day with an expenditure of 3000 litres of insecticide, giving a mean dosage of less than 5 gm active ingredient per hectare.

The numbers of locusts in swarms also illustrate the potential scale of the control problem. The swarms which invaded the Somali Republic in 1960 were estimated to be composed of 10^{11} locusts weighing nearly 200,000 tons, half this invasion in the form of daily sightings of swarms covering more than 300 km^2, thus consisting of more than 30 000 tons of live insects. Thus the control force had to be capable of treating at least a 30,000 ha of moving target per day, and to be able to disperse over it an adequate number of toxic doses. A great part of this population was in fact destroyed by the aerial application of 200,000 litres of insecticide concentrate containing about 2×10^{12} toxic doses, providing a mean efficiency of use of insecticide of about 3 % (that is the estimated number of locust corpses which was 3 % of the number of toxic doses applied).

The Desert Locust control is notable as being a prime example of an attempt to manage the numbers comprising an insect population. Through their great mobility an event affecting Desert Locust numbers in any part of the Distribution Region can affect any other part after one or two generations. Information is thus needed on day-to-day incidence of populations throughout the Distribution Region. This need defines the goal of Synoptic Survey to which the national and international survey teams contribute. The considerable international co-operation which is necessary to achieve these first steps towards Synoptic Survey have been provided by the Food & Agricultural Organisation of the United Nations in Rome, who co-ordinate the efforts in this field of some 40 countries constituting the Distribution Region, and have grouped them into Regional Organisations for the East, Middle East, Eastern Africa, North Africa and West African Regions, operating under its auspices.

Through Synoptic Survey, the analyses of which are disseminated as Forecasts, National and Regional control organisations can judge the scale of operation they must plan and select appropriate tactics to match this scale. Suitable tactics available are as follows:

Directed against hoppers:
  Poison bait distributed by hand or mechanical means (modified duster), ahead of marching bands. Typically the bait contains 0.1 % gamma BHC mixed with wheat bran.
  Vegetation spraying: applying by drift spraying, normally through a vehicle exhaust atomiser, very small quantities of a special formulation of insecticide, normally 20 % dieldrin, atomised to fine droplets which are selectively collected by vegetation on which the hoppers feed. Vegetation spraying may be used either against individual targets (hopper bands) or for barrier spraying where spray lines are placed across areas known to be infested in such a way that marching bands are likely to cross and feed in them. Barrier spraying can also be conducted using aircraft.

Directed against adults:
  Air-to-ground spraying: insecticide concentrates are aimed at locusts settled on trees and bushes. Economy dictates the use of droplets and spraying techniques which will provide maximum collection of the poison by locusts and the vegetation on which they feed over the widest possible swath. Drift spraying is normally employed and rotary atomisers found in practice to provide better control of the droplet spectrum than boom and nozzle.
  Air-to-air spraying: insecticide concentrates are sprayed into flying swarms. The droplet range selected must be able to penetrate the depth of the swarm but also remain airborne sufficiently long to provide a good chance of flying locusts collecting a toxic dose. Flying locusts are much more efficient droplet collectors than settled locusts. Since swarms move downwind at a speed less than the wind it is usually better to concentrate application to the densest sections of the swarms on the upwind edge.

Literature

FAO publications: Nos 1956/11, 1959/4, 1959/5 (Reports of FAO Panels of Experts on Desert Locust Control). – United Nations Special Fund Desert Locust Project. A series of reports published by FAO, Rome.
Anti-Locust Research Centre Reports (now Centre for Overseas Pest Research): The Locust Handbook: COPR, London. – Anti-Locust Memoirs nos 1 (Z. WALOFF, 1946), 3 (U. DONNELLY, 1947), 4 (D. E. DAVIES, 1952), 5 (J. FORTESCUE-FOULKES, 1953), 7 (C. R. RAINEY, 1963), 8 (Z. WALOFF, 1966), 10 (F. T. BULLEN, 1969). – Anti-Locust Bulletins Nos 9 (Z. WALOFF & R. C. RAINEY, 1951), 16 (V. D. DIRSH, 1953), 25 (P. E. ELLIS & C. ASHALL, 1957), 30 (W. J. STOWER, C. B. POPOV & D. J. GREATHEAD, 1958), 31 (C. B. POPOV, 1958), 32 (W. J. STOWER, 1959), 38 (C. ASHALL & P. E. ELLIS, 1962), 49 (R. D. MacCUAIG & M. N. D. B. YEATES, 1972), 50 (L. V. BENNET & P. M. SYMMONS, 1972). – Proceedings of the International Study Conference on the current and future problems of Acridology. London, July 1970.
WMO Publications: Technical Note no 54 (C. R. RAINEY, 1963), No 69 (1965). Other publications (in journals):0
COURSHEE, R. J. (1959): Drift spraying for vegetation baiting. Bull. ent. Res. **50**, 355–370.
JOYCE, R. J. V. (1962): Report of the Desert Locust Survey 1955–1961. EACSO, Nairobi, Kenya.
MacCUAIG, R. D. (1960): The toxicity of some insecticides to fifth instar nymphs of the Desert Locust. Ann. appl. Biol. **48**, 323–335.
MacCUAIG, R. D. (1962): The toxicity of some insecticidal sprays to adult locusts. Bull. ent. Res. **53** (3), 597–608.

RAINEY, R. C. (1951): Weather and the movements of locust swarms: a new hypothesis. Nature, London, **168,** 1057–1060.

RAINEY, R. C. (1958): The use of insecticides against the Desert Locust. J. Sci. Fd. Agric. **9,** 677–692.

SAYER, H. J. (1959): An ultra-low-volume spraying technique for the control of the Desert Locust. Bull. ent. Res. **50,** 371–386.

SAYER, H. J. (1962): The Desert Locust and tropical convergence. Nature, London, **194,** 330–336.

UVAROV, B. P. (1966): Grasshoppers and locusts. A handbook of general acridology. Volume I: Anatomy, physiology, development, phase polymorphism, introduction to taxonomy. Published for Anti-Locust Research Centre. Cambridge University Press.

Author: R.J.V. Joyce

Locusta migratoria ssp. (Plate 20 d)

Important subspecies and their geographical distribution: *L. migratoria migratorioides* (R. & F.) – Sahelian and Sudan savannah belt of Africa south of the Sahara, with extension into Uganda; *L. migratoria capito* (Saus.) – Malagasy Republic; *L. migratoria manilensis* (Mey.) – Tropical S. E. Asia including Philippines and S. China, Thailand and N. Borneo; *L. migratoria burmana* Ramme – Burma, Tibet, highlands of New Guinea (Farrow in litt.).

Populations peripheral to these centres, in Arabia, India, southern Africa and Australia certainly differ behaviourally and morphometrically from the named subspecies, but have not yet been defined and named themselves.

Common names: *L. m. migratorioides:* African migratory locust, Afrikanische Wanderheuschrecke, Criquet migrateur africain; *L. m. capito:* Malagassische Wanderheuschrecke; *L. m. manilensis:* Oriental migratory locust, Orientalische Wanderheuschrecke; *L. m. burmana:* Burmesische Wanderheuschrecke.

Host plants: Highly adaptable. Early rains breeding may occur on annual grasses, later breeding being among tall perennial grasses. Many different species are eaten, e. g. genera *Echinochloa, Andropogon, Chloris, Sporobolus, Sorghum, Heteropogon, Aristida, Hyparrhenia, Cynodon,* being representative. Fecundity and fertility may be dependent on the growth stage and type of predominant grass species consumed.

Habits change over a period of years. Thus the equivalent generation in subsequent years may be forced to occupy grass associations in different ecological zones. Cultivated crops attacked are all graminaceous species, e. g. maize, millet, sorghum, sugar cane, wheat, and rice. Extensive rice cultivation in lowland areas may, however, discourage the insects by limiting oviposition sites.

Symptoms: Principal damage is by defoliation though nibbling may cause lodging in plants, especially seedlings. Plants are often eaten down to the midrib. Attacks are often made by mobile populations which move so rapidly that inspection will be made after the insects have departed. In such cases the typical elongated faeces often form a matte on the ground among the defoliated plants. Damage is most severe on young plants, since older plants may 'tiller' and produce a crop of reduced size rather than die.

Economic importance: Attacks vary from local to widespread (as in the great plague years of 1930's to 1940's). Localised attacks may adversely affect pasture as well as loss to crops. "A swarm covering an area of 100 hectares may weigh 1000 tons (counting 1000 insects to the square meter) and consume 1000 tons of vegetation each day". The swarm may attack for 90 days. Estimates of the rice and sugar cane lost in an area of Madagascar over an area of 35,000 hectares in financial terms amounted from 1948–1951 to 510 million CFA.

Loss may be most severe at the end of the rainy season when the second sowings are sometimes made on suitable soils. At such time natural wild grass species may be almost totally lacking, while numbers of the insect in the late hoppers stages may be at a maximum after the succession of rainy season breedings. Recent outbreaks of a local nature, south of lake Chad in Africa, are estimated to have invaded 60 000 hectares in the late rains/early dry season period. Resurgence of high population levels can take place very quickly and seems to be largely dictated by the favourable temporal spacing and quantity of the rainfall. Indeed, in Madagascar, research has shown that in a system lacking the complication of dry season inundation, outbreaks can be predicted by a knowledge of the 'optimum pluviometric' conditions for the species.

Morphology: Hoppers. Young hatchlings are always brown in colour. When egg pods are laid in the ground at high density the crowding of the young insects induces a dramatic colour change which shows up in the second instar. These 'gregarious' forms become dark brown with black dorsal pigment and group or march together to form characteristic hopper bands. Under low density oviposition, with expanding supplies of green grass, e. g. at the onset of rains, hoppers disperse and rapidly develop brown, green, grey or even uniformly black colour forms. In general green forms predominate in these 'solitarious' hoppers when high humidities are encountered. Solitarious hoppers have a conspicuously high pronotal crest. If conditions favour continued crowding after the first instar, the hoppers retain the red-brown colour and black dorsal band. Such conditions arise when enormous populations have laid at any time of year, or after a slightly above average rainy season population encounters contracting habitats so often characteristic of the dry season.

Adults. Unlike other large locusts of the same size, *Locusta* adults have no prosternal tubercle between the bases of the front legs. In solitarious and gregarious populations individuals have hind wings which are coloured yellow basally when mature, the hind wing lacking any broad bands of pigment. The hind wing often bears a small diffuse light brown spot near the tip.

Two extremes of the adult form exist which are induced by low density conditions on the one hand (solitarious) and high density conditions on the other (gregarious). The gregarious form has adults which band together and which have a distinctly constricted pronotum deeply marked with black pigment above. The sexes approach equality of size, the tegmina being proportionately longer relative to the hind femur than they are in the solitarious form. The solitarious insects show larger sexual size difference, males being much smaller than the females. Solitarious insects show conspicuous green/brown colour polychromatism, the females usually showing more green forms than the males under any given set of circumstances.

Behavioural change is, however, always in advance of morphometrical change. It is thus common to find gregarious looking insects reverting to a secretive solitarious behaviour or solitarious looking adults caught up in swarming activity of their own and other species. Intermediates exist between the gregarious and solitarious form. These are commonly called 'transiens' types.

Life cycle and ecology: Adults fledge and then disperse after 5–7 days whatever conditions prevail in their old breeding area. Dispersal is by night flight in solitarious forms. 10 to 20 days after fledging they are mature. Females lay between 5 and 7 pods. Eggs are laid in moist but not waterlogged soils. Waterlogged pods or those subject to excessive dessication always die. Hatchlings emerge in 10 to 12 days (31–35 °C). Hoppers have 5–7 instars (e. g. *migratorioides* and *capito*). The longer life cycle is found in dry season populations. At such times hopper mortality is higher and adult longevity lower.

Under favourable conditions 5 generations may be completed in West African populations, 3 or 4 generations being the rule in *capito* and *manilensis*. Breeding appears to be continuous. In West Africa 3 generations occur in correlation with the advancing rains (April–September), and involve a rolling, northwards production, of adults following the ITCZ (inter-tropical convergence zone). The third generation is the widespread Sahelian breeding. The fourth and fifth generations coincide with the northward retreat of the floods which originate from the rains which fall in the mountains of the Central African Republic, Cameroon and the Guinea Republic. Present evidence thus points to no permanent breeding centre (likewise for N.W. India).

In S. W. Madagascar 3 habitat zones are recognised: A. a permanent habitat zone; B. a system of semi-arid zones within A (400–1000 mm, isohyet zone) from which swarming occurs occassionally and; C. an arid zone (300–400 mm, isohyet zone) of coastal plains and limestone plateaux from which durable swarms arise. A strong closed circuit migration of the type envisaged in Mali does not, therefore, occur although migration of 100 km. is not uncommon. A similar series of habitats probably occurs in Saudi Arabia occupying the coastal plain and inland plateaux of that region.

Maximum populations are reached when dry season mortality is minimal and all rainy season breeding is successful. This leads to high numbers of adults at the beginning of the dry season derived from hoppers which were concentrated into the decreasing habitats open to them at the end of the rains. This leads to gregarisation of the first dry season population. Large outbreaks probably require two complete annual cycles of successful breeding.

Natural enemies: Birds and egg parasites have been studied. Their controlling effect is marginal and the mobility of the species usually mitigates against the use of parasites or predators as a biological control method.

Control: Some improvement in yield might be achieved by the use of early maturing, high yield crops (but see section on grasshoppers, p. 269). It is for example the second sowing of sorghum, etc. which is most hard hit in many areas. Control is still best achieved by chemical methods. Where dieldrin is forbidden, or the large area of riverine and lake habitats would make its use a risk to the ecosystem, gamma BHC emulsion is useful and relatively safe. Hoppers should be attacked as treatment of adults is time consuming and expensive. The BHC is applied as a 5 % mixture, with water as a base under humid conditions, but with a light oil base under dry conditions (e. g. diesel oil). Other insecticides used with some success against *Locusta* include fenthion, fenitrothion and malathion. Dieldrin (5 %) applied with a motorised knapsac sprayer, produces successful control at 30–40 cc.active material/hectare. Application methods vary. In open country exhaust nozzle sprayers are successful. ULV (e. g. Holder) motorised knapsac sprayers can be used, but for larger infestations aerial application is infinitely preferrable. For this last helicopters should theoretically be the answer, since they afford a versatile survey and control vehicle able to land in marshy terrain.

Literature

BATTEN, A. (1966): The course of the last major plague of the African Migratory Locust, 1928 to 1941. Pl. Prot. Bull. F. A. A.: 14 pp., 1–16.

DAVEY, J. T. (1959): The African Migratory Locust in the Central Niger Delta. II. The ecology of *Locusta* in the semi arid lands and seasonal movements of populations. Locusta **7,** 1–180, 16 figs.

DESCAMPS, M. (1961): Comportement du Criquet Migrateur Africain en 1957 dans la partie septentrionale de son aire de gregarisation sur le Niger region de Niafounke. Locusta **8,** 1–280.

FARROW, R. A. (1972): The African Migratory Locust in its main outbreak area on the Middle Niger: quantiative studies of solitary populations in relation to environmental factors. Vols 1 and 2. Thesis; University of Reading, England.

TETEFORT, J. (1969): Les sauterelles migratrices et les recherches acridiennes a Madagascar. Bull. Madagascar Extract of 31 pp., 3 figs., 1 table.

UVAROW, B. P. (1966): Grasshoppers & Locusts, vol 1. Cambridge University Press.

WINTREBERT, D. (1970): Identité, Ecologie et comportement du criquet migrateur dans le Sud-Quest Malgache. Ann. Soc. ent. Fr. (N.S.) **6** (1), 35–152, 35 tables, 58 figs.

Author: N. D. Jago

Other harmful locusts and mole crickets:

Dociostaurus maroccanus (Thnb.), Moroccan or Mediterranean locust (Marokkanische Wanderheuschrecke). In the mediterranean region, in West and Central Asia and in parts of East Africa (Somalia) (CIE Map no 321). Adult swarms attack various plants, among them cereals, cotton, olive etc. Control by application of dieldrin or gamma-BHC, sometimes also by the use of baits.

Locustana pardalina (Wlk), the Brown migratory locust (Braune Wanderheuschrecke), has its outbreak areas in South Africa.

Nomadacris septemfasciata (Serv.), Red locust (Rote Wanderheuschrecke). Confined to Africa; outbreak centres in Tanzania, Zambia and Malawi.

Patanga succincta (L.), Bombay locust. Found in South and South East Asia. Increasing importance in Thailand in recent years. Damages maize, coconut palm, millet and other plants.

Schistocerca americana paranensis (Burm.) (= *S. urichi*) (Südamerikanische Wanderheuschrecke). Breeding centres of this locust are found in Northern Argentine, in Paraguay and Bolivia.

Gryllotalpa africana Beauv., African mole cricket (Afrikanische Maulwurfsgrille). Widely distributed in Africa and Asia (CIE Map no 293). Feeding on the roots of many plant species, but also a predator. Severe damage on young rice plants especially in South East Asia. Control by flooding affected fields or application of poison baits.

H. Sch.

Thrips; Blasenfüßer, Thripse; Thrips; Trips

Order: Thysanoptera

General features: Thrips are small or very small insects with a very slim body, which is mostly coloured yellowish, brown or black. With their asymmetrical, piercing-sucking mouth parts, they puncture plant cells and suck out their contents. The females of many species have a serrated ovipositor at the posterior end of the abdomen, with which eggs are inserted into plant tissues. Since metamorphosis is hemimetabolic, the life habit of thrips nymphs is similar to that of the adults. There are however prepupal and pupal stages which do not take up food.
The first symptoms of damage due to thrips attack on plant portions such as leaves and fruit consist of whitish to silvery discolourations at the feeding sites. The plant tissue can subsequently turn brown and die off. Fruit peel such as banana skin and citrus rind shows suberised areas at the places of feeding and oviposition. Some thrips species can transmit phytopathogenic viruses during the feeding process, e.g. on tomato.
Several thrips species are important pests in tropical and subtropical regions, one of the main ones being *Thrips tabaci* on onion, cotton etc. (see below). Other species are injurious on legumes, rice, tea, coffee, cocoa, olive, banana and citrus.

H. Sch.

Thrips tabaci Lind. (Plate 21 a)

Common names: Onion thrips; Zwiebelblasenfuß; Thrips de l'oignon; Trips de la cebolla.

Geographical distribution: This small insect is found in most countries of the world although it is particularly abundant in areas with rather hot dry climates. The Commonwealth Institute of

Entomology Distribution Map 20 (revised 1969) suggests that the species is not found in the larger areas of tropical rainforest. It is likely that the pest came originally from the eastern Mediterranean together with its most favoured host plant *Allium cepa*.

Host plants: The Onion thrips has been recorded from more than three hundred species of plants, although when given a choice it appears to prefer onions (*Allium cepa*). In temperate regions it is common on various Compositae (eg. *Achillea, Senecio*) and Cruciferae (eg. *Brassica*), whilst in warmer climates it is particularly abundant on cotton (*Gossypium*), tomatoes (*Solanum*), tobacco (*Nicotiana*), cucurbits (*Cucurbita, Cucumis*), and various weed Compositae (eg. *Emilia sonchifolia*). This wide range of host plants, together with the ease with which the insects are dispersed by wind and the rapidity with which they breed, makes *Thrips tabaci* an unpredictable pest which can be difficult to control.

Symptoms: Thrips usually feed on the lower surface of leaves. The cell contents are removed from the lower mesophyll, and as a result air spaces develop and the leaf becomes distorted. Attacked leaves frequently have a silvery sheen and they may bear small spots of faecal matter. Feeding damage on cabbages leads to russeting or bronzing of leaves, and young plants are particularly susceptible. Heavy thrips attack can cause sufficient leaf damage to kill young onion or cotton plants.

In addition to direct feeding damage, *Thrips tabaci* also carries Tomato spotted wilt disease to several crops. On pineapples (*Ananas*) this disease is known as Pineapple yellow spot due to the small round yellowish spots produced on the upper surface of the leaves. These spots increase to irregular streaks and a lethal necrosis may set in which can affect 40 % of a crop. The same virus disease on tobacco (*Nicotiana*) is known as Kromnek in South Africa. The apex of an infected plant bends over due to a check in growth on one side and this eventually leads to necrosis. Young tobacco plants with a severe infection usually die but older plants may recover.

Economic importance: Assessment of the economic importance of *tabaci* and of the virus disease it carries is difficult. The numbers of thrips on a crop can increase rapidly in dry weather and decrease rapidly after rain, and the virus disease is similarly erratic. Large numbers of thrips attacking a crop at the seedling stage can cause severe or even total losses with onions, cabbages or cotton. Similarly early infestation of a tobacco crop with tomato spotted wilt can lead to serious losses. However once established and growing vigorously most plants can tolerate both feeding damage and virus disease without economic loss.

Morphology: There are many other species of Thysanoptera which are more or less similar in appearance and biology, but *T. tabaci* can be distinguished by the following combination of characters: body length about 1,0 mm, colour variable from pale yellow to brown, usually darkest at lower temperatures but never blackish brown or with striped wings. Wings with two longitudinal veins each bearing a row of setae, the anterior vein with four setae in the distal half. Head with compound eyes and three ocelli but ocellar pigment never bright red. Antennae seven segmented with a forked sense cone on the third and fourth segment. Pronotum with two pairs of long posteroangular setae but without long setae on the anterior margin. Abdominal tergite eight with a complete comb of fine microtrichia along the posterior border; tergite nine with only one (not two) pairs of dorsal pores; pleurotergites with several transverse rows of fine pointed microtrichia. Second instar larvae with no spiracles on the second abdominal segment.

Life cycle and ecology: Adult *T. tabaci* may live for three weeks to four months or more depending on temperature and humidity. The life cycle can be completed in less than eighteen days at high temperatures although at lower temperatures development may take five weeks. Eggs are inserted singly into the tissue of green plants through a cut made by the ovipositor, and they hatch in from three to eight days depending on temperature. The two larval instars feed actively on leaves but the two pupal instars do not feed and are usually found in the soil. However a pupal cell is apparently not formed. The species overwinters as adults and there is no evidence of a diapause. Reproduction is probably usually parthenogenetic because males are rare in most parts of the world. The size of natural populations of thrips is probably controlled more by the weather and nutritional status of host plants than by predators and parasites. Populations tend to build up in hot dry weather but the number of individuals on a crop can be drastically reduced by heavy rain.

Natural enemies: Parasitic Hymenoptera can be effective in reducing the size of populations under some conditions. Five species of Eulophidae are listed from *tabaci*. Predators are probably less important, such as Anthocorids, Coccinellids and Arachnids.

Control: Control of alternative host plants is unlikely to be a useful method of reducing the numbers of *tabaci* on a crop, except under exceptional circumstances, because of the wide range of plants on which the insect breeds. However weed control can be important when the weeds are known to harbour Tomato spotted wilt, and decorative garden plants in surrounding urban areas can also be a source of this virus. Ploughing and harrowing of fields after a crop has been harvested can be useful in reducing subsequent thrips populations by killing both pupae in the soil and adults sheltering in grass stems and plant debris. Overhead and surface irrigation have both been found to be effective in controlling thrips damage, partly by killing thrips that are already present on the plants or in the soil, but also by stimulating the growth of a crop and so reducing the period during which it is most susceptible to damage. Similarly a crop may be protected by bringing forward the planting date so that the maximum population of thrips does not coincide with the seedling stage. Optimum plant density varies with the crop and the conditions under which it is being grown, but the distance between individual plants can be varied to reduce the numbers of thrips present or the damage which they cause. Crop loss has similarly been reduced, particularly in tomatoes, by growing varieties which are least susceptible to thrips damage.
The range of cultural practices by which losses to thrips may be contained is such that the use of insecticides may be avoidable or even uneconomic. Moreover attempts at chemical control of the spread of Tomato spotted wilt are usually unsatisfactory. In tobacco fields in Bulgaria control of *tabaci* and the virus disease was obtained by ploughing into the soil 50 kg/ha of 12 % gamma BHC dust both just after one crop and just before sowing the next, followed by monthly dustings with DDT. However such concentrations of insecticide would not be acceptable on a food crop. Both carbaryl and DDT are effective as foliar sprays at 0.5–1.0 lbs/acre in reducing thrips populations, and DDT can be used as a 5–10 % dust on bulbs in store or at about 20 lbs/acre in the field as a foliar dust. In glasshouses thrips are best controlled by gamma BHC or DDT smokes, or malathion aerosols rather than by spraying.

Literature

LEWIS, T. (1973): Thrips, their biology, ecology and economic importance. Academic Press, London and New York. 349 pp.
MOUND, L. A. (1971): The feeding apparatus of thrips. Bulletin of Entomological Research **60**, 547–548.
MOUND, L. A. (1973): Thrips and Whitefly: Chapter 13 in Viruses and Invertebrates (Gibbs, A. J., Editor), North Holland Publishing Company, Amsterdam, pp. 229–242.

Author: L. A. Mound

Other harmful Thysanoptera (Plate 21 b):

Caliothrips spp. *C. sudanensis* (Bagn. & Cam.), *C. impurus* (Pr.) (Plate 21 b) in North East Africa and *C. indicus* (Bagn.) in India damage leaves of groundnut. The two first named species also affect cotton in the Sudan, *C. indicus* damages pea in India. Malathion, gamma BHC, toxaphene, dieldrin, DDT etc. are used for control. *Taeniothrips sjostedti* (Tryb.) and *Sericothrips occipitalis* Hood attack flowers and leaves of various legumes in the African tropics.

Chaetanaphothrips signipennis (Bagn.), the Banana rust thrips (Bananenblasenfuß) and related species such as *C. orchidii* (Moult.) damage young banana fruit on oviposition (ovipositor damages plant tissue) and with their feeding activity. The banana skin is roughened, discoloured a reddish brown and may split. The flavour of the bananas is not affected, but the marketable value is much reduced. Such damage has been reported repeatedly from Central and South America, India, Sri Lanka, East Australia and the Fiji Islands. *Hercinothrips bicinctus* (Bagn.) causes similar damage in various parts of the tropics. Chemical control: Spray or dust application of phosphamidon, dieldrin, gamma-BHC or DDT.

Baliothrips biformis (Bagn.) (= *Chloethrips oryzae, Thrips oryzae*), Rice thrips (Reisblasenfuß). Distributed in South, South East and East Asia (CIE Map no 215). Attacks mainly young rice plants. Control with dimethoate, malathion, diazinon and gamma BHC sprays.

Diarthrothrips coffeae Will., Coffee thrips (Kaffeblasenfuß). Attacks leaves, twigs and berries of Arabica coffee in East Africa. Control by mulching the coffee trees with elephant grass and application of dicrotophos, fenitrothion or parathion.

Heliothrips haemorrhoidalis (Bché), Black greenhouse thrips (Schwarzer Gewächshausblasenfuß). Widely distributed in tropical and subtropical regions; in temperate regions in glasshouses (CIE Map no 135). On numerous host plants, such as avocado, tea, citrus, passion fruit, coffee, cocoa, cotton, cola, mango, coconut and date palm.

Liothrips oleae (Costa), Olive thrips (Olivenblasenfuß). Attacks leaves and inflorescences of olive in the mediterranean region. Control with parathion, DDT and other contact insecticides.

Selenothrips rubrocinctus (Giard), Cocoa thrips, Kakaoblasenfuß. This species has a worldwide distribution in the tropics and attacks cashew, mango, avocado, cocoa and some other crops. The nymphs have a broad red band around the base of the abdomen.

Scirtothrips aurantii Fauré, South African citrus thrips (Citrusblasenfuß). Widely distributed in Africa (CIE Map no 137). Attacks citrus fruit mainly in South Africa and Rhodesia. Control with malathion, parathion and other insecticides. *S. citri* (Moult.) affects citrus in California (CIE Map no 138) and *S. dorsalis* Hood tea in India.

H. Sch.

Order: Isoptera (Plates 21 c, d and 22 a, b)

Common names: Termites, White ants; Termiten, "Weiße Ameisen"; Termites, Fourmis blanches; Comejenes, termites.

Important species, synonyms and geographical distribution:
Mastotermes darwiniensis Frogg.: Australia; *Hodotermes mossambicus* (Hag.) (Harvester termite; Erntetermite): East, South East and South Africa; *Coptotermes curvignathus* Holmgr.: Malaysia, Indonesia, Indo-China; *Macrotermes subhyalinus* (Ramb.) (= *Bellicositermes bellicosus*): Tropical and subtropical Africa and the South West portion of the Arabian peninsula; *Microtermes thoracalis* Sjöst.: North East and Central Africa; *M. obesi* Holmgr.: Indian subcontinent; *Microcerotermes diversus* Silv.: Arabian peninsula (Irak, Saudi-Arabia, North and South Yemen); *Odontotermes formosanus* (Shir.) (= *Termes formosanus*): South China and Taiwan; *O. obesus* (Ramb.): India; *O. smeathmani* (Full.): Sudan; *Nasutitermes costalis* (Holmgr.): Caribbean Islands (Cuba, Puerto Rico, Barbados etc.) and Guayana.

Host plants: The termites are polyphagous plant pests and cause damage on various plant species
The above-mentioned species have been observed as pests on the following plants: *H. mossambi-cus:* cotton, peanut, wheat, barley, lucerne, beans and grasses (pasture); *C. curvignathus:* coco-nut, rubber tree, *Citrus,* mango, oil palm, kapok; *M. subhyalinus:* peanut, coffee, cocoa, sugar
cane, rice and tobacco; *M. thoracalis:* cotton, peanut, wheat, kenaf, sorghum, maize, sesame and
tomato; *M. obesi:* sugar cane; *M. diversus: Citrus,* date palm, cotton and guava; *O. formosanus:*
sugar cane, tea, cassava, banana, coffee, *Citrus,* mango, rice, sweet potato, guava, litchi etc.;
O. obesus: sugar cane, coconut palm, fruit trees, cotton, coffee, tea, sorghum, peanut, maize
etc.; *O. smeathmani:* date palm, wheat and *Citrus; N. costalis:* sugar cane.

Symptoms: Healthy plants which are well supplied with water and nutrients are rarely attacked
Feeding damage may occur on plants which are weakened, even if only temporarily, by certain
cultivation procedures, water deficiency etc. Drought seems to play a major part. Termite damage
has also often been observed during dry periods in the rainy season.
Subterranean plant portions are greatly at risk. *Microtermes* spp. often eat into the tap roots of
young cotton and peanut plants immediately below the soil surface, destroy the central root por-tions and fill the resulting cavities with soil. Plants damaged in this way die within a few days, par-ticularly under drought conditions. *C. curvignathus* and *M. diversus* also often penetrate into the
tap root. Termites may also eat up the roots of maize and sorghum, so that the damaged plants
topple. Peanut seed ripening inside the shell in the ground is attacked and destroyed by several
species. Sugar cane cuttings, consisting of cut pieces of stem, are damaged inside and outside by
Odontotermes-, Nasutitermes-, Microtermes- and *Macrotermes* species to such an extent, that no
shoots can form and large gaps arise in the field. Other species concentrate on aerial portions and
construct soil galleries above the feeding sites. *Macrotermes* species can peel the bark at the stem
base of coffee, tea and cocoa shrubs, resulting in the death of affected plants. Stem and branch
portions at some distance from ground level are also frequently damaged. In these cases the termi-tes enter chiefly through wounds, in which the central woody portions are exposed and accessible
They again advance in soil galleries, in which they are protected from environmental effects. The
Harvester termite *H. mossambicus* defoliates plants, especially on grazing land, where the turf is
destroyed.

Economic importance: Termites constitute one of the most important groups of pests in tropical
and sub-tropical regions. In the tree savannah, where they are particularly numerous, they do a
good deal of damage in a large variety of crops of both annual and perennial plants, especially on
newly cultivated land. Their economic significance extends to the destruction of turf and of wood
used in building and constructional work. They are, however, also beneficial and play a major part
in the decomposition of organic matter in the soil.

Morphology: The termites usually have a small to medium sized, soft skinned, whitish body. Dif-ferent, distinguishable castes, are present in all species (see "Biology and ecology"). The head in
sexual forms and worker termites is oval to round, in soldiers usually considerably larger and of
aberrant shape. The mouth parts are adapted for chewing and the mandibles of soldiers often stri-kingly large and powerful. Antennae are elongated and moniliform. Sexual forms have compound
eyes, which are reduced to a greater or lesser extent in the other castes. Until they start a colony
(see p. 285), they also have 2 pairs of very similar wings with a network of veins. Workers and sol-diers are at all times wingless. The legs are walking legs with relatively large coxae.
While the males retain their original shape and size throughout life, the abdomen of the queen in
large species (*Macrotermes* spp.) can extend to the length of a thumb of a grown human being.

Similarities to other pests: Termites are sometimes confused with ants, particularly if the species
live on trees. Soil termites are easily distinguished from ants by their white colour.

Biology and ecology: Termites are warmth loving animals and chiefly inhabit tropical and subtroɔical regions. In these regions they are only absent at high altitudes, where temperatures are too ɔow, or in desert land where there is no food. Termites are always social insects and form colonies (nests) such as are formed by ants, bees, wasps and bumble bees (Hymenoptera). As in the Hymenoptera, several castes can be distinguished in a termite colony, in which only the worker caste s of practical significance. Kings and queens function as sexual forms, while the soldier caste is ɔngaged in defending the colony against enemies. Since termites undergo incomplete metamorphosis, even the younger instars of their nymphs greatly resemble the adults and take on important functions in the nest at an early stage. In this they differ from Hymenoptera, which undergo a complete metamorphosis and only take on active functions in the nest as adults.

The colonies are startet by the sexual forms, which fly from the nests at the start of the rainy season and lose their wings before re-entering the soil or other hiding places. The sexes meet either in the air or on the ground and males are attracted to the females by pheromones.

Termites are usually heliophobic and withdraw into their nests during the day. In some species the nests can rise to a height of several metres, and are among the largest structures erected by animals. At night, the termites are very active and collect food at greater or lesser distances from the nest. On stems etc., they erect tunnel-like soil galleries for their protection.

Since cellulose is the decisive nutritional requirement for termites, they try to obtain it by feeding rapaciously on all kinds of wood, as well as on stalks and leaves. In this way they take a very active part in the turnover of organic substance in tropical rain forests and in the tree savannah, where they occur in large numbers, performing a vital utilitarian function.

In some of the more primitive termite groups, decomposition of cellulose is accomplished with the aid of symbiotic intestinal protozoa. More highly developed species (Termitidae) raise fungi in special chambers of their nests, on a spongy nutrient substrate consisting largely of wood fragments. The fungi facilitate digestion of the wood, while their fruiting bodies also serve as food.

Natural enemies: Termites suffer much persecution by man and many animals. In tropical Africa, masses of sexual forms are caught in simple traps and roasted in oil as a source of food rich in fats and proteins. As such they are greatly appreciated, especially in regions with protein deficiency. Dragonflies, ants, frogs, many kinds of birds, bats and larger mammals (ant bear, large anteater, pangolins, monkeys) also play their part. Despite the large number of predators, most species are well able to maintain a relatively high colony density by means of the mass production of sexual forms, provided sufficient cellulose and other organic substances are available for nutritional purposes.

Control: All methods of cultivation which promote the rapid growth of healthy crops are suitable means for avoiding termite damage. Unnecessary injuries, which facilitate the entry of termites, should be avoided. Despite the large number of natural predators, there are as yet no promising means to ensure biological control. Chemical control by seed dressing, treatment of field furrows or setts (sugar cane) with aldrin, dieldrin, chlordane and gamma-BHC is feasible. The latter has proved unsatisfactory in highly alkaline clay soils in Africa. Species which greatly impede crop cultivation methods with their large mounds, can be controlled by infiltrating the termite hills with the above mentioned insecticides, together with larger amounts of water. This kills the colonies and the hills can then be removed without the risk of seeing them built up again.

The amount of aldrin, dieldrin and chlordane used should be kept as low as possible, to avoid an accumulation of residues in the soil.

Literature

HARRIS, W. V. (1961): Termites. Longmans, London, 187 pp.
HARRIS, W. V. (1969): Termites as pests of crops and trees. Commonw. Inst. Ent. London, 41 pp.

Author: H. Schmutterer

Bugs; Wanzen; Punaises; Chinches

Order: Heteroptera

General features: Heteroptera are small to medium sized insects, which do not differ greatly from one another in appearance. They have forewings which are leathery in front, membranous and transparent towards the back. As a result of feeding activity with their piercing-sucking mouth parts, plant portions such as seed (Leguminosae seed, cereal grains) can shrivel, or large necrotic areas can arise at the feeding places, because the saliva is highly toxic. Fungi subsequently may invade these necrotic areas. Some species (*Dysdercus* spp., *Antestiopsis* spp., *Nezara viridula*) can transmit fungus spores. The fungi growing from these spores will rot fruit such as cotton bolls and coffee beans.

Bugs are hemimetabolic. Adults and nymphs therefore frequently have similar bionomics.

H. Sch.

Family: Pentatomidae

Eurygaster integriceps Put. (Fig. 109)

Common names: Wheat shield bug; Asiatische Getreidewanze; Punaise de blé.

Geographical distribution: Greece, Crete, Iran, Iraq, Israel, Jordan, Lebanon, Pakistan, Syria, Turkey, Soviet Union (Kazakhstan, Turkmenistan, eastern Ukraine). CIE Map no 40.

Host plants: Wheat, barley, oats, and wild Gramineae.

Symptoms: Whitish, dry stems of attacked cereals in March--April, and shrivelled grain in May-June.

Economic importance: Varies from negligible damage in the outer margins of the pest distribution area (e. g. Jordan, Israel, Greece), to about 90 % loss around the center (e. g., parts of Iran, Iraq, and Turkey). However, there is a marked periodic fluctuation in populations of this insect in most parts of its distribution range.

Morphology: Yellowish brown heteropteron 12–13 mm long with scutellum totally covering the hemielytra in the adult.

Similarities to other pests: Similar to *Eurygaster austriaca* of Central Europe and to *Aelia acuminata*.

Fig. 109. Adults of *Eurygaster integriceps* on barley (phot. A. S. Talhouk)

Life cycle: One generation per year. Young adults appear in early summer, feed for one to two weeks on dry wheat seeds, then fly to aestivation areas on adjacent hillsides[1]. Further feeding in summer quarters on wild Gramineae is usual. In the autumn a downward migration from the mountains is reported to take place for the rest of winter. The adults then bury themselves under *Astragalus, Acantholimon* or *Quercus* until spring when a return mass migration to cereal fields occurs. Feeding of both sexes on stems of cereals takes place for approximately two weeks after which the females mature sexually and copulation occurs. Females lay their eggs on broad-leaved weeds in cereal fields or on cereals. Oviposition occurs over 2 to 3 weeks, and egg-hatching over about 7–12 days. The bug has 5 nymphal instars completed in about 4 weeks. The first three instars feed on leaves and stems, and the last two mostly on the grain when it is in the "milk stage". In early summer, the young adult is formed and feeds on the maturing grain. It then migrates to the hills.

Ecology: In the cereal fields, a common plant, *Leontice leontopetalum* (Berberidacae) is particularly important because it provides the major site of oviposition. Several wild *Brassica* spp. (Compositae) are also important because they serve as food for other Pentatomids whose eggs act as hosts for different Scelionidae; the latter are important egg parasites of *Eurygaster* and *Aelia*. In the aestivation quarters, several Gramineae including species of *Hordeum, Bromus, Poa* and *Avena*, serve as food for young adults; in the hibernation quarters several species of *Astragalus, Acantholimon, Artemisia, Pistacia, Poterium spinosum* and the scrub oak *Quercus aegilops* serve as shelters below which the overwintering adults bury themselves.

At the hibernating sites in winter temperatures drop below freezing at night. The plants which shelter the insects often remain covered with snow for a few weeks. The relative humidity at these places is high during December–January (80–95 % RH) but low (25–35 % RH) during the rest of the year.

It is known that late spring and early summer rains result in a longer growth period of wild Gramineae thus affording more nourishment for bugs after leaving the cereal fields. Food reserves in the bug's "fat body" determine the ability of the population to survive winter. Cold winters favour overwintering populations and prevent exhaustion of food reserves.

Natural enemies: *Passer* spp. and *Corvus* spp. (birds); *Phasia subcoleoptrata* (Dipt.: Tachinidae); *Asolcus (Microphanurus) grandis, A. vasilievi* (Hym.: Scelionidae).

Control:
Cultural practices. Planting early-maturing cereal varieties and harvesting as early as possible.
Biological control. Release of laboratory-bred egg parasites (*Asolcus grandis*) as soon as first eggs of *Eurygaster* are found in the fields.
Chemical control. Application of trichlorphon (Diptrex) as dust or ULV spray when most nymphs have reached the second instar in order to avoid harming *Asolcus* which have either been released or are already naturally present in the fields.

Literature

BROWN, E. S. (1962): Researches on the Ecology and Biology of *Eurygaster integriceps* Put. (Hemiptera, Scutelleridae) in Middle East countries, with special reference to the overwintering period. Bull. ent. Res. **53**, 445–514.
TALHOUK, A. S. (1954): Further Trials with Parathion Dust against *Eurygaster integriceps*. Bull. ent. Res. **45**, 495–500.

Author: A. S. Talhouk

---

[1] Usually settle on a north exposure and at high altitudes (often above 2000 m).

Antestiopsis spp./ssp. (Plate 22 c)

Common names: Coffee bugs, Variegated bugs; Kaffeewanzen, Vielfarbige Kaffeewanzen; Punaises du caféier; Cinches del cafeto.

Important species or sub-species and geographical distribution: *Antestiopsis orbitalis bechuana* (Kirk.) (Rhodesia to East Kenya); *A. o. ghesquierei* (Car.) (Zaire, North West Tanzania and West Uganda); *Antestiopsis intricata* (Ghes. & Car.) (Ivory Coast up to West Kenya and Ethiopia); *A. facetoides* (Greath.) (Kenya and Tanzania).

Host plants: *A. o. bechuana. Coffea arabica, Gardenia* sp., *Pavetta elliottii, Psychotria nairobiensis, Rytigynia* sp., *Vangueria* sp. *A. o. ghesquierei. Coffea arabica, C. canephora, Canthium vulgare, Pavetta oliveriana, Vangueria apiculata. A. intricata. Coffea arabica, C. canephora, C. excelsa, C. liberica, Canthium golungense, Pavetta oliveriana, Vangueria apiculata. A. facetoides. Coffea arabica.*

Symptoms: Symptoms due to *Antestiopsis* spp. and ssp. occur on buds (blackening), young berries (berry drop) and on older and ripe coffee fruit (rotting of berries and zebra striped beans). The coffee bugs are vectors for the fungi *Nematospora coryli* and *N. gossypii,* which give rise to a dry rot of beans. These vector propensities, coupled with the high degree of mobility of the coffee bugs and their tendency to make many feeding attempts, have led to setting the injury threshold at a very low level. In Kenya it is set at 2 bugs per coffee tree in dry regions and 1/tree in regions with more rainfall.

Economic importance: The low injury threshold is a clear indication of the importance of this group of pests. In years with heavy infestation, up to 90 % of berries can be infected with *Nematospora* spp.. The risk of far-reaching damage is greatest on the smallholdings in some regions, where few insecticides are used. The outbreaks of *Antestiopsis* spp. are rare on plantations in which treatment is regularly given to control leaf miners or giant loopers.

Morphology: The bodies of *Antestiopsis* spp./ssp. are flattened and a little longer than wide. The size varies with the species/subspecies from 7.5–9.5 mm and females are usually larger than the males. The scutellum covers about $^2/_3$ of the abdomen. The black, white and orange colour patterns on hemielytra, scutellum and pronotum vary with the species and are very characteristic. The eggs are a mat white colour. The egg diameter averages 1 mm. Hatched nymphs are uniformly dark. The characteristic colour patterns of individual species are increasingly prominent in subsequent nymphal instars.

Similarities to other pests: *Antestiopsis* spp./ssp. differ remarkably from all other bugs attacking coffee.

Life cycle: The food preferred by coffee bugs consists of fully grown, green coffee berries. They do however also feed on shoots, leaves and coffee berries at any stage of development. *Antestiopsis* spp./ssp. are therefore found on coffee throughout the year. The population density increases in rainy periods, when the fruit sets. The egg batches of *Antestiopsis* spp./ssp. generally consist of 12 eggs and are laid on the undersurface of leaves. The number of batches produced in its lifetime by one female varies greatly. Normally, 10–12 are deposited, but in extreme cases, up to 40 have been observed. The life span of adults covers 3–12 months, and females have a higher life expectancy than males. The incubation period for eggs depends greatly on temperature (altitude and season). At 23 °C, the eggs of *A. o. bechuana* and *A. intricata* hatch after 5–6 days. Their fertility is about 95 %. *Antestiopsis* spp./ssp. have 5 nymphal instars. At 23 °C, the development from egg to adult takes 50–60 days. The developmental period again varies with season and geographical location.

Ecology: At higher altitudes, the bug occurs increasingly in less shaded plantations, in which the day temperature rises more rapidly. At lower levels, shade has a beneficial effect on the development of *Antestiopsis* spp./ssp., because high day temperatures are equalised. The high moisture requirements of the bugs are met by the dense, little ventilated growth of coffee shrubs, as well as by active fluid intake from young berries, dew and rain drops.

Natural enemies: *Antestiopsis* spp./ssp. are attacked by a large number of parasites in all developmental stages. The major egg parasites are *Hadronotus antestiae, Asolcus seychellensis, A. mopsus* and *A. suranus*. The first two Ichneumonid species parasitise all the *Antestiopsis* species and subspecies which have been mentioned, while the last two were only found in the eggs of *A. o. ghesquierei* and *A. facetoides*. Surveys carried out in Kenya gave degrees of parasitisation of between 70–95 %, taking all egg parasites into consideration.

Other important parasites are Braconidae, which attack adults and nymphs, depending on the species. *Aridelus rufus* and *A. taylori* are well known larval parasites. The Stylopid *Corioxenos antestiae* also plays a major part, but has a complicated life cycle and for that reason depends greatly on host population density.

Control:

Cultivation measures. The coffee shrubs should be kept open and accessible to wind effects, so that the micro-climate is affected adversely for *Antestiopsis* spp./ssp.. The flowering periods of coffee should, as far as possible, be kept close, not scattered. This ensures that the bug does not have berries at its disposal throughout the year.

Biological control. The introduction of effective parasites from Madagascar, India and South Africa has been tried, so far without marked success. The most practical procedure at the moment would appear to be the considered use of insecticides, in such a way that predators are largely spared (integrated control).

Chemical control. Trichlorphon (95 % and 85 % wettable powder), fenitrothion (50 % a. i.) and fenthion (50 % a. i.) can be used as effective sprays to control coffee bugs. The insecticides should be applied at a concentration of 0.075 % a. i. in 100 l water/ha with LV spraying. Treatment should be preceded by test sprays of several single trees, so that the number of bugs per tree can be roughly determined in order to avoid unnecessary treatments. Pyrethrum based sprays are suitable for this purpose, since the coffee bugs rapidly drop from affected bushes after their use.

Literature

GREATHEAD, D. J. (1965): A taxonomic study of the species of *Antestiopsis* (Hemiptera, Pentatomidae) associated with *Coffea arabica* in Africa. Bull. ent. Res. **56**, 515–554.

GREATHEAD, D. J. (1966): The parasites of *Antestiopsis* spp. in East Africa and a discussion of the possibilities of biological control. Tech. Bull. Com. Inst. Biol. Control **7**, 113–137, Farnham Royal.

KIRKPATRICK, T. W. (1937): Studies on the ecology of coffee plantations in East Africa II. The autecology of *Antestiopsis* spp. with a particular account of a Strepsipterous parasite. Trans. R. ent. Soc. London **86**, 247–343.

LE PELLEY, J. H. (1968): Pests of Coffee. Longmans, London, 590 pp.

TAYLOR, T. H. C. (1944): Recent investigations of *Antestia* species in Uganda. East Afric. Agric. Journ. **10**, 223–233.

Author: K. Leuschner

Family: Miridae

Helopeltis spp. (Figs. 110–111 and plate 22 d)

Important species and synonyms: *H. anacardii* Mill., *H. antonii* Sign., *H. ceylonensis* Forn., *H. clavifer* (Wlk.), *H. lalendei* (Caray.), *H. orophila* Ghesq., *H. poppiusi* Schmitz, *H. schoutedeni*

Reut. (syn. *H. sanguineus* Popp.), *H. theivora* Waterh., *H. theobromae* Mill., *H. westwoodii* (White).
Occurrence of different colour forms in the same species and similar colour patterns in different species has led, in the past, to many misidentifications.

Common names: Helopeltis bugs, Tea mosquito bug (*H. theivora*), Cotton helopeltis (*H. schoutedeni*), Cashew helopeltis (*H. anacardii*); Helopeltis-Wanzen/Teewanzen (*Helopeltis* spp.); Helopeltis; Chinches del algodón (*Helopeltis* spp.).

Geographical distribution: Some 20 *Helopeltis* species are recorded from the warm, humid areas of Africa, *H. schoutedeni* (CIE Map no 297) and *H. poppiusi* being the most important. In Asia and the Pacific Islands at least 10 other species are economically important, notably *H. theivora* and *H. antonii* (CIE Map no 296).

Host plants: All *Helopeltis* spp. are polyphagous living on a range of crop plants plus numerous weeds. The principal crops that act as host plants of the most important species are as follows: Cinchona, cocoa, cotton, cashew, tea: *H. poppiusi*. Cotton, castor, mango, sweet-potato, pigeon pea, cocoa: *H. schoutedeni*. Tea, cocoa, anatto: *H. theivora*. Tea, cinchona, avocado, cashew, guava, cocoa: *H. antonii*.

Symptoms: Both nymphs and adults feed by pushing their tube-like mouthparts into soft green tissues. Saliva is forced into the plant before feeding begins and is highly toxic to the cells. A dark water-soaked mark first appears around the feeding puncture which later turns into the characteristic lesion with a light brown centre and black edge. Stem lesions tend to split longitudinally and finally become corky as callous formation occurs. Young shoots often die off completely and this stimulates secondary branching which is also very susceptible to attack. Fungi often invade lesions on the fruit, causing shrivelling or rotting.
When cotton is attacked the plants become stunted and bushy with cupped leaves and the typical lesions on green shoots, leaf and flower stalks and leaves, especially on and near the main veins. The exposed parts of green bolls have crater-like lesions 3–4 mm in diameter. If the cotton plant is attacked when young it appears to have been scorched by fire.
On tree crops (cocoa, cashew, cinchona, tea) there is, of course, no damage to the main frame of the plant unless it is attacked when young. Otherwise, the damage is similar to cotton with circular black lesions on fruits and more elongated lesions on the green shoots, petioles and peduncles and on the main veins of leaves. Later, growth at the ends of branches appears bunched and distorted.

Economic importance: *Helopeltis* attacks are typically very localized with severe distortion of plant structure and loss of crop on one farm or part of a farm but nearby crops are free of the pest. Recurrent annual attacks on tree crops such as cocoa, cashew and cinchona are very serious because the tree never has a chance to grow into its natural size and shape.
The bugs are relatively long-lived (up to 3 months in some species) and make as many as 50 feeding punctures a day, each of which significantly damages the host plant, so that quite low populations can cause serious damage.

Morphology: *Helopeltis* are slender bugs about 7–9 mm long and 2 mm wide when full-grown. They have long legs and very long antennae. Colours vary from brown, red and orange through to yellow. The diagnostic feature in both nymphs and adults is the pin-like process which rises vertically from the thorax. It is about 2 mm long in the adult bug.

Similarities to other pests/diseases: Unless one is familiar with *Helopeltis* damage, it is very easy to believe that the lesions are caused by a fungus or bacterium, especially as the bugs may have disappeared from the plant by the time the symptoms are noticed. On cotton, fresh *Helopeltis* lesions may be confused with those of Bacterial blight caused by *Xanthomonas malvacearum*. Ho-

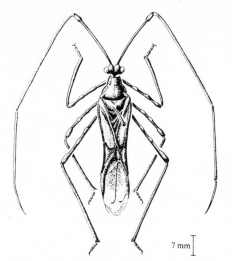

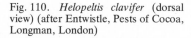

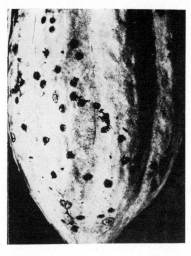

Fig. 110. *Helopeltis clavifer* (dorsal view) (after Entwistle, Pests of Cocoa, Longman, London)

› Fig. 111. Cocoa pod showing damage of *Helopeltis* sp. (phot. H. Schmutterer)

wever, old blight lesions are black and sunken and do not have corky callous tissue like bug damage. On cocoa pods, the Mirid *Sahlbergella* causes similar lesions to *Helopeltis* but these are concentrated near the stalk; *Helopeltis* lesions are more uniformily distributed. Several *Monalonion* spp. cause similar damage on cocoa pods in Central and South America.

Life cycle: The *Helopeltis* spp. that have been studied have a similar life history. The following is a generalized account.

The eggs are test-tube shaped, slightly curved with a rounded cap and two unequal hair-like filaments at one end. Eggs are white and 1.5–2.0 mm long. They are inserted singly into soft plant tissues, only the cap and filaments being visible externally. Most eggs are laid in the leaf stalk or main veins. Hatching takes place after 1–4 weeks, according to temperature.

The nymphs are slender delicate insects with red and yellow body colours in most species. The full-grown nymph has a body length of about 7 mm, the antennae being much longer. There are 5 nymphal instars, all except the first having a spine-like projection sticking up from the throax. The total nymphal period takes about 3 weeks in warm weather and up to 6 weeks in the cooler seasons.

After the final moult to the winged adult stage, several days may elapse before egg-laying begins. Adult females live 6–10 weeks and lay 30–60 eggs (up to 500 in some species).

Breeding is continuous with no evidence of diapause or other resting stage.

Ecology: *Helopeltis* spp. are typically pests of warm, moist forest areas (or former forest areas) with a rainfall of not less than 800 mm and an altitude of not more than 2,000 m. In such areas they have a wide host range of wild and exotic plants, mostly trees and shrubs. In cotton-growing areas certain swamp plants (*Jussiaea* spp., *Polygonum* spp.) are important hosts in the dry season. All stages avoid direct sunlight and adults fly readily if disturbed.

Natural enemies: Parasites and predators may be important in the control of *Helopeltis* populations on wild hosts. But when a crop is invaded, rates of parasitism are usually very low and only a few general predators, especially spiders, Mantids and Assassin bugs (Reduviidae) kill significant numbers.

Control:

Cultural practices. Cotton should be grown strictly as an annual with a dead season (legall enforced) between successive crops.

Hand collection has been used on peasant-grown cotton and tea and is moderately successful i areas where there is only a short period of immigration by the bugs into the crop.

Two crops that are *Helopeltis* hosts should not be grown next to each other. For example, sweet potatoes or pigeon pea should be grown apart from cotton. Tree crops in the nursery should b grown with minimal shade. *Helopeltis* damage is usually worse on crops grown on waterlogged o infertile soils and these should be avoided or ameliorated if possible. Fertilizer application may b beneficial on perennial crops but careful local studies are needed before a recommendation can b made to farmers.

Plants with abundant soft new growth generating a humid ecoclimate are particularly liable to *He lopeltis* attack. There is no clear evidence of varietal resistance conferred by any factor other tha growth habit.

Chemical control. There is little possibility of developing a biological or integrated control pro gramme in the near future. We have too little knowledge of the population dynamics of the pest on its alternative hosts. Chemical control of the bug when it invades the crop is at present the onl practical approach.

The following insecticides are effective as water-based sprays, dusts or as ultra-low-volum (ULV) waterless sprays:

DDT 0.5 kg a. i./ha, trichlorphon 0.8 kg a. i./ha, phenthoate 1.0 kg a. i./ha, carbaryl 1.0 k a. i./ha, BHC 0.35 kg a. i./ha.

DDT is to be preferred on cotton because of its cheapness and long persistence which gives pro tection against immigrating bugs for several days. It is not however generally recommended fo perennial crops because it kills parasites and predators and may lead to mite or scale outbreaks. I any case, it should be applied at least 3 weeks before harvesting on edible crops.

Fields must be inspected regularly during periods of flush growth and sprayed promptly if an in festation is found. Crop areas next to forest need special attention. Sprays should be applied to th infested area only – not the whole farm. Do not spray in hot sunshine when the bugs are sheltering Young cashew or cinchona trees up to 5 years old may need regular treatments in the main gro wing seasons in order to avoid stunting, and delay in the onset of cropping.

Literature

ENTWISTLE, P. F. (1972): Pests of cocoa. Longman, London. 779 pp.
HAINSWORTH, E. (1952): Tea pests and diseases and their control. Heffer, Cambridge. 130 pp.
PEARSON, E. O. (1958): The insect pests of cotton in tropical Africa. Emp. Cott. Grow. Corp. & Comm
    Inst. Ent., London, 355 pp.
SCHMITZ, G. (1958): Helopeltis du cotonnier en Afrique centrale. Publ. Inéac, Serie Sci. No 71, 178 pp

Author: T. J. Crowe

Distantiella theobroma (Dist.) (Fig. 112)

Synonym: *Sahlbergella theobroma*

Common names: Cocoa capsid; Kakaorindenwanze; Capsideo do cacau.

Geographical distribution: Ivory Coast, Ghana, Togo, Nigeria, Cameroun (rare). (CIE Map no 21, 1952.)

Host plants: Cocoa. Original hosts not known, probably various trees of order Malvales. Locally on *Citrus* spp. and *Ceiba pentandra,* also recorded on *Adansonia digitata.*

Symptoms: Injects copious digestive saliva into superficial tissues, causing sunken lesions that plit when they dry. On pods, round black lesions are clustered on sheltered side; primary damage superficial, but split lesions admit fungi and caterpillars. On seedlings and stems, oval black lesions on green tissues, less conspicuous sunken patches on hardened. Even a few lesions can ring shoot and cause dieback.

Categories of damage: 1. 'Blast' – lesions cause death of apical leaves; widespread and conspicuous in dry season, but trees may recover later. 2. 'Staghead' – excessive branching results from repeated dieback of apical shoots and development of lateral ones; the chronic condition of cocoa degeneration, especially where grown without shade, often covering large areas and with a complex of other insects and pathogens contributing. 3. Capsid 'pocket' – localised area of acute damage in which trees are largely reduced to regenerating basal shoots that are repeatedly killed back; the usual pattern where shade is left over cocoa.

Economic importance: Once capsid damage is established, its effects become part of a complex syndrome of degeneration involving fungal invasion of lesions (*Calonectria rigidiuscula*) and, where prevalent, mealybug-transmitted 'Swollen shoot' virus disease (SSVD), together with various other insects. In last 30 years, following main period of SSVD crisis, capsids generally regarded as main contributor. Estimates of annual loss range from 20 % to 30–40 %, and a survey in Ghana in 1956 showed about 1/5 of cocoa severely damaged.

Morphology: More robust appearance than most *Miridae,* and the large hooked spur on the adult scutellum is distinctive. Larvae dark chocolate-brown in colour.

Similarities to other pests: *D. theobroma* and *Sahlbergella singularis* are closely similar and occur together in many areas. All stages of latter are greyer in colour than *D. theobroma,* and antennae longer with less rounded segments. *Bryocoropsis laticollis* is sometimes common on pods; adults are smaller than the important pest species and larvae have a greenish colour.

Life cycle: Fully overlapping generations throughout year, generation time about six weeks. Eggs (commonly 30–50 per female) inserted in pod stalks and stems, buried except for respiratory filaments. Hatch 13–18 days, nymphal development 21–27 days with five instars of similar duration. Nymphs sedentary for first two instars, spread over tree in 3rd and 4th instars. Females release sex attractant from time first eggs mature, 4 or 5 days after emergence; mate once then lay eggs continuously. Live commonly 20–40 days, but large range. Main flight activity in afternoon. Dispersing insects are attracted to places where canopy broken.

Ecology: Seasonal population cycle usually well marked, but may be obscured on seedlings or in pockets of severe infestation. Numbers lowest March-May, at time of main leaf flush after dry season. Alternative hosts, notably *Ceiba,* may be locally significant as reservoirs at this time, but generally cocoa population self-contained. Numbers increase as pods develop from July or August to October, and often decrease temporarily at time of harvest. Also increase on vegetative tissues, especially vertical shoots ('chupons'), mostly from November onwards but sometimes earlier, and this continues to maximum in December-February.

This is time of main damage, increasingly aggravated by drought, both directly and by spread of *Calonectria* in wa-

8 mm

Fig. 112. *Distantiella theobroma* (dorsal view) (after Entwistle, Pests of Cocoa, Longman, London)

ter-stressed branches, as dry season progresses. Intermittently water-stressed tissues are ideal feeding sites, but late in dry season water stress approaching wilting point of trees results in slower growth, lower fecundity, and less survival of capsids, and finally leads to collapse of population.

Natural enemies: No important parasites. Where grown as understorey tree with forest shade, cocoa retains a diverse forest fauna including many ants, mantids, reduviid bugs, and salticid spiders which all eat some capsids; but no specialised predators. Role of ants controversial. Cocoa ant fauna in Ghana a mosaic of up to 12 species, many mutually exclusive. Some are negatively correlated with capsids, others positively correlated because they discourage general predators. *D. theobroma* mostly absent on trees with nests of *Oecophylla longinoda* (leaf-nests in canopy) but these trees seldom more than 20 % of total; the ants leave zones of unoccupied trees between conservative nest colonies, and attempts to spread them artificially not successful. Negative correlation also with *Macromischoides aculeatus* (carton nests on leaves). In spite of patchy influence of these ants as controls, role of ant-protected trees in containing and partly sheltering areas of damage very important, and control measures should preserve them.

Control:

Sanitary measures. Clearing of woody debris, pod husks etc. reduces nesting places of some ants (*Crematogaster striatula, Pheidole* spp.) that favour capsids by removing general predators. Cutting of ground herbage also reduces availability of extrafloral nectaries which are important food source for these species.

Cultural practice. The earliest possible formation of a closed canopy in a new planting is best defence against capsids and many other pests. Removal of chupons in mature cocoa reduces favoured capsid feeding sites.

Crop resistance. Amazon and Amazon hybrid varieties no less susceptible than traditional W. African Amelonado. Main resistance physiological: capsids favoured if trees already partly debilitated by water stress or absence of shade, and healthy trees regularly remain untouched alongside pockets of severe attack.

Integrated control. Recommendations have been put forward, but experience lacking even on experimental scale. Use of sprays should be based on local inspection and confirmation of capsid presence, not on a strict routine. This combined with measures (see above) to encourage capsid-predating members of ant mosaic and discourage their competitors that do not exclude capsids.

Insecticides. Gamma-BHC (Gammalin 20, Lindane etc.) in standard use, except in areas of resistance, where DDT sometimes used in absence of alternative.

Carbamates metalkamate and propoxur (Unden, Baygon) have shown to be good alternatives to gamma-BHC in field trials (Ghana, Cameroun).

Monocrotophos (Azodrin) can be brush-painted on young plants, with strict supervision. Four applications in period August to December effective on trees form first to fifth year.

Spraying schemes. Successful Government scheme in Ghana, 1956–58, and subsequent extension scheme, used knapsack mistblowers to apply gamma-BHC (active ingredient 3 oz/acre, 210 g/ha) in two pairs of sprayings each a month apart in June-July and November-December, with local retreatment if damage observed. Later experience showed earlier application effective only in isolated plots where risk of reinvasion slight; elsewhere spraying necessary through period of population increase, and four applications in period August or September to December found effective.

Resistance to insecticides. Localised resistance to BHC in Ghana 1961–63, then spreading more slowly when control widely neglected for several years. Survey in 1970 showed resistance persisted in original areas and had spread to several new areas.

Literature

see *S. singularis* (p. 295)

Author: D. G. Gibbs

Sahlbergella singularis Hagl. (Fig. 113 and plate 23 a)

Common names: Cocoa capsid; Kakaorindenwanze; Capside du cacao; Chinche del cacao.

Geographical distribution: Sierra Leone, Ivory Coast, Ghana, Togo, Nigeria, Cameroun, Fernando Poo, Central African Republic, Zaire, Uganda (CIE Map no 22).

Host plants: Occasionally found on a number of trees and shrubs of order Malvales (*Ceiba pentandra, Cola* spp., *Sterculia* spp., cultivated cotton), but present population overwhelmingly based on cocoa.

Symptoms: As *Distantiella theobroma* (see p. 292 and fig. 213). Preferred feeding sites of the two species overlap, and observed differences are not constant over whole range or over long periods in one place. At present in Ghana, *S. singularis* more on branches in canopy and on woody parts of stems, *D. theobroma* more on seedlings and green shoot tips. Important to note that pattern of attack has undergone various changes since capsids first noted on cocoa early in century, and may continue to do so.

Economic importance: As *D. theobroma* (see p. 293). Relative importance of the two species varies greatly between places and between years. *S. singularis* almost absent in much of Ghana from about 1956 to 1964, then quickly revived; eclipse largely coincided with period of effective gamma-BHC treatment, but this should not be assumed wholly responsible.

Morphological characteristics and similarities to other pests: See *D. theobroma*.

Fig. 113.   Young cocoa pods showing heavy damage by *Sahlbergella singularis* (phot. H. Schmutterer)

Life cycle: Stages of cycle take slightly longer than in *D. theobroma*. No sex attractant detected. Flight mostly at night, and unlike *D. theobroma* it comes to ultra-violet light traps.

Ecology: Differences from *D. theobroma* sometimes marked, but not consistent, and mostly result from fact that it occurs more often on branches in canopy, though preferring bases of chupons. Damage to canopy may occur at any time from about August, with peak numbers mostly November-December; goes on to reach later dry season peaks perhaps less often than *D. theobroma*.

Natural enemies: Braconid *Leiophron (Euphorus) sahlbergellae* in nymphs up to 5th instar or adult. Incidence commonly 20–40 % of 3rd and 4th instar nymphs, but much lower in some areas. Hyperparasitic ichneumonid *Mesorchus melanothorax* may reduce parasite incidence at some seasons.
General predators as *D. theobroma*, but less affected by ants and can co-exist even with *Oecophylla longinoda*.

Control: As *D. theobroma* (see p. 294). Incomplete penetration of the canopy by knapsack mistblowers in current use may result in poor control where canopy population important. Gradual spread of resistance to gamma-BHC in Western Region of Nigeria, 1964–69.

Literature

CLARK, L. R., P. W. GEIER, R. D. HUGHES & R. F. MORRIS (1967): The ecology of insect popula-
tions in theory and practice, chapter VI. Methuen, London.
COLLINGWOOD, C. A. (1971): Cocoa Capsids in West Africa: Report of International Capsid Research
Team 1965–71. International Office of Cocoa and Chocolate, 11 Green Street, London W1Y 3RF, U. K.
ENTWISTLE, P. F. (1972): Pests of Cocoa. Longman, London.
LESTON, D. (1970): Entomology of the cocoa farm. Annu. Rev. Ent. **15**, 273–294.
LESTON, D. (1973): The ant mosaic, tropical tree crops, and the limiting of pests and diseases. PANS **19**,
311–341.

Author: D. G. Gibbs

Family: Coreidae

Leptocorisa acuta (Thunb.) (Plate 23 b)

Synonyms: *Gerris varicornis* F., *Leptocorisa varicornis* (F.)

Common names: Rice bug; Gewöhnliche Reiswanze; Chinche común del arroz.

Geographical distribution: *L. acuta* occurs in oriental countries, e. g. Australia, Burma, Cambo-
dia, Sri Lanka, China, Indonesia, Fiji, Taiwan, Guam, India, Japan, Malaysia, New Hebrides,
New Zealand, Pakistan, Philippines, Samoa, Thailand, Tonga Islands, Vietnam and Tibet
(CIE-Map no 225).

Host plants: The adults feed and breed on rice, a number of wild grasses and other weeds, millet,
forest trees, etc. belonging to 81 important species.
Other alternate host plants of the rice bug are Catechu (*Acacia catechu*), Siris tree (*Albizzia* spp.),
Amaranth (*Amaranthus* spp.), Jack tree (*Artrocarpus chaplasha*), Toon (*Cedrela* sp.), Indian
hemp (*Crotolaria* sp.), Conifer tree (*Cryptomeria* sp.), Sedge, Indian red wood (*Dalbergia sissoo*),
Bean, Mango, Iron wood (*Mesua ferreae*), Champa (*Michella champaca*), Tobacco, Gram, Pea,
Guava, Sugarcane, Sal (*Shorea robusta*), Brinjal (Eggplant), Maize, Tea etc.

Symptoms: Both nymphs and adults suck the milky juice from developing grains of rice ears resulting in the grains failing to develop or shrivelling up completely. The characteristic symptom are
whitening ears, a whole field often turning colour in this way. The attack remains until the paddy
(rice) grain hardens. Late varieties of paddy escape damage since they mature late in November
when pest incidence is very low.

Economic importance: The rice bug is a major pest of rice (paddy). It occurs in epidemic form in
India, Indoniesia, Pakistan, Japan, Malaysia, Sri Lanka, Burma, Fiji Islands, Australia and the
Philippines, where it causes 10–40 % loss of crop. In cases of severe infestations it may cause
complete loss.

Morphology: *L. acuta* is very robust and more than 13 mm long. The basal joints of the antennae
and legs are pale and uniform in colour. The male claspers are wide at the base, with the extremity
curved and tapering. There are four pairs of brownish dots on the abdomen and in males the har-
pogones (hook-shaped structure of the external genitalia) are pointed at their ends. ·

Similiarities to other species: There are several species of *Leptocorisa* on rice in the oriental regions, e. g. *L. costalis*, *L. lepida*, *L. corbetti*, *L. discoidalis* and *L. geniculata*. They are classified
according to the structures of the male claspers, their colour, length and other external characteristics.

Life cycle: The longevity of the adults is 45–60 days in the field, but they can live for 105–115 days under controlled environments. The adults are active during the early morning and in the evening, while during the day the insects hide in the shade of the basal parts of the plants. The females are stronger fliers than the males. The males generally are ready for copulation soon after the last moult, but the females mate when they are 7–25 days old. 3–4 days after copulation the females lay 250–300 eggs by gradually moving forward and depositing one egg after another in one to three rows on the upper leaf surfaces; in captivity they may lay on any aerial part of the plant. The egg is yellowish brown, but its colour soon deepens. The incubation period varies from five to eight days. A newly hatched nymph is green and later becomes brownish. The nymphal stage lasts from 14 to 25 days. Each ecdysis takes about 10 to 15 minutes. The five instars are 2, 5, 8, 11 and 14 mm long und last 2–3, 2–5, 7, 3–8 and 4–9 days, respectively.

The insect overwinters from December to March and passes the summer (April–June) in the adult stage as scattered individuals on alternate hosts like grasses and other weeds. Later, the pest migrates to the paddy crop in the flowering and milk stages. In single cropping areas the insect usually has four overlapping generations, but in areas where temperatures are optimum and rice is grown all the year, the bugs remain active throughout the year without a distinct diapause; in such areas there is a heavy infestation.

Ecology: Early rains in May and June encourage the prolific growth of weeds and grasses on which the pest feeds. In subsequent months, this results in a severe outbreak of the bug in the paddy crop. The multiplication of bugs is favoured by light intermittent rainfall throughout the season, temperature of 27 °C to 28 °C and a relative humidity of 80 to 82 percent.

Natural enemies: There are 26 species of parasites and predators of *Leptocorisa* and the common ones are *Cicindela sexpunctata*, *Ommatius* sp., *Ooencyrtus analyensis*, *Hadronotus flavipes*, *Ooencyrtus malayensis* and *Telenomus comperei*.

Control:

Sanitary methods. Clean cultivation of banks around the paddy fields prevents infestation and breeding of rice bugs, especially between growing seasons.

Netting, smoking the fields, passing baskets or bags coated inside with a sticky material over infested fields have given promising results against the pest. Some scented aquatic plants like *Ceratophyllum* spp., *Lycopodium* sp., *Hydrilla* sp., etc., have been used to trap the bugs.

Cultural practices. Early sowing of early and late maturing paddy varieties generally prevents pest damage. The use of quick growing varieties evades bug attack.

Resistant varieties. Certain coarse grain-yielding, bearded rice varieties like Sathi, Soma and Mundagakutty are resistant to bug attack, because the panicle remains enclosed in the leaf sheath and thus offers a sort of mechanical resistance.

Chemical control. The bugs can be effectively controlled by dusting 5 % BHC, DDT or chlordane, or 10 % toxaphene, or 2.5 % aldrin (20 lbs/acre) or spraying with 0.25 % DDT, or 0.2 % nicotine sulphate, or 0.02 % parathion emulsion (50 gallons/acre). A new formulation containing 0.01 % nicotine sulphate and 1.25 % sesame oil as a synergist has proved very effective.

Resistance to insecticides. Strains of *L. acuta* exposed to BHC for the past 6 to 9 years have developed up to 2.7 times their original level of resistance. There is also a strain with a 6.6-fold resistance. Gamma BHC dust has been effective against both the most highly resistant and the least resistant bugs. Poor control of the most resistant strains of bugs, however, has been achieved with other chlorinated hydrocarbon dusts. Addition of diazinon dust to gamma BHC dust has reduced the toxicity of gamma BHC to all strains of the bug.

Literature

AHMAD, I. (1965): The Leptocorisinae of the World. Bull. Brit. Museum (N. H.), Entomol. Suppl. **5**, 1–156.

SRIVASTAVA, A. S. (1960): Control of the gundhi bug on paddy during 1958. Plant Protection Bull. XIV, Directorate of Plant Protection, Govt. of India, New Delhi.
SRIVASTAVA, A. S., & H. P. SAXENA (1964): Rice bug *Leptocorisa varicornis* Fabricius and allied species. Proc. Symp. Intern. Rice Res. Institute, 525–548.

Author: A. S. Srivastava

Family: Pyrrhocoridae

Dysdercus spp. (Figs. 114–115 and plate 23 c, d)

Important species and synonyms: *D. cardinalis* Gerst., *D. cingulatus* (F.) (syn. *D. ornatus* Bredd.), *D. fasciatus* Sign., *D. howardi* Ball., *D. intermedius* Dist., *D. koenigii* (F.), *D. melanoderes* Karsch, *D. nigrofasciatus* Stål, *D. peruvianus* (Guér.), *D. sidae* Mont. (syn. *D. insularis* Stål) *D. superstitiosus* (F.), *D. völkeri* Schmidt (= *D. superstitiosus* part.)

Common names: Cotton stainers; Rotwanzen, Baumwollwanzen; Punaises rouges du cotonnier, Les Dysdercus; Chinches rojos del algodonero, Chinches tintóreos.

Geographical distribution: At least 10 species of *Dysdercus* attack cotton in Africa, the most widespread being *D. fasciatus* (CIE Map no 266), *D. nigrofasciatus* and *D. völkeri*.
The Oriental group are found in various countries extending from Pakistan to Australia. The best known species are *D. cingulatus* (CIE Map no 265), *D. koenigii* and *D. sidae* (CIE Map no 267). The New World species are very numerous and include *D. howardi* and *D. peruvianus*.

Host plants: Cotton stainers are particularly associated with the family Malvaceae and most species attack cotton, wild and cultivated *Hibiscus* spp. (okra, roselle, kenaf etc.) and *Abutilon* spp.. The other families of the order Malvales – Bombaceae (kapok, baobab), Sterculiaceae and Tiliaceae also have members supporting certain *Dysdercus* spp.. *D. völkeri* is unusual in that is commonly breeds on sorghum and pennisetum (Plate 23 d).

Symptoms: Stainers feed on mature or developing seeds. They damage cotton because when (prior to sucking) they inject saliva into the cotton boll, they deposit inside spores of the fungus *Nematospora*. It is the subsequent growth of the fungus that does most of the damage. Attacks on young bolls are therefore, particularly serious since the fungus has a long period in which to grow. Small green bolls may abort and go brown or may be shed. No damage is visible externally on large green bolls but, if the inner boll wall is examined, warty growths or water-soaked spots can be seen which correspond to patches of yellow staining on the developing lint. Open bolls have lint hairs sticking to the boll wall causing a webbed appearance and the lint is stained a bright yellow colour. In severe attacks, whole locks may be brown and shrunken like small kidneys.

Economic importance: Major pests especially in the hotter drier areas where rain-feed cotton is grown. If large numbers of the bug enter the crop when young green bolls are present, the damage can be very serious. High populations at harvest time will not affect the lint, but germination percentage, weight and oil content of the seed will be reduced.
Seed cotton with stained lint commands only about half the price of clean cotton.

Morphology: Adult stainers are usually red-bodied bugs 12–15 mm long and 4.5 mm wide. The brown wings typically have a conspicuous black bar or pair of spots. The nymphal stages are bright red and gregarious. All stages tend to drop to the ground if the cotton bush is shaken.

Similarities to other pests/diseases: Bacterial blight, caused by *Xanthomonas malvacearum* also stains lint hairs when the boll is infected. But the stain is brownish-yellow compared with the greenish-yellow *Nematospora* stain. Blight also does not cause lint webbing or warty growths on the boll wall.

Other Pyrrhocorids, especially *Odontopus* spp., are often found under baobab and kapok trees feeding with the *Dysdercus*. The adults are easily distinguished from stainers but the nymphs are very similar. *Odontopus* nymphs are a dark red, not a bright crimson like *Dysdercus*.

Life cycle: The *Dysdercus* spp. that have been studied have a similar life history. The following is a generalized account.

The eggs are oval, about 1.5 mm long and 0.9 mm broad. They are yellow or white when first laid but change to orange as the embryo develops. Hatching takes place after about 5 days at 27 °C and 8 days at 23 °C. Eggs are laid in shady places (usually under host plants) in batches of about 100 in moist soil or plant debris. High humidity is essential for development. If the soil dries out, the eggs will die.

There are five nymphal instars. The full-grown nymph is a red bug with black wing pads and is 10 to 15 mm long according to species. The total nymphal period lasts about 21 days at 27 °C and 35 days at 23 °C. The first instar nymphs do not feed but require moisture and are usually found congregating near the egg shells from which they have emerged. The second and third instars usually feed gregariously on seeds in open bolls near the ground. Later instars wander freely over the plant seeking suitable seeds and fruits. Nymphs are often seen in large numbers on posts, tree trunks etc. where they prefer to moult.

Adult stainers mate 2–6 days after the final moult and begin egg-laying 3–8 days later. The egg-laying period and the number of eggs laid depends to a large extent on the availability of food. Most *Dysdercus* spp. need to feed on the seeds of Malvales to lay maximum egg numbers. A typical female may lay 8 batches of 100 eggs at 6-day intervals.

Breeding is normally continuous and there is no evidence of diapause. But some species can survive (without reproducing) on water alone for several weeks.

Ecology: The essential features in the ecology of stainers are:
a) breeding only takes place if ripe or riping seeds of the appropriate species of Malvales are available and moist soil is present for oviposition sites.
b) adult bugs can however survive for several weeks without reproduction on water and nectar.

Fig. 114.   Adults of *Dysdercus völkeri* on a pennisetum head (phot. H. Schmutterer)

Fig. 115.   *Phonoctonus* sp., a common predator of *Dysdercus* spp. in tropical Africa (phot. H. Schmutterer)

c) adult stainers tend to disperse from their breeding grounds as they approach maturity. They have a flight range of at least 10 miles.

In each cotton-growing area therefore it is necessary to identify the *Dysdercus* species present, determine their principal host plants and work out the seasonal fruiting cycle of these hosts in relation to rainfall and the actual or proposed cotton season. Only when this information is available can efficient cultural control measures be devised.

Natural enemies: No egg parasites have been recorded but soil-dwelling general predators (possibly Carabid beetles) eat some batches of eggs. Adults and fifth instar nymphs are attacked by Tachinid fly parasites (e. g. *Bogosia* spp.) in most countries. Parasitized bugs appear to be normal and take several days to die but may be recognized by the whitish fly egg stuck to their legs or body. Assassin bugs (Reduviidae), mostly of the genus *Phonoctonus* (Fig. 115), are common stainer predators in Africa. They closely resemble *Dysdercus* in their size and colour patterns but can be distinguished by their shorter, more beak-like mouth parts.

Control:

Cultural practices. Cotton should be grown strictly as an annual with a dead season (legally enforced) between successive crops.

If practicable, annual host plants should be cut down at the beginning of the dead season, to prevent fruiting. These are commonly *Abutilon*, *Hibiscus* and *Sida* spp. which are pioneer weeds in recently disturbed soil (roadsides, headlands, fallows etc.). If small trees are the main alternative host it may be possible to coppice them annually to prevent fruiting.

Resistant varieties. No commercial cotton variety has proven resistance to *Dysdercus* attack but those which produce their crop from many small bolls rather than a few large ones, may have to lose less crop when attacked by the same stainer population.

Biological control. Provided vegetative growth is not too lush, *Dysdercus* can be controlled effectively by caging chickens in the cotton field. About 30 birds will keep a quarter hectare almost free of bugs. This method should not be combined with a chemical treatment and is most appropriate to a small plot grown next to a peasant homestead.

Chemical control. The following insecticides are effective as water-based sprays, dusts or ultralow-volume (ULV) waterless sprays: Carbaryl 1.0 kg a. i./ha, phenthoate 1.0 kg a. i./ha, gamma-BHC 0.35 kg a. i./ha (ULV sprays are particularly effective).

If the cotton is carrying green bolls, spraying or dusting should begin when 5 % or more of the plants have one or more stainers.

In areas where baobab trees are the main wild host, excellent stainer control has been achieved by clearing the debris and vegetation from under the trees and spraying the trunk and exposed soil with 1 % chlordane. One application a year in the rainy season in all that is needed to prevent successful breeding.

Literature

PEARSON, E. O. (1958): The insect pests of cotton in tropical Africa. Emp. Cott. Grow. Corp. & Comm. Inst. Ent., London, 355 pp.

Author: T. J. Crowe

Other injurious Heteroptera (Figs. 116–117):

Agonoscelis pubescens (Thbg.) (= *A. versicolor*), Cluster bug, Sudan millet bug (Afrikanische Hirsewanze). Widely distributed in Africa south of the Sahara. Attacks sorghum, pennisetum, wheat, sesame, lucerne, sunflower and cocoa. Heavy outbreaks occur in the Sudan. Control: Application of gamma-BHC in winter against gregariously diapausing bugs.

Fig. 116. *Nezara viridula* on tomato (phot. H. Schmutterer)

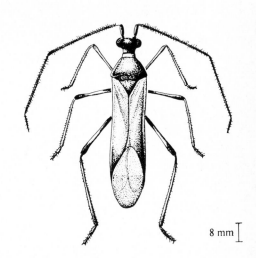

8 mm

Fig. 117. *Monalonion annulipes* (after Entwistle, Pests of Cocoa, Longman, London)

Bagrada spp., Harlequin bugs. Various species of this genus, for instance *B. hilaris* (Burm.) and *B. cruciferarum* (L.), destroy the leaves of cultivated crucifers by their sucking activity. They occur in the tropics and subtropics of the Old World.

Nezara viridula (L.) Green stink bug, Green vegetable bug (Grüne Reiswanze) (Fig. 116). Occurs in all tropical and subtropical regions, as well as in Southern Europe (CIE Map no 27). Attacks more than 200 host plant species including rice, cotton, groundnut, sorghum, okra, citrus, beans *(Phaseolus* and *Vigna* beans), tobacco, potato and castor bean. On cotton, fungus spores of the genus *Nematospora* can be transmitted with the act of feeding. Gamma-BHC, toxaphene, dieldrin and DDT are effective insecticides.

Scotinophara spp. *S. coarctata* (F.) (Black paddy bug, Schwarze Reiswanze) and *S. lurida* (Burm.) (Black Japanese rice bug, Schwarze japanische Reiswanze) feed mainly on leaf sheaths of rice plants in Asiatic rice growing regions.

Amblypelta coccophaga China. Feeds on the inflorescences of coconut palms on the Solomon Islands and causes dropping of young fruit. *Pseudotheraptus wayi* Brown does similar damage in East Africa and Zanzibar. Biological control of the former species by encouraging the ant *Oecophylla smaragdina* by eliminating other competitive species.

Acanthomia horrida (Germ.) and other species of the same genus feed in various parts of tropical Africa on the seeds of legumes *(Phaseolus* spp., *Vigna* spp. etc.). Other Coreid bugs attacking legume seeds in Africa belong to the genera *Riptortus, Mirperus* and *Anoplocnemis.*

Monalonion spp.. *M. bahiense* Costa Lima, *M. annulipes* Sign. (Fig. 117), *M. dissimilatum* Dist., *M. bondari* Costa Lima and *M. shaefferi* Stål take the place in the New World occupied in the Old World by *Helopeltis* spp. (see p. 289). They are considered to be major pests on cocoa in the South American tropics (Brazil etc.) and in Central America. Young pods damaged by feeding activity dry up and drop off. Even fully developed pods can burst, so that the beans are worthless. Normally however, the older fruit shows irregular growth and malformations. Fungi can penetrate the pods at the puncture sites and cause death of the surrounding tissue. Necrotic lesions also form on affected shoots. Chemical control can be carried out by repeated sprayings of contact insecticides (e. g. parathion).

Habrochila spp.. The Coffee bugs *H. placida* Horv. and *H. ghesquierei* Schout. are pests of coffee leaves in Central and East Africa. Chemical control: Application of parathion.

H. Sch.

Leafhoppers, White flies, Aphids, Scale insects etc.; Pflanzenläuse; Cicadelles, Pucerons, Cochenilles; Langostinos, Mosquitas blancas, Pulgones, Conchuelas

Order: Homoptera

General features: The usually small to very small Homoptera represent an insect group of special significance. They are all plant suckers. The most thoroughly adapted to a plant parasitic mode of life are the scale insects, particularly the Diaspididae. The apodous, pouchlike body of the Diaspididae is covered with a lide-like scale. Aphids appear in a variety of morphs, but in the tropics they do not generally exhibit the alternation of generations and hosts which is characteristic for temperate zones. Homoptera injure plants by their feeding activity (withdrawel of sap), by the physiological effect of their saliva (necroses, gall formation) and in many cases indirectly by giving off sugary honeydew, on which sooty mould develops to soil the fruit and inhibit assimilation and dissimilation by the leaves. Many Homoptera are attended by ants for their sweet excretions (trophobiosis).

Metamorphosis is hemimetabolic. Many Homoptera transmit phytopathogenic viruses and other plant pathogens (e. g. mycoplasma-like organisms) during the feeding process, as a result of which they can do much indirect damage in tropical and subtropical regions, especially on rice.

H. Sch.

Superfamily: Fulgoroidea
Family: Delphacidae

Saccharosydne saccharivora (Westw.) (Figs. 118–119)

Synonyms: *Delphax saccharivora, Stenocranus saccharivorus*

Common names: (West Indian) cane fly; Saltahoja de la caña de azúcar.

Geographical distribution: Entire Caribbean area as in CIE Map no 62, plus Belize (formerly British Honduras), Mexico and the Bahamas.

Host plants: Sugar cane. Wild hosts are *Andropogon bicornis, A. glomeratus,* and *Sorghum sudanense.*

Symptoms: Thick encrustations of sooty mould *(Capnodium* spp.) develop on the honeydew deposited by adults and nymphs on the lower leaves of the sugar-cane plant; egg punctures on the leaf midrib are marked by a conspicuous deposit of white fluffy wax and by some necrosis. Nymphs and adults are conspicuous on the leaves and in the funnels. Nymphal feeding causes a slight yellowish red mottling of the leaf. Heavily infested 2–3-week-old ratoon shoots may wilt.

Economic importance: A heavy infestation can cause losses of 5 tons cane/acre. Outbreaks of canefly have occured in different parts of the Caribbean at irregular intervals since the 18th century, but are most frequent and persistent in Jamaica.

Morphology: The adults are easily distinguished from any other sugar cane pests in the region by

Fig. 118. Nymphs of *Saccharosydne saccharivora* on a sugar cane leaf (reproduced by permission of the Commonwealth Agricultural Bureaux from the Bulletin of Entomological Research)

Fig. 119. Ovipositing female of *S. saccharivora* (reproduced by permission of the Commonwealth Agricultural Bureaux from the Bulletin of Entomological Research)

their pale green appearance and by the tuft of white wax surrounding the genitalia of the female. The nymphs are characterised by a filament of white wax, equal to or longer than the body, projecting from the posterior end, and by very fine lateral filaments. The five nymphal instars may be separated on the development of the wing pads and of the metathoracic tibiae and tarsi.

Life cycle: Rows of eggs, about 7 in each row, are inserted into the leaf midrib. After hatching, the nymphs and, later, the adults feed on the leaves, their sucking probes reaching the vascular bundles. At about 27 °C on normal vigorous cane plants the development times are for eggs 15–19 days, instar 1 6–7 days, instars 2–4 each 4–5 days, and instar 5 6–7 days; on unthrifty plants nymphal development is slower. There is a preoviposition period of 5.3 days, and egg production averages 12.0 eggs per female per day, the rate of production being directly related to the nitrogen content of the leaf lamina. The complete cycle takes $6^{1}/_{2}$–7 weeks.

Ecology: Canefly shows two features unique in a tropical insect with a capacity for continuous breeding, namely segregation and synchronisation of generations. The following remarks apply to Jamaica and Belize. In epidemic populations successive generations of canefly are segregated and their development is synchronised over areas of up to 80 miles^2. Segregation is due to the sterilising action of the parasite *Stenocranophilus quadratus;* in the drier months this spreads so rapidly through the nymph and adult population that oviposition ceases until the first adults of the next generation reach maturity. In the wet season this effect is complemented by the entomogenous fungus *Metarrhizium anisopliae.* Synchronisation is ensured by the dispersal of parasitised adult canefly before oviposition. In ratoon cane there are 6–7 generations between successive annual harvests; egg populations are highest in generations 1–3 and decline in old cane irrespective of season. In plant cane, egg populations do not show a decline with age and sometimes increase. The early stages of outbreaks are invariably associated with plant cane; heavy infestations rarely occur on cane subjected to adverse growing conditions. The essential prerequisite for an outbreak is plant cane growing under favourable climatic and agricultural conditions; a long harvest period, high standards of cultivation, irrigation and fertiliser practice together offer the minimum chance for a natural end to outbreaks.

Analysis of canefly population changes has shown dispersal of adults to be the key disturbing factor, while parasitism by *Stenocranophilus* is the only regulating factor. Adult dispersal depends on crop characters which can be altered by selective breeding or agronomic practice.

Natural enemies: Altogether 11 species of parasites, 72 species of predators and three species of entomogenous fungi have been recorded as attacking canefly. The most important are *Stenocranophilus quadratus, Tetrastichus* spp., Syrphidae, Reduviidae, and Miridae (*Tytthus* spp. – egg predators), swallows, and the fungi *Metarrhizium anisopliae, Fusarium* sp. and *Hirsutella* sp.

Control:

Biological control. Despite several attempts, *Tytthus mundulus,* a mirid which controlled *Perkinsiella saccharicidae* in Hawaii, has not become established in Jamaica.

Chemical control. a) **Insecticides** – Malathion (1/2 pt 97 % e. c./acre in 2 gals water) and fenitrothion (1 pt 50 % e. c./acre in 2 gals water).

b) **Spraying scheme.** The chemical control of canefly is tied closely to its biology and ecology. The combined effect of *Stenocranophilus* and *Metarrhizium* is to limit the oviposition period of each generation to 3–6 weeks. The result is a period, once in each generation, when the whole canefly population is in the nymph and early adult stages which, unlike the egg stage, are accessible to insecticide sprays. Therefore, one correctly timed spraying of all infested fields gives complete control. Extensive block spraying from the air in November-December when the average age of the crop is at its highest, and the canefly population at its lowest, gives complete control with minimum expenditure. Plant cane or young cane shoots, on which the oviposition period is longer, may need a second spray.

Spraying without regard to timing causes chaos. Synchronisation of generations breaks down and the benefit from the natural control by *Stenocranophilus* is lost.

c) **Prognosis.** Outbreaks in susceptible areas such as Jamaica may be expected whenever there is an extensive acreage of plant cane and/or when control of epidemic populations shortly before harvest has been neglected.

Literature

METCALFE, J. R. (1964): The chemical control of canefly *(Saccharosydne saccharivora* (Westw.) (Hom: Delphacidae) in Jamaica. Jl. Jamaican Sug. Cane Technol. **25,** 39–44.

METCALFE, J. R. (1968): Studies on the biology of the sugar-cane pest *Saccharosydne saccharivora* (Westw.) (Hom.: Delphacidae). Bull. ent. Res. **59,** 393–408.

METCALFE, J. R. (1970): Studies on the effect of the nutrient status of sugar-cane on the fecundity of *Saccharosydne saccharivora* (Westw.) (Hom.: Delphacidae). Bull. ent. Res. **60,** 309–325.

METCALFE, J. R. (1971): Observations on the ecology of *Saccharosydne saccharivora* (Westw.) (Hom.: Delphacidae) in Jamaica sugar-cane fields. Bull. ent. Res. **60,** 565–597.

METCALFE, J. R. (1972): An analysis of the population dynamics of the Jamaican sugar-cane pest *Saccharosydne saccharivora* (Westw.) (Hom.: Delphacidae). Bull. ent. Res. **62,** 73–85.

Author: J. R. Metcalfe

Family: Tropiduchidae

Ommatissus binotatus Fieb. var. lybicus de Berg.

Common names: Old world date bug; Dattelpalmenzikade.

Geographical distribution: Iraq, Egypt, Saudi Arabia, Trinidad.

Host plants: Only the date palm, *Phoenix dactylifera.* The nominotypical form, *O. binotatus,* however, lives on the wild palm *Chamaerops humilis* in North Africa, Spain, and in Southeastern Soviet Union.

Symptoms: Necrotic areas develop on the surface of fronds due to the egg-laying scars.
The fronds and fruits become covered with copious honeydew excretions of the pest which become coated with dust.

Economic importance: This insect is considered to be a serious pest in the Basrah area of Iraq where it often reduces the crop by over 50 percent. It is often quite serious in the western desert of Egypt, and in the Libyan date oases. Repeated attacks weaken the trees leading to their death.

Morphology: The female is 5–6 mm long, yellowish green in colour and bears up to 10 dark or black spots on the head and the 7th and 8th segments of the abdomen. The male is about 3 to 3.5 mm long with a tapered abdomen and has no dark spots on the 7th and 8th abdominal segments; its wings extend further beyond its abdomen when compared to the female. Individual differences in colour and size of the insect are quite common.

Similarities to other pests: Unlike any other pest known to feed on the date palm in the same areas. Differs from the nominotypical form in being longer, has a yellowish green abdomen instead of being ochrous yellow with a brownish abdomen. There is also a slight difference in the bifurcation of the median vein of the wing.

Life cycle: In October–November the eggs are laid in the axial veins and midrib of the date palm fronds. The eggs go into diapause until April, very occasionally until June, of the following year. After hatching the young nymphs disperse into "leaf" (frond) folds, or onto the young fruits and start to feed. The insect passes five nymphal instars which are completed in about four weeks from hatching. The large amount of honeydew they excrete smears the surface of the fruits and fronds and gets mixed with the insects' exuviae and dust, causing a reduction of the photosynthetic activity and suffocation of the tree by clogging the stigmata.

Eggs which hatch in April produce adults by early June. The adults copulate and lay again in the frond tissue. However, the eggs of the summer generation aestivate and do not hatch before the hot months are over. In late August, hatching of summer eggs starts and the nymphs reach maturity about the end of September, when adults of the autumn generation disperse to infest new trees in October–November. They then feed, copulate, oviposit and die. This means that the insect has two full generations per year. A few adults may survive the winter, hidden under palm bark; these become active early the following spring.

Ecology: The insect exists in date oases in different population densities. The damage caused by its feeding seems to increase inversely with the health of the trees. The injury caused is greater when the palm trees grow in water-logged soils with poor drainage, or where the desert sands invade the plantations on the periphery of neglected or unprotected date groves.

Natural enemies: Adults and larvae of a number of different species of Coccinellidae feed on the nymphs of this pest species particularly when its infestation is high in spring.

Control: Cultural practices which help to keep the trees healthy: in particular good drainage and windbreaks help to reduce injury by this pest.

Chemical control can be achieved by the use of short residual contact pesticides, such as nicotine sulfate or trichlorphon (Diptrex) at low concentration, in order to do as little harm to the Coccinellid predators as possible. Systemic insecticides, such as dimethoate, phosphamidon (Dimecron) and demeton-S-methyl (Metasystox-i) as sprays should be applied early when infestation is first noticed, and before dust accumulates on the leaf surfaces. Because of interactions with the large number of arthropod species that live in date palm groves, it is advisable to use chemical pesticides only when it is absolutely necessary, and when no other method really helps.

The height of palm trees makes it difficult to apply chemical pesticides by means of ground equipment, particularly when large acreages have to be treated in a short time. Aerial application is therefore the only solution. In private groves, air-blast power sprayers and dusters have been used effectively.

Application of pesticides is done only when honeydew droplets are found on the fronds or fruits. Ideally, crown inspection of a few trees in the grove should be done by means of a ladder, but often it is possible to see the glistening droplets against the green background from the ground.

Literature

LEPESME, P. (1947): Les insectes des Palmiers. pp. 170–172. Paul Lechevalier edit., Paris.
MARTIN, H. E. (1971): List of plant pests and diseases in Saudi Arabia. pp. 55. F.A.O. Reg. Office for N. E. Affairs, Cairo.

Author: A. S. Talhouk

Superfamily: Cicadoidea
Family: Cicadellidae (Jassidae)

Cicadulina spp. (Fig. 120)

Important species: *Cicadulina mbila* (Naudé), *C. storeyi* China, *C. bipunctella zeae* China, *C. parazeae* Ghauri, and *C. latens* Fennah.

Common names: Maize leafhoppers; Afrikanische Maiszikaden.

Geographical distribution: The maize leafhoppers, *Cicadulina mbila*, *C. storeyi*, *C. bipunctella zeae*, *C. parazeae* and *C. latens* are the known vectors of maize streak disease in Africa, Other *Cicadulina* species are found in Africa, and also in many warm regions of the world including South America, Asia and Australia. Even so, as *C. mbila,* the best known vector of maize streak disease, is found in the Yemen, India and several other parts of Asia, the disease could spread through movement of infective leafhoppers from Africa to regions where uninfected populations now occur. *C. mbila* and *C. bipunctella zeae* are also vectors of maize mottle in eastern Africa.

Host plants: *Cicadulina* spp. breed on a wide range of grasses and cereal crops. The few recorded from plants other than Gramineae may have settled temporarily on non-host plants. Most of the leafhoppers are sparsely distributed in natural grasslands. Dense populations of *C. mbila* and *C. storeyi* are found in pastures of *Pennesitum clandestinum* (Kikuyu grass) and on irrigated annual grass weeds such as *Eleusine indica* and *Urochloa panicoides* in Africa.

Symptoms of damage and economic importance: Maize streak virus is only transmitted by an infective leafhopper feeding on a healthy plant. After infection all new maize leaves show broken chlorotic lines parallel to the veins (Fig. 10). Plants infected at an early stage of growth become stunted and fail to produce a marketable cob. During a severe outbreak ninety percent of the crop may become infected within two months of germination and virtually the whole crop lost. In Rhodesia, streak is most serious on irrigated crops, and it is rarely found in maize grown away from irrigation schemes. Sometimes wheat plants may become stunted through early infection.

Morphology: All *Cicadulina* adults have a pair of small black spots between the eyes on the front of the head. The leafhoppers are about 3 mm in length, slender and cream in colour. *C. mbila* has dusky marks behind the eyes and these extend along the wings. The leafhoppers are easily seen in the funnels of young maize plants where they sit head upwards astride a vein. One leafhopper to three plants is a high level of infestation.

Life cycle and ecology: The life cycles of *C. mbila* and two other species which have been studied are similar. Eggs are deposited in the tissues of host plants and there are five nymphal stages. The period of development from egg deposited to adult stages is 21, 31 and 50 days for mean constant temperatures of 30 °, 25 °, and 20 °C respectively. The adult female matures in about five days and then lays several eggs a day for about six weeks.

The numbers of generations in an annual cycle are predictable from ambient temperatures, and the sizes of populations from abundance of suitable host grasses. In many parts of Africa rainfall is seasonal. At the end of the wet season *Cicadulina* populations are at their highest. As the natural grasses dry large numbers disperse, but only once they have reached adult stage. Consequently in areas

Fig. 120.   Female of *Cicadulina mbila* (phot. D. J. W. Rose)

where winter coincides with the dry season, development slows down and the flight period extends for several months. Many of the leafhoppers fly long distances during this period and alight on irrigated crops and grasses. Winter cereal crops may be directly infected with streak disease. Also, grasses sprouting on irrigation schemes are invaded, and it is the adults of the subsequent generations breeding in these grasses which infect maize crops planted close by.

Control: Control measures depend on recognition of these possible sources of vectors. Prevention of maize streak is most difficult in crops planted during the main flight of leafhoppers from the populations in drying natural grasses. Vectors alighting on susceptible crops are quickly replaced by others flying and streak is then only prevented by persistent and efficient protection with insecticides. This has been achieved experimentally with an application of aldicarb granules into the soil before planting maize. Unfortunately the treatment is costly and the toxic residues in maize need investigation before aldicarb can be recommended for prevention of streak in crops. Consequently maize is best not planted until the main flight of vectors is over.

The extent of the flight season depends on the condition of the grasses and the prevailing temperatures during the first part of the dry season. An extended wet season preceding cool dry winters causes a long flight period with a second peak flight of *Cicadulina* spp. in the spring just as irrigated maize crops are planted. It has been found that the amount of rain several months previously provides good warning of seasons in which widespread outbreaks of streak are likely and plantings must be delayed. After the main flight is over, the major sources of vectors are the populations breeding in grasses and cereals on irrigated lands. Most of these leafhoppers will not fly far. The ability to fly long distances is inherited and restricted to a small part of the population. A barrier of bare ground about ten metres wide stops the passage of most leafhoppers from grasses into crops and decreases streak infection.

The main danger periods occur when cereal crops are ripening, annual grass weeds are maturing, or silage crops are cut. Then adults fly downwind to infest late planted maize crops. Risk of streak infection may be reduced or largeley avoided by not planting a succession of cereal crops on irrigation schemes. If this is not possible then maize should not be planted downwind from earlier planted cereals, and these cereals and grasses should be sprayed with insecticides prior to the danger periods. Cover sprays with 0.5 % carbaryl are recommended for maturing crops.

If streak diseased plants are found in maize crops within a few weeks of germination then exponential increase of disease and severe losses are likely. Epidemic conditions may be delayed by spraying young maize plants with 0.1 % dimethoate or 0.1 % demeton-S-methyl (Metasystox-i) and then removing diseased plants. Rogueing, without firstly killing vectors, causes increase in spread of the disease through disturbance of leafhoppers.

Literature

GORTER, G. J. M. A. (1953): Studies on the spread and control of the streak disease of maize. Sci. Bull. Dep. Agric. For. Un. S. Afr. no 341, 20 pp.

ROSE, D. J. W. (1972): Times and sizes of dispersal flights by *Cicadulina* species (Homoptera: Cicadellidae), vectors of maize streak disease. J. Anim. Ecol. **41,** 495–506.

ROSE, D. J. W. (1973): Field studies in Rhodesia on *Cicadulina* spp. (Hem.: Cicadellidae), vectors of maize streak disease. Bull. ent. Res. **62,** 477–495.

ROSE, D. J. W. (1974): The epidemiology of maize streak disease in relation to population densities of *Cicadulina* spp. Ann. appl. Biol. **76,** 199–207.

RUPPEL, R. F. (1965): A review of the genus *Cicadulina* (Hemiptera: Cicadellidae). Publs. Mich. St. Univ. Mus. (Biological series), 385–428.

STOREY, H. H. (1925): The transmission of streak disease of maize by the leafhopper *Balelutha mbila* Naudé. Ann. appl. Biol. **17,** 691–719.

Author: D.J.W. Rose

Dalbulus maidis (DeLong & Wolc.)

Synonym: Cicadula maidis

Common names: American corn leafhopper; Amerikanische Maiszikade; Langostino americano del maíz.

Geographical distribution: D. maidis has been collected from the United States, Mexico, Central and South America, and islands in the Caribbean. It occurs most commonly below an altitude of 750 meters in tropical to semitropical areas, but does not occur above 2000 meters in more temperature areas.

Host plants: D. maidis has many herbaceous food plants, but egg laying and development of nymphs to adulthood is restricted to plant species in the Gramineae.

Symptoms: The direct damage caused by feeding is negligible. However, indirect damage is caused by transmission of the causal agent of the corn stunt disease.
The first symptoms of corn stunt disease appear as a general chlorosis at the base of newly developed leaves. Leaves become reddish-purple at the tips and along the margins. Older leaves have chlorotic streaks and red-purple blotches. Plants infected early are severely stunted due to shortening of upper internodes, and ears, if produced, may be small and incompletely filled.

Economic importance: D. maidis is a vector of the persistent corn stunt agent (CSA), causing the serious stunt disease of corn in the United States, Mexico, Guatemala, El Salvador, and Surinam. Strains of the pathogen are transmitted by several leafhoppers with varying degrees of efficiency, but D. maidis is the most efficient. Recently D. maidis was discovered to transmit the "rayado fino" pathogen in a nonpersistent manner to corn in Costa Rica, Central America.

Morphology: Nymphs and adults are pale yellow; adults have 2 round, black spots on the crown. Adult males are 3.5 to 4.0 mm and females 4.0 to 4.1 mm in length.

Life cycle and ecology: The average life of females in the field in Central Mexico was 44 days, whereas, adults lived 26–51 days in growth chambers at 21.1 °C and 60 % RH. The preoviposition period ranged from 1 to 7 days and the oviposition period from 10 to 51 days (32.9 days avg.) in the greenhouse at Chapingo, Mexico. Eggs are deposited in rows along the midrib of the corn leaf. The average number of eggs laid during the life span was 131.9. During the summer in Mexico, the incubation period was 23 days at an average temperature of 12.9 °C and 32.2 % RH. During the dry winter season eggs hatched in 36 days.
The length of nymphal development is 18, 15, 10 and 10 days at 21.1, 23.8, 26.7 and 32.2 °C, respectively. During the dry winter season at Chapingo, Mexico, the nymphal period was about 55 days. Nymphs have 5 stages and the sex ratio is 1:1.
D. maidis completes a generation in about 3 weeks; some generations require 18 days, others 24 days. In Central America, there are 2 generations on corn during the growing season in the summer, each generation lasting about 60 days. In El Salvador, Dalbulus sp. populations are high in August, September, December and March, and lowest in February and July.

Natural enemies: Dalbulus adults and nymphs are parasitized by the family Dyrinidae (Hymenoptera) in Mexico. However, parasites and predators are not important in regulating numbers of this leafhopper.

Control: Early planted corn is reported to escape much loss from corn stunt while later plantings are more severely damaged. In El Salvador in Central America, delayed plantings are exposed to lower populations of Dalbulus spp. and have lower incidence of disease.

Systemic insecticides (e. g. carbofuran) in furrow or in combination with sidedress applications control vectors and reduce disease incidence.

Literature

ARGUETA, J. MERINO & E. S. BONILLA (1967): Research in Salvador on maize varieties tolerant to stunt. In: Cimmyt News **2**, 4.
BHIRUD, K. M. (1972): Bioactivity of systemic insecticides in corn: Relationship of leafhopper vector control and corn stunt disease incidence. J. Econ. Ent. **65**, 1134–40.
BHIRUD, K. M. & H. N. PITRE (1972): Comparative susceptibility of three Cicadellid vectors of the corn stunt disease agent to carbofuran and disulfoton in greenhouse tests. J. Econ. Ent. **65**, 236–8.
COMBS, R. L. JR. (1967): Biological studies of *Dalbulus maidis* (DeLong and Wolcott), a leafhopper vector of corn stunt virus in Mississippi. Ph. D. Dissertation, Mississippi State University. 134 pp.
DAVIS, R. (1966). Biology of the leafhopper, *Dalbulus maidis,* at selected temperatures. J. Econ. Ent. **59**, 766.
GRANADOS, ROBERT R., JOHANNA S. GRANADOS, K. MARAMOROSCH & J. REINITZ (1968): Corn stunt virus: Transmission by three cicadellid vectors. J. Econ. Ent. **61**, 1282–87.
PITRE, H. N. (1967): Greenhouse studies of the host range of *Dalbulus maidis,* a vector of the corn stunt virus. J. Econ. Ent. **60**, 417–21.
PITRE, H. N. (1968): A preliminary study of corn stunt vector populations in relation to corn planting dates in Mississippi: Notes on disease incidence and severity. J. Econ. Ent. **61**, 847–9.

Author: H. N. Pitre

Empoasca lybica (de Berg.) (Fig. 121 and plate 24 a, b)

Common names: Cotton jassid; Baumwollzwergzikade; Mosquito verde.

Geographical distribution: South-, North-, Central-, North East- and East Africa, Middle East, Southern Spain and Mauritius (CIE Map no 223).

Host plants: Cotton, okra, tomato, potato, eggplant, paprika, lucerne, kenaf, roselle, field bean, cucurbits and other wild and cultivated herbaceous and woody plants.

Symptoms: On cotton, which can sustain severe damage, a yellow discolouration of leaf edges first arises as a result of the sucking activity of the jassids (toxic saliva effect!). Later the leaf edge rolls downwards and starts to dry up. In severe attack, a brownish or reddish discolouration also spreads gradually across the leaf blade between the main veins ("hopperburn"). On eggplants and okra, damaged leaves show yellowish to brownish discolourations. Growth of heavily infested plants is arrested considerably and there is a definite reduction in yield, as could be demonstrated repeatedly on irrigated cotton in N.E. Africa. Eggplants can be so severely damaged, that they form no fruit at all and wither slowly. Okra can also exhibit arrested growth and marked loss in yield.

Economic importance: *E. lybica* was a major pest of irrigated cotton in N.E. Africa until well into the sixties. Since then it has been regularly controlled along with other pests and lost much of its importance. In the absence of control measures, it still plays a major part as a pest of vegetables and can cause considerable losses.

Morphology: The males and females are about 2.5 mm long and pale green to yellowish green in colour. The wings are shiny and more or less transparent, the legs slender, with a fair number of bristles (front and hind legs). The nymphs resemble the adults but are smaller and do not have fully developed wings. Their colour is usually not as dark as that of fully grown insects. Eggs are banana shaped, whitish to greenish in colour and 0.7–0.9 mm long.

Fig. 121. Young eggplant, badly damaged by *Empoasca lybica* (phot. H. Schmutterer)

Similarities to other pests: Apart from *E. lybica,* some other very harmful species of the same genus also occur on Malvaceae (cotton, okra, *Hibiscus* species), Solanaceae (potato, egg plant), Leguminosae (beans) and other cultivated plants like castor bean, e. g. *E. fabae* (southern parts of the USA, South America, West Indies), *E. fabalis* (tropical and sub-tropical America), *E. facialis* (Central and South Africa) and *E. flavescens* (North Africa, Asia). These pests can be confused with *E. lybica,* especially if they occur together, not only in appearance but also because the damage they cause is very similar. The same applies to *Amrasca devastans* (see p. 318).

Life cycle and ecology: Adults and nymphs suck on the leaves, remaining on the leaf undersurface during the day, but also visiting the upper surface in the evening. If disturbed, they run rapidly sideways in characteristic fashion and endeavour to reach a shady part of the host. Adult jassids in flight can cover fair distances, especially if wind supported.

The females deposit their eggs with the aid of an ovipositor in the veins of the leaf undersurface and in leaf stalks. Young leaves are preferred for oviposition. No eggs are deposited at temperatures below 15 °C. The incubation period depends on temperature. In N. E. Africa (Sudan) it amounts to 6–10 days. The development of one generation depends on environmental conditions and takes from 2 weeks up to 3 months. Pronounced drought periods are survived on weeds or trees, unless irrigated cultivated crops are available.

Natural enemies: Some predators are known to occur in N. E. Africa, mainly Coccinellidae *(Coccinella rufescens, Cheilomenes vicina, Exochomus nigromaculatus)* and Chrysopidae *(Chrysopa carnea, C. corula).* Mymaridae *(Anagrus* sp.) occur as egg parasites and Dyrinidae as parasites of nymphs and adults.

Control: Jassids ready for oviposition are discouraged by very hairy cotton varieties. This observation was utilised in selective breeding of resistance to *Empoasca* spp. and related pests. Other factors, such as antibiosis, structure and moisture content of leaves, also contribute to resistance. Chemical control succeeds with many insecticides from all major chemical groups e. g. DDT, endosulfan, monocrotophos, phosphamidon, formothion, dimethoate, oxydemeton-methyl and carbaryl. In large scale cotton plantations, these chemicals are generally mixed with others and applied by aircraft as ULV formulations, so that other pests occurring with *E. lybica* can also be controlled. On vegetables such as eggplants, tomato and okra, insecticides without long lasting effect and with a low toxicity for warm blooded animals are to be preferred, and safety periods between application and harvesting must be maintained.

Literature

JACKSON, J. E., L. RAZOUX SCHULTZ & R. C. FAULKNER (1965): Effect of jassid attack on cotton yield and quality in the Sudan Gezira. Emp. Cott. Gr. Rev. **42,** 295–299.
PAINTER, R. H. (1951): Insect resistance in crops. Univ. Press Kansas, Lawrence & London, 520 pp.
SCHMUTTERER, H. (1969): Pests of Crops in Northeast and Central Africa. Gustav Fischer, Stuttgart & Portland, 269 pp.
TALHOUK, A. M. (1969): Insects and Mites Injourious to Crops in Middle Eastern Countries. Monogr. ang. Ent. no 21. Paul Parey, Hamburg & Berlin, 239 pp.

Author: H. Schmutterer

Idioscopus niveosparsus (Leth.) (Fig. 122 and plate 24 c)

Synonym: *Idiocerus niveosparsus*

Common name: Mango hopper.

Geographical distribution: This hopper species was first recorded from Saharanpur (Uttar Pradesh, India). Subsequently it has been reported from the Philippines, Taiwan, Vietnam, Indonesia, Sri Lanka, Burma, Bangladesh, and Pakistan. In India, *I. niveosparsus* is more destructive in the Southern peninsula than in the North-eastern States.

Host plants: *I. niveosparsus* is monophagous on mango *(Mangifera indica)*. However, it has been found on *Citrus* spp. and *Calophyllus inophyllum* though these do not act as alternate hosts.

Symptoms: Profuse egg-laying within the stalklets and florets causes physical injury, resulting in withering of affected parts. In addition nymphs and adults suck the cell sap of inflorescences during spring and of leaves during summer. The removal of inflorescence sap adversely affects fruit setting while on leaves, growth is stunted. The hoppers also exude 'honeydew' which encourages the development of the fungi *Capnodium mangiferum* and *Meliola mangiferae,* which produce black sooty mould on the dorsal leaf surfaces and branches. This interferes with the photosynthetic activity of the plant, ultimately resulting in failure of the flowers to set and dropping of immature fruits. A severe attack may result in total loss of the crop.

Economic importance: There are no reliable figures available regarding the monetary loss caused by this serious pest. The loss of inflorescences due to mango hopper attack varies from 20 to 60 %.

Morphology: The freshly emerged nymph is wedge-shaped and whitish in colour with two small red eyes; gradually with each moulting the colour changes to yellow, yellowish-green, green and finally to greenish-brown. The adult is also wedge-shaped having a greenish-brown body with a pale yellow vertex. The scutellum has three basal black spots, the central one being more or less rectangular. Forewings are thicker than hind wings, bronzy, sub-hyaline, with veins pale yellow and a white line along the costal margin forming a distinct mid-longitudinal line when the insect is at rest. The male is 3.9 to 4.3 mm, while the female is 4.9 to 5.3 mm in length.

Similarities to other pests: An allied species *Amritodus (Idiocerus) atkinsoni* (= *quinquepunctatus*) is more common, especially in Northern India. It is slightly larger (♂ 4.2–4.8 mm, ♀ 4.7–5.1 mm) and is a shy breeder. It causes damage mostly to the vegetative shoots. Both nymphs and adults are seen hiding during the day in cracks and crevices of the bark. Another species,

Idioscopus (Idiocerus) clypealis (= *I. nigroclypeatus*) is also found along with *I. niveosparsus*. This is smaller (♂ 3.4–3.7 mm, ♀ 3.6–3,9 mm) as well as narrower than the other two species. It is a most prolific breeder and though found all over India, it is predominant in South Gujarat, Maharashtra and Karnataka. Its maximum activity has been observed during January–February i. e. during the mango flowering season.

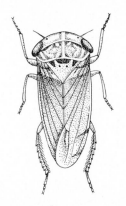

Fig. 122. Left: *Idioscopus niveosparsus;* right: *I. clypealis* (drawings D. K. Butani)

Life cycle: Around the end of January or early February, the females make tiny slits with their ovipositor in the tissues of flowering shoots, flower buds or tender leaves in which they lay their eggs singly. A female can lay as many as 200 eggs in her lifetime. The eggs hatch in 4–7 days. The nymphs undergo 4–5 moultings before becoming adults. The nymphal period ranges from 10 to 13 days in South India and 18–20 days in North India. In North India, there are two distinct generations a year; a summer generation during June–August and a spring generation in February–April; the latter being distinctly more destructive since it feeds on the inflorescences. Overwintering takes place in the adult stage when the insects hide in cracks and crevices in the bark of the trees.

Ecology: The hoppers are active throughout the summer and spring. The maximum damage is done during the flowering season. The hoppers prefer damp and shady places and their population rises to phenomenal proportions in neglected and water-logged orchards. The activity declines with the onset of monsoons and the adult hoppers remain inactive from August to January. A spell of cold weather, with the temperature dropping to 10–15 °C (50–60 °F) results in an increase in egg-laying.

Natural enemies: All the three species of hoppers are parasitised in India by *Epipyrops fuliginosa* and *Pipunculus annulifemer;* while in Java, *I. niveosparsus* is parasitised by *Centrodora idioceria.* In addition, *Isyndus* sp. (probably *I. heros*) and *Pyrilloxenus compactus* have been reported as predators from India.

In Bangladesh, two fungal parasites, namely *Aspergillus origer* and *Fusarium* sp. were recorded on adult hoppers.

Control:

Sanitary methods. Clean cultivation and avoidance of water-logging keeps the pest at bay.

Chemical control. Spraying with systematic insecticides like 0.03 % phosphamidon, diazinon, monocrotophos or methyl-demeton is recommended. More than one spraying is required to check this pest effectively; one before flowering (January), 1–2 after flowering and 2–3 during June–July. This will control all three species throughout the year. Broad spectrum pesticides such as DDT and carbaryl are also effective but may have more side effects on natural enemies than systemic insecticides.

Literature

BHATIA, L. J. (1967): Chemicals that take care of mango hoppers. Indian Fmg. **16** (10), 16.
BUTANI, DHAMO K. (1974): Insect pests of fruit crops and their control. 7: Mango. Pesticides **8** (3), 37–41.
BINDRA, O. S., G. S. SANDHU, G. C. VARMA & S. S. SEKHON (1972): Studies on the control of mango-hoppers, *Idioscopus clypealis* Leth. and *Idiocerus atkinsoni* Leth. (Cicadellidae: Hemiptera). Proc: 3rd int. Sym. Sub-trop. & Trop. Hort. (abstracts), 33, Bangalore.
REDDY, D. B. (1968): Plant protection in India, 454 pp. Allied Publishers, Pvt. Ltd., Calcutta.
SANTHIANANDAN, V. K., R. BETTAI GOWDER & T. SANTHANARAMAN (1972): Control of mango hoppers, *Idiocerus* spp. Proc. 3rd int. Sym. Sub-trop. & Trop. Hort. (abstracts), 83–84, Bangalore.
THOMPSON, W. R. (1944): A catalogue of the parasites and predators of insect pests. Sec. 1 (3), 57, Imperial Parasite Service, Ontario.

Author: Dhamo K. Butani

Nephotettix spp. (Fig. 123)

Important species and synonyms: *Nephotettix virescens* (Distant) (= *N. impicticeps*), *Nephotettix nigropictus* (Stål) (= *N. apicalis*).

Common names: Green rice leafhopper(s); Grüne Reiszikade(n); Cicadelle(s) verte(s) du riz.

Geographical distribution: Among Asian *Nephotettix* species, *N. virescens* and *N. nigropictus* are dominant both in number and in distribution. They are distributed throughout subtropical and tropical Asia, including India, Sri Lanka, Bangladesh, Burma, Thailand, Laos, Malaysia, South Vietnam, China, Taiwan, Indonesia, and the Philippines. They also occur in southern Japan which forms the northern limit of their distribution. A subspecies, *N. nigropictus yapicola*, is known from Micronesia. The closely related species *N. malayanus* and *N. parvus* are distributed similarly in tropical Asian countries, although they are relatively scarce and are not detrimental to rice. *N. sympatricus* is recorded only in Sri Lanka. *N. cincticeps* is distributed mainly in temperate Asia, China, Japan, and Korea. From Africa, Palestine and Madagascar, two different *Nephotettix* species, *N. modulatus* and *N. afer* have been recorded.

Host plants: *N. virescens: Oryza sativa.* The leafhopper is restricted to *Oryza* spp.. *N. nigropictus: Echinochloa crusgalli, Alopecurus pratensis, Eragrostis amabalis, Poa annua, Setaria italica, Eleusine indica, Cynodon dactylon, Cyperus rotundus, C. esculentus, C. scariosus, Oryza sativa,* etc. Rice is not the principal host of this species.

Symptoms of damage and economic importance: Generally, the nymphs and adults of *Nephotettix* spp. feed on the leaves of upper level of rice plants and suck the sap from the vascular tissues by their needle-like stylets. Although no direct feeding damage is apparent, they reduce the overall vigor of the plants by repeated piercing and intensive sap draining during feeding. Also, the honeydew excreted causes the development of sooty moulds. Usually, paddy fields which have received large amounts of nitrogenous fertilizers are most seriously infested.

In addition, *Nephotettix* spp. are dominant vectors of rice viruses such as tungro, transitory yellowing, dwarf and a disease caused by a mycoplasma-like organism, yellow dwarf (see p. 43). The damage resulting from these viruses is of much greater economic significance than that from direct feeding. Tungro particularly is one of the most widely distributed and most destructive rice diseases in tropical Asia. For example, an outbreak of tungro in 1971 affected hundreds of thousand hectares in the Philippines. In West Malaysia, thousands of hectares are damaged each year by the same kind of disease as tungro, penyakit merah. Tungro stunts rice plants and changes the leaf color to shades of yellow or orange. Yellowing starts from the tip of the leaf and may extend to the lower part of the leaf blade. Young leaves may appear mottled and old leaves may have rusty specks of various sizes. Infected plants also usually have somewhat fewer tillers than healthy plants. Transmission characteristics of rice virus diseases transmitted by *Nephotettix* species in tropical Asia are presented on page 32.

Morphology: Species of *Nephotettix* in tropical Asia can be distinguished from each other with the help of the following key, but the male genitalic characters should be examined as the final criterion (Fig. 123).

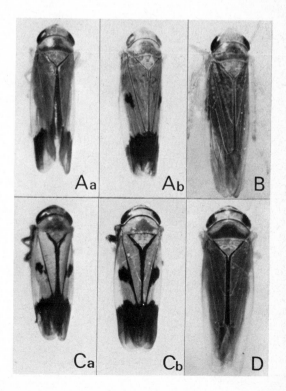

Fig. 123. Adults of *Nephotettix* spp. Aa–b = *N. virescens*, male; B = *N. virescens*, female; Ca–B = *N. nigropictus*, male; D = *N. nigropictus*, female (phot. K. Sōgawa & S. Nasu)

1. Vertex with black submarginal traverse band markedly and fully
   developed 4
   – Vertex without submarginal traverse band, or with band partially
   developed, or with its traces only behind ocelli 2
2. Vertex only slightly longer medially than next to eye, its anterior
   margin only slightly bulging; with traces of transverse
   black band in form of comma-shaped mark behind ocelli in males,
   not in females .... *N. malayanus*
   – Vertex much longer medially than next to eye, its anterior margin
   markedly pointed 3
3. Vertex with narrow marginal black band; submarginal black band
   interrupted in middle .... *N. sympatricus*
   – Vertex without traces of marginal and submarginal transverse
   black band in both sexes .... *N. virescens*
4. Anterior margin of pronotum marked by a black transverse band
   sometimes very narrow .... *N. nigropictus*
   – Anterior margin of pronotum without black marking 5
5. Anterior margin of vertex markedly pointed in center .... *N. parvus*
   – Anterior margin of vertex rounded in center .... *N. cincticeps*

Life cycle and ecology: The banana-shaped lactescent eggs (1.0 x 0.3 mm) are usually deposited in rows in the parenchyma or intercellular air spaces of the undersides of the leaves near the midrib. Embryonic development is completed in 5 days and nymphs emerge in 6–7 days at 30–33 °C. Nymphs usually hatch in the morning. They undergo 5 moults to reach the adult stage in about 21 days at 25 °C, and 15 days at 30 °C. The nymph of *N. virescens* varies from yellowish green to dark green in color. In the nymphs of *N. nigropictus,* the body color changes as they grow from pale yellow through reddish brown to black. Neither species have embryonic or post-embryonic diapause. The adults are 4.0–5.2 mm long, greenish in color with or without black spots on the wings. They live about 20 days, and usually have a preovipositional period for 6–10 days after emergence. The total number of eggs per female laid on rice plants is 140 in *N. virescens,* and 60 in *N. nigropictus,* on the average. In the warm and humid tropics, leafhoppers remain active all the year round, and have generally 6 and more generations a year if food plants are available. Their population fluctuates according to the quality of the food plants, natural enemies and environmental conditions. Generally an abundance of leafhoppers is attributed to high temperature, low rainfall, and abundant sunshine. A higher rate of nitrogen fertilizers applied in paddy fields also results in a high rate of reproduction of leafhoppers.

Natural enemies: In Japan, several araneid spiders such as *Oedothrax insecticeps, Lycosa pseudo-annulata, Pirate clerck,* and *P. piratica* are potential predators of *N. cincticeps.* An aquatic veliid bug, *Microvelia douglasi,* and a mirid bug, *Cyrtorhinus lividipennis,* are also important predators. As many as 60 % of eggs are parasitized by a trichogrammatid, *Japania andoi;* and more than 45 % of nymphs and adults by the doriliad flies, *Tomosuaryella oryzaetora, Dorilas tsuboii, D. cruciator,* and *D. orientalis.* Although there has been no detailed survey, *Nephotettix* spp. in tropical Asia are also attacked by a similar fauna of natural enemies.

Control:
Cultural control. Removing diseased plants is a reliable method to reduce the incidence and further spread of virus diseases.
Varietal resistance. Varieties such as Pankhari 203, ASD 7, Ptb 18, DK 1 and AC 435 are resistant to both *N. virescens* and *N. nigropictus,* but they are not always resistant to the viruses transmitted by them. Commercial varieties in Indonesia, namely Tjeremas, Bengawan, Peta, Intan, and Sigadis, are known to be resistant to tungro and other similar virus diseases. IR 20 and IR 26,

bred recently in the Philippines, are not only high-yielding but also resistant to both the tungro virus and the leafhoppers.

Chemical control. Diazinon and phorate granules at 2 and 3 kg/ha respectively, are effective when applied in paddy water on three occasions 10, 35 and 50 days after transplanting, for control of leafhoppers as well as for prevention of virus infection. Soaking the seed and dipping the seedlings in carbofuran solution (1000 ppm, 12–24 hr) protects the seedlings from virus infection for about 30 days, when it is most vulnerable to infection.

Literature

CHENG, C. H. & PATHAK, M. D. (1972): Resistance to *Nephotettix virescens* in rice varieties. J. Econ. Ent. **65**, 1148–1153.

GHAURI, M.S.K. (1971): Revision of the genus *Nephotettix* MATSUMURA (Homoptera: Cicadelloidea: Euscelidae) based on the type material. Bull. Ent. Res. **60**, 481–512.

LING, K. C. (1969): Testing rice varieties for resistance to tungro disease, in "The Virus Diseases of the Rice Plant". The Johns Hopkins Press, 277–291.

NASU, S. (1967): Rice leafhoppers, in "The Major Insect Pest of the Rice Plant". The Johns Hopkins Press, 493–523.

NASU, S. (1969): Vectors of rice viruses in Asia, in "The virus Diseases of the Rice Plant". The Johns Hopkins Press, 93–109.

OU, S. H. & K. C. LING (1966): Virus diseases of rice in the south pacific. FAO Pl. Prot. Bull. **14**, 113–121.

PATHAK, M. D., E. BEA & V. T. JOHN (1967): Control of insect vectors to prevent virus infection of rice plants. J. Econ. Ent. **60**, 218–225.

PATHAK, M. D. (1968): Ecology of common insect pests of rice. Ann. Rev. Ent. **13**, 257–294.

YASUMATSU, K. & T. TORII (1968): Impact of parasites, predators, and diseases on rice pests. Ann. Rev. Ent. **13**, 295–324.

Authors: Kazushige Sōgawa and Socho Nasu

Family: Cercopidae

Aeneolamia and Mahanarva spp. (Figs. 124–125)

Important species: *Aeneolamia (Monecphora, Tomaspis) varia saccharina* (Dist.) – Trinidad; *A. v. sontica* Fenn. – Venezuela; *A. postica postica* (Wlk.) – Mexico; *A. p. jugata* (Fowl.) – Belize, Guatemala; *Mahanarva (Monecphora, Tomaspis, Sphenorhina) fimbriolata* (Stål) and *M. posticata* (Stål) – Brazil.

Common names: Sugar cane froghopper, Spittlebug; Zuckerrohrschaumzikade; Crachat de coucou, Ecume printanière; Candelilla (Venezuela), Salivazo, Mosca pinta (Mexico).

Geographical distribution: South America: Argentina, Brazil, Bolivia, Venezuela, Guyana, Surinam. Caribbean: Trinidad and Tobago, Grenada. Central America: Panama, Honduras, El Salvador, Guatemala, Belize. North America: Mexico.

Host plants: Sugar cane (*Saccharum* spp. and hybrids), pasture grasses (*Panicum* spp., *Digitaria decumbens, Tripsacum laxum* and others), maize (*Zea mays*), rice (*Oryza sativa*) and various wild grasses and sedges.

Symptoms: The nymphs of most species feed on the roots, penetrating into the cortex (young nymphs) or the xylem (older nymphs) and sucking the sap. The punctured xylem elements may become occluded and heavy infestations may cause a stunting of stem growth and yellowing of the leaves.

Nymphs of some species (e. g. *Mahanarva posticata*) and the adults of all sugar cane froghoppers feed on the leaves, causing "froghopper blight". During feeding the adults pierce the border pa-

Fig. 124.   Adult of *Aeneolamia varia sac-charina* (phot. D. W. Fewkes)

Fig. 125.   Nymphs of *A. v. saccharina* on the roots of sugar cane (phot. D. W. Fewkes)

renchyma cells of the vascular bundles, injecting a complex mixture of enzymes and amino acids and withdrawing the cell contents. Blight develops over two to three weeks as necrotic streaks spread longitudinally from the feeding punctures and in heavy attacks whole leaves are destroyed, thin, stunted internodes are produced and the sugar content is lowered.

Economic importance: Froghoppers are major pests of sugar cane in Brasil, Venezuela, Trinidad, Belize and Mexico. The main damage is caused by the adults and yield losses of 25 to 40 % sugar are common in blighted cane. Without the use of insecticides, large areas may be devastated.

Morphology: The pale, soft-bodied nymphs are characterized by the production of a watery froth ("spittle" or "cuckoo spit") in which they become enveloped. The adults are about 1 cm long, dark brown with two transverse yellow, orange or red bands across the elytra. The flat head with its widely spaced eyes resembles that of a frog.

Similarities to other pests: The adults bear a superficial resemblance to those of some species of Jassidae. They may be distinguished readily by the shape of their tibiae, which are cylindrical in froghoppers but angular in Jassids.

Life cycle: All species have two or more generations a year and in most species the annual cycle is interrupted by a diapausing egg stage of variable duration. When development is direct most species complete their life cycle in about two months but with diapause the cycle may be extended by anything from a few weeks up to ten months.
The eggs are laid in the soil and non-diapausing eggs hatch in 2 to 4 weeks. The nymphs complete their development through five instars in 4 to 6 weeks and the adults may live for as long as 4 weeks, producing up to 300 eggs per female. Mating may occur on the day of emergence and eggs may be laid from the second or third day.

Ecology: Moisture has important effects upon the distribution and abundance of sugar cane frog-hoppers. In damp, grassy areas most species are capable of breeding throughout the year because the females commonly lay both diapause and non-diapause eggs. In sugar cane, however, bree-ding is usually interrupted by a period of dry weather lasting from three to six months, during which the crop is harvested.
The "first brood" populations that occur at the beginning of the rainy season stem from diapause

eggs that were laid at various times during the previous rainy season. Usually, a small first brood is followed by one or two large broods.

Natural enemies: The most important enemies of sugar cane froghoppers are the larvae of *Salpingogaster nigra* (Diptera: Syrphidae) that prey on the nymphs and an entomopathogenous fungus, *Metarrhizium anisopliae* (Entomophthoraceae) that attacks the adults. There are several egg parasites, notably *Anagrus urichi* (Hymenoptera: Mymaridae), but they rarely destroy more than 2 % of the eggs. Some species of ants (e. g. *Solenopsis* spp., *Monomorium* spp.) carry off the eggs and young, first instar nymphs and various spiders, predatory bugs (Heteroptera: Reduviidae), frogs, toads, lizards and birds are known to prey on the adults.

Control: The incidence of froghopper attack could be reduced by growing fewer ratoon crops and by rotating non-graminaceous crops with sugar cane, but this is not considered economical or practical. There is evidence that some varieties are more "tolerant" to froghopper attack or are somewhat less severely attacked than others. However, no truly resistant variety has been found. Various attempts at biological control have proved unsuccessful and control of sugar cane froghoppers depends upon the use of insecticides. Where the nymphs feed on the roots, insecticidal dusts or sprays may be applied to the bases of the sugar cane stools. This is laborious and expensive, requiring the use of insecticides with a long residual activity to avoid multiple applications. The most successful treatments have been with dust formulations of gamma BHC, dieldrin, toxaphene and carbophenothion.

In most areas aerial applications of insecticidal dusts or sprays are used against the adult froghoppers, particularly gamma BHC (Brazil, Mexico), carbaryl (Brazil), malathion, monocrotophos and omethoate (Trinidad, Venezuela).

The timing of treatments is based upon routine counts of froghopper nymphs per stool or adults per stem. Commonly treatments are applied during the second and third broods, when counts exceed 10 nymphs per stool or 50 adults per 100 stems. In Trinidad, Belize and some parts of Venezuela control measures are applied during the first brood to prevent the development of heavy second brood infestations. In these cases treatments are applied when the counts reach 5 adults per 100 stems.

Resistance of sugar cane froghopper nymphs to gamma BHC and several other organochlorine insecticides was first reported from Trinidad in 1954 and has since been noted in Venezuela. During 1969–1970 resistance of adult froghoppers to carbaryl, with cross-resistance to propoxur, was detected in Trinidad.

Literature

FEWKES, D. W. (1967): The control of sugar cane froghoppers. World Review of Pest Control **6** (1), 21–33.
FEWKES, D. W. (1969): The biology of sugar cane froghoppers. In: Pests of Sugar Cane (eds. J. R. Williams, J. R. Metcalfe, R. W. Mungomery and R. Mathes). Elsevier; Amsterdam, London, New York; 283–307.
EVANS, D. E. & D. A. BUXO (1973): Insecticidal control of the sugarcane froghopper. Proceedings of the International Society of Sugar Cane Technologists **14**, 507–515.

Author: D. W. Fewkes

Other injurious Fulgoroidea and Cicadoidea:

Nilaparvata lugens (Stål), Brown planthopper (Braunrückige Reiszikade) occurs in South-, South East- and East Asia as well as in Eastern Australia and on the Fiji Islands (CIE Map no 199; revised). It attacks rice and is known to be a serious vector of "Grassy stunt virus".
Perkinsiella spp. (*P. vastatrix* Bredd. and *P. saccharicida* Kirk.) (Zuckerrohrzikaden) inhabit chiefly South East and East Asia (CIE Map for *P. saccharicida:* no 150). They attack sugar cane.

P. saccharicida transmits "Fiji disease" of sugar cane in Australia (Queensland) and Madagascar, *P. vastatrix* in the Philippines.

Sogatodes orizicola (Muir), the American rice delphacid (Amerikanische Reiszikade), occurs in the southern parts of the USA, on the Caribbean Islands, in Central America and in Venezuela (CIE Map no 202). It is a vector of the "Hoja blanca" disease on rice. *S. cubanus* (Crawf.) also transmits the virus.

Pyrilla perpusilla (Wlk.), Indian sugar cane leafhopper, is found throughout India and Sri Lanka (CIE Map no 151). It attacks sugar cane, sorghum, wheat, maize, some wild grasses and dicotyledons. Control: Sprayings with fenitrothion or endosulfan.

Hilda patruelis Stål attacks in Africa (West, East, Central and South Africa) groundnut and some other legumes. Control measures are soil treatment before sowing or spraying of plant rows with dieldrin.

Peregrinus maidis (Ashm.), the Corn laternfly, has a world-wide distribution in the tropics where it transmits viruses on maize (see p. 25).

Amrasca devastans (Dist.) (= *Empoasca devastans*) attacks cotton, *Hibiscus* spp., potato, eggplant and other host plants in India, Sri Lanka and other parts of Asia. CIE Map no 326.

Inazuma dorsalis (Motsch.), Zig-zagged winged leafhopper (Zickzack-streifige Reiszikade). In South and South East Asia, Taiwan and Japan. Vector of the pathogens causing "Orange leaf" (virus) and "Yellow dwarf" (mycoplasma-like organism) on rice.

H. Sch.

Superfamily: Psylloidea
Family: Psyllidae

Euphyllura olivina (Costa) (Plate 24 d)

Synonyms: *Psylla oleae, Euphyllura oleae, Psylla olivina*

Common names: Olive psyllid; Olivenblattfloh; Teigne de l'olivier; Algodón del olivo.

Geographical distribution: The olive psyllid occurs in the entire mediterranean region, including Morocco and Portugal.

Host plants: Apart from *Olea europea*, *E. olivina* also lives on *Phyllirea media*.

Symptoms: The most easily recognised symptom consists of white, woolly larval wax secretions on inflorescences, leaves and young shoots. Severely affected trees look white from a distance. A heavy sooty mould deposit can later develop on the honeydew of the psyllids, which may remain visible for months. Fruit quality can be much reduced by the secretions after severe infestation in the autumn. Main damage results from the suction activity of nymphs on inflorescences, which dry up. This is particularly noticeable towards the end of the flowering period.

Economic importance: In extreme cases, heavy outbreaks can lead to total loss of flowers and hence also the yield. In most cases however, the damage is limited, so that special control measures are not necessary. The direct damage due to loss of inflorescences is not easy to assess, since most of the flowers dry up and drop off anyway. Heavy infestation probably also weakens the trees. On the whole, the olive psyllid is regarded as the worst olive grove pest after olive moth and olive fly, not least because it is widely distributed. The threshold for economic damage is sometimes taken to be 15 % of inflorescences affected.

Morphology: Adult olive psyllids are yellow to greenish brown in colour and 2.6–3 mm long. Some yellowish spots are present on the white, transparent forewings, while none are seen on the hind wings. Young nymphs are brown to orange, older ones greenish-grey. Eggs are yellowish and oval in shape.

Life cycle and ecology: Only adults are found in winter. Females oviposit on young shoots in the spring (February to April, depending on climatic conditions), as well as on the undersurface of young leaves and on unfolding flower trusses before these have fully developed. The period of oviposition differs in different countries. Depending on whether it is long or protracted, the generations can overlap with simultaneous occurrence of nymphs, eggs and adults or (parts of North Africa) one generation develops up to the main flowering period, another at the time of fruit setting. In the summer, development is interrupted to a greater or lesser degree as a result of higher temperatures, to be resumed in the autumn. The nymphs are situated in groups under a dense, woolly layer. This consists of secretions by epidermal glands, which produce a filamentous waxy substance, and sugar-containing drops of honey dew (excrements). Adults are freely mobile, able to fly and produce no waxy secretions.

Summer heat can lead to diapause and kill nymphal instars.

Natural enemies: *Encyrtus euphyllurae* (Hym., Chalcid.) is believed to be capable of preventing outbreaks. Larvae of various Syrphidae and Chrysopidae drain the nymphal instars of the pest.

Control: The olive psyllid is usually adequately controlled by the treatment applied at the start and after flowering to control olive moth. Separate treatment is necessary if infestation is severe in the pre-blossom period or if the control of olive moth is omitted. Heavy attack may require two treatments, one before flowering, the other on fruit setting.

At one time, gamma BHC and DDT were mainly used. Nowadays, a series of organic phosphates such as parathion and dimethoate are used both as sprays and dusts, from ground level and from aircraft.

Literature

ANDRES CANTERO, F. (1965): Enfermedades y plagas del olivo. Div. Gen. Agric., Madrid, 296 pp.

Author: K. Rolli

Other harmful Psylloidea (Fig. 126):

Trioza anceps Tuth., the Avocado psyllid (Avocadoblattfloh) (Fig. 126) attacks in Mexico and Central America avocado leaves and causes striking cyst-like galls on the upper surface of leaves.
Trioza erytreae (Del Guer.) (= *Spanioza erytreae*), Citrus psyllid (Citrusblattfloh). Occurs in South, East and Central Africa (CIE Map no 234). Nymphs produce galls on the leaves of citrus, adults transmit a serious citrus disease. A similar disease is transmitted by *Diaphorina citri* (Kuway.) in India and other parts of Asia. (CIE Map no 334).
Meshomatoma tessmanni (Aulm.) (= *Tyora tessmanni*), West African cocoa psyllid (Westafrikanischer Kakaoblattfloh). Attacks blossom, young pods, buds and shoots of cocoa in West and Central Africa.

H. Sch.

Fig. 126. Galls on avocado leaves, caused by *Trioza anceps* (phot. H. Schmutterer)

Superfamily: Aleyrodoidea
Family: Aleyrodidae

Bemisia tabaci (Genn.) (Plate 25 a)

Synonyms: *Bemisia gossypiperda, B. longispina, B. goldingi, B. nigeriensis*

Common names: Cotton whitefly, Tobacco whitefly; Tabakmottenschildlaus, Batatenmotten-schildlaus; Mosca blanca.

Geographical distribution: India, Micronesia, Taiwan, Indonesia, Madagascar, Rhodesia, Nige-ria, Zaire, Ivory Coast, Somalia, Sudan, Egypt, Libya, Morocco, Southern Italy, North America, Central America, Japan, Malaysia, Mauritius, Tanzania, Israel, Ethiopia, Ghana, Kenya, Mo-zambique, Fiji, Argentina, Malawi, Sierra Leone, Cameroon, and Uganda. CIE Map no 284.

Host plants: The Cotton whitefly has a very wide range of host plants. They include Malvaceae (*Gossypium* spp., *Hibiscus esculentus, H. cannabinus,* and other *Hibiscus* spp.), Papilionaceae (*Arachis hypogaea, Cajanus cajan, Cicer arientinum, Lablab niger, Medicago* spp., *Phaseolus* spp., *Pisum* spp., and *Vicia faba*), Solanaceae (*Capsicum annuum, Datura onium, Lycopersicum escu-lentum, Nicotiana* spp., *Solanum* spp.), Convolvulaceae (*Ipomoea batatas*), Cucurbitaceae (*Cu-cumis* spp., *Cucurbita pepo*), Euphorbiaceae (*Manihot utilissimia*), Compositae (*Carthamus tinc-torius*), Cruciferae (*Brassica* spp.), Myrtaceae (*Psidium guajava*), Pedaliaceae (*Sesamum indi-cum*), Tiliaceae (*Corchorus olitorius*) and many others.

Symptoms of damage and economic importance: *B. tabaci* is a serious leaf-sucking pest and a vec-tor of the leafcurl virus of cotton in the Sudan. In addition to removing plant nutrients, it produces numerous chlorotic spots on infested leaves, by the action of the saliva of feeding adults as well as by the removal of cell contents by the immature stages. Depending on the level of infestation, the chlorotic areas coalesce and cause an irregular yellowing of the leaf tissue which extends from the veins to the outer edges of the leaf; only the veins and narrow strips of tissue remain green. Later on the leaf becomes dry, very light brown in colour, and is eventually shed. Wilting and shedding of leaves and fruiting branches is associated with very heavy infestations. This results in a reduc-tion in yield and quality. The honeydew excreted by all the free juvenile stages covers the leaves and may affect the metabolic processes. In addition, it can contaminate seed cotton in open bolls, and thus causes trouble in processing the lint. Plant height, number of internodes, number of frui-ting points, number of leaves shed, number of picked bolls, number of bolls badly opened or shed, final yield, and grade are all detrimentally affected in proportion to the degree of whitefly infesta-tion. Boll characters such as weight of cotton per boll, lint index, seed weight, number of seeds per boll, are also more or less affected. *B. tabaci* is also an important vector of mosaic viruses of cotton in W. Africa and Central America and of leafcurl or other viruses on tobacco, tomato and beans (*Phaseolus* spp.). In addition, it is able to transmit the Cassava mosaic virus in tropical Africa (see p. 10).

Morphology: Egg. Elliptical, about 0.2–0.3 mm long, inserted into the plant tissue by the female by a short pedicel.
'Puparium' (pupal-like final juvenile stage) rather flat, oval, whitish to yellowish. Dorsal side with two tubercles, 0–7 pairs of submedian and submarginal and one pair of terminal setae (wide varia-tion).
Adults. About 1 mm long, male somewhat smaller than female. Body whitish to yellowish, co-vered with a mealy secretion. Wings white, similar in size and shape. Third antennal joint consi-derably longer than other segments of antennae.

Life cycle: The adult spreads its wings immediately after emergence usually for 8 to 15 minutes.

Plate 17

a Symptoms of red ring disease in the bole of a coconut palm
b Wilting tobacco plant (left), attacked by *Meloidogyne javanica*
c *Damage of Pratylenchus loosi* in a tea plantation
d Cysts of *Heterodera rostochiensis* on potato roots

Plate 18

a Adult female of *Tetranychus cinnabarinus*
b Symptoms of damage of *Tetranychus cinnabarinus* on lemon fruits
c Adult female of *Tetranychus urticae*
d *Tetranychus cinnabarinus* on the underside of a cotton leaf

Plate 19

a Adult female and egg of *Panonychus citri*
b Citrus leaves, damaged by *Panonychus citri*
c Nymphs *of Oedalus senegalensis* on *Pennisetum typhoides*
d Pennisetum field, badly damaged by grasshoppers

Plate 20

a

c

a Mating pair of *Zonocerus elegans*
b *Cyrtacanthacris tatarica*
c Mating pair of migratory phase of *Schistocerca gregaria*
d Female of solitary phase of *Locusta migratoria migratorioides* (brownish form)

Plate 21

a Damage of *Thrips tabaci* on onion leaves
b Damage of *Caliothrips impurus* on a cotton leaf
c Damage on the stem base of coffee, caused by *Macrotermes bellicosus*
d Young coconut plant, showing damage of *Macrotermes goliath*

Plate 22

a Damage of *Microtermes thoracalis* in groundnut pods
b Workers of *Microtermes thoracalis*
c *Antestiopsis orbitalis bechuana* on coffee
d *Helopeltis* sp. on cocoa pod

Plate 23

a   Adult of *Sahlbergella singularis* on a cocoa pod
b   Adult of *Leptocorisa* sp.
c   Mating pair of *Dysdercus fasciatus*
d   Nymphs of *Dysdercus völkeri* on pennisetum head

Plate 24

a Symptoms of hopperburn on cotton, caused by *Empoasca facialis*
b Nymphs and adult of *Empoasca lybica* on the underside of an eggplant leaf
c *Idioscopus* sp. on inflorescence of mango
d *Euphyllura olivina* on olive shoot

Plate 25

a   Adults and puparia of *Bemisia tabaci* on the underside of a sweet potato leaf
b Puparia of *Aleurocanthus woglumi* on a citrus leaf. One specimen (white spot) is infested by a parasitic fungus
c   Colonies of *Aphis craccivora* on broad bean leaves
d *Aphis gossypii* and larva of *Chrysopa* sp. on cotton leaf

Plate 26

a   *Aphis spiraecola* on citrus
b   *Macrosiphum euphorbiae* on potato leaf
c   *Myzus persicae* on cabbage
d   *Lipaphis erysimi* on radish

Plate 27

a *Rhopalosiphum maidis* on maize
b *Toxoptera citricidus* on citrus
c *Planococcoides njalensis* on a cocoa pod
d *Saccharicoccus sacchari* on a sugar cane stem

Plate 28

a Colony of *Icerya purchasi* on *Cajanus cajan*
b *Coccus viridis* (and predaceous coccinellid) on a coffee leaf
c *Aspidiotus destructor*, attacked by mealy bug-like larvae of Coccinellidae
d *Aonidiella aurantii* on a citrus fruit

Plate 29

a *Chrysomphalus ficus* on grapefruit (above)
b *Unaspis citri* on citrus leaf
c *Insulaspis gloverii* on citrus fruit
d *Lepidosaphes beckii* on citrus leaves

Plate 30

a *Oecophylla longinoda* on a mango fruit, attending colony of soft scales
b Nest of *Macromischoides aculeatus* on coffee leaves
c Nest of *Messor barbarus* in a pennisetum field (note the destruction of plants around the entrance of the nest)
d Workers of *Messor barbarus,* destroying a pennisetum plant

Plate 31

a Coconut palms, showing serious damage by *Oryctes rhinoceros*
b Larvae of *Oryctes rhinoceros*
c Young coconut palm, attacked by *Oryctes monoceros*
d Larvae of *Epilachna varivestis*

Plate 32

a Adult of *Cylas puncticollis*
b Adult of *Cylas formicarius*
c Cotton flower, damaged by adults of *Anthonomus grandis*
d Female of *Anthonomus grandis*

Soon afterwards, the adult males or females start to powder themselves with the white wax secreted by the ventral wax glands on the first and second abdominal segment of the male and on the third and fourth abdominal segment of the female.

Copulation takes place between 12 hours and 2 days after emergence, depending on the prevailing temperature. Adults copulate several times during their lives. The length of the pre-oviposition period varies during different seasons of the year.

The female usually deposits its first eggs on the lower surface of the cotton leaf on which she emerges, but soon it moves to the higher young leaves of the same plant or another neighbouring one where more eggs are laid than on the older lower leaves which the adults are no longer infesting. The attraction of the adult whiteflies to the upper leaves is possibly a combination of negative geotropism and nutritional selection for a feeding and breeding site. *B. tabaci* lays its eggs indiscriminately on the surface of the leaves of most of its host plants. The position of the female while laying is very characteristic. She stations herself with the stylets inserted into the tissue of the leaf, the abdomen is moved slightly up and down and finally the sharp tip of the ovipositor pierces the epidermis. The egg is guided gently, with its stalk coming out first, into the very fine slit made on the leaf surface. The ovipositor is then raised leaving the egg standing perpendicularly to the leaf surface.

From the same position, several eggs are laid by the female in an arc, if she is not disturbed. The extent of the arc is determined by the nature of the leaf surface, i. e. whether smooth or hairy. The egg-laying capacity of *B. tabaci,* as a mean, is 160.43 ± 8.8 eggs deposited by one female at an average daily rate of 1.88 eggs per female per day. Starvation completely stops the females laying their eggs and egg-laying is only possible on living plants.

The longevity of the adults varies widely and depends on environmental and other factors. The males are always short-lived. They live for an average of 9.54 to 17.20 days with a mean of 13.19 ± 3.65, and the female for 37.75 to 74.20 days with a mean of 61.51 ± 10.86.

The incubation period is 4–6 days in autumn when the temperature ranges from 26–32 °C and 10–16 days in winter when the temperature ranges from 18–22 °C and development ceases at 16 °C.

The eclosion of the first instar nymphs from the eggs takes from 42–80 minutes at 30 °C and 90 % R. H. This first free juvenile stage crawls about on the leaf surface for some time before settling and fixes itself on the lower surface 1–2 days after hatching. It then starts sucking and excretes tiny wax filaments from the edges of its body. The total larval stage takes 12–15 days in autumn (28–32 °C) and 28–32 days in winter (20–24 °C). The development period is shortened by warm temperatures of 30–34 °C and becomes longer with temperatures of 18–22 °C. Eleven to twelve generations per year arise in the field.

Ecology: Attempts were made in the Sudan to correlate whitefly numbers in cotton fields with weather conditions. At the time of the sharp increase in numbers in September and October, the relative humidity varies from 80 to 90 per cent and the temperature from 36–38 °C among the cotton plants. These conditions favour the development of the juvenile stages by shortening the duration of each stage. The decrease in numbers in January and February is correlated with very low humidity and low temperatures. There are indications that relative humidity of 10–16 per cent with low temperatures of about 9 °C in January, decrease the population sharply and is lethal to the free juvenile stages; there is an increase in the longevity of each stage which survives. However, warm spells increase the population tremendously. In March, April and May when the temperature is very high (43–45 °C) and the relative humidity low (8–17 per cent), the population decreases and a high mortality rate occurs among the eggs and free juvenile stages.

The amount of rainfall also affects the numbers of whiteflies. Heavy rains depress the population in fallow and cotton fields.

Natural enemies: Two hymenopterous aphelinid parasites of whiteflies are recorded from the Sudan Gezira, namely *Encarsia lutea* and *Eretmocerus mundus*. Parasitism by the two species reaches its peak in December. Sprayings by insecticides show that the parasites are more affected by

DDT alone and DDT + dimethoate than by dimethoate alone.
The whitefly eggs and first larval stages are preyed upon by the phytoseiid mites *Amblyseius aleyrodis* and *Typhlodromus sudanicus* in N. E. Africa.

Control: In the Sudan, reduction in yield and quality of cotton may be caused by unexpectedly low populations, namely 200 adult whiteflies per 100 cotton leaves. This is the economical threshold level which indicates that spraying, using the recommended insecticides at the right dosage rates, must be applied by aeroplanes, tractors or knapsacks. Effective chemicals are: Formothion 25 % E. C. at 0.5 lb a. i., monocrotophos 55.2 % E. C. at 0.25 lb to 0.5 lb a. i., dicrotophos 24 % E. C.at 0.5 lb a. i., dimethoate 32 % E. C. at 0.4 lb a. i., phosphamidon 50 % E. C. at 0.5 lb a. i., malathion 57 % E. C. at 1.0 lb a. i., malathion 96 % ULV at 0.8 litre of product, oxydemeton-methyl 25 % E. C. at 0.5 lb a. i., endosulfan 35 % E. C. at 0.9 lb a. i., endosulfan ULV at 1 lb of product, DDT + methyl-parathion + toxaphene (Torbidan 10) E. C. at 2.0 litres of product, aldicarb 10 G at 25 lb of product and monocrotophos 40 % at 0.4 lb a. i., dimethoat (Rogor) 30 % ULV at 0.6 l of product, monocrotophos (Nuvacron) 40 % ULV at 0.7 litres of product, monocrotophos (Azodrin) 40 ULV at 0.45 l of product, DDT + methyl-parathion + toxaphene (Torbidan) 10 ULV at 1.5 litres of product and triazophos (Hostathion D) at 1.25 litres of product per feddan (1 feddan = ca. 4200 m²).

Literature

GAMEEL, O. I.(1969): Studies of Witefly Parasites *Encarsia lutea* Masi and *Eretmocerus mundus* Mercet. Rev. Zool. Bot. Afr. **79**, 1–2.
GAMEEL, O. I. (1969): Summary of Cotton Pest Control Practices in the Sudan. PANS **15**, 168–170.
GAMEEL, O. I. (1971): The Whitefly Eggs and First Larval Stages as Prey for Certain Phytoseiid Mites. Rev. Zool. Bot. Afr. **84** (1/2), 79–82.
GAMEEL, O. I. (1972): A new Description, Distribution and Hosts of the Cotton Whitefly *Bemisia tabaci* (Genn.) (Homoptera: Aleyrodidae) Rev. Zool. Bot. Afr., **86** (1/2), 50–64.
GAMEEL, O. I. (1973): Field Evaluation of Insecticides for Jassid, *Empoasca lybica* De Berg. and Whitefly, *Bemisia tabaci* (Genn.) Control on Cotton. Bull. Ent. Soc. Egypt No. 7, 113.
MOUND, L. A. (1965): Effect of Whitefly *(Bemisia tabaci)* on Cotton in the Sudan Gezira. Emp. Cott. Gr. Rev. **42**, 290–294.
POLLARD, D. G. (1955): Feeding habits of the cotton whitefly *Bemisia tabaci* (Genn.) Ann. Appl. Biol. **43**, 664–671.

Author: O. I. Gameel

Aleurocanthus woglumi Ashby (Plate 25 b)

Common names: Citrus black fly; Schwarze Fliege; L'aleurode des citrus; Mosca prieta de los cítricos.

Geographical distribution: Native from Southeast Asia, it has spread throughout practically all the tropical and parts of the subtropical citrus areas. It is found in Pakistan, Malaysia, Indonesia, the Philippines, Taiwan, China, Korea, South Africa, East Africa, the Seychelles Islands, the Azores. On the American continent, it is found in the United States (Texas, Florida), Mexico, all Central American countries, Cuba and the West Indies, as well as South America (Columbia, Venezuela, Peru, Ecuador, Brazil). CIE Map no 91.

Host plants: *Citrus* spp.; guava (*Psidium guajava*); mango (*Mangifera indica*); *Melicoca bijuga;* cashew (*Anacardium occidentale*); *Annona muricata; Rosa* spp. etc.

Symptoms (on citrus): Nymphs produce copious honeydew, which encourages sooty molds on upper surfaces of leaves, followed by gradual weakening of the tree. The fruit is stained by the 'soot'. Heavy black colonies of the pest occur on the underside of leaves (see Plate 25 b).

Economic importance: Fruit production drops considerably when infestations are heavy and prolonged. Entire orchards or citrus areas may be rendered unproductive.

Morphology: Adults seldom over 1 mm long, aleyrodid type with bluish pubescence on body. They lay eggs on the underside of leaves in a typically spiral pattern. Nymphs sessile, with black straight bristles. Third nymphal instar black with whitish waxy secretions on edge of body.

Similarities to other pests: Morphologically, *A. woglumi* is very distinctive from other aleyrodids. However, the symptoms of attack (sooty mold, for example) can be confused, at first glance with those of citrus whiteflies *(Dialeurodes citrifolii* and *D. citri,* or woolly whitefly, *Aleurothrixus floccosus).* The orange spiny whitefly, *Aleurocanthus spiniferus,* somewhat resembles it.

Life cycle: Populations are more abundant and more widely distributed during the rainy season. Moderately high temperature and relative humidity are favourable for development. Under optimal conditions, duration of life stages are: egg, 8–10 days; first nymph, 8–10 days; second nymph, 9–12 days; third nymph, 10–14 days; pupa, 24–30 days. The whole life cycle can be completed in 60–72 days. There is considerable overlapping of generations, so that all stages may be present throughout the year. However, it is during the rainy season that activity and damage reach their peak.

Ecology: Moderately high temperatures (28–32 °) and relative humidities (70–80 %) are favourable for citrus black fly development. Citrus groves located above 3,000 feet (about 1,000 m) altitude seem to be less prone to attack by the pest.

Natural enemies: Predators as *Scymnus* spp. *(*Coleoptera: Coccinellidae) and *Chrysopa* sp. (Neuroptera: Chrysopidae) can eliminate tremendous amounts of nymphs. Pathogenic fungi as *Aschersonia aleyrodis,* are also important biotic mortality factors. All seem to reproduce more under favourable humidity, i. e., during the rainy season. These biotic factors, though important, do not provide an adequate control of the pest. Parasites as *Prospaltella opulenta, Eretmocerus serius, Amitus hesperidum, Prospaltella clypealis,* and *Prospaltella smithi,* are very effective in controlling the pest. Weather conditions or pesticide sprays may upset the excellent biological control achieved by these parasites. Successful biological control of the pest has been attained in Mexico, Cuba, South Africa, Panama, and more recently, in El Salvador.

Control: The possibility of achieving biological control of the pest should be given top priority. If spray programmes are needed for other pests, an integrated pest management programme should be implemented in which chemicals are judiciously applied at the proper timing and rates. Some botanicals as rotenone and sabadilla can be effective against thrips, for example, without upsetting biological control of the citrus blackfly. The use of narrow range oils also seems promising.

Literatur

CLAUSEN, C. P. & P. A. BERRY (1932): The citrus blackfly in Asia, and the importation of its natural enemies into tropical America. – U. S. Dept. Agric. Tech. Bull. 320, 59 pp.
QUEZADA, J. R. (1974): Biological Control of *Aleurocanthus woglumi (Homoptera: Aleyrodidae)* in El Salvador. Entomophaga **19** (3), 243–254.
SHAW, J. G. (1950): Hosts of the citrus blackfly in Mexico. U. S. Bur. Ent. and Plant Quar. E-798, 16 pp. (Processed).
SMITH, H. D., H. L. MALTBY & E. J. JIMENEZ (1964): Biological Control of the Citrus Blackfly in Mexico. USDA Techn. Bull. 1311, 30 pp.

Author: J. R. Quezada

Other injurious Aleyrodoidea:

Dialeurodes citri (Ashm.), Citrus whitefly (Citrus-Mottenschildlaus). In tropical America and in South and East Asia (CIE Map no 111). Attacks leaves of citrus and produces large amounts of honeydew. Other Aleyrodids affecting citrus, mainly in Asia, are *Aleurocanthus spiniferus* (Quaint.) (CIE Map no 112) and *Aleurolobus marlatti* (Quaint.). *Aleurothrixus floccosus* (Mask.) (CIE Map no 327) was successfully controlled by released *Cales noacki* How. (Hym.: Aphelinidae) in the western Mediterranean Basin.

H. Sch.

Superfamily: Aphidoidea
Family: Aphididae

Aphis craccivora Koch (Plate 25 c)

Synonyms: *Aphis laburni* part., *A. medicaginis* part., *A. robiniae, A. leguminosae, A. papilionacearum.*

Common names: Groundnut aphid, Cowpea aphid; Erdnußblattlaus; Puceron de l'arachide, Puceron de la gourgane; Pulgón de las legumbres.

Geographical disribution: Widely distributed in the tropics. Possibly represented by races or subspecies in temperate zones; immigration of the original strain in the summer cannot be excluded. CIE Map no 99.

Host plants: Mostly Leguminosae, also some Malvaceae (cotton), *Caesalpinia,* Caricaceae, Convolvulaceae (sweet potato), Chenopodiaceae, Cucurbitaceae, Compositae, Malpighiaceae, Mimosaceae, Oleaceae, Scrophulariaceae, Solanaceae, Tamaricaceae and ornamentals.

Symptoms: Young plants (Leguminosae, particularly peanut, broad bean and lucerne) are stunted by early attack; Severe attack at the time of flowering and seed formation affects the yield and can produce wilt symptoms. In addition, abnormalities due to virus diseases (rosetting, stunting, mosaic, mottle etc.) can be observed.

Economic importance: The greatest damage results from virus diseases which are transmitted by *A. craccivora.* A peanut crop attacked by the "rosette virus complex" may not give an economic return (yield may be reduced to 1/7 of normal crop). The groundnut aphid can act as vector for about 30 phytopathogenic viruses which can also do much damage in non-leguminous crops (cotton, papaya etc.).

Morphology: Virginaptera 1.5–2 mm long, blackish, shiny (only nymphs faintly dusted with wax), abdomen with large, dark, practically solid dorsal plate, segments II–V without marginal tubercles. Blackish, scaly siphunculi about $1^2/_5$–$1^4/_5$ times as long as the dark cauda, which is slightly pointed and has 5–6 bristles. Antennae markedly shorter than the body, very short hairs ($^1/_3$ to $^1/_2$ joint diameter), base of segment VI about $^1/_3$ to $^1/_2$ as long as processus terminalis. Winged parthenogenetic female 1.5 to 1.8 mm long, dark, dorsal abdominal plate dissolved into cross markings of varying number, often reduced in front, only very exceptionally with marginal tubercles on segments II–IV. Antennae, siphunculi and cauda blackish, antennal segment III with 3–8 rhinaria (absent on joint IV and V), with short hairs. Siphunculi $1^1/_3$–$1^3/_4$ length of cauda.

Life cycle and ecology: The groundnut aphid remains on Leguminosae (peanut etc.) throughout the year with varying population density. In drought periods it can take refuge on weeds or self-seeded peanut seedlings. It can also withdraw into cracks in the soil in such periods, provided the soil shows a tendency to fissure. As soon as the aphids are driven out again by rain, they once more colonise aerial plant portions. At a distance of 200 to 400 km inland from the coast conditions (in Africa) are so favourable, that yearly mass infestations are to be expected. From climatically suitable zones, *A. craccivora* often migrates over wide distances into dry zones where, given transient periods of sufficient rainfall, it can cause harm by transmitting the groundnut viruses it carries. Watered plants are more heavily infested than unwatered plants in the drought period. As soon as the drought period is over, plants which grow normally, without watering, are again preferred. Under reasonably suitable climatic conditions, the development of one generation takes 6–8 days (sometimes 5.5 days). With each generation, the degree of infestation on affected plants increases 5–8 fold. A progeny of 2–3 per day seems to be the rule. The mortality of nymphs is relatively high, less in temperate zones, there the progeny reaches up to 60 (India 50) individuals per virginaptera. Alatae produce only about half the progeny produced by apterae. Since the summer morph of *A. craccivora* is fairly susceptible to low temperatures, it succumbs to frost in cold regions and must later fill up the losses from frost free areas. Reports from India state that groundnut aphid attack starts 4–6 weeks after sowing, to reach its peak 3–4 weeks later (at about the time of flowering). Attack follows a similar course in other peanut growing areas, such as South or Central America. It is noteworthy that *A. craccivora* attack is slight in densely planted groundnut crops, whose plant rows soon close up. Moreover, there are hardly any alatae. Subsequent virus attack is confined to the edge of rows and free corners, a sign that virulent aphids are present very early. The formation of aphid and peanut races affect the extent of damage suffered by these plants. Slight attack and tolerance to the main viruses can affect the economy of a peanut crop considerably, so that selective breeding for these properties seems promising. Attack on other crops (subterranean clover in Australia, cotton, papaya), with migration from weeds, virus transport over large distances, peak and depression phase of attack, does not differ markedly in these respects from the circumstances described for peanut, except for time shifts and changes in alternating phases of population density, due to local climatic conditions. *A. craccivora* is consistently visited by ants.

Natural enemies: See species listed unter *Pergandeida craccivora* and *P. robiniae* in Börner & Heinze, 1957. Also *Chrysopa perla, Bulaea lichatschovii, Brumus 11-punctata, Xanthogramma (Ischiodon) aegyptium, Aphidius dauci* and *Lysiphlebus* sp..

Control: Densely planted groundnut fields sown as soon as possible (spacing 20–25 cm) discourage colonisation by aphids. The sooner the crop has closed before the plant lice migrate from wild plants, the more moderate the attack. Aphid resistant (or tolerant) peanut varieties allow only a much retarded increase of small aphid colonies; meanwhile, predators arriving from wild plants can build up populations, especially Syrphid larvae, and reduce the aphid population effectively. For chemical control, a large number of preparations with effective action against aphids are available, which are largely listed in the chapter on *Myzus persicae* (see p. 334). Other pesticides which have been tested against groundnut aphid are: monocrotophos (Azodrin), malathion, menazon, phosphamidon (Dimecron), trichlorphon, vamidothion. Residue problems may arise if granulates or similar preparations for soil application (phorate, disulfoton) are used.

Literature

See literature references for *Myzus persicae* (except HEINZE, K. 1960/1961); also

EASTOP, V. F. (1958): A study of the Aphididae (Homoptera) of East Africa. Her Majesty's Stationary Office London, 1–126.

REAL, P. (1955): Le cycle annuel du puceron de l'arachide *(Aphis leguminosae* Theob.) en Afrique Noire Française et son déterminisme. Rev. Pathol. végét. **34**, 3–122.

Author: K. Heinze

Aphis fabae Scop. (Fig. 127)

Synonyms: *Aphis papaveris, A. rumicis* (part.), *Doralis fabae*

Common names: Black bean aphid; Schwarze Bohnenlaus; Puceron du haricot; Pulgón negro de las habas.

Geographical distribution: Widespread in temperate regions. Introduced into East Africa (Uganda, Kenya, Tansania) in recent years. CIE Map no 174.

Host plants: *Vicia faba* and *Beta vulgaris* in temperate regions and *Phaseolus vulgaris* at high altitudes in the tropics. It is a virus vector in various horticultural crops as it feeds on many plants. *A. fabae* does not thrive in the hotter parts of the tropics where it is replaced by the (sub-)species *solanella* which feeds on few plants of economic importance including potato and numerous weeds, especially *Solanum* spp. (East Africa).

Symptoms: Direct damage is caused by the loss of sap, injury to plant tissues and indirect harm by virus transmission. Small populations may have little evident effect but large numbers of aphids may stunt the plant, reduce seed formation and in extreme cases kill the plant. There is often a strong 'edge effect' with a few rows on the windward side of the crop being heavily infested and with few aphids in the middle of the crop.

Economic importance: Important as a virus vector in sugar beet in Central Europe and reducing the yield of *Vicia faba* in Western Europe by feeding damage. *A. fabae* has recently become of importance in *Phaseolus vulgaris* crops in East Africa. It is known to transmit more than thirty viruses including Bean common and yellow mosaic, Beet mosaic and yellows, Cabbage black ring spot, Cauliflower mosaic, Celery mosaic, Cucumber mosaic, Dahlia mosaic, Iris mosaics, Lucerne and Narcissus mosaics, Soybean mosaic, Tobacco etch, Tomato dwarfing and Tulip breaking mosaics.

Morphology: *A. fabae* is a dark brownish green to almost black aphid, with black siphunculi and cauda, usually living on young shoots but dense colonies may eventually spread over most of the aerial parts of the plant. The femora bear many fine long hairs on all surfaces and the cauda bears 10–19 hairs.

Similarities to other species: Very similar to *A.(fabae)solanella* which has slightly longer siphunculi, shorter and less constricted cauda and shorter lateral abdominal hairs. Large specimens of *A. gossypii* may be very dark green, almost black but their cauda is usually paler and bears only 5–8 hairs and the femora bear short hairs on most surfaces with only a few long hairs along the posterior margin. *A. craccivora* is dark but the adults are shiny, have few caudal hairs and short femoral hairs.

Fig. 127.   Heavy infestation by *Aphis fabae* on bean (phot. H. Schmutterer)

Life cycle: In the temperate region *A. fabae* overwinters in the egg stage on *Euonymus, Viburnum* or *Philadelphus* and colonises many other plants during the summer. In the tropics the whole year is probably spent as a succession of parthenogenetic viviparous females, several generations of apterae being succeeded by a generation of winged individuals when the plant gets overcrowded.

Ecology: There is an enormous literature concerning the biology of *A. fabae. A. fabae* takes about a week from birth to maturity, the precise time depending mostly on temperature. Individuals developing faster into smaller adults at higher temperatures. A female may produce up to about 100 young at the rate of ten per day, but lower figures are likely from the smaller individuals produced at higher temperatures. *A. fabae* thrives best at about 14–15 °C and is often attended by ants.

Natural enemies: Numerous natural enemies are known from temperate regions. Predators include Dermaptera, Anthocoridae, Miridae, Carabidae, Cantharidae, Coccinellidae, Staphylinidae, Cecidomyiidae and Syrphidae. Parasites include *Ephedrus, Lipolexis, Lysiphlebus, Praon* and *Trioxys* spp. (Braconidae) and *Aphelinus semiflavus* (Aphelinidae) but their effectiveness may be limited by hyperparasites such as *'Charips' pusillus* (Cynipoidea), *Asaphes* and *Pachyneuron* spp. (Pteromalidae), *Aphidencyrtus* sp. (Encyrtidae).

Control:
Resistant varieties: In temperate regions, certain varieties of *Vicia faba* are resistant to the pest.
Chemical control: Menazon, dimethoate, demeton-S-methyl or oxydemeton-methyl can be used up to three weeks before picking but after that malathion or mevinphos can be applied. Small plots can be sprayed with derris or dusted with nicotine. Spraying should be done before flowering to reduce mortality in pollinating insects. If spraying must be carried out during the flowering period it should be timed to avoid the pollinating insects. In temperate regions spraying is usually best done late in the evening.
There is little evidence of commercially important insecticide resistance in *Aphis fabae*, perhaps because so small a proportion of each year's population is exposed to insecticides. That suitable detoxification processes are probably available to *A. fabae* is indicated by experimental work.

Literature

BERANEK, A. P. & R. J. BARRY (1974): Inherited changes in enzyme patterns within parthenogenetic clones of *Aphis fabae.* J. Ent. (A) **48**, 141–147.
BOMBOSCH, S. (1964): Untersuchungen zum Massenwechsel von *Aphis fabae* Scop. Z. angew. Ent. **54**, 179–193.
FRAZER, B. D. (1972): Life tables and intrinsic rates of increase of apterous black bean aphids and pea aphids, on broad bean (Homoptera, Aphididae). Can. Ent. **104**, 1717–1722.
HONEYBOURNE, C. H. B. (1969): Performance of *Aphis fabae* and *Brevicoryne brassicae* on plants treated with growth regulators. J. Sci. Fd. Agric. **20**, 388–390.
MÜLLER, H. J. (1966): Über die Ursachen der unterschiedlichen Resistenz von *Vicia faba* L. gegenüber der Bohnenblattlaus *Aphis (Doralis) fabae* Scop. Entomol. Exptl. App. **9**, 42–66.
SHAW, M. J. P. (1970): Effects of population densities on alienicolae of *Aphis fabae* Scop. Ann. appl. Biol. **65**, 191–196, 197–203, 205–212.
SWAINE, G. (1969): Studies on the biology and control of pests of seed beans *(Phaseolus vulgaris)* in Northern Tanzania. Bull. ent. Res. **59**, 323–338.
TAYLOR, L. R. (1970): Aggregation and the transformation of counts of *Aphis fabae* Scop. on beans. Ann. appl. Biol. **65**, 181–189.
WEARING, C. H. & H. F. VAN EMDEN (1967): Studies on the relations of insect and host plant. I. Effects of water stress in host plants on infestation by *Aphis fabae* Scop., *Myzus persicae* (Sulzer) and *Brevicoryne brassicae* (L.). Nature **213**, 1051–1052.
WEISMAN, L., & S. HALANDA (1968): The reaction of the black bean aphid *Aphis fabae* Scop. to qualitative changes in the contents of amino acids in the vegetative organs of spindle *(Euonymus europaeus)* and seed sugar-beet plants. Biologia (Bratislava) **23**, 849–856.

Author: V. F. Eastop

Aphis gossypii Glov. (Plate 25 d)

Synonyms: *Aphis cucumeris, A. cucurbiti;* some records at least of *A. frangulae* und *A. solanina.* Numerous other synonyms which seldom occur in economic literature.

Common names: Melon aphid, Cotton aphid; Gurkenblattlaus; Puceron du melon, Puceron du cottonier; Pulgón (amarillo) del algodonero.

Geographical distribution: Very widespread in the tropics and in warm temperate regions. CIE Map no 18.

Host plants: Cotton, cucurbits, citrus, coffee, cocoa, eggplant, peppers, potato, okra and many ornamental plants, including *Hibiscus.*

Symptoms: Rarely conspicuous, unless the plants are heavily infested when young when evident distortion and stunting occurs for instance in cotton and cucurbits. The upper surfaces of leaves may be contaminated with honeydew falling from aphids feeding on higher leaves and some of the viruses transmitted have distinctive symptoms.

Economic importance: *A. gossypii* is known to transmit more than 50 viruses and is often regarded as a serious pest on cotton and cucurbits owing to its large numbers and presumed feeding damage. Spraying however seldom seems to increase yield enough to justify the operation, perhaps because it is rarely carried out until large populations are seen on mature plants when any damage has been done. Contamination of cotton lint by honeydew carries problems during the spinning process. A vector of Pawpaw mosaic and distortion ring spot and possibly of some importance as a virus vector when feeding on citrus and cocoa in large numbers and also transmitting viruses in peppers, potatoes, groundnuts and cucurbits.

Morphology: Variable in colour, large specimens are dark green, almost black while the adults produced on overcrowded leaves at high temperature may be less than one mm long and very pale yellow to almost white. Commonly it is a light green aphid mottled with darker green, with dark siphunculi and pale cauda. The femoral hairs are short except for a few along the posterior margin. The eighth abdominal tergite bears only 2 hairs and the cauda only 5–8 hairs.

Similarities to other pests: Both *Aphis fabae* and *A. spiraecola* bear more numerous and longer hairs, and have a black cauda. *A. craccivora* bears short, sparse hairs but the black cauda is more pointed than in *gossypii* and the adult apterae are shiny black because of the pigmented dorsal carapace.

Life cycle: In temperate regions overwintering in the egg stage both on *Rhamnus* and on Bignoniaceae which may indicate that two similar polyphagous aphids are confused under the name *gossypii.*
In the tropics reproduction is continuously parthenogenetic and viviparous, on numberous dicotyledons and on the flower stems of many monocotyledons but seldom Gramineae. Females reach maturity in about 4–20 days depending on temperature and produce from 20 to 140 young, at a rate of from about 2–9 per day. The small individuals produced at very high temperature produce fewer young.

Ecology: Often attended by ants, belonging to various genera including *Acantholepis, Crematogaster, Oecophylla, Polyrhacis, Tapinoma, Techromyrmex, Pheidole* and *Wasmannia. A. gossypii* has been regarded as a beneficial insect in Peru as it is the winter host for the egg predator of a more important noctuid.

Natural enemies: Numerous natural enemies have been recorded. Predators include Neuroptera, Chrysopidae and Hemerobiidae members. Coleopterous predators include members of at least 20 genera of Coccinellidae and the tenebrionid *Epitragodes tomentosus*. Heteropterous predators include Reduviidae, Anthocoridae, Miridae and Pentatomidae. Dipterous predators include the larvae of Cecidomyiidae, Chamaemyidae and at least 11 genera of Syrphidae.

Primary parasites include *Aphidius, Lysiphlebus* and *Trioxys* spp. (Braconidae) and several species of *Aphelinus* (Chalcidoidea). *Asaphes* and *Pachyneuron* spp. (Pteromalidae) are recorded as hyperparasites through *Lysiphlebus*. The parasitic fungus *Entomophthora ? exitialis* has been recorded from *A. gossypii* in India.

Control:

Cultural practices. Too high a proportion of nitrogen in fertiliser may increase *A. gossypii* populations. Late sown crops of cotton usually suffer more from aphids than early sown crops. Some cotton varieties are more susceptible to *A. gossypii* than other cotton varieties.

Chemical control. DDT + methyl-demeton (Metasystox), phorate (Thimet); dimethyl-dimethoate and vamidothion (Kilval) at 0.5 % toxic ingredient per 100 gallons of water; dimethoate (Roxion); formothion (Anthio), methyl-parathion and carbophenothion (Trithion) at 0.25 lb per 100 gallons have controlled *A. gossypii* on cotton. Dimethoate can be added for aphids when spraying for other pests. DDT + gamma-BHC gave control and increased yield of cotton despite slight phytotoxicity in Uganda. Wettable mercaptodiamethur (Methiocarb) (Bayer 5024), carbaryl (Sevin) at about 1.35 lb toxicant per acre and azinphos-methyl (Gusathion) at 0.36 lb kept plants virtually free from aphids when applied at weekly intervals. This protection increased yields in late sown crops exposed to large aphid infestations. Carbaryl, endosulfan and fenitrothion have given good control without however reducing the amount of dirty or unpickable cotton. 20 % endrin at 1 fl. oz. per 2 gallons of water has increased cotton yields. 1 % phosphamidon dust can be used to economise water but should be applied while dew is still on the plants for best adhesion. Granules of phorate, UC 21149, and Niagara 10242 at 0.6–2.0 lb per acre have controlled *A. gossypii* for 4–9 weeks. Granules in seed furrows may give control for 4–6 weeks but cotton seed dressings have not given satisfactory control. Potatoes have been protected by 0.02 % parathion, 0.03 % dimethoate (Rogor) and mevinphos (Phosdrin). An emulsion of 1 oz 40 % dimethoate per 4 gallons of water or 1 oz of 20 % endrin in 2 gallons has given control on eggplant. The use of both DDT and dieldrin against other insects has been followed by outbreaks of *A. gossypii* on cotton and other crops, apparently as the result of reduction in natural enemies. The resistance of *A. gossypii* to HCN was reported in 1928 and since then resistance to demeton and to BHC has been recorded. Strains with LD 50 and LD 95, 135 times as great to demeton as susceptible populations have been reported.

Literature

BATCHELDER, C. D. (1927): The variability of *Aphis gossypii*. Ann. ent. Soc. Am. **20**, 263–278.

GOFF, C. C. & A. N. TISSOT (1932): The melon aphid, *Aphis gossypii* Glover. Bul. Univ. Fla Agr. Ept. Sta. 252.

KHALIFA, A. & N. EL-DIN SHARAF (1965): Biological and ecological study of *Aphis gossypii* Glover. Bull. Soc. ent. Egypt **48**, 131–154 (1964).

NASAR, S. A., S. K. EL-SAWAF, S. M. HAMMAD & H. ZAZOU (1962): The morphology of the cotton aphid, *Aphis gossypii* Glover (Homoptera, Aphididae). Alexandria J. Agric. Res. **10**, 133–144.

REINHARD, H. J. (1927): The influence of parentage, nutrition, temperature, and crowding on wing production in *Aphis gossypii* Glov. Texas Agr. Expt. St. Bull. **353**, 1–19.

THOMAS, K. H. (1968): Die Blattläuse aus der engeren Verwandtschaft von *Aphis gossypii* Glover und *A. frangulae* Kaltenbach unter besonderer Berücksichtigung ihres Vorkommens an Kartoffel. Entom. Abhandlung Staatl. Mus. Tierkund. Dresden **35**, 337–389.

Author: V. F. Eastop

Aphis spiraecola Patch (Fig. 128 and plate 26 a)

Synonym: *Aphidula spiraecola*

Common names: Spir(a)ea aphid; Grüne Citrus-Blattlaus; Pulgón verde del naranjo.

Geographical distribution: Original habitat North America – there with holocyclic (♂♀ and with oviposition in autumn) propagation. Now almost universally distributed in temperate and tropical latitudes. Anholocyclic (only asexual reproduction) in warm regions. CIE Map no 256.

Host plants: Citrus species (grapefruit almost immune), *Theobroma cacao, Carica papaya, Annona* sp., *Malus* sp., *Pirus* sp., *Prunus* sp., *Crataegus* sp., *Cotoneaster* sp., *Spiraea* (regional winter host), *Pittosporum* sp., *Viburnum* sp.. Occurrence on over 65 plant genera has been mentioned (but in part in mistake for *Aphis pomi,* the green apple aphid).

Symtoms: Leaves rolled tightly, sometimes almost spirally, inwards from the tip, as a result of aphid feeding. The earlier the attack, the more shoots are stunted. Branches no longer grow to normal size. On distorted tips of shoots, several leaves can be rolled in together. Leaf blades slightly wavy at feeding sites or buckled as a result of uneven growth. Leaves with heavy feeding damage are reduced in size. Such leaves and tips of branches may die prematurely. The distortions are irreversible, but uncolonised new shoots show normal growth. Old mature leaves are unsuitable for aphids and usually free from attack. Flowers and fruit are also damaged. Flower buds with feeding damage don't develop further. If already opened, they form no fruit. Fruit which had reached a certain size by the time of attack, is crippled.

Economic importance: On severely affected trees, the entire yield is in jeopardy. Heavy honeydew deposits on the fruit and the growth of sooty mould on the sticky honeydew make the fruit unsightly and reduce its marketable value. The growth of sooty moulds on the honeydew on leaves affects assimilation, which in turn also affects the yield. The species can transmit Tristeza virus of citrus trees.

Morphology: Virginaptera: 1.4–2.2 mm in size (largest in early spring), greenish lemon yellow to green. Upper abdomen without large sclerotic (more chitinised) plate. Antennae about $^3/_5$ of body length. Brown-black siphunculi tapered towards the end. Cauda about $^3/_4$ length of siphunculi, with 7–14 bristles[1]. Alatae 1.4 to 2.2 mm (summer forms smaller), greenish to faintly reddish, head thorax and siphunculi dark. Abdomen without extensive sclerotisation, with the exception of a few spots at the side. Antennae about $^3/_5$ of body length, with 5–11 rhinaria on segment III and 0–5 on joint IV. Cauda about $^3/_4$ length of siphunculi, with 7–14 bristles. Hairs on femora longer than diameter of femur at point of attachment to troachanter.

Similarities to other pests: Cannot be confused with green apple aphid on citrus (absent on citrus) but can be confused with it on other hosts which are suitable for *A. pomi.*

Life cycle and ecology: Attack by *A. spiraecola* starts in citrus growing regions with a few overwintered virginapterae on new shoots in early spring. In the mediterranean region, the first small colonies on young shoots can already be seen by early February. Seasonal variations in the different tropical regions can hardly be specified, not least because vegetative conditions are very different in northern and southern latitudes. The vegetative cycle of *Citrus* spp. is decisive for the occurrence of the species. The Spirea aphid depends on young developing leaves and shoots for the formation of sizable populations, but can increase rapidly if these are available. In hot weather,

---

[1]A good hand lens is required for observation. If necessary, boil in caustic potash, squeeze out abdominal contents and observe in lactic acid mixture under binoculars or microscope.

deposited nymphs can grow into adults within 5–6 days and in turn produce nymphs. On average, one aphid deposits 30 nymphs. Under favourable conditions, up to 14 generations are said to be produced in a year. With deterioration of food supply and overpopulation, the formation of winged forms increases rapidly. These alatae migrate within a short period from the *Citrus* species in search of other, more suitable host plants (see list p. 330). A residual number remains on the shoots emerging around grafts or other places inclined to shoot formation. As was observed in the mediterranean region, fruit formation and a change in vegetative conditions in the autumn enrich the sap stream and provide better conditions for *A. spiraecola,* which consequently increases in number. With approaching winter, the reproductive aphid activity declines until finally it almost ceases. Few aphids survive the cold weather period. Conditions in

Fig. 128.   Sooty mould on honeydew of *Aphis spiraecola* on citrus fruit (phot. H. Schmutterer)

the tropics are a little more favourable, since new shoot formation never stops entirely. In mixed populations of various citrus aphid species on one tree, *A. spiraecola* is generally present in greatest abundance, at least locally. Similar vegetative conditions prevail for coffee, cocoa and tea, especially as far as hardening of the foliage is concerned, so that the developmental conditions for the aphid on these hosts should not differ markedly from those on citrus plants. The species is visited by ants.

Natural enemies: Some 40 species of predators are known (see Börner & Heinze, 1957). They are mainly Chrysopidae, Coccinellidae and Syrphidae.

Control: Suitable chemicals are: Nicotine preparations (pure nicotine, e. g. 0.1 %), ethion 0.1 %, parathion-ethyl 0.035–0.05 %, parathion-methyl 0.05 %, dichlorvos 0.05–0.1 %, dimethoate (Perfekthion, Roxion) 0.05–0.1 %, fenitrothion 0.05–0.1 %, propoxur 0.1 %. Stem bandages soaked with dimethoate and oxydemeton-methyl (Metasystox R) were tested in Florida in February with good results. This procedure should also be suitable for the mediterranean region and areas with similar climatic conditions. Drenching with dimefox (1 % 1 l/m) should be tried on nursery plants.

Literature

BARBAGALLO, S. (1966): The aphis fauna of Citrus in Sicily. Entomologia (Bari) **2,** 201–260.
BARBAGALLO, S. (1966): Contributo alla conoscenza degli agrumi I. *Aphis spiraecola* Patch. Boll. Lab. Entom. agrar. Portici **42,** 49–83.
BÖRNER, C., & K. HEINZE (1957): Aphidina-Aphidoidea. Sorauer, Handb. Pflanzenkrankh. Bd. V, 5. Aufl., 4. Liefg. 1–402.
ESSIG, E. O. (1953): Aphids in relation to quick decline and tristeza of citrus. Pan. Pacif. Entom. **29,** 13–23.
WYNIGER, R. (1962): Pests of crops in warm climates and their control. Verl. f. Recht u. Gesellsch. Basel, 1–555. Appendix: V. Control measures 2nd Edit., 1–162, 1968.

Author: K. Heinze

Macrosiphum euphorbiae (Ths.) (Plate 26 b)

Synonyms: *Macrosiphum solanifolii, Macrosiphon solani, M. koehleri, M. gei* part., *Siphonophora solanifolii*

Common names: Potato aphid; Grünstreifige Kartoffelblattlaus; Puceron de la pomme de terre; Pulgón verde de la papa.

Geographical distribution: Common in temperate and tropical regions as anholocyclic form (with parthenogenesis). CIE Map no 44 (with supplements, e. g. East Africa).

Host plants: Several hundred host plants have been named. Some are only colonised temporarily, but long enough for virus transmission to take place. Cultivated plants which can be badly affected are: Potato, tomato, *Capsicum,* egg plant, sweet potato, papaya, *Passiflora,* cucurbits, lettuce, some Leguminosae, Cruciferae, Umbelliferae (celery, parsnip etc.), *Nicotiana* species, Chenopodiaceae (beet, spinach), maize, Liliaceae and a number of ornamentals from other families.

Symptoms: Severe attack by *M. euphorbiae* leads to stunted growth, particularly when the tips of shoots are covered with aphids. As with *Myzus persicae* however, the greatest damage results from viruses for which *M. euphorbiae* acts as vector. Depending on the type of virus, the various kinds of distortions are produced on different parts of the plant, which are described for *M. persicae* (see p. 333).

Economic importance: In fairly warm regions, where the potato aphid is not exposed to the population diminishing vicissitudes of winter conditions in Northern latitudes, it plays a major part as virus vector in potato crops. Altogether it transmits at least 75 viruses or virus strains.

Morphology: Virginapterae 2–3.5 mm long, green with dark green stripe across the back (Plate 26 b), at the side faintly covered with waxy powder. Greenish antennae, dark at the ends of joints, 2.9–3.7 mm long, clearly protruding beyond the pale, ensiform cauda which has 8–11 bristles. Antennal flagellum (slender end portion) of segment VI longer than segment III, which has 1–7 basal rhinaria. Siphunculi slender, almost $^1/_3$ body length, reticulated at terminal end and darkened.
Winged virginopara 2–3 mm long, green with brownish yellow head, brown thorax and dark green dorsal stripe on paler green abdomen, greenish siphunculi of about $^1/_3$ body length and long ensiform cauda. Antennae protrude beyond tail end, segment III with 16–20 rhinaria.

Life cycle and ecology: Reproduction of potato aphid in warmer regions is much like that of green peach aphid (cf.). It seems better able to withstand drought and as a rule reproduces at a greater rate on sprouting tubers in stacks or storage than *M. persicae.* In unfavourable climatic conditions it survives in foci for new population build-up on various weeds of different kinds, depending on country or continent, also on sprouting potato tubers left over from the previous year's potato crop (southern Argentine, tropical African regions) or on other self seeded plants. As usual, the population build-up reaches a maximum in the main growing period of plants up to the time of flowering. Environmental conditions for *M. euphorbiae* than worsen, physiological metabolic changes in the host connected with seed and tuber formation influence the availability of suitable sap compounds, so that the population density is much reduced at that time, especially as it coincides with the appearance of numbers of predators and parasites. Shortly before maturation of plants the physiological conditions for the nutritional requirements of the aphids once more improve, usually followed by a renewed steep rise in population density.

Natural enemies: See species listed unter *Macrosiphon solani* in the text by Börner & Heinze (1957).

Control: See *Myzus persicae* (p. 334).

Literature

As with *M. persicae,* except HEINZE, K., 1960/1961.

Author: K. Heinze

Myzus persicae (Sulz.) (Plate 26 c)

Synonyms: *Myzodes persicae, M. tabaci, Aphis dianthi, A. malvae*

Common names: Green peach aphid, Peach-potato aphid, Tobacco aphid; Grüne Pfirsichblatt-laus; Puceron vert du pêcher; Pulgón verde del duraznero.

Geographical distribution: Worldwide distribution, in regions with winter temperatures below – 12 °C depends on peach cultivation (sexual forms and oviposition). From there it colonises herbaceous plants, also dangerous pest in (temperate) glasshouses. Usually overwinters outdoors as winged and wingless virginogenia, both in temperate climates and in the tropics. CIE Map no 45.

Host plants: Well over 400 host plants are known, among them many crops. Major pest in potato crops and in crops of *Brassica-, Capsicum-, Cucumis-, Cynara-, Dahlia-, Fragaria-, Gerbera-, Gladiolus-, Gloxinia-, Gossypium-, Ipomoea-, Lycopersicon-, Nicotiana-, Phaseolus-, Pisum-, Pittosporum-, Prunus (persica and some others)-, Solanum (melongena)-, Streptocarpus-, Trifolium-, Vicia-* and *Zea*-species.

Symptoms: With few exceptions, the green peach aphid leaves no feeding damage on affected plants. Leaf distortion and chlorosis can occur on peach, as well as leaf drop of severely attacked young leaves. Mass infestation can greatly weaken the plants and lead to stunted growth. Heavy attack on tobacco plants can produce an inferior crop resulting from honey dew deposits and tearing of leaves around feeding places. The transmission of phytopathogenic viruses by *M. persicae* results in the most varied symptoms on affected plants. These depend on the virus and usually consist of mosaic or mottled speckling, chlorosis, leaf roll or crinkle, leaf enations and narrowing from slightly narrowed to filiform leaves.

Economic importance: As vector of over 150 viruses or virus strains, which may be persistent (transmitted repeatedly over a longer period) or non-persistent (only transmitted immediately after taking up) the green peach aphid can be described as the most important of all virus vectors and perhaps plant enemy number 1 (working in obsurity, since the damage is frequently not seen until after the aphids have disappeared). The damage resulting from both direct effects and transmitted viruses can lead to estimated losses totalling several milliards DM. Apart from typical potato growing countries in temperate zones, the green peach aphid plays a major part as vector in seed potato production areas in the tropics, which only is possible at high altitudes (e. g. Venezuela above 2100 m, Africa in the Kilimanjaro region at similar altitudes) or in locations where seed potato fields are much exposed to winds (Southern Argentine). Naturally, the rapid spread of virus infection resulting from green peach aphid attack necessitates crop rotation of potato crops for consumption after 2–3 (sometimes even 1) years, as is customary in temperate zones.

Morphology: Virginapterae 1.8–2.3 mm long, dull olive green or yellowish green, antennae about body length, segment III without rhinaria, on difinite frontal tubercles, frons therefore U-shaped. Siphunculi relatively long, about $^1/_5$–$^1/_3$ body length, slightly swollen, position mostly flat against the side of the body, cauda conical, with three bristles on each side. Nymphs (with wing rudiments) often with reddish tinge.
Alatae about 2–2.5 mm long, also with pronounced frontal tubercles. Head and thorax black-brown, abdomen yellowish green, in the middle (towards the back) with large, irregularly defined blotch, in front of it narrow cross markings or rows of spots . Siphunculi and tapered cauda relatively dark. Antennae body length; segment III with 8–10 rhinaria; siphunculi (summer form) slightly swollen.
Differs from *Aulacorthum solani* by the absence of a dark green spot at the place of attachment of each of the siphunculi (alatae of this species without black spot on the abdomen) and from *Macro-*

siphum euphorbiae by the absence of a dark green dorsal stripe (whose alatae also have no dorsal blotch). Other species found with *M. persicae* have short antennae and no frontal tubercles.

Life cycle and ecology: In the tropics, most damage is done by the summer form. The sexual generation only occurs at altitudes where peaches are grown. In these localities, the time of hatching frequently does not coincide with bud emergence, so that no food is available for prematurely hatched nymphs (fundatrices). Asexual reproduction of the summer form on herbaceous summer host plants is therefore the decisive factor for a mass population build-up. Since one generation develops within 6–7 days under tropical conditions (developmental zero point about + 3 °C, requisite cumulative daily temperature means for the development of one generation – minus 3 °C – = 170 °), a mass population builds up rapidly. On the other hand, excessive heat, heavy rainfall and increased occurrence of predators and parasites consitute more rapidly regulating factors than in the temperate zones of Europe. At persistent temperatures above 30 °C, the green peach aphid hardly reproduces. In regions with marked drought periods, colonies hidden in weeds can survive the unfavourable living conditions, so that a small number of aphids can persist into the next vegetative period. In the potato growing regions of the Argentine, storage in corn straw stacks, in which the tubers sprout relatively rapidly, provides a refuge for the summer form, so that initial attack in potato crops is often seen near such stacks. The rise and fall of attack is similar in all crops, e. g. tobacco, cabbage, Oleaceae, tuberiferous (including batata), cucurbits, ornamentals or berry fruit (strawberry). Local differences will obviously occur, such as migration from high altitude regions after the rainy season and the preference for weeds in periods which are unfavourable for *M. persicae*. Prevailing winds can also transport winged green peach aphids from their sheltered refuge into newly planted young crops and provide the impetus for a mass invasion. Initial migration and subsequent flight into and away from the crop by alatae is monitored in yellow dishes (tubs painted yellow on the inside or pans of at least 20 cm diameter) half filled with water containing a detergent and an insecticide. Sticky traps with a yellow backing are also suitable for observations of flight movements.

Natural enemies: See Börner & Heinze, 1957.

Control: Since some varieties of crops (e. g. potato, beet) have shown resistance to green peach aphid attack, attempts have been made to tackle the problem in that way. Cross breeding of resistant varieties usually reduces the quality of the crop, so that no marked successes have so far resulted from resistance breeding, apart from raising resistant potato varieties with reduced incidence of infestation. It is essential to ensure an absence of weeds in the vicinity of crops. Weeds form a frequent reservoir for renewed infestation. Chemical control in hot regions with nicotine, pyrethrum, rotenon (this last usually in combination) is decidedly advantageous despite their short term effect, which permits renewed infestation within 1–3 days after application. Other suitable insecticides are: Diazinon, dimethoate, mevinphos, omethoate, parathion, azinphos, dichlorvos, demeton-S-methyl, sulfotepp and thiometon (used as specified on the firm's packaging). For seed potato crops, carbofuran, disulfoton-granulate and phorate-granulate are recommended, used in plant hole or furrow or distributed. In other crops, these preparations are used on or shortly after sowing.

Literatur

BÖRNER, C. & K. HEINZE (1957): Aphidina-Aphidoidea, Sorauer Handb. Pflanzenkrankh. Bd. V, 5. Aufl., 4. Liefg., 1–402. Paul Parey, Berlin-Hamburg.
FRITZSCHE, R., E. KARL, W. LEHMANN & G. PROESELER (1972): Tierische Vektoren pflanzenpathogener Viren. VEB Gustav Fischer Verl. 1–521.
HEINZE, K. (1961): Systematik der mitteleuropäischen Myzinae. Beitr. Entomol. **10**, 744–842 1960; **11**, 24–96.
KENNEDY, J. S., M. F. DAY & V. F. EASTOP (1962): A conspectus of aphids as vectors of plant viruses. Commonwealth Inst. Entomol. (Commonw. agric. Bur.) London 1–114.
MOERICKE, V. (1951): Eine Farbfalle zur Kontrolle des Fluges von Blattläusen, insbesondere der Pfirsich-

blattlaus *Myzodes persicae* (Sulz.). Nachrichtenbl. deutsch. Pflanzenschutzd. (Braunschweig) **3**, 23–24.
Pflanzenschutzmittel-Verzeichnis Biol. Bundesanst. Braunschweig. Merkbl. **1**, 23. Aufl., 1973/1974 (und
spätere Aufl. bzw. Ergänzungen).

Author: K. Heinze

Lipaphis erysimi (Kalt.) (Plate 26 d)

Synonyms: *Rhopalosiphum erysimi (pseudobrassicae), R. pseudobrassicae, Hyadaphis erysimi,
H. erysimi pseudobrassicae, H. pseudobrassicae, Lipaphis erysimi pseudobrassicae, L. pseudobrassicae*

Common names: False cabbage aphid, mustard aphid, turnip aphid; Senfblattlaus.

Geographical distribution: It is found in all tropical and subtropical countries. CIE Map no 203.

Host plants: *L. erysimi* is a serious pest of mustard, cabbage, cauliflower, turnip, kohlrabi, radish,
chinese cabbage, rai *(Brassica juncea),* toria, brussels sprout, broccoli, kale and rutabaga. It is a
minor pest of bean, beet, spinach, pea, celery, onion, stock, soybean, cucumber, potato, and *Tropaeolum.*

Symptoms: The pest is found in colonies of hundreds and thousands sucking the plant sap. The attacked leaves curl and turn yellowish, the inflorescences fade and dry up, and the plants remain
stunted, wilt or may be completely killed. The pest excretes honey dew making the leaves sticky
on which a sooty mould also develops.

Economic importance: Although a minute insect it may destroy the plants even quicker than larger insects. It is a great limiting factor in the seed production of cruciferous crops. The growth of
sooty moulds on leaves interferes with the photosynthesis. The mere presence of aphids on the vegetables affects their market value very adversely. *L. erysimi* also transmits viruses like Bean
common mosaic, Beet mosaic, Cabbage black ring spot, Cauliflower mosaic, Celery mosaic,
Onion yellow dwarf, Pea mosaic, Radish mosaic, Stock mosaic, Soybean mosaic, Beet yellows,
Cucumber mosaic, Potato virus Y and Tropaeolum mosaic.

Morphology: This aphid is a soft bodied, yellowsih green or greenish coloured species measuring
about 2 to 2.5 mm in length when fully grown. The adults may be apterous or may have two pairs
of hyaline wings. The 5th abdominal segment bears a pair of cornicles. The winged adults usually
have black body markings and a blackish head.

Similarities to other pests: It resembles the cabbage aphid, *Brevicoryne brassicae,* with which it associates mostly on cruciferous crops. However, it is greener, produces less white secretions and
does not bear dark transverse sclerites on the dorsal side of the abdomen when compared with the
cabbage aphid.

Life cycle: The pest breeds parthenogenetically and has no sexual forms in tropical countries. The
nymphs are preferentially deposited on the undersides of leaves or inflorescences. The nymphs
undergo four nymphal stages and become adult in about 6 to 10 days. The adult stage may last for
13 to 15 days. The 1st, 2nd, 3rd and 4th stages last for about 2–4, 2–4, 3–4 and 3–4 days, respectively. A single female deposits about 100 to 200 nymphs.

Ecology: In the plains of tropical countries, *L. erysimi* is not found during hot summers. In India,
the infestation starts by November–December and lasts up to March, with a peak from the end of

December to the end of February when the temperature is about 11–14 °C and relative humidity 60–80 %. The aphid population declines sharply with heavy rainfalls. In India, in the plains, the pest has 5 to 6 generations in a year and during summer it is found on the hills.

Natural enemies: The larvae and the adults of the lady beetles *Coccinella septempunctata, Adalia bipunctata, Cheilomenes vicina* and the larvae of the hover flies *Xanthogramma scutellare* and *Betasyrphus adligatus* are predacious on *L. erysimi.* The larvae of *Diaeretiella rapae* (Braconidae) have been recorded as parasitizing 53 to 89 % or even more aphids. The fungi *Cephalosporium aphidicola* and *Entomophthora aphidis* also cause mortality.

Control:

Sanitary and cultural practices. Clean cultivation can help to reduce the infestation. In India, early maturing crops are preferred as they escape heavy infestations.

Resistance of crops. The rai *(Brassica juncea)* variety Laha 101 and *B. juncea* 6105 show a high to low level of resistance in India. Strains of yellow mustard *(B. campestris* var. yellow sarson) and brown mustard *B. campestris* var. brown sarson), namely L.G.L.G., G.B.S.I., Y.S. Cult. 31, K. Hotni 26, K. Hotni 27, G.B.S.203 and Assam Local are highly susceptible. Rape *(B. napus)* variety P.I. 171538 and turnip variety Pusa Sweti are quite resistant, whereas Dwarf Essex rape and Narrow Stem kale are fairly susceptible to this aphid. The waxiness of the plants determines their resistance.

Chemical control. The insecticides phosphamidon, endosulfan, dichlorvos, methyl demeton, monocrotophos, dimethoate, parathion, malathion, lindane, endrin, nicotine sulphate, carbaryl, diazinon, thiometon, mevinphos, safos, and aphidan are found to be very effective against *L. erysimi.* Three sprays of 0.1 % gamma-BHC at 16 day intervals or two sprays of 0.1 % methyl demeton, 0.05 % safos or 0.04 % endrin at 30 day intervals control *L. erysimi* on mustard. Granules of 10 % phorate, 10 % aldicarb or 5 % disulfoton at 1.5–2 kg per hectare also give good control of this aphid. Root dipping of radish in 0.1 or 0.25 % solution of thiometon or phorate gives good protection. At the flowering stage, spraying should be carried out in the afternoon when the bees have stopped visiting the flowers. Lindane, DDT, dimethoate, diazinon, parathion, malathion, methyl demeton and thiometon are toxic to bees. However, endosulfan, phosphamidon and safos are less toxic to them.

Literature

JAMES, L. J. (1970): Relative injury to some cruciferous oilseeds by the turnip aphid. J. econ. Ent. **63,** 1498–1502.
LAL, O. P. (1969): Field studies for varietal resistance in rape and mustard against mustard aphid, *Lipaphis erysimi* Kalt. Z. ang. Ent. **64,** 394–400.
LAL, O. P. (1971): Effect of certain antibiotics on the development and reproductivity of *Lipaphis erysimi* Kalt. on cabbage plant. Ibid. **70,** 42–48.
LAL, O. P. (1973): Effect of aphid infestation on plant growth and chlorophyll contents of cabbage. Ibid. **73,** 260–262.
SCHMUTTERER, H. (1969): Pests of crops in Northeast and Central Africa. Gustav Fischer Verlag, Stuttgart & Portland, 296 pp.
SCHMUTTERER, H. (1972): Zur Beutespezifität polyphager räuberischer Syrphiden Ostafrikas. Z. ang. Ent. **71,** 278–286.
SRINIVASACHAR, D. & R. S. MALIK (1972): An induced aphid resistant, nonwaxy mutant in turnip, *Brassica rapa.* Curr. Sci. **41** (22), 820–821.

Author: O. P. Lal

Pentalonia nigronervosa Coq. (Fig. 129)

Synonym: *Pentalonia caladii*

Common names: Banana aphid; Bananenblattlaus; Puceron noir du bananier; Pulgón (negro) del plátano.

Geographical distribution: More or less co-extensive with banana cultivation in tropical and sub-tropical regions. CIE Map no 242.

Host plants: Banana, Manila Hemp (Abacá), Taro or Coco-yam *(Colocasia)*, *Caladium* spp., Ginger *(Zingiber* spp.) and related members of Musaceae, Araceae and Zingiberidaceae.

Symptoms: Not causing evident symptoms to the plant except when transmitting phytopathogenic viruses. Living inconspicuously under the old leaf bases and rarely found unless searched for.

Economic importance: Virus vector in banana and Manila hemp and in Cardamon (see p. 5). The most important virus transmitted is the Banana bunchy top virus occuring in Australia, Asia and Africa.

Morphology: No other small brown aphid living under the leaf bases of the plants mentioned above is known. The forewing has a characteristic venation with the radius and media being fused for part of their length giving a closed cell which is most unusual in aphids. The weakly clavate siphunculi and short pentagonal cauda are also characteristic for both apterae and alatae. Confusion with other economically important aphids is almost unknown.

Fig. 129. Colony of *Pentalonia nigronervosa* on a leafsheath of banana (phot. H. Schmutterer)

Life cycle: Most populations are probably continuously parthenogenetic although sexuales have been recorded from India.

Ecology: Usually attended by ants including *Tetramorium, Pheidole* and *Wasmannia* spp.. *P. nigronervosa* may have 20–26 generations per year. The apterous females are recorded as producing 24–58 young each and the alatae 6–29. The young take about two weeks from birth to maturity at the optimum temperature of 24–28 °C.

Natural enemies: Often preyed on by wax covered Coccinellid larvae such as *Cryptogonus orbiculus. Paragus* spp. (Syrphidae) are important predators in East Africa. Parasitism by *Lysiphlebus staccipes* has been recorded in Cuba and an internal Cecidomyiid parasite is present in Brasil.

Control:

Resistance of crops. Some varieties of bananas seem more susceptible to banana aphids than others in India (Kerala).

Chemical control. Phosphamidon (Dimecron) at 300 grammes of active ingredient per hectare or dicrotophos (Carbicron) as an overall spray at 0.025 % a. i. or 0.1 a. i. injected into suckers at a height of 2–4 feet above ground level is recommended. Oxydemeton-methyl (Metasystox R) and demeton-S-methyl [Metasystox(i)] sprays at 0.025 a. i. have also been used. Spraying to run off on uprooted plant of demeton-S-methyl [Metasystox(i)] is also recommended. Endrin 0.05 % spray at 50 gallons to the acre directed at the plant crown and base of pseudostem, below soil level between outer leaf sheathes and stem and over the surrounding soil is another effective method. The injection of systemics was too expensive to be considered in Africa.

Literature

ILHARCO, F. A. (1968): *Pentalonia nigronervosa* Coquerel na ilha da Madeira. Bocagiana **17**, 1–25.

Author: V. F. Eastop

Rhopalosiphum maidis (Fitch) (Plate 27 a)

Synonym: *Aphis maidis, Rhopalosiphon maidis*

Common names: Maize aphid, Corn leaf aphid; Maisblattlaus; Puceron du mais; Pulgón verde del maíz.

Geographical distribution: Widespread in all tropical and warm temperate parts of the world (CIE Map no 67).

Host plants: Mainly on young leaves of *Zea mays, Sorghum vulgare, Hordeum vulgare* and members of more than 30 other genera of Gramineae including *Avena sativa, Secale cereale, Triticum, Oryza, Saccharum officinarum* and occasionally Cyperaceae and Typhacaceae.

Symptoms: Heavy attacks may stop earing or prevent pollen shedding in maize. The honeydew arrests both pollen and dust and sooty moulds develop on this mixture and reduce photosynthesis. In some varieties of sorghum large red spots develop on the leaves as a consequence of the feeding activity of *R. maidis.*

Economic importance: Heavy attacks may result in poorly filled heads of maize and sorghum but controlling populations of up to several hundred aphids per plant may not increase yield, perhaps because their damage has already been done. In other cases increases of yield of up to 12 % have been obtained by aphid control. *R. maidis* tends to delay maturity rather than reduce yields but barley has been damaged in temperate regions. Sorghum grains from heavily infested heads have lower germination than usual. The aphids may also have an indirect effect in that their honeydew acts as food for the adults of maize borers and other lepidopterous pests.
R. maidis transmits viruses of barley, maize and sorghum and can also transmit viruses of abacá and sugarcane (see p. 51).

Morphology: *R. maidis* is a rather elongate aphid with short antennae and short dark siphunculi. It varies in colour from pale green to dark olive green and is sometimes noticeably dusted with wax.

Similarities to other pests: *Rhopalosiphum padi* is a more rounded aphid with longer antennae and siphunculi also feeding on many Gramineae and sometimes confused with *maidiis.*

Life cycle and ecology: Reproduction is mostly or entirely parthenogenetic and viviparous on Gramineae in most parts of the world but there may be host plant alternation in Eastern Asia. If a primary host does exist it is likely to be a member of the Rosaceae and probably Prunoidea or Pomoidea. Up to 45 generations per year may be produced in the warmer parts of the world. Adult females may give birth to from 3 to 67 young at a rate of 1 to 9 per day. Females start producing young from 6–15 days after birth, largely depending on temperature. The large adults produced at 16 °C may live for 50 days while the small specimens which develop rapidly at 28 °C only live for about 20 days. Most take off for flight takes place between 20–40 °C and above a light intensity of 1 foot candle.

Natural enemies: Internal parasites include species of Aphidiinae belonging to the genera *Aphidius, Lysiphlebus* and *Praon* and of *Aphelinus* (Aphelinidae). Hyperparasites belonging to the

Pteromalidae, *Asaphes* and *Pachyneuron* spp.; Encyrtidae, *Aphidencyrtus* and Ceraphrontidae, *Dendrocerus,* have been reared from primary parasites.

Recorded predators include member of 12 genera of Coccinellidae; 11 genera of Syrphidae and the predaceous cecidomyid *Aphidoletes aphidimyza.* The record of *Trilobiella siphae* was in error, the aphid concerned being *Sipha maydis* and not *R. maidis. Leucopis* spp. (Chamaemyiidae) are also recorded as predators. *Orius* spp. (Anthocoridae), Chrysopidae and *Doru lineare* (Dermaptera) are also predators of *R. maidis.*

Control:

Cultural practices. Early planting is important in regions where *R. maidis* is abundant. Heavy attacks may only delay maturity while late crops tend to be more seriously damaged.

Resistance of crops. Some varieties of cereals are more resistant than others but the existence of biotypes of the aphid with different preferences has limited their use.

Biological control. Attempts to arrest or attract predators by spraying with sugar have had partial success but do not seem an economic proposition.

Chemical control. Control has been achieved with little effect on natural enemies by an emulsion spray of demeton at 0.5 lb toxicant per acre of *Sorghum.* Other systemic insecticides, such as dimethoate and oxydemeton-methyl are efficient on wheat.

Literatur

EVERLY, R. T. (1967): Review of factors affecting the abundance of corn leaf aphid. Proc. Indiana Acad. Sci. **76,** 260–264.

HASSAN, M. H. (1957a): Studies on the morphology and biology of *Aphis maidis* Fitch, in Egypt. Bull. Soc. Ent. Egypt **41,** 199–211.

HASSAN, M. H. (1957b): Studies on the damage and control of *Aphis maidis* Fitch, in Egypt. Bull. Soc. Ent. Egypt **41,** 213–230.

Author: V. F. Eastop

Schizaphis graminum (Rond.) (Fig. 130)

Synonyms: *Toxoptera graminum, Rhopalosiphum graminum, Hysteroneura graminum*

Common names: Green bug, Spring grain aphis, Wheat aphid, Common wheat louse; Grüne Getreideblattlaus; Puceron vert des graminées; Pulgón verde de los cereales.

Geographical distribution: Spread presumably from the southern parts of the USSR into the temperate zones of the Old and New World and the tropics (India, Sri Lanka, Africa except West Africa, East Australia, Philippines etc.). CIE Map no 173.

Host plants: *Triticum* sp., *Hordeum sativum, Avena sativa, Secale cereale, Panicum* sp., *Sorghum* sp., *Zea mays, Oryza sativa, Saccharum officinarum,* also *Bromus* sp., *Andropogon* sp., *Eragrostis* sp., *Elymus* sp., *Dactylis* sp., *Digitaria* sp., *Festuca* sp., *Cynodon* sp., *Phalaris* sp., *Setaria* sp., *Trisetum* sp., *Lolium* sp., *Poa* sp., *Cyperus* sp. and other Gramineae and Cyperaceae.

Symptoms: The feeding activity of the aphids first produces pale areas on the leaf, which can turn into a reddish colour around the actual puncture. These discolourations are due to chlorophyll damage. With increased attack, the leaves show a blotchy and striated chlorosis, which spreads until the leaves are yellowed entirely. In some Gramineae species, reddish discolouration of the leaf surface is more pronounced and infested areas of plants can look as though they had been burnt. The formation of foci of infestation in the crop is typical for *Schizaphis* damage. In hot regions, high temperatures lead to rapid aphid increase, which soon spread across huge areas, so that large crops are destroyed in a short time. Red and yellow discolourations and stunting of plants can also be due to virus infection, transmitted by *Sch. graminum.*

Economic importance: In catastrophic years, the losses in some States in the USA can reach 50 %. In the La Plata countries, the wheat aphid is, after migratory locusts, one of the most danger ous pests. In 1944/45, losses of 80–100 % occurred in the wheat fields of Uruguay. Catastrophic damage can also result in Africa (South Africa) at altitudes between 900 and 1500 m. *Sch. grami num* is also a major vector of viruses of Gramineae. It transmits cereal yellow dwarf (barley yellow dwarf, red leaf of oats) and the related virus of *Setaria italica,* the Italian millet (red leaf disease of fox-tail millet). It is a persistent vector for both viruses. It also transmits western wheat mosaic vi rus and sugar cane mosaic.

Morphology: Virginapterae 1.4–2 mm long, narrow, pale green with dark green longitudinal stri pes on the abdomen. Cauda and siphunculi pale, the last sometimes darkened and grey-black at the distal end (Fig. 130). Marginal tubercles usually only on 1. and 7. (Fig. 130) abdominal seg ment present. Antennae 0.5–0.8 times the size of the body, pale towards point of attachment. Fla gellum (end portion) of the segment VI $2^3/_5$ to $3^3/_4$ times as long as its basal portion. Hairs on the segment III shorter than its diameter. Pale cauda, not much narrowed at the centre, with 4–5 bristles (Fig. 130), about 0.64–0.8 times as long as siphunculi, these $^9/_{15}$ to $^1/_6$ of body length or 2–3 times as long as hind leg (without claw). Terminal segment of proboscis (Fig. 130) $^7/_{10}-^{17}/_{20}$ length of hind leg segment II (without claw), with 2 (rarely 3) secondary bristles.
Winged morph a little smaller than virginaptera, elongated, head yellowish brown to dark brown, thorax dark, almost black, abdomen greenish with dark middle line, cauda yellowish green, often dark towards the tip. Cylindrical siphunculi yellowish green. 3. lateral vein on fore wings (counted from wing insertion), usually only forked once. Antennae 6-segmented, pale at the base, almost of body length. End portion of segment VI about 3–4 times as long as its basal portion. Segment III with 4–8 (IV only exceptionally with 1) rounded rhinaria. Cauda with 4–5 bristles. Siphunculi 6–8 times as long as their diameter in the middle. Terminal segment of proboscis $^2/_3$ to $^3/_4$ times the length of hind leg segment II (without claw)[1].

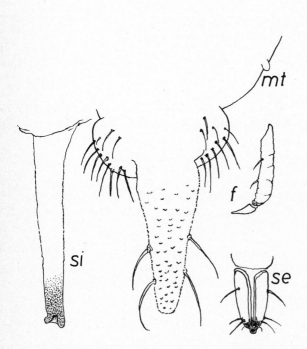

Fig. 130. *Schizaphis graminum.* si = siphunculus; mt = marginal tubercle and cauda; f = second hind leg segment; se = terminal segment of proboscis (drawings K. Heinze)

[1] For species identification see also footnote with *A. spiraecola* (p. 330).

Life cycle and ecology: In the chiefly affected regions in warm climates, the wheat aphid overwinters as the summer form. A sexual generation only forms in northern temperate zones with cool winters. While biotype formation does not occur with parthenogenic reproduction of the aphid, it occurs relatively often when copulation processes intervene. As a result, forms adapted to a small number of host plants have developed in Central Europe, which can also show morphological differences. The formation of aphid biotypes is of great importance for cereal resistance breeding in the USA. Here again, wheat aphid biotypes will avoid certain cereal species or varieties or grasses. In warmer climates, *Sch. graminum* has the opportunity to overwinter after harvest, not only on grasses in pastures but also on young seedling plants growing from dropped, germinating grain – mostly as virginaptera. Such plants are numerous after rainy periods, e. g. in 1957 in South Africa, where in conjunction with a moist spring and low rate of increase of parasites, an aphid calamity resulted. Once a number of colonies have developed in cereal crops, dry weather can also favour aphid development. Mass infestation results, if temperatures are high enough to promote rapid aphid increase, but not high enough to effect an equivalent increase in parasites; for the parasites have a higher temperature optimum than the wheat aphid. The temperature effect alone does not suffice to produce a calamity. Numerous other factors are involved and contribute, some independently, to the aphid increase, but weather conditions remain the main factor. Greatest increase occurs at temperatures between 22 and 24 °C. At 7 °C it virtually ceases and the rate of increase slows down markedly at temperatures between 29 and 33 °C. Temperatures above 40 °C (42 °C) are lethal for wheat aphid. Flight activity of alatae also depends markedly on prevailing temperatures (little flight activity below 20 °C, none above 40 °C), while light seems to play a subordinate part. In flight promoting weather conditions, alatae are wind dispersed over large distances, e. g. from the southern parts of the USA to Canada. The development of hatching nymphs (fundatrix) in temperate regions is much retarded by the normally low spring temperatures; it can take up to 3 weeks. The developmental period of subsequent parthogenetic generations is reduced to about a week and can be completed in an even shorter period at the height of summer. In hot climates, over 30 generations can be expected in one year.

Natural enemies: Over 50 species (see Börner & Heinze, 1957).

Control: Resistance breeding has led to good results in the USA. A series of resistant varieties of various cereal species (including sorghum) and fodder grasses are now available. Biological control with parasites and predators is still in its infancy. Under suitable weather conditions, parasites and predators can reduce wheat aphid infestation to reasonable proportions, but are often not effective until after damage has occurred. Integrated control measures have also so far not passed beyond the experimental stage. Chemical preparations kill parasites as well as aphids, unless parasitisation has occurred at least one week before treatment. Suitable for chemical control are: Demeton (Metasystox), diazinon (Basudin et al.), ethion (Nialate), malathion, parathion, phosphamidon (Dimecron), TEPP, and thiometon (Ecatin). Good results were achieved with systemic insecticides, which are suitable for soil treatment. These are above all disulfoton- and phorate (Thimet)-granulates, which are applied to the soil at the time of sowing. Seed dressing with menazon (2–2.5 kg/100 kg seed) was a good protection against aphid attack on *Sorghum* till 42–45 days after sowing and increased the yield by 62 %.

Literature

BÖRNER, C. & K. HEINZE (1957): Aphidina-Aphidoidea, Sorauer, Handb. Pflanzenkrankh. Bd. V, 5. Aufl., 4. Liefg. 1–402. Paul Parey, Berlin-Hamburg.
EASTOP, V. F. (1958): A study of the Aphididae (Homoptera) of East Africa. Her Majesty's Stationary Office, London, 1–126.
HEINZE, K. (1959): Phytopathogene Viren und ihre Überträger. Duncker & Humblot, Berlin, 1-290.
SCHMUTTERER, H. (1969): Pests of crops in Northeast and Central Africa. G. Fischer Verlag, Stuttgart, Portland/USA, 1-296.

SMIT, B. (1964): Insects in Southern Africa: How to control them. Oxford Univ. Press, Capetown, Salisbury, Johannisburg, 1–399.
WYNIGER, R. (1962): Pests of crops in warm climates and their control. Verl. f. Recht u. Gesellsch. Basel, 1-555, Appendix: V. Control measures. 2nd Edit., 1–162, 1968.

Author: K. Heinze

Toxoptera aurantii (B.d.F.)

Synonyms: *Toxoptera aurantiae, Aphis camelliae, A. coffeae, A. citrifoliae*

Common names: Black Citrus aphid, Black-orange aphid, Camellia aphid; Schwarze Citrusblattlaus; Puceron noir de l'oranger, Puceron du café; Pulgón de los agrios, Pulgón (negro) del naranjo.

Geographical distribution: Indigenous in the tropical and subtropical regions of the Old World, spread overseas with citrus cultivation. East Asia, Philippines, New Guinea, Asia Minor, Mediterranean regions, Africa, Southern parts of the United States (California to Florida), Central America, Caribbean region, South America, Hawaii, Pacific Islands (Australasia) New Zealand, East and South Australia; CIE Map no 131.

Host plants: First of all citrus species, *Theobroma cacao, Coffea* sp., *Thea* sp., *Ficus* sp., *Cola* sp., *Piper* sp., *Mangifera indica, Morus* sp., *Annona squamosa, Litchi chinensis, Camellia* sp., *Gardenia* sp., *Hibiscus* sp., *Cydonia japonica, Pirus* sp., *Cinchona* sp., *Chaenomeles* sp., *Eugenia* sp., *Evodia aromatica, Loranthus* sp., *Macadamia* sp., *Magnolia* sp., *Murraya exotica, Styrax* sp., *Pittosporum* sp.; altogether more than 120 host plants have been named.

Symptoms: Most severe attack by *T. aurantii* is usually observed in young plantations; young shoots are densely colonised in spring. Leaves colonised by aphids are slightly rolled at the succulent shoot apices and usually curve downwards at the tip. They are not generally rolled as much as with *A. spiraecola* attack, but can twist on occasion into an open spiral. The affected leaf is not infrequently crinkled along the midrib. On flowers and flower buds, the black citrus aphid is more rarely seen. If they are attacked at en early stage, they die off. On older trees, leaf damage remains slight.

Economic importance: With mass attack, the entire new growth on Citrus trees, especially on young trees, can be destroyed; shoots wither at the tip. *T. aurantii* can occasionally transmit Tristeza disease on citrus and is a vector of a virus disease causing leaf mottle on *Citrus vulgaris* (citrus infectious mottling virus) and of little leaf and lemon ribbing virus of lemon. It also transmits two viruses of coffee shrubs, blister spot of arabica coffee and ringspot of excelsa coffee.

Morphology: Virginaptera 1.5–1.8 (2.0) mm long, brown-black to black, cauda and siphunculi black, abdomen (ventrally) with stridulation pattern and spines typical for *Toxoptera* spp. (see *T. citricidus*), also marginal tubercles characteristic for the group, ciliation as in alatae, hairs on pale antennal segment III at most as long as diameter of this segment, usually not as long, flagellum of joint VI $1^1/_4$–$1^1/_2$ times as long as joint III, cauda with 10–28 bristles (hairs). Winged morph 1–1.2 (to 1.8) mm in length, head, thorax, siphunculi and cauda black, abdomen dark brown to brown black. Costa of fore wings after broadening (towards the end) black, 3rd. accessory vein (media) usually forked only once. Antennae about $^5/_6$ of body length, antennal joint III dark at the outermost part, otherwise pale, with 3–8 rhinaria arranged in rows. Antennal joint IV free of rhinaria, longest hairs on antennal joint III always shorter than its basal diameter. Cauda with 8–13 (16) bristles (hairs), siphunculi at most up to $1^2/_5$ length of cauda. Lateral body ciliation (abdomen) shorter than terminal diameter of siphunculi. Hairs on legs less than $^2/_3$ length of tarsal joint II (without claw). Nymphs dark brown.

T. aurantii produces a scratching noise by vibrant stroking of the posterior part of the body against the legs (stridulatory movement), which is plainly audible when larger, excited aphid colonies are approached.

Life cycle and ecology: In temperate zones (mediterranean region), *T. aurantii* does not usually reach epidemic proportions. If the temperature falls to 15 °C, a generation takes almost 3 weeks the develop, whereas it takes no more than 6 days at 25 °C. Development can also be retarded in hot regions, as temperatures approach 30 °C. In protracted hot and dry weather, very few black citrus aphids are left on citrus trees, especially if temperatures rise well above 30 °. In the tropics, the species may adapt to humid heat conditions and survive a rise in temperature more readily than in dry regions. Like all other species inhabiting citrus, *T. aurantii* depends on the young growth and young fruit. As the foliage hardens, the proportion of alatae increases rapidly. These endeavour to reach new young shoots or change to other host plants. Towards the end of summer, renewed aphid attack on citrus can again be noted (in the tropics at the time of increasing sap flow for fruit formation, which hardly ever ceases entirely) and highly populated colonies may result, since one virginopara can produce over 50 offspring – up to 7 per day. No sexual forms have so far been observed in the open. Alatae are not as productive, but play an important role in establishing new colonies. They also spread virus diseases if they have had the opportunity to become infective on diseased plants. The citrus viruses concerned are not persistent, i. e. they remain active on the vector's stylets only for a short period (up to 1 day, usually less). The species is visited by ants.

Natural enemies: Over 70 species have so far been discovered (see Börner & Heinze, 1957).

Control: Biological control measures should be improved by enlarging the number of parasites (and predators), in conjunction with the careful use of chemicals in infested regions. Indigenous parasites are generally not effective until after damage has occurred. The efficacy of predators and parasites is enhanced if ants are kept away by tying dieldrin saturated cloth around the trees, since they tend to be molested or chased off by the ants. Chemical control as for *T. citricidus* (see p. 345).

Literature

BODENHEIMER, F. S. (1951): Citrus Entomology in the Middle East. Uitgev. Dr. W. Junk, 'S-Graven-hage 1–663.
BODENHEIMER, F. S. & E. SWIRSKI (1957): The Aphidoidea of the Middle East. Weizmann Sci. Press of Israel, Jerusalem 1–378.
BÖRNER, C. & K. HEINZE (1957): Aphidina-Aphidoidea, Sorauer, Handb. Pflanzenkrankh. Bd. V, 5. Aufl., 4. Liefgg 1–402. Paul Parey, Berlin-Hamburg.
ESSIG, E. O. (1949): Aphids in relation to quick decline and tristeza of Citrus. Pan-Pacif. Entomol. **25**, 13–23.
HEINZE, K. (1959): Phytopathogene Viren und ihre Überträger. Verl. Duncker & Humblot Berlin, 1–290.
LE PELLEY, R. H. (1968): Pests of Coffee. Longmans, Green & Co. LTD, London and Harlow, 1–590.
PIGUET, P. (1960): Les Ennemis Animaux des Agrumes en Afrique de Nord. Société Shell d'Algérie 1–117.
SCHMUTTERER, H. (1969): Pests of crops in Northeast and Central Africa. G. Fischer Verlag, Stuttgart–Portland/USA, 1–296.
STROYAN, H.L.G. (1961): Identification of aphids living on Citrus. F.A.O. Plant Prot. Bull. **9**, 45–65.
WYNIGER, R. (1962): Pests of crops in warm climates and their control. Verl. f. Recht u. Gesellsch. Basel 1–555, Appendix: V. Control measures 2nd Edit. 1–162, 1968.

Author: K. Heinze

Toxoptera citricidus (Kirk.) (Plate 27 b)

Synonyms: *Toxoptera citricida, T. tavaresi, T. citricola, Paratoxoptera argentinensis, T. rotundiventris, T. theobromae*

Common names: Tropical Citrus Aphid, Oriental black or Brown citrus aphid; Braune Citrus-blattlaus; Puceron tropical de l'oranger; Pulgón café (de los cítricos).

Geographical distribution: Predominantly in humid tropical regions (Africa south of the Sahara, South America, Caribbean region, Hawaii, Australasia, New Guinea, Indonesia, Philippines, Formosa, Thailand, Malaysia, India), widely distributed, also found in temperate zones, where it has been reported in South Africa, South America (up into tropical regions), East and South Australia, New Zealand, Japan and China. Presumably carried on Rutaceae from East Asia. CIE Map no 132.

Host plants: Almost exclusively on Rutaceae, especially *Citrus* species and on *Poncirus trifoliata*. Reports of occurrence on *Diospyros kaki, Ficus carica* and *Eriobotrya japonica* not confirmed.

Symptoms: Even smaller colonies on young shoots inhibit the development of flower buds by their feeding activity and bud drop results. Moderate attack on young leaves leads to distortions, rolling and stunting, usually on the entire shoot. It seems typical that the margins of many of the leaves are rolled upwards and inwards, while the tip of the leaf bends downwards. Rolling downwards has also been observed. Severely affected leaves turn brittle. Shoot and leaves are stunted, badly affected shoots gradually die off. In addition, pronounced honey dew production with subsequent growth of sooty mould on the sticky deposit interferes with the assimilatory processes of the leaf. As a result of sooty mould on the honey dew deposit, the fruit looks black and unsightly.

Economic importance: Not only is the marketable value of the fruit reduced by the sooty mould deposit, but losses up to 50 % can result from feeding damage. The most serious losses are however due to phytopathogenic viruses, for which *T. citricidus* is the main vector. It transmits the Tristeza virus of oranges, the 'stem-pitting' virus, Eureka-seedling virus and 'bud onion decline' of lemon and orange (see also p. 18).

Morphology: In *Toxoptera* species, irregular lines of serrate ridges on the ventral abdomen at the side, near siphunculi, a little larger in *T. aurantii* than in *T. citricidus*. Tibiae (hindlegs) with short, thick, dorsal spines. Both together make a stridulation organ (vibrant stroking of hind part of body against legs); no audible stridulation noise in *T. citricidus*. Virginapterae 2.3–2.8 mm long, reddish dark brown to brown-black, antennae about $^2/_3$ body length, flagellum (end of segment VI) $1^1/_{10}$ to $1^1/_4$ x segment III.. Antennal hairs 1.5 to 2 x as long as diameter of this joint. Siphunculi $1^1/_{10}$ to $1^1/_2$ times as long as cauda, this last with 19 to 54 (on average 25 to 35) bristles. Long and widely spaced ciliation at body margin (there longer than distal siphunculi apertures) and on the legs, on these $^3/_4$ to $^1/_1$ the length of tarsal joint II (without claw).
Winged morph about 2.1–2.6 mm long, head, thorax, siphunculi and cauda black, abdomen brown without markedly chitinised plate in the middle, only behind the siphunculi two dark intermittent cross bands. Costa of fore wings pale after broadening (towards the end), not black, 3rd. accessory vein nearly always with a lateral vein which is forked. Antennae about $^4/_5$ body length, antennal segment III black with 8–20 rhinaria, also 0–4 rhinaria on (pale) antennal segment IV. Longest hairs on antennal segment III longer than basal diameter of this segment. Siphunculi $1^1/_4$ to $1^3/_4$ times as long as cauda, this last with 22–40 (usually 22–32) bristles. Ciliation of legs as in apterae $^3/_4$ to $^1/_1$ length of tarsal joint II (without claw). Nymphs brown.

Similarities to other pests: Other species found on Citrus (apart from *T. aurantii)* differ from *T. citricidus* by their shining yellow, green to grey or slightly brownish green colour.

Life cycle and ecology: The tropical citrus aphid lives on *Citrus* species throughout the year only as the summer morph, no males or females are present. At colder times of the year, the winter of northern and southern latitudes, only insignificant colonies with few individuals survive on the young branches. As the temperature rises and more young shoots are formed, conditions for *T. ci-*

tricidus improve drastically, leading to mass infestation on young shoots which reaches a peak in the summer just before new growth is completed. Normally, one generation takes no more than about 6–8 days to develop, so that the number of generations per year – with about 4 generations per month – is considerable. The aphid colonies are usually visited by ants.

Natural enemies: Over 40 species have been recorded (see Börner & Heinze, 1957).

Control: Control measures should be applied as soon as the first distorted leaves or the first small aphid colonies are seen on Citrus plants. They prevent extensive damage on shoots in form of crinkle (which is irreversible), damaged flowers and fruit and they suppress the formation of alatae, which are largely responsible for the spread of Citrus viruses. At least recognised foci of infestation should be treated immediately, for which a dust application, e. g. parathion dust, is recommended. Young trees should be treated with systemic insecticides such as dimethoate, demeton-S-methyl [Metasystox(i)] or fenitrothion. Other suitable substances are malathion, diazinon, propoxur, parathion-ethyl and p.-methyl, chlorfenvinphos, endosulfan (Thiodan), ethion and parathion-oil (Folidol-oil) in recommended concentration. See also for *A. spiraecola* (p. 331).

Literature

BÖRNER, C. & K. HEINZE (1957): Aphidina-Aphidoidea, Sorauer Handb. Pflanzenkrankh. Bd. V, 5. Aufl. 4. Liefg., 1–402. Paul Parey, Berlin-Hamburg.
ESSIG, E. O. (1949): Aphids in relation to quick decline and tristeza of Citrus. Pan-Pacif. Entom. **25,** 13–23.
HEINZE, K. (1959): Phytopathogene Viren und ihre Überträger. Duncker & Humblot Berlin, 1–290.
HEPBURN, G. A. & H. J. BISHOP (1954): The insect pests of Citrus in South Africa. Bull. Dept. Agric. South-Africa, **333,** Ent. Ser. No 41, 1–31.
SCHMUTTERER, H. (1969): Pests of crops in Northeast and Central Africa. Fischer Verlag, Stuttgart–Portland/USA, 1–296.
STROYAN, H.L.G. (1961): Identification of aphids living on Citrus. F.A.O. Plant Prot. Bull. **9,** 45–65.
WYNIGER, R. (1962): Pests of crops in warm climates and their control. Verl. f. Recht u. Gesellsch. Basel, 1–555. Appendix (1968): V. Control measures. 2nd Edit. 1–162.

Author: K. Heinze

Other injurious Aphidoidea (Figs. 131–132):

Brevicoryne brassicae (L.), Mealy cabbage aphid (Mehlige Kohlblattlaus) (Fig. 131). This aphid, whose body is covered with a whitish waxy layer, has a worldwide distribution in tropical, subtropical and temperate regions (CIE Map no 37). It attacks wild and cultivated crucifers, especially cabbage. Feeding activity on cabbage leaves results in stunted growth, yellowing and distortions. In addition, host plants are very sticky with honey dew deposits. In temperate climates, *B. brassicae* can transmit various phytopathogenic viruses on crucifers. Dimethoate, demeton-S-methyl and mevinphos can be used for chemical control.

Fig. 131. *Brevicoryne brassicae* and larvae of hover flies on the underside of a cabbage leaf (phot. H. Schmutterer)

Fig. 132. *Melanaphis sacchari* (and larva of a hover fly) (phot. H. Schmutterer)

Melanaphis sacchari (Zhnt.) (= *Longuinguis sacchari*) (Fig. 132), Dura aphid (Gelbe Hirseblattlaus). In the African tropics, in the Middle East, in South, South East and East Asia (Taiwan) and on the Caribbean Islands. Attacks chiefly sorghum, but also sugar cane and wild grasses. In India, it transmits "Grassy shoot disease" on sugar cane. Chemical control with malathion or thiometon.

Sipha flava (Forb.). In Mexico and on the Caribbean Islands on the leaves of sugar cane.

H. Sch.

Superfamily: Coccoidea
Family: Pseudococcidae

Planococcoides njalensis (Laing) (Plate 27 c)

Synonym: *Pseudococcus exibitialis*

Common names: West African cocoa mealybug; Westafrikanische Kakaoschmierlaus.

Geographical distribution: Apparently restricted to West and Central Africa where it ranges from Sierra Leone to Zaire. It is a truly tropical forest species which seems not to have been found beyond the southern edge of the Guinea Savannah Woodland zone. CIE Map no 332.

Host plants: A highly polyphagous mealybug recorded from over 100 species in at least 28 families of plants. The principle economic host plants are cocoa, coffee, cola *(Cola acuminata)* and avocado pear. Internal cavities (domatia) in the stem and branches of the forest tree *Canthium glabriflorum* may be occupied by thousands of individuals.

Symptoms: On Robusta coffee *(Coffea canephora)* injurious feeding in the base of the inflorescence and among the berries causes flower and fruit fall, but is not very prevalent.
Despite occasional very heavy infestations *P. njalensis* has not been found to cause direct damage on cocoa. It is nevertheless extremely important as a vector of viruses pathogenic in cocoa. Virus can be acquired by feeding for as little as one hour and a half and can be transmitted in an even shorter period. By far the bulk of transmissions are by first instar nymphs (crawlers). Virus diseases of cocoa occur throughout West Africa but are at their most virulent in Ghana. Three main types have been recognised, namely Cocoa swollen shoot virus (CSSV), Cocoa mottle leaf virus (CMLV), and Cocoa necrosis virus (CNV) (see p. 8).

Economic importance: CSSV is by far the most widespread of the viruses. Many isolates have been described some of which, for instance New Juaben which kills trees in three years, are extremely virulent. The adverse effects of all isolates of CSSV are exacerbated by poor agronomy and inadequate control of pest insects. Because of the complexity of interactions between these factors it is impossible to identify losses consequent solely on virus diseases, but they are undoubtedly enormous. In Ghana, where for a long time it was policy to destroy infected trees, by 1963 113, 535, 831 trees had been grubbed out for which Government had paid farmers Ł11, 376, 136 in compensation.

Morphology: In appearance all life stages are typical mealybugs. Fortunately macroscopic characters (only a hand lens is necessary) serve to distinguish the adult female, which of course is wingless and neotenic, from other mealybug species on coffee or cocoa. The white mealy wax secretion covering the dorsum is thinnest along the intersegmental membranes and is absent in each segment along the mid-dorsal line in a series of small oval areas which are widest and deepest on the second and third thoracic segments and taper off gradually on the abdominal segments. There are 18 pairs of marginal wax filaments of which the anal pair is the longest (about one fith of body length), the 17th and 16th pairs a little shorter but still longer than the remainder. Beneath the wax covering the body colour varies from light chocolate brown merging into flesh pink ventrally to a uniform flesh pink or light yellow or even dark reddish brown. In shape it is much more nearly circular than such other common cocoa or coffee mealybugs as *Planococcus citri* and *P. kenyae* from both of which it is also distinguished by its broader mid-dorsal line.

Life cycle: Reproduction in *P. njalensis* is exceptional among mealybugs in that it may be either sexual or parthenogenetic, when only female progeny result (thelytoky). The extent of parthenogenesis seems to vary regionally. Adult females live about four weeks during which they produce 30–40 eggs which hatch within ten minutes of being laid. The female passes through three nymphal stages before maturing to the adult. The male nymph ceases to feed at the end of the second stage and spins a cocoon in which it moults successively to prepupa, pupa and adult. The adult male, which like that of other coccoids cannot feed, leaves the cocoon two days after entering the imaginal state and lives only another 5–6 days. The sex ratio, following sexual reproduction, is unity. A realistic estimate of the period from egg to adult on cocoa seems to be 30–60 days, but under some circumstances it may be longer.

Ecology: *P. njalensis* is very closely associated with ants especially of the genus *Crematogaster,* but also of *Pheidole, Camponotus* and many others. In the presence of species of *Crematogaster* mealybugs occur in colonies, containing from very few up to 3000 individuals, each colony being protected by a tent composed of vegetable fibres and fungal hyphae. Species of *Pheidole* construct tents from soil particles.

The nests of the majority of *Crematogaster* species are on trees shading cocoa, but the principal species of *Pheidole, P. megacephala* nests on the ground.

On cocoa all parts of the plant are attacked but the bulk of individuals (over 85 per cent) occur in the canopy 3 to 4 m above ground level where new shoots are most preferred.

Changes in population density are evident as changes in numbers of colonies and less in colony size. A five to six-fold order of seasonal change has been demonstrated on cocoa in Ghana. Populations decline during the first six months of the year and rise to a maximum during October–November. In contrast the proportion of trees infested is highest during the first three months of the year. Populations of crematogasterine ants closely follow the seasonal changes in incidence of *P. njalensis* in Ghana.

The dispersal behaviour of *P. njalensis* (and of other species of mealybug) assumes importance in relation to the spread of cocoa virus diseases of which these insects are the only known vectors[1]. Over 90 per cent of moving individuals are first stage nymphs (crawlers); adult females seldom walk. In contrast most movement in *P. citri* is by pre-gravid adults though second and third stage nymphs also move. There are two main methods of movement. Firstly, by walking 'crawlers' can cover a distance of 8 m and may easily travel across the canopy from one tree to another. This assists radial increase in size of virus outbreaks. Secondly, passive dispersal of crawlers in wind currents occurs regularly and in Ghana is most pronounced in the main dry season, December–February, probably because mealybug populations are then at their highest. By this means 'jump spread' of virus disease probably occurs. Movement across the ground is ineffective. Some ants contribute heavily to the dispersal of coccoids but do not appear to do so with cocoa mealybugs in Africa.

---

[1]Other mealybugs transmitting viruses of cocoa are *Planococcus* sp. nr. *celtis, P. citri, P. lilacinus, P. kenyae, Pseudococcus concavocerarii, P. hargreavesi, P. longispinus, P.* sp. nr. *fragilis, P.* sp. nr. *proteae, Dysmicoccus brevipes,* and *Ferrisia virgata.*

In Ghana *P. njalensis* constitutes between 50 and 98 percent of mealybugs on cocoa but in Nigeria, where it is codominant with *P. citri* and where *P. kenyae* is an important part of the complex, it composes only about 25 percent.

Natural enemies: The mean annual level of parasitism of *P. njalensis* in Ghana is low (2.7–3.4 percent recorded) and has not been seen to exceed an annual maximum of 10 percent. The main parasites are *Anagyrus* (a complex of species), *Neodiscodes martinii,* four *Clausenia* species and *Leptomastix bifasciatus* (all Hymenoptera, Encyrtidae). In Nigeria *L. bifasciatus* and *N. martinii* are the most important species. Small orange-red larvae of the cecidomyiid fly *Schizobremia coffeae* are predatory on eggs and nymphs and occassionally on pre-gravid adults. Adults and larvae of the coccinellid beetles *Platynaspis higginsi* and of four species of *Scymnus* prey on eggs, nymphs and adults.

Control: Restriction of the spread of cocoa virus diseases by control of their mealybug vectors has been approached in three unsuccessful ways. Early attempts concentrated on direct chemical control and were followed by extensive introductions of exotic parasites. Attempts to reduce mealybug numbers indirectly by chemical control of attendent ants with dieldrin and other chlorinated hydrocarbon insecticides met with limited and short term success and were accompanied by alarming increases in numbers of insects normally of only minor importance (*Spulerina* spp., *Eulophonotus myrmeleon, Metarbela* spp. (Lepidoptera) and *Tragocephala* spp. (Coleoptera)). Control measures have therefore emphasised the elimination or containment of virus by grubbing out infected trees (see p. 10). Meanwhile a search for varieties of cocoa resistant to virus diseases has been in progress.

All known types of cocoa are attacked by mealybugs but varietal differences influence population densities.

Literature

BIGGER, M. (1972): Recent work on the mealybug vectors of cocoa swollen shoot disease in Ghana. PANS **18** (1), 61–70.
ENTWISTLE, P. F. (1972): *Pests of Cocoa.* Longman, London. 779 pp.
LE PELLEY, R. H. (1968): *Pests of Coffee.* Longman, London. 590 pp.
LEGG, J. T. (1972): Measures to control spread of cocoa swollen shoot in Ghana. PANS **18** (1), 57–60.
MAGNIN, J. (1953): Developpement et mode de reproduction de *Pseudococcus njalensis* Laing. Agron. trop. Nogent, **8** (3), 292–299.
WOOD, G.A.R. (1975): Cocoa. Longman, London. 292 pp.

Author: P. F. Entwistle

Saccharicoccus sacchari (Ckll.) (Plate 27 d)

Synonyms: *Dactylopius sacchari, Trionymus sacchari, Pseudococcus sacchari*

Common names: Sugar cane mealybug; Zuckerrohrschmierlaus; Chinche harinosa de la caña de azúcar, Chanchito blanco de la cãna de azúcar.

Geographical distribution: This insect is present in all biological regions of the world except the Nearctic and Australian regions. CIE Map no 102.

Host plants: The host range of this insect seems to be limited to a very small group within the family Gramineae. Apart from on sugar cane the mealybug has been recorded in Egypt on *Sorghum vulgare, S. halepense, Panicum colonum* and *Saccharum biflorum.*

Symptoms: All stages of the insect usually aggregate around the nodes of cane underneath the leafsheaths. The damage is caused partly by the insect sucking the plant sap which leads to thin and stunted canes but mostly from the honeydew excretions and the gums exuded from the wounded parts which thus interfere with the synthesis of raw sugar juice leading to a reduction in the amount of sugar which can be crystallised commercially.

Economic importance: *S. sacchari* is considered to be a major pest of sugar cane in Egypt and elsewhere mainly because of the reduction in sugar which it causes.

Morphology: This mealybug species is pink in colour. It has the typical characters of Pseudococcidae. The body is clearly segmented and is covered by a mealy secretion. The circulus is large with a median transverse constriction. Each lateral margin of the abdominal segments (6–9) bears a long seta.

Similarities to other pests: *S. sacchari* resembles to some extent *Dysmicoccus boninsis* with which it is often found unter the leafsheaths of sugar cane.

Life cycle: The longevity of *S. sacchari* is influenced by temperature being shorter at high temperatures. Males are shorter lived than females at the same temperature. The male lives for 2.65 ± 0.03 days at 30 °C compared to 35.4 ± 0.33 days for the female.
The preoviposition and oviposition periods are also affected by temperature. The male is capable of fertilising 3–5 females while each female is fertilised only once. Shortly before oviposition, the female begins to secrete waxy threads along the posterior end of the body below which it then deposits eggs. The fact that the incubation period of eggs is short, ranging from few minutes to few hours, gives the impression that the insect is viviparous. Parthenogenesis does not occur in this species. The highest number of eggs (185–193 eggs/female) are produced at 24 °C or in May under Egyptian conditions. At higher or lower temperatures, fewer eggs are produced, 49 and 72 eggs/female at 35 and 16 °C, respectively.
The number of females usually exceeds that of males but the difference in the sex ratio is more marked in cold months.
There are three different forms of males, namely winged with 4 nymphal instars, apterous with 3 nymphal instars and intermediates with or without wing buds. In cold months, the apterous forms exceed in number the winged ones while the reverse occurs in hot months. The upper lethal temperatures have been found to be 48 and 50 °C for the male and female, respectively after 4 hours exposure.
After egg hatching, the crawlers seek a feeding site beneath the leaf sheaths and, after the first moult, differentiation of both sexes begins. The male nymph stops feeding near the end of the second stage when it shelters inside a waxy cocoon in protected crevices, while the female nymph feeds during the three instars before moulting to the adult stage. The shortest nymphal duration occurs at 30 °C, being 15.4 ± 0.2, 14 ± 0.3 and 17.8 ± 0.6 days in the female, apterous and winged nymphs respectively. The duration increases to 82 ± 0.80, 69 ± 0.91 and 81.3 ± 0.65 days for the same forms at 16 °C. The life cycle of this insect is always shorter for the male than the female.

Ecology: Ecological studies in Egypt indicate that this mealybug has one annual peak of seasonal abundance. The calculated quotient of increase shows that the favourable time for annual increase is September/October when the temperature ranges between 26 and 28 °C. The insect passes through 4–5 annual generations in Egypt. Usually the insects live in a microhabitat in which the temperature change is proportional to that in the outer atmosphere. Microclimatic humidity is always higher than in the outer atmosphere and ranges from 70–95 %. In sugar cane, 3 or 4 crops can be obtained from the first year stools. The first year crop is the least susceptible to insect infestation whereas the fourth year crop is severely infested. The sugars and amino acids detected in the honeydew of this insect explain the close relation between these mealybugs and ants since the latter can obtain their nutritional requirements from this excretion and also serve as a means of dispersion of the insect from one place to another.

Natural enemies: A parasitic fungus, *Aspergillus flavus,* attacks this insect in Egypt and plays a significant role in its natural control. The percentage of mealybugs attacked by this fungus may be up to 26.9 %.

Control: The fact that this mealybug lives on sugar cane stems sheltering beneath the leaf sheaths makes its chemical control rather difficult when the stalks are at full height in the field. In Egypt is usually recommended that cane cuttings to be planted are soaked in kerosene to kill the insects that might live on them. Thorough ploughing of the soil is also recommended to remove weeds which might serve as alternative hosts for the insect after the crop is harvested. Observations have shown that cane varieties with adhesive leaf sheaths are more susceptible to infestation than those with loose leaf sheaths, since they provide a better protected shelter for mealybug development. Irrigation and systemic insecticides can also be recommended.

Literature

HAFEZ, M. & H. S. SALAMA (1969): Ecological studies on the sugar cane mealy bug *Saccharicoccus sacchari* (Ckll.) in Egypt. Bull. Soc. ent. Egypte **53**, 21–39.
HAFEZ, M. & H. S. SALAMA (1969): Biological studies on the sugar cane mealy bug *Saccharicoccus sacchari* (Ckll.). Bull. Soc. ent. Egypte **53**, 499–516.

Author: H.S. Salama

Planococcus citri (Risso) (Fig. 133)

Synonym: *Pseudococcus citri*

Common names: Citrus mealybug; Zitrusschmierlaus; Cochenille farineuse de l'oranger, Cochenille farineuse de la vigne; Chanchito blanco de los cítricos, Cochinilla harinosa.

Geographical distribution: *P. citri* with various sub-species (races) is represented worldwide in tropical and subtropical regions, in some areas it also occurs in climatically suitable zones outside subtropical regions, e. g. in mediterranean and Black Sea regions, in Japan and Portugal. In temperate zones it occurs in glasshouses.

Host plants: *Citrus,* grapevine, coffee, cocoa, potato, rubber, papaya, yam, banana, annona, mango, fig, *Eugenia* and many other wild and cultivated plants. Extremely polyphagous species.

Symptoms: Like other Homoptera, *P. citri* is directly and indirectly damaging in various ways. Much sap is withdrawn from heavily infested plants, leading to pronounced arrested growth and lowered yield, for instance as a result of premature fruit drop. Soiling of fruit, leaves and other plant portions with honey dew and sooty mould is often more conspicuous. The fruit can also be soiled with the white, thread-like secretion of the mealybug if the infestation is severe. Special conditions prevail if *P. citri* is associated with fungi of the genus *Polyporus* on the roots of *Coffea arabica* and *C. liberica*. Plants affected in this way are surrounded on their roots by a thick layer of mycelium, wilt badly and may die.
In West Africa and the West Indiens, the Citrus mealybug was shown to transmit various isolates of swollen shoot virus of cocoa (see p. 9).

Economic importance: *P. citri* is one of the most widespread and most damaging mealybugs in tropical and subtropical regions, where it occurs predominantly on *Citrus* and coffee, but can also cause considerable damage on other tropical fruit trees by feeding activity and/or soiling of fruit with honey dew (sooty mould).

Morphology: The oval, pale yellow to brownish-orange female is distinctly segmented and has a body length of up to 4 mm. The skin is covered with a white, powdery glandular secretion, while a median, longitudinal dorsal strip remains almost clear (Fig. 133). Laterally at the body edge are short secretory processes (17 pairs) which gradually lengthen towards the back. The two hindmost processes reach about $1/12$–$1/8$ of the body length. Legs and antennae are well developed.

Males are no more than 1 mm long and violet to yellowish in colour. On the head are four ocelli and relatively long antennae with many bristles. The forewings are transparent and shiny, the hind wings are reduced to small halteres. The legs are slender and very hairy. The abdomen is clearly segmented and

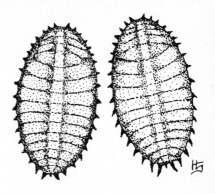

Fig. 133. Females of *Planococcus citri* (drawing H. Schmutterer)

carries two long, white secretory processes at the posterior end. The males develop in small cocoon-like structures formed of filiform secretions.

Similarities to other pests: A number of Pseudococcidae resemble *P. citri* and some of them are found on the same host plants, e. g. coffee and *Citrus*. *P. kenyae* and *P. lilacinus* (East Africa) on coffee, *Planococcoides njalensis* (West Africa) on cocoa and *Pseudococcus gahani* (America) on *Citrus* can be confused with *P. citri*. If in doubt, the female must be examined microscopically by an expert.

Life cycle and ecology: *P. citri* colonises branches, leaves, flowers and fruit of the host, but the "root form" is found on subterranean plant portions (see below).

The female is freely mobile until oviposition. A few days after mating she settles in some sheltered spot on the host plant, usually after migrating over a short distance. An ovisac consisting of filiform secretions is then secreted posteriorly, into which the yellowish eggs are deposited. The deposits consist of about 50 to 600 eggs, depending on the nutritional state of the female. They hatch after 3–10 days or more, depending on temperature. The period of oviposition lasts for several weeks. Male developmental instars are found fairly frequently in *P. citri* colonies. The number of generations per year depends on climatic conditions. In hot, dry areas up to 10 successive generations can be expected, while at high altitudes and in some mediterranean regions there may be no more than 3–4.

A sub-species ("root form") occurs on *Coffea arabica* in East Africa. It colonises the main roots of coffee plants in unsuitable localities (soil conditions.). A fungus of the genus *Polyporus* forms a dense mycelium which envelops the root portions affected by the mealybug, offering protection while allowing the passage of visiting ants. Similar associations between Pseudococcidae and root fungi on coffee are also known in other parts of the world (Madagascar, Central America, Indonesia).

Natural enemies: Coccinellidae of the genera *Scymnus*, *Hyperaspis* and *Cryptolaemus (C. montrouzieri)* are among the main predators. Neuroptera of the genera *Chrysopa* and *Sympherobius* also play a part. The most important parasites belong primarily to the Encyrtidae *(Prochiloneurus, Anagyrus, Leptomastix* and *Leptomastidea)*. The population density of Citrus mealybug can also be reduced considerably by parasitic fungi such as *Empusa fresenii* (e. g. on coffee in Indonesia) during the rainy season.

Control: A biological control of *P. citri* is carried out in the southern USA, where good results have been obtained with *Cryptolaemus montrouzieri* (Coccinellidae) and *Leptomastidea abnormis* (Encyrtidae). These natural enemies have also been successfully acclimatised in other parts of the world.

The chemical control of the Citrus mealybug can be carried out by repeated sprays with parathion, diazinon, malathion, dimethoate and azinphos. The effect of parathion and malathion can be enhanced considerably by the addition of light oil.

Where *P. citri* is visited by ants, it is advisable to treat the base of affected stems with gamma BHC, aldrin or dieldrin against ants, so that they are kept away from the mealybug colonies. The infiltration of the main root region with aldrin has proved effective against root mealybugs in East Africa. The ants are probably primarily affected by this measure.

Literature

EBELING, W. (1959): Subtropical fruit pests. University of California, 436 pp.
ENTWISTLE, P. F. (1972): Pests of cocoa. Tropical Science Series, Longmans London, 779 pp.
LE PELLEY, R. H. (1968): Pests of coffee. Tropical Science Series, Longmans London, 590 pp.
DE LOTTO, G. (1964): Observations on African mealybugs (Hemiptera. Coccidae). Bull. Br. Mus. nat. Hist. Ent. **14**, 343–397.

Author: H. Schmutterer

Family: Coccidae

Coccus viridis (Green) (Plate 28 b)

Synonym: *Lecanium viride*

Common names: Green coffee scale, (Soft) green scale; Grüne Kaffeeschildlaus; Cochenille verte; Conchuela verde del cafeto.

Geographical distribution: Owing to some confusion with other *Coccus* species, a fully accurate account of the exact distribution cannot yet be given. The scale insect is definitely widely distributed in tropical Africa (East and West Africa) and also occurs in Sri Lanka. It has been reported in the Indo-Malaysian region (India, Indonesia) and in tropical Central and South America (West Indies, Central America, Brazil etc.) but these reports have to be confirmed.

Host plants: Coffee, *Citrus,* tea, mango, guava and other wild and cultivated hosts.

Symptoms: The Green coffee scale tends to rapid multiplication, especially on young coffee plants and primarily causes damage by removing the sap, so that plants are considerably weakened and arrested in their growth. Sooty mould develops on honey dew excretions and can cover fruit and leaf surface as a thick black layer, interfering with the process of assimilation. The older literature reports repeatedly of such heavy damage, that coffee cultivation in particular localities had to be abandoned.

Economic importance: *C. viridis* must be regarded as a major pest on young coffee plants, whose growth is considerably retarded by heavy attack.

Morphology: The female is oval, sometimes asymmetrical, fairly flat and coloured pale green. In the middle, dorsally, are a few black spots. Length is up to about 4 mm, width up to about 2.2 mm. The skin is soft and elastic, the body edge very thin. Males are rarely found.

Similarities to other pests: Two very similar species are found with *C. viridis* on coffee in East Africa. They are *Coccus alpinus* and *C. africanus*. These species greatly resemble the Green coffee scale in appearance and bionomics. In case of doubt, identification by an expert may be necessary. On *Citrus, C. hesperidum* (see p. 370) can be mistaken for Green coffee scale. It is a widely distributed species, but is usually much darker (brownish) than *C. viridis*.

Life cycle and ecology: *C. viridis* is an ovoviviparous scale insect. The eggs are deposited under the body and hatch within a few hours after oviposition. Several hundred eggs are usually deposited per female and their number can rise above 500 if the parent is well nourished. The larvae remain under the mother insect for several days and eventually leave to settle on the undersurface of leaves and on shoots and fruit. Three instars can be differentiated during the post-embryonic development of females, which can change their position. Only after the start of oviposition, does the female generally remain in the same place until death. The period of development of one generation varies from one to several months, depending on temperature and food supply. The length of the reproductive period is also very variable. In extreme cases, it can extend over almost 4 months. No males are yet known, so that it can be concluded that reproduction is purely by parthenogenesis.

The Green coffee scale is always visited by ants and these protect it against predators. It has also been observed that the rate of reproduction of the scale insect is increased by certain ant species. In East Africa, *C. viridis* occurs mainly at low altitudes.

Natural enemies: Ladybirds of the genus *Chilocorus* (Africa, Asia) and caterpillars of the Noctuid genus *Eublemma* (East Africa) are important predators. Among the parasitic Hymenoptera, Aphelinidae of the genus *Coccophagus* are the most prominent in Africa and Asia. Some Encyrtid and Eulophid species have also proved parasitic in various parts of the world. Of great importance are parasitic fungi, chief among them *Cephalosporium lecanii,* not least because it is widely distributed in tropical America, Africa and Asia. This fungus is particularly effective in the rainy season, when it can kill large colonies of the Green coffee scale within a short period of time. *Empusa lecanii* is considered important in southern India.

Control: Since *C. viridis* is associated with ants, it is sometimes possible to reduce attack greatly by controlling ants with lindane, aldrin or dieldrin, provided the effect does not have to be immediate. Direct control can be carried out with malathion, azinphos, parathion, dimethoate, diazinon and white oil.

Literature

DE LOTTO, G. (1960): The green scales of coffee in Africa south of the Sahara. Bull. ent. Res. **51**, 389–403.
LE PELLEY, R. H. (1968): Pests of Coffee. Tropical Science Series, Longmans London, 590 pp.

Author: H. Schmutterer

Family: Diaspididae

Aspidiotus destructor Sign. (Fig. 134 and plate 28 c)

Synonym: *Aspidiotus cocotis*

Common names: Coconut scale; Kokospalmenschildlaus; Conchuela del cocotero.

Geographical distribution: Worldwide in the tropics in most major coconut palm growing regions. CIE Map no 118.

Host plants: Above all coconut palm *(Cocos nucifera).* Also on oil palm, phoenix palm, *Pandanus* spp., banana, mango, avocado, guava, *Citrus,* cocoa, papaya, rubber, breadfruit, tea and other wild and cultivated plants.

Fig. 134. Damage caused by *Aspidiotus destructor* on leaves of coconut palm (phot. H. Schmutterer)

Symptoms: On coconut palm, the undersurface of leaves is chiefly attacked, but frond stalks, flower clusters and young fruit can also be affected. Affected leaves first show a yellow discolouration around areas of sucking activity (Fig. 134), followed by brown necroses. In extreme cases the leaves dry up, entire fronds drop off, the crown dies and the whole crop is lost. On banana leaves, yellowish discoloured zones also form on the affected areas.

Economic importance: *A. destructor* is one of the most dangerous pests of coconut palm. Yield losses can be particularly high if the scale insect has been recently introduced.

Morphology: The scale of the female is circular, fairly flat, transparent, whitish to grey white and about 1.8 mm in diameter. The cast skins of the first and second instar nymphs lie at the centre of the scale and are of a yellowish colour. The female is almost pear-shaped and coloured yellow to yellowish green. At the posterior edge of the pygidium she has three pairs of lobes, between which considerably longer, deeply serrated plates are situated. The scale of the male is oval and much smaller than that of the female.

Similarities to other pests: Alongside *A. destructor* and the sub-species *A. d. rigidus,* which is sometimes considered to be even more destructive, other Diaspididae also occur on coconut palm, such as *Aspidiotus nerii, Chrysomphalus dictyospermi, Hemiberlesia lataniae* and *Selenaspidus articulatus.* None of these species have a transparent scale and can thereby be distinguished from *A. destructor.*

Life cycle and ecology: The female deposits about 20–50 eggs under her scale in the course of a few days. The nymphs crawl under the scale edge out into the open after hatching and soon colonise the leaf undersurface not far from the parent. These "crawlers" can easily drop off or be carried over larger distances by the wind. Other insects can also contribute to the spread of young nymphs. The developmental period of females takes about one month in Indonesia. With the sub-species *A. d. rigidus,* which occurs in Indonesia and on the Philippines, it takes $1\frac{1}{2}$ to almost 2 months. For this reason, 6–12 generations can be expected in a year. In mass attack, 20–30 insects will occupy one square centimetre of palm leaf surface, and a total of 30–60 million scale insects are present on fully grown palm trees.

Natural enemies: Predators play a significant part as a natural limiting factor for *A. destructor.* They are mainly *Chilocorus* species, *Azya trinitatis, Cryptognatha nodiceps, Lindorus lophanthae* and *Pentilia castanea* (Coccinellidae). Parasites of the genera *Comperiella* (Encyrtidae), *Aphytis* and *Aspidiotiphagus* (Aphelinidae) have a more local significance.

Control: Biological control is of foremost importance, especially if *A. destructor* is introduced into new regions in which it was formerly absent. If the main predators (see above) can be successfully acclimatised, the attack is noticeably contained after a little while.

Chemical control from below is difficult owing to the great height of grown trees and so costly that it is hardly a commercially viable proposition. Young palm trees can be treated successfully with diazinon, malathion and parathion.

Literature

LEVER, R. J. A. W. (1969): Pests of the coconut palm. FAO Agricultural Studies no 77, Rome 1969.
MENON, K. P. V. & K. M. PANDALAI (1958): The coconut palm: a monograph. Ernakulam, Indian Central Coconut Committee.
REYNE, A. (1948): Studies on a serious outbreak of *Aspidiotus destructor rigidus* in the coconutpalms of Sangi (North Celebes). Tijdschr. Ent. **89**, 83–120.
SIMMONDS, F. J. (1960): Biological control of coconut scale (*Aspidiotus destructor*) in Principé, Portuguese West Africa. Bull. ent. Res. **51**, 223–237.

Author: H. Schmutterer

Aonidiella aurantii (Mask.) (Plate 28 d)

Synonyms: *Aspidiotus aurantii, Chrysomphalus aurantii*

Common names: California red scale; Le pou de Californie; Rote Kalifornische Schildlaus, Rote Orangenschildlaus; Escama roja de los cítricos, Cochinilla roja de California.

Geographical distribution: The California red scale is of Oriental origin. It has spread with citrus practically all over the world, and is now present in the Far East (China, southeastern Asia), all around the Mediterranean Basin, western and southern Africa, Australia, New Zealand, southern USA, Mexico and South America.

Host plants: Very polyphagous, infesting a wide range of arboreal plants, including many important fruit trees and ornamentals. Citrus and roses are usually the main hosts suffering serious economic damage, but numerous others may serve as sources of re-infestation.

Symptoms: *A. aurantii* may infest all the above-ground parts of citrus trees – trunk, limbs, branches, twigs, leaves and fruit – causing severe injury apparently both by direct feeding and by the injection of toxic substances into the infested tree. Infested leaves may turn yellow and drop prematurely. Branches and twigs may become encrusted with live and dead scale insects and eventually die back. Young fruits may become deformed with deep pits, whereas mature fruits may become encrusted with scale insects.

Economic importance: The California red scale is considered one of the most serious pests of citrus in the world. It is regarded as the most important pest of citrus in California, northwestern Mexico, Australia and South Africa, and as a major pest of citrus in the eastern Mediterranean Basin, North Africa and parts of South America. Heavy infestation may result in defoliation, fruit drop, extensive die-back of twigs and branches, culling of the entire crop, reduction in subsequent crops, retardation of development of young trees, and even death of entire trees.

Morphology: The covering scale of the adult female is circular, rather flat, about 2 mm in diameter, translucent, with the orange-red body of the adult insect showing through it and imparting it a reddish hue; exuviae concentric, central or sub-central. A thin, greyish-white ventral scale is also present. The body of the adult female is strongly reniform, the cephalothoracic region extending backward in a large, rounded lobe on each side of the retracted pygidium. In the mated female, the body cannot be readily separated from the covering scale.

23*

The scale of the male is smaller, elongate-oval, paler than in the female; exuvia slightly towards anterior end. Body of male pupa orange, with red-brownish eyes.

Similarities to other pests: The yellow scale, *Aonidiella citrina,* was formerly thought to represent a "biological variety" of *A. aurantii.* Yellow scale usually occurs only on the leaves and fruit of citrus, rarely infesting the branches, and can be distinguished from the California red scale by the yellow color of the adult female and microscopic features (apophyses on the pygidium).

Life cycle and ecology: *A. aurantii* is a biparental species, no embryo formation occurs without fertilization. The species is viviparous: the eggs hatch within the body of the female, giving birth to young crawlers. The crawlers may remain for a day or two under the mother scale; their emergence is influenced by both temperature and light intensity, so that most of them emerge in the morning. They may wander for 3 hours and may cover a distance of up to 3 m before settling down. Passive dispersal by wind or man also occurs during the crawler stage; the crawlers are capable of surviving for several hours without feeding while being carried with the wind. They prefer to settle down in the tiny depressions marking the site of oil glands on the fruit, or along the midrib and prominent veins of leaves.

Once settled, the female never changes her position again. The female molts twice, losing the legs and prominent antennae of the crawler in the first molt. Both exuviae are incorporated in the scale covering. In the male, only the first exuvia is incorporated in the scale. The male undergoes the prepupal and pupal stages under the unchanged scale of the second instar, and eventually is transformed into a winged adult, possessing well-developed antennae and legs. Development of males and females is synchronized, the male emerging when the female is in the receptive young adult stage. Male emergence usually occurs in the evening. Mating commences as soon as the male emerges. The adult male lives for only a few hours, does not feed, and may mate with several females. It is attracted to a specific pheromone released by the unmated female, and may cover a distance of 100–200 m in search for females.

At 25 °C and 70 % RH, male emergence peaks on the 26th day, and crawlers begin to emerge 43 days after insemination. Two or three crawlers may emerge daily over a period that may last up to several months. Total fecundity averages 50–150 crawlers per female on citrus leaves, dependent on the temperature, and about 350 on citrus fruit.

Two generations develop annually on citrus in coastal areas of California, 3 in inland areas, 2–3 in South Africa, 3–5 in Rhodesia, 5–6 in Queensland. In Israel, 4 major generations develop in the coastal plain, 5 in the hot Jordan Valley. Considerable overlapping of generations usually occurs, due to the relatively long life of the producing female. The population usually peaks at the beginning of the picking season of citrus, in late autumn.

The California red scale is apparently able to survive under almost all climatic conditions suitable for citrus. It usually appears to prefer young trees and outer rows in the grove, but in warmer areas it may infest also mature, dense trees. Low relative humidities are detrimental and may cause a reduction of the population, especially if combined with high temperatures.

Natural enemies: The natural enemies of the California red scale include predators, endoparasites and ectoparasites. Predatory coccinellids – especially *Lindorus lophanthae, Orcus chalybeus* and *Chilocorus* spp. – often decimate severe infestations but are usually dependent on high prey densities and are incapable of keeping the pest at subeconomic levels.

Endoparasites usually play a more significant role than predators. Most important of these are the encyrtids *Comperiella bifasciata* and *Habrolepis rouxi,* and the aphelinids *Prospaltella perniciosi, Pteroptrix (= Casca) chinensis* and *Aspidiotiphagus* spp. Although apparently inferior to ectoparasites, they often complement the work of the latter in bringing about effective biological control.

Ectoparasites of the aphelinid genus *Aphytis* are by far the most effective natural enemies of the California red scale. *A. chrysomphali* and *A. lingnanensis* are dominant in coastal, climatically mild areas, whereas *A. coheni* and *A. melinus* are more adapted to the extreme climatic conditions of inland areas. *A. africanus* is important in South Africa. *A. melinus,* originally from India, is currently considered the most promising natural enemy of the California red scale.

Control:
Biological control. In California, repeated attempts to introduce *P. chinensis,* a presumably efficient parasite from China, failed due to lack of essential information on its biology. After numerous failures, *H. rouxi* was obtained from South Africa and established in 1937, followed by *C. bifasciata* from China in 1941, *P. perniciosi* from China in 1947, and *A. lingnanensis* from China in 1948. Eventually, *A. melinus* was introduced from India and Pakistan and established in 1957. A general decline of red scale infestations was evident by 1962, and the introduced parasites have demonstrated their ability to maintain satisfactory control of the pest in numerous untreated citrus plots. *A. melinus* and *C. bifasciata,* which are the dominant natural enemies in inland citrus areas of California, have been successfully introduced into several other countries. *A. lingnanensis* and *P. perniciosi* are still dominant along the coast of California.
Chemical control. It can normally be achieved with light-medium or medium grade petroleum oil ("summer oil"), applied as a high-volume, thorough-coverage spray of a 1.75–2 % emulsion which is effective against all stages of the pest throughout the year. Oil treatments are recommended during winter, preferably after picking, and should be avoided during the flowering season of citrus in spring and during periods of draught or excessive heat. Weak trees may be sensitive to oil treatment. Late autumn application of petroleum oil may retard the formation of ripe coloring in early citrus varieties.
Being highly selective, oil treatments do not disrupt the natural equilibrium in citrus groves and should therefore be preferred to organophosphorus insecticides. The latter (e. g., malathion, parathion, ethion, methidathion (Supracide) etc.) may be used, in combination with reduced concentrations of petroleum oils, to control severe outbreaks. However, such combinations are highly detrimental to natural enemies, possess high mammalian toxicity and may be phytotoxic to certain citrus varieties under certain conditions, hence should be avoided except in extreme emergencies.
Traps containing a lemon infested with about 200 virgin females may be used to detect very light infestations of the California red scale. Males attracted to the pheromone released by the females are trapped on an index card coated with glue. Such traps may prove useful also in determining the timing of oil treatments.

Literature

AVIDOV, Z. & I. HARPAZ (1969): Plant pests of Israel. Israel Universities Press, Jerusalem, 549 pp.
COMPERE, H. (1961): The red scale and its insect enemies. Hilgardia, **31,** 173–278.
DEBACH, P., D. ROSEN & C. E. KENNETT (1971): Biological control of coccids by introduced natural enemies. Chapter 7 in: Huffaker, C. B. (Ed.), Biological Control. Plenum Press, New York & London, 511 pp.
EBELING, W. (1959): Subtropical fruit pests. University of California, Division of Agricultural Sciences, 436 pp.
MORENO, D. S., J. FARGENLUND & J. G. SHAW (1973): California red scale: Capture of males in modified pheromone traps. J. Econ. Entomol. **66,** 1333.
TASHIRO, H. & J. B. BEAVERS (1968): Growth and development of the California red scale, *Aonidiella aurantii.* Ann. Entomol. Soc. Amer. **61,** 1009–1014.
TASHIRO, H. & C. MOFFITT (1968): Reproduction in the California red scale, *Aonidiella aurantii.* II. Mating behavior and postinsemination female changes. Ann. Entomol. Soc. Amer. **61,** 1014–1020.

Author: David Rosen

Chrysomphalus ficus Ashm. (Plate 29 a)

Synonyms: *Aspidiotus ficus, Chrysomphalus aonidum*

Common names: Florida red scale; Schwarze Tellerschildlaus; Cochenille rouge de Florida; Cochinilla roja de Florida.

Geographical distribution: In North America, Florida red scale is found in the United States and Mexico and was introduced into Florida from Cuba in 1874. In California, it's only a pest in greenhouses. In Mexico, it's distributed mainly along the Atlantic coast. In Central America, in all countries, particularly along the Atlantic coast as well as the Antilles Islands of Cuba, and Trinidad and other Caribbean Islands. In South America, it is also found along the Atlantic coast countries of Colombia, Venezuela, Brazil (where at times it is a major citrus pest), and the Entre Ríos, Missiones Corientes, Tucumán, and Jujuy areas of Argentina. In Europe, Florida red scale is found along the Mediterranean, in Italy, Lebanon, Syria, and in Israel and Egypt where it was regarded as the number-one pest and it is called Black Scale by the Egyptians. It is also a pest at times in some areas of South Africa, India, and the Queensland area of Australia as well as some areas of China. CIE Map no 4.

Host plants: More than 630 plants are listed as hosts. The important tropical crops are annonas, apples (and related species), avocados, bananas, various types of berries, cedar trees, various types of cherry trees, various types of citrus, eucalyptus, various types of figs, guavas, mangos, olives, various types of palms, pears, peppers, different types of pine trees, plums, rubber trees, vanilla trees, yucca plants. Citrus is the most important host plant.

Symptoms: Florida red scale generally causes yellow chlorotic spots when feeding on leaves. When citrus fruits are attacked, yellow spots appear at the feeding sites and the presence of scales on the citrus fruit presents a very unattractive appearance.

Economic importance: Before the introduction of an effective biological control agent, this scale insect was a very serious pest of citrus in Florida and Israel. At one time, heavy populations of this scale caused severe defoliation with resulting loss of crops and subsequent yields. The unattractiveness of the fruit due to the presence of this scale and the difficulty of the complete removal of the insect from the fruit with available fruit handling methods causes lower prices for the fruit in the fresh fruit market.

Morphology: The scale covering is circular and convex and made up of three rings. The central ring is nearly central, it is light-brown where the second ring is reddish-brown. The third ring is wider than the other two combined and is reddish-brown to black with a thin gray margin. Florida red scale can be differentiated from California red scale by the ease in which the body can be lifted away from the armor, whereas the body of the California red scale remains attached to the armor. Also Florida red scale lays egg where California red scale gives birth to living young. The body of the California red scale is reddish and kidney-shaped where Florida red scale is bright-yellow colored with the shape of a wide, short top.

Similarities to other pests: Although the morphological characteristics are very similar to California red scale, Florida red scale has very different habits. California red scale can in time severely infest the wood besides the leaves and the fruit where Florida red scale infests only the leaves and fruit.

Life cycle: The eggs are laid beneath the dorsal scale covering and are oval-shaped lemon-yellow colored with an average of 145 per female. Crawlers (1st instar nymphs) are ovoid-like in shape, bright-yellow colored and very active before permanently settling down. The female goes through two molts before reaching maturity. Males also molt twice with a free flying adult emerging after the last molt. Females must be fertilized before laying eggs. Life cycle from egg to egg takes 78 days at 61 °F while only 28 days are required at 83 °F. In Florida, there are four to six generations per year, while three to four occur in Israel.

Ecology: This scale insect does not appear to have a specific ecological pattern. Florida red scale appears to be cosmopolitan and to adapt itself to a wide range of hosts and over a wide range of growing conditions.

Natural enemies: Florida red scale is parasitized by a wide range of hymenopterous parasites. Several species of Coccinellid beetles have been reported feeding upon Florida red scale.

Control: The control of *C. ficus* in Florida and Israel is depended upon the integration of an effective biological control agent and the occasional use of pesticides when necessary due to misuse of pesticides in the ecosystem. A classic example of outstanding biological control is the case of the Florida red scale of being completely controlled by the introduction of the parasite *Aphytis holoxanthus* (Hym. Aphelinidae). Today, rarely are chemicals (azinphos, diazinon, parathion, parathion-oil etc.) needed to control this scale insect in Florida.

Literature

BROOKS, R. F. & W. L. THOMPSON (1963): Investigations of new scalicides for Florida. Fla. Entomol. **46**, 279–284.
DEKLE, G. W. (1965): Arthropods of Florida Volume III: Florida armored scale insects. Fla. Dept. of Agr., Div. of Plant Ind.
EBELING, W. (1959): Subtropical fruit pests. Regents of the University of California, Div. of Agr. Sci., 436 pp.

Author: R. F. Brooks

Parlatoria blanchardii Targ. (Figs. 135–136)

Common names: Date palm scale; Dattelpalmenschildlaus; Cochenille blanche du palmier-dattier.

Geographical distribution: Like the date palm, the scale insect *Parlatoria blanchardii* almost certainly originated in Mesopotamia (Iran, Iraq). Today it stretches from the oases of Punjab (India) to the plantations of Maghreb (Tunisia, Algeria, Morocco), and is found in Turkey, Syria, Israel, Egypt,Sudan, Arabia, Somalia, Tripolitania, Mauritania and Niger.
From the 18th century and during the 19th, the pest was successively introduced into California, Arizona (1890), Australia (1894), Argentina (1928), Brazil (1929) and Turkestan (1935).

Host plants: *P. blanchardii* only occurs on palms, in particular on the date palm *(Phoenix dactylifera)* but also on *P. canariensis, P. reclinata, Hyphaene thebaica* (tropical Africa and Madagascar) and *Washingtonia filifera* (California, Arizona).

Symptoms: The scales prefer to infest the pinnules and the main veins of the fronds. In severe cases they even attack the leaf bases, the fruits, and also uniformly cover the old fronds which acquire a characteristic white colour instead of their normal green tint.

Economic importance: The density of the pest varies from a few individuals (15 scales/cm^2) to a complete encrustment (320 scales/cm^2). When the leaves are totally covered with scales, photosynthesis is reduced and the survival of the trees, especially young plants, is jeopardized. Severe attacks can kill trees. The fruits are not marketable if infested. The importance of this pest on date palm is comparable with that of *Aspidiotus destructor* on coconut palm (see p. 353).

Morphology: The pest is an oval-shaped, diaspidid scale insect. The scale (shield) of the adult female measures 1.2–1.6 mm by 0.3 mm; that of the male is 1.0–1.3 mm by 0.15 mm.

The scale of the mature female is brown with a white border. This appearance is due to dark nymphal skins, visible through the scale secreted by the female. The scales of the males are white because the nymphal skins are pale yellow and invisible beneath the scale.

Similarities to other pests: On date palms this scale cannot be confused with any other pest except *Phoenicoccus marlatti* (a red scale).

Life cycle: The oviparous females lay eggs (8–15) under their scales after they have been fertilized by winged or micropterous males. The ovaries mature in 15–20 days according to season. The eggs hatch 8–18 days after laying to produce mobile nymphs which attach themselves in less than 3 days and then pass through two nymphal moults. The 2nd instar lasts 2–3 weeks and the 3rd instar (an immature female) 10–15 days. Then the scale becomes a mature female. The life of the last two nymphal stages can be extended if a winter diapause is initiated.
The males undergo a slightly different development. Under their scales they pass through, in addition, prepupal and pupal stages before becoming mobile adults.

Ecology: The life-cycle of *P. blanchardii* varies from 50–60 days in summer to 75–85 days in autumn and spring. In the northern part of its area of distribution (North Africa), the cycle lasts 130 days in winter. Annually there are 3–4 generations in the Maghreb and 5–6 in Mauritania. *P. blanchardii* prefers a hot, dry, Sahara-type climate. In such an environment the date palm scale populates relatively humid situations where it is protected from direct sunlight. Accordingly, the scale generally occupies the centre of oases where it invades, in particular, the lowest fronds and the suckers at the base of the trees.
The edges of plantations and vegetation exposed to dry winds are much less attacked.

Natural enemies: No parasites specific to *P. blanchardii* are known; at the most, *Aphytis mytilaspidis* (Hymenoptera, Aphelinidae) attacks it occasionally.
However, there are many predators of this scale among the Coleoptera and Neuroptera. Of the Coleoptera there are two genera of Coccinellidae which are strictly restricted to predating on diaspidid scales: *Pharoscymnus* spp.—very well adapted to deserts an sub-deserts. Small insects, with a low voracity and fecundity, they normally attack scales towards the end of an outbreak when the pest density is low. *Chilocorus* spp. – much more cosmopolitan, voracious and fecund than *Pharoscymnus,* they attack severe outbreaks of the pest. The family Nitidulidae (Coleoptera) is repre-

Fig. 136. *Chilocorus bipustulatus,* an important predator of *P. blanchardii* (phot. G. Iperti)

Fig. 135. *Parlatoria blanchardii* on a date palm leaf (phot. G. Iperti)

sented by *Cybocephalus* spp., the value of which is comparable to that of *Pharoscymnus.* Of the Neuroptera, a few species, two of which belong to the genus *Chrysopa,* sometime exercise a significant predatory role.

In certain countries a predacious mite, *Hemisarcoptes malus* has been recorded.

Control: The separate or combined use of cultural, physical, biological and even chemical methods is recommended.

Cultural methods. It is important to maintain a good state of vegetative growth. Irrigation, application of fertilizers, periodical pruning of the trees and the removal of unwanted suckers are some of the good management measures needed to restrict pest development.

Physical methods. These comprise stripping the tree of all its fronds except those at the very top, and burning all the trash. Hot, salty water is then poured over the crown of remaining leaves. This operation is harsh, but sometimes alleviates the problem.

Resistant varieties. Certain varieties are acknowledged to be very susceptible to *P. blanchardii,* but there has been no attempt to select for resistance.

Biological control. The possibility of achieving this type of control was verified with the successful introduction of a coccinellid, *Chilocorus bipustulatus* (Fig. 136), from Iran (centre of origin of the pest) to Mauritania in 1967. In three years the population of *P. blanchardii* at Atar (about 250 000 palms) fell from a mean infestation index of 4 (start of encrustment) to $^1/_2$–1 (slight infestation). This success led to a new action which began in 1970 in a much larger plantation at Tidjikja, and the results were as conclusive. Biological interventions of this nature must gradually extend to the plantations of Niger and North Africa (beginning with Morocco).

Chemical control. The application of pesticides is not suited to poor and desert countries, but can be valuable in new plantations to protect the young, non-cropping plants during establishment.

a) Insecticides. The use of hydrocyanic acid as a fumigant appears too complicated whereas parathion with oil can be considered.

b) Application. Fumigation is under tended trees. Sprays are applied from the ground, but their toxicity, short persistence and costs are among factors which do not encourage their general introduction.

c) Prognosis. A single scale is sufficient warning of a rapid and inevitable increase in the pest population.

d) Resistant strains. Except in Israel, there has been no serious investigation of this subject.

Literature

BALACHOWSKY, A. S. (1953): Monographie des Coccoidea – Diaspidinae; IV *Odonaspidini Parlatorini.* Hermann édit. Paris 207 pp. 45 pl.

IPERTI, G. & Y. LAUDEHO (1969): Les entomophages de *Parlatoria blanchardii* Targ. dans les palmeraies de l'Adrar. I – Etude biologique et écologique préliminaire. Perspectives d'acclimatation de nouveaux prédateurs Coccinellidae. Ann. Zool. Econ. Anim. **1** (1), 17–30.

IPERTI, G. & J. BRUN (1969): Rôle d'une quarantaine pour la multiplication des Coccinellidae coccidiphages destinés à combattre la cochenille du palmier-dattier *(Parlatoria blanchardii* Targ.) en Adrar mauritanien. Entomophaga **14** (2), 149–157.

IPERTI, G., Y. LAUDEHO, J. BRUN & E. CHOPPIN DE JANVRY (1970): Les entomophages de *Parlatoria blanchardii* Targ. dans les palmeraies de l'Adrar. III–Introduction, Acclimation et efficacité d'un nouveau prédateur Coccinellidae: *Chilocorus bipustulatus* L. variété *iranensis* (var. nov.). Ann. Zool. Ecol. Anim. **2** (4) 617–638.

KEHAT, M. (1967): Some notes on the life cycle of the date palm scale, *Parlatoria blanchardii* Targ. in Israel. J. Agric. Res. **17**, 175–179.

KEHAT, M. & E. SWIRSKI (1964): Chemical conrol of the date palm scale *Parlatoria blanchardii* and the effect of some insecticides on the lady beetle *Pharoscymnus* aff. *numidicus* PIC. Israel J. Agric. Res. **14** (3), 101–110.

LAUDEHO, Y. & C. BENASSY (1969): Contribution à l'étude de l'écologie de *Parlatoria blanchardii* Targ. en Adrar mauritanien. Fruits **24** (5), 273–287.

SMIRNOFF, W. (1957): La cochenille du palmier-dattier *(Parlatoria blanchardii* Targ.) en Afrique du Nord: comportement, importance économique, prédateurs et lutte biologique. Entomophaga **2** (1), 1–99.

Author: G. Iperti

Aulacaspis tegalensis (Zhnt.) (Fig. 137)

Common names: Sugar cane scale insect; Zuckerrohrdeckelschildlaus.

Geographical distribution: Malaysia, Thailand, Indonesia (Java), Taiwan, Philippines, Mauritius, Reunion, Madagascar, Kenya, Tanzania, Uganda. The insect is considered to be indigenous to S. E. Asia and to have been accidentally carried to the Mascarenes, Madagascar and E. Africa with sugar cane imported for planting material. CIE Map no 187.

Host plants: The insect is a pest only of sugar cane. It has been found also on sorghum in Tanzania and on the wild grass *Erianthus arundinaceus* in Java.

Symptoms: The part of the sugar cane plant usually infested is the stem, but the insect can also be found at times on the rhizome, the leaf sheaths and the leaves. On the stems, the only part of the plant where intensive multiplication occurs, the massed individuals form whitish crusts that partly or entirely cover the internodes. The leaf sheaths usually hide these scale crusts and have to be stripped off to observe the extent of stem infestation. Because the insect is essentially a stem-feeder, it cannot multiply to any great extent until stem (cane) formation is well advanced. Crop infestation therefore develops to economically important levels only in the later stages of growth.

Economic importance: The insects feed in the parenchyma (storage) cells of the stem and by doing so prevent the accumulation of sucrose. Infested canes show reduced pol % cane accompanied

by reduced refractometric brix and low purity, but absolute juice is unaffected. In other words, total sucrose content of infested cane is low not because it contains less juice but because the juice contains less solids in solution. Since the proportion of sucrose to other solids in solution is also diminished, the purity is lower in infested canes and this leads to additional loss in the factory, where the lower the purity the lower is the percentage recovery of sucrose from the juice. These effects of the insect on cane composition are directly proportional to the number of living insects on a stem and tend to be restricted to the infested parts; they are not necessarily permanent and may disappear to a large extent if the insects die.

Death of canes may also result from heavy infestation but whether or not this occurs depends on a variety of factors – duration of intense infestation, age of the canes, weather, and the inherent intolerance of some varieties such as the thin-stemmed NCo 376. Generally speaking, the economic importance of the insect centres on loss of sugar per unit weight of cane rather than on loss of cane weight per unit area.

Fig. 137. *Aulacaspis tegalensis* on a stem of sugar cane (phot. J. R. Williams)

Life cycle[1]: The life cycle is complicated and is similar to that of other armoured scale insects (Diaspididae). The adult female is sedentary and morphologically degenerate, having no legs or wings, and lives inside a white envelope (the "scale") which it makes with wax threads secreted from special glands. The scale is stuck to the host plant and the female within feeds through a comparatively long stylet or proboscis which is embedded in the plant tissues. A female is about 1.8 mm long by 0.9 mm wide, the diameter of her scale is about 2.5 mm and the length of her stylet about 2.4 mm. The male is minute and is free living: it does not feed at all and has a very short life of less than 48 hours. It has a special sharp organ to penetrate the female's scale covering.

The fertilised female lays eggs inside her scale and these hatch into mobile nymphs or "crawlers", which escape from under the scale, wander over the host plant and eventually fix themselves by inserting their mouth parts into the plant tissues and secreting a scale over themselves. Several moults follow, and development differs according to sex, the males eventually becoming free-living adults while the females remain sedentary.

Ecology: Infestations are favoured by dry environments and in some cane growing countries the insect is a pest only in the lower rainfall areas. While distribution and abundance can be correlated with dry climates, abundance in any particular area is apparently increased by dry weather if the stage of crop growth is not a limiting factor. Dry conditions are believed to favour survival and dispersion of the infective "crawler" stage.

Apart from weather and climate, age of the host plant and natural enemies are the important factors regulating abundance.

Natural enemies: The natural enemies may be divided into 3 groups: predacious Coleoptera (Coccinellidae), parasitic Hymenoptera (Encyrtidae and Aphelinidae), and a miscellany of predacious and parasitic organisms comprising mites, fungi, and other insects. Wherever the scale insect occurs they are important and at times suppress the pest population to low levels.

Control:

Sanitary methods. Clean planting material should be used because insects on the setts can survive for lengthy periods under some circumstances and later spread up on to the shoots. If clean setts are not available, a hot water dip (52 °C for 20 min) will destroy all stages of the insects on them: a less satisfactory method of treating infested setts is to dip them in malathion (3 ml 50 % e. c./litre) immediately before planting.

Infested cane should be burnt before harvest if other agronomic considerations permit. A harvested field to be ratooned should present adverse conditions for survival of the insect to minimize within-field carryover: the stubble should be short, water-shoots should not be left standing, discarded pieces of cane bearing insects should not be left lying about.

Cultural methods. The scale insect multiplies intensively only on stem surfaces that are covered by leaf sheaths. This is a consequence of the habits of the infective "crawler" stage and also of the protection that leaf sheaths afford from weather, friction of vegetation, and from the action of certain natural enemies. No infestation develops on an uninfested stem if the dry leaf sheaths are removed from it: similarly, if the dry sheaths are removed from infested stem surfaces, most of the insects on those surfaces will die or disappear. Trashing of cane (stripping off dead leaves) as it grows is therefore an advocated control measure; the objective being to keep the canes as free of clinging trash as is practicable.

Free trashing cane varieties (varieties that tend to have exposed or partly exposed stems, as opposed to those whose stems remain invested with dry leaf sheaths) are the least infested by scale insect. Such varieties are M 13/56 in Mauritius and POJ 3016 in Java. There is also some evidence that thick-stemmed varieties are more tolerant of heavy infestation than thin-stemmed varieties.

Biological control. Biological control by importation of parasitic and predacious insects has been employed with some success in Mauritius and East Africa. The object is to fill gaps in the spectrum

[1] Including Morphology

of natural enemies in a particular region and to achieve this it is first necessary to have an appreciation of the action of natural enemies in the region concerned in the general context of factors affecting the pest's populations. The insects that have been employed for biological control to date are Coccinellid beetles and Aphelinid parasites.

Chemical Control. Application of insecticides during crop growth is not feasible for control of the scale insect. Diaspidid scale insects are notoriously difficult to destroy with insecticides, while the difficulties of obtaining a good spray cover are prohibitive, particularly as the infestations on the stems are partly covered and protected by leaf sheaths. Spraying is thus liable to do more harm than good by destroying natural enemies more effectively than the pest insect. Systemic insecticides applied to the soil have not given good results. The control methods used have consequently been a combination of cultural and biological methods.

Literature

WILLIAMS, J. R. (1970): Studies on the biology, ecology and economic importance of the sugar cane scale insect, *Aulacaspis tegalensis* (Zhnt.) (Diaspididae), in Mauritius. Bull. ent. Res. **60,** 61–95.
WILLIAMS, J. R. & D. J. GREATHEAD (1973): The sugar cane scale insect *Aulacaspis tegalensis* (Zhnt.) and its biological control in Mauritius and East Africa. PANS **19** (3), 353–367.

Author: J. R. Williams

Unaspis citri (Comst.) (Plate 29 b)

Synonyms: *Chionaspis citri, Dinaspis annae, Prontaspis citri, Dinaspis veitchi*

Common names: Citrus snow scale; Schneeweiße Zitrusschildlaus; Piojo blanco, Cochinilla blanca.

Geographical distribution: Citrus snow scale is reported as having worldwide distribution in the citrus belt. However, the more temperate citrus regions such as California are reported as not having this pest. Citrus snow scale is a serious pest in Mexiko, Cuba, El Salvador, Columbia, in the Entre Ríos and Tucumán areas of Argentina and the New South Wales and Queensland areas of Australia. It is also a minor pest at times in Peru and Brazil. It has been reported to be a serious pest at times in certain parts of China (CIE Map no 149). A closely related species, *Unaspis xanonensis* (Kuwana), is a very serious pest in Japan and has been recently introduced into the citrus area along the French Riviera.

Host plants: Citrus snow scale is considered to be host specific on citrus species. It has been reported on all varieties of citrus but mandarins as a rule do not harbor nearly as many individuals as lemons and oranges. It has been reported that the 'Dancy' tangerine variety is immune to snow scale attack.

Symptoms: *U. citri* is a wood inhabiting species and feeds almost exclusively in the sieve tube portions of the phloem. The detrimental effect of Citrus snow scale on a citrus tree results from the insect feeding on the sap of the trunk, limbs, and twigs and occasionally the leaves and fruit. When a tree becomes infested and the population of scale remains uncontrolled, the following sequence of events may take place: reduced tree vigor, reduced fruit production, dead limbs and branches, partial defoliation, large cracks in the bark, and if heavy infestations persist, the whole tree may die. See also chapter on Geographical distribution.

Morphology: The female scale armor is described as oyster shell or fusiform in shape, brown to blackish brown in color with a central longitudinal ridge and gray border. The length is 1.5 to 2.25 mm. The female body beneath the armor is a bright orange in color. The male armor is described as snow white in color with parallel sides and three longitudinal ridges, one prominent center ridge and two less prominent marginal ridges. The male armor is approximately 1 mm. Adult males are a delicate flylike insect with a light-yellow body and two wings. The crawlers (first instar nymphs) are described as oblong and light-orange to reddish in color.

Similarities to other pests: Citrus snow scale is similar to other bark inhabiting scale insects but differs in the female characteristics of having a longitudinal ridge running the length of the armor and the orange color of the female body beneath the armor. Several species of scale insects have males very similar to the Citrus snow scale male.

Life cycle: *U. citri* has four widely overlapping generations or broods per year in Florida citrus groves. The following observations on the life cycle of Citrus snow scale under laboratory conditions were made at 80 ± 4 °F and at 70 ± 10 % relative humidity; the eggs are laid singly and are hatched in 30 minutes to 3 hours. Given egg is always hatched before the following one was deposited. The female snow scales take 62.5 days to complete development to adults. The male takes 28 to 31 days to complete its development to adult. Males have a longevity of 31.5 to 35.4 days. Adult females live from 112.3 days to 190.1 days. Length of life cycle crawler to crawler is 60.2 days minimum and 76.4 days maximum.

Ecology: Citrus snow scale generally infests the woody portions of citrus trees. The portions of the trees that are generally attacked the severest are the trunk and the main scaffolding limbs. The leaves and fruit are only infested after the main branches have developed heavy infestations.

Natural enemies: Results of a 2-year (1970–72) natural enemy survey conducted in Florida indicate that Citrus snow scale had few natural enemies. The most frequently occurring species of natural enemies found in Florida were *Aspidiotiphagus citrinus* and *A. lounsburyi* and *Aphytis lingnanensis* was recorded in very small numbers at three or four times during the year but at no time were more than 7 % of the females parasitized.

Control:
Biological control. Recently a hymenopterous parasite of the *Aphytis lingnanensis* group was introduced from Hong Kong. This parasite shows great promise of controlling Citrus snow scale in Florida.
Chemical control. Insecticides used in Florida for the control of *U. citri* are: Parathion, azinphos (Guthion), malathion, diazinon, ethion, carbophenothion (Trithion), or ethion combined with oil. Petroleum oil sprays against Citrus snow scale are very ineffective.

Literature

BROOKS, R. F. (1964): Control of citrus snow scale, *Unaspis citri* (Comst.) Florida Proc. Fla. State Hort. Soc. **77**, 66–70.
BROOKS, R. F. (1973): Citrus snow scale control in Florida. Proc. of 1st Intl. Citrus Cong. Murcia, Spain (In press).
DICKENS, T. H. (1968): Life history of citrus snow scale *Unaspis citri* (Comst.). Thesis-University of Florida.

Author: R. F. Brooks

Insulaspis gloverii (Pack.) (Plate 29 c)

Synonyms: *Coccus gloverii, Aspidiotus gloverii, Mytilaspis gloverii, Mytiella sexspina, Lepidosaphes gloverii*

Common names: Glover scale; Schmale Kommaschildlaus; Serpette; Escama larga.

Geographical distribution: North America – the southern States and Mexico; Central and South America and the Antilles Islands; Europe–along the Mediterranean Coast; France (Corsica), Italy and Spain; Africa–throughout the continent; Asia–China, Sri Lanka, Mauritius, Iran, Pacific Islands of Philippines, Japan, and Hawaii. CIE Map no 146.

Host plants: Citrus; different varieties of cherry and ivy; several varieties of palms, mangos, and magnolia.

Symptoms: On the bark, leaves, and fruits of the host. On citrus, it is found more commonly on the twigs and smaller branches of the trees, rather than the leaves and fruit. It can be a serious pest of citrus in Florida. It can cause green spots on the fruit which lowers the grade for fresh fruit. It also kills small twigs and in some cases, major limbs of trees.

Economic importance: This insect can cause weakness of the host, bad appearance of the tree, and a significant reduction in yields if left uncontrolled.

Morphology: The female is long (2.5–3.25 mm) and very slender, with nearly parallel sides; sometimes the body is straight or curved. The color varies from light to dark brown, the margins and terminals of the body lighter.

Similarities to other pests: Glover scale is often associated with purple scale, *Lepidosaphes beckii.* However, there are morphological and behavioral characteristics that are different among them. Morphologically, Glover scale adults have a ventral covering extending almost to the edge of the scale and divided lengthwise at the middle while on the other hand, purple scale has a broadly oyster shell-shaped armor with a ventral covering totally covering the insect and without a median division. Glover scale females deposit their eggs in two rows beneath the scale armor while purple scale females deposit them irregularly beneath their armor. Purple scale also shows a preference for the lower north side of citrus trees while this preference is seldom exhibited by Glover scale.

Life cycle: Eggs are oval-shaped, whitish in color, with a small granulated, roughened surface. The time required for the eggs to hatch varies according to the environmental temperature i. e. from 2 weeks in the summer to 2 months in the winter. Crawlers are ovally flat in shape, whitish in color with a brown posterior tip, 6-segmented annulated antennae and are very mobile before permanently settling. Glover scale goes through 3 instars, 2 molts, before becoming an adult. Females reach maturity after the second molt and must be fertilized before any eggs are laid. Males can be distinguished from the female after the first molt because it is smaller and more slender than the female and after the last molt it emerges from the scale as a winged adult. The life cycle of Glover scale from egg to egg varies widely from 4 to 11 months.

Ecology: Restricted to the condition of the host and generally prefers humid environmental conditions.

Natural enemies: In Florida, Glover scale has had many hymenopterous parasites and several species of Coccinellid predators reported attacking it. However, none of these appear to be the regulatory factor in suppressing populations of Glover scale.

Control:
Biological control. As indicated above, Glover scale is attacked by several species of hymenopterous parasites, also several species of Coccinellid beetles will feed upon the scale crawlers.
Chemical control. *I. gloverii* is controlled by applications of petroleum oil, parathion, azinphos (Guthion), malathion, dimethoate, parathion-oil, malathion-oil, or ethion-oil.

Literature

BROOKS, R. F. & W. L. THOMPSON (1963): Investigations of new scalicides for Florida. Fla. Entomol. **46**, 279–284.
BROOKS, R. F., W. L. THOMPSON & P. J. JUTRAS (1963): Evaluating spray equipment for Florida citrus. Proc. Fla. State Hort. Soc. **76**, 18–21.
DEKLE, G. W. (1965): Arthropods of Florida Vol. III: Florida armored scale insects. Fla. Dept. of Agr., Div. of Plant Ind.

Author: R. F. Brooks

Lepidosaphes beckii (Newm.) (Plate 29 d)

Synonyms: *Lepidosaphes citricola, Lepidosaphes pinnaeformis, Mytilococcus beckii, Cornuaspis beckii*

Common names: Purple scale, Citrus mussel scale; Zitrus-Kommalaus; La cochenille virgule des orangers; Cochinilla coma de los cítricos, Serpeta de los cítricos, Serpeta gruesa.

Geographical distribution: Apparently of Oriental origin, this species has spread widely and now occurs on citrus practically throughout the world. It is common in the Far East (Japan, China, Southeast Asia) and has been considered a serious pest in parts of Australia, South America, Central America, Mexico, the United States, various Mediterranean countries and South Africa. It also occurs in Eastern and Western Africa. CIE Map no 49.

Host plants: *Citrus* is the principal host of *L. beckii.* It occurs also on *Buxus, Eleagnus* and *Ilex,* but other host records are doubtful, due to possible misidentification.

Symptoms: *L. beckii* may infest the leaves, fruit and bark of citrus. The areas surrounding the scale insects on the leaf turn yellow, and in severe infestations the entire leaf may be discolored and drop prematurely. Similar areas on the fruit remain green long after the rest of the fruit attains its normal color. Twigs and branches may become encrusted with live and dead scale insects, and eventually dry up.

Economic importance: *L. beckii* is potentially one of the most serious pests of citrus, capable of culling a large proportion of the crop and, if infestations are left unchecked, even of killing trees. Severe defoliation and widespread death of branches are quite common in heavy infestations.

Morphology: The adult female scale is 2–3 mm long, purplish or dark brown, elongated, usually curved in the shape of a comma, widening posteriorly, with the exuviae at the anterior end. The elongated, light yellowish body of the adult female itself is also enclosed by a thin white ventral scale.
The scale of the male is shorter and more slender, similar to the female in color.

Similarities to other pests: Another pest of citrus, *Insulaspis gloverii* (see p. 365), is rather similar to the purple scale but differs in being more elongated, slender, with the sides of the female scale nearly parallel. Microscopic examination of the female body reveals *I. gloverii* to be heavily sclerotized on the dorsum of the thoracic region and first abdominal segment, and to possess sclerotized spurs on the lateral lobes of the abdomen. Both characters are lacking in *L. beckii.*

Life cycle: The female lays about 40–80 eggs underneath the dorsal scale, fecundity being much higher on fruit than on leaves. The crawlers are capable of migrating for a considerable distance, but usually settle near their mother; they prefer to settle under the calyx or on the upper half of the fruit. The female larva molts twice, the two exuviae being incorporated in the dorsal scale. In the male, only the first exuvia is incorporated; the male undergoes the prepupal and pupal stages underneath the unchanged scale of the second instar, then emerges as a winged adult.
Development of the female takes 50–60 days in summer, up to 110 days in winter. In California and Israel, 3–4 generations develop annually.

Ecology: The purple scale thrives under both humid and semi-arid conditions, but reaches its greatest development in the more humid areas. It prefers thickly-foliaged trees, and infestations are usually heaviest at the center of the tree and on the north or northeast quadrants. The threshold of development is 8 °C, and 1104 days-degrees are required for the production of one generation.

Natural enemies: *Myiophagus* sp., a chytrid fungal disease, is apparently quite important in the humid areas of Florida. Predatory coccinellids (e. g. *Chilocorus* spp.) and mites (e. g. *Hemisarcoptes*) frequently attack the purple scale but are usually dependent on high prey densities and are not effective. Endoparasites *(Physcus, Aspidiotiphagus* spp.) are usually rare.
Aphytis lepidosaphes (Hymenoptera: Aphelinidae), a specific gregarious ectoparasite of Oriental origin, is by far the most efficient natural enemy of *L. beckii*.

Control:
Biological control: *Aphytis lepidosaphes* was introduced from China into California in 1948, and soon became a major factor in the control of purple scale in that state. That effective parasite has since been introduced into 8 other states or countries, and has established itself by ecesis or unintentional introduction in 13 additional areas. It appears to be responsible for substantial to complete biological control in nearly every one of those countries.
Chemical control: When chemical control is required, this can be achieved with light-medium or medium grade petroleum oil ("summer oil"), applied as a high-volume, thorough-coverage spray of a 1,75–2 % emulsion around the middle or later part of summer (July–September). Oil spray is most effective against young instars of purple scale, and should be carefully timed accordingly. Late application of petroleum oil may retard the formation of ripe coloring in early citrus varieties.
Severe outbreaks may be controlled by organophosphorus insecticides [e. g. malathion, parathion, methidathion (Supracide), ethion], applied in combination with a reduced concentration of petroleum oil. However, such combinations are highly detrimental to the natural equilibrium, possess high mammalian toxicity and may be phytotoxic to certain citrus varieties at certain periods, hence should be avoided except in extreme emergencies.
Integrated control: The availability of an effective natural enemy has enabled the development in California of integrated control by strip treatment. This involves spraying alternate pairs of rows across a grove with petroleum oil in a given year, leaving the other pairs untreated, and then the next year spraying the rows left untreated in the previous year.

Literature

AVIDOV, Z. & I. HARPAZ (1969): Plant pests of Israel. Israel Universities Press, Jerusalem, 549 p.
DEBACH, P. & J. LANDI (1961): The introduced purple scale parasite, *Aphytis lepidosaphes* Compere, and a method of integrating chemical with biological control. Hilgardia **31**, 459–497.
QUAYLE, H. J. (1938): Insects of citrus and other subtropical fruits. Comstock Publishing Co., Ithaca, 583 pp.

Author: David Rosen

Other injurious Coccoidea (Plate 28 a and figs. 138–139):

Drosicha mangiferae (Green), Mango mealy bug, Giant mealy bug (Riesenschmierlaus) attacks many host plants, especially mango and other fruit trees in India, Pakistan, Bangladesh and South China. Control is by spraying with monocrotophos or diazinon (0.04 %).

Icerya purchasi Mask. (= *Pericerya purchasi)*, (Australian) Cottony cushion scale (Australische Wollschildlaus) (Plate 28 a). Extremely polyphagous, widely distributed citrus pest in tropical and subtropical regions, but also found in climatically suitable areas in South and West Europe (CIE Map no 51). Biological control with the Australian ladybird *Rodolia cardinalis,* chemical control with malathion or parathion (+ white oil).

Dysmicoccus boninsis (Kuw.), Grey sugar cane mealybug (Graue Zuckerrohrschmierlaus). Resembles *Saccharicoccus sacchari* (see p. 348) in bionomics and geographical distribution (CIE Map no 116). Control: Planting of cuttings free from attack and chemical ant control.

Dysmicoccus brevipes (Ckll.) (= *Pseudococcus brevipes*), the Pineapple mealybug (Ananasschmierlaus), is a polyphagous species which occurs in tropical and subtropical regions in all parts of the world (CIE Map no 50). Other cultivated plants affected are sugar cane, cocoa, groundnut, coffee, oil palm, banana and soybean. On pineapple, the subterranean parts are mainly affected, but the basal part of the leaves and fruit is also colonised. Toxins are introduced into the plant with the saliva on feeding, and their effect is held to be responsible for "Pineapple wilt disease". The symptoms of this disease are reddish discolouration of leaves, stunted growth and loss in yield. In a more advanced stage of the disease, the leaves roll (upwards). Since two different types of symptoms are observed, the assumption is that *D. brevipes* can produce two kinds of toxin (geographical or biological races of the mealy bug?). In Trinidad, *D. brevipes* transmits a cocoa virus isolate. The colonies of the pest are regularly attended by ants, which may also play a part in spreading the pest in pineapple plantations. The control of ants is therefore advisable. Another recommendation is to dip pineapple cuttings in a solution containing aldrin, before planting out.

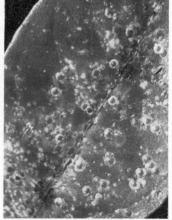

Fig. 138. *Ferrisia virgata* on a guava leaf (phot. H. Schmutterer)

Fig. 139. *Selanaspidus articulatus* on a citrus leaf (phot. H. Schmutterer)

Ferrisia virgata (Ckll.) (= *Ferrisiana virgata*) (Lamtorolaus) (Fig. 138). In tropical and subtropical regions of Africa, Asia and America (CIE Map no 219). It thrives on cocoa, coffee, guava, jute, cotton, rubber, tomato, citrus, avocado, *Hibiscus* spp., oleander, *Leucaena glauca*, *Erythrina* spp. etc. In West Africa and Trinidad, *F. virgata* can transmit various cocoa virus isolates (see p. 347). Methyl parathion and methyl azinphos are used for control.

Planococcus spp.. *P. kenyae* (Le Pell.) (Afrikanische Kaffeeschmierlaus) was previously a serious pest of Arabica coffee in Kenya, but its economic importance decreased as a result of effective biological control with parasitic Hymenoptera. *P. lilacinus* (Asiatische Kaffeeschmierlaus) attacks coffee, cocoa, annona, guava and other plants in South and South East Asia (CIE Map no 101). In Sri Lanka it transmits a cocoa virus isolate.

Ceroplastes spp., **Gascardia** spp. and **Chloropulvinaria** spp.. Several species of these genera are pests in tropical and subtropical regions on mango, guava, coffee, citrus, fig and other fruit trees.

Coccus hesperidum L. (= *Lecanium hesperidum*), Soft scale (Weiche Schildlaus). Widely distributed in hot countries, but also found in South and West Europe and fairly common in glasshouses and on house plants in colder climates (CIE Map no 92). Host plants include citrus, papaya and cotton. Chemical control with malathion, diazinon, azinphos-ethyl and dimethoate.

Saissetia coffeae (Wlk.), Hemispherical scale (Halbkugelige Napfschildlaus). Worldwide distribution in the tropics (CIE Map no 318). Host plants are coffee, avocado, tea, rubber, citrus, fig, guava, annona, *Hibiscus* spp. and many others.

Saissetia oleae (Oliv.), (Mediterranean) black scale (Schwarze Ölbaumschildlaus). Widely distributed in warm climatic regions including the mediterranean basin (CIE Map no 24); in temperate climates in greenhouses. Attacks olive, citrus and many ornamental plants such as oleander. Control with natural enemies (e. g. *Metaphycus* spp.; Encyrtidae) and application of light-medium or medium grade oil, carbaryl, omethoate and methidathion + oil against nymphs and young females.

Aspidiotus nerii Bché. (= *A. hederae*), Oleander scale (Efeublattlaus). Mainly in the mediterranean and in subtropical regions (CIE Map no 268) on citrus, olive, apple, palm trees, mango and many ornamentals.

Chrysomphalus dictyospermi (Morg.), Dictyospermum scale (Rote Tellerschildlaus). Occurs in the Western mediterranean basin, in the American tropics and in Iran (CIE Map no 3) on citrus, avocado, mango, tea, palm trees and other host plants. Control: Application of parathion or parathion + oil.

Selenaspidus articulatus (Morg.), Rufous scale, West Indian red scale (Westindische Citrusschildlaus) (Fig. 139). Widely distributed in hot countries of the Old and New World. The host plant spectrum includes citrus, coffee, avocado, banana, fig, palm trees and ornamentals. Control with oil sprays.

Parlatoria spp.. *P. zizyphus* (Luc.), *P. oleae* (Colv.), *P. pergandii* Comst. and *P. crypta* Mc Kenz. occur as pests in various parts of the world, e. g. *P. zizyphus* and *P. pergandii* on citrus, *P. oleae* on olive and *P. crypta* on mango.

H. Sch.

Ants, Bees, Wasps, Ichneumon flies etc.; Ameisen, Bienen, Wespen, Schlupfwespen etc.; Fourmis, Abeilles, Guêpes, Ichneumons etc.; Hormigas, Abejas, Avispas, Ichneumónidos etc.

Order: Hymenoptera

General features: As well as pests, most of which are ants (Formicidae), the Hymenoptera include many parasites, and a large number of such species have already been utilised effectively in biological or integrated control projects. They are either endo- or ectoparasites. Ants are social insects which can bite off plant portions with their biting-chewing mouth parts, e. g. the subtropical *Atta* and *Acromyrmex* spp. (leaf cutting ants). These use the leaf material for culturing a fungus which serves as their food. Direct plant pests are otherwise rare among the Formicidae. Many ants do indirect damage by tending honey dew producing Homoptera, which are spread and protected against enemies. In some cases, predatory ants like *Oecophylla* spp. can be very useful, by keeping pests from trees on which leaf nests of the ants are situated. On the other hand, these aggressive ants can be a nuisance while picking or cultivation procedures are in progress.

The honey bee is an important useful insect in the tropics as well as elsewhere, not only as a producer of honey and wax, but also as a pollinator of fruit trees. It should be taken into consideration, when chemical pest control measures are employed.

Metamorphosis is complete (holometabolic) in the Hymenoptera.

H. Sch.

Familiy: **Formicidae** (Fig. 140 and plate 30 a–d)

Common names: Ants; Ameisen; Fourmis; Hormigas.

Important species and their common names[1]: *Acropyga* spp.; *Anoplolepis longipes* (Jerd.) – Gramang ant (Java); *Azteca chartifex* Forel – Balata ant (Trinidad); *A. chartifex v. spiriti* Forel – Cacarema ant (Brazil); *A. paraensis* Forel *v. bondari* Borg. – Enxerto ant (Brazil); *Crematogaster* spp. – Acrobat ant (W. Indies); *Dolichoderus bituberculatus* Mayr – Black cacao ant, Black ant or ireng (Java); *Macromischoides aculeatus* (Mayr) (Plate 30 b); *M. africanus* Mayr – Venomous ant (Zaire); *Messor* spp. – Harvester ants (Africa, Near East) (Plate 30 c, d) *Myrmelachista ambigua* Forel *v. ramulorum* Wheeler; *Oecophylla longinoda* (Latr.) – Tailor ant, Red fire ant (Plate 30 a); *O. smaragdina* (F.) – Tailor ant, kurukum (Papua New Guinea) and kerengga (Malaysia); *Pheidole megacephala* F.; *Solenopsis geminata* F. – Fire ant; *Technomyrmex albipes* (Fr. Smith) – Crazy ant (E. Achipelago); *Wasmannia auropunctata* (Roger).

Geographical distribution: *Acropyga* spp.: New World Tropics; **Anoplolepis longipes:* E. Archipelago, New Guinea, Solomon Islands, Zanzibar and Mexico; *Azteca chartifex:* Trinidad and Brazil; *A. chartifex spiriti:* Brazil; *A. paraensis bondari:* Brazil; *Crematogaster* spp.: New and Old World Tropics; *Dolichoderus bituberculatus:* Eastern Archipelago; *Macromischoides aculeatus:* W. Central and E. Africa; *M. africanus:* Central Africa; *Messor* spp.: Africa, Mediterranean

---

[1] The Leaf-cutting ants are considered in a separate chapter (see p. 375)

*Because of their especially close association with man a few ants have spread widely outside their natural range. Such are often referred to as homophylous or 'tramp' species.

24*

countries, Near East; *Myrmelachista ambigua ramulorum:* Puerto Rico; *Oecophylla longinoda:* Africa; **O. smaragdina:* India to E. Archipelago and N. Australia; **Pheidole megacephala:* New and Old World Tropics; **Solenopsis geminata:* New and Old World Tropics; **Technomyrmex albipes:* Old World Tropics; **Wasmannia auropunctata:* New World Tropics and Cameroun.

Host plants: Most ants are not specific to particular host plants but rather to ecologically suitable habitats. The following list is merely one of economic plants with which particular ants have significant associations, beneficial or otherwise.

Acropyga spp.: coffee, cocoa; *Anoplolepis longipes:* cocoa, coconut, coffee; *Azteca* spp.: cocoa, coffee, coconut; *Crematogaster* spp.: cocoa, coffee, citrus, avocado pear; *Dolichoderus bituberculatus:* cocoa, coffee; *Macromischoides aculeatus:* cocoa, coffee; *M. africanus:* coffee; *Messor* spp.: millets, groundnut, cotton, sesame, cowpea etc.; *Myrmelachista ambigua ramulorum:* coffee; *Oecophylla longinoda:* coconut, cocoa, coffee, mango, citrus, guava, clove;
O. smaragdina: coconut, cocoa, coffee, mango, oil palm; *Pheidole megacephala:* coffee, cocoa, pineapple, coconut; *Solenopsis geminata:* coffee, cocoa; *Technomyrmex albipes:* coffee, cocoa; *Wasmannia auropunctata:* coffee, cocoa.

Symptoms:
1. **Direct damage.** To obtain mucilage for use in nest building the Enxerto ant, *Azteca paraensis bondari,* bites the young apical shoots of cocoa. This leads to terminal defoliation, loss of apical dominance and the growth of many less vigorous shoots giving a broom-like appearance. Below the broom the leaves arise in a cluster forming a very characteristic picture which enables detection of attack from a distance. In the presence of *Azteca* ants in Trinidad cocoa trees are said never to do so well and to have pods which are often dwarfed and generally disfigured with scars and brown patches.
Species of *Crematogaster* occasionally damage cocoa and coffee. For instance in W. Africa *C. depressa* may feed on cocoa flowers and the exocarp of pods causing wilting of cherelles (young pods) whilst *C. africana* may carry off large numbers of flowers. In Java *C. treubi* ssp. *vastatrix* bores in branches of Robusta coffee.
In Brazil a *Camponotus* species strips bark from the roots of coffee and was once involved in the death of over 50,000 bushes. *Myrmelachista ambigua ramulorum* is a primary pest of coffee in Puerto Rico boring in live twigs and inducing formation of knotty galls, injuries which lead to greatly reduced yields in the most heavily infested fields. On coffee, cocoa and citrus the habit of *Oecophylla* of spinning leaves together is more of a nuisance than it is injurious (Fig. 140). The wilting and death of avocado pear trees in W. Africa may be a joint consequence of this habit and that of the encouragement of large numbers of coccoids.

Fig. 140.   Nest of *Oecophylla longinoda* on a mango tree (phot. H. Schmutterer)

In Africa *Messor barbarus* collets the seeds of various crops after sowing and destroys the plants around the entrance of its nests (Plate 30 d). This leads to bare patches in the fields measuring several square metres (Plate 30 c).

2. **Indirect damage.** Direct injury to clove trees in Zanzibar is caused by the scale *Saissetia zanzibarensis* which exists in a mutually interdependent association with the ant *Oecophylla longinoda*. The rates of development and survival of the Green Scale, *Coccus viridis* on coffee, citrus, tea, mango, etc., are considerably increased by the presence of *Anoplolepis longipes* and probably also to some extent by other ants. As *C. viridis* ranks as a major pest of coffee and because infestations tend to vanish in the absence of ants the ant-coccid association is extremely injurious. The dominant mealybug vector of cocoa swollen shoot viruses, *Planococcoides njalensis* tends to vanish from cocoa in the absence of ants (especially *Crematogaster* spp.) indicating a similarly significant relationship. This mealybug and the symptoms of the virus diseases it spreads are discussed on pages 346 and 8–9. *Planococcus lilacinus,* which acts as a vector of the relatively mild cocoa virus diseases in Sri Lanka, also lives in obligatory association with ants, at least in Java where it is attended by *Dolichoderus bituberculatus*. The increase in size of populations and spread of the mealybug *Dysmicoccus brevipes,* associated strongly in wilt disease of pineapple, is rapid in the fields in Hawaii where the ant *Pheidole megacephala* is present. A swiftly lethal phloem necrosis disease of coffee in Surinam is probably spread by mealybugs which feed on the roots (hypogeic mealybugs) in very close trophobiosis with *Acropyga* ants. As noted with *Oecophylla* some ants causing direct damage are also pests because they support the development of sap-sucking insects. A further example of this is *Azteca paraensis bondari* which tends *Horiola* and other membracids as well as mealybugs, aphids and white fly.

Economic importance:

1. **Direct and indirect crop losses.** The ravages of *A. paraensis bondari* are one of the major entomological problems of the Brazilian cocoa industry. In the mid-1950's it was estimated that plantations in Bahia harboured 20 to 25 million nests which annually caused losses of 100 million cruzeiros. The indirect effects of ants fostering *C. viridis* on coffee have not been established but must be enormous. Following the historic epiphytotic of coffee leaf disease (caused by *Hemileia vastatrix*) the rapid spread of this coccid in Sri Lanka sounded the death knell of the island's coffee industry. Very severe damage has also been caused in India, Java and Réunion. The catastrophic consequences of spread of cocoa virus diseases by *P. njalensis* are discussed on page 346. Hypogeic mealybugs on coffee roots generally decrease yields though not always until some years have elapsed. Their association with phloem necrosis disease in Surinam is very serious.

In Africa large areas for crop production are lost year after year by the activity of Harvester ants.

2. **Interference in plantation operations.** Heavy infestations of aggressive species of ants may be an embarrassment in the conduct of pruning and harvesting, e. g. *Macromischoides* spp., *Dolichoderus bidens* (in Surinam), *Oecophylla* spp., *Solenopsis geminata, Wasmannia auropunctata* and *Paraponera clavata* (Central America), but whilst control may occasionally be necessary such problems have probably been generally exaggerated. However, by avoiding areas infested with *M. africanus* pickers of coffee may initiate dangerous reservoirs of coffee berry beetle, *Hypothenemus hampei.*

3. **Beneficial aspects of ants.** Some ant species are directly beneficial as agents of control of pest insects. For instance *O. longinoda* is a successful predator of *Theraptus* bugs (Coreidae) on coconut in Zanzibar but where it is replaced by *A. longipes* this method of control breaks down. Another coreid pest of coconut in the Solomon Islands, *Amblypelta coccophaga* is controlled by *O. smaragdina* but control breaks down when this ant is replaced by *P. megacephala*. In the same way control of capsid bugs *(Helopeltis)* on cocoa in Java by the ant *D. bituberculatus* can be broken by invasion by *A. longipes.* On the other hand *A. longipes* is very promising as a predator of the intractible weevil pests, *Pantorhytes* spp., of cocoa in Papua New Guinea. Another ant *W. auropunctata* is being used successfully to control a capsid bug, *Sahlbergella singularis,* on cocoa in Cameroun. There is evidence that in Brazil *A. chartifex spiriti* is associated with a higher rate of

pollination of cocoa, possibly by emiting a substance attractive to pollinating midges (Ceratopogonidae). The ants themselves do not pollinate.

Morphology: Like certain other groups of taxonomically difficult insects identification of ants is, in general, a specialist task. However, certain of the species mentioned in this text can be readily identified by their nesting habits. *Oecophylla* species make nests on the tree of living leaves spun together with 'silk' secreted by the ants' larvae. Nests of *A. paraensis bondari* are arboreal and roughly spherical, up to 45 cms diameter, and often with a growth of epiphytic plants which originate from seed collected by the ants: the orchids *Coryanthes maculata* and *Epidendrum immatophyllum* are characteristically associated with nests of this ant and *Codonanthe formicarium* (Geresnaceae) is not known to occur elsewhere. *Macromischoides* nests are small, up to 7 cms diameter, and on the underside of living leaves or between leaves. Many *Crematogaster* species construct very large nests of carton (dark brown chewed plant fibres) on the outside of forest and planted shade trees, but some which nest cryptically in decaying wood are not so easily distinguished. Many ants nest in soil, e. g., *P. megacephala, S. geminata, A. longipes* and *W. auropunctata.*

Life cycle: The sexually functional males and females are winged and usually mate outside the parent nest in the course of the nuptual flight. In *D. bituberculatus* there is no swarming and females are fertilised by males of the same colony. Fertilised females initiate new nests and most of the eggs laid give rise to the wingless, generally infertile, worker class of adult females which do most of the food collection, nest construction and brood tending. The fertilised female, or queen, sheds her wings at about the time of nest formation. She may live from one to several years during which she lays large numbers of eggs. There are several larval stages, the last being followed by an exarate pupal stage in a cocoon. Workers of *A. longipes* develop from egg to adult in 50–65 days and live about 6 months. Some nests may contain more than one reproductively active queen.

Ecology: Trophobiotic associations play a part in the economy of nearly all ants mentioned here. The association may embrace any honeydew-producing insect, viz., coccoids, aphids, white fly and membracids. Ants may construct small tents composed of chewed vegetable material or soil particles over such insects or they may excavate cavities in the soil in which coccoids or aphids feed on roots. In addition to collecting secretions of honeydew (a source of sugars and some amino acids) some ants, e. g. *Oecophylla,* are known to be predacious on the coccoids they tend, a habit which may be especially pronounced at times of ant colony recession. Reduced rates of parasitism, predation by coccinellid beetles, etc., increased rates of growth and survival of ant tended Homoptera have all been demonstrated. Some ants actually disperse coccoids: young *Acropyga* females each leave the parent nest for the nuptial flight carrying in their jaws an immature female hypogeic mealybug. *A. longipes* workers disperse *C. viridis* scales. However this is not a habit universally well developed and, for instance, in W. Africa crematogasterine ants seem little disposed to disperse cocoa mealybugs. Trophobiotic associations are not exclusive of other types of ant feeding: *Oecophylla* spp., *A. longipes, W. auropunctata* and many other ants are very general feeders despite close relationships with a variety of Homoptera. However, on clove *O. longinoda* seems unable to survive in the absence of *Saissetia zanzibarensis.*

The nesting site of ants is often outside their sphere of general foraging and may well not be on the economic plants with which man is concerned. Many *Crematogaster* and *Azteca* species favour plantation shade trees rather than, for instance, coffee or cocoa. *A. longipes* and *W. auropunctata* nest in the soil but forage much on the trees. For successful establishment species of *Oecophylla* require a continuous canopy of evergreen trees. *A. longipes* cannot establish where there is a growing ground cover.

The ant fauna of the tropics is complex. The pattern of spatial distribution of species in particular habitats is known as the "ant mosaic" and is determined by habitat considerations compounded by mutual incompatibilities. For example *O. longinoda* is incompatible with *A. longipes* on coconut in Zanzibar, *M. aculeatus* with *Camponotus* on cocoa in Ghana and *D. bituberculatus* with *A. longipes* on cocoa in Java. Because of the number of species present such interactions may be very complex; for instance 250 species are present in Ghanian cocoa farms and 128 species have been found in an area of only 250 m².

The pattern of seasonal fluctuations in numbers of ants tends to be less extreme than that of none social insects because of the continuous presence of the reproductive cast and a general continuity in food supply to some degree provided by tended Homoptera. Ant numbers are not, however; immune from the influence of seasonal changes in their environment.

Natural enemies: The significance of natural enemies in the economy of tropical ants is virtually unknown.

Control and encouragement: It may be necessary to control some ant species but to encourage others. Both aspects are dealt with in this section.

1. **Control.** Depression of ant populations is not easy either culturally or chemically. Control of *Coccus viridis* on coffee in India has been achieved with joint applications of 0.01–0.02 percent parathion against the scale and dusts of either BHC or aldrin against ants. In Brazil *A. paraensis bondari* is controlled by injecting about 15 g of a 1.0 percent BHC dust into each nest using a hand pump fitted with a sharp tipped delivery tube. In the Solomon Islands competition of *P. megacephala* with *O. smaragdina* causes breakdown in ant control of *Amblypelta coccophaga* on coconuts. *P. megacephala* can be suppressed by 15 percent dieldrin used at 0.002 lit/lit of water in three monthly treatments, a dose which is tolerated by *O. smaragdina*. Supression of ground vegetation with a herbicide prevents re-establishment of *P. megacephala*. A disastrous attempt at mealybug control by dieldrin control of ants is mentioned in the section of *Planococcoides njalensis* (p. 348). Where the objective of ant control is control of a homopterous vector of plant disease it is important to know to what population density the vector must be reduced to give an economically acceptable decrease in spread of disease.

2. **Encouragement.** The encouragement of ant species as agents of pest control has usually been achieved by dissemination of ant nests. These may be obtained either by collection or by providing artificial nests and ensuring they become occupied by the ants. In the former method it is important to ensure the 'nests' are occupied by a queen ant for this is not always so e. g. *Oecophylla* spp. and *M. aculeatus*.

Transfer of *D. bituberculatus* and *W. auropunctata* for control of capsid pests of cocoa has been successfully achieved by contriving nests, respectively, sections of bamboo stuffed with dry leaves and bundles of raffia leaves which are first left for a while in ant infested places to ensure colonisation.

Literature

ENTWISTLE, P. F. (1972): Pests of Cocoa. Longman, London, 799 pp.
LE PELLEY, R. H. (1968): Pests of Coffee. Longman, London, 590 pp.
ROOM, M. P. (1971): The relative distributions of ant species in Ghana's cocoa farms. J. Anim. Ecol. **40**, 735–751.
SILVA, P. & G. A. C. BASTOS (1965): Polyvilhadeira-injetora PG para combater formiga-de-enxerto. Cacau Atual, **2**, 20–23.
WAY, M. J. (1954): Studies on the association of the ant *Oecophylla longinoda* with the scale insect *Saissetia zanzibarensis* Williams. Bull. ent. Res., **45**, 113–134.

Author: P. F. Entwistle

Acromyrmex and **Atta** spp. (Figs. 141–144)

Important species: *Acromyrmex octospinosus* (Reich), *A. landolti* (For.), *Atta capiguara* Gonç., *A. cephalotes* (L.), *A. laevigata* Smith, *A. sexdens sexdens* (L.).

Common names: Leaf-cutting ants, Fungus-growing ants, Parasol ants; Blattschneiderameisen; Fourmis fongueuses, Fourmis champignonistes. Many species of this group of ants are called by different names in different countries in South and Central America, e. g. Argentina, Paraguay – hormiga isau *(A. vollenweideri);* Brazil – sauva *(A. sexdens);* Belize, Nicaragua – wee wee *(A. cephalotes);* Colombia, Panama – hormiga arriera *(Atta* spp.); El Salvador, Guatemala – zompopos *(A. cephalotes);* Peru – coqui *(A. cephalotes, A. sexdens);* Trinidad – bachac *(A. cephalotes);* Venezuela – bachaco *(A. cephalotes, A. sexdens).*

Geographical distribution: These ants occur only in the New World ranging from North America (USA) (approx. 40 °N), through Central and S. America to Argentina (approx. 40 °S) (including some Caribbean islands but excluding Chile). There are about 200 species.

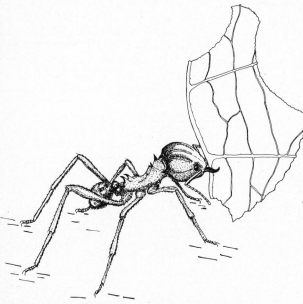

Fig. 141. Leaf-cutting ant carrying a leaf fragment (drawing T. Lewis)

Fig. 142. Leaf-cutting ants cutting fragments from citrus leaves (phot. T. Lewis)

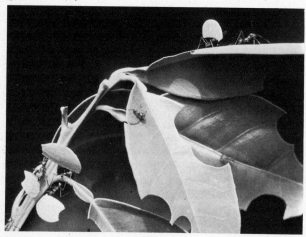

Host plants: The economically important species can be divided into two main groups. One group (e. g. *A. octospinosus, A. cephalotes, A. s. sexdens*) attacks dicotyledonous crops including citrus, coffee, cocoa, cassava, *Eucalyptus,* many forest trees and garden flowers. The other group (e. g. *A. landolti, A. capiguara*) are grass-cutters and are mainly a pest of range land. A few species (e. g. *A. laevigata*), cut both dicotyledonous and monocotyledonous plants.

Different species occur in different regions and their economic importance in each depends on the relative value of the local crops.

Symptoms: Leaves and often flowers are cut from host plants. In instances of minor attack damage is recognisable by U-shaped fragments cut from the edges of leaves (Figs. 141 and 142) but severely attacked dicotyledonous plants may be completely defoliated and grass blades cut near to ground level.

Economic importance: This group of ants is one of the most serious agricultural and forest pests in the New World and the losses caused may be comparable to those caused by locusts in the Old World. Damage valued at millions of dollars per annum occurs in Central and S. American

Fig. 143. Part of nest of *Atta vollenweideri* showing entrance holes and ventilation turrets (phot. T. Lewis)

countries due to destruction of food, cash crops and forest trees, and to reduced stock-carrying capacity of pastures.

Morphology: The fungus growing ants possess three distinct castes: workers, females and males. The workers are polymorphic and show a gradual and continuous change from the smallest to the largest (the largest workers of *Atta* have huge heads and are often called "soldiers"). Thus many species are only morphologically distinguishable by a specialist, but often the characteristics of the mound covering the nest are diagnostic. For example, mature colonies of *A. vollenweideri* produce a large (up to 10 m diameter) mound covered with entrance holes and ventilation turrets (Fig. 143), *A. capiguara* produces a ring of mounds, circling a relatively undisturbed central area, and *A. landolti* builds small nests surmounted by turrets of interwoven grass stalks. *A.s. sexdens* emits a powerful and diagnostic smell of citronella (lemon) when the head capsule is crushed.

Similarities to other pests: Whilst superficially similar in appearance to other ants, only Attini cut and carry leaves along well-worn trials, so they are unlikely to be confused with other pests.

Life-cycle: Leaf-cutting ants use the fragments of vegetation they cut as a nutritious medium for the growth of specific fungi on which immature stages and adults feed. The life-cycle comprises the usual stages: – egg, larvae, prepupa, pupa, (callow) and adult. These ants differ from all other insects in embedding their brood in a fungus garden. The complete life-cycle, depending on species and temperature lasts about 50–60 days.

Ecology: Colonies are founded by a single queen, who, after mating on a nuptial flight, sheds her wings, burrows into the ground and establishes a fungus garden, with remnants of fungus carried in her infrabuccal pocket from the parent nest. After workers are produced the colony increases in size and more chambers are excavated to accommodate fungus gardens. Nests of some species e. g. *A. octospinosus* comprise only a few fungus gardens containing several thousand individual ants, whereas other species e. g. *A. s. sexdens* and *A. vollenweideri* have nests with hundreds of interconnected fungal chambers extending several metres into the ground and containing perhaps up to 2 million individual insects. Such large nests also include refuse chambers where spent fungus, dead ants and rubbish are dumped. Leading from them are well-worn trails, often 25–30 cms wide, formed by the frequent passage of foragers.
The distance travelled by foragers depends on the species of ant and size of nest. Some of the grass-cutting species e. g. *A. capiguara,* which is common in the savannahs of southern Brazil and

of Paraguay, have huge nests but collect only within a 30–40 metres radius along a diffuse network of trails. Others, and especially the leaf-cutting *A. cephalotes* of the wet tropical forest of Northern and Central South America and the Caribbean, may travel up to 300 metres along

well-defined and sparsely branched trails leading to cutting sites (Fig. 144).

The density of colonies ranges from several per m^2 (e. g. *A. landolti* in grasslands) to 1–4 per ha (e. g. *A. cephalotes* in forest).

Natural enemies: Probably the most vulnerable stage in the life cycle is the young queen, many of which are eaten by birds and predatory wasps before they have burrowed into the ground. Army ants (*Eciton* and related genera) sometimes prey on the brood. Toads and reptiles eat large numbers of adults but probably not enough to usefully decrease populations. In Paraguay and Venezuela, armadillos tunnel into nests and anteaters probably destroy many more.

Control: Generally, the more intensively cultivated the ground, the less likely are leaf-cutting ants to establish, because their nests are disturbed. Crops grown within foraging range of forest-dwelling colonies are more vulnerable.

Fig. 144. Trail from large nest of *Atta cephalotes* (phot. T. Lewis)

The most satisfactory, convenient and safest method of control is by toxic baits. The wide variety of baits now available all incorporate a chlorinated hydrocarbon insecticide with a vegetable carrier, usually soyabean meal, dried citrus pulp or cassava flour, which also act as attractants. Most proprietary baits are formulated as cylindrical pellets and are applied by hand to the ants' trails for the foragers to collect and carry back to their nests. Once there, they are quickly chewed and spread throughout the fungus gardens, killing the mature ants and brood.

The most successful toxicant now available is mirex. After bait containing 0.45 % mirex applied at 5–10 g/m^2 of nest has been collected by foragers for several days, 90 % of colonies are killed. Cheaper baits containing aldrin, heptachlor, nonachlor, or chlordane are generally less effective either because they repel the ants, or because they kill the foragers before enough insecticide has been collected to destroy the entire nest.

Cheap bait for many species of dicotyledonous cutters can be based on unprocessed (flakey) dried citrus meal, mixed with 0.2–0.4 % aldrin, 5 % soya-bean or sunflower oil. This bait has been successfully applied from aircraft at 2–3 kg/ha to control small nests of *Acromyrmex,* but to kill large colonies of *Atta* it would need to be applied by hand directly to nests or preferably trails.

Literature

LEWIS, T. (1973): Aerial baiting to control leaf-cutting ants in Trinidad II. Field application, nest mortality and effect on other animals. Bull. ent. Res. **63**, 275–287.

LEWIS, T. & F. J. PHILLIPS (1973): Aerial baiting to control leaf-cutting ants in Trinidad I. The bait, its production and the effect of weathering on attractiveness and persistence of toxicant. Bull. ent. Res. **63**, 263–273.

MARICONI, F. D. M. (1970): As sauvas. Editora Agronomica "Ceres" Ltd São Paulo (in Portuguese).

WEBER, N. A. (1972): Gardening Ants, the Attines. American Philosophical Soc. Philadelphia.
Author: Trevor Lewis

Beetles; Käfer; Escarbots; Escarabajos

Order: Coleoptera

General features: Beetles are very varied in colour and size. Some tropical species are among the largest and strongest of all insects. A common feature are the hard elytra (fore-wings) which protect the membranous hind-wings underneath. The mouth parts are biting-chewing, so that adults can be pests when attacking plants. In the tropics, some species do damage by chewing leaves, others penetrate into stalks, shoots, or developing, folded leaves and destroy them. Other species may attack the fruit or subterranean plant portions.

Beetle larvae vary greatly in appearance and are far more important plant pests than the adults. They gnaw subterranean parts of plants with their biting-chewing mouth parts, bore into shoots and stems, destroy fruit or feed on the leaves.

Metamorphosis of beetles is complete (holometabolic).

H. Sch.

Superfamily: Scarabaeoidea
Family: Scarabaeidae

Oryctes rhinoceros (L.) (Figs. 145–146 and plate 31 a, b)

Common names: Coconut (palm) rhinoceros beetle, Coconut black beetle; Indischer Nashornkäfer; Oryctes du cocotier.

Geographical distribution: From West Pakistan eastwards across the entire South- and South East Asian region. Carried from there to islands of the Indian- and above all the South Pacific Ocean. CIE Map no 54.

Host plants: The adults preferably attack coconut palms, but young oil palm plantations are also greatly at risk. Moreover, they can also feed on many other cultivated and wild palms. Occasionally, banana, sugar cane, papaya, sisal, pineapple etc. may also be damaged.

Symptoms: Adult beetles feed at the crowns of palms by boring into the central spear cluster of emerging fronds, and from there they usually tunnel downwards towards the vegetative cone. Signs of infestation: Bore holes and discarded drilling material. Typical symptoms appear as the palm continues to grow: Wedge shaped notches in frond outlines, shortened and broken fronds (Plate 31 a), damaged inflorescences. Young plants are often destroyed, while the relatively resistant older palm trees only succumb to massive and repeated attack. *Oryctes* attack is often followed by further damage and losses due to secondary rotting in the bud (budrot) or to breeding of palm weevils (*Rhynchophorus* spp.) in the wounds.

Economic importance: Both private and public copra production often seriously affected and much reduced due to: Damaged inflorescences, reduction of leaf mass, retarded growth and death of palms. A survey in the Pacific has shown that numerically assessed damage on fronds of 15–100 %/coconut palm occasions a proportionate loss in yield of 0–60 %. Added to this is a considerable outlay for special cultivation-, control- and quarantine procedures, as well as for new plantations. Very large losses are often experienced in newly affected regions, which offer a surfeit of breeding places but scarcely any natural antagonists.

Morphology, life cycle and ecology: Eggs are deposited in nearly every kind of rotting plant material, where larval development also takes place. Decaying coconut palm stems (upright and prostrate) and stumps are however preferred, although rotting oil palms, rubber trees etc. also offer excellent breeding facilities. Other substrates frequently used for breeding are dunghills, compost heaps, sawdust and refuse dumps, garbage refuse and enriched humus.

Newly deposited eggs are white (2.3 x 3.5 mm); larvae hatch after about 11–13 d.; width of head capsule of the 3 larval instars: about 0.3, 0.5 and 1 cm; length of late 3rd instar larvae about 10–11 cm. Under favourable conditions, the entire larval period takes only about 80–130 d., but it can last up to 200 d. and more. The prepupa moults after about 1 week to a yellowish brown pupa (length about 4–5 cm), from which the beetle emerges after about 16–28 d. The beetles leave the pupal chamber after 1–3 weeks. They are about 3.5–5 cm long, of robust build, dorsally black and glossy, ventrally reddish brown. In the male, the pygidium is smooth and rounded, in the female it is hairy and relatively pointed (Fig. 145). Males tend to have a longer horn than females, but horn length may overlap in both sexes. Life span of beetles up to about 6 months, with repeated alternation between feeding and breeding places. Average number of eggs/female about 90–100. Under optimum conditions, one generation (from egg to egg) takes only 4–5 months.

Fig. 145.   Female (left) and male (right) of *Oryctes rhinoceros* (phot. A. Huger)

Fig. 146.   Female of *Oryctes monoceros* (phot. H. Schmutterer)

Similarities to other pests: There are altogether 42 *Oryctes* species, most of which attack palm trees. In Africa, those mainly found are *O. monoceros* (Fig. 146 and Plate 31 c; CIE Map no 188 rev.), *O. boas, O. gigas* and *O. owariensis*. Their mode of life is much like that of *O. rhinoceros.*

Natural enemies: Predators: In general, many non-specific Arthropods and Vertebrates have little or no significance as limiting factors if separately considered, but their cumulative effect may exert a certain control. Arthropods: Carabidae, Elateridae, Histeridae, Reduviidae, Chilopoda and many others. Vertebrates: Birds, pigs, small mammals, lizards etc.

Parasites: Under suitable conditions, *Scolia* spp. can exert a certain limiting effect. Larvae ectoparasitic.

Diseases: The most effective natural control is provided by a virus disease (so-called Malaya disease; pathogen: *Rhabdionvirus oryctes*), which is easily transmitted perorally to larvae and beetles. Natural and artificial epizootics. Virus infected larvae usually transparent with symptoms of "dropsy". Infected adult beetles play a central part in epizootics and in the persistence of the virus disease in the field (see below).

A fungus disease by *Metarrhizium anisopliae* is enzootically occurring in most *Oryctes* populations and may on occasion also rise to epizootic proportions (e. g. in the monsoon season in India). Infected larvae display black-brown spots and post mortem a velvety green conidial pad.

Control: Successful control of *Oryctes* requires a combination of several procedures (see below) in an integrated programme. Owing to the direct correlation between extent of damage and available breeding sites:

a) **Cultural procedures.** Especially sanitary precautions are indispensable. Thus, all potential breeding sites (see above) must be cleared away consistently in plantations and on surrounding land. Dunghills, compost heaps and refuse dumps must be inspected regularly. Breeding substrates are rendered less attractive for oviposition if naturally or artificially overgrown with ground vegetation (e. g. Leguminosae). Large plantations are more easily protected than scattered plantings.

b) **Physical and biotechnical procedures.** Among these are: Collection of all *Oryctes* stages from breeding places and palm crowns; special beetle traps baited with ethylchrysanthemumate ("Rhinolure"); attraction of beetles in monolayers of split coconut palm stems (about 1.2 m long), which must be inspected for beetles and eggs every 2–3 days.

c) **Biological control.** So far, only the above mentioned virus disease has practical significance. The method at present adopted in the UN/SPC-*Oryctes* project on the South Sea Islands is simple and cheap: Captured beetles are infected perorally by swallowing a virus suspension or bathing in homogenised virus diseased larvae (about 10 mins.) and then liberated. The virus is reproduced and spread autobiologically by these beetles, whose mid-gut develops into a formidable virus reservoir. As flying virus producers, they effect directed contamination of the species specific habitats with their infective faeces, so that populations are continuously infected and kept in check for a longer period. Oat grain inoculum of the fungus *Metarrhizium anisopliae* is recommended for *Oryctes* control in local piles of breeding substrates; efficacy 1–2 years.

d) **Insecticides.** Can be used against larvae and beetles, but owing to the peculiarities of *Oryctes* habitats, their use is costly and has great limitations, e. g. treatment of palm crowns with a 1:9 mixture of gamma BHC (6.5 %) and sawdust. Control of breeding foci and prophylactic infiltration of breeding substrates (e. g. dung, compost, sawdust) with 0.05–0.1 % gamma BHC, isobenzan, aldrin, dieldrin, diazinon, or carbaryl; usually effective for several months. Caution, domestic pets at risk from poisoning!

e) **Quarantine measures.** In order to prevent the continued spread of *Oryctes,* statutory regulations must be in force in areas at risk, e. g. for inspection of ships and aircrafts and for the importation of plants with soil balls.

Literature

CATLEY, A. (1969): The coconut rhinoceros beetle *Oryctes rhinoceros* (L.) (Coleoptera: Scarabaeidae: Dynastinae). Pans **15** (1), 18–30.
GRESSITT, J. L. (1953): The coconut rhinoceros beetle (*Oryctes rhinoceros*) with particular reference to the Palau Islands. Bernice P. Bishop Museum, Honolulu (Hawaii), Bulletin No. 212, 157 pp.
HUGER, A. M. (1966): A virus disease of the Indian rhinoceros beetle, *Oryctes rhinoceros* (Linnaeus), caused by a new type of insect virus, *Rhabdionvirus oryctes* gen. n., sp. n. J. Invertebrate Path. **8**, 38–51.
HUGER, A. M. (1972/73): Grundlagen zur biologischen Bekämpfung des Indischen Nashornkäfers, *Oryctes rhinoceros* (L.), mit *Rhabdionvirus oryctes:* Histopathologie der Virose bei Käfern. Ztschr. angew. Ent. **72**, 309–319.
LATCH, G. C. M. & R. E. FALLOON (1976): Studies on the use of *Metarrhizium anisopliae* to control *Oryctes rhinoceros.* Entomophaga, **21**, 39–48.
MARSCHALL, K. J. (1970): Introduction of a new virus disease of the coconut rhinoceros beetle in Western Samoa. Nature (London) **225**, 288–289.
UN/SPC (FAO) Rhinoceros Beetle Project: Semi Annual Reports 1966–1970, Annual Reports 1970–1973; South Pacific Commission, Noumea, New Caledonia.
WOOD, B. J. (1968): Pests of oil palms in Malaysia and their control. Yau Seng Press, Kuala Lumpur, Malaysia, 204 pp.
ZELAZNY, B. (1973): Studies on *Rhabdionvirus oryctes.* J. Invertebrate Path. **20**, 235–241, 1972; **22**, 122–126, 359–363.

Author: A. M. Huger

Superfamily: Dermestoidea
Family: Dermestidae

Trogoderma granarium Ev. (Figs. 147–148)

Common names: Khapra beetle; Khaprakäfer; Trogoderma du grain; Gorgojo de khapra.

Geographical distribution: All tropical and sub-tropical regions except South and Central America, and South East Asia. Mass incidence especially in India, Burma, Sudan, Tunisia and Nigeria

Stored products attacked: All cereals, especially wheat, cereal products, oil cakes and peanuts.

Symptoms: On cereal, larvae first attack the embryo, later also the endosperm. Seed coat chewed in irregular manner.

Economic importance: Under conditions favourable for the pest – drought, high temperatures – wheat can be destroyed completely within 6 months. Most dangerous storage pest in the tropics and in sub-tropical regions. Can cause major damage in malt houses in Europe. Strict quarantine measures in force in most American and many European countries.

Fig. 147.   Female (left) and male of *Trogoderma grana-rium* (phot. G. Brünner)

Fig. 148.   Larva of *T. granarium* (phot. G. Brünner)

Morphology: ♂♂ 2, ♀♀ up to 3 mm long (sexual dimorphism) (Fig. 147), egg-shaped, antennal club can be placed in antennal groove. Larvae very hairy. Tufts of barbed hairs (Fig. 148). Cannot be confused with other cereal pests.

Life cycle: Oviposition loose and single, on average 65 per ♀. Start of oviposition and number of eggs per day depend greatly on temperature. Developmental period at 30 °C: Egg 7 days, larva 34 days, pupa 4–5 days. Life span of adults 12–19 days. In India 4 generations per year. Under favourable conditions in the store, one generation per month. Total developmental period at 21 ° up to 310 days, at 34–35 ° only 25–29 days. In case of nutrient deficiency, accumulation of excrement in the food or drop in temperature, some of the larvae crawl into cracks in the store, where they remain in a dormancy-like state (facultative diapause). The ability to enter diapause is genetically determined.

Ecology: ♀♀ entirely, ♂♂ almost entirely unable to fly. Hence no attack in the field. Spread only if carried, especially larvae which, with their barbed hairs, easily adhere to sacks etc., also by direct or indirect (rodents) contact of affected with unaffected goods, on residues of affected ware in emptied stores and ships and by larvae (diapause larvae!), which are hidden in cracks and fissures.

Control:

a) **Preventive measures.** Storage chambers should have smooth walls and floors. Affected parts of goods in store must be kept separate from unaffected ones. Used sacks must be fumigated (methyl bromide, phosphine-PH_3) before they are used again and/or impregnated (phoxim = Baythion) and emptied store space thoroughly cleaned and sprayed (malathion, phoxim). Fumigation of any remaining residues.

b) **Chemical control.** Owing to diapause of some of the larvae, the Khapra beetle is particularly hard to control. See fumigation schedules (p. 385). When fumigating larger amounts of loosely stored products (not in sacks), the concurrent use of phosphine (PH_3) and methyl bromide acting over a 3 day period, has proved effective.

Literature

BURGES, H. D. (1959): Dormancy of the Khapra Beetle. Quiescence or Diapause. Nature **184**, 1741–1742.
LINDGREN, D. L., E. V. LLOYD & H. E. KROHNE (1955): The Khapra Beetle *Trogoderma granarium* Everts. Hilgardia **24**, 1–36.
VÖLKEL, H. (1924/25): Zur Biologie und Bekämpfung des Khaprakäfers *Trogoderma granarium* Everts. Arbeiten aus der Biologischen Reichsanstalt **13**, 129–171.

Author: H. Piltz

Superfamily: Bostrychoidea
Family: Bostrychidae

Rhizopertha dominica (F.) (Fig. 149)

Synonyms: *Rhyzopertha dominica, Rhyzopertha pusilla, Dinoderus pusillus*

Common names: Lesser grain borer; Getreidekapuziner; Capucin des grains; Gorgojo de los cereales.

Geographical distribution: Cosmopolitan throughout tropical, sub-tropical and warm temperate zones on all continents.

Stored products attacked: Cereal grains of all types; cereal products; also on other grains (including pulses) and root crops in store.

Symptoms: Both larvae and adults bore through the stored produce usually causing characteristic round tunnels (up to 1 mm diameter) which are easily observed in most grain and root crops.

Economic importance: It is an important pest of stored cereals especially in hot tropical areas (because of its greatly increased rate of development at high temperatures, see below). Its general importance as a primary pest of stored cereals is less than that of *Sitophilus* spp. because it does not infest the grain before harvest and has lower powers of dispersal than the weevil species. However, it is a very important pest when established since both larvae and adults are voracious feeders and cause substantial weight loss. Furthermore, as a primary pest it facilitates greater damage by subsequent secondary pests. Infestations of this species may often be underestimated because adults and larvae remain hidden inside the grains.

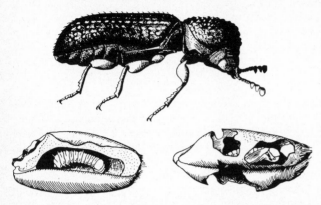

Fig. 149. *Rhizopertha dominica*. Above: adult beetle; below: larva (left) and pupa (right) in a wheat grain (Imperial Chemical Industries)

Morphology: The adults of Bostrychidae found on stored produce are characterized by their narrow cylindrical shape, dark brown colour and the position of the head which is ventral to the prothorax and usually invisible from above (Fig. 149). Additionally, the adults of this family have straight antennae with a large 3-segmented club (apical segment ovoid and the two sub-apical segments strongly triangular) and have numbers of tubercles on the pronotum (especially anteriorly). *R. dominica* is the commonest member of this family found on stored produce but may be distinguished from similar species by the following characters: length 2–3 mm, width 0.6–1 mm, pronotum rounded in front and with flattened tubercles covering its posterior median surface; lateral edges of pronotum indicated by an irregular ridge in the posterior half only; tarsi of hind leg shorter than its tibia. The larvae are white and somewhat slow-moving with a small head-capsule and a cylindrical, parallel-sided body not tapering posteriorly.

Similarities to other pests: The damage caused to cereal grains is characteristic to the experienced worker but may sometimes be confused with that caused by *Sitophilus* spp.. However, the latter hollow out individual grains, whereas *R. dominica* (during the earlier stages of an infestation) bores distinct tunnels. In later stages of infestation, *R. dominica* may also hollow out the grains but inspection of the remaining seed coat reveals characteristic circular holes (compared with the irregularly shaped holes caused by the weevils). The other members of this family infesting stored cereals cause very similar damage but the adults can be distinguished: in Central America, *Prostephanus truncatus* is larger (3–4.5 mm) than *R. dominica,* and *Dinoderus* spp. are somewhat stouter and have punctures on the posterior median surface of the pronotum.

Life cycle: Eggs are laid on the surface of, or among, the produce. The larvae bore slowly through the produce eating as they go. The number of larval instars varies with the physical conditions and the quality of food. After a short quiescent prepupal stage, pupation occurs, usually inside a grain. The adults are long-lived and a female may lay up to 550 eggs over a period of three to six weeks. Under optimum conditions, development from egg to adult takes 25 days; development is prolonged by sub-optimal conditions so that, for example, at 23 °C and 70 % r. h. the egg to adult period is extended to 84 days.

Ecology: Optimum conditions for maximum rate of increase are 34 °C and 50–60 % r. h. The limiting conditions for completion of development are 18 and 39 °C and 25 and 70 % r. h. From this it can be seen that this species can survive in a wide variety of climatic areas but that (because of marked response of development time to temperature) it is only a really important pest in the hotter tropical areas. It has been suggested that this species (like other Bostrychidae) was originally a wood-borer and it is still often found boring in wood. For this reason, it is particularly difficult to eradicate from wooden stores using normal storage control techniques.

Natural enemies: The most important natural enemy of this species is the hymenopteran parasite *Lariophagus distinguendus* which is commonly found in association with infestations of *R. dominica* and may reduce the rate of increase of the pest in such situations. Two other parasitic Hymenoptera have been noted as parasites of *R. dominica,* namely *Choetospila elegans* and *Anisoptero-*

malus calandrae. Predatory mites have also been reported as feeding on eggs or first instar larvae of this pest, but the species concerned are probably incapable of exerting any substantial influence on the pest's rate of increase.

Control: Admixture with malathion at 12 ppm. 2 % dusts should be applied at 600 g per ton and emulsifiable concentrates at 1.2 litres of 1 % spray per ton. Standard treatments with dichlorvos at 7 to 14 ppm for short term or in transit control are effective against all stages. Fumigation is effective at normal dosage schedules (see p. 385). In Australia where *R. dominica* is a serious problem due to resistance to organophosphates, the use of bioresmethrin has shown promise. Much work has been done showing that the pest may be controlled by gamma-irradiation but this is not likely to find widespread commercial application.

Resistance. Resistance to lindane and malathion is widespread and commercially important. Some resistance to phosphine and methyl bromide has also been demonstrated. Control of resistant strains is only poor to fair with alternative organophosphate insecticides suitable for stored products application.

General situation. The future outlook for control of this serious primary pest is uncertain and it seems likely that heavy reliance (in the short term) may be placed on the use of dichlorvos and fumigants. Some varietal differences in rice susceptibility have been reported but it seems unlikely that this will be of any practical significance.

Store hygiene. Store hygiene is most important. All stores and bins should be thoroughly cleaned and sprayed with fenitrothion or alternative approved insecticides at 0.5 to 1 g a. i. per square metre before filling with fresh grain.

Appendix: Store Pest Control by Fumigation

Fumigation Schedules

Although the following rates of application of some fumigants may be useful in certain circumstances it cannot be over emphasised that fumigant chemicals are dangerous and fumigation procedures require considerable expertise. Fumigation should therefore be left to experienced personnel individually trained in fumigation techniques.

a) Methyl bromide.

The dosage rates required to kill common insect pests with methyl bromide vary from species to species but in practice it is not necessary to vary the dosage for each insect. Fumigation dosage rates for methyl bromide are therefore based on temperature and commodity. The simple schedules adhered to in Europe give CT (concentration x time) products which give 100 % kill of most common species.

	Exposure period	Space dosage g/m^3		Commodity dosage g/ton	
		10-20 °C	Above 20°C	10-20 °C	Above 20 °C
Rice, barley, peas, beans, dried fruit	24	15	10	0	0
Wheat, maize, oats	24	15	10	30	20
Sorghum, nuts, dates, figs	24	15	10	60	40
Flour, bran, groundnuts, oilseeds	48	15	10	60	40
Oilseed cakes and meals, fish meal	48	15	10	120	80

It is necessary to add together the space dosage and the commodity dosage to get the correct dosage. However for filled containers and under gas proof sheets the following simplication based on volume is possible.

	Exposure period	Dosage (g/m³)	
		10-20 °C	Above 20 °C
Rice, barley, peas, beans	24	15	10
Wheat, maize, oats	24	35	24
Sorghum, figs	24	55	40
Oilseeds, groundnuts	48	50	40
Oilseed cakes	48	90	60
Flour	48	50	40

For mites or *Trogoderma granarium* increase dosage by 50 %.

b) Phosphine.
Dosages for bulk fumigations vary from 2 g to 10 g of phosphine per ton. Fumigations in bags with non-permeable liners require 0.2 to 0.4 g of phosphine per bag. Proprietary preparations are available in the form of tablets releasing 1 g of phosphine, pellets releasing 0.2 g, and sachets releasing 11 g of phosphine each. Phosphine fumigations require 5–7 days for completion.

c) Liquid fumigants.
(i) Ethylene dichloride – carbon tetrachloride (EDCT), a mixture of 3 parts ethylene dichloride to 1 part carbon tetrachloride is used to fumigate grain in bags or in bulk less than 6 ft deep. For greater depths equal parts of the liquids are used.
(ii) Ethylene dibromide may be used for small depths of grain or in-bag fumigations.

Literature

POTTER, C. (1935): The biology and distribution of *Rhizopertha dominica* (Fab.). Trans. R. ent. Soc. Lond. **83** (4), 449–482.

Authors: C. P. Haines and D. J. Webley

Family: Anobiidae

Lasioderma serricorne (F.) (Fig. 150)

Common names: Cigarette beetle; Tabakkäfer; Moucheron, Coléoptère des cigarettes; Gorgojo del tabaco.

Geographical distribution: Humid tropical and sub-tropical regions. World-wide distribution in stocked tobacco stores.

Stored products attacked: Tobacco, wheat flour (providing better developmental conditions than tobacco!), cereal, bran, peanuts, cocoa beans, cottonseed, beans of various sorts, spices and even

Fig. 150. Larva of *Lasioderma serricorne* (phot. G. Brünner)

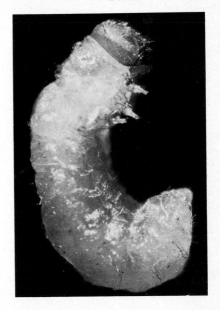

insecticides containing pyrethrum, meat- and fish meal. Chief pest on cocoa beans in West Africa.

Symptoms: Circular, pin-head sized bore holes on processed tobacco. No other typical feed marks.

Economic importance: Main pest on tobacco and tobacco products. Tobacco storage and processing without control measures not possible anywhere.

Morphology: Adult: Antennae serrated, prothorax and fore wings not punctated.
Larva. Head in front view round, with long hairs and brown spots (Fig. 150).

Similarities to other pests: Drugstore beetle (Brotkäfer, Vrilette du pain, Escarabajo del pan) *Stegobium paniceum* is similar. Antennae with three long terminal segments, not serrated. Prothorax punctated, forewings with rows of dots.
Larval head in front view a little pointed towards the top, few hairs, no brown spots.

Life cycle: Oviposition singly in hiding places, from 45–115 per female, only at temperatures above 20 °C. Young larvae hatch after $5^1/_2$ to $6^1/_2$ days at the earliest, at 32 °C and 75–90 % rel. humidity (optimum). Larvae do not hatch at temperatures below 20 °C, above 37.5 °C or at low rel. humidities. Developmental optimum of larvae et 35.5 ° and 70–80 %.
Developmental period under such conditions only 16 days (in wheat flour), at 20 ° between 68 and 78 days. Between 19.5 and 15.5 °C, larval activity ceases. They enter a state of dormancy, in which they can remain for months and overwinter. Pupation in a loose cocoon on some firm part of the food, e. g. the mid-rib of a tobacco leaf. Pupal period from 4 days at 37.5 ° to almost 13 days at 20 °. Emerging beetles remain for from 5 (at 37.5 °) to 12 days (at 20 °) in the cocoon. They are then sexually mature. The ♀♀ mate repeatedly. Oviposition starts 2–5 days after leaving the cocoon. Total period of development at 30 °C and 70 % rel. hum. 26 days in wheat meal and 105 days in unbroken cocoa beans. Development in tobacco 42–90 days, depending on temperature. Life span of beetles 11–45 days. Under favourable laboratory conditions, up to 11 generations per year. In practice, 6–8 generations can be expected if temperatures never drop below 20 °C.

Ecology: The beetles drink, but do not take solid food. They nevertheless burrow into tobacco bales. They avoid bright light and are attracted by twilight. Their main activity is confined to the evening hours. If disturbed, for instance by reloading of affected ware, they will also fly in bright daylight. They spread from store to store by flight or may be carried manually, especially with tobacco.

Natural enemies: *Tenebroides mauritanicus* and *Thaneroclerus buqueti* feed on the larvae of cigarette beetle.

Control:
a) In tobacco. All stages are killed by the customary steaming of tobacco, including those inside

the "hogsheads", if a vacuum is first created. 50 °C kill in 24 hours, 60 ° kill all stages within a few minutes. Severe infestation in "hogsheads" is also susceptible to low temperatures and can be eradicated at storage temperatures of 4.4 °–7.2 ° and 8.9 ° in 12, 20 and 32 weeks respectively. Good results were also obtained in a tobacco store with an automatic dichlorphos sprinkler. All pests are definitely destroyed by prophylactic fumigation with ethylene oxide in a vacuum chamber before tobacco storage. Fumigation with methyl bromide can have an adverse effect on the aroma. Light traps should guard against renewed infestation. If necessary, store should be fumigated with phosphine.

b) Other wares as in fumigation schedules (p. 385).

Literature

CHILDS, D. P. (1965): Effect on the Cigarette beetle of flowing steam vapour under vacuum. Tobacco. N. Y. **160**, 32–36.
CHILDS, D. P., G. L. PHILLIPS & A. F. PRESS jr. (1966): Control of the Cigarette Beetle in Tobacco Warehouses with Automatic Dichlorphos Aerosol Treatments. J. Econ. Ent. **59**, 261–264.
CHILDS, D. P., J. E. OVERBY & B. J. WATKINS (1968): Low Temperature Effect on Cigarette Beetle Infestation in Tobacco Hogsheads. J. Econ. Ent. **61**, 992–996.
HOWE, R. W. (1958): A Laboratory Study of the Cigarette Beetle, *Lasioderma serricorne* (F.) (Col. Anobiidae) with a Critical Review of the Literature on its Biology. Bull. Entom. Res. **48**, 9–56.

Author: H. Piltz

Family: Silvanidae

Oryzaephilus mercator (Fauv.)

Common names: Merchant grain beetle; Getreideplattkäfer.

Geographical distribution: See *O. surinamensis*.

Stored products attacked: Oilseeds (especially groundnuts), rice, rice bran, dried fruits, spices.

Symptoms: Some superficial surface damage to whole grains caused by feeding of adults and larvae; in damaged grain, etc. the actual damage is not easily visible. Close examination will show cast larval skins, excreta and cocoons.

Economic importance: A secondary pest of moderate importance, it may sometimes assume greater importance on high-value export crops (e. g. groundnuts for human consumption). An important problem is that this species infests a wide range of produce thus leading to cross-infestation of other produce.

Morphology: The larvae of *Oryzaephilus* spp. are slender and are pale cream in colour with two patches of darker greyish-cream colour on the dorsal surface of each segment. The adults of *Oryzaephilus* species are small, narrow, flattened beetles (2.5–3.5 mm long) which are dull dark brown in colour. Their most distinctive feature is the shape of the prothorax which has six large teeth on each side and three longitudinal ridges on the dorsal surface. The adult of *O. mercator* may be distinguished from the common and similar *O. surinamensis* only by the length of the temple behind the eye; namely in *O. mercator* the distance from the hind margin of the eye to the hind angle of the head is much less than half the longitudinal diameter of the eye.

Similarities to other pests: The damage caused by this species is indistinguishable from that caused by several other secondary storage pests. On rice (and occasionally other cereals) this species may be present in the company of *O. surinamensis*.

Life cycle: See *O. surinamensis*.

Ecology: Optimum conditions for population increase are approximately 30 °C and 70 % r. h. The range of physical conditions for successful development is from 18 to 38 °C and from 10 to 90 % r. h. It is not particularly tolerant of cold conditions and is therefore less of a problem in cool temperate climates; however, its heat and dryness tolerance allows it to persist in hot dry tropical conditions.

Natural enemies: There are few records of natural enemies of this species and it is unlikely that any of the recorded predators exert any significant control over *O. mercator* populations.

Control: Admixture with malathion at 12 ppm. 2 % dusts should be applied at 500 g per ton or emulsifiable concentrates at 1 litre of 1 % spray per ton but these volumes may be modified depending on the flow rate of the cereal. Surfaces of bags or stores may be sprayed with pirimiphos methyl at 0.5 g a. i. per square metre. Surfaces other than those in contact with foodstuffs may be sprayed with other insecticides, fenitrothion, pirimiphos methyl or phoxim at 0.5 g per square metre. Fumigation is effective at normal dosage schedules (see fumigation schedules, p. 385).

Alternative recommendations: See *O. surinamensis* (see below).

Resistance: Lindane resistance is widespread and some malathion resistance has been reported. Malathion resistant strains may show high levels of resistance to most available alternative organophosphates.

General situation: Since this insect is mainly a pest of oilseeds and oilseed cake, fumigation is likely to be the most important control method. Good hygiene in bins and containers is most important to prevent re-infestation of clean commodities.

Literature

HOWE, R. W. (1956): The biology of the two common storage species of *Oryzaephilus* (Coleoptera, Cucujidae). Ann. appl. Biol. **44** (2), 341–355.

Authors: C. P. Haines and D. J. Webley

Oryzaephilus surinamensis (L.) (Fig. 151)

Common names: Saw-toothed grain beetle; Getreideplattkäfer; Gorgojo aserrado de los granos.

Geographical distribution: Cosmopolitan. It is widespread from tropical to temperate areas on all continents.

Stored products attacked: Cereals and milled cereals, especially rice, sorghum and wheat.

Symptoms: Some superficial surface damage to whole grains caused by feeding of adults and larvae; in damaged grain and flour the actual damage is not easily visible. Close examination will reveal cast larval skins, excreta and cocoons. Heavy infestations usually lead to mould growth in the infested area.

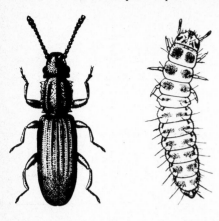

Fig. 151. Adult (left) and larva of *Oryzaephilus surinamensis* (Courtesy of Imperial Chemical Industries)

Economic importance: A secondary pest of moderate importance on whole grain in the tropics, it assumes greater importance on previously damaged grain or on milled cereals. It causes loss in weight, and quality reduction (increased by the mould damage with which it is often associated).

Morphology: The larvae of *Oryzaephilus* spp. are slender and are pale cream in colour with two patches of darker greyish-cream colour on the dorsal surface of each segment (Fig. 151). The adults of *Oryzaephilus* species are small, narrow, flattened beetles (2.5–3.5 mm long) which are dull dark brown in colour. Their most distinctive feature is the shape of the prothorax which has six large teeth on each side and three longitudinal ridges on the dorsal surface. The adult of *O. surinamensis* may be distinguished from the similar *O. mercator* only by the length of the temple behind the eye; namely, in *O. surinamensis,* the distance from the hind margin of the eye to the hind angle of the head is somewhat more than half the longitudinal diameter of the eye.

Similarities to other pests: The damage caused by this species is indistinguishable from that caused by several other secondary storage pests. On rice (and occasionally other cereals) *O. mercator* may be present in the company of this species.

Life cycle: Approximately 300 eggs are laid in the produce by the female over a period of 10 weeks. The larvae are active and move through the produce on which they feed until they are fully grown. Pupation occurs inside a silken cocoon spun by the mature larva. The emerged adult also feeds on the produce and is long-lived (often up to three years). The egg to adult development takes less than 25 days under optimum conditions.

Ecology: Optimum conditions for population increase are 35 °C and 90 % r. h. The range of physical conditions for successful development are from 18 to 38 °C and from 10 to 90 % r. h. It is tolerant of both cold conditions and hot dry conditions and is therefore found both in cool temperate countries and in hot tropical areas.

Natural enemies: There are few records of natural enemies of this species but the predator recorded most frequently is the predatory hemipteran *Xylocoris flavipes*. It is doubtful whether this (or any other predator) exerts any significant control over the rate of increase of *O. surinamensis*.

Control: Admixture with malathion at 10 ppm. 2 % malathion dust may be applied at 500 g per ton or emulsifiable concentrate at 1 litre of 1 % spray per ton but these volumes may be modified depending on the flow rate of the cereal. Surfaces of bags or stores may be sprayed with pirimiphos methyl at 0.5 g a. i. per square metre or surfaces not in contact with foodstuffs with fenitrothion or other approved insecticides at 0.5 g a. i. per square metre. Standard short term protection with dichlorvos is effective against all stages at 5 to 10 ppm, the dosage being determined by the withholding period. Fumigation is effective at normal dosage schedules (see fumigation schedules, p. 385). Pirimiphos methyl at 5 ppm is recommended in the United Kingdom.

Resistance. Resistance to lindane is widespread and some malathion resistance has been reported. Malathion resistant strains may also be resistant to other organophosphates and carbaryl.

General situation. *O. surinamensis* infestation takes place only after grain is brought into store and therefore store hygiene is most important. Thorough cleaning of the store and spraying into all parts of the store with malathion, pirimiphos methyl or fenitrothion is essential. Normally 1.0 or 1.5 % sprays are applied at a rate of 5 litres per 100 m². Containers may be disinfested with dichlorvos at rates of up to 70 mg per cubic metre. Pockets of infestation such as old sacks and feedingstuff containers should be eliminated. In countries where temperatures fall below 18 °C at night, ventilation with cool air is useful as the insect does not breed below 18 °C. The moisture content of the cereal should be below 13 %.

Literature

HOWE, R. W. (1956): The biology of the two common storage species of *Oryzaephilus* (Coleoptera, Cucujidae). Ann. appl. Biol. **44** (2): 341–355.

Authors: C. P. Haines and D. J. Webley

Family: Coccinellidae

Epilachna varivestis Muls. (Plate 31 d)

Synonym: *Epilachna corrupta*

Common names: Mexican bean beetle; Mexikanischer Bohnenkäfer; Coccinelle du haricot; Escarabajo mexicano del frijol, Conchuela del frijol.

Geographical distribution: The Mexican bean beetle is believed to be native to the plateau region of southern Mexico. Its range of distribution extends today from Panama to Southern Ontario, Canada. CIE Map no 46.

Host plants: Hosts of the Mexican bean beetle are restricted to plants of the family Leguminosae, of the Fabaceae group. The preferred hosts are most varieties of snap or common beans, *Phaseolus vulgaris;* lima beans, *P. lunatus;* and cowpeas, *Vigna sinensis.* Soybeans, *Glycine max,* are heavily attacked by certain localized populations in the Atlantic Coast states, and in south-central Indiana. The most likely wild hosts are weeds of the genus *Desmodium.* Other 12 species in 13 legume genera were also recorded as more or less acceptable hosts. A few records mention feeding on non-leguminous plants such as maize, rye, squash, eggplant, and potato.

Symptoms: Larvae and adults feed on the underside of the leaves of bean plants. In heavier infestations they may attack green pods and stems after the leaves have been destroyed. The Mexican bean beetle has a peculiar feeding mechanism. The mandibles scrape and crush the lower epidermal and parenchymatous tissues, expressing the cellular contents that are then sucked into the food channel. The crushed tissues remain on the leaves as ridges that present a typical lacework aspect (Plate 31 d). Adult beetles may open irregular holes, especially when feeding on young or thinner leaves. The leaves thus attacked may not display the characteristic lacework appearance.

Economic importance: The Mexican bean beetle is most damaging to snap and lima beans, the preferred hosts. In many portions of its geographic range the cultivars of *P. vulgaris* and *P. lunatus* cannot be commercially grown without insecticidal protection.
In the U.S. the economic impact of the pest on soybeans is becoming more serious as the acreages of soybeans are expanded. Populations requiring control measures on soybeans occur in Maryland, Virginia, the Carolinas, Georgia, and Alabama. Soybeans in certain areas in the southern half of Indiana are also subject to damaging attacks.

Morphology: Eggs are elliptical, elongated, about 1.4 mm long, and orange-yellow.
Larvae are oval and yellow, and each segment is covered with 4–6 branched, yellow, black-tipped spines. Under cold conditions the spines turn totally black. The larvae grow to a maximum length of 8 mm.
Pupae are about 6 mm long, rounded, convex, and bright yellow. They are usually found attached to the leaves by the tip of the abdomen which remains partially covered with the folded cast larval skin.
Adult beetles are somewhat rounded and convex. They are dark yellow with a copper sheen, and the elytra present 16 black spots in two rows of 6 spots and one distal row of 4 spots. They are 6–8 mm long and 4–6 mm wide. Male and female beetles are very similar, but they can be distinguished by the shape of the last abdominal segment (8th sternite), which in the male has a small indentation.

Similarities to other pests: Adult Mexican bean beetles resemble some of the native beneficial ladybeetles, but the plant-feeding habit of the former prevents any mistakes. On superficial examination the beetles may also be confused with the bean leaf beetle, *Cerotoma trifurcata*.

Life cycle: Eggs are laid in clusters of 40–60 on the underside of bean leaflets. An average of 500 and a maximum of over 1,500 eggs per female are oviposited in about 40 days.
Eggs hatch in the field within 5–15 days at temperatures of 24.2 and 13.2 °C, respectively. At 27 °C in the laboratory eggs hatch in 5 days.
The newly emerged larvae start eating as soon as the exoskeleton hardens, and they remain initially aggregated. They disperse while eating the leaf tissues in an irregularly circular front centered around the egg cluster.
There are four larval stages, and the total larval period varies, depending upon the climatic conditions, from 15 days to 5 weeks. Fully grown 4th instars stop eating, attach themselves by the tip of the abdomen to the plant substrate, and become prepupae. After 2–3 days the larval exuviae are shed and the pupal period begins, lasting 7–10 days at temperatures averaging 25 °C. The emerging adults are pale yellow and without black spots, which slowly appear sometime after emergence as the elytra harden.
Females begin ovipositing about 10 days after emergence. The total developmental period from egg to egg is, therefore, from 35–40 days under optimal field conditions. One to four generations per year occur at the various latitudes according to the prevailing climatic conditions.

Ecology: Mexican bean beetle population levels vary from field to field, depending upon a number of physical and biotic factors. Some of the critical physical factors are the location of the field, the slope, prevailing air currents, and type of soil. Beetles seem to be more abundant in plantings on sandy soils than on those on heavier soils.
Heavy precipitation in the summer is detrimental to the beetles, which may be washed off the plants and buried in the mud. Drought periods may directly affect beetle populations by increasing egg and larval mortality due to exposure, or may indirectly affect development of immature forms and adult oviposition through the effect on the food plant.
Optimal temperatures for adult oviposition and survival and larval development are between 22 ° and 27 °C with relative humidity around 60 percent. In a few hours a temperature of 37 °C kills beetles, embryos in the eggs, and larvae. Below 17 °C oviposition drops very sharply and development slows down very markedly. By the success with which the species has colonized regions in a variety of climates, it is evident that it can tolerate a wide range of temperatures.
Weight gain and food consumed vary with the nature of the food. Optimal growth was obtained with snap beans on which the larvae gained an average of 43.1 mg (fresh weight) in 14 days, each larva consuming an average of 51.3 mg (dry weight) of foliage. On the most suitable soybean variety tested ("Harosoy" normal) under identical conditions, larvae gained 36.3 mg in 15.8 days, but consumed only 38.5 mg of foliage. It is therefore apparent that the rates of development are greatly influenced by the quality and condition of the plant, and this is particularly important during the spring migration period.

Natural enemies: Adults and immature stages of the Mexican bean beetle are attacked by several parasitoids, predators, and diseases. Among the most active predators are the hemipterous *Podisus maculiventris, Stirethrus anchorago, Nabis* spp., and *Orius insidiosus;* the coleopterous *Collops bipunctatus,* and various coccinellids; and the neuropterous *Chrysopa* spp.

Control:

Cultural control. In cultures of snap and lima beans the destruction of the crop remains after the beans have been picked is recommended. Fields should be plowed at least 15 cm deep, and all the foliage should be covered for the control to be effective (USDA 1960). Planting of quick-maturing varieties may reduce injury by summer Mexican bean beetle populations, since the beans mature before these populations reach a peak.

In soybeans attempts are being made to use as a trap a strip of rows planted to a faster growing, earlier variety than that planted in the bulk of the field. The colonizing adults are attracted to these more developed plants, where they are killed with insecticide sprays.

Plant resistance. Although most varieties of snap and lima beans are very susceptible to attack by the Mexican bean beetle, certain ones show some resistance. The least damaged snap bean varieties tested in North Carolina were: "Idaho Refugee", "Wade", "Logan", "Supergreen", "Black Valentine", and "Refugee U.S. no 5". The least damaged lima bean varieties were: "Baby Fordhook", "Bush Lima", "Triumph", "Burpee's Bush Lima", "Evergreen", and "Henderson Bush".

A high level of resistance was identified in the soybean plant introductions 171451, 227687, and 229358. Both behavioral and physiological functions of the Mexican bean beetle are affected by the resistant lines. Active breeding programs are under way to incorporate these sources of resistance into commercial varieties in early maturity groups at Illinois, in intermediate groups at North Carolina, and in late maturity groups at South Carolina and Mississippi.

A soybean variety, "Shore", with partial resistance was developed at Maryland and Virginia and seed production was increased for release.

Biological and integrated control. The tachinid fly, *Paradexodes epilachnae,* native to Mexico, was introduced into the United States in 1922, but it has not become established. Two hymenopterous species were more recently introduced from India. *Tetrastichus ovulorum* is an egg parasitoid, and *Pediobius foveolatus* is a larval parasitoid. *T. ovulorum* did not successfully complete development on *E. varivestis* eggs, but larvae were an adequate host for *P. foveolatus.* The success of the establishment of *P. foveolatus* in the United States has not been assessed at this time.

The rather rich predator fauna in soybean fields is not detrimentally affected when the plants are sprayed against the Mexican bean beetle, using minimum effective rates of carbaryl (see below). These minimum rates coupled with proper timing of sprays are an effective integrated control practice.

Chemical control. Effective control of larvae and adult beetles was obtained with dosages lower than those normally recommended. The following compounds and rates gave 80 percent mortality or better 48 hours after the treatments: carbaryl at 0.10 lb a. i. (active ingredient)/acre, methomyl at 0.05–0.13 lb a. i./acre, methyl-parathion at 0.20–0.25 lb a. i./acre, and toxaphene and methyl-parathion 0.40 + 0.20 to 0.50 + 0.25 lb a.i./acre.

No spraying schedules are suggested. In all crops fields should be periodically surveyed and treatments made only when populations approach the economic threshold.

For snap and lima beans conservative thresholds seem to be one adult beetle or one egg mass per meter of row. In soybeans thresholds have not been defined, but no sprays are recommended until defoliation reaches about 30 percent of the total leaf area prior to bloom, 15 percent at bloom and pod development, and 35 percent after pod maturation, and active adults and larvae are observed on the plants.

The Mexican bean beetle is naturally tolerant to DDT, but the species is very susceptible to most organophosphorous and carbamate compounds.

Literature

AUCLAIR, J. L. (1959): Life history, effects of temperature and relative humidity, and distribution of the Mexican bean beetle, *Epilachna varivestis* Mulsant (Coleoptera: Coccinellidae) in Quebec, with a review of the pertinent literature in North America. Ann. Soc. Entomol. Que. **5**, 18–43. Illus., refs.
CAMPBELL, W. V. & C. H. BRETT (1966): Varietal resistance of beans to the Mexican bean beetle. J. Econ. Entomol. **59**, 899–902.
KOGAN, M. (1971): Feeding and nutrition of insects associated with soybeans. 2. Soybean resistance and host preferences of the Mexican bean beetle *Epilachna varivestis*. Ann. Entomol. Soc. Amer. **65**, 676–83.
KOGAN, M. (1972): Intake and utilization of natural diets by the Mexican bean beetle, *Epilachna varivestis*. A multivariate analysis. In: Rodriguez, J. G.-edit. Insect and Mite Nutrition-Significance and Implication in Ecology and Pest Management. No. Holland Pub. Co., Amsterdam, p. 107–126.
NICHOLS, M. P. & M. KOGAN (1972): The literature of arthropods associated with soybeans. 1. A bibliography of the Mexican bean beetle *Epilachna varivestis* Mulsant (Coleoptera: Coccinellidae). Ill. Nat. Hist. Survey Biol. Notes 77, 20 pp.
TURNIPSEED, S. G., J. W. TODD, G. L. GREENE & M. H. BASS (1974): Minimum rates of insecticides on soybeans: Mexican bean beetle, green cloverworm, corn earworm, and velvetbean caterpillar. J. Econ. Entomol. **67**, 287–91.
VAN DUYN, J. W., S. G. TURNIPSEED & J. D. MAXWELL (1971): Resistance in soybeans to the Mexican bean beetle. I. Sources of resistance. Crop Sci. **11**, 572–573.

Author: M. Kogan

Family: Tenebrionidae

Tribolium castaneum (Hbst.)

Common names: Red flour beetle; Rotbrauner Reismehlkäfer; Petit ver de la farine; Gorgojo rojo de la harina.

Geographical distribution: Flour beetles of this species are easily transported from one place to another in stored food products. *T. castaneum* is best characterized as a subtropical species, however, due to the utilization of heated granaries and other storage places, it is cosmopolitan in distribution.

Stored products attacked and symptoms: Refer to *T. confusum* (p. 385)

Morphology: Adults 2.3–4.4 mm in length with sexes externally alike and reddish to blackish in color. The body is somewhat flattened with a pronotum that is broader than it is wide. The sides of the abdomen are parallel. This species has 11 segmented antennae with the terminal three segments forming a pronounced club. The margins above the eyes are not elevated. Usually one or more of intervals four through seven of the elytra are strongly carinate from base to apex.

Similarities to other pests: Refer to *T. confusum* (p. 385)

Life cycle: The life cycle of this species is similar to that of *T. confusum*. Under optimal laboratory conditions, adults of *T. castaneum* have a mean lifespan of approximately six months and an oviposition rate of approximately 5–15 eggs per female per day. The eggs have a sticky external surface which becomes coated with the medium in which they are laid. The developmental time of the eggs is approximately 5 days at 29 °C. There are typically 7 or 8 larval instars, although this number can vary from 6 to 11 or more. At 29 °C the period from egg to pupa is approximately 23 days in duration. The duration of the pupal stage is about 6 days. *T. castaneum* females can be fertilized within three hours of eclosion and commence oviposition of fertilized eggs at an age of 96 to 108 hours.

Ecology: A great deal of information has been gathered on the population dynamics of *T. casta-neum* under controlled conditions. Both temperature and humidity are very important factors in determining rates of birth and death. In addition, both the adults and larvae of *T. castaneum* cannibalize eggs and pupae. This cannibalism is the major factor limiting population growth in laboratory environments.

In addition to the foods listed above, it has been found that *T. castaneum* is able to complete its life cycle on at least 8 species of fungi that commonly occur in stored grains. Thus, along with decaying organic matter, it is likely that flour beetles utilize fungi in their native habitats.

Natural enemies: Refer to *T. confusum* (see below).

Control: Refer to *T. confusum.*

Literature

KING, C. E. & P. S. DAWSON (1972): Population biology and the *Tribolium* model. Evolutionary Biology **5**, 133–227.
SOKOLOFF, A. (1972): The biology of *Tribolium,* with special emphasis on genetic aspects. Vol 1. Oxford University Press, London, 300 pp.

Authors: C. E. King and P. S. Dawson

Tribolium confusum Duv. (Fig. 152)

Common names: Confused flour beetle; Amerikanischer Reismehlkäfer; Gorgojo confuso de la harina.

Geographical distribution: Although African in origin, this species has been transported in foodstuffs by man and is now cosmopolitan in distribution. Because of its greater tolerance to cool weather, *T. confusum* tends to occur at higher latitudes than some other members of this genus (e. g., *T. castaneum*).

Stored products attacked: Beetles of this genus are important pests in a wide variety of food products, including whole-wheat flour, bran, rice flour, rye flour, corn meal, barley flour, oat meal, chocolate, spices, various nuts, snuff, orris root, ginger, slippery elm, peas, and beans. *T. confusum* is also able to exist in unpulverized grain, though its survival and reproduction is much reduced in comparison to the flour habitat.

Symptoms: Adult beetles are readily observed in even moderately infested stored foods. These pests construct tunnels as they move through flour and other granular food products. In addition, they release gaseous quinones to the medium which may produce a readily identifiable acrid odor in heavy infestations.

Economic importance: A heavy infestation by *T. confusum* will render some stored foods unpalatable for human consumption. This beetle is one of the most dangerous store pests.

Morphology: Adults 2.6–4.4 mm in length with sexes externally alike and generally reddish-bronze in color. The body is somewhat flattened with a pronotum that is broader than it is wide. The sides of the abdomen are parallel. This species has 11 segmented antennae with a feebly differentiated club of 5 segments. The margins above the eyes are distinctly elevated. The narrowest part of the eye is no broader than a facet. Elytra of *T. confusum* have first and second intervals flat or at most carinate only at the apex.

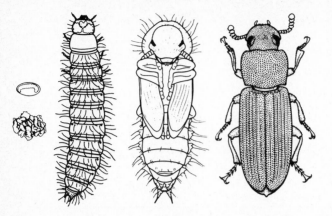

Fig. 152. Developmental stages of *Tribolium confusum*. From left to right: egg, larva, pupa, adult (drawings P. S. Dawson & C. E. King)

Similarities to other pests: There are more than 30 species in this genus, many of which also infest various cereal products.

Life cycle: Under optimal laboratory conditions, adults of *T. confusum* have a mean lifespan of more than six months and an oviposition rate of approximately 5–15 eggs per female per day. An average female may produce more than 1,400 eggs in her lifetime under optimal conditions. The eggs have a sticky external surface which becomes coated with the medium in which they are laid. The developmental time of the eggs is approximately 6 days at 29 °C. There are typically 7 or 8 larval instars. At 29 °C, the period from egg to pupa is approximately 25 days in duration. The duration of the pupal stage is about 6 days. *T. confusum* females can be fertilized within 17–20 hours of eclosion and commence oviposition at an age of 114–126 hours.

Ecology: More information has been gathered on the population dynamics of *T. confusum* under controlled conditions than any other species of organism. Both temperature and humidity are very important factors in determining rates of birth and death. Both the adults and larvae of this species cannibalize eggs and pupae. This cannibalism is the major factor limiting population growth in laboratory environments.
In addition to the foods previously listed, it has been found that *T. confusum* is able to complete its life cycle in at least seven species of fungi that commonly occur in stored grains. Thus along with decaying organic matter, it is likely that flour beetles utilize fungi for food in their native habitats.

Natural enemies: *T. confusum* is parasitized by several species of sporozoans. Severe parasitic infections decrease both survivorship and fecundity, but seldom to the extent that they produce population extinction under laboratory conditions.

Control: Good sanitation is the easiest and best prevention for all stored grain insect pests. Storage bins should be thoroughly cleaned prior to use by removing all old grain and sweeping ceilings, walls and floors. After cleaning and about one week before filling bins, treat interior with malathion, methoxychlor, or pyrethrin bin sprays. Clean up all grain spills outside storage facility and spray outside area. Store only dry, clean grain containing less than 12 percent moisture and free from weed seeds, broken kernels and dirt. Infestation can usually be prevented for up to a year by adding a protectant (malathion, piperonyl butoxide or pyrethrins) to the grain as it enters the bin. Infestations in bulk grain are best controlled by fumigation (see p. 385).
In home, sanitation is again the best control. Inspect packages of susceptible food products before buying, sterilize doubtful products in oven or freezer, store items in tightly sealed containers, wipe up spills immediately, and periodically check stored items. When an infestation is located, thoroughly clean shelves and use a prepared household surface spray on the empty shelves.

Literature

KING, C. E. & P. S. DAWSON (1972): Population biology and the *Tribolium* model. Evolutionary Biology **5**, 133–227.

SOKOLOFF, A. (1972): The biology of *Tribolium,* with special emphasis on genetic aspects. Vol 1. Oxford University Press, London. 300 pp.

Authors: P. S. Dawson and C. E. King

Superfamily: Chrysomeloidea
Family: Cerambycidae

Anthores leuconotus Pasc. (Fig. 153)

Common names: White coffee borer; Ostafrikanischer weißer Kaffeebohrer; Foreur blanc du tronc; Barrenador blanco del cafeto.

Geographical distribution: This beetle is widely distributed in Africa from about latitude 5 °N reaching as far south as Natal, and also in Zanzibar. CIE Map no 196.

Host plants: This borer breeds in all species of coffee. Other trees and shrubs in which it has been found breeding are *Vangueria* sp., *Oxyanthus speciosus, Rytigynia schumannii, Rothmannia urcelliformis, Erythroxylum emarginatum.*

Symptoms: The chief damage is by the larvae boring in the trunk. At first the young larvae burrow in the inner layers of the bark, often ringbarking the bole and main roots. Later the larva bores into the wood. Young attacked trees are nearly always killed. Older trees turn yellow and do not produce a crop. Mature trees are not usually killed outright but sometimes die later in unfavourable conditions.

Economic importance: The importance of this beetle in infested coffee districts can hardly be exaggerated, it makes coffee growing quite uneconomic unless effective control measures are undertaken.

Morphology: The adult is a robust beetle about 21–29 mm long. It is greyish with characteristic white markings covering about three quarters of the elytra (Fig. 153). The antennae of the female are slightly longer than the body and almost twice as long as the body in the male.
The egg is light cream in colour about 5 mm long by 2 mm broad. The newly hatched larvae are small white somewhat flattened grubs. As they grow older they become more cylindrical and yellowish.

Similarities to other pests: *Anthores* is unlikely to be confused with any other pest but there are several other borers which also breed in coffee stems, the most important being *Bixadus sierricola* which is a very severe pest of coffee in the whole of West and Central Africa, the damage being very similar.

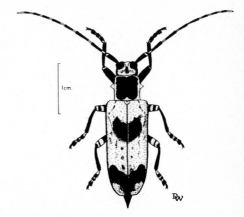

Fig. 153. Adult of *Anthores leuconotus* (after Le Pelley, Pests of Coffee, Longman, London)

Life cycle: The incubation period of the egg is about 21 to 23 days. There are thought to be 7 larval instars and the duration of the larval stage varies widely. Pupae are found with head uppermost in a pupal chamber under the bark, the pupal stage lasting several weeks and the beetle remaining in the pupal chamber for some time. The life cycle is from 12 to 25 months, most beetles completing their development in from 16 to 20 months. Therefore, calculated on an 18 month period the approximate duration of the different stages in weeks is egg $3^1/_2$, larva ring-barking 16, wood-boring 42, preparing pupal chamber 10, pupa $4^1/_2$, adult before breaking out of chamber $1^1/_2$

Ecology: The original natural hosts of this beetle must be considered to be various Rubiaceous trees and shrubs, among them those already listed, since in places where arabica coffee is an introduced plant it is attacked near forested areas in which they occur. Attempts to reduce the attack on coffee by eliminating these native host plants have been unsuccessful and are in any case now unnecessary.

Natural enemies: Natural mortality is great and it has been found that only one of every four eggs laid finally develops into a living adult. Most eggs hatch normally, only a few are parasitized by a species of *Aprostocetus* (Eulophidae). Large numbers of ring-barking larvae die, though the causes of this mortality are not fully known. Parasites play a part. *Iphiaulax varipalpis* (Braconidae) is known to attack the larvae and five other species of different families are believed to do so. In the wood-boring larvae there is also considerable mortality and three species of Ichneumonidae have been found in larval burrows. Other enemies are woodpeckers which destroy many larvae and sometimes ants attack larvae in galleries.

Control: The present control with dieldrin is so effective that it is unnecessary to give any detailed description of earlier methods.
The method previously employed in Kenya and enforced by law, was to remove the soil round the collar of the trees to find the infested trees by the frass thrown out of the burrows, and then to kill the larvae with a wire or with fumigants such as carbon disulphide or carbon tetrachloride. This did much to keep the borer under some degree of control, but where dieldrin can be made available such uncertain and time consuming measures are not now required.
Treatments with DDT, endrin, chlordane, and dieldrin were tried and of these dieldrin has proved entirely satisfactory. This is applied by mixing 500 ml of 18 percent dieldrin miscible liquid with 20 litres of water. To this is added 15 g of methylene blue as a marker. The mixture is applied to the trunks of the coffee trees from ground level to a height of 45 cm, preferably just before the rains. The application may be made by spray or brush. This should be repeated 1 year later and thereafter every second year. The adult beetles have been found to die after touching the sprayed bark during oviposition or emergence. The young ring-barking larvae are killed by residual insecticide in the bark. The methyl blue warns operators of the presence of dieldrin on skin or clothing and helps them to ensure that the stem is completely covered. The use of this persistent insecticide applied to a limited portion on the plant has not been shown to have any detrimental side effects and does not suffer from the objections of persistent sprays applied to foliage. This control measure has been found to be so effective that when applied as recommended the borer is no longer a pest of economic importance.

Literature

LE PELLEY, R. H. (1968): Pests of Coffee, Longmans London, 590 pp.
TAPLEY, R. G. (1966): The White Coffee Borer *Anthores leuconotus* Pasc. and its control. Bull. ent. Res. **51**, 279–301, London.

Author: R. H. Le Pelley

Family: Bruchidae

Callosobruchus maculatus (F.)

Synonyms: *Bruchus maculatus, B. quadrimaculatus, B. ornatus, B. vicinus, B. ambiguus, B. sinuatus.*

Common names: Cowpea weevil; Vierfleckiger Bohnenkäfer; Bruche à quatre taches.

Geographical distribution: Cosmopolitan: spread by international trade in pulses: Africa, Middle East, Southern United States, Japan.

Host plants/stored products attacked: Cowpeas (*Vigna unguiculata, Vigna sinensis*). *C. maculatus* has also been reared on Soya bean *(Glycine max), Phaseolus* spp., Bambara groundnut *(Voandzeia subterranea), Dolichos lablab,* and other legumes.

Symptoms: *C. maculatus* attacks seeds of cowpeas and related legumes in store. Holes about 2 mm diameter are left by the emerging adults. Heavy attack causes severe powdering and weight loss.

Economic importance: This insect is the major pest of stored cowpeas in Africa, in the United States, and elsewhere.

Morphology: Size 2.5–3.5 mm. The antennae are serrate but not pectinate. The body is oval in outline and the elytra pubescent, with rust coloured background and two brown or black spots on each side. These are more obvious in the female. Two forms of the female, one with a white pygidium and the other having a black pygidium with a white central line have been recorded.

Similarities to other pests: *C. maculatus* is polymorphic. It has been confused with *C. analis* which has non-serrate antennae, with *C. chinensis* which has a more angular outline and with *C. subinnetatus* which lacks the dark spots on the elytra and is larger, 4.5–5.5 mm.

Life cycle: The eggs are laid on the outside of the cowpea to which they adhere. The number of eggs laid varies from about 55–85 per female.
The development takes place inside the bean and takes 25–33 days before the adults emerge. The pupal and pre-adult stages are normally about 10 days in duration. The adults normally live for about seven days but the female form with the white pygidium is more active and slower to mature and if unmated, it may live for several months.
Primarily, a pest of cowpeas in store *C. maculatus* can spread to mature pods in the field from infested stores. Infestation has been shown to start in the field before harvest in drier areas. In more humid zones, low pre-harvest infestation is recorded. Optimum conditions for development are given at 32.5 °C and 90 % R. H.

Natural enemies: The parasites *Dinarmus laticeps* (Hym.: Pteromolidae) and *Bruchocida vuilletti* (Hym.: Eupelmidae) are known to restrict growth of populations of *C. maculatus.*
However, their effect is only significant with very heavy Bruchid infestation. The presence of these parasites can be recognised by the small emergence holes (1 mm).

Control:
Cultural practices and hygiene: Threshing should be carried out immediately after harvest and the cowpeas stored in metal drums, earthenware pots or rhumbus. To reduce field infestation, cowpea pods should be picked as they become dry rather than at a single final harvest.

Store hygiene is essential. Care should be taken to ensure that spillage in processing and storage areas is cleared away and either utilised or burned.

The control of *C. maculatus* in small quantities of cowpeas for household use can be achieved by heating to 64 °C for 10 minutes or cooling to 18 °C for four days with subsequent storage in glass jars with lids.

Cowpeas for seed can be stored by admixture of dried sand which fills intergranular air spaces and prevents free movement of adults for egg laying. This will not kill the insects present inside the beans but will prevent increase of infestation levels.

Chemical control: Where larger quantities of cowpeas are to be stored, fumigation and post-fumigation protection by means of physical barriers gives the best results.

The instructions of the manufacturers of fumigants should be followed with regards to safety precautions. Adjacent accommodation should be vacated and operators should use gas masks if working in enclosed spaces. (See Appendix "Fumigation Schedules", p. 385). Practical recommendations for the main fumigants can be found in the "Manual of Fumigation" (Munro, 1961).

The use of methyl bromide and hydrogen cyanide is recommended in the United States (USDA Agric. Inf. Bull., 303) at dosages of 2 lbs per 1000 cu. ft. for methyl bromide and 1.5 lbs per 1000 cu.ft. for hydrogen cyanide at temperatures above 15.6 °C (60 °F). Phosphine gas for fumigation is adaptable to a wide range of different types of fumigation i.e. small containers, drums, silos and large warehouses. It has the advantage that heavy equipment such as gas cylinders, scales and piping are not required.

Fumigation with phosphine under gas proof sheets is recommended for stacks of bagged cowpeas. After application of the fumigant and before off-sheeting, it is desirable that the store should be sprayed with a good knock-down insecticide such as dichlorvos to kill any bruchids not enclosed under the fumigation sheet. Fumigation of small containers such as oil drums may be conducted by simply adding one tablet or 2–3 pellets of aluminium phosphide and sealing the container. Polythene or polythene lined bags may similarly be fumigated but care should be taken that fumigation immediately follows filling of the bags as emerging adult *C. maculatus* will bore straight through polythene.

Aluminium phosphide tablets can be applied to small silos containing cowpeas by means of applicator tubes provided that there is adequate head room for the operators above the grain surface. The success of this operation depends on the efficiency of sealing the silos against leakage. 100 % success is rare. Covering the surface of the grains with polythene sheeting and spraying of the air space above with dichlorvos can improve efficiency in ventilated silos.

Carbon tetrachloride/ethylene dichloride (1:3) mixture has been used with some success against *C. maculatus* in silos at a dosage of 1 gallon per 5 tons. Application to the surface of the beans can be made by means of a pump or watering can. Care should be taken not to inhale the fumes. (See appendix p. 385).

Hermetic storage: Where no fumigants are available storage of cowpeas in clean oil drums may be recommended. If the drums are well filled and sealed with bitumen the *C. maculatus* will, after a short time, use up available oxygen and increase in visible damage should be contained. Note well: that inadequate sealing can be disastrous.

Literature

CALDERON, M. (1962): The Bruchidae of Israel, Rivista di Parasitologia **23** (3), (Includes keys) 207–216.

CASWELL, G. H. (1960): Observations on an abnormal form of *Callosobruchus maculatus* (F.). Bull. ent. Res. **50**, 671–680.

MUNRO, H.A.U. (1969): Manual of Fumigation for Insect Control. F.A.O., pp. 381.

HOWE, R. W. & J. E. CURRIE (1964): Some laboratory observation on the rates of development, mortality and oviposition of several species of Bruchidae breeding in stored pulses. Bull. ent. Res. **55** (3), 437–477.

PREVETT, P. F. (1962): The Reduction of Bruchid infestation of Cowpeas by post-harvest storage methods, pp. 7. Federal Ministry of Information, Lagos, Nigeria.

PREVETT, P. F. (1971): The larvae of some Nigerian Bruchidae (Coleoptera). Trans. R. Ent. Soc. Lond. **123** (3), 247–312.
SOUTHGATE, B. J. (1958): Systematic notes on species of *Callosobruchus* of economic importance. Bull. ent. Res. **49**, 591–599.
SOUTHGATE, B. J., R. W. HOWE & G. A. BRETT (1957): The specific status of *Callosobruchus maculatus* (F.) and *Callosobruchus analis* (F.). Bull. ent. Res. **48**, 79-89.

Author: M. A. Cornes

Family: Chrysomelidae

Dicladispa armigera (Oliv.) (Fig. 154)

Synonyms: *Hispa armigera, Hispa aenescens*

Common names: Hispa, Rice hispa; Asiatisches Reisigelkäferchen.

Geographical distribution: Bangladesh, Burma, Cambodia, Southern China, Taiwan, India, Indonesia, Korea, Laos, Malaysia, Nepal, New Guinea, Pakistan, The Philippines, Sri Lanka, S. Vietnam and Thailand. CIE Map no 228.

Host plants: a) Cultivated plants. – Rice and occasionally sugarcane and turnip; b) Alternate/collateral hosts. – *Paspalum sanguinale, Mnesethia laevis, Eleusine indica, Dactyloctenium aegyptium, Echinochloa colonum, Digitaria adscendens, Leptochloa filiformis, Leersia hexandra, Zizania latifolia, Vetiveria zizanioides, Panicum proliferum* and wild rice species.

Symptoms: At first the beetles scrape the leaf lamina between the veins giving an appearance of white parallel lines. Later, due to indiscriminate feeding even on veins, white blotches devoid of chlorophyll appear on the leaves. The larvae bore into the leaf between the epidermal layers and feed on the mesophyll between the veins tunelling in the tissue towards the leaf sheath and producing irregular longitudinal white patches. In severe cases of damage, the leaves dry up completely and the fields appear as if scorched.

Economic importance: The yield losses from hispa infested fields range from 10 to 65 percent in Bangladesh and 39 to 65 percent in India. Annual yield losses vary from 20 to 50 percent in parts of Bihar, Assam and West Bengal (India). For every unit percent increase in damaged leaf area, estimated at 50 percent flowering of crop, a corresponding loss in yield of 0.78 to 1.52 percent has been reported.

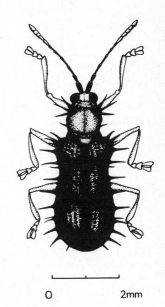

Morphology: The beetles are oblong in shape, metallic blue in colour with long and well developed spines on the prothorax and elytra (Fig. 154). Four strong spines project somewhat laterally on the dorsal side of the pronotum; a pair of spines arise from the metanotum likewise. The forewing contains a row of 10 spines along the lateral margins and 9 dorsolateral spines. The antennae are 11-segmented. The femur is heavily spinose. The females are slightly larger (4.4 to 4.8 mm long) than the males (3.6–4.1 mm).

Fig. 154. *Dicladispa armigera* (after PANS Manual no 3, Pest Control in Rice, Crown Copyright 1970)

O   2mm

Similarities to other pests: The other related genera and species of beetles infesting rice and causing broadly similar symptoms of damage are *Hispa (Hispella) stygia, Rhadinosa lebongensis, Leptispa pygmaea* and *Chaetocnema coccipennis* from India, *Asamangulia (Hispa) wakkeri* and *Rhadinosa parvula* from Indonesia, *Dicladispa boutani* (= *Hispa similis*) from South China, Japan, Korea, Taiwan and Southern Ryukyu islands, *Dicladispa irridicyanea* from Zaire, Rwanda and Burundi, *Hispellinus moestus* from Malaysia, *Dicladispa paucispina, Dorcathispa bellicosa, Polygonia spinicornis* from Cameroun, *Onchocephala gestroi, Dicladispa gestroi, Dactylispa echinata* and *Dactylispa spinulosa* from Nigeria and *Oediopalpa guerini* from Venezuela and Brazil

Life cycle: The eggs are 1 to 1.5 mm in length, shaped like sesamum seeds and are inserted singly inside mesophyll tissue towards the leaf tips. Up to 60 eggs are laid singly by one female. The incubation period lasts for 3–5 days. The average duration is 3.0, 3.6, 4.1 and 4.8 days, respectively for the 4 larval instars. The mature larva (5.1/1.6 mm) reaches the blind end of the tunnel and pupates between upper and lower epidermal layers of the leaf. The pupal period lasts for 4–6 days. The emerging beetle cuts its way out of the larval tunnel and copulates within 3 to 4 days. The gravid female commences to oviposit 4 to 5 days after mating and continues for 22 to 40 days. The adult females and males can live up to a maximum of 78 and 46 days, respectively. Oviposition to adult emergence takes 22 to 25 days. No distinct diapause is known but the adults emerging from rice after September in Taiwan and after October in W. Bengal (India) hibernate in basal parts of grasses near rice fields.

Ecology: Three to 5 generations, usually 3, are reported to occur in Taiwan, the 2nd causing greatest damage to rice. In India 6 generations occur, the 2nd and 5th causing greatest damage to kharif and rabi crops in Andhra Pradesh. Adults prefer tender seedlings in nurseries and rice crops 20 to 60 days after transplanting for feeding and oviposition. Crops raised early in the season escape or suffer negligible damage. Top dressing a rice crop with nitrogen during hispa abundance produces greater damage. Grass and weed hosts play a major role in their initial multiplication at the beginning of the crop season and also in their continued survival in low numbers out of season. Unusually heavy rains in early July followed by abnormally low rainfall and more sunshine hours than usual in August and September are attributed as mainly responsible for the hispa epidemics of 1948 and 1962 in Orissa, India. Continuous or heavy rain has a negative effect on the activity of adults and immature stages.

Natural enemies: The hymenopterous parasites *Isotima* sp., *Bracon* sp., *Pediobius* sp., *Campyloneurus* sp., *Macrocentrus* sp., and *Achrysocharia cardigaster* have been recorded on larvae and *Eupteromalus* sp., *Trichomalopsis apanteloctenus* and *Derostenus* sp. on pupae. Natural parasitism varies from 15–82 %. Braconids are the common larval parasites but are found to be of no practical value. Under artificial conditions, the entomophilic nematode *Neoaplectana dutkyii* parasitizes and kills the hispa beetles.

Control:
Sanitary methods. Removal and destruction of wild grasses and weeds from rice fields and bunds during and after the crop season; collection of adults by nets in early morning hours.
Cultural practices. Raising crops very early in the crop season; cutting off leaf tips and burying or burning them to destroy eggs and larvae.
Resistance of crops. The rice cultivars Monkompu-1, Patnai-23, Ashpata, T.1242, BAM.6 and AC.1951 are reported to be less susceptible in India. Shorter vegetative period, rough leaf surface, more sclerenchyma and silica and less succulence and nitrogen content in the leaf might confer resistance of rice against hispa attack though these aspects have not been studied.
Integrated control. Keep nurseries free from the pest; clip leaf tips, dip seedlings in 0.04 percent solution of effective insecticides and transplant; destroy weed and grass hosts of hispa; adopt chemical control in transplanted crops only when the situation warrants.
Prognosis. About 5 percent of damaged leaf area, or 1 beetle or 5 to 10 leaf-mining immature

tages per hill, is arbitrarily a situation to warrant control action. This, if followed by prolonged rainless periods with bright sunshine hours and vulnerable vegetative growth stage of the crop, is a forerunner of an impending outbreak of hispa epidemic.

Chemical control. Insecticides found effective against hispa are DDT, dieldrin, phosphamidon, demeton-S-methyl, diazinon, lindane, ethyl parathion, EPN 0.3 to 0.5 kg a.i./ha. as foliar sprays or BHC 5 or 10 percent dust 25 or 20 kg/ha. or granular lindane application in standing water 2.0 kg a.i./ha.

Literature

ACHARYA, L. A. (1967): Life history, bionomics, and morphology of the rice hispa *Hispa armigera* Olivier. M. Sc. thesis. College of Agriculture, Bhubaneswar, (India).
GRIST, D. H. & R.J.A.W. LEVER (1969): Pests of rice. Longmans, Green and Co. Ltd., London, 520 pp.
PANS manual no 3. Pest control in Rice (1970): Ministry of Overseas Development, London, 270 pp.
PRAKASA RAO, P. S., P. ISRAEL & Y. S. RAO (1971): Epidemiology and control of the rice hispa *Dicladispa armigera* Olivier. Oryza **8** (2 Suppl.), 345–359.

Author: P. S. Prakasa Rao

Superfamily: Curculionoidea
Family: Apionidae

Cylas puncticollis Boh. (Plate 32 a)

Common names: Sweet potato weevil, Schwarzer Batatenkäfer.

Geographical distribution: *C. puncticollis* is found throughout tropical Africa to which it is confined. CIE Map no 279.

Host plants: *C. puncticollis* is primarily a pest of sweet potato, *Ipomoea batatas*. Other host plants include wild species of herbaceous Convolvulaceae.

Symptoms: Adult weevils feed on foliage and produce circular feeding holes. Adults are also found feeding on tender stems and tubers producing characteristic feeding punctures. The larva is the most harmful stage. It bores into the stem both above and below ground level causing serious mortality of sweet potato seedlings. On established sweet potato plants, the larvae feed in tubers and stems and the infested plants exhibit drought stress, symptoms of wilting and, in the case of severe infestation, they may dry up. Infested tubers show larval tunnels and exit holes of adult weevils.

Economic importance: The Sweet potato weevil is the most important pest of sweet potato. It causes damage both in the field and in store. Weevil-infested tubers cannot be stored for a long period.

Morphology: The adult *C. puncticollis* is a shiny metallic black, very slender, ant–like weevil.

Similarities to other pests: *C. formicarius* (Plate 32 b), a closely related species, has world-wide distribution as a major pest of sweet potato. This beetle has brown thorax, legs and antennae. It resembles *C. puncticollis* very closely except for its colour and slight differences in behaviour.

Life cycle and ecology: The female lays its eggs singly, in small hollow punctures made by it for this purpose. Eggs are laid in the tubers and at the base of the stem. The larva hatches in about one week and tunnels into the tubers and vines. The larva remains inside the plant feeding and tunnelling for about 2 to 4 weeks. It has a shorter larval period during dry summers. Adult weevils are also more active during dry summers and multiply faster. The larvae pupate within the tubers or vines, the pupal stage lasting for about one week. The adults are active for a long time depending upon the weather conditions. Sometimes they have been found to survive for over a month in storage buildings. Several overlapping generations are found in the field. If the sweet potato crop is grown continuously throughout the year, the insect is found to be active throughout. During the rainy season its activity is slowed down.

Natural enemies: A fungus (*Beauveria* sp.) has been found in Nigeria during the rainy season infesting the adults. Sometimes ants have been found associated with the larvae of the weevil but their role is not clear since it is difficult for the ants to reach the larvae within the tubers.

Control: Continuous cropping of sweet potato can keep the weevil population at a high level. Therefore crop rotation is one method of reducing the losses. Very dry soils also assist the movement of adult weevils and increase their infestation levels. Varietal resistance to weevil both in planted vines and tubers in storage has been recorded at the International Institute of Tropical Agriculture, Ibadan, Nigeria. It has also been observed that drought resistant, leafy sweet potato varieties tend to maintain more moisture in the ground and reduce the activity of adult weevils; this encourages infestation of the adults by *Beauveria* sp.
After harvest, destruction of infested material by burning also reduces the level of infestation. Planting of healthy vines and an early harvest can also reduce the damage.
DDT and gamma-BHC dusts or sprays have been found to be effective. Due to residue problems in the tubers, no long lasting insecticides should be applied to the soil.

Literature

BOHLEN, E. (1973): Crop pests in Tanzania and their control. Verlag Paul Parey, Berlin–Hamburg, 142 pp
SCHMUTTERER, H. (1969): Pests of crops in northeast and central Africa. Gustav Fischer Verlag, Stuttgart, 296 pp.

Author: S. R. Singh

Family: Curculionidae

Anthonomus grandis Boh. (Figs. 155–156 and plate 32 c, d)

Common names: Boll weevil; Baumwollkapselkäfer; Anthonome, Charançon américain de la capsule; Picudo del algodonero.

Geographical distribution: The boll weevil is native to Mexico and Central America, but it has spread into other areas and now occupies also the southeastern U.S.A., Cuba, Haiti and northern Colombia/Venezuela. CIE Map no 12.

Host plants: Wild and cultivated cotton is the primary host. Other wild Malvaceae are also attacked (see p. 405).

Symptoms: The cotton squares show tiny punctures and yellow crumbs (pollen) on the surface as a result of weevil feeding. Larger, protruding, sealed injuries stem from oviposition (Fig. 155). Later the bracts open away from the bud ("flaring") which becomes yellowish and drops to the ground. The interior of squares and bolls is eaten and stained from frass and rot, and a white, curved, plump, wrinkled, legless larva with brown head capsule is found (Fig. 156).

Fig. 155.   Oviposition scar of *Anthonomus grandis* on a flower bud of cotton (phot. H. Schmutterer)

Fig. 156.   Larva of *A. grandis* in a flower bud of cotton (phot. H. Schmutterer)

Economic importance: The boll weevil, where it occurs, is usually the number-one pest of cotton. In the U.S.A. it causes annually $200 million of crop loss and $75 million control expenditures. Nearly one-third of all agricultural insecticides applied in the U.S.A. are used against this insect.

Morphology: The adult is a reddish- to dark brown curculionid, 8 mm in size, densely covered with grey pubescences, with a long thin proboscis (Plate 32 d).

Similarities to other pests: The boll weevil is similar to *Anthonomus vestitus* occurring in Peru, but is geographically well separated from this other species.

Life cycle: The female lays 100–300 eggs preferably into squares. There are three larval instars, and one generation is completed in 17 days at 30 °C. The development is faster in squares than in bolls: 11 days in squares, 31 days in bolls (Texas). Five generations/year develop in the U.S.A.. The adults enter facultative diapause under adverse environmental conditions. In the U.S.A. they overwinter in forest litter and emerge again by mid-June; in Central America (Nicaragua) they diapause in cotton bolls and other refuges when the host plants become unsuitable (absence of fruiting forms) in the dry season, and the humidity is low.

Ecology: In Nicaragua, the boll weevil depends totally on cultivated cotton for mass reproduction and on volunteer, cultivated and wild cottons for survival. It was not found on other hosts. In Mexico and the U.S.A. it can survive on alternate hosts like *Hampea, Cienfuegosia, Thespesia,* and *Sphaeralcea,* but mass reproduction only occurs on cotton. The time of peak square and boll formation is also the time of highest weevil reproduction rate in Nicaragua, and population growth is practically unaffected by predators and parasites. The major factor determining population dynamics is temperature causing mortality of larvae in the squares dropped to the sun-heated soil surface. When suitable oviposition sites become scanty due to boll maturation and/or complete puncturing of the available squares, the weevil population starts a mass migration in mid- to late season in search for fresh hosts. In Central America (Nicaragua), development of the boll weevil populations continues as long as squares or young bolls are available which in the dry season (January–May) are provided by stalk, ratoon and wild cotton.

Natural enemies: Forty-two arthropod species are known as parasites of the boll weevil. The more effective among them are *Bracon mellitor* in the U.S.A. and *Heterolaccus grandis* in western Mexico and Central America. In Nicaragua, *Zatropis* sp. was recently found to parasitize the boll weevil. Here parasitism is higher in the dry season than in the cotton season.

Control:

Resistance of crops. Frego-type cotton whose bracts are rolled and grow away from the bud ex
posing it fully, alters the behaviour of the weevils visiting the squares and suppresses oviposition
Red-leaf cotton varieties are also less infested. Excess production of fruiting structures is a tole
rance factor in the cotton plant in Nicaragua which sheds 80-odd % of its total production ever
without insect attack. This surplus is a buffer against boll weevil injury.

Integrated control. The area-wide integrated control program developed by USDA-researcher
in Mississippi has suppressed weevil populations there to a very low level. The program include
the following chemical, biotechnical and cultural measures:

1. "Reproduction-diapause control". Several applications of malathion in the fall reduce the pen
ultimate and the last generation of the year destined to enter diapause. The latter is further suppressed by chemical defoliation using a high dosage that also causes late squares and small bolls tc
drop, and by early stalk destruction.

2. Pheromone traps used in the spring baited with grandlure, the synthetic sex pheromone of the
boll weevil, catch a high percentage of the surviving overwintered population.

3. Rows of trap cotton planted very early, treated with systemic aldicarb and made more attractive by grandlure bait stations attract and kill weevils having by-passed the traps.

4. One application of azinphos-methyl at the appearance of first squares reduces the remainder of
the weevil population that has survived all foregoing treatments.

In Central America, hand-picking of weevils and fallen squares in early season has prevented the
weevil population from rising during that time. Insecticide sprays, in the early season, are directed
only to "hot spots" of infestation using ground equipment.

Chemical control. Toxaphene-DDT, methyl parathion, azinphos-methyl, malathion. Low-volume and ultra low-volume formulations are more effective but present environmental hazards.
Carbofuran used as seed treatment and sidedressing gave effective control of emerging overwintered boll weevils but is known to affect beneficial insects.

Prognosis. Pheromone traps indicate the onset of weevil migration from diapause sites to the cotton fields. The traps detect lower levels of infestation than visual field inspections.

Resistance to insecticides. Resistance of the boll weevil to certain insecticides has occurred
throughout its range. Resistance to organo-phosphorous insecticides is fortunately still low.

Literature

CROSS, W. H. (1973): Biology, control, and eradication of the boll weevil. Ann. Rev. Ent. **18**, 17–45.
HARDEE, D. D. (1972): A review of literature on the pheromone of the boll weevil, *Anthonomus grandis*
  Boheman. US Dep. Agr. Coop. Econ. Insect Rep. **22**, 200–207.
MITLIN, L. & N. MITLIN (1968): Boll weevil, *Anthonomus grandis* Boh.: Abstracts of research publica-
  tions, 1961–65. US Dep. Agr., Agr. Res. Serv. Misc. Publ. **1092**, 32 pp.
MAXWELL, F. G., J. N. JENKINS & W. L. PARROT (1972): Resistance of plants to insects. Advan.
  Agron. **24**, 187–265.

Author: R. Daxl

Cosmopolites sordidus Germ. (Fig. 157 and Plate 33 a, b)

Common names: Banana weevil; Bananenbohrkäfer; Charançon du bananier; Gorgojo, Picudo
negro del plátano.

Geographical distribution: The banana weevil is now found in most areas of the world where bananas are grown except in Egypt, Israel and Hawaii. Its centre of origin is probably the Ma-
laya/Java/Borneo region (Malesia) as it is here that the weevil's natural predators occur. By 1900
however the insect had been recognised in the Far East, Australia and Brazil and during the following twenty years was observed in Central Africa, Central America, the Pacific Islands, the Indian Ocean Islands and the Caribbean. CIE Map no 41.

Host plants: All host plants lie within the family Musaceae and no members are known to possess any acceptable degree of resistance. Bananas, plantains and Manila hemp *(M. textilis)* are the major crops within the genus *Musa* and weevil damage often achieves economic importance during their cultivation.

Symptoms: The weevil damage is primarily the result of the destruction of corm tissue by the tunnelling larvae (Plate 33 b). Young suckers especially show symptoms of wilting and die but older plants are checked in their growth and though infested plants can fall during violent weather conditions. Large scale falls in plantations are attributed usually to nematode damage as *Cosmopolites* larvae do not attack root tissue though they can leave the corm and migrate to the pseudostem itself on occasions. The larvae's characteristic tunnels in the corm increase in size as the larval stage grows and the root primordia and vascular bundles surviving the voracious appetite of this grub can often be destroyed by secondary fungal and bacterial infection which accelerates the process of plant decline.

Economic importance: *C. sordidus* is considered to be the most serious insect pest of bananas. It causes by preventing the formation and storage of nutrients a stunted plant growth and consequently a reduction in crop yield. In well managed plantations however the effects of the weevil are reduced and good cultural practices often obviate the need for specific control measures. In Malesia the weevil is not considered a serious pest, probably on account of the presence of its naturally occuring parasites and predators.

Morphology: Adult weevils are about 10 mm in length and have a large curved snout (Fig. 157). The newly emerged adult is however reddish brown before turning black. The larvae are white, legless grubs with pronounced dark brown mouthparts and are also about 10 mm in length. The eggs are approximately 1 mm in length but on account of their white colour are rarely seen in the corm tissue.

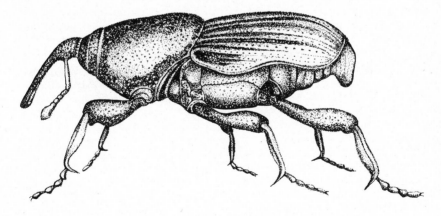

Fig. 157.   *Cosmopolites sordidus* (side view) (Courtesy of Imperial Chemical Industries)

Similarities to other pests: In the Caribbean and Latin America the W. Indian cane weevil *(Metamasius hemipterus)* also inhabits banana plantations but this weevil, though similar to *Cosmopolites* is brown and in contrast to the banana borer is active during the day. In E. African banana gardens *Temnoschoita nigroplagiata* also resembles *Cosmopolites* but this banana weevil always pupates in a cocoon.
In Hawaii, a new species of *Cosmopolites*, namely *C. pruinosus*, has been described as pest of bananas.

Life cycle: Adult borers which feed on dead or dying debris are sluggish and nocturnal, living under cut pseudostems where the humidity is high. The female bites a small hole in the corm at ground level and after preparing the incubation chamber deposits a single egg. The drying of the tissue adjacent to the egg causes it to shrivel and thus the chamber is almost completely closed. Oviposition is greatest during the rainy season but the incubation period depends on temperature and can be from 7–30 days. In a lifetime a single female can lay up to 100 eggs but usually the number does not exceed 50.

After emergence the larvae tunnel into the corm for 20–100 days but after a series of moults turn towards the periphery to pupate. This pupatory stage is accomplished in 10 days but the immature adult often remains longer within the plant before biting through the external sheath. Adults live for up to two years and can live without food for six months. Little is known about their migratory habits though they move mainly at night by crawling, only flying on very rare occasions.

Ecology: The spread of the weevil within banana areas is generally accomplished in two ways; in planting material from infested plantations or by crawling to adjacent clean plantings. Of these the former is the most important and in Australia for example legislation exists to control the movement of plants within the genus *Musa* in an attempt to curb the insect's distribution. A third factor which can play a part in dispersal is rain, since when bananas are planted on steep slopes flood water does carry infected material as well as adults from high to low areas.

Natural enemies: *C. sordidus* has a number of natural enemies most of them originating like itself from Malesia. The most important are the histerid beetles *Plaesius javanus* and *Hololepta quadridentata* but amongst other species the leptid fly, *Chrysophilus ferruginosus,* the hydrophilid beetles, *Dactylosternum hydrophiloides, D. abdominale* and *D. subdepressum* from Trinidad.

Control:

Assessment of infestation. Before any programme for borer control is considered it is essential to estimate the degree of infestation. This assessment can be achieved by trapping adults or by directly surveying corm damage. This second method is in many cases an improvement on conventional traps as no relationship has been established between the adult population and the extent of plant damage.

Currently the Jamaican Banana Board recommend the following assessment technique. Ten corms within a 50–80 m radius are clean trimmed and the extent of larval tunnelling is noted over 25 %, 50 %, 75 % or the complete exposed surface, it being unnecessary to count the actual tunnels. The scoring of 0, 20, 40, 60 and 100 for tunnel damage visible throughout all the exposed surface is then made. If a mean score from these ten corms rises above 20 the infestation is considered serious and it is suggested that such a rating in the first crop can lead to a 10 % production decrease, a score of 40 resulting in a 20 % cropping loss.

Three types of trap are in use. The most efficient trap type embodies the use of two 10 cm fresh pseudostem discs superimposed on each other and placed between the plants. In Central America 25 such traps are sufficient to assess populations in a hectare and when a mean of 15–20 weevils are recovered from this stump trap after three 2-day counts control measures are considered necessary. This trap appears to be 3–4 times more attractive to borers than other types.

Sanitary methods. Since the banana weevil lives on plant debris it is essential to clear plantations of rotting vegetation and so reduce the areas suitable for harbouring the pest. After harvesting or wind damage pseudostems should be chopped up and scattered so that they quickly dry off and thus do not attract the pest. At reaping the pseudostem should be cut close to the ground and in certain areas the covering of the cut surface with soil is said to prevent the weevil's entry and deter oviposition.

Cultural practices. Regular desuckering and the cleaning of matts of dead leaves and decaying matter must also be observed. Good husbandry practices such as weeding and fertilizing help to produce vigorous banana plants which are more able to tolerate weevil damage. Infested land should not be planted while old corms remain or where insufficient time has elapsed for adult weevils to die after remnants of the previous crop has been removed. At replanting, suckers free from weevil damage should be used but if this is not possible corm trimming to reduce egg and larval numbers must be practiced. At no time should cleaned "seed" material be left in plantations overnight as it could attract the egg laying female weevil. The soaking of suckers in water will kill neither eggs nor larvae in the corm but dips in insecticide solutions are effective.

Resistance of crops. Indications that certain banana cultivars exhibit degrees of resistance to *Cosmopolites* have been recorded but no commercial cultivars possess this highly desirable characteristic to any useful extent. *Musa* (AAA Group) "Gros Michel" has been described as being more susceptible than either "Valery" or "Lacatan" clones of the group's Cavendish subgroup but the plantains in the (AAB) subgroup are generally recognised as being the most susceptible of all the *Musa* cultivars. Of the wild species *Musa acuminata* is usually susceptible but *M. balbisiana* from the Trinidad collection appears to be rather resistant as perhaps could be expected from the absence of the A genome. However, no breeding work has yet been specifically carried out to look into the incorporation of weevil resistance as a feature for a new commercial clone.

Biological control. Only in the Fiji and Tahiti Islands has the hysterid beetle, *P. javanus,* a natural enemy of *C. sordidus* shown success in reducing the weevil numbers and chemical control in these areas is consequently limited. None of the introductions of the potentially predacious or parasitic pests of *Cosmopolites* mentioned earlier, have been successful in reducing its population in various parts of the banana growing world.

Trapping. Though not a recommended practice in all areas it is cheap and effective in some. Pieces of fresh pseudostem described previously are positioned throughout the plantations and the migratory adults can be regularly collected by hand or poisoned by the use of a material such as 0,5 % gamma-BHC, DDT or dieldrin powder dusted onto the trap's cut surface. Despite the use of attractants poisoned baits do appear to be relatively ineffective and severe infestations cannot be controlled by this way alone.

Dipping new planting material. Before planting clean trimmed suckers should be immersed into a bath of a persistent soil insecticide. Various worldwide practices exist ranging from 10 mins–24 hours dipping in solutions of 0.1–0.4 % aldrin, dieldrin, chlordane and even a clay/endrin emulsion and all will successfully reduce larvae and egg populations in the corm as well as extending to it some degree of protection after planting. Levels of resistance to the organo-chlorine compounds have however been exhibited by *C. sordidus* in many banana growing areas including Ecuador and Jamaica and so a range of newer organo-phosphorus chemicals such as diazinon and fenchlorphos have been tested in dip solutions but with relatively poor results. Dusting the holes prior to planting with a powder formulation of the organo-chlorine materials is also useful and it is attractive to small growers who lack dipping facilities.

Field treatment of infested plants. About 30 days after planting new bananas in infested zones plants should be dusted or sprayed to protect them from weevil attack. This treatment should be repeated at regular intervals and this schedule should be based on local recommendations and the result of trap counts. The chlorinated hydrocarbons are again the most widely recommended post planting insecticides and a 0.1 % aldrin or dieldrin spray using 500 ml/matt is usually effective. Granular dieldrin at 2 kg a.i./ha is also active as well as 5 % gamma-BHC or dieldrin dusts at 20 g/matt and treatments such as these should give control, where weevil resistance is not a local feature, for at least 6 months.

The prolonged persistence of aldrin and dieldrin, which has assured the place of these two insecticides in the past over other less persistent materials such as DDT and gamma-BHC has led in recent years however to a reluctance to use these products, particularly in the export crop. This situation, coupled with the development of weevil resistance, has led to worldwide investigations into the suitability of a range of other chemicals for weevil control. Fensulfothion, carbofuran, phoxim, dichlorvos, trichlorphon, chlordecone and pirimiphos-ethyl being some of the newer introductions into this important field. Applications as sprays or granules at rates between 1.5–3.0 g a. i./matt, of one plant and a follower, have been found to be effective but application of these materials must be made to the base of the plant in order to prevent the approach of female egg layers and the emergence of new adults from the pupal chambers.

Literature

BRAITHWAITE, B. M. (1963): The banana beetle borer. Agric. Gaz. NSW 74, 396–399.
CHAMPION, J. (1968): El Plátano. Barcelona: Editorial Blume.
FEAKIN, S. D. (1972): Pest control in bananas. PANS Manual No 1 London: ODA.
FOREMAN, P. L.: Banana weevil borer. Bulletin No 1 Kingston: Banana Board.
FOREMAN, P. L. (1973): Investigation into the resistance of the banana weevil *(C. sordidus)* to dieldrin.
     Ann. Report 26–7 Kingston: Banana Board.
FOREMAN, P. L., & A. C. ROWLE (1973): Effectiveness of seven insecticidal compounds against the ba-
     nana weevil *(C. sordidus)*. Ann. Report 28–30 Kingston: Banana Board.
FRÖHLICH, G. & W. RODEWALD (1970): Pests and diseases of tropical crops and their control. London:
     Pergamon.
OSTMARK, H. E. (1974): Economic Insect Pests of Bananas. Ann. Rev. Ent. **19**, 161–176.
PULLEN, J. (1973): The control of the banana weevil *(Cosmopolites sordidus)* in Latin America and the Ca-
     ribbean with pirimiphos-ethyl. PANS **19** (2), 178–181.
SIMMONDS, N. W. (1966): Bananas. 2nd edn. London: Longman.
SWAINE, G. & R. J. CORCORAN (1973): A field trial on a suspected dieldrin resistant population of ba-
     nana weevil borer. Qd J. agric. Anim. Sci. **30**, 79–83.

Author: R. I. Smith

Rhynchophorus ferrugineus F. (Fig. 158)

Synonym: *R. signaticollis*

Common names: Red palm weevil; Indomalaiischer Palmenrüßler.

Geographical distribution: This species is confined to India, Sri Lanka, Burma, Thailand, Indonesia (Java), New Guinea, and the Philippines. CIE Map no 258.

Host plants: Date palm *(Phoenix dactylifera)*, sago palm *(Metroxylon sagu)* and toddy palm
(Phoenix sylvestris) are important host plants as well as coconut palm *(Cocos nucifera)* which is
the major host. Palmyra palm, oil palm, talipot palm, sugar palm, serdang palm, nibong palm,
royal palm, areca palm and some other ornamental palms are also attacked.

Symptoms: Infestation by the Red palm weevil
is broadly of two types (a) from the crown and
(b) through different parts of the stem including the leaf-axil and the bole. Observational
studies have revealed many symptoms associated with infestation. Associated with infestation from the crown, wilting or yellowing of the
inner fronds is invariably observed. Rotting of
the crown due to infestation by the red weevil
produces a characteristic odour which can easily by detected. Where entry is through the
leaf-axils, the green "leaves" may easily detach
when pulled because their basal parts have
been eaten away by the borer. After these leaves wilt, dry up and fall, small holes can be observed on the stem. An exudation of a thick,
reddish-brown, viscous fluid as well as an ex-

Fig. 158.   Larvae of *Rhynchophorus ferrugineus* in
a bole of a coconut palm (phot. C. Kurian)

trusion of the chewed-up and discarded fibres arises from these holes. The bases of attacked leaves split and an extrusion of fibres is seen in the cracks. The presence of cocoons, weevils or chewed-up fibres in leaf-axils, or at the base of the palm, offers further evidence of the presence of the pest. The gnawing or nibbling sound produced by the grubs while feeding is often easily audible.

Economic importance: This tissue-boring insect is one of the most dreadful and damaging among the major pests of coconut and is becoming an increasing menace to the coconut palm in southeast Asia. Once the palm is attacked it dies within six to eight months. Attacks by the weevil are more serious among younger palms (5–20 years old).

Morphology: The weevil is about 35 mm long and 12 mm wide, rusty-brown in colour, cylindrical in shape with a long prominent and anteriorly curved rostrum, and with no appreciable differences between the sexes. The male weevil has a tuft of reddish-brown hairs along the dorsal aspect of the snout. The larva is conical in shape, swollen in the middle and pointed towards both ends. It is yellowish-white, with a reddish-brown head, stout, fleshy and without legs. Its average length is 50 mm and the mean width in the middle is 20 mm.

Similarities to other pests: Both the Rhinoceros beetle and Red palm weevil have a characteristic anterior projection, but that of the former is recurved. The weevil is smaller in size. Consequent upon attack by either, chewed-up plant fibres may be noticed in and around the region of attack, especially the crown. *Rhynchophorus schach* and *R. papuanus* cause damage to coconut palms in South-east Asia similar to *R. ferrugineus*. *R. phoenicis* (Plate 33 d) attacks palms in Africa, *R. palmarum* in tropical America (see p. 423).

Life cycle: A female weevil lays about 200 eggs during its life span of about 3 months. Eggs are laid in wounds of palms and hatch in two or three days into grubs which bore into the plant. They feed on the soft succulent tissues, discarding all fibrous material. The larval period is about 2 months. The pupae are covered by a cylindrical cocoon made of fibrous strands. The pupation period lasts two to three weeks. The total life cycle is about three and a half months.

Ecology: *R. ferrugineus* attacks palms in the tropics and subtropics. There is no seasonal variation in its occurrence. Though polyphagous it has a preference for coconut and is multivoltine. Being a tissueborer it is not dependent to any great extent on the environment. Injuries on young palms attract the adult females for oviposition. *Oryctes* is a precursor for its entry.

Natural enemies: *Scolia erratica* parasitizes the larvae in Java. In India, a mite, *Tetrapolypus rhynchophori* is found as an external parasite on pupae and adults and a Calliphorid fly *Sarcophaga fuscicauda* has also been recorded as a parasite. In India, *Chelisoches moris,* a species of earwig, is encounted predating on the eggs and early instar grubs. *Platymeris laevicollis,* a Reduviid predator, imported for the control of *Oryctes* in India, feeds on the pest.

Control:
Sanitary methods. Maitenance of plant and field sanitation is essential. Dead and badly infested palms should be cut and burnt. A thorough search should be made in the leaf-axils for adults which should then be collected and killed. It is also necessary to prohibit cutting footholds in the trunks and cutting off green "leaves". If necessary, "leaves" can be cut at a distance of 120 cm from the stem which reduces the chances of entry by the weevil.
Integrated control. Integrated control to include the following conventional/sophisticated methods would be expected to control the pest satisfactorily. Mechanical with sanitational control methods are essential prerequisites for effective pest management. By using toddy-smeared coconut logs, weevils can be attracted and killed. Prevention of injury is also an essential prerequisite for controlling the pest. As a prophylactic measure, the damage caused by Rhinoceros beetle, leaf rot and bud rot diseases must be prevented with appropriate pesticides. Prophylactic leaf-axil

treatment and curative insecticidal injection have already proved their worth and would both be important components of integrated control. A male sterilization technique should also be included in the schedule.

Chemical control

a) Prophylactic. Filling the leaf-axils with an insecticide-sand mixture three times each year, is effective in protecting the palm against the red weevil and black beetle. The application of gamma-BHC or coal tar on wounds in palm trees checks the laying of eggs by the weevil.

b) Curative. Infestation is effectively controlled in India by the administration of pyrethrins + piperonyl-butoxide or carbaryl at 1 % concentration. A specially devised funnel (injector) and an auger are required for the purpose. All the holes in the stem are plugged and a hole is made just above the infested region. The tip of the funnel is inserted into the hole and the insecticide suspension poured in. If the entry of the pest is from the top to crown, the infested area should be cut off and the insecticide suspension poured slowly over it. In Thailand an alternative method consists of pouring diluted oxydemeton-methyl into a hole drilled into the trunk about 5 cm deep, just above the injury.

Literature

KURIAN, C. (1970): Pests of coconut and their control. Food, Farming and Agriculture **2** (7), 4–9.
KURIAN, C. & K. MATHEN (1971): Red palm weevil – hidden enemy of coconut palm. Indian Farming **21** (1), 29–31.
LEVER, R. J. A. W. (1969): Pests of coconut palm. FAO Agricultural studies: Food and Agriculture Organization of UN, Rome. pp. 113–119.
MATHEN, K. & C. KURIAN (1966): Prophylactic control of *Rhynchophorus ferrugineus* F., the red weevil of coconut. Indian J. agric. Sci., **36** (6), 285–286.
MATHEN, K. & C. KURIAN (1967): Insecticidal trials against *Rhynchophorus ferrugineus* F., the red weevil of coconut. Indian J. agric. Sci. **37** (6), 521–523.

Author: C. Kurian

Sitophilus oryzae (L.) (Figs. 159–160)

Synonyms: *Calandra oryzae, Sitophilus sasakii*

Common names: Rice weevil; Reiskäfer; Charançon du riz; Gorgojo del arroz.

Geographical distribution: Cosmopolitan. It is widespread throughout tropical, sub-tropical and temperate areas on all continents.

Host plants and stored products attacked: Most cereal grains (rice, sorghum, wheat, barley, maize) before harvest and in store.

Symptoms: The larva develops inside a single cereal grain and larval damage is thus hidden from visual inspection. The adult eats through the outer layers of the grain, after emergence from the pupa, leaving a roughly circular hole approximately $1^1/_2$mm in diameter. The feeding adult attacks whole or damaged grains causing irregularly shaped holes. In badly infested grain the endosperm may be completely consumed by larvae and adults, leaving only the shell of the grain perforated by feeding and emergence holes.

Economic importance: One of the most important primary pests of cereals after harvest causing loss in weight and leading to quality deterioration and fungal growth. Its activities as a primary pest attacking whole grains increase its importance by facilitating the development of secondary pests.

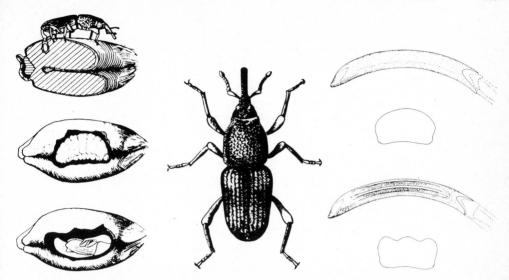

Fig. 159.   *Sitophilus oryzae*. Left (from above to below): egg-laying female, larva and pupa in a wheat grain; right: adult beetle (Courtesy of Imperial Chemical Industries)

Fig. 160.   Above: male aedeagus of *Sitophilus oryzae;* below: male aedeagus of *S. zeamais* (after Halstead)

Morphology: The stout, legless larva is seldom seen since it develops within a single grain. The adult is 2.5–4 mm long, dark brown with a long, narrow snout and 8-segmented, elbowed, clubbed antennae. Adults of *S. oryzae* and *S. zeamais* may be distinguished from those of *S. granarius* by the following characters: the possession of hind wings, the round (instead of oval) punctures on the thorax, and the presence (usually) of two reddish-brown areas on each elytron. The adults of *S. oryzae* and *S. zeamais* cannot be distinguished effectively by external characters. The sculpturing of the male aedeagus is the most useful taxonomic character (see Fig. 160); in *S. oryzae* the convex surface of this structure is smooth and shining.

Similarities to other pests: This species can only be distinguished from *S. zeamais* by the form of the aedeagus, and the damage caused by the two species is indistinguishable. However, in terms of control practices, there is an important behavioural difference between these two species, namely that, although both species are winged, *S. oryzae* rarely flies. Also, the two species exhibit differing food preferences; *S. oryzae* tends to prefer the smaller grains, especially rice. In many respects the damage caused by this species is similar to that caused by the moth *Sitotroga cerealella* but the two types may be distinguished by the form of the adult emergence holes, and the presence of adult feeding damage in the case of *Sitophilus*.

Life cycle: The female bores holes in the surface layers of grains either in the field or in store; in each hole she deposits a single egg and then plugs the hole with a hard secretion. The larva feeds and develops within a single grain and pupates there. After pupation the adult bites its way out of the grain. The adults feed and live for up to five months. Under optimum conditions, the life cycle from oviposition to adult emergence takes 26 days and the female lays up to 300 eggs over a period of many weeks.

Ecology: Optimum development occurs at 30 °C and 70 % r.h. and the physical limits for successful development are 17 to 34 °C and 45 to 100 % r.h. This species is restricted to cereal grains which are large enough to allow complete development of a single larva per grain.

Natural enemies: Three hymenopteran parasites *(Anisopteromalus calandrae, Lariophagus dis-*

tinguendus and *Choetospila elegans*) have been noted as parasitic on the larvae of *S. oryzae*. They may reduce the rate of increase of this pest in certain situations.

Control: Malathion at 12 ppm is the recommended treatment for protection of stored cereals. This may be applied as a dust at the rate of 600 g of 2 % dust per ton or as an emulsifiable concentrate at rate of 1.2 litres of 1 % spray per ton or equivalent dosages at alternative flow rates. Alternative insecticides such as bromophos, pirimiphos methyl and tetrachlorvinphos are also effective at rates of the order of 10–12 ppm and may be used where local Insecticide Regulations permit. Where maize is stored on the cob or sorghum on the ear, the recommended treatment is 10 ppm of lindane, calculated on a shelled weight basis. This is sometimes given as 450 g of 1 % dust per cubic metre of cobs but may vary with the variety. Protection of unthreshed or unshelled cereal is difficult and control is best achieved by drying, shelling or threshing and then treating with insecticides as given above.
Cereals may be cleared of infestation by fumigation at the scheduled dosage rates (see appendix, p. 385). Disinfestation of maize cobs stored in polythene lined sacks or tightly sealed metal containers may be effected by in-bag fumigants such as phosphine, ethylene dibromide and carbon tetrachloride.
The surfaces of stores may be kept free from residual pockets of infestation by spraying monthly with fenitrothion, chlorpyrifos (or other approved insecticide) at 0.5 to 1 g active ingredient per square metre. These sprays should not be applied to the commodity either loose or in hessian bags, but bags of commodity may be sprayed with malathion or pirimiphos methyl.

Resistance: Resistance to lindane is widespread. Resistance to malathion has been demonstrated in *S. oryzae* but not to any significant extent at present.

General situation: *S. oryzae* can fly from stores to infest cereals in the field pre-harvest. It is therefore desirable to keep storage centres away from the growing crop. Reduction of residual infestation with hygienic measures and spraying of emptied stores with insecticides will help to avoid reinfestation of the new crop. Provided the crop is dried, shelled and treated as recommended, successful control is possible but protection of inadequately dried, unshelled or unthreshed cereals presents a difficult problem.

Literature

HALSTEAD, D.G.H. (1964): The separation of *Sitophilus oryzae* (L.) and *S. zeamais* Motschulsky (Col., Curculionidae), with a summary of their distribution. Entomol. mon. Mag. **99,** 72–74.

Authors: C. P. Haines & D. J. Webley

Sitophilus zeamais Motsch. (Figs. 160–161)

Synonyms: *Calandra oryzae* (misid.), *Sitophilus oryzae* (misid.)

Common names: Maize weevil; (La-Plata-)Maiskäfer; Gorgojo del maíz.

Geographical distribution: Cosmopolitan. It is widespread throughout tropical and warm temperate areas on all continents.

Host plants and stored products attacked: Most cereal grains (especially maize, sorghum, rice, wheat) before harvest and in store.

Symptoms and economic importance: See *S. oryzae*.

Fig. 161. *S. zeamais* on a maize cob in the field before harvest (phot. H. Schmutterer)

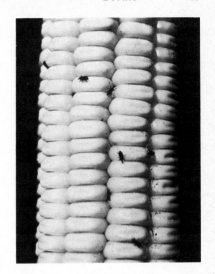

Morphology: The stout, legless larva is seldom seen since it develops within a single grain. The adult is 2.5–4.5 mm long, dark brown with a long, narrow snout and 8-segmented, elbowed, clubbed antennae. Adults of *S. zeamais* and *S. oryzae* may be distinguished from those of *S. granarius* by the following characters: the possession of hindwings, the round (instead of oval) punctures on the thorax, and the presence (usually) of two reddish-brown areas on each elytron. The adults of *S. zeamais* and *S. oryzae* cannot be distinguished effectively by external characters. The sculpturing of the male aedeagus is the most useful taxonomic character (see Fig. 160); in *S. zeamais* the convex surface of this structure has two longitudinal furrows.

Similarities to other pests: This species can only be distinguished from *S. oryzae* by the form of the aedeagus (Fig. 160), and the damage caused by the two species is indistinguishable. However (unlike *S. oryzae*) *S. zeamais* is a strong flier and is able to easily invade ripening seeds in the field. Also, the two species exhibit differing food preferences; *S. zeamais* tends to prefer the larger grains, especially maize. In many respects the damage caused by this species is similar to that caused by the moth *Sitotroga cerealella* but the two types may be distinguished by the form of the adult emergence holes, and by the presence of adult feeding damage in the case of *Sitophilus*.

Life cycle: The female bores holes in the surface layers of grains either in the field or in store; in each hole she deposits a single egg and then plugs the hole with a hard secretion. The larva feeds and develops within a single grain and pupates there. After pupation the adult bites its way out of the grain. The adults feed and live for up to five months. Under optimum conditions, the life cycle from oviposition to adult emergence takes 30 days and the female lays up to 300 eggs over a period of many weeks.

Ecology: See *S. oryzae* (p. 413).

Natural enemies: Two hymenopteran parasites (*Anisopteromalus calandrae* and *Choetospila elegans*) have been noted as parasitic on the larvae of *S. zeamais*. They may reduce the rate of increase of this pest in certain situations.

Control: See *S. oryzae* (p. 414).

Resistance. Resistance to lindane is widespread.

General situation. See *S. oryzae*.

Literature

HALSTEAD, D.G.H. (1964): The separation of *Sitophilus oryzae* (L.) and *S. zeamais* Motschulsky (Col., Curculionidae), with a summary of their distribution. Entomol. mon. Mag. **99**, 72–74.

Authors: C. P. Haines and D. J. Webley

Family: Scolytidae

Hypothenemus hampei (Ferr.) (Figs. 162–163)

Synonym: *Stephanoderes hampei*

Common names: Coffee berry borer; Kaffeekirschenkäfer; Scolyte du grain (de café); Barrenillo del grano del café.

Geographical distribution: The distribution of *H. hampei* is shown in CIE Map no 170. The insect is indigenous to Africa where it is widely spread and has been introduced to Brazil and more recently to Guatemala, and to the main growing areas of Asia, excluding India, and to several of the Pacific Islands.

Host plants: The insect lives and breeds normally only in *Coffea* spp. and all the main commercial species of coffee are attacked. Records on other plants are of no economic importance.

Symptoms: The damage is to the young fruits and older seeds. The insect bores into the young fruit while the seeds are soft and following this many berries may fall. In Zaire it was found that *H. hampei* was responsible (in 1953) for a shedding of 14 percent out of a total shedding of 17 percent of the crop. The chief damage results from the breeding in the seeds which occurs from the time when the endosperm first becomes hard up to the time when the berry is ripe and even afterwards in the overripe berry on the tree or after it has fallen to the ground. The bean becomes riddled with borings.

Economic importance: There are records of up to 80 percent, or even 90 percent of the berries having been damaged, and this is a direct loss since either the attacked beans do not pass through the original curing process, or they have to be removed before final grading and if used at all can only go into the lowest grades. In Brazil losses of 60 to 80 percent have been recorded in plantations where control measures were not applied. This pest is of great economic importance, it has caused very great losses in Central African countries and in Indonesia. In Brazil it has caused incalculable losses and is still a serious primary pest of the crop.

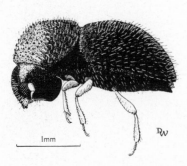

Fig. 162. *Hypothenemus hampei* (after Le Pelley, Pests of Coffee, Longman, London)

Fig. 163. Coffee berries with entry holes of *H. hampei* (phot. H. Schmutterer)

Morphology: The insect is a small dark Scolytid beetle which when found together with its typical damage to the coffee seeds cannot be mistaken for any other insect, except a few other species of Scolytid that do similar damage to the berries but are comparatively rare. The white legless larvae with brown heads are unmistakable since they always occur in the characteristic tunnels in the beans. The pupal stage is also passed in the bean.

Similarities to other pests: The only similar coffee pests are other species of Scolytidae which bore in twigs or branches.

Life cycle: The life cycle does not vary greatly in different parts of the world. Females always predominate, at periods of full reproduction in the crop the ratio of females to males is about 10 to 1, at times when the old crop has been collected and laying has not begun in the new crop the residual population consists mainly of females since females live longer than males. The female beetle enters the coffee berry by a circular hole which it makes usually in the tip of the berry. It tunnels in the bean and lays eggs in the tunnel. The eggs hatch in 5 to 9 days and the larvae feed on the substance of the bean. The larval stages occupy about 14 days and the pupal stage is between 4 and 9 days. Complete development from egg to adult is between 25 and 35 days. The life of the female beetle averages about 160 days which is sufficient to enable the insect to carry over from one coffee crop to the next, and stresses the need for thorough removal of old berries in which it breeds.

Ecology: Conditions suitable to the beetle are limited by altitude, and it is more common in low altitude coffee. In East Africa it is rare above 1500 m. In Java severe attacks occur between 250 and 1100 m. Damp conditions favour the borer and in Brazil and several countries of Africa it has been found that infestation is greater in damp shaded plantations than in dry, open ones.

Natural enemies: There are three important parasites found in Central Africa, two Bethylids *Prorops nasuta* and *Cephalonomia stephanoderis* and a Braconid *Heterospilus coffeicola*. Together *P. nasuta* and *H. coffeicola* are considered to be of value in some African countries though they do not prevent some serious attacks occurring. *P. nasuta* has been imported into Brazil, Sri Lanka and Indonesia (Java), it has not proved of great value anywhere but has been considered useful in Brazil in conjunction with other control measures. *H. coffeicola* was imported into Indonesia (Java) apparently without beneficial results. *C. stephanoderis* is present in the Ivory Coast where it has been responsible for a considerable reduction of the berry borer. This parasite has not been introduced to other countries but would be worth a trial.
Two fungi attacking *H. hampei* occur in Java namely *Beauveria bassiana* and *Spicaria javanica*. They cause appreciable mortality of the beetle when conditions are favourable. *B. bassiana* is present also in Africa and Brazil where it is of value in favourable conditions. In view of recent successes with this fungus further study of its possibilities against *H. hampei* would perhaps be useful. The few other occasional enemies known, including Pyrrhocorid bugs, ants and some birds are of no real importance.

Control:
Legislative. Any country or island that may still be free from this pest should take particular precautions against its importation in coffee beans. Legislation should require any trade coffee to be dried to a moisture content below 12.5 percent. Seed for planting or ordinary marketing can be disinfected by carbon disulphide at a dosage of 300 ccs to 1 cubic metre for 15 hours, this has been reported not to affect germination.
Sanitary and cultural practices. This is one of the insects for which sanitary and cultural practices are more useful for control than the use of insecticides. Since in conditions which favour the beetle and when coffee berries are present throughout the year continuous breeding occurs, a great measure of control can be achieved by preventing this breeding. This is done by ensuring that for at least three months, preferably longer, each year there is a period free from berries, which entails the laborious task of the most careful and thorough collection from the trees and ground of all the

overripe, ripe and bored green berries. In many places satisfactory yields are dependent on this being done and it has been proved that if it is scrupulously done the damage by the beetle is greatly reduced.

Chemical control. Several chemicals have proved satisfactory as dusts or sprays. In Brazil two or more applications of a dust containing 1 percent gamma-BHC applied first when 5 percent of the berries had been entered was found satisfactory, and not to cause any change in flavour of the coffee. In the Central African Republic large scale spraying was done with endrin using 4 litres (800 g of active insecticide) in 11 litres of oil per hectare; only one treatment was required. In Kenya spraying with dieldrin 18 percent miscible liquid at the rate of 625 ml in 200 litres of water is recommended at three week intervals after the main crop, but only as a supplement to the cultural control measure mentioned above.

Literature

LEPAGE, H. S. & O. GIANNOTTI (1950): Atividade de alguns inseticidas modernos sôbre a broca do café *Hypothenemus hampei*. Archos Inst. biol. **19**, 299–308, S. Paulo.
ALMEIDA, P. R. & R. D. CAVALCANTE (1964): Ensaio de campo novos inseticidas orgânicos no combate à broca do café *Hypothenemus hampei* (Ferr. 1867). Archos Inst. biol. **31**, 85–90, S. Paulo.
BERGAMIN, J. (1943): Contribuição para o conhecimento da biologia da broca do café. Archos Inst. biol. **14**, 31–72, S. Paulo.
(1960): Les Problèmes Insecticides Outre-Mer. IRAT Journées Francaises d'études et d'information consacrées aux insecticides agricoles, Paris.

Author: R. H. Le Pelley

Xyleborus and Xylosandrus spp. (Fig. 164)

Important species and synonyms: *Xylosandrus compactus* (Eichh.) (syn. *Xyleborus morstatti*), *X. morigerus* (Blandf.) (syn. *Xyleborus coffeae* Wurth), *Xyleborus ferrugineus* (F.) (syn. *X. confusus*, *X. bispinatus*, *X. fuscatus* etc.), *X. fornicatus* Eichh.

Common names: *X. compactus:* Coffee-twig borer, Schwarzer Kaffeezweigbohrer, Scolyte des rameaux; *X. morigerus:* Brown coffee-borer, Brauner Kaffeezweigbohrer; *X. fornicatus:* Tea shot-hole borer, Teezweigbohrer.

Geographical distribution:
X. compactus: Japan, Vietnam, Malaysia, Indonesia, India and Sri Lanka, West and Central Africa, Kenya, Tanzania, Fiji, Hawaii and Florida. CIE Map no 244.
X. morigerus: an Oriental species but now recorded from East Africa, Madagascar, Réunion, Sri Lanka, Vietnam, Malaysia, Indonesia, Philippines, Papua New Guinea, Queensland, Samoa, Fiji, Caroline Islands, Colombia and Brazil. CIE Map no 292.
X. ferrugineus: througout the tropics, but, apart from Malaya, not on the Asiatic mainland. Present in Papua New Guinea, Samoa, Solomon Islands, Fiji and many other Pacific islands. CIE Map no 277.
X. fornicatus: Sri Lanka, India, Burma, Indo-China, Java, Borneo, New Guinea, Taiwan, Fiji and Hawaii. In this account we shall be dealing mainly with the morphologically recognisable race *fornicatior* Egg. responsible for damage to tea and prevalent in Sri Lanka. It is relatively rare in southern India and unknown elsewhere.

Host plants: All four species are highly polyphagous amongst woody plants but the following are the non-forest tree hosts which are of most general importance.
X. compactus: coffee (especially Robusta), cocoa, avocado pear, mango, tea.
X. morigerus: coffee (especially Robusta), tea, camphor.
X. ferrugineus: cocoa, rubber, mango, coconut.
X. fornicatus: tea, castor, avocado pear, citrus, cocoa.

Symptoms: Only a minority of species of scolytid beetles are primary pests of healthy woody plants, the majority selecting unthrifty or moribund hosts. *X. fornicatus* and *X. compactus* are outright primary pests, whereas *X. morigerus* and *X. ferrugineus* can be primary pests in some host plant species.

All four species attack only woody tissue, *X. compactus, X. morigerus* and *X. fornicatus* generally in stems of small diameter (1–2 cm) but *X. ferrugineus* not usually in stems of less than 10 cm diameter. *X. compactus* and *X. fornicatus* usually select healthy plants but though *X. morigerus* prefers weak or senile plants infestation is usually primary. Structural weakness results and, consequently, broken stems may be symptomatic of infestation. Fungal attack occurring via the gallery causes discolouration of wood and bark with frequent wilting above the site of beetle entry. Except for its two economically most important hosts, cocoa and rubber, *X. ferrugineus* seldom attacks healthy plants and therefore in general tends to exacerbate pre-existing conditions. In cocoa its attacks are associated with a fungal wilt of the tree caused by *Ceratocystis fimbriata* which is often lethal (see also p. 100). External symptoms of infection by this fungus are wilting of the whole tree, or part of it, followed by rapid death of the affected parts. Mature leaves become pendulous like flush leaves. Wilt is invariably associated with boring by scolytid beetles, especially in the basal trunk region, the activities of which may precede wilting. Following fungal attack there is intense discolouration of the wood just above soil level and in the region of scolytid tunnels the bark internally is brown or claret coloured. Zones of yellow, red and brown occur in xylem and phloem and streaks of blue corresponding with medullary rays are present in the xylem vessels. However, the appearance of affected tissues may be very variable. In Trinidad diseased areas of tissue are said to have a smell strongly resembling that of sardines.

Economic importance: *X. compactus* is an important pest of Robusta coffee causing losses of up to 20 percent of the crop. The extent to which it attacks Arabica coffee varies regionally. In the Seychelles, Mauritius and Fiji it damages avocado pear and in West Africa can be injurious to seedling cocoa. In Java *X. morigerus* is very injurious to Robusta coffee, but less so to Excelsa. *X. ferrugineus* may attack rubber through tapped bark thus allowing fungal invasion of the host tissues; attack itself is generally repelled by the rubber tree. It is especially important on cocoa in the Neotropics because of its involvement in *Ceratocystis* wilt. There is reason to believe that this condition is the feared 'blast' of cocoa of which records in the West Indies and Central America go back almost to the time of the Spanish Conquistadores. Losses may be extremely heavy. In the state of Aragua, Venezuela, 20 percent of trees died between 1951 and 1956 and in Colombia nearly half a million were lost between 1925 and 1941. A severe epidemic occurred in Trinidad in the 1950's.

X. fornicatus has been a serious pest of tea in Sri Lanka for over 60 years, but elsewhere is of little importance except on castor. Repeated attacks cause severe debilitation of the bushes with a yield loss of at least 20 percent; responses of infested bushes to fertilisers are actually reversed.

Morphology: The females of all four species are small (4–5 mm long) cylindrical beetles; in all but *X. ferrugineus* the male is markedly smaller than the female. The identification of scolytid beetles is best left to the specialist.

Similarities to other pests: Great care must be taken to distinguish between species causing primary and those causing secondary damage, a category into which most Scolytidae fall. For instance, over 60 species have been recorded from cocoa trees which have initially been weakened by other agencies. On coffee *X. compactus* and *X. morigerus* must not be confused with the ubiquitous coffee berry borer, *Hypothenemus hampei,* an insect restricted solely to the fruit.

Life cycle: All four species are ambrosia beetles, their larvae feeding on fungi growing on the gallery walls rather than directly on host plant tissues. Eggs are laid in the galleries, there are three larval instars followed by an exarate pupal stage. Development from egg to adult is in the region of 20 to 40 days. The males are flightless and there is a disparate sex ratio of about one male to

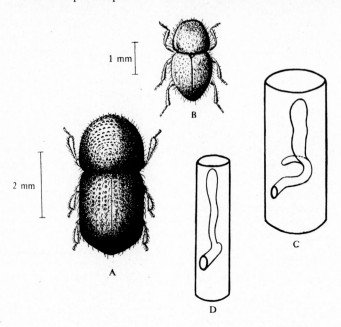

Fig. 164.   A = adult female of *Xylosandrus compactus;* B = adult male; C = typical gallery form in cocoa; D = gallery form in the thinner stems attacked (after Entwistle, Pests of Cocoa, Longman, London)

20 females in *X. morigerus* and about one male to 10 females in the other species dealt with here. Females are normally fertilised in the parent gallery before flight. There is very little doubt that in *X. compactus* and *X. ferrugineus* males are haploid and are produced arrhenotokously. Evidence that adult females of *X. ferrugineus* may aestivate in soil exists.
The galleries excavated by *X. fornicatus* in tea and *X. compactus* and *X. morigerus* in coffee are rather similar, consisting of a single short entrance tunnel, at right angles to the stem's long axis, leading from which is a chamber of rather irregular shape in which the brood develops. The galleries of *X. ferrugineus* in cocoa usually follow the vascular rings in a cross sectional plane, but occasionally extend transversely, or even longitudinally, and may be much branched in an irregularly dichotomous fashion.

Ecology: Flight in *X. ferrugineus* is known to be controlled by an endogenous circadian rhythm and is crepuscular. The other three species fly in daylight. Adult females of *X. compactus, X. fornicatus* and *X. ferrugineus* carry the ambrosia fungus to the new gallery in small pockets of their bodies called mycangia. Investigation will probably show *X. morigerus* to behave similarly. Whilst *X. compactus* attacks healthy coffee its ability to attack healthy cocoa seedlings is not clear cut and may vary regionally. *X. ferrugineus* seems to attack both healthy cocoa trees and trees already infected by *C. fimbriata*. Attack is concentrated in a region ± 10 cms about the soil line though a rather higher trunk region seems to provide conditions conducive to greater reproductive success. A similar disparity between zones of preferred attack and optimal reproductive success occurs in *X. compactus* on seedling cocoa in Nigeria. The role of *X. ferrugineus* in cocoa wilt disease is twofold. Firstly, where attack is truly primary beetles may act as vectors of the fungus. Secondly, following attack, millions of spores are extruded daily, with wood dust and frass, from beetle galleries so tending to increase the epiphytotic rate. In this way in Trinidad it has been estimated 17 million chlamydospores are liberated per infected tree per day.

Little is known about the population dynamics of most scolytid beetles. In both Cameroun and the Ivory Coast peak densities of *X. compactus* on coffee occur from September to November for which physiological changes in coffee twigs combined with climatic influences are said to be responsible. Pruning of tea is practised on a three year cycle in Sri Lanka. Attack by *X. fornicatus* usually begins about six months after pruning and the population then increases to a peak in the second half of the second year, after which there is a decline, thought to be a consequence of depletion of breeding sites. Manurial treatments designed to increase yields have, by favouring rapid increase in *X. fornicatus,* had the reverse effect.

Natural enemies: Few parasites, and no predators, are known. Where control by removal of infested branches was practised *Tetrastichus xyleborum* (Hymenoptera, Eulophidae) parasitised 22 percent of broods of *X. morigerus* in E. Java and 43 percent where it was not. However, as it lays its eggs between the bark and the wood it can only reach broods in very slender twigs. In the same area a similar, if not identical species of *Tetrastichus* is said to have parasitised *X. compactus.* An undescribed bethylid (Hymenoptera, Bethylidae) has been recorded attacking *X. compactus* in Java.

Control: Cultural and sanitary methods of control have been of no avail with *X. fornicatus.* Early tests with dieldrin showed promising results, but outbreaks of tea tortrix moth, *Homona coffearia* (see p. 510), continued for up to six months following spraying and constituted a serious side effect. Until very recently *X. fornicatus* has been controlled by a single post-pruning application of 1.5 lb dieldrin per acre (= 1.78 kg per ha.) following which tea tortrix was controlled with one or two applications of DDT or, in areas prone to red spider mite (*Oligonychus coffeae,* see p. 268), with trichlorfon. It has now been found that the tortrix effect is less if heptachlor is used. This is used at the rate of 2.0 to 2.5 lb per acre (= 2.2 to 2.8 kg per ha.) in 80–100 gallons of water (= 800 to 1000 lit per ha.) as a single application 12 to 15 months after pruning. An interval of three weeks must be allowed between spraying and plucking and leaves from two subsequent pickings should be mixed in the ratio of one to ten with leaves from unsprayed tea. Control of tea shot-hole borer allows response to fertiliser and large yield increases are then often possible. Adequate control of *X. compactus* and *X. morigerus* on coffee has not been achieved either by manual removal of infested twigs or by insecticides. However, in West Africa application of a combined dieldrin (0.2 percent) – Bordeaux mixture (0.5 percent) is more effective than dieldrin alone against *X. compactus,* the Bordeaux mixture being said to act partly as a sticker for the dieldrin and partly by destroying the fungi on which larval beetles feed in the galleries. A minimum of two applications are recommended. This method, which has reduced infestations by 70 percent, might well prove equally successful against the very similar *X. morigerus.* Insecticides have so far failed to prevent injury by *X. compactus* to cocoa seedlings in Nigeria or on tea in Japan. Control of the *X. ferrugineus – C. fimbriata* association depends on prevention of injury by the beetle and on minimising the effective spread of fungal inoculum. In Ecuador trunk sprays of 1 percent lindane with 20 percent Estab® (a plastic sticker) every six months gave over 70 percent reduction in disease, presumably by controlling beetle attack. Prevention of wounds to the tree during weeding, regular sterilisation of implements, application of fungicide to pruning and other cuts and rapid destruction of infected trees all help greatly to reduce disease spread. In general disease occurs at a much higher incidence, and is more virulent, in cocoa with a preponderance of Criollo characters.

Literature

BROWNE, F. G. (1961): The biology of Malayan *Scolytidae* and *Platypodidae*. Malay. Forest Records **22.** 255 pp.

BROWNE, F. G. (1962): Notes on *Xyleborus ferrugineus* (F.), *(Coleoptera, Scolytidae)*. Rep. W. Afr. Timber Borer Res. Unit **5,** 47–55.

CRANHAM, J. E. (1966): Tea pests and their control. Ann. Rev. Entomol. **11**, 491–514.

ENTWISTLE, P. F. (1972): Pests of Cocoa. Longman, London, 779 pp.

LE PELLEY, R. H. (1968): Pests of Coffee. Longman, London, 590 pp.
MEIFFREN, M. & M. BELIN (1961): Essai de traitement mixte insecticide et fongicide contre le scolyte des rameaux du caféier *Xyleborus morstatti* Hag. Café-Cacao-Thé **4**, 150–158.

Author: P. F. Entwistle

Other harmful Coleoptera (Figs. 165–171 and Plate 33 c):

Batocera spp. [*B. rubus* (L.) and *B. rufomaculata* (de Geer)]. Larvae feed in stems and branches of mango and other fruit trees in India. *B. rufomaculata* (Tropischer Ficusbockkäfer) has also been introduced into the eastern mediterranean region.

Bixadus sierricola (White), West African coffee borer (Westafrikanischer Kaffeebohrer) (Fig. 165). This is the most serious of all the longicorns on coffee in West and Central Africa. Young trees are completely ringbarked by its larvae and die, older trees survive very enfeebled and may show several incomplete girdlings. When many larvae are present mines are made in all parts of the heart-wood and sap wood. Up to 60 percent of the trees in a plantation have been said to be killed by this insect. Treatment with dieldrin has also been shown to be an effective control for *Bixadus* (see p. 398).

Steirostoma breve (Sulz.) (= *S. depressum*), Cocoa beetle (Kakaobockkäfer) (Fig. 166). This grey coloured, 1.2–3 cm long beetle is a major cacoa pest in the South American tropics and on the Caribbean Islands. The most important alternative hosts are *Pachira insignis* and *Hibiscus tiliaceus*. The larvae hollow out galleries inside branches and young stems, which often kills the affected plant portions. The construction of pupal chambers can have similar consequences. Until a few years ago, chemical control was carried out effectively with lead arsenic + linseed oil (sticker). Repeated spraying with DDT or chlordane is effective in the dry season.

Xylotrechus quadripes Chevr., Coffee stem borer (Indischer Kaffeebohrer) (Fig. 167). The larvae of this very agile long-horned beetle are about 2–2.5 cm long in full-grown stage and bore into the bark and wood of coffee stems and roots in Southern India and South East Asia. Eggs are deposited in small groups in crevices of the bark. Young plants can be killed rapidly by larval feeding, while older ones remain alive for a longer period, but are increasingly unproductive. *Coffea arabica* is attacked more heavily than *C. canephora*. Several alternative hosts are known, inclu-

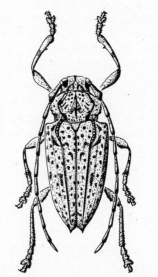

20 mm

Fig. 165.   Coffee stem, damaged by larvae of *Bixadus sierricola* (phot. H. Schmutterer)

Fig. 166.   *Steirostoma breve* (after Entwistle, Pests of Cocoa, Longman, London)

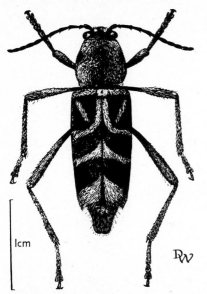

Fig. 168. Larvae of *Schizonycha* sp. on banana roots (phot. H. Schmutterer)

Fig. 167. *Xylotrechus quadripes* (after Le Pelley, Pests of Coffee, Longman, London)

ding teak *(Tectona grandis)*. Since the beetles are sun-loving insects, very shady plantations are only slightly affected. For this reason, the cultivation of shade trees is recommended in areas which are at risk. Repeated spraying with gamma-BHC on stems and main branches distinctly reduces the degree of infestation (India).

Cochliotis sp., **Dermolepida** spp., **Eulepida** sp., **Lachnosterna** spp., **Phyllophaga** spp., **Leucopholis** sp., **Schizonycha** spp. (Fig. 168) et al. do damage in various parts of the world owing to their white, C-shaped larvae (chafer grubs, Engerlinge), which feed in the soil on roots and other subterranean plant portions (see Fig. 168). Considerable damage is done on sugar cane in East Africa and Australia (Queensland) and on some Caribbean Islands, but rubber in South East Asia, coconut palm in South India and groundnut and tobacco in parts of Africa and India are also affected.

Heteroligus spp., Yam beetles (Yamskäfer). Adults and larvae of *H. meles* (Billb.) (= *H. claudius*) and *H. appius* (Burm.) attack yam tubers in the ground mainly in West Africa. *Prionoryctes* spp. do similar damage.

Pantorhytes spp. (*P. batesi* Faust, *P. proximus* Faust, *P. szentivanyi* Mshl.) (Fig. 169). These beetles are conspicuous for their oval abdomen and long legs. They are destructive cocoa pests, especially in New Guinea. Their apodous larvae bore into stems and branches. With repeated attack, the stems may split open and affected plants die off. The development of one generation takes about 10 months. Planting of barrier crops (the beetles cannot fly) of sweet potato, taro, *Leucaena glauca, Imperata* around the cocoa crop has proved of value. Beetles can be controlled by repeated spraying with trichlorphon, larvae with fenthion and dichlorvos. The removal of alternative host plants from cocoa growing areas is an important aspect of plant hygiene.

Rhabdoscelus obscurus (Boisd.). Larvae bore in stems of sugar cane in New Guinea, East Australia, on the Pacific Isles and in Hawaii (CIE-Map no 280). Other host plants are banana, sago palm, coconut palm, oil palm and papaya. *Metasmius anceps* (Gylh.) (= *M. bilobus*) attacks sugar cane stems in Bolivia and Peru.

Apion spp. *A. godmani* Wagn. is a serious pest of *Phaseolus* beans in Central America, *A. varium* Wagn. of *Vigna* beans in West Africa. The larvae of both species attack the seeds.

Rhynchophorus palmarum (L)., South American palm weevil (Neotropischer Palmenrüßler) (Fig. 170 and Plate 33 c). This species occurs on the Caribbean Islands and in Central and South America (CIE Map no 259), where it takes on much the same important role played by *R. ferrugineus* in Asia (see p. 410). It attacks not only coconut trees but also other palm trees belonging to different genera, such as *Elaeis, Livistonea* and *Phoenix*. The eggs are deposited by the female of this brown-black to black beetle (Plate 33 c), in wounds and cracks in the bark of boles. A total of over 700 eggs can be produced per female. The larvae hatch after about 3 days and gradually bore into the stem, in which they produce large burrows (Fig. 170) in the course of their development up to pupation, lasting about $1^1/_2$–2 months. These burrows are filled with coarse threads which have an acid smell. The cylindrical cocoon also consists of coarse threads and is placed beneath the bark. Pupal period lasts about $^1/_2$–1 month. The total developmental period from egg to adult takes about $2^1/_2$ months. The newly emerged beetle remains for a few days inside the cocoon and then works its way out into the open. Severely affected palms gradually die off. The economic importance of *R. palmarum* is heightened by the fact that the beetle transmits the nematode *Rhadinaphelenchus cocophilus* (see p. 241), which gives rise to the davastating red ring disease of coconut palm. Another beetle, *Rhinostomus barbirostris,* is also capable of such transmission, but far less important.

Fig. 169.   *Pantorhytes szentivanyi* (after Entwistle,.Pests of Cocoa, Longman, London)

Fig. 170.   Burrows of larvae of *Rhynchophorus palmarum* in a bole of a coconut palm (phot. H. Schmutterer)

Damage of palm stems resulting form cultivation procedures must be avoided. Affected trees must be felled as quickly as possible and burnt. The beetles can be caught in traps containing iso-amylacetate, malt extract and maize meal. In Venezuela, cylindrical wire-mesh traps are recommended ($\varnothing$ 0.5 m, height 1 m), which are filled with plant residues and whose bottom layer is treated with methomyl. These traps should be emptied at least once a week, when trapped beetles should be killed and plant residues should be destroyed. Aldrin sprays reduce the severity of attack, but the efficacious use of insecticides is doubtful for economic and ecological reasons.

Sternochetus spp., Mango stone weevils. Several species attack mango in Asia and/or parts of Africa. The larvae feed in the stones and destroy the young fruit.

Sycophorus interstitialis Gylh., Sisal weevil (Sisalrüßler) occurs in East Africa and elsewhere (CIE Map no 66). The beetle feeds on young, soft leaves whereas the larvae bore in leaves and in the stem.

Henosepilachna elaterii (Rossi) (= *Epilachna chrysomelina*), African melon ladybird (Gefleckter Gurkenkäfer). Larvae and adults attack leaves of cucurbitaceous plants in the Near and Middle East and in large parts of Africa. *H. vigintioctopunctata* (F.) (= *Epilachna vigintioctopunctata*) is a serious pest of eggplant, cucurbits, tomato, potato and tobacco in India.

Aulacophora africana Weise (= *Aulacophora, Raphidopalpa foveicollis*), Red melon beetle (Zinnoberroter Kürbiskäfer). In the mediterranean region, in Africa and Asia. Adult beetles attack leaves, larvae roots and recumbent fruit of cucumber, pumpkin, melon etc.

Colaspis spp. Larvae live in several Latin American countries on the roots of wild grasses and banana, adults gnaw holes into the peel of young banana fruit.

Diabrotica spp. Larvae of some species are pests of legumes (*Vigna* spp., *Arachis hypogaea*), maize and other crops in Central and South America. They attack subterranean parts of the host plants. Adults feed holes in the leaves and can transmit highly infectious viruses, such as cowpea mosaic virus.

Podagrica spp. Several *Podagrica* spp., e. g. *P. puncticollis* Weise, *P. pallida* (Jac.), *P. sjostedti* (Jac.) and *P. uniforma* (Jac.) cause damage by feeding on the leaves of cotton, okra, kenaf and other *Hibiscus* spp. in tropical Africa.

Prometheca spp. (*P. coeruleipennis* Blanch., *P. cumingi* Baly, *P. opacicollis* Gestro, *P. papuana* Csiki). The larvae mine in South East Asia in the basal portion of coconut palm leaves, while the adults feed on the distal end. Biological control by the Eulophid wasp *Pediobius parvulus*.

Necrobia rufipes de Geer. Store pest with worldwide distribution in the tropics. Attacks especially copra in South East Asia and on the Pacific Isles.

Carpophilus spp., Dried fruit beetles (Saftkäfer). In the field, these beetles are generally secondary pests in maize cobs, cotton bolls or fruit. In stores or mills they can be primary pests, attacking dried fruit, copra, groundnut, cocoa beans or palm kernels.

Phloeotribus scarabaeoides (Bern.), the European olive bark beetle (Europäischer Ölbaumborkenkäfer), occurs in the mediterranean region and to the east of it as far as the Iran. After overwintering, the beetles bore into young twigs. The females later make holes in the cortex of branches and sometimes also stems, to construct a parent gallery in the cambial layer, in which the eggs are deposited at regular intervals. The larvae hollow out mines by feeding in the cambial layer and pupate at the blind end of these. Emergent young beetles bore through the bark and disperse. Weak and diseased trees have a special attraction for the bark beetles, but healthy trees are also attacked. Strict plant hygiene is advisable to counteract the pest, i. e. immediate removal and burning of affected twigs and branches. In addition, the olive trees must be maintained in as good a state of health as possible by appropriate cultivation measures (cutting back, manuring etc.).

Apate monachus F., Black borer (Schwarzer Kaffeebohrer). This black, cylindrical Bostrychid is about 1–2 cm long and bores into the stems of cocoa, coffee and other deciduous trees in Africa. It does its main damage in young plants by constructing galleries in the wood, though development of the beetles takes place in felled trees.

Acanthoscelides obtectus (Say), Bean weevil (Speisebohnenkäfer). Occurs in tropical and temperate zones throughout the world as an outdoor and store pest. Larvae feed in seeds of Leguminosae, such as *Phaseolus* spp., *Vigna* spp., pea, chick-pea, and lentil. Control: See *Callosobruchus maculatus* (p. 399).

Callosobruchus chinensis (L.), the Adzuki bean beetle (Kundekäfer) (Fig. 171), comes originally from East Asia and now has a worldwide distribution. In hot countries, this Bruchid is found in the open, in colder climates it is confined to stores. The female is conspicuous for its deeply serrated antennae, which distinguish it from *C. maculatus* (see p. 399) which has less markedly serrated antennae. Eggs are deposited on the seed of various legumes, such as peas, field bean, chick-pea, *Vigna* spp., *Phaseolus* spp., soybean and lupin. The larvae destroy the seed by feeding, or reduce germination capacity. In more heavily attacked crops, several larvae can develop inside one seed. Control as for *C. maculatus* (see p. 399). **H. Sch.**

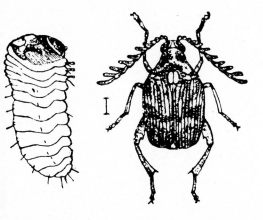

Fig. 171. Larva (left) and adult beetle of *Callosobruchus chinensis* (after Chittenden)

Butterflies and Moths; Schmetterlinge; Papillons; Mariposas y Polillas

Order: Lepidoptera

General features: Moths and butterflies range from small to very large insects. They possess two pairs of wings, covered with numerous scales. The body is also covered by scales. The most conspicuous are the brightly coloured species, which are mostly active during the day, but the majority is of an inconspicuous brown, black or yellowish white colour with nocturnal habits. Most characteristic of the mouth parts is the proboscis, which is spirally coiled in repose. It serves to take up liquid nourishment such as nectar and other plant juices. In some Noctuid moths, the fruit piercing moths, it is so strongly developed, especially at the tip, that it can be used to pierce ripening fruit. In these exceptional cases, even the adult is therefore a pest.

From an economic point of view, the larvae or caterpillars are by far the most important developmental stage. They have a well developed head with biting-chewing mouth parts and an elongated-cylindrical body. Many caterpillars live on plants and require relatively large amounts of food for their development. For this reason they can do considerable damage, both outdoors and in stores.

On a global scale, moths and butterflies can be regarded as the insect order of highest economic significance. Stem borers are particularly notable pests, which attack chiefly cereal species. Leaf devouring species, which often appear very suddenly in large numbers (army worms), are also much feared in the tropics. Finally there are species which destroy fruit or seed and are therefore also of great economic importance.

Moths and butterflies develop from larva (caterpillar) to pupa and adult, i. e. they are holometabolic.

H. Sch.

Superfamily: Tinaeoidea
Family: Gelechiidae

Pectinophora gossypiella (Saund.) (Figs. 172–174 and Plate 34 a)

Synonym: *Platyedra gossypiella*

Common names: Pink bollworm; Roter Baumwollkapselwurm; Ver rose; Gusano rosado del algodonero.

Geographical distribution: *P. gossypiella* was first reported from India in 1842 and from there spread to all major cotton-producing countries of the world, and probably occurs in every country where cotton is grown.

Host plants: Although the plants of worldwide distribution representing 7 families, 24 genera, and 70 species have been recorded as alternate hosts *Gossypium* is the preferred host of the pink bollworm. Most of the hosts belong to the family Malvaceae, of which, the genus *Hibiscus* ranks high in the insect's preference. The six cultivated plants which serve as alternate hosts are okra (*Hibiscus esculentus*), kenaf (*H. cannabinus*), roselle (*H. sabdariffa*), muskmallow (*H. abelmoschus*), castorbean (*Ricinus communis*), and jute (*Corchorus olitorius*).

Fig. 172. Cotton flower spun together by larva of *Pectinophora gossypiella* (phot. H. Schmutterer)

Fig. 173. Damage by *P. gossypiella* in a cotton boll (photo T. F. Watson)

Symptoms: Early in the season before bolls are available, pink bollworm infestations can be detected by the presence of "rosetted blooms." Later, the first-instar larva may denote its presence in bolls by conspicuous mines along the inner carpel wall, a result of not burrowing directly into the inner part of the boll. Other visible signs of damage include the small, round holes from which the larvae exit the bolls, and discolored lint and seed, showing the actual feeding signs (Fig. 173). Rotted bolls may also indicate the presence of pink bollworms as the exit hole allows the entrance of bollrotting fungi.

Economic importance: Cotton losses attributable to the pink bollworm are indicative of the world-wide importance of this pest. Losses averaging 15 to 25 percent have been reported from India and Egypt. Heavy losses have also been reported from China and USSR. Although average annual losses of 20 to 25 percent have been reported from Brazil, losses amounted to 60 to 70 percent in the 1949–50 cotton crop. Losses in Texas (U.S.) have been reported as high as 34 percent in the Brownsville area and 50 to 80 percent in the Rio Grande Valley. Where uncontrolled, losses in Arizona have ranged from 25 to 60 percent.

Morphology: The adult of the pink bollworm is a small, slender moth about $^3/_8$ inch long (Fig. 174). The moth is greyish-brown in color with dark brown forewings which have irregular black areas; the hindwings are silvery-grey.
The oval, white egg is about 0.5 mm by 0.3 mm in size. The first 3 larval instars are creamy white with dark brown heads and thoracic shields. At times the third larval instar will show transverse pinkish lines, changing into dark-pink bands in the fourth instar (Plate 34 a). Pupae are about 8 mm in length by 2.5 mm wide and exhibit the typical mahogany brown color.

Life cycle: A generalized life cycle of the pink bollworm for a temperature of 30 °C is as follows: egg, 4–5 days; larval stage, 15–20 days; pupal stage, 7–9 days; and, the preoviposition period, 2 days, or a total of 28–36 days.

Fig. 174. Adult moth of *P. gossypiella* (phot. T. F. Watson)

In arid, semi-tropical areas such as Arizona where the cotton-growing season may last 9–10 months, there may be 6–8 generations per year. In more temperate regions having shorter growing seasons, 4–6 generations are more likely.

Short-cycle generations will continue until daylength falls to 13 hours, after which increasingly higher proportions of the population enters diapause. The long-cycle or diapausing larvae overwinter in cotton seed, lint, surface trash, or in free cocoons in the soil.

Ecology: Temperature, moisture, and photoperiod are important factors affecting the pink bollworm. Termination of diapause is primarily a function of temperature and moisture. Temperatures in excess of 15 °C are necessary for initiating pupation of overwintering larvae. Contact moisture or high relative humidity enhances survival and pupation, especially at higher temperatures. Temperature of about 22 °C and contact moisture appear to be most optimum for survival and the highest rate of pupation.

During the growing season moth activity is adversely affected by unusually high temperatures. Longevity and oviposition are reduced when temperatures exceed 35 ° to 40 °C.

Winter mortality of diapausing larvae is generally high. Areas with cold, wet climates are most detrimental to diapausing larvae.

Natural enemies: Several species of parasitic and predacious insects, and predacious mites have been reported to attack the pink bollworm. Spiders have also been observed feeding on adults. None of these, however, has effectively reduced field populations.

Control:

Sanitary and Cultural Practices. The overwintering phase is the weakest link in the seasonal cycle of the pink bollworm and cultural control is the preferred method of suppressing this pest. A number of cultural practices effectively reduce overwintering populations. Practices that adversely affect the pink bollworm are shredding the stalks, disking the soil, deep plowing and winter irrigation. Additionally, shortening the growing season by early crop termination has significantly reduced overwintering populations.

Host-Plant Resistance. The status of resistant cotton varieties has been summarized as follows: "A cotton possessing both resistance and desirable agronomic characters has not as yet been developed."

Chemical control. In many areas of the world where pink bollworm usually reaches the economic infestation level each year, profitable cotton production can only be achieved by the timely application of chemical insecticides. The best control has been obtained with azinphos-methyl at the rate of 0.5 lb./acre or carbaryl at 1.5 to 2.0 lbs./acre. Generally, several applications, made at intervals of 6–7 days, are required to bring an infestation under control.

Although there is no indication of insecticidal resistance by the pink bollworm in Arizona and California, or other areas of the world where insecticidal control is necessary, in all likelihood resistance will develop if current control practices are continued. High levels of resistance to DDT have been reported in the Torreón area of Mexico and certain areas of Texas.

Integrated control. Pink bollworm control is a complex matter. No single practice will suffice for long. All available tools – sanitation, cultural practices, biological and chemical control, field sampling, etc. – can be effectively integrated, however, to manage this pest in any cotton agroecosystem for continued production of high quality cottons.

Literature

HUNTER, W. D. (1918): The pink bollworm with special reference to steps taken by the Department of Agriculture to prevent its establishment in the United States. U. S. Dept. of Agric. Bul. 723, 27 pp.

MARTIN, D. F. & R. D. LEWIS (ed.): A summary of recent research basic to the cultural control of pink bollworm. Agric. Expt. Sta. of Ariz., Ark., La., Puerto Rico and Tex., and the Agric. Res. Serv., USDA. Misc. Publ. 579. 28 pp.

NOBLE, L. W. (1969): Fifty years of research on the pink bollworm in the United States. Agric. Handbook no 357, 62 pp.

SLOSSER, J. E. & T. F. WATSON (1972): Population growth of the pink bollworm. Ariz. Agr. Expt. Sta. Tech. Bul. 195, 32 pp.

WATSON, T. F., K. K. BARNES, J. E. SLOSSER & D. G. FULLERTON (1974): Influence of plowdown dates and cultural practices on spring moth emergence of the pink bollworm. J. Econ. Entomol. **67**, 207–210.

WATSON, T. F., L. MOORE & G. W. WARE (1976): Practical insect pest management: A self-instruction manual. W. H. Freemann & Co., San Francisco, 196 pp.

Author: T. F. Watson

Phthorimaea operculella (Zell.) (Figs. 175–176)

Synonym: *Gnorimoschema operculella*

Common names: Potato tuber moth; Kartoffelmotte; Teigne de la pomme de terre; Polilla de la papa (patata).

Geographical distribution: Generally found wherever hosts occur between the 50 ° parallels e. g. in India, Africa, the Americas, Southern Europe, Australia and Asia (CIE Map no 10).

Host plants: Among cultivated plants potato *(Solanum tuberosum),* tobacco *(Nicotiana tabacum),* tomato *(Lycopersicum esculentum),* and egg fruit *(Solanum melongena)* are attacked.
Some wild plant species of the following genera serve as alternative hosts: *Solanum, Datura, Nicotiana, Capsicum, Physalis, Fabiana, Hyoscyamus, Lycium* and *Nicandra.* Of the above only *Nicandra physalodes* sustains significant tuber moth populations in Southern Africa.

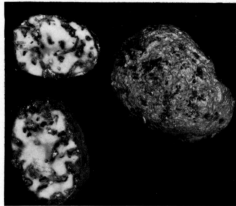

Fig. 175.   Mines of *Phthorimaea operculella* in a potato leaf (phot. S. W. Broodryk)

Fig. 176.   Potatoes, showing damage by *P. operculella* (phot. S. W. Broodryk)

Symptoms: Larvae perforate potato tubers and leave accumulations of excrement near the entrance hole (Fig. 176). Leaves (Fig. 175) and stems of growing potato and tobacco plants are mined and perforated, often already in the young stage. Tomato and egg fruit foliage is mined.

Economic importance: Potato foliage may be totally destroyed, resulting in severe crop reduction. Tuber infestations of up to 45 % have been recorded in the field and damage to stored potatoes may range from slight to total infestation and loss.

Damage to tobacco seedlings leads to unproductive plants. Larval mines in tobacco leaves ruin the quality and reduce returns to the grower.

Mining damage to tomato and egg fruit foliage usually does not reach economic levels. Damage to fruit of both is on record.

Morphology: Newly laid eggs are oval and pearly white (0.5 mm x 0.4 mm). Newly hatched larvae are about 1 mm long and grow to a size of 11 mm x 1.5 mm after four moults. A fully grown larva has six stemmata on each side of the head, mouth parts with spinneret, a cervical and an anal plate, nine pairs of spiracles and five pairs of prolegs on abdominal segments III to VI and X. Fully grown larvae are pale green with pink markings and before pupation, spin frail off-white cocoons covered with soil and debris.

Pupae are dark brown, about 6 mm long. The male genital aperture is situated medially on the ninth abdominal segment and the female aperture medially on the eighth.

The grey moths are from 6 to 10 mm long and the span of the fringed forewings varies from 13 to 17 mm. The abdomen in females terminates in a cone while males bear two apical claspers.

Similarities to other pests: The tuber moth larva is similar in appearance to larvae of pink bollworm *(Pectinophora gossypiella)* and *Mometa zemiodes,* both occurring on cotton. Its close relative, *Phthorimaea heliopa,* bores into tobacco stems and is occasionally of economic importance.

Life cycle: Eggs hatch within 108 hours at 26.5 °C, the low threshold being 9.5 °C with the favourable range between 15 and 35 °C. Larval development is completed in 67 days at 11 °C, 12 days at 25 °C and nine days at 32 °C. The pupal stage occupies 18 days at 11 °C, $6^{1}/_{2}$ days at 25 °C and five days at 32 °C. All above refer to constant temperature regimes.

Moths mate about 16 hours after emergence and start ovipositing soon afterwards. They live about 13 days at 25 °C and 65 % RH on a honey diet.

Ecology: Humidity does not influence egg incubation and hatch, nor does it affect pupal development and emergence.

The growing crop is invaded by egg laying moths at any stage, causing a build up of larvae in the foliage. As soon as the foliage and stems decline nutritionally, larvae leave the plant in search of tubers. Swelling tubers cause the soil to crack providing access to larvae which bore into the tubers. At least 100 kg/ha of tubers are usually overlooked at harvesting and the infested ones tide the population over until the new season starts. Weeds may sustain the population but are usually not frost hardy and lose importance where winters are severe. Moths usually disperse in the direction of prevailing winds with short flights at ground level. Distant or isolated areas usually become infested by planting of infested tubers.

Natural enemies: Non specific parasites occur abundantly in most areas invaded by potato tuber moth. Their contribution to control is usually surpassed by specific parasites once the latter are established. A number of specific natural enemies are available from the Commonwealth Institute of Biological Control. Of these, *Copidosoma koehleri* and *Apanteles subandinus* have been the most successful.

Control: In the absence of insecticides, foliar damage is usually kept below the economic level by natural enemies. Damage to tubers can be avoided by planting seed tubers deeper than 20 cm and keeping the developing tuber crop covered with about 25 cm of fine, loose soil. Three ridgings usually achieve this cover, the final ridging immediately following the first signs of foliar decline. Where natural enemies are lacking and more than 10 % of plants become heavily infested, or where effective ridging is impossible, two to three sprays of DDT at 1 kg active ingredient per ha should be applied in the latter half of the season. After prolonged excessive use of DDT, however, resistance to chlorinated hydrocarbons has occurred in Southern Africa and Australia. In this event only more hazardous pesticides like monocrotophos, methomyl and azinphos-ethyl remain effective but they are all unsafe for use in hand-held equipment.

Harvested tubers should not be left in the fields overnight. Infested tubers must not be mixed with healthy ones for storage. Stores should be cleared of old tubers and sprayed with 1 % malathion or 0.6 % diazinon before use. Stored table potatoes should be protected with liberal applications of 2.5 % diazinon or 2 % malathion dust. DDT 5 % dust should only be used on seed potatoes. Partially damaged tubers can be planted as seed after three months of effective chemical protection.

The fungicides zineb, mancozeb, maneb and fentin acetate (Brestan) at field concentrations do not suppress populations of parasites markedly.

Literature

BROODRYK, S. W. (1971): Ecological investigations on the potato tuber moth, *Phthorimaea operculella* (Zeller) (Lepidoptera: Gelechiidae). Phytophylactica **3**, 73–84.

REED, E. M. (1971): Factors affecting the status of a virus as a control agent for the potato moth *(Phthorimaea operculella* Zell.) (Lep.: Gelechiidae). Bull. ent. Res. **61**, 207–222.

WATMOUGH, R. H., S. W. BROODRYK & D. P. ANNECKE (1973): The establishment of two imported parasitoids of potato tuber moth (*Phthorimaea operculella*) in South Africa. Entomophaga **18** (3), 237–249.

Author: S. W. Broodryk

Sitotroga cerealella (Oliv.) (Fig. 177)

Synonyms: *Gelechia cerealella, Tinea cerealella*

Common names: Angoumois grain moth; Getreidemotte; Alucite des céréales; Polilla de los cereales.

Geographical distribution: Cosmopolitan. It is widespread throughout the tropics and in most temperate areas on all continents.

Host plants and stored products attacked: Most cereal grains (especially paddy rice, sorghum, maize, wheat and barley) before harvest and also in store.

Symptoms: The larva develops inside a single cereal grain and larval damage is thus hidden until emergence of the adult. The adult pushes its way through a thin layer of seed coat left by the larva leaving a characteristic hole approximately 1 mm in diameter; the seed coat remains as a flap partially covering the hole either in the form of a trapdoor or as a shallow cone.

Economic importance: The loss in weight of an individual maize grain attacked by one larva is more than 10 %; in smaller cereal grains this weight loss is proportionately greater. Damage to the cereal crops is greatest immediately prior to and just after harvest; in store, this pest only attacks the surface layers of stored grain. However, since it is a primary pest, its economic importance is heightened by the opportunities that its damage provides for increased attack by secondary pests in store.

Morphology: The following characters distinguish the adult from all other common moth pests found on cereals after harvest: upper forewing (when moth is newly emerged) pale ochreous brown often with a small black dot in the distal half; upper hindwing with a whitish stripe from the base of the wing to just beyond the centre; labial palps long, slender, sharply pointed and curved upwards in front of the head; hindwing with a long fringe of hairs (the hairs are longer than half the breadth of the wing) and with the apex elongate and sharply pointed. The larva is rarely seen but can be distinguished by the very small size of its abdominal false legs.

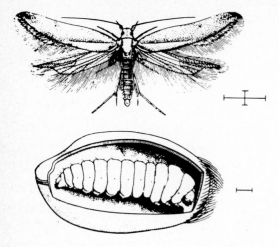

Fig. 177. *Sitotroga cerealella*. Above: adult moth; below: larva in a wheat grain (Courtesy of Imperial Chemical Industries)

Similarities to other pests: Most of the moths found on cereals after harvest quickly lose the colour patterns on their wings but this species can easily be distinguished by the form of the hindwings and labial palps. The emergence holes of adults from the grain can be distinguished from the damage caused by other primary cereal pests (notably *Sitophilus* spp. and *Rhizopertha dominica*) by the characteristic appearance noted above.

Life cycle: The female lays eggs on the surface of grains in the field or in store. The newly emerged larva immediately bores into a grain where it remains and feeds until fully developed. The final instar larva pupates near the surface of the grain leaving only a thin layer of the seed coat intact. (In very small grains, e. g. sorghum, the larva sometimes leaves the grain and pupates in the space between two or more grains.) The adult then pushes its way through the seed coat and after mating searches for a suitable oviposition site. In most tropical climates the developmental period from egg to adult takes approximately five weeks. In very dry conditions and in cool temperate climates the mature larvae may enter a variable period of quiescence, though it is not yet known whether this is a true diapause. The adults are shortlived and do not feed.

Ecology: Optimum development occurs at 32 °C and 75 % r. h. and the physical limits for successful development are 16 to 35 °C and 25 to 80 % r. h. This species is apparently restricted to cereal grains and does not infest cereal products or other grains. The adult is a good flier and thus may cause cross-infestation problems; this is particularly important in storage on small farms where adults from stored grains may often infest growing cereals in nearby fields.

Natural enemies: The hymenopteran parasites *Habrocytus cerealella* and *Bracon hebetor* are often found parasitizing the larvae and may sometimes contribute substantially to a reduction of the potential increase of the pest. Species of the hymenopteran genus *Trichogramma* may also parasitize the moth eggs. The mite *Pyemotes ventricosus* is an ectoparasite of the larvae and pupae of this pest and the predatory mite *Blattisocius tarsalis* feeds on the moth eggs. There are also reports of predation by the young larvae of *Cryptolestes ferrugineus*, a secondary beetle pest of stored cereals.

Control:
Recommended treatment. For storing maize on the cob or sorghum on the ear the recommended treatment is 10–12 ppm lindane calculated on a shelled weight basis. This is sometimes given as 450 g of 1 % dust per cubic metre but may vary with the variety. For shelled or threshed cereals, 10 to 12 ppm malathion is the recommended treatment. On a single bag scale this is commonly applied as 100 g of 1 % dust per 90 kg bag but malathion emulsifiable concentrate applied as a 1 % spray may be more appropriate for large scale treatment.
Alternative treatment. *S. cerealella* may be controlled by normal dosages of fumigants (see p. 385). In trials several organophosphate dusts applied at 12–15 ppm have given promising results but no insecticide has yet been officially recommended as an alternative to malathion or lindane.

General situation. *S. cerealella* is an important pre-harvest pest which can readily fly from stores into fields of the growing crop. Store hygiene is therefore important. All residual pockets of infestation should be cleaned out at the end of the storage season to minimise re-infestation of the new crop. Separation of stores from fields is advantageous. In store the moth only abounds in unthreshed or unshelled cereal as it is unable to multiply within bulked grain. In bulked grain, the moth is readily controlled by admixture of insecticides or by surface spraying. The shelling or threshing of grain is therefore indicated where conditions permit.
S. cerealella is sensitive to changes in varieties and older traditional varieties are frequently unattractive. There is scope for breeding of new varieties with a low susceptibility to this pest. The moth is also attacked by predatory mites but it is unlikely that this will be important in controlling the pest.

Literature

BOLDT, P. E. (1974): Effects of temperature and humidity on development and oviposition of *Sitotroga cerealella*. J. Kans. ent. Soc. **47** (1), 30–36.
STOCKEL, J. (1973): Influence des relations sexuelles et du milieu trophique de l'adulte sur la reproduction de *Sitotroga cerealella* Oliv. (Lepidoptère Gelechiidae). Consequences écologiques. Thesis pres. Univ. François-Rabelais de Tours pour Grade Docteur-Ingénieur, duplic. 171 + 8 pp.

Authors: C. P. Haines and D. J. Webley

Family: Cosmopterygidae

Batrachedra amydraula Meyr. (Plate 34 b)

Common name: Lesser date moth; Kleine Dattelmotte.

Geographical distribution: Bangladesh, India, Iraq, Egypt, Libya, Isreal, Saudi Arabia and South Yemen.

Host plant: The date palm, *Phoenix dactylifera.*

Symptoms: Inflorescences are eaten up and become entangled with caterpillar frass and webs. Young fruits turn brown instead of green. Stalks served from common fruit strand are cut but remain attached to it by a silken thread. Black larval frass is ejected by caterpillars from tiny entrance holes in the fruits.

Economic importance: *B. amydraula* destroys up to 80 % of young fruits in some years and localities. In some oases, total loss of fruits has been observed.

Morphology: The moth has a wing span of 10–13 mm. The front wings are lanceolate, white-ochrous and finely speckled with brownish scales. The hind wings are narrow, light grey, and long-fringed.
The fully-grown caterpillar reaches 15 mm in length. Head and prothoracic shield are brown, while the rest of the body is translucent white. Each segment of the larval body bears one dark tubercle on each of its pleura and four on the tergum; the pleural tubercles have shorter setae than the tergal ones. Prolegs are found on the abdominal segments III–VI and on the last. The pupa is slender and long and yellowish-brown in color.

Similarities to other pests: Dissimilar to any other caterpillar that infests fresh dates on the tree. Caterpillars of *Arenipses sabella,* the "Greater date moth", may be found together with those of *B. amydraula* but differ in being rose in color and reaching a length of 20–22 mm. Attack by caterpillars of *A. sabella* also severs the fruits and attaches them to the spadix by a silken thread before cutting the fruit stalk and causing the fruit to shrivel; the shrivelled fruits assume a greyish color instead of brown.

Life cycle: The fully-grown caterpillars of *B. amydraula* pass the winter protected in a cocoon which is spun between fruit strands, fronds, and other tissues of a palm tree. Early in April pupation occurs and moth emergence usually begins by the middle of the same month. Following moth emergence and copulation, egglaying takes place in the inflorescence on which the newly emerged caterpillars feed. Their feeding can cause about 20 percent damage to the inflorescences. In about four weeks, the insect completes one generation. Moths of the second generation appear during the first week of May and lay eggs on the young fruit strands. The ensuing caterpillars attack the young fruitlets after fastening them to the common fruit strand, or spadix, by a silken thread, and they finally bore through their calices into the fruit. The fruitlets later shrivel, turn brown and rot. To reach maturity, the caterpillar consumes more than one fruitlet. The full-grown caterpillars pupate during the first half of June, and emerge as moths of the third generation by the middle of the same month. Again, copulation takes place, but egg-laying occurs on the fruits. Caterpillar-feeding continues as with those of the second generation. During the second half of July, the caterpillars attain their full size, leave the fruit and go into diapause throughout the rest of summer, autumn and winter. In late March or early April the following year, they pupate and then emerge as moths of the first generation.

Ecology: Not much is known about the ecology of *B. amydraula*. However, it is so widely distributed in the date oases all over Iraq, the Gulf States, Arabia, Egypt and North Africa to illustrate that under existing climatic conditions in these oases, the insect finds suitable environmental conditions.

Natural enemies: The insect is parasitized by a number of hymenopterous species, mostly Braconids, but the amount of parasitism is low.

Control: Control is possible with organic phosphates, particularly with trichlorphon (Diptrex) and azinphos (Gusathion). However, due to the fact that organic phosphates may kill a number of natural enemies, particularly of the scale insect *Parlatoria blanchardii*, it is recommended that *Bacillus thuringiensis* sprays should be tried against the caterpillars when they first appear.

Literature

LEPESME, P. (1947): Les Insectes des Palmiers. P. Lechevalier edit. Paris, 903 pp.
TALHOUK, A. S. (1969): Insects and Mites Injurious to Crops in M. E. Countries. Paul Parey, Hamburg–Berlin, Monog. Ang. Ent. no **21**, 157–158.

Author: A. S. Talhouk

Family: Yponomeutidae

Prays oleae (Bern.) (Plate 34 c)

Synonym: *Prays oleellus*

Common names: Olive moth; Olivenmotte; Teigne de l'olivier; Polilla del olivo.

Geographical distribution: The olive moth does damage in all natural olive tree habitats and in the entire Mediterranean region. It is also found in Portugal, Morocco and on the Canary Islands. CIE Map no 123.

Host plants: Species of the family Oleaceae other than *Olea europea* also serve as host plants, for instance those belonging to the genera *Jasminum, Ligustrum* and *Phyllirea*.

Symptoms: Dead inflorescences are found in the spring, towards the end of the flowering period, held together by fine webbing. Round larval bore holes can be seen in the withered petals of unopened flowers.
Fruit drop occurs increasingly in the summer months. The kernel contains a caterpillar or the contents are destroyed. The winter generation produces larval mines in the leaves which remain visible throughout the year.

Economic importance: Alongside the olive fly, *P. oleae* is the most important pest in olive groves. The flower generation alone can destroy the entire crop. On the whole, the annual loss in yield is in some countries estimated at 20 %. The tolerable threshold is frequently cited as 5 % attack on inflorescences.

Morphology: Egg. – Whitish, elliptic and slightly flattened. Larva. – Greenish to reddish, with one darker mid-dorsal and two lateral lines running along the body. Length of fully-grown caterpillar about 8 mm. Pupa. – Brown, embedded in a silken cocoon. Adults. – Silvery-grey, narrow fore wings with some dark spots. Hindwings light grey. Wingspan 12–14 mm.

Life cycle: Shortly before flowering, eggs are deposited singly in the calyces of unopened flowers. From there, the caterpillars penetrate to the interior, eat up the contents and leave through a hole in the petals. In the course of 3–4 weeks, about another 20 flowers are destroyed in the same way. Pupation takes place inside dead inflorescences, in the soil or on the bark. The next generation oviposits on the calyx of very young fruit and the caterpillars enter the calyx. This leads to increased fruit drop in June and again in September when the caterpillars bore their way out. The succeeding moth generation oviposits on the upper surface of leaves in around October. The larvae burrow successively in usually 4 leaves altogether, producing variously shaped larval mines and the final instar may feed on the surface. They pupate in hiding places in the bark, or among leaves.

Ecology: The incidence of olive moth fluctuates greatly from year to year. This probably depends on climatic factors (low relative humidity on oviposition, temperatures below 7 °C in winter and above 40 °C when young larval instars are present), as well as on various predators and parasites.

Natural enemies: The main natural enemies belong to the genera *Xanthadrus* (Dipt.), *Trichogramma* (Hym.), *Ageniaspis* (Hym.) and *Chelonella* (Hym.).

Control: The effect of measures of cultivation and choice of varieties on attack have been observed. Tests with biological methods have brought some good results. *Bacillus thuringiensis* can be effective, but correct timing is no easy matter. Chemical control with parathion, dimethoate, fenthion and endosulfan has been widely explored, and a whole series of other chemicals are also used. In dry regions, dusts (frequently parathion 1 %) play a major part in the control of the "flower generation". In less intensive grove management, control is confined to treatment of the "flower generation", while all three generations are treated in intensive cultivation.
Suitable times for treatment are:
Winter generation: Between cropping and pupation – usually February.
Flower generation: At the start of flowering – usually end of April/early May.
Fruit generation: After flowering, when fruit about pepper corn size. Usually end of May/early June.
The use of aircrafts for dust and spray applications has brought good results. Trials with the application of ULV formulations are also under way.
For prognostic purposes, a count of larval mines made in the leaves by the winter generation, provides a suitable method.

Literature

ARAMBOURG, Y. (1966): La teigne de l'olivier. In A. S. Balachowsky, Entomologie Appliquée à l'Agriculture.
PELEKASSIS, E. D. (1962): A contribution to the study of nomenclature, taxonomy, biology, ecology and the natural parasitisation of the olive kernel borer. Annales de l'Institut Phytopathologique, Benaki 185–300.

Author: K. Rolli

Family: Lyonetiidae

Leucoptera coffeella (Guér.-Ménev.) (Plate 34 d)

Synonyms: *Cemiostoma coffeella, Perileucoptera coffeella*. Until 1958 the East African species *L. meyricki* was thought to be *L. coffeella*

Common names: White coffee leaf miner; Kaffeemotte; Teigne de cafétier, Mineuse des feuilles de caféier; Minador de la hoja del cafeto.

Geographical distribution: Coffee-growing areas of Central and South America and the West Indies. Also Madagascar and Réunion. CIE Map no 315.

Host plants: *L. coffeella* has only been recorded from cultivated coffees, notably Arabica *Coffea arabica,* Robusta *C. canephora* and Liberica *C. liberica. L. meyricki* in East Africa can breed on the indigenous forest coffee *C. eugenioides.*

Symptoms: Irregular brown blotches on the upper surface of fully-expanded leaves (Plate 34 d). If the leaf is bent across the blotch, the upper surface cracks open revealing in a fresh mine small white caterpillars. Mined leaves are usually shed prematurely.

Economic importance: A major pest especially in areas where Leaf rust caused by *Hemileia vastatrix* is also a problem.
To a considerable extent, each fruiting branch of a coffee bush is a separate physiological unit. If it is carrying berries it should also carry enough leaves to feed those berries. Any agent, therefore, that causes heavy leaf-fall, especially in the two months prior to harvest, will have serious consequences. Not only will the current crop fail to develop normally but also the fruiting branches will die back from the tip. The tree may take more than one season to recover.

Morphology: Eggs are oval in outline and just visible to the naked eye (about 0.3 mm long). They are laid scattered in small groups (2 to 6) not touching and orientated at random on the upper leaf surface. They are silvery-white when first laid, turning brown just before hatching.
Larvae, in the mines, are flattened whitish caterpillars with distinct segmentation. They are about 4.5 mm long when full grown. The pupa is found in a white H-shaped silk cocoon about 6 mm long which is often spun on the underside of leaves.
Moths are small (2 mm long) and white with dark wing tips.

Similarities to other pests: *L. meyricki* in East Africa causes similar damage to leaves of arabica coffee. *L. coma* and *Crobylophora* spp. attack robusta coffee in Central Africa. Other insects also mine coffee leaves but such mines are silver coloured (not brown) and serpentine (not blotch-like) and are thus easily distinguished from *Leucoptera* mines.

Life cycle: Eggs hatch after 5 days in hot summer weather but after 21 days or more in the colder months.

The larva bores through the base of the egg straight into the leaf. Mining takes place in the palisade tissue under the upper epidermis. At first there are separate small mines, one for each larva, but later they coalesce to form a single blotch. When the larva is full-grown it cuts a semi-circular (c. f. the parasitic wasp) slit in the dead epidermis above the mine, crawls out and lowers itself towards the ground on a silk thread. The larval period varies from about 10 to 42 days according to the season. Larval development is always completed in a single leaf. If the leaf is shed before the caterpillar is full-grown it will die or produce an under-sized moth.

The mature larva seeks a concave surface on the underside of a leaf, on trash on the ground or in a crack in the soil on which to spin its cocoon. The pupa which is inside a spindle-shaped bag at the centre of the cocoon, cannot, of course, be seen. The pupal period lasts from 5 to 22 days according to the season.

The emerging moth squeezes out from one end of the cocoon, leaving it intact. Mating takes place in the evening and egg-laying at night. The female moth may live 2 to 4 weeks and lay about 40 eggs. Much depends on the availability of food. If the moth has access to nectar or honeydew she may lay 90 eggs or more.

No diapause or other resting stage is known, but cool weather greatly slows the rate of reproduction.

Ecology: Damage is usually greatest in unshaded coffee since direct sunlight accelerates the shedding of a mined leaf. But, if the larval population is very high, severe leaf fall is also possible in shaded plantations.

There is some evidence from both South America and East Africa that *Leucoptera* is a more important pest when regular sprays of copper fungicide are applied.

Natural enemies: No egg parasites are known but several general predators including mites, thrips and lace wings (Neuroptera) sometimes suck out the egg contents.

Fifteen species of small parasitic wasps, mainly braconids and eulophids, are recorded attacking the larvae in the mines. Development is usually completed inside the mine and the adult wasp emerges from a small circular hole in the roof of the mine.

Caterpillars which have left the mine and are seeking pupation quarters are sometimes eaten by ants. But, after the cocoon has been spun, the pupa is usually safe from predation.

Control:

Resistance of crops. There is evidence from East Africa that the selection of resistant varieties is possible but no such varieties are yet commercially available.

Biological control. This does not seem to be a promising prospect, but the spray programme should always be designed so that the least possible harm is done to the parasitic wasps which attack the larvae in the mines. Persistent contact insecticides (e. g. DDT) kill adult parasites as they search for a host larva and are to be avoided if possible.

Chemical control. The following insecticides, which penetrate into the leaf tissues, are effective as water-based sprays: Fenitrothion (1.0 kg a. i. per hectare), fenthion (1.2 kg a. i. per hectare) and diazinon (1.0 kg a. i. per hectare).

Mature coffee leaves should be dipped in the prepared spray mixture. If the film of liquid breaks up immediately after the leaf is taken out, then extra wetting agent should be added to improve penetration of the toxicant into the leaf.

Special insecticide-oil formulations are available in some countries which give control at roughly half the dosage rates listed above. 1 % gamma-BHC dust has been widely used in Brazil for *Leucoptera* control and has the advantage of also controlling the Berry borer *Hypothenemus hampei* but it is unlikely to be as effective as a spray. Spraying should be done as far as possible when a very low proportion of the population is in the cocoon stage. A sample of cocoons should be squeezed with the thumb. If a drop of thick yellow fluid exudes from one end of the cocoon it contains a living moth pupa. If the cocoon is quite dry, the moth has already emerged.

The correct time for spraying is about one week after the period when moths were most numerous. Most of the population will then be eggs or young larvae and a good kill will be obtained. Trees should be shaken at regular intervals and the number of moths that flutter out should be estimated. If the trees are already short of leaves, and especially if they are carrying crop, any area that had more than 20 per tree at the peak will require spraying. In very severe attacks, a second spray may be needed 5 to 10 days after the first.

Literature

LE PELLEY, R. H. (1968): Pests of Coffee. Longmans, London, pp. 218–223.

Author: T. J. Crowe

Superfamily: Psychoidea
Family: Metarbelidae

Indarbela quadrinotata (Wlk.) (Plate 35 a)

Synonyms: *Cossus quadrinotata, C. abruptus, C. tesselatus, Arbela quadrinotata, Zeuzera pardicolor*

Common name: Bark eating caterpillar.

Geographical distribution: Burma, Bangladesh, Sri Lanka and throughout India.

Host plants: Mango, citrus, guava, jamun *(Syzygium cuminii),* loquat, mulberry, pomegranate, a number of forest and ornamental trees, ber *(Ziziphus jujuba),* drum stick *(Moringa oleifera),* litchi *(Litchi chinensis),* aonla *(Emblica officinalis),* rose, etc.

Symptoms: Thick, ribbon like, fine silken webs consisting of wooden particles and excreta are seen hanging on bark and main stems, especially near forks. Below these webs zigzag galleries occur made by the freshly hatched caterpillars and the holes where the caterpillars have bored in. As many as 15–16 holes may be seen on one tree and one caterpillar or pupa occupies each hole. A severe infestation may result in death of the stem but not of the main trunk though there may be interference with translocation of cell sap resulting in arresting of the growth of the tree and its fruiting capacity being adversely affected.

Economic importance: *I. quadrinotata* is considered to be a serious pest of fruit trees in India but no systematic studies have been carried out so far to study the extent of loss caused by this pest.

Morphology: Freshly hatched larvae are dirty brown while the full grown caterpillars (50–60 mm) have pale brown bodies with dark brown heads. Pupae (18 x 5 mm) are stout, reddish brown with 2 rows of spines on each abdominal segment arranged transversely on anterior and posterior margins. Adults are pale brown with head and thorax rufous; forewings are pale rufous with numerous dark rufous bands of strigae; abdomen and hind wings are fuscous (♂ 36 mm, ♀ 40 mm).

Similarities to other pests: *I. tetraonis* differs from *I. quadrinotata* in being pale brown and with markings less rufous; forewings have a prominent submarginal series of conjoined spots; hindwings are whitish with some brown spots and streaks; abdomen has brown tufts: ♂ 35–38 mm, ♀ 46–50 mm. *I. dea* has forewings arrotated with few dark scales, hindwings being blackish brown, ♂ 24 mm, ♀ 29 mm. Also similar are *I. theivora* which has been reported from Assam (India) on mango and *I. baibarana* on litchi from China. Moths of all the five species have no proboscis; male antennae are bipectinate to the apex with short branches and vein 1 c is present in hind wings but absent in forewings.

Life cycle and ecology: The moths appear in May–June and start laying eggs within 25 hours of emergence. The eggs are laid in clusters (15–25) under the loose bark of the trees. The egg laying continues throughout the summer. A single female lays as many as 2,000 eggs which hatch in 8–10 days. Freshly hatched larvae nibble the wood and after 2–3 days bore inside the wood. The larval period is 9–11 months. The caterpillars become fully grown by December but continue feeding until March–April. With the rise in temperature they start pupating within the tree trunk or main branches. The pupal period is 3–4 weeks. The adults are short lived; males die soon after mating (within 24 hours of emergence) and the females live for 2–3 days more to lay eggs. There is only one generation each year.

Natural enemies: No parasites and predators have been recorded so far on *Indarbela* spp. in India. However, in Sri Lanka, *Zenillia heterusiae* is recorded on *I. quadrinotata*.

Control:
Cultural and mechanical practices. Keeping the orchards clean and avoiding overcrowding of trees help to minimize attacks of the pest. It has been suggested that an iron spike be inserted into the bored hole to kill the caterpillar inside. This is quite effective and may be practised in small orchards or when the infestation is low.
Chemical control. During September–October, before much damage has been done, the tree trunks and main branches should be cleaned by removing all the webs and a swab of cotton wool soaked in any fumigant, such a carbon bisulphide, petrol, etc. inserted in each hole. Half a litre of fumigant will suffice for 500 holes which should be sealed with mud. Those holes which reopen need to be retreated. The injection of ethylene glycol and kerosene (1 : 3), 0.013 % dichlorvos (DDVP), 0.05 % trichlorfon or 0.05 % endosulfan is also to be recommended. Spraying with 0.2 % gamma-BHC or 0.04 % endrin, gamma-BHC + DDT after removing webs can also be performed.

Literature

BUTANI, D. K. (1973): Les ravageurs et les maladies des Citrus en Inde. Fruits **28** (12), 851–856, Paris.
BUTANI, D. K. (1974): Insect pests of fruit crops and their control – 7: Mango. Pesticides **8** (3), 37–40, Bombay.
CHEN TING-YU (1964): A study of two species of litchi stem borers. Acta ent. sin. **13** (2), 159–171.
DAVID, B. VASANTHARAJ, S. VIJAYARAGHAVAN & P. S. NARAYANASWAMY (1963): *Indarbela tetraonis* Moore – a new bark borer pest on curry leaf tree and its control. Madras agric. J. **50** (5), 195–199.
KHURANA, A. D. & O. P. GUPTA (1972): Bark-eating caterpillars pose serious threat to fruit trees. Indian Farmers' Digest, **5** (4): 51–52.
REDDY, D. BAP (1968): Plant Protection in India, 243–244, Allied Publishers.
SRIVASTAVA, A. S. & M. S. SIDDIQI (1962): A preliminary study of the life history and control of *Indarbela quadrinotata* Wlk., Metarbelidae: Lepidoptera. Proc. nat. Acad. Sci. India **32** (3): 265–270.

Author: Dhamo K. Butani

Superfamily: Pyralidoidea
Family: Galleriidae

Corcyra cephalonica (Staint.) (Fig. 178)

Common names: Rice moth; Reismotte; Pyrale du riz; Polilla del arroz.

Geographical distribution: Tropical and sub-tropical regions, provided the minimum temperature of 18 °C for development and a minimum relative humidity of 30 % are reached for a longer period in the year.

Stored products attacked: Maize, peeled rice, other cereals, milled products, cocoa beans, peanuts only after prolonged storage, cottonseed, other seed, raisins et al.; occurs in mills in Egypt together with *Ephestia kuehniella*.

Symptoms: Dense webbing indicates attack.

Economic importance: Similar to that of *Plodia interpunctella*.

Morphology: Moth with ochre-yellowish green fore wings and grey-white hind wings. Span 14–24 mm. ♂ smaller than ♀. Fore wings very pointed. Larva easily recognised by the dark chitinous peritreme of spiracles, whose anterior part is not as broad as the posterior margin (Fig. 178).

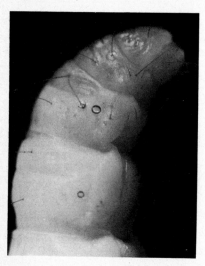

Fig. 178. Posterior end of body of larva of *Corcyra cephalonica* (phot. G. Brünner)

Similarities to other pests: Moths of *Ephestia* spp. distinguishable by the colour and shape of fore wings and the difference in size between ♂ and ♀. For comparison of larvae, see *Plodia interpunctella* and Figs. 179 & 180.

Life cycle: ♀♀ oviposit on day of hatching or within the first 9 days as follows:
104–155 eggs per ♀ in 1–3 batches. At higher temperatures and increased relative humidity more eggs are deposited, in the tropics up to 400. Incubation period (egg dormancy) between 4 and 10 days, also depending on temperature. The duration of larval development depends greatly on temperature and food. With higher moisture contents of the food, the larval period is reduced. Developmental period in corn meal at 18.2, 22.5 and 25.7 °C averages 116, 64 and 35 days. Wheat meal is far less suitable for development. In Egypt, larvae and pupae overwinter. Pupal dormancy at 17.6 °C on average 24, at 25.4 °C 10 days. Entire period of development in Egypt between 64 and 101 days. Shortest developmental period in the tropics 40 days. Under laboratory conditions, 6 generations on corn meal and 5 generations on wheat meal per year.

Ecology: The larvae, which can starve far up to 2 days, migrate far afield in search of suitable food. They spin profusely and fabricate much webbing to inhabit. Pupation takes place in dense white material.

Control: Chemical control as for *Plodia interpunctella* (see p. 444).

Literature

KAMEL, A. H. & M. A. HASSANEIN (1967): Biological studies on *Corcyra cephalonica* Staint. (Lepidoptera: Galleriidae). Bull. Soc. ent. Egypte **51**, 175–196.
HOSNY, M. M., H. H. HASSANEIN & A. H. KAMEL (1968): Ecological studies on *Anagasta kuehniella* and *Corcyra cephalonica* infesting flour mills in Cairo (Lepidoptera: Phycitidae and Galleriidae). Bull. Soc. ent. Egypte **52**, 445–456.

Author: H. Piltz

Family: Phycitidae

Ephestia cautella (Wlk.) (Fig. 179)

Synonym: *Cadra cautella*

Common names: Tropical Warehouse Moth, Almond Moth, Dried-currant Moth; Dattelmotte; Teigne de l'amandier; Polilla del almendro.

Geographical distribution: Cosmopolitan. Widespread throughout the tropics to around 2500 m.

Host plants/Stored products attacked: Cereal grains, cocoa, animal feeding-stuffs, nuts, spices, dried fruits, oilseeds, milled cereals, coffee beans, pulses, hides and skins; also recorded on citrus fruits causing superficial damage.

Symptoms: Larval pellets webbed into the commodity by silk and silk-strands on the surface of the commodity or the packages containing it. With heavy infestation there may be extensive sheets of silk over the surface. The adults fly actively, especially at dusk, and are conspicuous even at low infestation levels. Late instar larvae are seen on the surface of infested commodities and pupal cocoons are found especially on bagged commodities (at the line of contact between bags). Feeding damage on cereal grains is characteristically in the region of the embryo, especially on wheat.

Economic importance: On cereal grains, less important than weevils and other beetles. Important on high value commodities and packaged consumer goods (because of the obvious spoilage) and on seed-grain.

Morphology:
Adult (7–8 mm). Distinguished from Tineid and allied moths in stored produce by the broad hindwing with a relatively short fringe of hairs. Distinguished from other moths in stored produce by the markings on the forewing, readily seen on recently emerged adults. The forewings are brownish-grey, with no division into pale anterior and reddish-brown posterior halves as in *Plodia interpunctella,* but with a distinct, slightly sinuate, dark band at right-angles to the insect's long axis across the anterior half and a pale band bordering this anteriorly. In other *Ephestia* species these bands are indistinct or oblique to the long axis and in *Corcyra cephalonica* there are no transverse markings.

Larva. Distinguished from other genera by the distinct small dark spots on all body segments. Distinguishable from other *Ephestia* species only by microscopic examination (The minute seta anterior to the spiracle of abdominal segment 8 is separated from it by a distance equal to or less than the diameter of the spiracle).

Similarities to other pests: Can be confused with other *Ephestia* species but *E. kuehniella* is common only on cereal flour and *E. elutella* is very rare in the tropics.

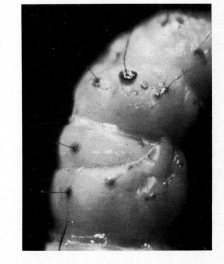

Fig. 179. *Ephestia cautella.* Posteror end of body of larva (phot. G. Brünner)

Life cycle: The adults do not feed and are short-lived (10–20 days or less). Up to 300 eggs per female are laid mostly in the first 3–4 days. The larvae (usually 5 instars) move actively, feeding until they are mature and excreting frass and silk. Prior to pupation there is a wandering phase, of varying duration, in which most of the obvious silk-webbing is produced. The pupal cocoon is thin and transparent. Total development occupies about 30 days at 30–32 °C and 70–80 % r. h. increasing to about 145 days near the lower developmental limit (15 °C) and to about 40 days at the upper limit (about 36 °C). Limiting humidities are about 95 % and 20 % r. h. at 25–32 °C with the lower limit rising markedly at unfavourable temperatures. The egg, larva and pupa respectively occupy about 10 %, 70 % and 20 % of the total developmental period.

Ecology: Aspects relevant to the assessment and control of populations are the distinct periodicity of adult flight activity, with a major peak at dusk and a smaller peak just before dawn, and the larval habit of seeking pupation sites which permits the use of refuge traps to compare population levels. The recent identification of adult sex pheromones is also of interest.

Natural enemies: The larvae are commonly parasitized by Hymenoptera, notably *Microbracon hebetor*. Egg-predation by the mite *Blattisocius tarsalis* has been recorded. Bacterial epidemics (usually caused by *Bacillus thuringiensis*) are common in heavily infested stores.

Control:
Sanitary methods. Store hygiene is important but rapid infestation of clean commodities is always likely in conventional stores.
Cultural practices. Pre-harvest infestation is negligible but cultural or harvesting practices leading to under-drying or grain damage will cause greater susceptibility to post-harvest infestation.
Crop resistance. Rice in husk (paddy), oats and rye are less readily attacked than other cereal grains. T'ef *(Eragrostis abyssinica)* is almost immune.
Biological control. Deliberate control by *B. thuringiensis* has been demonstrated. Arthropod enemies generally offer little promise except as natural population checks. Synthetic sex pheromones offer possibilities.
Integrated control. Effective control depends upon integration of sanitary methods and chemical methods. Biological control merits further investigation.
Chemical control. Fumigant gases give short-term control but repetitive fumigation is uneconomic and undesirable. Long-term control requires the use of contact insecticides to supplement fumigation. Many insecticides used on stored products are relatively ineffective but notable exceptions are straight pyrethrins (synergists are generally of little value against this pest), dichlorvos, bromophos and chlorpyrifos.
Spraying regimes. Pyrethrins and dichlorvos require frequent application preferably by daily fogging or mist-spraying at dusk when adult flight activity is greatest. Fair control can be achieved in cool uplands by monthly applications of pyrethrins as a deposit on all exposed surfaces of the commodity or the packages containing it. Similar or longer intervals may be possible with bromophos and chlorpyrifos. Dichlorvos is particularly suited to daily space-treatments and although often used for intermittant single-dose treatments the best results are obtained by continuous application from slow-release generators or, more economically, from automatic mist-blowers delivering a low volume dose daily at dusk.
Recommended dosage rates:
Fumigant gases: See fumigation schedules (p. 385).
Contact insecticides: as space-treatments (mists or fogs).
(Not suitable for stores with extensive permanent ventilation).
Dichlorvos: 5 mg per cu.m. daily at dusk; best applied as a 100 % wt/vol concentrate from automatic mist-blowers, or from proprietary slow-release generators.
Pyrethrins: 0.5 % solution in a non-combustible fogging mixture at 1 litre per 1000 cu.m. daily at dusk using a thermal-fog generator. (With less frequent application higher dosages are necessary and equally good results, nevertheless, may not be obtained.)

Contact insecticides: as surface treatments on store fabric, bagged commodities and exposed surfaces of commodities in bulk.

Pyrethrins: 0.5 % in technical white oil at 2 litres per 100 sq.m. at monthly intervals. (Higher concentrations may be necessary in low-altitude tropics. Added synergists give little advantage except where required for formulation stability).

Pirimiphos methyl: For spraying of surfaces including the surfaces of bags containing foodstuffs, pirimiphos methyl may be applied at 0.5–1.0 g per square metre monthly.

Chlorpyrifos: May be sprayed on hessian sheets covering bags in store at 0.5–1.0 g per square metre monthly, but should not be sprayed directly on to hessian bags containing foodstuffs.

Resistance to insecticides. This insect is relatively tolerant to a number of commonly used insecticides including DDT, lindane and malathion. Acquired resistance to other insecticides can be expected in areas of extensive or protracted use.

Literature

BURGES, H. D. & K. HASKINS (1965): Life-cycle of the Tropical Warehouse Moth, *Cadra cautella* (Wlk.) at controlled temperatures and humidities. Bull. ent. Res. **55** (4), 775–789.

CORBETT, A. S. & W. TAMS (1943): Keys for the identification of the Lepidoptera infesting stored food products. Proc. Zool. Soc. Lond. Ser. B, **113**, 55–148 + 5 plates.

GRAHAM, W. M. (1970): Ecological observations of an infestation by *Ephestia (Cadra) cautella* (Wlk.). J. stored Prod. Res. **6**, 157–167.

Author: J. A. McFarlane

Plodia interpunctella (Hübn.) (Fig. 180)

Common names: Indian meal moth; Dörrobstmotte; Pyrale des fruits secs; Palomilla indiana de las harinas.

Geographical distribution: Worldwide in the tropics and in subtropical regions, but only if relative humidity is above 40 %. Can develop in temperate climates, but only as long as temperatures are above 18 °C.

Stored products attacked: Dried fruit and vegetables, cereal – especially maize –, farinaceous products, nuts, sweets.

Symptoms: Dense webbing on the surface of affected products. In wheat (and rye) only the embryo is consumed. In maize, the endosperm is also attacked.

Economic importance: Important pest, especially on dried fruit and maize. With fairly severe infestation, the moisture content of stored products is increased. Secondary pests develop under the dense mass of felted grains, which can be up to 5 cm thick.

Morphology: Moths: Outer half of fore wings copper red with lead grey, wavy markings. Inner half cream coloured.

Larva: Without clearly distinguishable dark dots at the base of dorsal setae. Peritreme of spiracles only faintly chitinous (Fig. 180). Frons about twice as long as entire coronal suture.

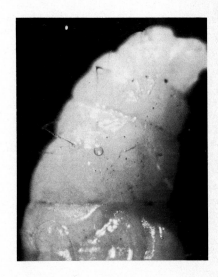

Fig. 180. *Plodia interpunctella.* Posterior end of body of larva (phot. G. Brünner)

444   Pests in tropical crops

Similarities to other pests: Moths unmistakable. Larvae of *Ephestia cautella* with clearly visible dots at the base of dorsal setae (Fig. 179). Frons about as long as entire coronal suture. Larvae of *Corcyra* with distinctive dark chitinous peritreme of spiracles, especially on 1st thoracic segment and 8th abdominal segment (Fig. 178). Posterior part of peritreme thickened.

Life cycle: Per ♀, 20–400 eggs are deposited, which are sticky and adhere to the support. Larvae hatch after a few (at 25 ° after 4–5) days. Fully grown larvae usually leave the nutrient medium and migrate in search of some suitable site for pupation. They pupate inside a loose cocoon. The duration of all developmental stages depends greatly on temperature and humidity. The entire developmental period egg – adult takes 24–31 days in trials at 35 ° and 41 % rel. humidity and 51–59 days at 20 °and 58 % rel. humidity. Under natural conditions, some 2 generations per year were counted in unheated warehouses in Germany and up to 8 under very favourable conditions in California. Temperatures below 20 ° can induce dormancy in fully grown larvae, but not in all individuals and to a varying degree in different populations. The total developmental period can extend over more than 200 days in that way. Dormancy can be prevented by photoperiods of 13 hours and this can facilitate control measures.

Ecology: Spread by moth flight and carried larvae. Larvae spin profusely and always leave a silk thread behind them.

Control:
Resistance. Different sweet corn varieties show very variable susceptibility to *Plodia*.
Chemical control. With adequate observation of moth flight, timely application of sprays (pyrethrum, malathion), fogs (pyrethrum, malathion, dichlorphos) or vapours (dichlorphos) can prevent oviposition.
Larvae can only be successfully controlled with fumigants. See fumigation schedules (p. 385).

Literature

ABDEL-RAHMAN, H. A., A. E. HODSON & C. M. CHRISTENSEN (1968): Development of *Plodia interpunctella* (Hb.) (Lepidoptera, Phycitidae) on Different Varieties of Corn at Two Levels of Moisture. J. stored Prod. Res. **4**, 127–133.
BELL, C. H. & D. J. WALKER (1973): Diapause Introduction in *Ephestia elutella* (Hübner) and *Plodia interpunctella* (Hübner) (Lepidoptera, Pyralidae) with Dawn-Dusk Lightning System. J. stored Prod. Res. **9**, 149–158.
MÜLLER, H. J. (1966): Probleme der Insektendiapause. Zool. Anz. 29. Suppl., 192–222.
TZANAKAKIS, M. E. (1959): An Ecological Study of the Indian meal moth *Plodia interpunctella* (Hübner) with Emphasis on Diapause. Hilgardia **29**, 205–246.

Author: H. Piltz

Family: Pyralidae (Pyralididae)

Antigastra catalaunalis (Dup.) (Plate 35 b)

Synonyms: *Botys catalaunalis, B. venosalis*

Common names: Sesame leaf roller, Sesame webworm; Sesamzünsler.

Geographical distribution: India, Bangladesh, Burma, Cyprus, USSR, Somalia, Sudan, Zaire, South Africa, East Africa, West Africa, Malta and Turkey.

Host plants: *Sesamum orientale, S. indicum, S. angustifolium, S. occidentale, S. prostratum, Antirrhinum majus, Linum* spp. (toad flax), *Linaria* sp., *Russelia juncea,* and *Martynia diandra.*

Symptoms: Caterpillars roll a few terminal leaves and make a web inside which they take shelter and feed on the leaves. They also feed on buds, flowers, immature capsules and seeds. Heavy infestation makes the plant unhealthy and dirty in appearance.

Economic importance: This is one of the major pests of sesame in various parts of the world, including India. It attacks the sesame crop when it is about 15 days old and continues until the crop matures. In the plant's initial stage of growth the pest damages the leaves and terminal shoots resulting in stunted growth. Heavy infestation at this stage results in the plant's death. At the flowering stage the caterpillars feed inside the flowers making them barren. The yield of the crop is thus greatly reduced.

Morphology: Egg. The egg is elongate oval in shape measuring about 0.43 mm in length and 0.28 mm in breadth. It is transparent when freshly laid but gradually changes to pale yellow, grey and finally to pink, just before hatching. Larva. The freshly hatched caterpillar is small (measuring about 2.5 mm in length) and dirty white in colour with a black head. The fully-grown caterpillar is light green in colour with black spots bearing small setae. It measures about 15 mm in length. Pupa. The pupa is light green in colour when freshly formed but changes to light brown later on. Adult. The moth is straw coloured with orange red wings having prominent veins and a fringe of hairs on outer margin of each one. It measures about 8 mm in length and its wing span is about 15 mm. The under surfaces of the wings are shiny grey in the centre and yellowish white on the sides, with three blackish spots on the fore wings but only one on the hind wings, placed towards the anterior margin.

Life cycle: The moth lays eggs singly on terminal shoots and leaves, though several eggs may be found close together. The fecundity of the moth is about 70, although up to 223 eggs have been reported by some workers. Eggs are laid successively over a period of 4–8 days. The incubation period is about 4–5 days.

The caterpillar undergoes five larval instars over a period of 10–20 days, depending upon the season, before transforming into pupa. Cannibalism among the larvae has been reported. Pupation takes place either inside the fallen leaves on the ground, or inside the web on the plant. The pupa is generally covered with whitish silken threads. The pupal period lasts 3–7 days. The moth matures sexually soon after its emergence and starts copulation within 24 hrs. The oviposition starts 2–4 days after emergence. The longevity of sugar-fed moths is 6–8 days while that of unfed moths is 2–3 days. Generally, females live longer than males.

Ecology: In India, the pest is active throughout the year. The infestation starts in July when the crop is in it's early stage and the pest continues to breed up to the end of November. Thereafter, it migrates to a winter annual, *Antirrhinum majus,* on which it regularly breeds upto the end of February. The insect passes the period from March to end of June on volunteer plants of *A. majus* and on old sprouting sesame plants. It continues to live in small numbers until the new sesame crop is sown towards the middle of June or early July. The insect passes through six overlapping generations on the sesame crop from July to November. In Northeast Africa, the pest survives the long dry season as a diapause larva.

Natural enemies: *Apanteles aethiopicus, Microbracon brevicornis, Bracon hebetor* (Braconidae); *Camptothilipris antigastrae, Cremastus* sp., *C. flavoorbitalis,* and *Hymenobosmina* sp. (Ichneumonidae).

Control:
Sanitary methods. (a) Affected portions of the plant may be destroyed immediately after the appearance of the pest. (b) Old sprouting plants of sesame may be destroyed since they serve as alternate hosts during the host's absence.
Cultural practices. (a) Early sowing of the crop may be a good practice because late sown crops

become more infested in India. (b) Application of different fertilizers should be in the proper ratio. Infestation is directly proportional to the quantity of nitrogenous fertiliser applied.

Resistance of crops. Less susceptible varieties (like C-1036 and Chanda – 3 in India) may be grown in the absence of resistant varieties.

Integrated control. Various possible combinations of the control measures mentioned above and the timely application of insecticides may ensure good control.

Chemical control. 0.05 % endosulfan emulsion and 0.01 % carbaryl suspension has proved to be effective. Either of these two insecticides may be sprayed in about 500 l of water/ha at intervals of 20 days starting from when the pest appears.

Literature

DESAI, M. T. & R. M. PATAL (1965): Studies on the sesame leaf roller *(Antigastra catalaunalis* Dup.) in Gujarat. Indian Oilseed J. **9** (2), 109.
MENON, M. G. R., R. LAL & N. S. BHATTA CHARJEE (1960): Studies on *Antigastra catalaunalis* Dup. The til leaf roller II. Bionomics and Biology. Indian J. Ent. **22** (1), 1–6.
PRASAD, S. K. (1970): Varietal differences in the incidence of *Antigastra catalaunalis* Dup. on sesame *(Sesamum indicum* L.). Indian J. Ent. **32** (3), 27–28.
SINGH, J. P. (1970): Insect pests of Sesamum – Labdev J. Sci. & Tech. **8**B (2), 84.
TEOTIA, T. P. S. & RISHAD HUSSAIN (1965): Bionomics of the Til leaf roller and pod borer, *Antigastra catalaunalis* Dup. (Pyralidae: Lepidoptera). Labdev J. Sci. & Tech. **3** (3), 195–197.
THOMPSON, W. R.: A catalogue of the parasites and predators of insect pests. Sec. **1** (5), 53.

Author: S. K. Prasad

Chilo infuscatellus Snell.

Synonyms: *Chilo tadzhikiellus, Chilotraea infuscatellus*

Common names: Early shoot borer; Gelber Zuckerrohrbohrer.

Geographical distribution: This species is widely distributed from Tadzhikistan (USSR) to the Philippines including Pakistan, India, Bangladesh, Burma, China, Taiwan, Korea and Indonesia. CIE Map no 301.

Host plants: The most preferred host is sugarcane from which the pest may migrate to wild *Saccharum* spp., viz., *Saccharum arundinaceum, S. munja, S. spontaneum, S. fuscum, Erianthus* sp. and other grasses, namely, *Rottboellia compressa, Panicum maximum, P. colonum, Cynodon dactylon, Cyperus rotundus, Coix lachryma jobi, Eragrostis cynosuroides, Echinochloa colonum, Sorghum halepense,* if they are present in the vicinity of sugarcane fields. Among crops of economic importance the pest has been recorded, though rarely, on sorghum (*Sorghum vulgare*), maize (*Zea mays*), bajra (*Pennisetum typhoidees*), barley (*Hordeum vulgare*) and oats (*Avena sativa*).

Symptoms: The caterpillars attack sugarcane in the early stage of crop growth (before node formation) but their activity often continues even after node formation depending upon the climatic conditions.

The freshly hatched and 2nd instar larvae usually feed on outer leaves. The 3rd instar larvae bore through the core of the plants and damage the growing points. As a result, the central whorls begin to dry up yielding dead-hearts. The larvae come out and enter the adjacent healthy shoots; thus a single larva is capable of causing several dead-hearts in a single clump. These dead-hearts begin to rot at their bases and when pulled out give off an offensive smell.

After node formation, the borers make small circular holes in the stem and feed and pupate within, hindering the normal growth of the crop. A number of holes may be seen on an affected stalk with frass extruding from these holes, while the tunnels inside are hollow, straight and free of frass.

The larvae of the 2nd, 3rd and 4th brood cause comparatively more damage than those of the 1st and last generations.

Economic importance: According to estimates of various workers, this borer causes losses of 8–85 %. The percentage loss has been reported to be 10.36, 0.55 and 6.69 % on a stalk, weight and sucrose basis, respectively. Other estimates indicate that an early shoot borer attack may destroy 57.5 % of mother shoots, 75 percent tertiary, 27.1 % secondary and 6.4 % primary tillers and, in addition, by boring into the internodes it may cause a loss of 0.6 tonnes of commercial cane sugar per hectare.

Morphology: Egg. Tiny, scale-like, oval-shaped and whitish in colour.
Larva. Dorsal side with five longitudinal, light-violet stripes; spiracles open, oval in outline with black rim; crochets on prolegs multiordinal, arranged in incomplete circles. In the last instar, the larva loses all but one thin, median, dorsal stripe making identification difficult.
Pupa. Yellowish-brown, abdominal segments 5, 6 and 7 having flattened wavy ridges which almost touch one another and make a complete circle on segment 7; cremaster short and blunt with fairly deep lateral grooves; anal end rounded and smooth with no horny processes or hairs; anal opening terminating in λ.

Adult. Front of frons bearing a small corneous apex; ocelli present; antennae of male lamellate and flat while those of female filiform. Wing colouration very variable (brownish-yellow to chocolate brown); veins 11 and 12 in forewing running upto costa rather close together.

Life cycle: Normally lasts 25–47 days, though the winter brood in North India lasts for 155–277 days. The actual duration of each stage varies with the prevailing temperature and relative humidity. On an average, egg, larval and pupal stages last for 3–6, 15–35 (over 140 days for the overwintering larva) and 7–12 days, respectively; longevity of moths is 4–5 days. There are normally 5–6 generations each year.

Ecology: High temperature and low relative humidity are very conducive to rapid multiplication of the insect. In general, it is a pre-monsoon pest. Duration of development of egg, larva and pupa decreases with increasing temperature, the lower and upper limits being 12 ° and 40 °C. In Northern India, the larva enters into physiological diapause during winter, while in South India there is no diapause and the pest is found all the year round. Maximum activity of the pest has been observed at 37 ° to 41 ° and 40–50 percent relative humidity coupled with the absence of rainfall. The population remains low during the rains (high humidity). Heavy infestation has been observed during April, May and June in Northern India and during February–March in eksali (one year) and September–October in adsali ($1\frac{1}{2}$ years) cane in South India.

Natural enemies: Egg parasites in India include the hymenopterous *Telenomus beneficiens*, *T. dignoides*, *Tetrastichus schoenobii*, *Trichogramma australicum*, *T. japonicum* and *T. nana*. Larvae are parasitized by *Apanteles flavipes*, *A. phytometrae*, *Bracon chinensis*, *Campyloneurus mutator*, *Drapetis* sp., *Elasmus zehntneri*, *Exorista quadrimaculata*, *Goniozus indicus*, *Gotra marginata*, *Stenobracon nicevillei*, *Tropobracon schoenobii*, *Vipio deesae* (Hymenoptera) and *Sturmiopsis inferens* (Tachinidae). Pupal parasites are *Aprostocertus israeli*, *Centeterus alternecoloratus*, *Isotima javensis*, *Brachycorphus nursei*, *Tetrastichus ayyari*, *T. israeli*, *Xanthopimpla punctata* and *X. stemmator*. A nematode (*Mermis* sp.) has been found in the body of the larva.

Control:
Sanitary methods. Clean cultivation is very essential to prevent the carry-over of this pest. Remove all wild gramineaceous plants and other alternate host plants growing in the vicinity of cane fields. Soon after harvest, collect and destroy all the stubble and trash by burning or by burying deeply.
Cultural practices. Earlier workers suggested a change in the sowing dates to avoid the peak incidence period, 2–3 light earthings in the early stage of crop growth followed by irrigation to reduce dead-hearts and trash mulching to trap the borer moths. Trash mulching, beside reducing the bo-

rer population, reduces the evil effects of drought, conserves soil moisture and adds organic matter to the soil thereby improving its texture. Planting in deep trenches also reduces the borer damage. It has been reported that attacks were greater in thin varieties than in thick ones while quick-growing varieties escaped heavy infestation.

Mechanical methods. Hand collection and destruction of egg masses, removal and quick disposal of dead-hearts, collection of moths by the use of light traps are some of the measures which, though laborious, are very effective. They may not be practicable on a large scale and in the advanced stage of crop growth but, when adopted in the early growth of the cane crop, can keep the incidence of this borer at a low level.

Biological control. Due to unfavourable climatic conditions, natural parasitism is rather low. Studies have been undertaken in different parts of India on mass breeding and liberation of the egg parasite, *Trichogramma australicum* (erroneously recorded as *T. evanscens minutum*). It is doubtful whether its use is adequate to give a constant economic benefit to the final yield.

Chemical control. Soil application of gamma-BHC at a rate of 1 kg a. i. per hectare is effective in keeping the pest population low, though the pest does not respond well in soils with a pH above 7.5. Spraying with 0.1 % endrin or phosphamidon (400–1000 ml/hectare) has also proved effective in reducing the pest population. Two to three sprayings may be necessary. These must synchronise with hatching of eggs so that the freshly hatched larvae are killed before they enter the plants.

Integrated control. The only rational approach to check this borer is integrated pest control, viz., clean cultivation, soil application with 1.0 kg a. i. gamma-BHC at the time of planting, collection and destruction of egg-masses and dead-hearts, 2–3 light earthings followed by irrigation in the early stage of crop growth coupled with 1–2 sprayings of 0.05 to 0.06 % phosphamidon against the later broods of the pest.

Literature

BUTANI, D. K. (1956): A key for identification of sugarcane borers. Indian J. Ent. **18** (3), 303–304.

BUTANI, D. K. (1969): Bionomics and control of sugarcane shoot borer, *Chilo infuscatellus* Snellen. Labdev J. Sci. Tech. 7-B (2), 104–118.

JAGANNATHA RAO, E. & R. JAGANNATHA RAO (1960): Some studies on the control of shoot borer *(Chilotraea infuscatellus* Snell.) in Bobbili tract (Andhra Pradesh). Indian J. Sugarcane Res. & Dev. **5** (3), 149–154.

KALYANARAMAN, V. M., A. LEELA DAVID & P. S. NARAYANASWAMY (1963): Distribution season of occurrence and control of the early shoot borer of sugarcane, *Chilotraea infuscatellus* (Snellen) in Madras State. Indian J. Sugarcane Res. & Dev. **7** (2), 89–95.

KHAN, M. Q. & B. H. KRISNAMURTHY RAO (1956): Assessment of loss due to *Chilotraea infuscatellus* Snell. in sugarcane. Proc. 9th Cong. int. Soc. Sug. Cane Tech., India **1**, 870–879.

PRADHAN, S. & S. K. BHATIA (1956): The effect of temperature and humidity on the development of the sugarcane stem borer, *Chilotraea infuscatellus* Snell. Proc. 9th Cong. int. Soc. Sug. Cane Tech., India, **1**, 856–869.

SIDDIQI, Z. A., V. G. RAJANI & O. P. SINGH (1959): Simultaneous control of sugarcane termite and shoot borer through soil application of gamma-BHC liquid and its boosting effect on crop yield. Indian J. Sugarcane Res. & Dev. **3** (4), 227–232.

SINGH, O. P., & J. S. SANDHU (1961): Preliminary studies on the translocation of gamma-BHC in sugarcane and its residual effects. Indian J. Sugarcane Res. & Dev. **5** (3), 142–145.

TEOTIA, T.P.S., V. G. RAJANI & GANGA SAGAR (1963): Additional findings on the use of gamma-BHC against termites and shoot borers in sugarcane crop in Uttar Pradesh. Indian J. Sugarcane Res. & Dev. **8** (1), 33–38.

Author: Dhamo K. Butani

Chilo partellus (Swinh.) (Plate 35 c)

Synonym: *C. zonellus*

Common names: Spotted (sorghum) stemborer, Spotted stalk borer; Gefleckter Stengelbohrer.

Plate 33

a Adults of *Cosmopolites sordidus*
b Pseudostem of banana, showing damage caused by larvae of *Cosmopolites sordidus*
c Adult of *Rhynchophorus palmarum*
d Larvae of *Rhynchophorus phoenicis*

Plate 34

a Larva of *Pectinophora gossypiella* in a cotton flower
b Damage of *Batrachedra amydraula* on date palm fruits
c Olive fruits, showing damage by larvae of *Prays oleae*
d Mines of *Leucoptera coffeella* in a coffee leaf

Plate 35

a Feeding damage of larvae of *Indarbela quadrinotata* on a mango stem
b Damage of *Antigastra catalaunalis* on sesame
c Larva of *Chilo partellus* in inflorescence of maize
d Female of *Chilo suppressalis*

Plate 36

a Larvae of *Chilo suppressalis* in rice stems
b Larva of *Maruca testulalis* in a cowpea pod
c Larva of *Ostrinia furnacalis* on maize cob
d Adult moth (female) of *Tryporyza incertulas*

Plate 37

a Larvae of *Agrotis ipsilon*
b Adult moth of *Agrotis ipsilon*
c Adult moth of *Alabama argillacea*
d Larva of *Busseola fusca* on sorghum

Plate 38

a   Larva of *Diparopsis castanea* in a cotton boll
b   Adult moth of *Diparopsis watersi*
c   Larva of *Diparopsis watersi* in a cotton boll
d   Egg of *Diparopsis watersi*

Plate 39

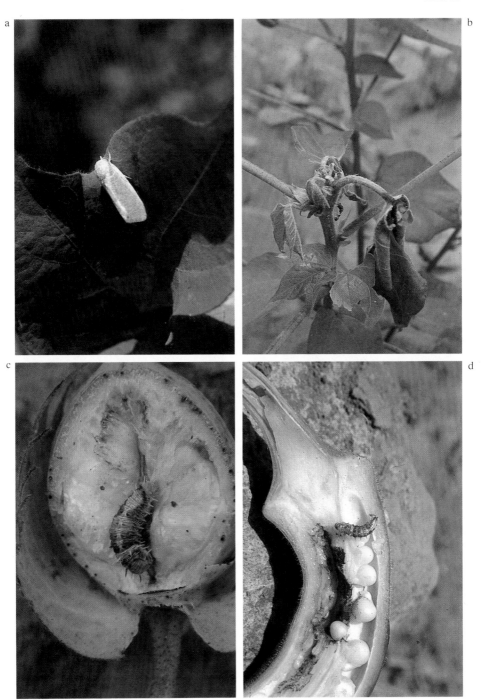

a Adult moth of *Earias insulana*
b Wilting shoot of a young cotton plant, damaged by a larva of *Earias insulana*
c Larva of *Earias biplaga* in a cotton boll
d Larva of *Earias biplaga* in an okra fruit

Plate 40

a Adult moth of *Heliothis armigera*
b Larva of *Heliothis armigera* on a cotton boll
c Green larva of *Heliothis armigera* on a sorghum head
d Tomatoes, showing feeding holes caused by larvae of *Heliothis armigera*

Plate 41

a Larvae of *Heliothis virescens*
b Adult moth of *Heliothis virescens*
c Green larva of *Heliothis zea* in a cotton flower
d Brown larva of *Heliothis zea* on a cotton flower bud

Plate 42

a Green larva of *Heliothis zea* feeding on a young cotton shoot
b Adult moth of *Heliothis zea*
c Adult moth of *Sesamia calamistis*
d Larva of *Sesamia calamistis* in a sorghum stem

Plate 43

a Larva of *Sesamia cretica* on a maize cob
b Dead hearts on sugar cane, caused by larvae of *Sesamia calamistis*
c Larva of *Sesamia inferens* in a sugar cane stem
d White heads of rice, caused by *Sesamia inferens*

Plate 44

a Larvae of *Spodoptera exigua* on a cotton leaf
b Feeding damage of larvae of *Spodoptera exigua* on cotton leaves
c Larvae of *Spodoptera frugiperda* on maize
d Eggs and newly hatched larvae of *Spodoptera frugiperda*

Plate 45

a Larva of *Spodoptera littoralis*
b Adult moth (female) of *Spodoptera littoralis*
c Adult moth of *Trichoplusia ni*
d Larva of *Trichoplusia ni*

Plate 46

a Rice plants, showing symptoms of attack ("onion shoots") by *Pachydiplosis (Orseolia) oryzae*
b Young sorghum plant, showing dead heart caused by larva of *Atherigona (varia) soccata*
c Adult flies of *Ceratitis capitata* on citrus fruit
d Orange fruit, attacked by *Ceratitis capitata*

Plate 47

a   Adult fly of *Dacus dorsalis*
b   Larvae of *Dacus dorsalis* in a papaya fruit
c   Egg laying scars of *Dacus ciliatus* on a zucchini fruit
d   Olives, damaged by larvae of *Dacus oleae*

Plate 48

a Male of *Quelea quelea* in breeding plumage
b *Rattus rattus mindanensis*
c Rat damage on maize cobs
d Rat damage on tomatoes

Geographical distribution: *C. partellus* occurs in India, Pakistan, Sri Lanka and other neighbouring countries. Records in Africa refer to Somalia, Ethiopia, Kenya, Uganda, Tanzania, Malawi and the Sudan.

Host plants: Sorghum, maize, Sudan grass, wheat, finger millet, *Pennisetum,* sugar cane and wild grasses. In the Sudan, *Pennisetum* and sugar cane are slightly attacked and in India sorghum, maize and bajra *(Pennisetum)* in a decreasing order of susceptibility, are the most susceptible host plants.

Symptoms: After hatching from the eggs the young larvae feed gregariously on the soft folded leaves (funnel). When these leaves are fully developed, the damage appears as characteristic rows of small, uniformly shaped holes. A few days later the larvae separate and penetrate the midribs of the leaves and eat their way downwards, passing the growing point until they enter the stem. Others penetrate the stem directly. The destruction of the growing point leads to cessation of growth, known as "dead heart". The larvae entering the stem via the growing point, or through small holes in the side of the stem itself, tunnel further downwards leaving behind frass and excrement. Such damage disturbs the water-transport system of the plant thus causing its partial or complete failure to form a head. In maize, cobs are also infested late in the season.

Economic importance: *C. partellus* is the primary cause of grain losses in sorghum in the Sudan. It is also a major pest of sorghum and maize in other parts of Africa and in India.

Morphology: Egg. Oval, flat and whitish. Larva. 20–25 mm long in the fully-grown stage, whitish to yellowish-brown. Dorsal side with longitudinal rows of light-brown to brown warts of different sizes. Head capsule brown, spiracles black. Pupa. Slender, 10–15 mm long, shining brown. Female. Yellowish to yellowish-brown, body slender, wing span 20–25 mm. Forwing terminating with an acute tip, straw-coloured with one or two transverse rows of small, dark brown dots. Hindwing white with marginal fringe. Male. Darker and smaller than female.

Similarities to other pests: The pest is similar in its damage and habits of feeding to a number of other stem-boring pests e. g. *Sesamia cretica* (North Africa, Near and Middle East), *S. calamistis* (West Africa), *Busseola fusca* (Africa south of the Sahara) and *Ostrinia nubilalis* (North Africa, America, and Europe).

Life cycle: Under field conditions in the Sudan, eggs are deposited in one or more oval discs, on the lower surface of leaves at night. About 300 eggs are laid by a single female. Hatching begins after 3–5 days and the young caterpillars feed on leaves for a further 5–6 days, after which they penetrate the midribs of leaves. They enter the stem directly or through the growing point. The caterpillars feed inside the stem until they become fully-grown after 10–14 days. In the stem they enter the pupal stage in special pupal chambers provided with an exit hole and "window" for the hatching moth. After 7–9 days the moth emerges, usually just after sunset. The entire life-cycle takes about 3–4 weeks, sometimes longer in colder months but shorter in hot ones.

Ecology: Continuous development occurs during the rainy season, or under otherwise favourable conditions in irrigated areas, the whole year round. In places where there is a dry season, the pest enters a larval diapause sometime after the rainy season. Diapausing larvae remain in the dry stalk or stubble until the next rainy season. After the first rain showers they pupate, and the moths hatch some days afterwards.

Natural enemies: Larvae of the braconid wasps *Glyptomorpha deesae* (= *Vipio deesae)* and *Euvipio* sp. are important external parasites of the caterpillars. The pupa is parasitized by the wasps *Hyperchalcidia soudanensis* and *Pediobius* sp.. The coccinellids *Menochilus sexmaculatus* and *Coccinella undecimpunctata* have been observed as predators of young larvae.

Control:
Sanitary methods. Graminaceous weeds should be removed from the field since some act as alternate hosts of the pest.
Remains of the crop of the previous season (stubble) should be removed and burnt before establishing the new crop. A sequence of crop rotations in which cereals are followed by crops of other species is beneficial in reducing infestations.
Resistance of crops: Growing resistant varieties seems to be the best procedure to avoid crop losses. In maize, certain germplasms are known to be resistant to *C. partellus,* e. g. Antiqua Gr 2, Antiqua Gr 1 (India), Antiqua Gr 1 (USA) and Antiqua 8 D. The basis of their resistance could be the presence of toxins or repellent materials, or the absence of certain nutrients.
Chemical control: In N.E. Africa, carbaryl (Sevin) w. p. at 1 kg a.i./feddan (1 feddan = 0.42 hectare), DDT e.c. at 1 lb a.i./fedd., endosulfan e. c. at 1 lb a.i./fedd. and toxaphene e. c. at 2 litres a. i./fedd., applied 3 times in intervals of 14 days has controlled *C. partellus* on maize very well. Carbaryl has given a significant increase in grain yield. Monocrotophos, tetrachlorvinphos and chlorfenvinphos are also effective, when repeatedly applied.

Literature

AHMED, S. M. & W. R. YOUNG (1969): Field observations on the susceptibility of sorghum, maize and bajara to *Chilo zonellus* (Swinhoe). Ind. J. Ent. **31** (3), 235–339.
CHATTERJI, S. M., V. P. S. PANWAR, K. H. SIDDIQUI, W. R. YOUNG & K. K. MARWAHA (1970): Field screening of some promising maize germ plasm against *Chilo zonellus* Swinhoe under artificial infestation. Ind. J. Ent. **32,** 167–170.
SCHMUTTERER, H. (1969): Pests of Crops in Northeast and Central Africa. Gustav Fischer, Jena and Portland, 296 pp.
SHARMA, A. K. (1971): Preferential oviposition and antibiosis in different maize germplasms against *C. zonellus* under cage conditions. Int. J. Ent. **33**, 299–315.
JEPSON, W. F. (1954): A critical review of the world literature on the lepidopterous stalk borers of tropical Graminaceous crops. Commonw. Inst. Ent. London, 127 pp.

Author: S. A. Siddig

Chilo polychrysus (Meyr.) (Fig. 181)

Synonyms: *Proceras polychrysa, Chilotraea polychrysa, Diatraea polychrysa, Chilo polychrysa*

Common names: Dark-headed rice borer; Schwarzköpfiger Reisstengelbohrer.

Geographical distribution: Oriental region: Bangladesh, Brunei, Burma, China, Hongkong, India, Indonesia (excluding West Irian), Khmer, Laos, Malaysia, Philippines, Thailand, Vietnam.

Host plants: Primary host: Rice. Secondary hosts: maize, sugar cane, *Scirpus grossus, Hymenachne pseudointerrupta, Setaria pollidefusca, S. italica, Echinochloa crusgalli,* and *Panicum crusgalli.*

Symptoms: Refer to *Chilo suppressalis* (p. 452).

Economic importance: The dark-headed rice borer is a major pest of rice in Malaysia and parts of India. Its importance has been increasingly recognized in some other countries. A heavy infestation of this borer may cause a loss in yield of up to 60 %.

Fig. 181.   *Chilo polychrysus*. From left to right: egg mass, larva, pupa, femala and male (phot. IRRI, Los Baños)

Morphology: Egg – laid in masses of overlapping rows, transparent, white, scale-like, naked, about 0.75 mm long.

Larva – last instar is 21 mm long. The head is brownish black (in contrast to *C. suppressalis*) while the body is creamy white with five brown stripes along the back of the body. The thoracic plate behind the head is also dark, causing the head, when viewed from above by an untrained observer to appear larger than its actual size.

Pupa – white which gradually changes to dark brown. The length is about 11 mm.

Adult moth – yellowish brown with small purple spots. Two or three spots appear in the center part of the forewings. The wing span is 16 to 25 mm.

Similarities to other pests: Refer to *Chilo suppressalis* (p. 453).

Life cycle: The moths are active during the night and lay their eggs between 7 to 11 p. m. in masses containing 20 to 150 eggs each. A single female moth can lay up to 480 eggs in 3 days. The incubation period is 4 to 7 days. The larvae hatch early in the morning and feed beneath the leafsheath for a period of time. The mature larvae feed within the stem and can destroy the growing point of the rice plant. The larval stage lasts 20 to 41 days.

Ecology: Depending on the climatic conditions and the availability of host plants as a source of food, the number of generations of the borer per year varies up to 12; no dormancy or diapause has been reported. Overlapping generations may occur throughout the year. The second and succeeding generations are usually more destructive. In the absence of rice plants, the insects move to their alternate hosts, i. e., maize (corn), sugar cane, and others.

Natural enemies: Two egg parasites, *Telenomus beneficiens* and *Trichogramma japonicum,* have been recorded as natural enemies of the dark-headed rice borer. *Bracon albolineatus* and *Tetrastichus* species, and *Apanteles flavipes* (wasps) parasitize the larvae or the pupae.

Control:

Sanitary methods. Refer to *Chilo suppressalis* (p. 454).

Cultural practices. Corn should not be grown after rice in areas where the dark-headed rice borer is abundant because the borer can shift from rice to corn as an alternate host. For other cultural practices, refer to *Chilo suppressalis* (p. 454).

Resistance of crops. Very little information is available regarding rice varieties that are resistant to *C. polychrysa.* Under field conditions rice varieties IR 20, IR 22, Karta, Latisail, Jaya, and TKM-6 exhibit a low incidence of dead heart damage and effected poor larval survival.

Biological/integrated control. The possibility of utilizing parasites to control this borer has been extensively explored. However, when borer parasites were imported into Malaysia, there was no build-up of the parasite population in the borer-infested areas. The use of rice varieties which are less susceptible to this pest as a principal measure or as an integral part of an insect control program may minimize the crop loss. The lower incidence of borer infestation in the less susceptible rice varieties can complement the effect of insecticides to give better control.

Chemical control. Refer to *Chilo suppressalis* (p. 454).

Prognosis. The moths caught from light traps have been useful in the study of the seasonal abundance of borers throughout the rice growing season. The resulting information has been used as a guide in determining the proper time for sowing to minimize borer damage to rice crops.

Literature

Refer to *Chilo suppressalis* (p. 455).

Author: Ibrahim Manwan

Chilo suppressalis (Wlk.) (Fig. 182, plates 35 d and 36 a)

Synonyms: *Crambus suppressalis, Chilo simplex, Chilo oryzae*

Common names: Striped rice borer; Gestreifter Reisstengelbohrer; Barrenador del arroz.

Geographical distribution: Australia (Northern Territory), Bangladesh, Brunei, Burma, China, Hongkong, India, Indonesia, Japan, Khmer, Korea, Malaysia, Nepal, New Guinea, Pakistan, Papua, Philippines, Ruykyu, Sri Lanka, Taiwan, Thailand, U.S.A. (Hawaii), U.S.S.R. (Soviet Maritime Province), Vietnam. CIE Map no 254.

Host plants: Primary host: rice *(Oryza sativa).* Secondary hosts: kibi *(Panicum miliaceum),* millet *(Echinochloa* spp.), *Phragmites communis,* ikri *(Saccharum fuscum),* great reedmace *(Typha latifolia:* Typhaceae), makono *(Zizania aquatica),* and maize *(Zea mays).*

Symptoms: Larvae bore and tunnel into the stem. Their feeding on the vascular tissue within the stem produces two characteristic symptoms found upon visual inspection of a field:
1. Dead heart – internal girdling of young tillers at the base causes the portion above to wither and die.
2. White head – similar to above in feeding after panicle initiation, causes the panicle to dry up, stopping grain development or causing grains which are already formed to shrivel.

Fig. 182.   White heads of rice caused by *Chilo suppressalis* (phot. H. Schmutterer)

Economic importance: The striped rice borer has historically been considered the most serious pest of rice in Japan, Korea, Taiwan, and China. Severe infestations may kill the plant in the vegetative stage. Normally the greatest yield loss is due to the borer feeding on the stem before flowering, which prevents panicle and grain formation. The rice plant can, to some extent, compensate and recover from tiller damage during the vegetative phase if the insect population is arrested before panicle initiation. The plant produces new tillers and the only effect is a lengthening of the period before flowering. Every 1 percent of white head damage may cause a 1–3 percent loss in yield. In addition to dead heart and white head where whole stems are affected, larval feeding can cause reduced plant vigor, fewer tillers, unfilled grains, and plant lodging in high winds.

Morphology: Egg – scale-like, white to dark yellow, laid in masses formed of overlapping rows, naked.
Larvae – last stage 20–26 mm long, recognized by 5 longitudinal dark stripes running down the pale brown back. The middle stripe is less distinct. The head capsule is light brown in contrast to *Chilo polychrysus*.
Pupa – reddish brown, naked, 11–13 mm.
Adult moth – 13–16 mm in length, wings straw-colored to light brown. The forewings have a row of small spots along the tip.

Similarities to other pests: There are some other rice stem borers in Asia, belonging to various genera of Pyralidae and Noctuidae. The damage caused by them resembles that of *C. suppressalis*. These borers can be erroneously identified as striped rice borer, especially in the early instars. However, the fully-grown larva of *C. suppressalis* can be recognized by its clearly striped body and its light brown head capsule (Plate 36 a).

Life cycle: Adult moths are active in the early evening. A female will lay from 100 to 550 eggs in batches of 50 to 80 depositing one batch each night over a 3–5 day period. Egg masses are found on the basal half of the leaves or occasionally on the leaf sheaths along the midrib of either the upper or lower surface. Upon hatching, the larvae will crawl up the plant and will congregate eventually beneath the leaf sheath at the juncture of the leaf. All larvae will enter a common hole. During the first three larval periods the larvae are found in clusters. Larval feeding generally occurs in the middle portion of the stem. The larval stage normally lasts from 20 to 48 days. Pupation takes place within the stem; the full-grown 5th-instar larva prepares an exit hole in the internode through which the soon-to-develop moth can escape. No silken cocoon is formed around the pupa. Mating usually occurs during the night of emergence. The life cycle takes from 35 to 60 days under favourable nondormancy conditions. In the more temperate regions, where cold winters occur, the larvae undergo a dormancy period during the last instar and development resumes in the spring with warmer temperatures. Striped rice borers can have one to five generations per year. Overlapping generations are common in tropical regions typified by continuous cropping.

Ecology: The striped rice borer is adapted to temperate regions; the larvae are cold-hardy and are able to withstand temperatures as cold as – 14 °C for short periods of time. A larval dormancy has been identified in temperate zones. Both the availability of the host and the occurrence of favorable temperatures appear to determine the number of generations in a year. The longer the time of host availability, the more the population is built up through more generations per year. Generally, the first crop sustains only slight damage, but this varies depending to a major extent on the overwinter mortality. The mortality can be high in years of mild winters or early springs that affect the early development of moths which lay eggs on young rice seedlings not sufficiently developed to accomodate the young emerging larvae. The mortality is lower during the years of cool springs where the rice is planted relatively earlier and the plant stems are available for the newly emerged larvae. A period of sudden warm weather following the peak oviposition period further promotes the development of this rice pest. More oviposition occurs on lush rice plants, especially those to which high rates of nitrogen have been applied.

Natural enemies: Numerous insect parasites of the striped rice borer have been reported in the literature. The egg parasites, notably *Trichogramma* spp. (minute wasps) parasitize 40 to 60 percent of eggs during certain seasons. They are superparasities (not restricted to lay one egg per host egg), however, and even when mass-reared and released, seldom exceed these figures. The low season mortality of less than 5 percent year after year of the striped rice borer larvae and pupae caused by the *Trichogramma* parasites reflects the protected habitat occupied by the stem borer larvae. Spiders are known predators of small striped rice borer larvae and have been reported to cause between 55 and 87 percent predation. The anthocorid bug, *Eusupaeus beneficus,* preys on larvae and newly-emerged adults. Nematodes and disease (viral, bacteria, and fungal) have a minimal effect for the most part. The fungus *Isaria farinosa* has also been identified as a pathogen of the striped rice borer in Japan.

Control:

Sanitary methods. After harvest the rice stubble usually harbors the developing larvae or pupae which were not removed with the straw. The recommended practice to minimize infestation on succeeding crops includes flooding plus harrowing or plowing under the stubble when it is uprooted. Destruction of volunteer rice between succeeding crops can also serve as sanitation method.

Cultural practices. Depending on the local conditions, the time of planting the first crop may be altered to reduce borer infestation by minimizing larval feeding in the stems at panicle initiation. The use of an earlier maturing rice variety will impair the population buildup because harvest will be sooner and will disrupt the life cycle of the striped rice borer. Where two crops are grown in succession, all farmers in a region must synchronize their first plantings to allow a rice-free period between crops. Harvest the stems close to the ground to remove the larvae from the stubble tops which can then be destroyed. The stubble can be grazed by livestock. To delay borer build-up, avoid placing the seedbed nursery for the second crop concurrently with the first crop.

Crop resistance. Generally tall rice varieties with long wide leaves and large stems are more susceptible than shorter varieties. Some highly resistant varieties are TKM 6, Taitung 16, Chianan 2, Su-Yai 20, Szu-Mizo, Yabami Montakhab 55, CV 136, and PTB 10. Semi-dwarf varieties such as IR 20 and IR 26 are classified as moderately resistant. The borer exhibits a lower preference for laying eggs on these varieties and such varieties effect a degree of larval mortality, thus affording these semi-dwarf rice varieties 10 to 20 times more protection from dead heart or white head damage than some tall rice varieties which are susceptible to the striped rice borer.

Biological/integrated control. The use of more resistant, early maturing rice varieties and applying treatments only when a problem arises rather than by the calendar can reduce the number of chemical applications. Granular systemic insecticidal treatments are preferable to foliar, nonsystemic sprays because the systemics generally are less harmful to the predators and parasites of the striped rice borer.

Chemical control. Insecticides for stem borer control are: Gamma BHC, mephosfolan, carbofuran, chlordimeform, diazinon, cartap, methyl parathion, phosmet, azinphos-methyl, azinphosethyl, endosulfan, chlorpyrifos, fenthion, metalkamate (Bux), monocrotophos, fensulfothion, fenitrothion, endrin, dimethoate, EPN, phosphamidon, phorate, triazophos, and chlorfenvinphos. Although recommendations made in the past suggested granular applications every 20 days or sprays every 2 weeks. wherever possible, treatments should be made based on insect numbers. For example, from 10 to 40 days after transplanting, inspect the rice fields, and only when an average of 10 % dead hearts occur, apply insecticide. For 41 to 70 days after transplanting, the rice fields should again be inspected. If an insecticide has not been applied within the past 2 weeks and if 5 percent dead hearts occur, an insecticide should be applied. Between panicle initiation and booting, if the abundance warrants, apply one granular treatment or two spray treatments. For lowland rice, when applying insecticide granules, fill the paddy field with 5–8 cm of water, close all outlets, and repair the dikes. Prevent the outflow of water for 4 days while the insecticide is active. For upland rice, use a foliar spray at 200–300 liters/ha.

Always read the label on the insecticide container for exact instruction.

Prognosis – predicting outbreaks. Numbers of moths attracted to light traps at night have been used to designate peak egg-laying periods and the time of subsequent larval damage have been correlated with meteorological factors. The rice fields are inspected at prescribed times as dictated by the meteorological associations.

Resistance to insecticides. Resistance of the striped rice borer to insecticides is very local in nature. Methyl parathion resistance has been reported for parts of Japan.

Literature

FEAKIN, S. D. (edit.) (1970): Pest Control in Rice. Ministry of Overseas Development (Great Britain). PANS Manual No 3, 270 pp.
GRIST, D. H. & R.J.A.W. LEVER (1969): Pests of rice. Longmans, London, 520 pp.
IRRI (1967): The major insect pests of the rice plant. Proceedings of a symposium, September 1964, Los Baños, Philippines. John Hopkins Press, Baltimore, Maryland, 729 pp.
JAPAN MINISTRY OF AGRICULTURE AND FORESTRY (1971): Symposium on rice insects. Proceedings of a symposium on tropical agriculture researches, 19–24 July, 1971. Tropical Agriculture Research Series No 5. Tokyo, 332 pp.
JEPSON, W. F. (1954): A critical review of the world literature on the lepidopterous stalk borers of tropical graminaceous crops. Commonwealth Inst. of Entomol., London, 127 pp.
PATHAK, M. D. (1968): Ecology of common insect pests of rice. Ann. Rev. Entomol. **13**, 257–294.
PATHAK, M. D. (1969): Insect pests of rice. IRRI, Los Baños, Philippines. 77 pp.
PATHAK, M. D. & V. A. DYCK (1973): Developing an Integrated Method of Rice Insect Pest Control. PANS **19** (4), 534–544.
UNIVERSITY OF THE PHILIPPINES (COLLEGE OF AGRICULTURE). Rice Protection Manual. 382 pp.
PHILIPPINES (NFAC) (1974): Integragency insect control guide for lowland rice in the Philippines. 27 May 1974. (Mimeo) 20 pp.

Author: J. A. Litsinger

Diatraea saccharalis (F.) (Fig. 183)

Common names: American sugarcane borer; Amerikanischer Zuckerrohrbohrer; Barrenador de la caña de azúcar.

Geographical distribution: This species of the New World genus *Diatraea* is widely distributed in the southern U.S.A., in Central and South America to Argentina and throughout the West Indian islands.

Host plants: The borer can be a major pest of sugarcane and can also infest maize, rice and sorghum. Several wild grasses act as natural hosts.

Symptoms: If a host plant is attacked during the first or second month of growth, the central shoot often dies, forming a "deadheart". Sometimes only a fibrous plant mass remains. Attack on older plants results in retarded growth and breaking and lodging of stalks. Internodes of sugarcane, maize and sorghum, containing one, or sometimes 2 larvae, can become riddled. Larvae also tunnel through the nodes and may perforate the stem wall in some places. The tunnels are more or less plugged with frass which is often extruded as a wet mass visible on removal of the sheathing leaves from the stem. In rice, the inner tissue of the stem wall is destroyed whereas nodes are tunnelled.

Economic importance: Injury varies in intensity in different regions. In Louisiana, losses in sugar yield were estimated to have averaged 13 % annually from 1937–1957. In 1972, sugarcane fields in Trinidad showed averages of 18 % joints (internodes) bored by *Diatraea* spp. in plant cane and 5 % joints in ratoon cane.

Percent joints bored, i. e. the number of bored joints as a percentage of the total number of joints in millable cane, has been widely used as an index and correlated with loss of sucrose. Usually, su-

Fig. 183.   Male of *Diatraea saccharalis* (phot. H. Hummelen)

gar-losses are assumed to be 0.5–0.7 % for each 1 percent of joints bored. Since this is a rather crude estimate, detailed damage assessment within local areas is needed.

Damage to maize and sorghum is highly variable in the neotropics. Maize stands, especially young plants, can become completely destroyed by *D. saccharalis* and *D. lineolata*. There are few records of losses in rice crops.

Morphology: Adult moths have a wing span of 18–39 mm. The fore wings are straw-coloured and each has two oblique, brown, more or less continuous lines and a dark discal dot (Fig. 183). Because the moths are highly variable in size and colouration and because they closely resemble other *Diatraea* species, the genitalia are the only reliable diagnostic character. The ground colour of the larvae is creamy white to pale yellow; a series of dark-brown, wartlike spots is present along the back and the sides.

Similarities to other pests: A number of other *Diatraea* species also attack sugarcane, maize and sorghum. They can be more important than *D. saccharalis,* with which they may occur simultaneously. Examples: *D. centrella* in Guyana and Surinam, and *D. rufescens* in Bolivia, both in sugarcane, and *D. lineolata* which is the dominant stem borer of maize in many neotropical countries.

Life cycle: Eggs are deposited on the leaves of the food plant. Young larvae start feeding on the epidermis and until about one week old often live in the leafsheaths or between the leafsheaths and the stem. They penetrate into the stem wall and arrive in the stem interior where they complete development and pupate after having made an exit hole. Normally 5 to 6 larval instars can be distinguished, though up to 8 may occur. The life cycle from egg to adult can be completed in 35 to 50 days. Four and a partial fifth generation appear each year in the northern and southern limits of its range. Here, larvae overwinter (diapause) in stubble and pieces of broken stalks that remain in the field after harvest. In the tropics, as many as 7 generations develop annually.

Natural enemies: Several parasites and predators prey on this pest, e. g.: a) the hymenopterous egg-parasite *Trichogramma fasciatum* and the hymenopterous larval parasites *Agathis stigmaterus* and *Iphiaulax grenadensis;* b) the tachinids *Metagonistylum minense, Lixophaga diatraeae* and *Paratheresia claripalpus;* c) the ladybird *Coleomegilla maculata* and a number of ant species.

Control:
Sanitary and cultural practices. The following measures help to reduce damage: 1. Remove and burn plant residues from the field after harvest (sugarcane) and apply clean cultivation to fallow fields (maize, rice, sorghum). 2. When double-cropping, sow and harvest separately, as fast as possible to reduce carry-over of the moth between crops (maize, rice, sorghum). 3. Plant borer-free sugarcane setts, soaking the setts for 20 minutes in water at 50 °C (used for disease control, this treatment also kills many borers).
Crop resistance. Low levels of resistance are present in quite a number of commercial sugarcane and maize varieties grown in Louisiana and the neotropics. Awareness of their availability offers growers some opportunity to reduce losses by *D. saccharalis* and related borers. Breeding of new resistant varieties is continuing, although it is realized that complete resistance to borers is unlikely to be achieved. In rice breeding programmes, resistance to borers has also been incorporated. The present tendency to replace rice varieties having longer growth periods (130–140 days) with those reaching maturity after 110–120 days, may help to reduce the extent of damage.

Biological control. This method has been used extensively to control *D. saccharalis* and related species in sugarcane in Florida and in several South American countries. Biological control has received much attention in the neotropics, where there are no discrete moth generations and where the application of insecticides is costly and not feasable.

Many introductions of exotic parasites and mass-rearings and releases of indigenous species have failed to give satisfactory control. However, some examples of successful programmes are: 1. The mass-rearing and annual liberation of *Metagonistylum minense* in a number of sugarcane estates in Venezuela. The percentages of joints tunnelled by *D. saccharalis* and other *Diatraea* spp. dropped from 16 % in 1947 to less than 3 % to date. 2. Annual releases of *Lixophaga diatraeae* in cane fields in Cuba resulted in an overall level of *D. saccharalis* damage of less than 5 % being maintained. 3. Mass-rearings and releases of *L. diatraeae* since 1960 and of *Apanteles flavipes* (origin India) since 1966, both at Barbados has resulted in the average 15 % joint infestation decreasing to 6 % in 1970.

Chemical control. Chemical control of *D. saccharalis* in sugarcane is applied only in the southern U.S.A.. Here, the winter produces a clear-cut spring generation which gives rise to rather well separated summer generations. This situation is not found in the tropics.

In Louisiana, insecticides are recommended for control of second and third generation borers only. Weekly surveys are made for young larvae feeding beneath the leaf sheaths which have not yet bored into the cane stalks. A 5 % stalk infestation of this type is used as the threshold for treatment. The maximum number of three insecticide applications is advised.

Insecticides (applied from airplanes): 1. Endrin granules 2 %, at the rate of 0.28 kg a.i./ha, was used almost exclusively from 1958 to 1963, when resistance to it developed. 2. Azinphos-methyl granules 5 %, at the rate of 0.85 kg a. i./ha or azinphos-methyl e.c., at the rate of 0.85 kg a. i. in 19 l of water/ha. 3. Monocrotophos and carbofuran at 0.85 kg a. i./ha (foliar sprays).

Control recommendations for maize pests *(Spodoptera frugiperda, D. saccharalis, D. lineolata)* at CIMMYT experimental fields, Mexico, are (pers. communication Dr. Ortega): 1. seed dressing with carbofuran 0.5 kg a. i./ha, 2. whorl granular hand applications with carbaryl 2.5 %, trichlorphon 2.5 % or chlorfenvinphos 2 % at 10 kg/ha, 2–3 weeks and 6 weeks after plant emergence.

Literature

BENNETT, F. D. (1971): Current status of biological control of the small moth borers of sugarcane *Diatraea* spp. (Lep. Pyralididae). Entomophaga **16** (1), 111–124.

DINTHER, J. van (1971): A method of assessing rice yield losses caused by the stem borers *Rupela albinella* and *Diatraea saccharalis* in Surinam and the aspect of economic thresholds. Entomophaga **16** (2), 185–191.

HENSLEY, S. D. (1971): Management of sugarcane borer populations in Louisiana, a decade of change. Entomophaga **16** (1), 133–146.

HENSLEY, S. D. (1972): Control of the sugarcane borer, *Diatraea saccharalis* (F.), in Louisiana. Proceed. 14th Congress ISSCT: 454–461.

HUMMELEN, P. L. (1973): Relations between two rice borers in Surinam, *Rupela albinella* (Cr.) and *Diatraea saccharalis* (F.) and their hymenopterous larval parasites (Thesis, Wageningen).

METCALFE, J. R. (1969): The estimation of loss caused by sugarcane moth borers. In: Pests of sugarcane (ed. Williams et al.), 61–79.

Author: J. van Dinther

Maruca testulalis (Gey.) (Plate 36 b)

Common names: Pod borer, Mung moth, Spotted borer.

Geographical distribution: This pest is found all over the tropical and subtropical countries. It has been reported as a major pest of legumes from West, Northeast, East and South Africa, Fiji Islands, Indonesia, West Indies and South America. CIE Map no 351.

Host plants: *M. testulalis* is primarily a pest of legumes and attacks a large number of different species. It becomes of major concern on the predominant legume of a given locality. It attacks groundnut *(Arachis hypogaea),* pigeon pea *(Cajanus cajan),* cowpea *(Vigna unguiculata)*, Egyptian bean *(Dolichos lablab*), and soybean *(Glycine max*). It has also been reported as a pest of *Canavalia ensiformis, Lablab niger, Lupinus* sp., *Pisum sativum, Ricinus communis,* and of several species of *Phaseolus.*

Symptoms: The most obvious damage by the larva is to the pods and shoots. The larva bores into the green stem, shoot tips, and pods, it feeds on flowers and buds and by webbing the leaves together, also feeds on the leaves. The characteristic symptom is webbing together of pods, inflorescences and leaves and the presence of frass on pods, stem, and shoot near the larval entry holes.

Economic importance: *M. testulalis* is a major pest of legumes. In Indonesia 25 percent damage of the soybean crop has been reported. In Nigeria it is considered as the most important pest of cowpea, in the Fiji Islands as a major pest of pigeon pea, in the Sudan as a serious pest of Egyptian bean and *Phaseolus* sp. and in East Africa as a major pest of French bean.

Morphology: The moth has a wing span of 20–25 mm. The forewings are light brown with characteristic white spots. The hind wings are greyish white with light brown markings at the tips. The larva is dull white or yellowish-white in color with dark spots on each body segment forming dorsal longitudinal rows. The full grown larva is about 18 mm long.

Similarities to other pests: The adult moth and the larvae are distinctly different from most lepidopterous pests of legumes. The nature of damage can also be recognised with no difficulty.

Life cycle and ecology: The female moth lays eggs liberally all over the host plant. In certain legumes, most eggs are laid on flowers, buds and tender leaves. There is no information on the exact number of eggs laid by a female. Some reports indicate from 10 to 200 during the female's life span. There are five larval instars, the duration of each varying from 2 to 4 days, depending on the host plant and climatic conditions. The prepupal stage varies from 1 to 2 days. During this stage, the larva usually becomes uniformly green and loses all its other pigments. It then descends to the surface of the soil on a silken thread and crawls underneath leaf debris. Later, it constructs a double-walled pupal cell inside which it pupates. The outer wall of the pupal cell consists of silken threads woven together with soil and other debris. The inner wall comprises loose strands of whitish threads woven together and with an anterior opening. The pupal stage may last from 5 to 15 days. The emergence of the moth is favoured by rainfall or high moisture content in the soil. The adult moth has a life span of 5 to 7 days.
The insect is most active during the rainy season. The larva is primarily a pod borer but comes out and wanders about on the host surface during the night.

Natural enemies: Few natural enemies of this pest have been recorded. The parasites belong to the Braconidae and Ichneumonidae families.

Control: Since *M. testulalis* attacks a wide range of legumes, voluntary legume crops should be destroyed. Continuous cropping of different legumes can maintain the population throughout the year.
Resistance to this pod borer in cowpea cultivars has been investigated at the International Institute of Tropical Agriculture at Ibadan. From a world germ plasm collection of 7,000 cowpea cultivars only relatively few less susceptible or moderately resistant cultivars have been identified. *M. testulalis* is best controlled by the application of insecticides. Several insecticides have been found to be effective, namely lindane, endosulfan, carbaryl, methomyl, monocrotophos and chlorpyriphos. The first insecticide application should be made at least one week before flowering begins. Later, insecticides should be applied as and when necessary. It has been found that 400 g a. i./ha of the above insecticides per application give good control of the pest.

Literature

BOHLEN, E. (1973): Crop pests in Tanzania and their control. Verlag Paul Parey, Berlin–Hamburg, 142 pp.

OEI-DHARMA, H. P. (1969): Use of pesticides and control of economic pests and diseases in Indonesia. E. J. Brill, Leiden, 199 pp.

SCHMUTTERER, H. (1969): Pests of crops in northeast and central Africa. Gustav Fischer Verlag, Stuttgart, 296 pp.

TAYLOR, T. A. (1967): The bionomics of *Maruca testulalis* Gey. (Lepidoptera: Pyralidae), a major pest of cowpeas in Nigeria. J. West. Afric. Sc. Assoc. **12**, 111–129.

Author: S. R. Singh

Ostrinia furnacalis (Gn.) (Plate 36 c)

Synonyms: *Pyrausta salentialis, Ostrinia salentialis, O. damoalis, O. nubilalis* (part.), *Pyrausta nubilalis* (part.)

Common names: Asian maize borer; Asiatischer Maiszünsler.

Geographical distribution: *O. furnacalis* is widely distributed in Asia. It has been recorded in Sri Lanka, China, Taiwan, parts of India, Bangladesh, Pakistan, U.S.S.R. (Ussuri region, Uzbekistan, Turkmenistan and Soviet Far East), Indonesia, Japan, Korea, Vietnam, Laos, Cambodia, Malaysia, Burma, Thailand, Philippines, Mariana Islands, Solomon Islands, and New Guinea. The pest also occurs in eastern Australia. CIE Map no 294.

Host plants: *Zea mays, Sorghum vulgare, S. saccharatum, Eleusine coracana* and many wild grasses.

Symptoms: Maize plants are usually attacked 3 to 4 weeks after sowing in Malaysia. The larvae attack almost every part of the plant. They feed on leaf tissue, tunnel into midribs, attack tassels or silks, bore into stalks and ears and sometimes even the stubble. The greatest injury occurs when numerous borers tunnel into the same stalk and into the ears. In the former case, development of the plants or production of tassels, silks or ears may be affected and often strong winds easily break the tassels or stalks, especially when the stalks bear developing ears. When the breaks occur towards the base of the plant the plant collapses, dries up and dies. When very young ears are attacked bacteria or decay-causing organisms stop the development of grain.

Economic importance: *O. furnacalis* is an important pest of maize in various countries of Asia, for instance in Malaysia, Indonesia, and the Philippines. It causes heavy crop losses.

Similarities to other pests: *O. furnacalis* resembles the European corn borer *O. nubilalis* in habits and bionomics. For this reason, both species for a long time have been confused. *O. nubilalis* occurs in Europe, Middle East, western parts of U.S.S.R., North Africa, North and Central America. It overlaps with *O. furnacalis* in Central Asia.

Morphology: Newly laid eggs are pale yellow, shiny and soft but will turn deeper yellow after a day. Newly hatched larvae are greyish yellow in colour with a black prothoracic plate and head. The mouth-parts are brown and the body is sparsely covered with short black hairs. The mature larva is about 20 mm in length; the head is dark brown or more often black. The upper part of the body is light grey brownish or pinkish.
The pupa has an average length of about 13 mm and a width of 3.5 mm, and is initially yellowish white but assumes a brown or almost black colour before emergence.
The female moth is yellow to light brown in colour, with a wing span of about 27 mm. The male has a tapering abdomen and the wings are darker brown in colour than in the female.

Life cycle and ecology: Eggs are usually laid on the underside of leaves in flat masses of irregular shape. Sometimes they are also laid on the upper side of leaves or on the sheath of ears. The incubation period is, on the average, 3 days.

Newly hatched larvae feed within the whorls of leaves under a protective cover of silken webs for about 9 days (then they are in the 3rd or 4th instar) and migrate downwards and bore into the stem. The larval period is about 18 days and during this time the larva undergoes 4 moults or 5 instars.

Normally pupation takes place in tunnels of the stem, or in the maize ear if this is attacked, and sometimes between the ear sheaths or on the ear stalks. The average pupal period is 6 days. The average life span of mated and unmated adults under laboratory conditions is about 6 days. Eggs are generally laid by adults 2 days after emergence and egg-laying continues daily for as long as 7 days. Under field conditions where maize is planted throughout the year the generations overlap.

Natural enemies: Two pupal parasites, namely *Brachymeria obscurata* (Chalcididae) and *Xanthopimpla stemmator* (Ichneumonidae) have been recorded. The importance of these two parasites in the population dynamics of the borer and the effects of chemicals on the parasite populations have not yet been investigated.

Control:

Cultural practices. Removal and destruction of maize stubble or mature stalks aimed at eliminating or reducing available feeding and hiding material for the pest. Where farm machinery is employed clean ploughing practices should also be adopted.

Chemical control. Insecticides: Gamma-BHC granules and dicrotophos have proved to be effective.

Spraying schemes. Four applications of insecticides are necessary to obtain satisfactory control. The first has to be made 1 month after sowing and the three subsequent applications at fortnightly intervals.

Literature

YUNUS, A. & H. T. HUA (1969): The biology and chemical control of the maize borer *Ostrinia salentialis* Gnellen, in West Malaysia. Malay. Agric. J. **49**, 109–140.

Author: A. Yunus

Scirpophaga nivella (F.) (Fig. 184)

Common names: Sugarcane top borer; Weißer Zuckerrohrbohrer.

Geographical distribution: *S. nivella* is reported from Burma, Sri Lanka, China, Taiwan, India, Indo-China, Japan, Malaysia, Pakistan, Philippines, Ryukyu Islands and Thailand.

Host plants: The top borer attacks *Saccharum officinarum, S. spontaneum, S. arundinaceum, S. bengalense, S. ravennae, Sclerostachya fusca, Chloris barbata, Echinochloa colonum,* and *Oryza sativa.*

Symptoms: Leaves which have been freshly damaged show one to several fine white tunnels on the upper side of the midribs. Later the tunnels appear reddish. In young canes dead-heart symptoms appear. The larva penetrates into the interior and damages the bud leaves which unfurl with new growth. They become brown and appear as though burnt. Such leaves are conspicuous by possessing holes like gun shotholes. If the borer attacks after node formation, the growing point is killed and the plants produce side shoots giving the appearance of bunchy tops (Fig. 184). These side shoots do not produce millable canes.

Fig. 184.   Shoot of sugar cane, showing bunchy appearance due to attack by *Scirpophaga nivella* (phot. R. A. Agarwal)

Economic importance: The pest causes a high mortality in tender shoots, up to 50 percent shoots dying after 8 weeks. Although there is practically no death of older shoots, the content of sucrose is reduced in weight. However, losses from 25–50 percent in yield and 1–2 units in sucrose content are reported due to top borer attack.

Morphology: Eggs. – The eggs are laid in masses and are covered by reddish-brown hairs. Larva. – The newly hatched larvae are greyish-brown and mature larvae creamy yellow in colour. The dorsal vessel can be seen through the transparent integument as a thick line in between the fat globules. Pupa. – It is slender, transparent and pale yellow. The posterior segments in the female pupa are buff coloured. Adult. – The wings of the male and female are silvery white in colour. The latter bear an anal tuft or reddish-brown or rosy or buff-coloured hairs.

Life cycle: The moths are active in the mornings. They lay eggs on the underside of the leaves for 3–4 days from the day after their emergence. A female lays 5–6 egg masses. Each mass may contain 47 to 216 eggs. The eggs hatch in 6–15 days.
The freshly hatched larvae penetrate into the midrib from the underside of the tender opened leaf and gradually bore downwards until they reach the growing point. They construct a cavity in the tip and cut an exit hole before pupation. The larval period varies from 19–45 days. The pupal period ranges from 4–20 days. In India, the life cycle takes 53–72 days from March–May, 45–55 from May–June, 35–49 from June to August, 60–71 from August–September and 100–208 days from September–February. There are 5–7 generations each year and profuse multiplication takes place from the third to the fifth generation i. e. mainly during July to October.

Ecology: The top borer starts its activity with the start of the monsoon rains. It prefers moderate temperatures (32.2–35.5 °C) and high relative humidity (80–86 %). Serious multiplications take place in years of heavy and evenly distributed monsoon rains. Late or scanty rains reduce the fecundity. Maximum hatching of eggs takes place at 21.6–30 °C and 92 % R. H.

Natural enemies: 68 species of natural enemies have been listed. Of these, 10 species are important. Amongst them *Telenomus beneficiens* and *Trichogramma minutum* parasitize the eggs during March–April and July–October, whereas *Apanteles flavipes, Elasmus zehntneri, Rhaconotus scirpophagae, Shirakia* sp., *Stenobracon nicevillei, S. deesae, Melcha ornatipennis* and *Isotima javanensis* parasitize the larvae and *Tetrastichus* sp. parasitizes the pupae.

Control:

Sanitary methods. The remaining stalks and stubble etc. should be burnt after harvest. Alternate host plants should be destroyed and borders of fields kept free of gramineaceous weeds. Dried leaves and leaf sheaths should be stripped off plants every month after 6–7 internodes have formed.

Mechanical methods. Collection of egg masses. These egg masses may be kept in wire gauge recepticles to allow parasites to emerge. Removal of infested plants. Up to the tillering phase the infested shoots may be cut at ground level and destroyed. This method needs to be carried out as a campaign.

Resistance of crops. Resistant varieties like EK 28, Co 331, Co 421, and Co 617 may be grown.
Biological control. *Isotima javanensis* as an important larval parasite may be released in the field after its multiplication in the laboratory.
Integrated control. Involves growing of resistant varieties, release of egg parasites collected from fields and supplemented with *Trichogramma* sp. against eggs and *I. javanensis* against the larvae. The infested shoots should be sprayed with 0.1 % endrin from the 3rd generation of the borer onwards. The remaining stubble, top leaves and leafsheaths etc. should be burnt after harvest. No more than one ratoon or long duration crops in top borer-infested areas should be grown.
Chemical control. Endrin, 3–4 times at 1–2 litres a. i. per hectare, may be sprayed from the initation of the third borer generation and synchronizing with peak oviposition period.

Literature

AVASTHY, P. N. (1969): The top borer of sugarcane, *Scirpophaga nivella* (F.). Pests of sugarcane. Pub. Int. Soc. Sugarcane Technologists.
GUPTA, B. D. (1959): Insect pests of sugarcane in India. III. The top borer, *Scirpophaga nivella* (F.). Indian Sugar **9** (3), 127–140.

Author: R. A. Agarwal

Tryporyza incertulas (Wlk.) (Plate 36 d)

Synonyms: *Schoenobius incertulas, S. bipunctifer, S. punctellus, S. minuletus*

Common names: Yellow rice borer; Gelber Reisstengelbohrer; Pyrale jaune; Piral amarilla.

Geographical distribution: Oriental region and neighbouring Palaearctic region: Australia, Brunei, India, Indonesia, Khmer, Laos, Labuan, Malaysia, Pakistan, Philippines, Sri Lanka, Taiwan, Vietnam.

Host plants: *T. incertulas* is monophagous to rice. Records of its occurrence on sedges and grasses are probably unreliable.

Symptoms: Refer to *Chilo suppressalis* (p. 452).

Economic importance: *T. incertulas* ranks as the most destructive rice pest in Bangladesh, India, parts of Indonesia, Pakistan and Philippines. Losses of up to 80 % have been reported.

Morphology: Egg – creamy white to dark, scale-like in appearance. The eggs are laid in masses covered with short, pale-brown, felt-like scales.
Larva – last instar is light yellow to greenish with a brown head capsule. It is 20 mm long.
Pupa – straw colored, the abdominal region is pale. The pupa which is 17 mm in length, is encased in a whitish silken cocoon which is attached to the exit hole made by the larva before pupation.
Adult moth – shows sexual dimorphism. The forewings of the female moth are yellowish brown with a black spot in the center (Plate 36 d). The wing span is 22 to 30 mm. The male is smaller and its forewings are light brown and have no spots.

Similarities to other pests: Refer to *Chilo suppressalis* (p. 453).

Life cycle: The eggs are laid in the evening on the lower or on the upper surface of the leaf blade. There are between 56 and 96 eggs per mass. In Japan with two generations of the borers, more eggs are laid per mass in the second generation than in the first generation. The moth lays one egg mass per night for 5 to 6 successive nights. The eggs hatch in 5 to 14 days. During hatching the larvae make two to three exit holes underneath the egg mass through the leaf blade. The larvae crawl upwards to the tip of the plant, suspend themselves from silken threads, and swing in the wind to move to other plants. The larvae which fall on water can swim using an air layer around their bodies to float. Some larvae travel down the space between leaf blade and inner sheath, and eventually bore into the leaf sheaths. During the earlier stages, the larvae are found in clusters. However, as the larvae grow they feed singly and complete their larval and pupal stages in the stem. The full-grown larvae tend to feed on the basal parts of the plants. After the rice crop is harvested a large number of larvae or pupae remain in the stubble below the soil level. The larval period varies from 23 to 43 days depending on the local environmental conditions. Under unfavorable weather and food conditions, the yellow rice borer will undergo dormancy.

Pupation takes place within the basal part of the stem. A large number of pupae are usually found below the soil level. Before each larva pupates, it prepares an exit hole in the stem internode by which the moth can escape. The pupal period is 6 to 8 days. Emergence and mating occur during the night. The total life cycle is 33 to 68 days under favorable conditions. In winter it may last from 83 to 210 days. The number of generations varies from two to at least six, depending on the location.

Ecology: Environmental factors and the availability of a suitable host determine the seasonal abundance of the yellow rice borer. Low temperature, short daylength, the lack of an available host, and a host plant at an immature stage of development cause the last instar larvae to undergo dormancy. Dormancy has never been reported in Indonesia, Malaysia, Sri Lanka, and the southern part of India. Where rice is grown continuously, the growth and development of the borer is uninterrupted throughout the year. Where overlapping generations occur, the insect is found at any of the four stages of development at any time of the year. The later generations of the borer are usually more destructive due to population build-up, causing more damage to the late-planted crops. Mild temperature in the winter and spring are associated with high mortality of the first generation larvae because the moth emerges earlier when the rice seedlings are not sufficiently developed to support the larvae. However, when the late spring is cool and the rice plants are transplanted slightly early, more damage can be expected due to the rapid build-up of the population. The moths deposit more eggs in fields receiving more nitrogen and the larvae grow better on the lush rice plants. The moths deposit more eggs on younger plants than on older plants.

Natural enemies: A large number of parasites of the yellow rice borer have been noted in different countries. The egg parasites (minute wasps) *Telenomus beneficiens, Tetrastichus schoenobii, Trichogramma japonicum,* and *Telenomus rowani* can effectively reduce the borer population. These species may occur singly or in mixed populations. *T. japonicum* can parasitize up to 70 percent of yellow rice borer eggs. *Telenomus schoenobii* is the most effective parasite of *T. incertulas.*

Control:
Sanitary methods. A large number of larvae and pupae remain in the stubble after harvest and serve as an important source of infestation for succeeding crops. Refer to *C. suppressalis* (p. 454).

Cultural practices. Continuous rice cropping promotes the build-up of the borer population through the year. Where two crops are grown in one year, lengthening the interval between the first and the second crop can significantly reduce the borer infestation of the second crop. Planting an early-maturing rice variety can lengthen the period between the first and second crop. However, the success of this method depends upon the participation of all the rice farmers in the region. Introducing another short duration commercial crop after rice should markedly reduce the borer infestation.

Resistance of crops. Thousands of rice varieties have been tested against the yellow rice borer (*T. incertulas*) in various countries. A few varieties such as IR 1820-52-2, TKM 6, WC 1251, WC 1253, WC 1263, Kipusa, exhibited less susceptibility to this borer than other rice varieties. So far, however, none of these varieties possess good agronomic characteristics combined with pest resistance. Planting commercial varieties which are more resistant to the borer in the field can help to minimize crop losses caused by this rice borer.

Biological/integrated control. Although eggs of *T. incertulas* are highly parasitized, this borer still remains an important pest of rice in several countries. Refer to *Chilo* for integrated control practices.

Chemical control. Stem borers are difficult to control because they remain outside the plant for only a short period of time after hatching and spend most of their life inside of the stem. The population pattern of the borer varies according to the area; therefore, no uniform timing of insecticidal treatments can be recommended. When two different and separate broods usually occur, the insecticide can be applied during the stage when the insect is most vulnerable to the pesticide. In the tropics, where a host plant is available throughout the year, the control of overlapping generations is difficult. On a wet season crop, various insecticides (see p. 454) are applied when 10 percent of the tillers exhibit dead heart damage. Chemical protection is continued beyond the tillering phase, when the plant loses its capacity to compensate for damaged tillers.

If granulated insecticides, such as diazinon, gamma-BHC, and carbofuran, are used, two applications – at 40–50 and 70–80 days after transplanting – generally provide satisfactory control. In some cases, additional chemical treatments may be required for protection against other pests.

Prognosis. Refer to *Chilo suppressalis* (p. 455).

Resistance to insecticides. Very little information on the resistance of the yellow rice borer to insecticides is available from different countries. The only data is on the resistance of the borer to methyl parathion in Japan.

Literature

Refer to *Chilo suppressalis* (p. 455).

Author: Ibrahim Manwan

Superfamily: Noctuoidea
Family: Noctuidae (Agrotidae)

Agrotis ipsilon (Hfn.) (Plate 37 a, b)

Synonyms: *Agrotis ypsilon, Euxoa ypsilon, Scotia ipsilon*

Common names: Greasy cutworm; Ypsiloneule; Gusano cortador.

Geographical distribution: According to the CIE distribution map no 261 (December 1969), this species is cosmopolitan occurring in all continents. In Europe, it is found in almost all countries extending from Ireland and Portugal in the west to Bulgaria and Rumania in the east and from Norway and Finland in the north to Sicily in the south. In Asia it occurs from Turkey, Saudi Arabia, India and Sri Lanka to Korea and Northeast China and in Africa from the Cape to the Mediterranean coasts. It occurs also in North, Central and South America, in Australasia and in the Pacific Islands.

Host plants: Common host plants are tobacco, cotton and crucifers. In Egypt, clover *(Trifolium alexandrinum)* and cotton (seedling stage) are seriously attacked; other host plants include maize, wheat, barley, bean, pea, lentil, tomato, potato, sweet potato, onion, beet, artichoke and pepper.

Symptoms: The main damage is caused by the mature larvae. These hide in the soil near the food plants and first cut the stem below the soil surface, then nibble at it for a time, leave it and then attack another plant. The injured plants wilt and wither. Perforations on the leaves due to the chewing activities of young caterpillars are also encountered.

In cotton seedlings, the severed cotyledons and bits of stems may be pulled or partly pulled into the soil thus acting as indicators of the position of the concealed cutworms. The larvae are also in the habit of cutting down a great deal more food material than they consume at one feeding. Small uneaten bits of the plants are therefore commonly encountered.

Economic importance: *A. ipsilon* is a highly polyphagous insect attacking many species of host plants in the temperate, subtropical and tropical zones. In most countries (e. g. Egypt and Syria) it is a serious pest of cotton, clover and other crops, and the farmer is frequently obliged to re-sow his crop only a few weeks after the first crop germinates. As a consequence of this delay, a heavy infestation of cotton with leaf- and bollworms ensues.

Morphology: Egg. – Subspherical or more usually dome-shaped, with 30–40 longitudinal ribs and about 0.5 mm in diameter; cream-coloured and then turns reddish-yellow as incubation proceeds and finally to blackish before hatching.
Larva. – The young larva (neonate) is pale yellowish-green with a blackish head and pronotal shield; it is covered with small dusky tubercles each bearing a seta. When fully-grown, the larva is 40–50 mm long, slate-grey or dark green in colour and with shiny, greasy looking skin in which the hairs and hair tubercles are not conspicuous. Each body segment has four or more distinct spots on each side. On the dorsal surface, along the median line, two bright lines run longitudinally. The ventral surface is lighter grey.
Pupa. – Obtect, brown glossy, measuring about 20 to 30 mm in length and with two small spines at the tip of the abdomen.
Moth. – Medium sized, about 22 mm long with a wingspan of 40 to 50 mm. Fore wings grey-brown in colour with black undulating lines along the side margins. On the disc there are several irregular black markings together with the typical oval concentric orbicular spot. Hind wings are pearly white with dark brownish margins and veins.

Life cycle: Four to six days after mating, the female begins to oviposit. The preoviposition period may be prolonged to two weeks in the winter at 15 °C. Oviposition continues for up to about 15 days but usually most of the eggs are laid during the first few days. A single female may lay up to 2,000 eggs or more. These are laid singly or in small groups on moist soil, weeds or leaves of host plants. The incubation period in Egypt lasts about 3 days in summer, 7–8 days in the spring and autumn and as long as 3 weeks in winter.
The newly hatched larvae actively feed on the leaves and later as the caterpillars advance in age on the stems of their host plants. They are nocturnal, hiding in the daytime in the soil. Cannibalism is common among larvae. They moult six times and become fully grown in 18 days at 27 °C or 65 days at 15 °C. Before pupation, the larva constructs a cell a few centimeters deep in the soil in which it pupates. In Egypt the pupal stage lasts about 2 weeks in the summer, 3 weeks in the spring and autumn and 6 weeks in the winter. The male lives only a short while whereas the female lives about 2 weeks.

Ecology: In Egypt and other neighbouring countries the moth occurs all the year round apart from the summer. It produces 4 or 5 generations each year, the duration of each generation varying from 1–4 months. The first and smallest generation appears in the autumn (September–October–November) on fodder and food crops such as clover and wheat. This is followed by a second, very large generation in mid-winter attacking also barley, beans etc. The third and largest generation is in March–April and it is this one which attacks seedling cotton. Then follow the much smaller fourth and fifth generations which occur on seedling maize, vegetables and ornamental plants. From June onwards and with the continuous rise in temperature, infestation by this pest begins to decline. The moth appears again in September or late in August. No resting stage or diapause is known and development is inhibited at about 32 °C.
Evidence of migration of this species has been reported in Egypt and in India. Apparently moths from Upper Egypt migrate northward, and the following generation migrates still further north in response to too warm weather.

The nature of the soil and the ecological conditions of the field have a large influence on the rate of infestation. Crops on heavy soils are usually more infested than those on sandy soils; irrigated fields are frequented by ovipositing females to a greater extent than non-irrigated ones. Moths are attracted more to fields with a dense growth of weeds than to fields with sparse vegetation. Soils containing 10 % R. H. have been found to be most favourable for pupating larvae.

Natural enemies: Parasites. *Apanteles ruficrus* (Braconidae-Hymenoptera) is the most important parasite in Egypt from October to April. Many *Apanteles* larvae may live in the body of a single cutworm. Another active parasite which is common in April, May and November is *Gonia capitata* (Tachinidae-Diptera). Other parasites recorded from Egypt include *Meteorus laeviventis* (Braconidae) and *Eulimneria xanthostoma* (Ichneumonidae). In the Sudan and in South Africa two important internal parasites occur, namely *Gonia bimaculata* and *Sturmia inconspicua* respectively.
Predators. Various bird species *(Ardea cornix, Corvus cornix, Motacilla* sp.) destroy larvae and pupae.

Control:
a) Early destruction of weeds, as these are very attractive to ovipositing females and hence harbour the first larval instars which later migrate to attack cotton seedlings.
b) Flooding of soil induces caterpillars to vacate their hiding places during daytime and thus become exposed to unfavourable environmental conditions and to predators. The larvae (and also the weeds) cannot tolerate a succession of irrigations.
c) Hand removal of larvae may be also performed at the beginning of infestation.
d) Tilling and ploughing soil intended for sowing of cotton, especially after the clover harvest, is most necessary to kill existing cutworms through their exposure to the sun and other adverse conditions.
e) Chemical control. Young larvae feeding on the foliage can be exterminated by spraying the infested plants with insecticides. Wettable endrin or endrin-dicrotophos may be used at the rate of 1.5 litre/acre. Dusting with DDT 10 % may be also effective. Older caterpillars which live in the ground are killed with baits consisting of endrin, bran and water applied close to the plants. Gamma-BHC dust is also very effective when broadcast at the rate of 1–5 kg per hectare. DDT/lindane (30/9) is also used as bait (3 litres/acre + 25 kg bran + 1 litre molasses + 25 to 30 litres water).

Literature

BISHARA, I. (1932): The greasy cutworm *(Agrotis ypsilon* Rott) in Egypt. Bull. Minist. Agric. Egypt, 114, 55 pp.
FLETCHER, T. B. (1925): Migration as a factor in pest-outbreaks. Bull. ent. Res. **16**, 177–181.
PEARSON, E. O. (1958): The Insect Pests of Cotton in Tropical Africa. Empire Cotton Growing Corporation & Commonwealth Insitute of Entomology, London.
RIVNAY, E. (1962): Field Crop Pests in the Near East. Monographiae Biologicae, Dr. W. Junk, Den Haag.
SCHMUTTERER, H. (1969): Pests of Crops in Northeast and Central Africa. Gustav Fischer, Stuttgart & Portland.
TALHOUK, A.M.S. (1969): Insects and Mites Injurious to Crops in Middle Eastern Countries. Mon. z. Angew. Entom. Paul Parey, Hamburg–Berlin.
WILLIAMS, C. B. (1925): Notes on insect migration in Egypt and the Near East. Trans. Ent. Soc. London, 1924, 439–456 pp.
WILLCOCKS, F. C., & S. BAHGAT (1937): The insect and related pests of Egypt. Vol. **1** Part 2, 792 pp., Cairo, Roy. Agric. Soc. Egypt.

Author: Mahmoud Hafez

Alabama argillacea (Hb.) (Fig. 185 and plate 37 c)

Common names: Cotton leaf worm; Baumwollblattraupe; Gusano medidor (del algodonero).

Geographical distribution: *A. argillacea* is native to the tropics of America. Each year during May–June the adults migrate from South and Central America into Mexico and the U.S.A., at times up to the Great Lakes. In South America the insect occurs throughout Colombia, Ecuador, Venezuela, Brazil, Peru to Argentina.

Host plants: Cotton is the principal host. In Venezuela, *Cienfuegosia affinis* and *C. heterophylla* serve also as hosts. In the U.S.A. the larvae feed only on cotton, and the adults sometimes cause injury to ripe peaches, grapes and other fruits by lacerating them with spines on the end of the proboscis.

Symptoms: The larvae feed on the cotton leaves stripping them so that often the main ribs only are left, causing a skeletonized appearance to the foliage. Bracts of squares and bolls, and sometimes even squares, are also eaten.

Economic importance: In Central America the cotton leaf worm is an important key pest next to the boll weevil and the *Heliothis* complex. *Alabama* can appear in damaging numbers in the early season destroying the young plants. In most situations, however, its populations are effectively regulated by biological control agents. The leaf worm is considered a key pest only because its presence traditionally has triggered the use of broad-spectrum insecticides causing *Heliothis* outbreaks and starting the pesticide treadmill. In the U.S.A. it can occasionally be an important cotton pest, but spray treatments against the boll weevil and *Heliothis* spp. usually prevent the buildup of damaging infestations.

Fig. 185.   Larva of *Alabama argillacea* on a cotton leaf (phot. H. Schmutterer)

Morphology: The rather flat eggs are laid singly and are pale green-blue. The larvae are slender, greenish looping caterpillars with 2 broad velvet-black dorsal stripes separated by a thin white line, and more black and white stripes toward the sides. Characteristic are the numerous round black spots scattered over the body, four of which form a square on the back of each segment. The last of the 5 proleg pairs protrudes conspicuously behind the body. Small larvae may lack the stripes. Pupation occurs on the foliage in the shelter of rolled and spun-together leaves, or the pupae hang by their tips from the foliage. The adult has uniformly greenish-brown forewings with a jagged pattern across and a small dark spot near the center of each; a narrow white fringe with brown dots borders the hind edge of the wings.

Life cycle: The female lays 400–600 eggs singly on the underside of cotton leaves. There are 6 larval instars after which the worms measure up to 3.75 cm. In the cotton regions of the U.S.A. one generation is completed in about 4 weeks, and 3–7 generations can occur per year.

Ecology: In Nicaragua, moth flight activity starts in March and reaches its highest peak in May–June. It drops off sharply then and has a second very small peak in September/October after which the moth populations decline to an almost indetectable level. Larval abundance follows the same pattern. The second half of the May–June peak coincides with the cotton planting period, and the leafworm can develop as an early-season pest. However, it is held in check usually by the beneficial insect fauna abundant at that time; parasitization of the eggs by *Trichogramma* and of larvae by Tachinidae are the essential mortality factors.

Natural enemies: *Euschistes, Geocoris, Orius, Nabis, Podisus, Proxya, Zelus* spp. (Heteroptera); *Coleomegilla, Coccinella, Cycloneda, Hippodamia, Olla* spp. (Coccinellidae); *Chrysopa, Calosoma, Cicindela* are among important predators. Parasites are *Trichogramma* spp., *Copidosoma truncatellum* (Encyrtidae), *Eucelatoria* spp. and *Euphorocera floridensis* (Tachinidae), *Microcharons* sp. (Ichneumonidae), and *Euplectis* spp..

Control:

Resistance of crops. Nectariless cotton varieties lack the food source for the adults and are of less attractiveness. Egg deposition is therefore reduced on these varieties.

Biological/integrated control. Since the leafworm is only a key pest when it escapes natural biological control triggering pesticide use and *Heliothis* outbreaks, everything must be done to preserve the pest's antagonists. This is best done by using a low dosage of a selective insecticide like trichlorfon (Dipterex 95 %, 143 g/ha), or *Bacillus thuringiensis,* applied by ground equipment and directed only to the local points of infestation signalled by the field checkers. In this early season between planting and appearance of first squares the cotton plant can tolerate up to 50 % foliar damage. So before deciding to spray, this damage level has to be considered as well as the abundance and impact of the beneficial organisms, and the population trend of the pest (egg numbers and parasitization, proportion of larval sizes and parasitization of larvae, moon phase). *Alabama* populations, as all Noctuids, tend to decline toward full moon and to increase towards new moon. Adults damaging fruits can be baited using sliced fruits poisoned with sodium arsenite or another stomach poison, and hung into the orchards.

Chemical control. a) Insecticides. Trichlorfon and *Bacillus thuringiensis,* especially useful in early season. b) Prognosis. Light trap collections can be used to warn of infestations. First catches are usually followed in a few days by the appearance of larvae in the field. In the U.S.A., a sudden large increase in catch indicates invasion from southern areas (June–July) and impending development of infestations. Decisions to spray, however, must be based only on ecological data obtained through field inspections.

Literature

METCALF, C. L. & W. P. FLINT (1962): Destructive and useful insects. 4. edition. Mc Graw Hill Co. New York.

Author: R. Daxl

Busseola fusca (Full.) (Fig. 186 and plate 37 d)

Synonym: *Calamistis fusca*

Common names: Maize stemborer; Maisstengelbohrer.

Geographical distribution: *B. fusca* is restricted to the Ethiopian region of Africa, stretching from West to East and South Africa. The insect has been recorded from sub-tropical South Africa, Tanzania, Zaire, Cameroon, Angola, Rhodesia, Kenya, Ethiopia, Uganda, Southern Sudan, Nigeria and Ghana. In West Africa it is a serious pest in the wetter parts of both the tree savanna and rain forest zones but is less important in the drier region of the thorn scrub savanna. In East Africa it does not occur below 550 m altitude.

Host plants: *B. fusca* has been recorded on 9 crops and 2 grasses, namely maize *(Zea mays),* gui-

Fig. 186.   Adult moth of *Busseola fusca* (phot. H. Schmutterer)

nea corn *(Sorghum vulgare)*, millet *(Pennisetum typhoides)*, rice *(Oryza sativa)*, finger millet *(Eleusine coracana)*, sugar cane *(Saccharum officinarum)*, elephant grass *(Pennisetum purpureum, P. pedicellatum)*, job tears *(Coix lachryma-jobi)*, guinea grass *(Panicum maximum)* and fodder cane *(Saccharum sp.)*.

Symptoms: The epidermis of young maize leaves are scarified by the first and second instar larvae. Within 4–6 days, small holes, referred to as 'window panes', appear on the leaves as they grow out of the funnel or leaf whorls. Further feeding in the funnel results in destruction of the meristematic tissues of the shoot. This results in what is termed 'dead heart'. Advanced 4–7 instar larvae migrate down the maize stem boring into it. Entry holes of these larvae into the stems are characterized by the presence of frass pushed out from the interior of the stems.

Economic importance: Maize varieties in Nigeria do not tiller, hence stems attacked by borer larvae are lost and cannot be replaced. In 2nd crop maize in Nigeria, a loss of 10–20 % has been recorded, but severe borer attack early in growth may result in permanent loss of stands. Insecticide trials with endrin have shown that sprayed plots significantly out-yield unsprayed controls. An overall increase of 26 percent has been recorded. In regard to the effects of borer larvae on maize yield, it has been shown that the presence of one or two larvae in a maize stem reduces the yield highly significantly by 25–28 percent. Losses due to borer larvae on maize has been put at about 4.2 million Nairas in Nigeria alone in 1969.

Morphology: *B. fusca* is a medium-sized moth, heavily infuscate with head and thorax light to dark brown, lightly streaked light ochreous or white. Fore-wing fuscous-black to black with some ochraceous suffusion at base and obliquely from apex to inner margin.
Eggs are hemispherical, flattened, butter-yellow in colour and measuring 0.78 mm in diameter with about 72–84 ribs on chorion.
Larva in full grown stage has a mean length of 31.4 mm and a dark brown head, yellowish to deep brown prothorax, dorsal surface of body pinkish-white.
Pupa 18–20 mm long, dark brown with projectionless convex front.

Similarities to other pests: Larvae of *B. fusca* resemble those of *Manga basilinea*. They also slightly resemble larvae of *Sesamia* spp.. Separation is possible by chaetotaxic features.

Life cycle and ecology: Adult moths emerge from the pupae between 7–9 in the evening. Mating starts from about midnight. Eggs are laid on the inner surface of the leaf sheath by the female inserting the ovipositor between the leaf sheath and the stem. Each female lays an average of about 400 eggs. Eggs hatch in 6–7 days. Newly hatched larvae are gregarious but disperse during the following night migrating to the terminal whorl of leaves or funnel where the first and second instar larvae feed. The third and subsequent instar larvae leave the whorl and migrate down the stem, boring and destroying it. There are usually 6 or 7 larval instars. In the wet rainy season, the larval period is about 33–42 days for non-diapause larvae.
B. fusca pupates within the maize stem, and prior to pupation, the larva cuts an exit hole through which the adult would emerge. The average pupal period is about 14 days. The life span of the adult moths is about 3–10 days for males and 4–11 days for females.
Three or four generations of *B. fusca* are produced in Nigeria. The third or fourth generation is

the diapause generation. Although there is evidence of larval diapause all the year round, the main diapause generation commences from about November. Diapause development is completed about February and, with the rains, adult moths emerge from about April until July when maize of a suitable age is available. It has been shown that diapause in *B. fusca* is induced largely by the state of maturity and composition of food consumed by the larvae. The incidence of diapause larvae increases with the maturity of the food plants in which larvae feed. Carbohydrate, protein and water content of the food plants are probably the crucial elements associated with the induction of diapause.

Natural enemies: The ant *Dorylus affinis* (Formicidae) attacks late-instar larvae. *Sturmiopsis parasitica* (Tachinidae) is a pupal parasite, whereas *Enicospilus* sp. (Ichneumonidae), *Apanteles sesamiae* (Braconidae), *Eupelmus* sp. (Eupelmidae), and *Tetrastichus atriclavus* (Eulophidae) are pupal parasites. *Pediobius* (= *Pleurotropis*) *furvus* and *Telenomus busseolae* (Scelionidae) have been reared from eggs. Larvae are attacked by the bacterium *Bacillus thuringiensis* and the fungus *Aspergillus flavus*. *A. sydowii* has been found on pupae.

Control:
Cultural practices. A good measure of control has been effected by burying maize stubble under a few centimetres of earth or by making the stubble into compost or burning it. High mortality of the larvae has been obtained when infested maize stems are cut and left lying on the ground to be exposed to the intense heat of the sun. Other methods of cultural control employed include eradication of wild grasses which often act as reservoirs, and planting maize, guinea corn and millet early in the planting season. Resistant maize varieties have now been produced at research institutes.
Chemical control. The first promising chemical for the control of the borer was carbaryl. This at 0.7 kg a. i. carbaryl (Vetox) 85 % wettable powder in 75 litres of water per acre and applied twice at intervals of 10–14 and 20–24 days, gave good control. Carbofuran, when placed in gelatin capsules 0.3 g (3 % a. i.) and inserted about 2.5 cm below soil surface in the root zone at the time of planting, has also given good protection during the first fifty days of growth.

Literature

HARRIS, K. M. (1962): Lepidopterous stemborers of cereals in Nigeria. Bull. Ent. Res. **53,** 139–171.
NYE, I. W. B. (1960): The insect pests of graminaceous crops in East Africa. Col. Res. Studies No 31. 48 pp., Lond. HMSO.
TAMS, W. H. & J. BOWDEN (1953): A revision of the African species of *Sesamia* Guenée and related genera (Agrotidae-Lepidoptera). Bull. Ent. Res. **43,** 645–678.
USUA, E. J. (1970): Some notes on the Maize Stemborers, *Busseola fusca* and *Sesamia calamistis*. J. econ. Ent. **63,** 776–778.
USUA, E. J. (1970): Diapause in the Maize Stemborer. J. econ. Ent. **63,** 1605–1610.
USUA, E. J. (1973): Induction of Diapause in the Maize Stemborer, *Busseola fusca*. Ent. exp. & appl. **16,** 322–238.

Author: E. J. Usua

Diparopsis castanea Hmps. (Plate 38 a)

Common names: Red bollworm; Südostafrikanischer Baumwollkapselwurm.

Geographical distribution: *D. castanea* is confined to the African continent, south of the equator and occurs in cotton growing areas of the Republic of South Africa, Swaziland, Botswana, Mocambique, Rhodesia, Malawi and Zambia. It, also, occurs in the extreme south of Tanzania. A closely related species, *D. tephragramma,* is found in Angola. CIE Map no 142.

Host plants: *D. castanea* is confined in its host plant range to the cultivated and wild cottons of the genus *Gossypium* and the shrub, *Cienfuegosia hildebrandtii*. The wild cottons are *G. herbaceum* race *africanum* found in the lowveld areas of southern Africa and *G. bardadense* var. *brasiliense,* the kidney cotton, associated with villages in parts of Malawi and Zambia and possibly elsewhere.

Symptoms: The larvae tunnel into and feed inside the buds, flowers, bolls and, less commonly, the stems of the cotton plant. The bracts of attacked buds and young bolls turn yellow, the fruiting points eventually shedding. Older infested bolls remain on the plant with subsequent total or partial failure of boll opening. In the absence of fruiting points, larvae will tunnel into the main stem causing wilting and death of the terminal growing point although this type of damage is more usually associated with the spiny or Egyptian bollworm (*Earias* spp.). In the early stages of larval development, frass may be found between the bracts and the bud or boll but later, unlike the American bollworm (*Heliothis armigera*), the frass is often not noticeable on the outside of the bud or boll.

Economic importance: The red bollworm is one of the major pests of cotton in Africa causing considerable loss of yield and down grading of seed cotton. The down grading results from damaged and stained lint being picked from infested bolls which have partially opened.

Morphology: Egg. Approximately 0.6 mm in diameter and pale blue in colour changing to grey before hatching. Under a hand lens it will be seen that the egg is spherical with a flattened base, and the surface sculptured with vertical and horizontal ribs with small spines at the rib junctions.
Larva. Has characteristic dull-red chevron markings on each segment except the first and last with a cream to light greenish background except the newly hatched larva which is greyish-white in colour. The fully-grown larva has a shiny distended appearance and a length of 25–30 mm.
Pupa. Contained within a hard earthen cocoon, it is seldom found unless special soil sampling techniques are employed.
Moth. Stoutly built moth with a wing expanse of 25–35 mm. Forewings vary in colour from light pink, brown to dark greenish brown with light coloured hind wings. Moth is nocturnal and not readily seen during the day.

Similarities to other pests: The larva can be confused with that of the Pink bollworm (*Pectinophora gossypiella*) and False codling moth (*Cryptophlebia leucotreta*) both of which may be found feeding in bolls. The former is distinguished by the red markings occuring as two distinct bands on each segment, the front one being broader than the other and the length of the larva not more than 12.5 mm when fully-grown. The latter larva has a diffuse red or purplish-red colouring with no distinct markings and is 15–18 mm long when fully-grown.

Life cycle and ecology: The moths are sexually mature on emergence from the pupa and mating and oviposition occur on the night of emergence. Eggs, which are laid singly on the stems, leaves, buds and bolls of the cotton plant, develop within 6 to 13 days depending upon temperature. The larva, on hatching, moves over the plant in search of a fruiting point which it penetrates. It is during this period that the larva is most exposed and susceptible to residual insecticide deposits. Otherwise, except for one or two transfers to another fruiting point, normally a boll, it remains protected within the bud or boll. The larval period may vary from 2–6 weeks during which the larva passes through five instars. When fully developed the larva vacates the boll on which it has been feeding, drops to the ground and penetrates the soil to a depth of 10–150 mm where it pupates. The duration of the pupal period is extremely variable. In certain cases, development of the pupa will take only some two to four weeks, while in other cases development is not completed for some months or even years. The former pupae, known as the 'short term' fraction serve to maintain the current season's infestation while the latter or 'long term fraction' (diapause pupae) enable the insect to carry over from one season to another. The proportion of larvae forming diapause pupae increases as the season advances and may reach 100 per cent towards the end of the season. In Rhodesia and Malawi, for example, subsequent emergence of moths from diapause pupae may extend from the beginning of October to the middle of April of the following year with a main period of emergence from mid-November or early December to mid-February or later. Thus with cotton planted in November and December the crop is subject to infestation derived directly from moth emergence from diapause pupae over the major part of the growing period apart from any build-up occasioned by moth emergence from short term pupae.

Natural enemies: Various parasites have been recorded but little is known of their importance. Of the predators, ants are considered of importance in attacking both larvae and pupae with up to 70 per cent mortality having been recorded. Other predators of larvae include spiders and *Neuroptera* larvae.

Control:

Sanitary methods. All cotton plants should be uprooted or ploughed under at the end of the season to prevent ratooning and subsequent survival of larvae prior to the sowing of the next season's crop.

Cultural practices. A high standard of cultural practice should be maintained to realise the maximum response from control measures.

Chemical control. Insecticides offer the only satisfactory method of control and reference is made to a spraying programme which is widely followed in southern Africa on both small scale and estate farms. It is emphasised that the control of red bollworm cannot be considered in isolation and any spray programme, the timing of which should be based on regular field inspections, must take into account the insect pest complex as a whole.

a) Insecticide. The carbamate, carbaryl, is probably the most effective and widely used insecticide for red bollworm control. It is formulated as a wettable powder containing 85 % active ingredient or as an oil based preparation with 25 or 40 percent a.i. for ultra low volume spraying. It is not effective against American bollworm (*Heliothis* sp.) except under conditions of low rainfall.

b) Timing of spray application. Spraying against red bollworm with carbaryl should commence as soon as eggs are seen on the plants, which normally coincides with first flower buds (six weeks after germination). Carbaryl sprays are then generally applied at weekly intervals, provided egg laying continues, until such time as control of American bollworm (*Heliothis*) is required with an accompanied change in insecticide. A return to carbaryl sprays is made when the American bollworm attack diminishes. These later sprays are necessary to control damaging infestations of red bollworm larvae which produce predominantly diapause pupae. The red bollworm spray programme cannot usually be divorced from that of American bollworm and reference to the section dealing with the latter pest should be made.

c) Method of application. The choice of a particular type of spray equipment will depend largely on the system of cotton production. For the smallholder or where labour is not limiting, the knapsack sprayer fitted with a rear mounted vertical boom carrying four pairs of nozzles directed upwards and outwards (tailboom) or the battery operated spinning disc hand sprayer for ultra low volume application can be used. Tractor mounted or animal drawn sprayers fitted with several tailbooms are appropriate for large cotton areas or, alternatively, aerial spraying can be employed.

In tailboom spraying, carbaryl wettable powder is used at a constant spray concentration of 0.5 percent a. i., with a dosage rate of 0.25–1.00 kg/ha according to plant height. In aerial spraying, wettable powder sprays may be applied at 23 l/ha with a 15 m swath and at a concentration of 2.5–5.0 percent a. i. depending upon plant height. The ultra low volume formulations are applied at 2.5 l/ha with a swath of two and 18 metres for hand and aerial spraying, respectively. A recent development has been the application of wettable powder formulations with hand held ultra low volume sprayers.

Literature

PEARSON, E. O. (1958): The insect pests of cotton in Tropical Africa, 355 pp. London, Emp. Cott. Gr. Corp. and Commonw. Inst. Ent.

Cotton Handbook of Malawi (1971): Published by Extension Aids Section, Ministry of Agriculture & Natural Resources, Government of Malawi.
Cotton Handbook (1971): Published by Rhodesian Farmer Publications, Rhodesia.

Author: J. P. Tunstall

Diparopsis watersi (Roths.) (Plate 38 b, c, d)

Common names: Sudan bollworm; Sudanesischer Baumwollkapselwurm.

Geographical distribution: Tropical Africa south of the Sahara but north of the equator including the following countries: Somalia, Ethiopia, Sudan, Central African Republic, Chad, Northern Nigeria, Cameroon, Ghana, Niger, Ivory Coast, Mali and Senegal. The pest has also been recorded in the Yemens on the Arabian peninsula.

Host plants: Cultivated varieties of cotton (*Gossypium* spp.). Records on *Hibiscus* spp. are doubtful.

Symptoms: Larvae of *D. watersi* damage mainly the flower buds, flowers and bolls of the cotton plant. They penetrate into these organs of the host plant and feed on the contents. Older damaged bolls may remain on the plants and rot either partly or completely, whereas young bolls, flower buds and flowers are shed sooner or later after the attack takes place. In heavy outbreaks, however, single caterpillars can penetrate into the main stems which then may break during heavy rainstorms.

Economic importance: The Sudan bollworm is a major pest, especially of rain-grown cotton in most countries of its distribution area. The destruction of flower buds, flowers and especially bolls results in a heavy yield loss as has been demonstrated in a number of control experiments in various parts of Africa. Cotton which is picked from partially destroyed bolls is stained and therefore of a very low quality.

Morphology: Egg. Spherical with horizontal and vertical ribs, bluish to bluish-green but darkening towards the end of the incubation period; diameter about 0.6 mm.
Larva. In later instars, mostly with apple green to pale green ground colour. All segments, except first and last with a median dorsal and two oblique rose-red markings on each side which can be diffuse or even absent in the fully-grown larva, reaching a length of about 3 cm. Head capsule brown, thoracic legs black.
Pupa. Stout, shining yellowish-brown, up to 1.5 cm long.
Moth. Body stout, up to about 2 cm long. Colour of forewings brown, reddish-brown, pinkish or greyish-brown; wing span up to 3.5 cm. Hindwings light coloured. Head and thorax rose to brownish, abdomen somewhat lighter.

Similarities to other pests: Confusion of the larvae with those of the Pink bollworm and the False codling moth is possible (see section on *D. castanea,* p. 471).

Life cycle and ecology: The nocturnal female lays its eggs singly on the young growth of the cotton plant and prefers young leaves and flower buds. Depending upon the prevailing temperature, the incubation period lasts from 3–5 days. The first instar larvae hatch in the early morning. They usually penetrate a fruiting point and leave it as soon as its contents are consumed in order to search for another one or a boll. Six or more flower buds may be destroyed by one larva during its life. If large capsules are attacked, a caterpillar may obtain sufficient food to complete its development. The larval period lasts about 2–3 weeks under the conditions of the Sudan Central Rainlands. Pupation takes place in the top layer of the soil in an earthen cell which is constructed by the larva. The duration of the pupal period varies greatly as short-term pupae (non-diapause pupae) and long-term pupae (diapause pupae) can be formed. Short-term pupae give rise to adults within a period of about 2–5 weeks depending on the prevailing temperature. These pupae enable the pest to develop several generations during the current season. The percentage of long-term pupae increases step by step towards the end of the season. The moths emerge from the diapause pupae either during the following rainy season or later, sometimes after several years. According to investigations in Chad, high diurnal temperatures of 30 °C combined with low nocturnal temperatures of 15 °C during the incubation and larval periods, followed by low (15 °C), high (30 °C) and very high (38 °C) daily temperatures during pupation, result in the induction of diapause, in most cases. *D. watersi* is a typical pest in the savannah belt south of the Sahara desert, where cotton is grown during the rainy season which is followed by a long dry season.

Natural enemies: *D. watersi* is attacked by a number of predators and parasites from various orders. Most of them seem not to be very effective. However, several ant species prey upon eggs, whereas others attack the caterpillars when they enter the soil for pupation. Pupae are destroyed by termites. Among the larval parasites, Braconidae, as *Bracon brevicornis* and *Apanteles* spp., have been recorded as well as some Tachinid flies. Virus and bacterial diseases may be of some importance under certain conditions, especially in West Africa.

Control:

Sanitary methods. All cotton plants in infested areas should be uprooted after harvest and destroyed by burning or ploughing under.

Cultural practices. Flooding for a period of about two weeks or longer destroys the pupae in the soil or terminates their diapause.

Biological control. Some attempts at biological control with rather a limited number of released parasites were not successful. Several trials with *Bacillus thuringiensis* in West Africa also gave unsatisfactory results.

Chemical control. The use of conventional insecticides seems to be the only economic way to control *D. watersi* at present. However, successful chemical control is difficult and expensive mainly because both that the larvae are internal feeders and the moths emerge during an extended period during the rainy season. Because of the latter, and the development of several generations during the season, a number of carefully-timed sprays at intervals of about 8–10 days are needed, at least during heavy outbreaks.

Carbaryl, endosulfan and endrin are recommended insecticides which are often combined with other chlorinated hydrocarbons and organophosphorous pesticides in order to control other major pests of cotton at the same time.

Literature

GALICHET, P. F. (1964): *Diparopsis watersi* Rothschild, Lepidoptera, Noctuidae, ravageur du cotonnier en Afrique Centrale. Cot. et Fibr. trop. **19**, 437–518.
PEARSON, E. O. (1958): The insect pests of cotton in tropical Africa. London & Reading, 355 pp.
PROCTOR, J. H. (1962): The biology and control of the Sudan bollworm, *Diaropsis watersi* (Roths.) in the Abyan delta, West Aden Protectorate. Bull. ent. Res. **53**, 311–335.
SCHMUTTERER, H. (1964): Zur Bekämpfung der *Podagrica*-Arten (Col., Chrysomel.) und von *Diaropsis watersi* Roths. (Lep., Agrot.) an Baumwolle in den Nuba-Bergen im Sudan. Z. ang. Ent. **54**, 316–324.
SCHMUTTERER, H. (1969): Pests of crops in Northeast and Central Africa. Gustav Fischer, Stuttgart & Portland, 296 pp.
TUNSTALL, J. P. (1958): The biology of Sudan bollworm, *Diparosis watersi* (Roths.) in the Gash Delta, Sudan. Bull. ent. Res. **49**, 1–23.

Author: H. Schmutterer

Earias biplaga Wlk. (Plate 39 c, d)

Synonym: *Earias citrina*

Common names: (Southern) spiny bollworm; Chenille épineuse du cottonier.

Geographical distribution: Africa, south of the Sahara. CIE Map no 281.

Host plants: Cotton (*Gossypium* spp.), cocoa *(Theobroma cacao),* okra, most other Malvaceae, some Sterculiaceae, Tiliaceae and Bombacaceae.

Symptoms: Young cotton plants are damaged by 'tip boring'. The larva enters near the terminal bud, then burrows down inside the stem thus killing the growing point. Such damage is not generally of concern for the side branches develop, producing a bushy plant that can yield well, but the fruiting is delayed. On older plants the fruiting bodies are attacked; flower buds and flowers being preferred to the bolls.
On cocoa the larvae feed mainly upon the leaf buds and cause damage both in nurseries and on mature trees.

Economic importance: *E. biplaga* is of most concern on rain grown cotton in Central Africa, where it occasionally causes sufficient loss of fruiting bodies to merit the status of a major pest. It has also been rated as a common, but minor, pest of cocoa, in West Africa.

Morphology: The blue-green eggs are spherical, 0.5 mm diameter and are difficult to find on cotton leaves. The larva reaches a length of 20 mm, is stout and spindle shaped, with long hairs on each segment and, on the last two thoracic segments and all the abdominal segments, there are two pairs of fleshy tubercles, one dorsal the other lateral. These tubercles, which give the insect its common name, are long and slender in *E. biplaga.* The basic colour of the larva is brown with some grey markings. The pupa is enclosed in a tough brown silk cocoon shaped like an inverted boat and is found attached to the plant or plant debris. The moths are about 12 mm long. They rest with the wings folded neatly along the sides of the body. The abdomen and hindwings are silvery or creamy white. The fore wings are usually metallic green with a dark brown, marginal fringe. The female can generally be distinguished by a median, brown blotch of irregular outline between the discoidal spot and the posterior edge of the wings. In each dry season the fore-wing coloration becomes yellow or light brown, rather than green.

Similarities to other pests: *E. biplaga* will usually be found in mixed populations with *E. insulana,* on rain grown cotton in Africa. The larvae can be readily distinguished, for the former is browner, more "spiny" and the dorsal tubercles on the 8th abdominal segment are brown, instead of white.

Life cycle: The length of the life cycle varies with the temperature, but at 24 °–30 °C, egg incubation takes 4 days, larvae 10–20 days, pupae 9–16 days. The moths can live for up to 50 days and lay up to 500 eggs. No diapause has been recorded, but moths have emerged after 60 days as pupae.

Ecology: *E. biplaga* is generally most abundant in more humid areas and towards the end of each rainy season. Populations are greatly reduced by prolonged dry seasons.

Natural enemies: Many hymenopterous parasites have been recorded, the most common being *Agathis aciculatus, Rogas aligharensis* and *Apanteles* spp.. Many larvae collected from the field die, with a variety of disease symptoms.

Control:
Sanitary methods. The cotton stalks and trash should be cleared and destroyed soon after harvesting is complete.
Cultural practices. Timely sowing of cotton may help to produce a crop before this pest has time to build up to damaging levels.
Resistance of crops. There is some indication that the more hairy cotton varieties attract greater egg laying and that glandless cottons are more susceptible to the larvae. No appreciable resistance has been reported.

Biological control/Integrated control. Some attempts have been made to supplement the natural control by introducing *Trichogramma brasiliense* into Uganda and Tanzania, but without noticeable effect.

Chemical control. a) Insecticides. Endosulfan at 0.75 kg. a. i., per ha appears to be the most efficient insecticide against this pest. Carbaryl at 1 kg. a.i. per ha is also generally effective.

b) Spraying schemes. In most African cotton growing areas the spraying regimes are usually designed to control the more damaging pests *Heliothis armigera* and *Diparopsis* spp. and providing an effective insecticide is used, *E. biplaga* is also controlled. When DDT is used, severe infestations of *E. biplaga* can develop, for the natural enemies are killed but not the pest.

c) Prognosis. Endosulfan or carbaryl may be sprayed whenever counts show that populations exceed one larva on five plants.

Literature

ENTWISTLE, P. F. (1969): The biology of *Earias biplaga* Wlk., (Lep.: Noctuidae) on *Theobroma cacao* in Western Nigeria. Bull. ent. Res. **58,** 521–535.
MATTHEWS, G. A. (1966): Investigation of the chemical control of insect pests in Central Africa. Bull. ent. Res. **57,** 69–91.
PEARSON, E. O. (1958): The insect pests of cotton in tropical Africa. 355 pp. London, Emp. Cott. Gr. Corp. and Commonw. Inst. Ent.
REED, W. (1974): Populations and host plant preferences of *Earias* spp. (Lep.: Noctuidae) in East Africa. Bull. ent. Res. **63,** 33–44.

Author: W. Reed

Earias insulana (Boisd.) (Plate 39 a, b)

Synonym: *Earias smaragdina*

Common names: Spiny boll worm, Egyptian boll worm; Ägyptischer Baumwollkapselwurm; Chenille épineuse, Ver épineuse du cotonnier; Oruga espinosa.

Geographical distribution: Africa, including adjacent islands, southern Europe, Asia Minor, Pakistan, India, South East Asia, Japan, Taiwan, Philippines, and Australia. CIE Map no 251.

Host plants: Cotton (*Gossypium* spp.), okra, and many other Malvales, particularly *Abutilon* spp. Sometimes also found on maize (*Zea mays*), for instance in Egypt.

Symptoms: Young cotton plants are damaged by "tip boring". The larva enters near the terminal bud and then burrows down inside the main stem. The main stem growing point is killed, but this is not generally serious for the side branches grow in compensation, thus producing a bushy plant with a large yield potential, but fruiting may be delayed. On older cotton this pest feeds in buds, flowers and bolls. It tends to be an internal feeder and is more commonly found in bolls than *E. biplaga,* which prefers surface feeding.

Economic importance: This pest is most damaging on irrigated cotton in drier countries, particularly in Egypt, Sudan, Israel, Pakistan and North India. Although the early attacks by this pest can be compensated for by later plant growth, the delayed crops are often totally destroyed by pink bollworm *(Pectinophora gossypiella).*

Morphology: The eggs are blue, spherical, 0.5 mm diameter. The larva grows to a length of 20 mm, is stout and spindle shaped, with hairs on each segment and with two pairs of fleshy tubercles, one dorsal, the other lateral, on the last two thoracic segments and all abdominal segments. These tubercles, which give the spiny bollworm its name, are shorter than those of *E. biplaga* but more pronounced than those of *E. vittella.* The larva is dull grey-brown with grey markings.

The pupa is enclosed in a tough, off-white silk cocoon, shaped like an inverted boat, attached to the plant or its debris.

The moths are generally 11 mm long and rest with their wings folded straight along their sides. The abdomen and hind wings are silvery white, the forewings are uniformly silvery-green, but tend to be straw-yellow in drier areas and seasons. There is no dark marginal fringe to the forewing. Very rarely, specimens have a brown blotch in the centre of the forewing similar to that on female *E. biplaga.*

Similarities to other pests: In Africa, *E. insulana* is often found in mixed populations with *E. biplaga* on cotton. *E. insulana* can be distinguished by its less 'spiny' appearance and by the dorsal tubercles on the 8th abdominal segment being white, instead of brown.

In India, mixed populations of *E. insulana* and *E. vittella* frequently occur on cotton. *E. insulana* larvae are rather more 'spiny' than *E. vittella* which are more strongly marked with a black and white colouration.

Life cycle: At 28 °C, egg incubation takes 3 days, larvae 9 days, and pupae 9 days.

The moths lay up to 300 eggs. No diapause has been recorded.

Ecology: This pest appears to survive better than other *Earias* spp. in the drier areas, perhaps because it is generally an internal fruit feeder.

Natural enemies: Many hymenopterous parasites have been recorded, the most common being *Apanteles* spp., *Linnaemya agilis* and *Bracon brevicornis.* Larvae collected from *Abutilon* spp. in Tanzania were frequently 80 % parasitized and the larvae from cotton often have a high disease incidence.

Control:
Sanitary methods. It is important that old cottons stalks should be destroyed after harvesting.
Cultural practices. Cotton should be timely sown, for later sown cotton can be severely infested. In some countries the destruction of *Abutilon* spp. has been undertaken with some success.
Chemical control. a) Insecticides. Endosulfan at 0.75 kg. a. i. per ha or carbaryl at 1 kg a.i. per ha. Azinphos-methyl at 0.6 kg a.i. per ha is also reported to be effective.
b) Spraying schemes. Although schedules involving weekly sprays against this and other cotton pests are frequently used, it is far better to spray against this pest only when field counts indicate damaging populations.
c) Prognosis. Since this pest can often feed inside bolls, the cotton must be closely examined. Populations of larvae greater than one on five plants probably merit insecticide use.
d) Resistance to insecticides. Resistance to endrin, formerly widely used for the control of this pest, has been reported from Israel in 1956. DDT is widely reported to be ineffective against this pest and may increase infestations by killing the natural enemies.

Literature

PEARSON, E. O. (1958): The insect pests of cotton in Tropical Africa. 355 pp. London. Emp. Cott. Gr. Corp. and Commonw. Inst. Ent.

RIPPER, W. E. & L. GEORGE (1965): Cotton pests of the Sudan, their habits and control. Oxford, Blackwell Sci. Publ., 345 pp.

YATHOM, S. (1965): Biology of the spiny bollworm *(Earias insulana* Boisd.). Ktavim (Engl. Edn.) **7,** 43–57.

Author: W. Reed

Earias vittella (F.)

Synonym: *Earias fabia*

Common name: Cotton spotted bollworm.

Geographical distribution: *E. vittella* is found all over South East Asia. Among the related species, *E. insulana* extends even to Africa whereas *E. hügeli* is recorded from Australia and *E. cupreoviridis* is restricted to China, Formosa, the Philippine Islands and India.

Host plants: *E. vittella* is a major pest of cotton (*Gossypium* spp.) and also attacks a few other malvaceous plants e. g., *Abelmoschus, Abutilon, Althaea, Hibiscus, Malva, Malvastrum, Sida* and *Urena.* The closely related species *E. insulana* and *E. cupreoviridis* attack a slightly wider range of host plants.

Symptoms: The larvae feed on and damage growing vegetative buds, developing seeds in the cotton bolls, shoots of the main axes, succulent internodes, tops of side branches, young leaves, flower buds and flowers. This results in the shedding of flower buds and bolls, delayed flower formation, premature opening of the attacked bolls, hollowing of the seeds and weakening and staining of cotton fibres.

Economic importance: The damage caused by the pest in South and South East Asia results in an enormous loss of cotton fibres, an inferior quality of the lint and a low yield of cotton seed oil.

Morphology: Eggs. Small, spherical, bluish green with parallel longitudinal ridges projecting upward. Larva. A newly hatched larva is 1.3 mm long, brownish white with dark head and prothoracic shield. A well developed larva is 19 mm long, with brown dorsum showing a white median longitudinal streak and pale yellow or green venter. Pupa. Dark brown, 13 mm long and is enclosed in a dirty white to light brown, though silken, boat-shaped cocoon. Adult. Buff coloured, 12.5 mm long, wing expanse 25 mm, fore wings are buff coloured with a green wedge.

Similarities to other pests: In the nature of its damage to cotton crops, *E. vittella* resembles, beside other *Earias* spp., the pink bollworm *Pectinophora gossypiella* and the cotton bollworms *Heliothis armigera* and *H. zea*.

Life cycle: On the 1st night after mating, or 3–5 days later the female begins to lay eggs either singly or scattered in small groups on the hairy parts of the plant, such as tender shoots, stalks of flower buds and bolls and on the lower surfaces of leaves. A single female may lay 63–697 eggs during the oviposition period. The incubation period varies from 3–4 days in summer to 5–7 days in winter. The newly hatched larvae wander about for a few hours before boring into tender shoots, flower buds or bolls. The larval period varies from 10–12 days in summer to 14–16 days in winter during which the larva passes through 5 instars. The last instar larvae, after they cease feeding, descend from the plant and usually penetrate 25–30 mm deep into the soil for pupation though they may pupate on the plant surface. The pupal period varies from 8–14 days. The entire life cycle occupies 22–35 days and the insect has 7–8 or 12 generations per year, depending upon climatic conditions. The adults live for 8–22 days or longer. There is no regular diapause but in regions with cold weather, the insect overwinters in the last larval instar within the bolls.

Ecology: Rainfall and temperature greatly influence relative abundance of the pest. Its population density is higher during some months in the monsoon season, when there is good rainfall and a sudden drop in summer temperature, than during the rest of the year. The period of development of different stages is prolonged during winter. The longevity, fecundity and colouration of the adults also fluctuates with the environmental temperature and humidity.

Natural enemies: *Eumenes petiolata* (Hymenoptera) and *Cantheconidae furcellate* (Hemiptera) act as larval predators. A number of parasitic wasps attack different stages of the pest. Egg parasites – *Trichogramma evanescens*. Larval parasites – *Actia aegyptia, A. hyalinata, Apanteles* sp., *Bassus* sp., *Elasmus johnstoni, Microbracon brevicornis, M. greeni, M. hebetor, M. lefroyi, Microdus fabiae, Polyodaspis compressiceps, Rogas aligharensis* and *R. testaceous.* Pupal parasites – *Brachymeria techardiae, Centrochalcis* sp., *Chalcis responsonator, C. techardiae, Chelonus rufus* and *Melcha nursei.*

Control:

Sanitary methods. a) Remove all cotton stalks after harvest. b) Remove stray cotton plants and alternate host plants during the off-season.

Cultural practices. a) Cultivate a single cotton crop instead of two per season in order to prevent heavy outbreak of the pest on the succeeding crop. b) Discourage growing alternate host plants in the absence of cotton crops in order to check carry-over of the pest.

Chemical control. The following chemical treatments have been used for satisfactory control of the pest in different cotton-growing areas. a) Dusting. Gamma-BHC 0.025 or 2 % endrin on tender leaves and bolls or a mixture of 5 % DDT and 5 % BHC starting from the middle or end of May. b) Spraying. 0.05 % endrin, 0.4 % toxaphene or a mixture of 0.05 % endrin, 0.4 % toxaphene and 0.2 % DDT at 130 gallons per acre; 0.025 % parathion and 0.03 % endrin in 2–3 rounds at fortnightly intervals after the pest begins to appear; 0.25 % DDT, 0.25 % BHC or 0.1–0.15 % malathion emulsion at 100 gallons per acre; 0.6 lb endrin or 0.7 lb parathion at 100 gallons per acre at tri-weekly intervals commencing when the crop is 9 weeks old; 0.2 % carbaryl or 0.25 % carbaryl followed by 0.04 % endrin in a 10–15 day schedule.

Literature

DESHPANDE, B. P. & N. T. NADKARNY (1936): The spotted bollworms of cotton *Earias fabia* Stoll and *Earias insulana* Boisd., in South Gujerat, Bombay Presidency. I.C.A.R. Sci. Monogr. **10**, 1–208.
KHAN, Q. & V. P. RAO (1960): Insects and Mite Pests in Cotton in India. A Mongraph. Indian Central Cotton Committee, Bombay, 217–301.
MEHTA, R. C. (1968): Some factors governing establishment of *Earias fabia* Stoll (Lepidoptera: Arctiidae) on various plants. Ph. D. thesis, University of Delhi, India.
SOHI, G. S. (1964): Pests of Cotton. in Entomology in India Ed. N.C. Pant. Ent. Soc. India, 111–148.

Author: R. C. Mehta

Heliothis armigera (Hb.) (Plate 40 a–d)

Synonyms: *Heliothis obsoleta, Helicoverpa armigera*

Common names: "American" bollworm; Afroasiatischer Baumwollkapselwurm; Oruga del tomate.

Geographical distribution: The pest occurs in Southern Europe, probably the whole of Africa, the Near and Middle East, India and Central and South-East Asia to Japan, the Philippines, Indonesia, New Guinea, the eastern part of Australia, New Zealand and a number of Pacific Islands. CIE Map no 15.

Host plants: A wide range of host crop plants occur including cotton, tobacco, maize, sorghum, pennisetum, sunflower, various legumes, citrus, tomatoes, okra and other horticultural crops. Wild plant hosts which are considered of importance include species of Euphorbiaceae, Amarantaceae, Malvaceae, Solanaceae, Compositae, Portulacaceae and Convolvulaceae, but many other plant families are also hosts.

Symptoms: The larva prefers to attack the reproductive parts of the plant including buds, flowers and fruits although it will feed upon the leaves. On cotton, the symptoms of damage are a hollowing out of buds and bolls leaving a clear cut entrance hole. Attacked buds and young bolls are shed following yellowing and flaring of the bracts while older bolls remain on the plant and fail to open. Occasionally, young shoots are also damaged. On maize, the silks and soft grain at the top of the cob are attacked while with tobacco the larva feeds upon the vegetative buds and older leaves of the plant. On tomato, the larvae bore into the fruits.

Economic importance: *H. armigera* is one of the most important crop pests and probably reaches its most devastating proportions on cotton although serious attacks can occur on other crops necessitating control measures.

Morphology: Egg. 0.4–0.5 mm in diameter, nearly spherical with a flattened base, glistering yellowish-white in colour changing to dark brown prior to hatching. Under a lens, the surface will be seen to have 24 longitudinal ribs, alternate ones being slightly shorter, with numerous fine transverse ridges between them.
Larva. The fully grown larva, about 40 mm in length, varies in general colour from almost black, brown or green to pale yellow or pink and is characterised by having a dark band along the back to each side of which there is a pale band, followed by another dark band and then a very light band.
Pupa. The light brown pupa, being in the soil, is seldom seen unless special sampling techniques are used.
Moth. Stout bodied moth with a wing span of 40 mm. General colour varies from dull yellow or olive grey to brown with little distinctive marking. Being nocturnal the moths are seldom seen during the day.

Similarities to other pests: The larval stage, to the inexperienced observer, might be confused with army worms (*Spodoptera* spp.), maize stalk borer (*Busseola fusca*) and possibly other caterpillars found feeding on the aerial parts of crop plants.

Life cycle and ecology: The moths become sexually mature and mate about four days after emergence from the pupae having fed from the nectaries of plants. The moth is only active at night and lays its eggs singly on the plant. On cotton, while most parts of the plant may be selected for oviposition, the majority of eggs are found on the upper half of the plant. Eggs are reported to be laid on the underside of young tobacco leaves and for other crop plants there may be preferred oviposition sites. The incubation period may vary from two to eight days depending upon temperature. On hatching, the larva normally eats some or all of its egg shell before feeding on the plant. On cotton the larva prefers buds and the younger bolls which it will completely hollow out. Unlike the red bollworm *(Diparopsis castanea)* it will commonly feed with much of its body exposed on the outside surface of the bud or boll and frass is commonly found within the enclosing bracts. The larva passes through six instars and the larval period may vary from 15–35 days.
Pupation normally occurs in the soil at a depth of 25–175 mm but on maize pupation may occur in the tip of the cob. The pupa is enclosed within a thin layer of silk. Both non-diapause and diapause pupae are produced, the latter towards the end of the season. The pupal period of the non-diapause pupae may vary from 15 to 52 days while that of diapause pupae is very variable, moths from such pupae generally emerging over a period of several weeks at the beginning of the following season.
Major attacks of *H. armigera* generally correspond to the flowering and fruiting periods of the crop and during the season there may be a succession of attacks on various crops as they come into flower. For example in southern Africa, the incidence of the pest on cotton is particularly associated with that on maize and other crops which may be grown in rotation or within close proximity to cotton, and to some extent on wild host plants.

Natural enemies: Egg and larval parasites together with predators such as ants and Neuroptera larvae are considered of importance in effecting a degree of control but are frequently unable to prevent outbreaks of economic importance. A polyhedral virus is also believed to be an important natural control factor.

Control:
Sanitary measures. No particular sanitary measures are advocated. Cotton plants should be destroyed at the end of the season to avoid ratoon growth supporting an early generation of bollworm.

Cultural measures. Ploughing to destroy the overwintering pupae in the soil has been recommended, but the effectiveness is not fully known.

The interval between the sowing dates and thus period of flowering of various crops should be as short as possible to avoid a successive build up of *Heliothis* from one crop to the other. Early sown maize followed by late sown cotton, for example, will favour a heavy incidence of bollworm on the latter crop. The use of diversionary crops or trap cropping has been suggested as means of controlling bollworm in cotton but has not been generally successful.

Biological control. No methods of biological control have been proved successful although the effective utilisation of the polyhedral virus as a control measure may prove possible in the future.

Chemical control. The application of insecticides offers an effective means of controlling *Heliothis* and, as protection of the cotton crop has probably received the most attention, the control of the pest in this crop will be primarily considered.

a) Insecticides. DDT and endosulfan give effective control of American bollworm and are both extensively used on cotton either as water based or ultra low volume formulations. DDT waterbased formulations are generally used at a spray concentration of 0.5 percent active ingredient and those of endosulfan at 0.25–0.5 percent a.i. Ultra low volume formulations of both insecticides may be used at the rate of 2.5 l/ha. Carbaryl has proved effective for the control of *Heliothis* in areas of low rainfall, but is not recommended for moderate or heavy rainfall areas. The addition of molasses to the carbaryl spray provides improved *Heliothis* control.

b) Timing of spray applications. The accurate timing of sprays in relation to the onset of attack, which may be sudden, is of paramount importance in the effective control of *Heliothis*.

Regular scouting of crops for eggs is the only sure basis on which to judge when to commence spraying and on cotton in southern Africa, it is recommended that control measures should be applied when twice weekly egg counts show an average of one half an egg per plant or a distinct rise in number of eggs over two or three consecutive counts. If control measures are delayed, larvae as they grow will become increasingly tolerant to the insecticide. Weekly sprays are usually necessary while the attack persists. One of the main problems encountered in a cotton spray programme where control of the red bollworm, *Diparopsis castanea* has also to be considered, is the timing of the changeover from carbaryl to DDT or endosulfan sprays. This difficulty can be minimised if one or two interim sprays of a carbaryl/molasses mixture are used which will give control of both bollworms. Alternatively, carbaryl may be added at half strength to the DDT or endosulfan sprays.

c) Method of application. For cotton, the various methods of spray application considered unter the section on red bollworm *(D. castanea)* are equally effective for controlling American bollworm. As the American bollworm tends to be generally found on the upper and outer parts of the plant feeding on buds and young bolls, spray coverage of the inner framework of the plant is of less importance.

Resistance to insecticides. No resistance of American bollworm to either DDT or endosulfan has been reported from southern Africa where both insecticides have been extensively used over 10 or more years. An increasing tolerance has been observed in Central Africa.

Literature

PEARSON, E. O. (1958): The insect pests of cotton in Tropical Africa. 355 pp. London. – Emp. Cott. Gr. Corp. and Commonw. Instit. Ent.
Cotton Handbook of Malawi (1971): Published by Extension Aids Section, Ministry of Agriculture and Natural Resources, Government of Malawi.

Author: J. P. Tunstall

Heliothis virescens (F.) (Plate 41 a, b)

Common names: Tobacco budworm, Flaxworm; Amerikanische Tabakeule; Bolillera, Gusano del brote.

Geographical distribution: New World between Canada and Argentina. CIE Map no 238.

Host plants: Cotton, tobacco, flax, corn, groundcherry, chickpea (*Cicer arietinum*), lettuce, squash and practically all hosts listed under *H. zea* (see p. 484). In Argentina, the budworm is specific to tobacco, cotton and flax.

Symptoms: On tobacco the terminal buds of the plants are attacked and often destroyed, mostly with one larva/bud. Leaves other than those in the immediate bud area are rarely infested. Feeding damage increases with the size of the larvae. For symptoms on other host plants, see *H. zea*.

Economic importance: Due to its high level of resistance against all insecticides the tobacco budworm is now a major threat to cotton growers in many areas of its range. This insect has destroyed the cotton industry in Northeastern Mexico where cotton acreage went down from more than 700,000 acres (1950–60) to less than 1,000 acres (1970). Combined losses due to enormous costs of insecticidal treatments and reduced yields forced the Mexican farmers out of business who had relied unilaterally on regularly scheduled insecticide applications. Farmers in Texas are now faced with the same problem. In the lower Rio Grande Valley of Texas the budworm in 1970 destroyed 25 % of the cotton crop and now threatens to make cotton an unprofitable crop there.

Morphology: The setigerous tubercles (chalazae) on the abdominal segments 1, 2 and 8 of the larvae bear microspines, and there is a processus (retinaculum) on the oral surface of the mandibula. The adults have yellowish-green forewings with three prominent whitish oblique bands, paralleled by darker green on their outer sides. The hind wings are white with a dark band on the margin which varies greatly in extent. In all other aspects, *H. virescens* instars closely resemble those of *H. zea*.

Similarities to other pests: *H. virescens* is very similar to *H. zea* with regard to biology, ecology, morphology and damage caused to crops. The two species mostly occur together forming the *Heliothis* complex. Moths of *H. virescens* and *H. subflexa* have the same coloration.

Life cycle: The life cycle information given for *H. zea* (see p. 484) applies equally to *H. virescens*. However, development time for one budworm generation on cotton in Colombia averages only 32 days.

Ecology: Similar to *H. zea,* spring populations of *H. virescens* in the southern U.S.A. build up on wild host plants, important species of which are *Nicotiana repanda, Gaura parviflora* and crimson clover. The wild hosts are more important for the budworm's spring development than for the bollworm's. The summer main hosts are cotton and tobacco. When cotton matures, *H. virescens* populations decline to low numbers and maintain themselves on alfalfa and uncultivated hosts such as morning glory plant *(Ipomoea trichocarpa)* and carelessweed *(Amaranthus polmeri)* during fall. The budworm has a narrower host range than the bollworm, and is less attracted to corn.

Natural enemies: The natural enemies listed under *H. zea* are also antagonists of *H. virescens*. On tobacco, *Jalysus spinosus, Geocoris punctipes, Oecanthus* spp., *Cyrtopeltis varians* (a suckfly) and *Polistes* wasps are important predators of the budworm; *Cardiochiles nigriceps* is an important parasite of the larvae on cotton.

Control:
Cultural practices. Such practices mentioned for *H. zea* also suppress *H. virescens* populations.

Tobacco stalk destruction soon after harvest, and sucker (shoot) control by means of maleic hydrazide reduces budworm populations by depriving them from an important source of late-season food. In Peru, reduced irrigation of cotton fields discourages succulent growth of leaves and stems that presumably attracts ovipositing moths, and favours the predator *Paratriphleps laeviusculus* which does not attack the pest effectively in the humid microclimate of heavily irrigated fields.

Resistance of crops. The budworm prefers villous, hirsute plant part surfaces for oviposition. Glabrous cotton varieties offer therefore resistance to this pest. Otherwise, the same resistance factors in host plants that work against *H. zea* (see there) are also effective against *H. virescens*.

Biological/integrated control. The concept of integrated control presented in the *H. zea* chapter includes also *H. virescens*. A crude economic injury level has been established for flue-cured tobacco in North Carolina; control action is required when more than 5 *Heliothis* spp.–larvae/50 plants are found prior to the beginning of flowering. One budworm larva/flue-cured tobacco plant consumes 7 leaves/plant and destroys 11 % of the buds.

Bacillus thuringiensis is registered against *H. virescens* for use on tobacco and, in view of the near overall resistance of the budworm to chemical insecticides in many areas, is a promising tool in an integrated control programme.

Chemical control. Insecticides. The same insecticides listed against *H. zea* (see p. 486) will also suppress budworm infestations provided that no resistance is manifest. On tobacco, bait and granualr formulations offer increased selectivity. Flue-cured tobacco is best protected by coating the terminal portion of plants with an effective insecticide shortly after the larvae hatch. This is most efficiently accomplished by directing sprays, dusts or baits into the terminal growth with hand equipment. Power sprayers are less efficient with the result that even heavier and/or more frequent applications give poorer plant protection.

Spraying schemes and prognosis. See *Heliothis zea.*

Resistance. The budworm has in recent years become resistant to chlorinated hydrocarbons and carbamates in many parts of the Americas: U.S. cotton belt, Colombia, Peru, Northwest Mexico, so that organophosphates became the major means of control. Then in the lower Rio Grande Valley of Texas resistance to methyl parathion developed; it was 5–9 fold in 1968, 11-fold in 1969 and 54-fold in 1970. In Central Texas it increased to 26-fold in 1970. Even greater resistance developed in the Mante-Tampico area of Mexico: 31-fold in 1968, 169-fold in 1969, and in 1970 the pest was beyond chemical control. Levels of methyl parathion resistance in *Heliothis* spp. are increasing in Mississippi, and a 3-5 fold increase was found in Arkansas and Louisiana. Populations in western and southern Mexico and South America seem to be still susceptible to methyl parathion.

The restricted host range of the tobacco budworm may be one of the reasons for its greater resistance to insecticides compared with the bollworm. The budworm is mainly confined to cotton, so each application of insecticides is an application to the total budworm population present at this time. *H. zea* is distributed on several hosts, so that an application to cotton affects only a portion of the total bollworm population. In other words, *H. virescens* has been under much greater selection pressure.

Literature

Refer to *Heliothis zea* (p. 486).

Author: R. Daxl

Heliothis zea Boddie (Plates 41 c, d and 42 a, b)

Common names: Cotton bollworm, Corn earworm etc.; Amerikanischer Baumwollkapselwurm; Ver de la capsule; Gusano bellotero, Gusano de la cápsula del algodonero.

Geographical distribution: Its range is confined to the New World. It occurs throughout the Americas between Canada and Paraguay/Argentina including the West Indies. CIE Map no 239.

Host plants: Cotton and corn (maize), beans, tobacco, tomato, sorghum, cabbage, okra, pumpkin, sesame, chickpea, strawberries, sunflower, alfalfa, chili peppers, cowpea, sudan grass, johnson grass, clover and vetch. Numerous weed species are also attacked.

Symptoms: The host's fruiting points are usually consumed entirely or in part. The feeding provides gates of entry for moulds, bacteria, and other insects.
Cotton. Flower buds (squares), flowers and young bolls are attacked. The larvae bore into the fruiting points and eat out the interior. One average-sized larva can damage 3.8 squares and 2.2 bolls. Occasionally, young shoots and leaves are also damaged, especially in the absence of fruiting points.
Corn (maize). Larvae feed on the tender leaves in the whorl. When tassels emerge, the larvae migrate down the stalk to the ears where the severest damage is caused.

Economic importance: The bollworm is among the worst pests of crops in the Western hemisphere due to (a) its wide host range, (b) wide geographical range, (c) attacking the plant parts to be harvested, (d) its large-sized larvae with high food requirements leading often to the total loss of infested fruits, supplemented by secondary rot organisms, (e) the increasing insecticide resistance of the pest. Annual corn losses in the U.S.A. due to *H. zea* are estimated at $ 75–140 million.

Morphology: Eggs. Shiny white at first, darkening before hatch. Hemispherical, taller than wide, ridged along the sides, a little smaller than a pinhead. Deposited singly. Larvae. They show wide variation in color: light- to dark green, pinkish, brown to nearly black, bearing a double middorsal line the length of the body and alternating light and dark stripes along its sides. The larvae reach a length up to 4.5 cm and have 3 pairs of dark true legs, 5 pairs of prolegs. The skin is rough and thorny under magnification. The setigerous tubercles (chalazae) have no microspines; there is no process (retinaculum) on the oral surface of the mandibula. Pupae. Dark brown, about 2 cm long, found 5–15 cm below soil surface in earthen cells. Adults. Front wings of a light grayish brown marked with dark irregular lines and a dark area near the tips. Hind wings white with irregular dark spots.

Similarities to other pests: *H. zea* is very similar to *H. virescens* in all aspects (see p. 482). In Argentina, similarity exists to *H. gelotopoeon,* a pest of cotton, sorghum and flax.

Life cycle: Life cycle data differ from one geographical area to another. The eggs hatch in 2–5 days. There are 5 larval instars. Development time for one generation can vary from 62 days (March) to 28 days (July) in the southern U.S.A.; in Colombia the average is 41 days. One female lays up to 2,500 eggs. The insect overwinters or estivates in the pupal stage in the soil. Pupal diapause is induced by temperature and photoperiod regimes, but terminated only by temperature conditions in the U.S.A. Diapausing pupae retain the larval eye-spot in the post-genal region. In the southern U.S.A., peak diapause occurs in September/October, peak emergence of moths in May.
The life cycle of *Heliothis* spp. is influenced by the moon. Greater numbers of moths are active and higher numbers of eggs are deposited during new-moon phases than at full moon. An 80 % reduction in increase of *Heliothis* populations occurs during full moon.

Ecology: The ecology of *H. zea* varies with the geographic region. Generally, larval populations do not occur uniformly in an area but are concentrated on a variety of host plants and change to other species as the season progresses. In the subtropical U.S.A., spring populations build up on wild geranium *(Geranium carolinianum),* legumes (vetch, *Vicia* spp.; crimson clover, *Trifolium* *incarnatum;* alfalfa) and wild hosts *(Nicotiana repanda, Verbena neomexicana, Ruellia runionii,* and others). Low temperatures as well as predators and parasites slow the development of this first generation in some cases; in others this brood can develop great numbers on alfalfa and corn. Corn becomes the principal host in June, and in the silking stage has the highest attractiveness of all host plants. Development of the population here is rapid, the larvae in the ears are more protected against natural enemies. Cannibalism from the third instar on inhibits development of more than one or two larvae per ear. The large populations built up on corn invade then cotton after corn matures. Cotton prior to squaring is less attractive. The populations on cotton usually do not reach levels as high as on corn; biological control agents are mostly adequate to prevent damaging infestations unless impaired by insecticides. However, where corn acreage has markedly declined, *H. zea* outbreaks occur regularly in cotton even without prior use of insecticides. In August–September the populations fall to a low level when cotton, the main host in summer, matures and other plants are not available. It is not until rains in September cause alfalfa to resume growth that *H. zea* numbers increase again to high levels on this crop that together with regrowth cotton and wild hosts is utilized in the fall by the larvae destined to enter diapause.

In Central America (Nicaragua) there are 3 marked peaks of abundance of moths: January–February at the height of the dry season; May, at the onset of rains; October–December during peak cotton fruiting.

Natural enemies: Eggs. Eggs are attacked by Heteroptera *(Geocoris* and *Orius* spp.), Coccinellids *(Hippodamia, Coleomegilla, Coccinella, Chilocorus, Cycloneda, Olla), Collops balteatus, Chrysopa, Lebia analis* and certain spiders; and parasitized by *Trichogramma.*
Small larvae. Ants, lady beetles, *Collops* spp., *Chrysopa, Conocephalus fasciatus* (Tettigoniidae), *Nabis, Geocoris, Orius, Zelus* spp. and spiders are predators, and *Campoletis* sp., *Microplitis croceipes, Euplectrus* spp., *Chelonus texanus* (all Hymenoptera), *Eucelatoria* spp., *Lespesia* spp. (Tachinidae) are among important parasites. Fungi *(Spicaria rileyi, Beauveria* spp., *Entomophthora* spp.), bacteria *(Bacillus thuringiensis)* and viruses (nuclear polyhedrosis) cause diseases.
Large larvae and pupae are attacked by *Polistes* wasps, *Calosoma* beetles, *Sphecidae* and *Podisus maculiventris* (Heteropt.); *M. croceipes* and *Cardiochiles nigriceps* are important parasites.
Moths. Dragonflies, spiders and *Calosoma* spp. prey on the adults. In Nicaragua cotton, predators and parasites are abundant in the early season (June–September) and in the dry season (January–May), and virtually absent during the peak of cotton fruit formation in the wettest months (September–December). In Colombia, beneficial insects are more abundant from planting to first square formation.

Control:
Cultural practices. Prompt shredding of cotton stalks and fall clipping of alfalfa deprives the overwintering *Heliothis* populations from their host plants in the southern U.S.A. Fall or spring ploughing destroys the exit tunnels of pupae in the soil and reduces the number of emerging moths. In Central America, early cotton stalk destruction exposes the soil during the dry season to erosion. Besides, the stalks harbour a rich fauna of beneficial insects. Uniform and well-timed planting dates shorten the presence of susceptible crop stages and avoid their coincidence with abundance peaks of *Heliothis.*
Resistance of crops. Glabrous and nectariless cotton strains cause significant reduction in *Heliothis* oviposition. High gossypol content in the plants exerts an antibiotic effect on the larvae. Factors of resistance in corn include a) longer, tighter, thicker husks with massive, compressed silk balls hampering penetration of larvae; b) short silking period not coinciding with major oviposition activity; c) nonpreference, antibiosis and tolerance qualities. In soybeans, besides antibiosis factors, resistance lies mainly in the plant's capacity to compensate for pod loss. This tolerance is influenced by stage of maturity, moisture conditions and previous damage to foliage and pods. Soybeans with closed canopies are less infested. The cotton plant's tolerance lies in its excess production of squares and small bolls.
Biological/integrated control. The *Heliothis zea-virescens* complex on cotton is a secondary pest

ordinarily held to subeconomical levels by beneficial arthropods. Preservation of this fauna is therefore of paramount necessity. Once insecticidal treatments have begun, the pest usually gets unleashed from antagonists, and its repeated resurgences start the well-known pesticide tread-mill. Areawide insecticidal applications against other, earlier-occuring pests like fleahopper (Texas), *Lygus* (California), boll weevil and cotton leafworm (Nicaragua) must be deferred until the crop becomes seriously endangered, and when all other control measures have failed. The use of chemicals against *Heliothis* has almost everywhere resulted in pest resistance and resurgence, pollution of the environment and increased cost to farmers. The beneficial fauna can be fomented in its efficiency by maintaining diversity in the crop ecosystem, applications of food sprays (11.25 kg wheast + 11.25 kg sugar + 95 l water/acre for *Chrysopa,* sprayed in alternate 10 m-swaths), supplementary mass releases of *Trichogramma,* restricted use of broad-spectrum insecticides, etc. The strong influence of the moon on the pest's life cycle allows to predict the times of high egg and larval densities. The planting date of cotton then must be chosen so that the susceptible period of critical fruit formation (60–115 days after planting in Nicaragua) lies as favourably as possible between two new-moon induced peaks of oviposition and small larvae activity. This scheme can be adapted to other crops.

Regular field scouting is the base of an integrated control program. The number of pest instars, beneficial organisms, healthy and damaged fruits per ha or per 100 plants should be counted twice weekly. When pest densities have reached the economic damage threshold which in California is between 8–20 larvae/100 cotton plants, in Nicaragua 5700 larvae/ha before the first application, 7000 small larvae/ha after the first application and before the crop is 100 days old, 8600 small worms/ha when the crop exceeds 100 days in age, ecologically sound control measures should be used. They include: a) Microbial control agents. Preparations of nuclear polyhedrosis virus (Biotrol VHZ, Viron/H) combined with pH-buffer and UV-filter, and *Bacillus thuringiensis* (Thuricide, Dipel) are often as effective as chemical insecticides and do not harm natural enemies. b) Selective use of chemical insecticides. 5.7–8.0 l/ha toxaphene-DDT, or 2.7–5.7 l/ha Sevimol (2.3 kg/l water) are recommended for cotton in Nicaragua. c) Combinations of a resistant crop variety with microbial or chemical insecticides.

An integrated control program against *Heliothis* spp. should comprise the populations on all host crops in a given ecosystem throughout the year.

Chemical control.

a) Insecticides. Endosulfan (short residual action), toxaphene-DDT, Lorsban, Celathion, carbaryl for use in an integrated control program. Adding molasses can improve performance and residue-life. Toxaphene-methyl parathion, toxaphene-DDT-methyl parathion, leptophos, methyl parathion and chlordimeform-methyl parathion, as potent emergency formulations.

b) Spraying schemes. They must take into account the moon phase-governed reproduction rate of the population and the behaviour of the pest. Spraying during population increase (full to new moon) can keep the pest from surpassing economically dangerous levels. On corn, treatment of young larvae in the whorl or tassel stage with a DDT-virus combination effectively reduces ear damage.

c) Prognosis. Ultraviolet blacklight traps serve as short-term warning devices. Increased catches of moths are usually followed by a rise in numbers of eggs and larvae in the field. Several traps are to be placed across an area. Control action must never be initiated on trap catch data but only on field checking information. On cotton, first flower appearance is often an indicator for the start of bollworm infestations.

d) Resistance to insecticides. In recent years the bollworm has developed resistance to chlorinated and carbamate insecticides in the U.S.-cotton belt and Colombia. High resistance to methyl parathion is reported from Nicaragua, and in other countries the susceptibility to this insecticide is on the decline.

Literature

ALLEN, J., D. GONZALEZ & D. W. GOKHALE (1972): Sequential sampling plans for the bollworm, *Heliothis zea.* Environm. Entom. **1**, 771–780.

FALCON, L. A. & R. F. SMITH (1973): Guidelines for integrated control of cotton insect pests. Food and Agriculture Organization, AGPP: MISC/8, Rome.

HARTSTACK, A. W., J. P. HOLLINGWORTH, R. L. RIDGWAY & J. R. COPPEDGE (1973): A population dynamics study of the bollworm and the tobacco budworm with light traps. Environm. Entom. **2**, 244–252.

INTERNATIONAL ATOMIC ENERGY AGENCY, Vienna (1971): Ecology and behaviour of the *Heliothis* complex as related to the sterile male technique. Tech. Rep IAEA – **129.**

LINCOLN, C., J. R. PHILLIPS, W. H. WHITCOMB, G. C. DOWELL, W. P. BOYER, K. O. BELL JR., G. L. DEAN, E. J. MATTHEWS, J. B. GRAVES, L. D. NEWSOM, D. F. GLOWER, J. R. BRADLEY JR. & J. L. BAGENT (1967): The bollworm – tobacco budworm problem in Arkansas and Louisiana. Louisiana Agr. Expt. Sta. Bull. **720.**

METCALF, C. L. & W. P. FLINT (1962): Destructive and useful insects. 4. edition. McGraw Hill Book Co. New York.

QUAINTANCE, A. L., & C. T. BRUES (1905): The cotton bollworm. US Dep. Agric. Bur. Entomol. Bull. **50**, 97–103.

STADELBACHER, E. A., M. L. LASTER & T. R. PFRIMMER (1972): Seasonal occurrrence of populations of bollworm and tobacco budworm moths in the central delta of Mississippi. Environ. Entom. **1**, 318–323.

WOLFENBARGER, D. A., M. J. LUKEFAHR & H. M. GRAHAM (1973): LD_{50} values of methyl parathion and endrin to tobacco budworms and bollworms collected in the Americas and hypothesis on the spread of resistance in these Lepidopterans to these insecticides. J. Econ. Entomol. **66**, 211–216.

Author: R. Daxl

Sesamia calamistis Hmps. (Plate 42 c, d)

Synonym: *Sesamia vuteria*

Common names: Southern pink borer, Pink stalk borer, African pink borer; Afrikanischer Stengelbohrer; Borer rose, Sesamie; Sesamia. This species is often confused with *S. nonagrioides.*

Geographical distribution: The savanna and dry tropical zones of the African region: Madagascar, Réunion, Mauritius, Angola, Cameroon, Congo, Ivory Coast, Gambia, Ghana, Upper Volta, Rwanda, Burundi, Senegal, Tanzania, Sudan.

Host Plants: Wild and cultivated Gramineae: Sugar cane, maize, sorghum, rice, pennisetum millet (bulrush millet), wheat, *Tripsacum, Paspalum, Andropogon, Hyparrhenia rufa, Pennisetum purpureum, P. subangulatum, Rottboellia compressa, R. exaltata, Setaria splendida, Vossia cuspidata, Sorghum halepense, Coix lachryma jobi.*

Symptoms: The damage is caused by caterpillars which excavate galleries in the stem. The caterpillars of *S. calamistis* generally attack the upper parts and the plants die when the growing zone is reached; this type of damage is seen in young stems of sugar cane, maize and rice. In the latter crop the young caterpillars, 2nd and 3rd instars, occupy the thin part of the stalk at the base of the panicle, which is then lost. Older caterpillars feed lower down the stalk, and in this position the stem is not always a total loss.

The effect on maize is similar to that due to *S. nonagrioides.* On very young plants the caterpillars feed first on the rolled leaves, and then descend to the growing point. The shoot continues to grow normally until the plant suddenly permanently withers as a result of the many galleries bored by the caterpillars. Attacks may lead to breakage of the stems, this depending upon the severity of boring and the toughness of the tissues. Even if maize escapes these attentions of the pest the caterpillars can attack the ears and eat the grains beneath the husks.

On sugar cane, the attacks take place on very young stems. The narrow rolled leaves are the first to wilt, leaving the inferior leaves intact, but the entire shoot is eventually lost. The new growths which then appear at the base may, in turn, also be attacked.

Sorghum has a defense mechanism in the form of a gelatinous exudate which traps young caterpillars.

Economic importance: The species of *Sesamia* are unevenly distributed according to local climate and host plants, but each is to be found on the majority of cultivated Gramineae in Africa. In this situation it is only possible to give an idea of the economic importance of the genus as a whole. The "Pink borer" is a major pest of young sugar cane plantations in Madagascar, Réunion and Mauritius. Maize is everywhere the most severely attacked plant, and damage to rice, wheat and sugar cane is often associated with nearby maize, cultivated before or at the same time as these other crops. The degree of damage depends upon the age of the crop when the pest arrives. Maize does not readily tiller and so a single caterpillar can destroy a plant, whereas millet and rice tiller freely and are therefore much more tolerant. In general, irrigated rice suffers less than the rain-grown crop.

Morphology: The adult moth is coloured light beige more or less striped with brown. The margin of the anterior wings is wide, whitish and in part smoky. The posterior wings are pearly white with an equally wide but yellowish margin. There are considerable differences in colour and markings between geographical areas. The genitalia must be examined before it is possible to identify the species with certainty.

The larvae, which can reach 4 cm in length, are even less distinctive than the adults. The caterpillars are smooth, uniformly yellowish-pink and dirty rose on their dorsal side, with greyish lateral and dorsal lines. The surrounds of the spiracles are black and clearly visible. The head capsule and thoracic plate are a dark, shiny brown.

The eggs are subspherical, flat at the poles, and with numerous longitudinal striations.

Similarities to other pests: It is easy to confuse the damage due to *S. calamistis* with that of *S. nonagrioides*, *S. cretica*, *S. botanephaga* and *S. poephaga*. These are similar species that can only be distinguished by their genitalia. However, it is possible to specify the species concerned: only *S. nonagrioides* is found in southern France, Italy and the Iberian peninsula; in Morocco and the Azores *S. cretica* also occurs and is spread around the Mediterranean basin, especially the southern part and in the Middle East. Further south, *S. nonagrioides* is replaced by *S. calamistis* which is distributed throughout Africa south of the Sahara, and in Madagascar, Réunion and Mauritius. Also found in central Africa are *S. botanephaga*, *S. poephaga* and *S. penniseti*.

Biology, ecology and life-cycle: The adults have a nocturnal habit and are able to travel large distances; they appear less active when breeding. Mating usually takes place as early as the first night after emergence and egg-laying begins at once. The female inserts her ovipositor beneath the leaf sheath which surrounds the upper internodes. On adult maize plants the eggs are deposited on the inner face of the sheath below the cob.

The caterpillars first feed within the tissues of the sheath, subsequently entering the main stem through a horizontal cavity and then moving vertically downward, sometimes through several internodes. They stay within the shelter of the sheaths or stems. The frass which fills the vertical galleries is partly ejected through scattered openings beneath the sheaths. Pupation takes place at the foot of the stem or in the folds of the withered sheaths.

In the wet climate of tropical countries the life-cycle is practically uninterrupted. In contrast, drought and cool temperatures can induce a slowing down of development. Mature caterpillars become quiescent from the start of the dry season until the rains return or the temperature increases, but this behaviour is only possible if the host plant has withered, as happens with maize, sorghum and rice. In the case of sugar cane the plant remains turgid throughout the year so that active winter populations of *Sesamia* are supported.

In the intertropical zone of Africa the life-cycle of *S. calamistis* is rapidly completed and can result in 5–6 generations. In favourable conditions the eggs hatch after 7–10 days, the life of the larva is 4–5 weeks, the pupal stage 10–14 days and the adult 4–5 days, giving an average of 2 months for one generation. Towards the end of the crop season the length of this cycle may be extended, but without any notable discontinuity.

Control:

Cultural methods. Maize has often been used as a trap plant to protect sugar cane plantations in Réunion and Mauritius, being sown as interlines between the canes.

Cereals of the right varieties, well maintained with dressings of balanced fertilizers, can resist the effects of *Sesamia*.

Biological control. The following is a list of the most important natural enemies of *S. calamistis* which have been established with a view to the biological control of this pest on sugar cane:

Scelionidae *Platytelenomus* sp. Mauritius

Trichogrammatidae *Trichogramma australicum* Madagascar, Mauritius

Eulophidae *Tetrastichus* sp. (?*atriclavus*) Mauritius; *Pediobius furvum* Réunion

Chalcididae *Brachymeria feae* Nigeria

Braconidae *Apanteles ruficrus* Somalia; *Apanteles sesamiae* Mauritius, Réunion; *Bracon chinensis* Mauritius

Ichneumonidae *Amesospilus* sp. Madagascar; *Enicospilus* sp. Mauritius, Réunion; *Enicospilus antakarus* Madagascar; *Xanthopimpla citrina* Mauritius; *Xanthopimpla stemmator* Mauritius, Réunion, Madagascar; *Braunsis occidentalis* Nigeria

Tachinidae *Sturmiopsis inferens* Madagascar; *Sturmiopsis parasitica* Ghana

Nematoda *Mermis* sp. Mauritius

Among several countries, Mauritius, Madagascar and Réunion have introduced parasites with varying success. For example, in Madagascar *Apanteles sesamiae* has been introduced on several occasions without success, whereas *Pediobius furvum*, brought from Kampala in 1968, rapidly established itself on the Madagascan plateau and in two years significantly reduced the *Sesamia* population.

The writer has no knowledge of any introductions into continental Africa, but this should certainly be considered in the context of looking for natural enemies of all species of *Sesamia*.

Resistant varieties. This approach to control has been explored very little. It is recognized that there are considerable differences in susceptability between varieties of sugar cane which differ, in particular, in their growth rate and tillering, and the situation is similar for maize. Much can be done, for it should be possible to test each world collection in order to select lines best fitted as parents for breeding programmes.

Chemical control. This is only feasible with crops which have a sufficiently high value, such as sugar cane, maize and sometimes rice. Excellent results have been obtained with DDT and gamma-BHC, dusted or sprayed, separately or mixed, and other insecticides have also been used with success: azinphos-methyl, camphechlor, carbaryl, endosulfan, trichlorphon, disulfoton. These chemicals are used early in the cropping season before the caterpillars have penetrated deeply. Finally, monocrotophos, a systemic which also acts as a contact insecticide, can be used if adequate precautions are taken with respect to its high toxicity.

Literature

ABUL-NASR, S. E., A.K.M. EL NAHAL & S. K. SHAHOUDAH (1968): Field experiments on the chemical control of the corn borer, *Sesamia cretica* Led. Bull. Ent. Soc. Egypt no 2, 131–142.

APPERT, J. (1971): Les insectes nuisibles au mais en Afrique et à Madagascar. Agro. Trop. **26**, 476–499.

BADAWY, A. (1969): The dura stem borers and their parasites in the Sudan. Bull. Soc. Ent. Egypt **51**, 233–241.

BRENIERE, J. (1966): Dix années de recherches sur les ennemis du riz en Afrique francophone et à Madagascar – Agro. Trop. **21**, 514–519.

BRENIERE, J. (1970): Les problèmes des lépidoptères foreurs des graminées en Afrique de l'Quest. Conf. Symp. sur foreurs des graminées – VIIème Congrès International Protection des Plantes – Résumé des communications – 21–25/9/70 – p. 506–508.

GRIST, D. H. & R. J. A. LEVER (1969): Pests of Rice. 520 pp., Longmans.

NICKEL, J. L. (1964): Biological control of Rice stem borers. IRRI Tech. Bull. 2, 111 pp.

NYE, I. W. B. (1960): The insect pests of graminaceous crops in East Africa. Colonial Research Studies no 31, Colonial Office.

PATHAK, M. D. (1969): Insect pests of rice. IRRI 77 pp. typewritten.

TAMS, W. H. T. & J. BOWDEN (1952): A revision of the African species of *Sesamia* Guenée and related genera (Agrotidae – Lepidoptera). Bull. Ent. Res. **43**, 645–678.

YÜRÜTEN, O. (1971): Investigations on the biology and control of the maize stem borer *Sesamia cretica* Led. attacking maize in the Marmara region. Bitki Koruma Bülteni **11** (3), 133–156 Istanbul.

Author: J. Brenière

Sesamia cretica Led. (Plate 43 a, b)

Common names: Pink borer of sugar-cane, Sorghum borer; Hirsestengelbohrer.

Geographical distribution: Tropical and subtropical countries growing maize, sorghum and sugar-cane, for instance Egypt, Sudan, Ethiopia, Somalia, Saudi Arabia, Iraq and Iran. The pest has also been reported in Southern Italy and some other countries of the Eastern Mediterranean basin.

Host plants: Maize, sugar-cane, sorghum, wheat, pennisetum, broom corn, Sudan grass, and some wild grasses.

Symptoms: In Egypt, maize is the most susceptible host plant. Plants are attacked in the seedling stage, one to two weeks from the date of sowing. Infestation usually reaches its highest level on plants which are one month old. Infested plants can be identified by three main symptoms. The top leaves may have long, narrow holes arranged in one or more horizontal rows. The hearts of infested plants may appear shrivelled, dry and yellowish, easily separated by a slight pulling action. The stems of infested plants, when free of the leaf sheaths, show several holes along their length down to the soil level or even beneath. If infested plant stems are cut lengthwise, mid and peripheral tunnels which may contain larvae or pupae become apparent. Symptoms of infestation on sugar-cane are similar to those on maize, except for the holes in the leaves, which are very rare. The tunnels inside the sugar-cane stem become pinkish in colour. In sorghum, sterile heads may develop as a consequence of attack.

Economic importance: In places where there are severe attacks by the pest, the heavy losses of dead or badly damaged maize, sugar-cane or sorghum plants means that the pest becomes a limiting factor in the cultivation of these crops. The toll may reach over 60 % of mature plants, those escaping infestation remaining sparsely scattered over the field.

Morphology: Adult moth is of medium size; wing span 3.4–3.7 cm, body length 1.7–1.9 cm, fore-wings light yellowish brown, with darker main veins, hind wings silvery. Full grown larva 3.5–3.8 cm long, yellowish cream with pinkish shadow over the dorsum, the head capsule dark brown. Pupa light brownish, usually enclosed in a light silken cocoon.

Similarities to other pests: In some countries corn, sugar-cane and sorghum may be subject to infestation by more than one species of insect borer. In Egypt, two important insect borers may exist together with *S. cretica*, namely *Chilo agamemnon* and *Ostrinia nubilalis*. In the Sudan, *Chilo partellus* (Northern Sudan) and *Sesamia calamistis* (Southern Sudan) may infest the same maize or sorghum plants.

Life cycle: At the end of the host's growing season, full grown larvae of the insect hide themselves at the end of their tunnels near to the stem surface but mostly at the stem bases above or beneath the soil surface. They remain as resting or diapause larvae from late autumn until early spring. The resting larvae turn to pupae in their resting places after making exit holes. Emergence of the moth takes place and mated female moths start to lay their eggs in small batches.

A batch contains 15–75 eggs set in two to three rows. A single female may lay 10–12 egg batches. Oviposition starts on seedling maize with a single leaf; the plants become unattractive when bearing seven or more leaves. The egg batch is laid at the base of the leaf-blade or at the top end of the leaf-sheath. The incubation period takes 4–7 days and the tiny larvae crawl towards the heart of the plant where they bore their way through the whorled leaves thereby causing the symptoms of the holes in rows and dead heart of infested plants. A good number of larvae may remain in the heart area (dead heart) causing disintegration of tissue, a bad smell and a slimy secretion. Full grown larvae may pupate at the end of their tunnel or leave to rest in corners between the leaf blades and sheaths to pupate inside light silken cocoons.

In Egypt there may be 3–4 generations during the active season, from mid-March to mid-September. The larvae of the last brood enter a resting stage. The first generation is usually the most active and destructive.

Natural enemies: Eggs are parasitized by *Platytelonomus hylas* (Scelionidae). Also, eggs may be attacked by predaceous mites and by the larvae of the Neuropteroid *Chrysopa carnea* in Egypt. Larvae are destroyed by *Apanteles* spp. and pupae by Chalcidids in the Sudan.

Control:

Sanitary methods. As resting larvae hibernate inside host plant stems, all maize stems should be destroyed by burning or chopping into fragments before the beginning of next season. The basal portions of maize plants, which may remain in the field, should be collected and treated similarly.

Cultural practices. Change of sowing date: By studying fluctuations of the insect it should be possible to arrange cultivations so that plants escape from the period of high pest incidence, mostly by the first generation. Planting at a later date, in the case of maize and sugar-cane, has proved to be effective in keeping infestation below an economically destructive level.

Chemical control. Motorised spraying of insecticides from the ground at the time of initial infestation, to be followed by two or three sprays at 15-day intervals. Carbaryl (80 % W.P.) is used successfully against the borer, at a rate of one kilogram to each 200–300 litres of water. One acre of maize may need 200–300 litres for the first spray, which is increased to 400 litres for the following sprays. It is essential that the insecticide liquid should reach the hearts of the plants. Use of emulsifiable insecticides are not advised as they cause scorching to the tender leaves of the plant's heart.

Literature

SALAH E. ABUL-NASR, SALAH E., A. K. EL-NAHAL & S. K. SHAHOUDAH (1968): Field experiments on the chemical control of the corn borer, *Sesamia cretica* Led. (Lepidoptera: Agrotidae-Zenobiinae). Bull. Soc. ent. Egypte Econ. Ser. II, 131–142.

SALAH E. ABUL-NASR, SALAH E., A. K. EL-NAHAL & S. K. SHAHOUDAH (1969): Some biological aspects of the corn stem-borer, *Sesamia cretica* Led. (Lepidoptera: Agrotidae-Zenobiinae). Bull. Soc. ent. Egypte **52**, 429–444.

BADAWY, A. (1969): The dura stem borers and their parasites in the Sudan (Lepidoptera and Hymenoptera). Bull. Soc. ent. Egypte **51**, 233–241.

DAMIANO, A. (1967): Contributo alla conoscenza della biologia della *Sesamia cretica* Led. (Lepidoptera Agrotidae) in Tripolitania. Riv. Agric. subtrop. trop. **61**, 261–270.

Author: Salah E. Abul-Nasr

Sesamia inferens (Wlk.) (Plate 43 c, d)

Synonyms: *Leucania inferens, Nonagria inferens*

Common names: Pink borer; Violetter Reisstengelbohrer.

Geographical distribution: Andaman Islands, Bangladesh, Brunei, Burma, China, Hongkong, India, Indonesia, Japan, Khmer, Korea, Laos, Malaysia, Nepal, New Guinea, Pakistan, Papua, Philippines, Ryukyu, Sikkim, Singapore, Solomon Islands, Sri Lanka, Taiwan, Thailand, Vietnam.

Host plants: Primary hosts: Rice *(Oryza sativa),* Sugar cane *(Saccharum officinarum).* Secondary hosts: Maize *(Zea mays),* Wheat *(Triticum aestivum),* Barley *(Hordeum vulgare),* Sorghum *(Sorghum vulgare),* Finger millet, Ragi *(Eleusine coracana),* Guinea grass *(Panicum maximum),* Jove grass *(Rottboellia compressa),* Serch *(Andropogon nardus),* Golmootha *(Scripus affines),* Markat *(Phragmites karka),* Ikri *(Saccharum fuscum),* Minogome *(Beckmania erucaeformis),* Sedge *(Cyperus japonicus),* Brischloa villosa, Banyard grass *(Panicum crusgalli),* Sama *(Panicum frumentaceum),* Paspalum thunbergii, P. commersoni, Polypogon hiyegawari,* Sar, Kanra *(Saccharum arundinaceum),* Glagah *(Saccharum spontaneum),* Indian millet *(Setaria italica).*

Symptoms: Refer to *Chilo suppressalis* (p. 452).

Economic importance: The pink borer is probably the least important pest among the rice stem borers. Outbreaks in rice usually result from a build-up in adjacent sugar cane fields or in fields of other alternate hosts. Refer also to *Chilo suppressalis* (p. 453).

Morphology: Egg – hemispherical, creamy white to dark, ridges running down the sides from the top, laid in rows, naked.
Larva – last stage 28–35 mm long, light yellow with a pink tinge, distinctly segmented with no stripes.
Pupa – reddish brown, naked, 12–18 mm long.
Adult moth – robust, 14–17 mm long, brown in color. The forewing has faint stripes up to the tip which is bordered by a light stripe.

Similarities to other pests: Refer to *Chilo suppressalis* (p. 453).

Life cycle: The life history of the pink borer is similar to the striped rice borer, *Chilo suppressalis,* with the following differences. Pink borer eggs are less exposed, being laid between the leaf sheath and the stem in two to three rows. The larvae do not tend to cluster and disperse early. The pink borer has seven larval stages. The larger size of the larvae and the greater number of stages result in a longer life cycle which can last from 45 to 90 days under nondormancy conditions. There can be up to six generations annually. Pupation occurs within the stem or between the leaf sheath and stem. Because the larvae are polyphagous, they can move to adjacent fields or border areas to complete their development after the rice has been harvested.

Ecology: The pink borer has been studied very little. Apparently, its ecology is similar to that of the striped rice borer, except that it is not as well adapted to the more temperate environments.

Natural enemies: Because the pink borer eggs are protected by their location under the leaf sheath, predators and parasites can inflict only slight injury – rarely exceeds 5 percent for a given season. Parasites, predators, and the incidence of disease organisms have only a minimal effect on the larvae and pupae. The tachinid fly, *Sturmiopsis inferens,* however, can parasitize up to 80 percent of the pink borer larvae.

Control:
Sanitary methods and cultural practices. Refer to *Chilo suppressalis* (p. 454).
Resistance of crops. Those rice varieties found to be resistant to the striped rice borer have not been tested against the pink borer.
Integrated control/biological control. Refer to *Chilo suppressalis* (p. 454).

Insecticides. The pink borer is not controlled by gamma-BHC (lindane). Refer to *Chilo suppressalis* (p. 454) for effective insecticides.

Literature

See *Chilo*.

Author: J. A. Litsinger

Spodoptera exigua (Hb.) (Plate 44 a, b)

Synonym: *Laphygma exigua*

Common names: Lesser cotton leaf worm, Beet army worm; Zuckerrübeneule; Gusano soldado.

Geographical distribution: *S. exigua* has been recorded from Europe, Asia, Africa, Australia, and America; it is more common in warm climates. In the tropics and sub-tropics it is found in countries such as Indonesia, India, Arabia-Southern Yemen, Somalia, Ethiopia, Sudan, Kenya, Nigeria, Mali, Senegal, Cameroon, Benin, Madagascar, Guatemala, El Salvador, Nicaragua etc. CIE Map no 302.

Host plants: The larva attacks almost all kinds of field crops including cotton, sugar beet, lucerne, maize, sorghum, tobacco, groundnut, broad bean, sesame, jute, citrus and such vegetables as tomato, onion and potato. On weeds it has been found on various species of *Chenopodium, Portulaca, Convolvulus, Sida* and *Amaranthus*.

Symptoms: The young larvae feed mainly on the lower surface of the leaves where they eat the leaf lamina avoiding larger veins. The upper surface may be left intact ("windowing"), or sometimes they puncture the leaves producing irregular holes. Fully-grown caterpillars devour the foliage completely, leaving only the main veins. Damage may extend to flowers and fruits.

Economic importance: *S. exigua* is mostly a pest of sugar beet in the U.S.A., Iraq and Syria, a major pest of cotton in Soviet Central Asia, Ethiopia and Central America; it seriously attacks lucerne and young maize in Egypt and in northern Sudan it is a menace to broad beans and lucerne.

Morphology: The moth is 10–14 mm long, and has a wing span about 25–30 mm. The fore wings are light grey with a small round, rust-coloured spot in the middle beyond which there is a second smaller kidney-shaped spot. The hind wings are white with dark brown veins and edges. The pupa is 10–12 mm long and its general colour is shining brown. The fully-grown caterpillar is about 30 mm long, its colour is light green with conspicuous stripes running along the sides of the body.

Similarities to other pests: *S. exigua* is closely related to the true army worm *Spodoptera exempta* with which it is very similar in appearance. It also resembles *Spodoptera (= Laphygma) latebrosa*, reported from Egypt on cotton.

Life cycle: The sexes attain maturity soon after emergence and then mate. The preoviposition period is one day in summer and extends to 3 days in wintertime in the Sudan. Eggs are laid in clusters on the lower surfaces of the leaves and the average per female is about 600. The incubation period is about 2–4 days and after hatching larvae disperse as they age and may march in bands to adjacent fields. The average larval period is about 11 days; pupation occurs in soil and the moth emerges in about 6 days. These periods are longer in winter, but no diapause has been noted.

Ecology: Light trap catches in Northeast Africa (Sudan) have indicated that the insect is active throughout the year. *S. exigua* is known to be migratory in temperate regions and has been collected in high-level traps.

Pest incidence has been reported to be affected by factors such as sowing date and abundance of weeds. Food type also affects the duration of development.

Natural enemies: Several Braconids *(Chelonus texanus, Disophrys lutea* and *Zelomorpha sudanensis)* have been reported to attack the immature stages of *S. exigua.* Two Tachinids *(Palexorista quadrizonula* and *Lespesia archippivora)* have also been found to parasitize *S. exigua.* One Eulophid, *Euplectrus laphygmae,* has been noted on larvae in the Sudan and two Ichneumonids have been recorded from Egypt.

Microbial agents pathogenic to this insect, such as bacteria, have been identified in the U.S.A.

Control: Clean cultivation and weeding are generally recommended as cultural practices. Cutting has been recommended when lucerne grown as fodder becomes infested.

Glandless strains of cotton have been reported to be more susceptible to attack by the pest.

Baits, as used for cut-worms, are successful for control of *S. exigua* caterpillars. The larvae can also be controlled by most contact insecticides and stomach poisons. Application of chemicals is recommended after the first appearance of damage symptoms. Dusting or spraying with DDT have proved effective. For spraying, DDT at a rate of 2 lb. per acre is recommended. Carbaryl also offers good control at a rate of 1.5 lb. a. i. in 20 gallons of water per acre. Hand spraying of maize in Nigeria by wettable carbaryl at the rate of about 2 lb. of 85 % active material per acre killed 90 % of the larvae. Dimethoate (32 % E.C.) used in trials at the rate of 0.4 lb. has given the best kill in lucerne fields in the Sudan, followed by endosulfan, malathion, carbaryl and formothion.

ULV (ultra-low-volume) spraying of various organophosphorous insecticides (malathion, azinphos-methyl, methyl-parathion, fenitrothion) is also effective according to experiences in the southern U.S.A. and in Iran.

Literature

AFIFY, A. M., M. H. EL KADY & F. N. ZAKI (1970): Biological studies on *Spodoptera (Laphygma) exigua* Hbn. in Egypt, with record of five larval parasites. Z. ang. Ent. **66,** 362–368.

BASHIR, M. O. & T. V. VENKATRAMAN (1968): Insect parasites complex of Berseem army worm *Spodoptera exigua* (Hb.) (Lepidoptera: Noctuidae). Entomophaga **13**, 151–158.

EL SARRAG, M.S.A. (1971): Studies on *Spodoptera exigua* HB. (Lepidoptera: Noctuidae). A pest of *Medicago sativa* L. (Berseem). M.Sc. (Thesis) University of Khartoum.

MUINI, M. & S. H. HODJAT (1971): A comparison between the effects of U-L-V and conventional methods of spraying on *Spodoptera exigua* (Hb.). Pl. Pests Dis. Res. Inst. Tehran. Techram CENTO Res. Proj. **2,** No 4: 34–37.

Author: E. El Khidir

Spodoptera exempta (Wlk.) (Fig. 187)

Synonym: *Laphygma exempta*

Common names: African armyworm, South African mystery worm etc.; Afrikanischer Heerwurm.

Geographical distribution: *S. exempta* occurs in Africa south of the Sahara, and in Asia (Yemens, Sri Lanka, Malaysia and Singapore), Australia (Queensland, New South Wales and Western), Hawaii, Indonesia (Java) and the Philippine Islands. (CIE Map no 53).

Fig. 187.   Maize plant, heavily infested and damaged by *Spodoptera exempta* (phot. EAAFRO, Moguga)

Host plants: These are predominantly grasses (Gramineae) and sedges (Cyperaceae). In E. Africa, any grass is a potential host plant. The most frequently attacked agricultural crops are: Maize (*Zea mays*); Finger millet (*Eleusine coracana*); Millet (*Sorghum* spp.); Rice (*Oryza sativa*); Wheat (*Triticum vulgare*); but Sugar cane (*Saccharum officinarum*), is only seldomly attacked.

The list probably reflects host availability rather than host preferences. In Queensland and Hawaii, sugar cane is frequently attacked. In Rhodesia and South Africa oats (*Avena sativa*) and barley (*Hordeum vulgare*) are attacked. Of the fodder and wild grasses, the following genera: *Cynodon, Chloris, Eragrostis, Pennisetum, Panicum, Urochloa* and *Brachiaria* are frequently attacked. In Queensland *Paspalum* sp. is a preferred species.

Symptoms: Armyworm larvae attack the leaf. Early instar (I–II) larvae scrape away the under surface of the leaf, leaving the transparent upper epidermis, thus giving a "window" effect. Later instars eat the complete thickness of the leaf starting at the margins and moving inwards. The leaf is left with a characteristic tattered appearance or laminae may be completely eaten leaving only the mid rib.

Economic importance: The economic effects of armyworms can result from: 1. Direct crop loss; 2. Loss of grazing lands; and 3. Possible direct toxic action of ingested larvae on cattle (this has been reported but not confirmed experimentally).

Armyworm larvae destroy the leaf thus reducing crop yield or causing complete crop loss. In rangeland the larvae compete directly for grasses with game, cattle, sheep and goats.

The degree of damage by armyworms varies from year to year. In E. Africa, a severe outbreak can cover over 6,000 m^2, with a density of up to 3,000 larvae/m^2, while in non-outbreak years larval density is often low and size of area negligible.

The economic importance of *S. exempta* can be attributed to 4 main factors:
1. The previously unpredictable occurrence of high concentrations of larvae over large areas.
2. The short life cycle (which results in a succession of generations in one season).
3. The first instars are inconspicuous, while the major damage occurs during the last instars.
4. Young plants are preferred.

Armyworms can produce devastating losses to maize crops. The 1954 famine in Central Province of Tanzania was attributed to heavy armyworm infestations associated with low rainfall. The degree of damage to crops depends on a) the stage of development of the crop; b) the climate prevailing at the time; and c) the density of armyworm present and area affected.

Maize crops beyond the 10 leaf stage (2–3 ft high) are unlikely to be attacked by armyworm. If the crop is more or less completely defoliated the farmer is likely to replant, in which case he risks a total failure if the rains fail.

Morphology:
a) Moth. The adult insect has a wing-span of about 25–35 mm. The fore-wings are pale, mottley-brown in males and uniform dark-brown in females. The hind-wings are white with the veins usually distinctly darker or partially smoky black.
b) Eggs. Small, almost spherical and slightly flattened (diameter 0.55 mm, height 0.42). Eggs are laid on leaves or sometimes on other surfaces, in masses of one to three layers thick. The female moth covers them with black hairs from her abdomen.
c) Larva. The caterpillars exhibit a marked colour variation, as a density dependent colouration or "phase change" similar to that in locusts occurs. After each moult, a new skin starts as an almost colourless 1st instar, becoming progressively greener, then darker with the growth of numerous black bristles. The darkening of the larvae is often associated with increasing density ("gregarious phase") which differs from the predominantly green or brown larvae growing singly ("solitary phase"). A common form is brown along the back and green along the sides and underside.
d) Pupa. The pupa which is found in the soil, averages some 17 mm long, and has a smooth, membraneous skin, at first greenish-brown, but later becoming darker brown and finally almost black.

Similarities to other pests: The word "Armyworm" describes the habits of the larvae of certain insect species which intermittently occur in such large "gregarious" numbers that they have to travel en masse from one feeding ground to another in search of food to complete their development. It has been applied to some 20 species representing nine genera.

Life cycle: The life cycle from egg to egg lasts approximately 22 $^1/_2$ days at 90 °F (32.2 °C) to 82 at 65 °F (18.3 °C) in the laboratory. In Tanzania under field conditions with an average temperature of 70 °F (26.1 °C), it lasts approximately 25 days, in Hawaii 27–43 and in Rhodesia 37–40 $^1/_2$.
a) Moths. Live on average from 7 days at 90 °F (32.2 °C) to 12 at 60 °F (15.6 °C) in the laboratory. The pre-oviposition period ranges from 2 days at 90 °F (32.2 °C) to 5 at 60 °F (15.6 °C); it can also be longer. In Kenya, the longevity of the female is 13 days and that of the male 12 days.
b) Larvae. Last from 6–8 days at 90 °F (32.2 °C) to 25–36 at 60 °F (15.6 °C) in the laboratory. Under field conditions they last 10–12 days in Zambia, 21 in Queensland, 14–21 in Java and Hawaii, and 18–24 in Transvaal.
In E. Africa, the larval stage lasts 14–21 days under outdoor conditions.
c) Pupae. Last from 10–15 days at 90 °F (32.2°C) to 43–55 at 65 °F (18.3 °C) in the laboratory. Lower temperatures tend to increase mortality. In the field the pupal period can last 9–11 days in Tanzania, 7–48 in Malawi, 10–12 in Rhodesia, 12–36 in Transvaal, 10 in Queensland and 8–14 in Hawaii.
d) Eggs. Incubate from 28–30 hours at 90 °F (32.2 °C) to 11 days at 50 °F (10.0 °C) in the laboratory. Under field conditions, incubation can last 3 days in Tanzania, 3–7 in Malawi, 1–7 in Transvaal and 3–4 in Java and Hawaii.
e) Diapause. No stage of the insect has been found to have a diapause.

Natural enemies: Include a large range of natural enemies varying from virus and bacteria to birds. The viruses, e. g. Nuclear Polyhedrosis and others sometimes act as a natural controlling factor during outbreaks of larvae, and also as a nuisance in laboratory cultures, disrupting experiments with the latter. Their use as biological control agents are currently under investigation.

Ecology: The most striking facet of the ecology of *S. exempta* is the sudden appearance of larvae in large numbers in widely separated areas. This characteristic has been attributed to migration of the moth which is most probably determined by wind direction. These migrations have been found to follow a more or less similar pattern year after year in Eastern and Southern Africa.

In E. Africa outbreaks usually occur first in East Central Tanzania during December or January, followed by subsequent ones at intervals of about a month moving further north. By January or February larval populations are to be found in northern Tanzania and southern Kenya and by February or March outbreaks may occur in Uganda. Moths sometimes continue to migrate northwards and outbreaks first appear in Ethiopia in March or April. The origin of the first infestations is, however, yet unknown.

In Southern Africa outbreaks sometimes occur first in Zambia, Rhodesia or Malawi during December or January, and move progressively further south to reach Transvaal by late February. Return movement is occasionally observed.

An alternative to migration is that moths occur in small populations in several areas during the whole year, but when climatic conditions improve the populations build up to outbreak proportions. More ecological studies are planned to elucidate this hypothesis.

The moths, in their wind determined migrations tend to move into zones of wind convergence where the resulting precipitation favours fresh vegetative growth. Temperature affects development rates, and in S. Africa at least 70 °F (21.1 °C) is necessary before an outbreak will occur, while in Malawi it is 65 °F (18.3 °C).

The studies of wind systems in E. Africa and the biogeography and ecology of *S. exempta* have resulted in the implementation of a forecasting service which is able to predict the occurrence of larval outbreaks in defined areas a week before they occur. A similar system is proposed for Ethiopia, and a grid network of light traps exists in S. Africa for internal forecasting purposes.

Control: The migratory nature of the moth, together with the short larval period, half of which is inconspicuous, makes effective control of armyworms a difficult proposition.

In areas in which the forecasting service is in operation, once a positive forecast is given, insecticide and spraying equipment should be made ready for immediate dispatch, and agricultural departments, through the agency of field and extension workers, should establish the area in which armyworm larvae are present. Once the area of infestation is established, the susceptibility of the crop to damage should be determined, bearing in mind the age of crop and density of larvae. Timely action is vital.

Sanitary methods. Most crops contain a number of graminaceous weeds. In the case of *Cynodon dactylon* and *Eleusine indica,* the larvae sometimes prefer the weed to the crop. There is therefore some advantage in leaving weeds until the larvae are fully-grown and can do no more damage. The risk is great, though.

Biological control. No method of biological control is as yet effective against armyworms. Work on the NPV virus as a biological control agent will hopefully rectify this. Sex-pheromone traps are being tested against the moths as another alternative. The effects of predators and parasites have not been reliable.

Chemical control. The only effective way to control an outbreak at the moment is by the use of insecticides.

The most useful insecticides have so far been: DDT, fenitrothion, tetrachlorvinphos, malathion, endosulfan and trichlorphon. As yet no resistance to insecticides has been detected in *S. exempta*. The most suitable methods and rates of application have been: 10 percent DDT dust applied by hand to individual plants, through the meshes of a small sack beaten with a stick, or from a tin with a perforated lid. The same material can be applied on a large scale by any mechanical dust applicator, at a rate of 13 kg per hectare (12 lbs. per acre). A minimum safety period of 2 weeks must elapse between applying this insecticide and harvesting or allowing livestock to feed. Safety periods for other insecticides are indicated below by a figure in brackets.

With standard crop-spraying machines applying diluted spray mixtures at 100–500 litres per hectare (8–40 gallons per acre), sprays can be prepared by adding the appropriate quantities of water to the following materials:

75 % DDT wettable powder at $1^1/_2$ kg. per hectare (20 oz per acre) (2 weeks), 25 % DDT miscible liquid at 4 litres per hectare (3 pints per acre) (2 weeks), 50 % malathion miscible liquid at 3 litres per hectare (2 pints per acre) (2 days), 80 % trichlorphon wettable powder at 300 grams

per hectare (4 oz per acre) (1 week), 35 % endosulfan (Thiodan) miscible liquid at $1^{1}/_{2}$ litres per hectare (1 pint per acre) (2 weeks).

Substantial improvements in speed and economy of operation and in reduced environmental contamination are now possible with ultralow-volume (U.L.V.) spraying methods, in which special concentrated and involatile formulations are applied without dilution as very fine sprays using the wind for distribution and for penetration of plant cover. Examples of U.L.V. spray-equipment already used successfully for armyworm control are a) the Turbair battery-operated electric hand-sprayer, capable of achieving an effective swath-width of 20 metres, and b) Sayer exhaust sprayer, mounted on a four-wheel-drive vehicle to utilize exhaust pressure to atomise and disperse the spray. It is capable of an effective swath-width of 100 metres. Appropriate formulations are 20 or 25 % DDT – U.L.V. at 1 litre per hectare ($^{3}/_{4}$ pint per acre) (2 weeks), technical malathion at $1^{1}/_{2}$ litres per hectare (1 pint per acre) (2 days), technical fenitrothion (Accothion, Sumithion) at $^{3}/_{4}$ litre per hectare ($^{1}/_{2}$ pint per acre) (2 weeks) and 40 % tetrachlorvinphos U.L.V. at $1^{1}/_{2}$ litres per hectare (1 pint per acre) (2 weeks).

With aircraft, U.L.V. spraying using such formulations will likewise be the method of choice in most cases. If rotary atomisers such as the Micronair are not available, boom-and-nozzle spray-gear can be used for U.L.V. spraying, selecting the smallest nozzle and the highest convenient operating pressure.

Certain insecticides, notably dieldrin and endrin, have been used and are known to be effective against armyworm, but are not recommended because of the poison hazard due to their high mammalian toxicity.

Literature

BROWN, E. S. (1962): The African Armyworm *Spodoptera exempta* (Walker) (Lepidoptera: Noctuidae). A review of the literature 57 pp. multigraph London Commonw. Inst. Ento.

BROWN, E. S. (1970): Control of the African Armyworm, *Spodoptera exempta* (Walk.) – an appreciation of the problem. E. Afr. Agric. For. J. **35**, 237–245.

BROWN, E. S. & C. F. DEWHURST (in preparation): The genus *Spodoptera* in Africa and the Near East.

BROWN, E. S. & A. K. A. MOHAMED (1971 d): The relation between simulated armyworm damage and crop-loss in maize and sorghum. E. Afr. Agric. For. J. **37**, 237–57.

BROWN, E. S. & P. O. ODIYO (1968 c): The rate of feeding of the American armyworm, *Spodoptera exempta* (Walk.) and its significance for control operations. E. Afr. Agric. For. J. **33**, 245–56.

Authors: P. O. Odiyo and P. D. Stickler

Spodoptera frugiperda (J. E. Smith) (Plate 44 c, d)

Synonym: *Laphygma frugiperda*

Common names: Fall armyworm; Amerikanischer Heerwurm; Gusano cogollero.

Geographical distribution: *S. frugiperda* occurs in the Americas. It overwinters only in tropical or subtropical regions, but the moths disperse into temperate regions during the growing seasons. In the United States, it overwinters in Florida and Texas, and by fall infestations may extend into Canada. Therefore, it was given the name "fall armyworm". CIE Map no 68.

Host plants: Larvae attack many plant species, including corn, sorghum, and rice.

Symptoms: Young larvae in corn feed on the upper leaf surface, without penetrating the leaf. The remaining lower epidermis is transparent, and is sometimes called "window pane" feeding. The growth stage of the host plant affects the amount and kind of damage caused by larvae. For example, if corn plants are attacked when they are small, larvae may penetrate to the bud and the plants may be killed. Corn is the most susceptible to yield reduction by defoliation when it is small and again just before the tassels appear. When the tassels emerge from the whorl of leaves, larvae lose their protective retreat, and move down the plant and bore into the ears. If corn plants are nearing maturity and ears are present, larvae feed on the ears but not the foliage.

Economic importance: *S. frugiperda* is one of the most destructive insect pests of corn in the Americas. It reduces the crop value by 1) destruction of foliage, 2) destruction of grain, 3) destruction of the apical growing point resulting in killing or stunting of the plant, 4) destruction of flowering parts resulting in incomplete fertilization, 5) weakening of plant stems, and 6) lowering the quality of food products.

Morphology: Adults of *S. frugiperda* are grey with black and white markings, and have a wing-span of 35 mm on the average. Young larvae are light coloured with dark head capsules and a prominent dark cervical shield. As they grow, dark lateral stripes develop.

Similarities to other pests: A contrasting light coloured inverted "Y" on the head capsule of the larva separates this species from other species commonly found with it in the field.

Life cycle and ecology: Eggs are deposited on many surfaces, including plants, fences, and buildings. Egg masses are usually more than one layer deep, and are covered with scales from the moths' abdomen. Freshly deposited eggs are green, but become brown prior to eclosion. Eggs hatch in about 5 days.

Larval behaviour is important in selection of a feeding site on the host and therefore in the resulting damage. Newly emerged larvae are positively phototactic and move to the highest part of the plant or leaf. Light wind stimulates them to drop on silken threads, and many are blown to nearby plants. Feeding sites are selected within 24 hours after eclosion.

As the larvae develop, they become negatively phototactic and move downward into the whorl of leaves of corn or sorghum. There are 6 larval instars, and under ideal conditions the larval stage is completed in 12 days.

Mature larvae leave the plants and burrow into the soil. Pupal chambers are formed near the soil surface. The pupal stage lasts about 9 days.

Adult *S. frugiperda* emerge and feed on nectar of various plants. They are nocturnal, and remain hidden in plants during the day. They are attracted to lights during the night, and are easily caught in light traps. Eggs are laid after 3 days, and adults live for about 13 days.

Natural enemies: Many fly and wasp parasites have been recorded. Also birds, frogs, and lizards feed on adults and larvae. Outbreaks of diseases of larvae sometimes occur. Unfortunately, no practices have been developed to increase the prevalence of these biological factors.

Control:

Resistance of crops. Resistance to larval feeding damage has been found in some strains of corn, millet, and bermudagrass, but at this time, no resistant varieties have been marketed. Healthy plants are more tolerant to defoliation and are less likely to be killed by larvae. Fertilization, irrigation, and early planting all are important in reduction of plant damage.

Chemical control. During times of outbreaks, chemical control programs are needed. In general, chemicals should be applied as soon as possible after the outbreak has been detected. For foliage protection of corn, sprays should be directed downward into the whorl of leaves. Sprayers should deliver at least 5 gallons of water for ground equipment. For ear protection, applications may be necessary at about 2-day intervals. In sorghum, treatments should be made when 2–3 or more larvae are found in each plant. A number of chemicals have been used for controlling *S. frugiperda*, and include carbaryl, malathion, methyl-parathion, parathion, trichlorfon, toxaphene, naled and methomyl.

32*

Literature

JANES, M. J. & G. L. GREENE (1969): Control of fall armyworms and corn earworms on sweet corn ears in central and south Florida. J. Econ. Entomol. **62**, (3), 1031–1033.
LUGINBILL, P. (1928): The fall armyworm. U.S. Dept. Agr. Techn. Bull. **34**, 91 pp.
MORRILL, W. L. & G. L. GREENE (1973): Distribution of fall armyworm larvae. I. Regions of field corn plants infested by larvae. Environm. Entomol. **2** (2), 195–198.
MORRILL, W. L. & G. L. GREENE (1973): Distribution of fall armyworm larvae. 2. Influence of biology and behaviour of larvae on selection of feeding sites. Environm. Entomol. **2** (3), 415–418.

Author: W. L. Morrill

Spodoptera littoralis (Boisd.) (Plate 45 a, b)

Synonym: *Prodenia litura* (part.)[1]

Common names: (Egyptian) cotton leafworm; Ägyptischer Baumwollwurm; Ver du cotonnier; Rosquilla negra.

Geographical distribution: According to the revised CIE distribution map of pests no 232 (June 1967), this species occurs in southern Europe, the Mediterranean islands, Africa, the islands of the eastern and western coasts of Africa, and in south-western parts of Asia as far east as Iran and Bahrain. In Egypt in particular this species occurs throughout the country.

Host plants: As many as 73 host plants have been recorded for this species in Egypt, 16 of which serve as hosts for oviposition and 45 as hosts for oviposition and feeding. Among the important host plants are cotton, clover, alfalfa, maize, potato, tomato, sweet potato, okra, cowpea, peanut, cabbage, pepper, tobacco, soya bean, castor, beet, onion, egg plant, rice, melon and other cucurbits, fruits including citrus, grape, fig, banana, apple and plum. However, in different countries the attractiveness of host plants to *S. littoralis* varies as also does the damage caused.

Symptoms: The damage caused by this pest is mainly because of defoliation since the caterpillar is principally a leaf-feeder; it also has the habit of boring into and feeding in the interior of fruits such as tomato, young melon and pepper which are near to or rest on the soil. In clover and alfalfa, the larvae which remain in the field after harvest attack the young buds and hinder the development of the next crop. In cotton the young larvae feed on the lower sides of leaves, and strip away the tissues; the dead leaf tissue becomes crisp and pale brown in colour. The dead leaves fall off and in a heavily infested field the ground below the plants is littered with fallen leaves or portions of leaves. Wherever the lower tissue of a leaf has been eaten away the light shines through the white, translucent upper epidermis in spots and patches imparting a distinctive speckled appearance to the foliage. After the third moult the larvae eat holes through the leaves, and later still the entire tissue is eaten away leaving the thick, main veins. The tissues around the edges of the holes dry up and acquire a pale brown colour. At this stage many larvae seek shelter from the sun within the epicalyces of the flower buds. As the larvae advance in age they become more destructive attacking buds and green bolls which fall on the ground and they may cause complete defoliation of the plant. A noticeable feature of a severe infestation is the condition of the foliage, which is riddled with holes or is skeletonised and either brown or turning brown. In addition there is a characteristic acrid or warm sour smell of the infested field.

---

[1] Previously misidentified as *Prodenia litura* which is the Asiatic species now known as *Spodoptera litura* which occurs in India, South-East Asia, Australia and Australasian Islands (see p. 503).

Economic importance: *S. littoralis* is a highly polyphagous species and is considered to be a major pest of great economic importance in many countries since it attacks a multitude of host plants and inflicts heavy losses on foddercrops, truck crops and in particular on industrial or cash crops such as cotton and sugar beet. In Egypt the annual losses due to its ravages may amount to 20 to 40 million Egyptian pounds. This is additional to costs incurred in control campaigns which amount to ten million pounds or more every year.

Morphology: Egg. Spherical and slightly flattened, about 0.5 mm in diameter and 0.3 mm in height; the egg shell is sculptured with numerous vertical and horizontal ridges or ribs; its colour is at first pearly white or yellowish green with an iridescent lustre but later, prior to hatching, changes to blackish.

Larva. When newly hatched greenish in colour with a shining black head and thoracic plate; body with conspicuous black tubercles each bearing a dark coloured long hair. Upon moulting the colour changes into olive green or dark grey or brown, and as the larva becomes older it acquires certain characteristics, i.e. it bears three pale yellowish, longitudinal lines (one median dorsal and two lateral) running along the body and a dark green broad band on each of the sides. In addition the first and eighth abdominal segments each bear two distinct large black triangular dots on either side. Meso- and metathorax each bear two black spots (with yellow edges) on either side. The lower surface of the body is green or yellowish-white in colour. The full grown larva varies from 30 to 50 mm in length.

Pupa. Brown in colour and varies from 15 to 20 mm in length and about 5 mm in width, and bears two small, slightly curved spines on its tip.

Moth. Brownish-grey in colour; body length 15–20 mm with a wing expanse of 30–40 mm. The fore wings are brown with longitudinal, transverse and oblique lines of a pale yellowish colour which are more distinct in the male. Near the outer edge of the wing are short yellowish bands alternating with brown ones. There are also two bluish areas, a large one at the tip of the wing and a smaller one near the base, these being less distinct in the female. The rear wings are pearly-white with greyish-brown outer margins and with dark lines running along the veins.

Life cycle: Under Egyptian conditions, the moth becomes sexually mature about two days after emergence. Mating then takes place during the night followed either immediately or within 24 to 48 hours by oviposition.

The moth hides during the day in the soil or under fallen leaves and becomes active at night, feeding and ovipositing particularly in the early morning before sunrise. Oviposition continues for about four days in the summer and for about ten days towards the end of the autumn. The female lays 1,000–1,500 eggs or more in batches or clusters of 300–600 (or more) at a time. Each female lays 3 to 7 batches, the first batch containing as a rule the highest number of eggs. The eggs are laid in one or more layers, usually on the underside of leaves of the host plant and covered with hair-like scales from the body of the female. The incubation period lasts 2–3 days in summer and 15–22 days in winter. The hatching larvae remain in groups close to the ovipositional site and feed for some time on the epidermis of leaves; later they tend to disperse on the surface of the leaf. Their movement from one plant to another is effected by swinging on silken threads which they secrete and fasten to the edge of the leaf. As the larvae grow older (3rd or 4th instar) they fall on the soil, hide during the day and climb the host plant at night for feeding. The larva moults five times and passes through six larval instars, the last being the longest and most voracious. Larval development is completed in 12 days at 29–35 °C, 2–3 weeks at 24–28 °C and 30 days at 18–20 °C. When ready to pupate, the larva seeks a suitable site in the soil at a depth of 2–5 cm. The pupal period lasts 7–8 days at 23–30 °C and 14 days at 18–20 °C. The moth lives on the average 4–10 days during the summer and there is no obligatory period of winter diapause.

Ecology: This species favours a warm climate. In Egypt breeding is continuous all the year round, with 7 generations each year. Of these, four generations occur on clover (*Trifolium alexandrinum*) covering the autumn-spring period (September–May). The two succeeding generations occur principally on cotton in June and July while the 7th generation occurs in August on cotton, alfalfa and maize.

Newly irrigated fields are very attractive to ovipositing females. The heaviest infestation in a crop takes place 3 days after it is irrigated. Soils which have a water content of 20 % are highly preferred for pupation as well as for adult emergence.

Natural enemies: Parasites. Among the larval parasites in Egypt are the tachinid flies, *Tachina larvarum* which is the most important parasite, *Actia aegyptia* and *A. palpalis*. Other less important parasites (hymenopterous) include *Eulimneria xanthostoma, Zele chlorophthalma, Z. nigricornis* and *Barylypa humeralis*. *Conomorium eremita* is a chalcid parasite of the pupa. *Trichogramma evanescens* is an egg parasite.

In addition to the above mentioned indigenous parasites there are some imported parasites in Egypt e.g. the egg parasites *Telenomus neuvaii* and *T. spodopterae* (Scelionidae), the larval parasites *Actia nigritula* and the braconid wasp *Microplitis demolitor*.

In other countries the following tachinid larval parasites occur: *Sturmia inconspicua* in the Sudan; *Sturmia zonata* and *Wagneria* sp. in Malawi. In the latter country *Metopius discolor* (Ichneumonidae) also occurs as a larval parasite.

Predators. Various beetles have been recorded, namely *Coccinella undecimpunctata* (Coccinellidae), as a predator on eggs and young larvae; *Paederus alfierii* (Staphylinidae), a predator on eggs; and *Calosoma chlorostictum chlorostictum* (Carabidae).

Other predators include *Chrysopa vulgaris* (Neuroptera), *Labidura riparia* (Dermaptera), wasps (especially *Polistes gallica, Ammophila tydei*) mantids, ants, spiders etc.

A polyhedrosis virus disease is of common occurrence among larval populations of *S. littoralis;* also the scorching heat of the sun in many countries kills large numbers of egg masses and neonate larvae.

Control:

Destruction of weeds. Wild host plants may harbour developing larvae that migrate to cotton fields.

Tilling and ploughing. This is carried out to allow existing larvae to be killed through exposure to the sun.

Cessation of irrigation. The irrigation of clover fields after May 10th is prohibited by law to deny favourable breeding conditions for *Spodoptera* during the spring.

Hand-collection and burning of egg masses. This is intensified in June and July when parasites and predators are most active.

Biological control. Parasites and predators of *Spodoptera* certainly play a significant role in killing appreciable numbers of this species. A mortality of 32 % during the summer months and as high as 75 % among the population of the winter brood has been reported. The introduction of parasites of *Spodoptera* (e. g. *Telenomus* spp.) may also be advocated, but in Egypt these exotic parasites have proved of no great practical value as they fail to establish themselves in numbers large enough to be effective biological control agents. In Egypt the role of native parasites and predators is enhanced by hand-picking of egg masses and less use of insecticides in the early season. Other biotic control agents include the use of polyhedrosis virus for infecting the larvae in the field. The virus has proved to be highly potent; in field trials however, control was insufficient to be considered of likely economic value. The use of *Bacillus thuringiensis* as a microbial control agent is also being investigated in Egypt and other countries. More recently the sex pheromone of *S. littoralis* has been extracted, identified and synthesized and is now in use in Cyprus as an attractant for males in bait stations (D. Campion: personal communication).

Chemical control. The use of insecticides is often inevitable in spite of collecting egg masses by hand, the activities of natural enemies and other factors. The general trend in recent years is to limit the extensive use of pesticides through the integration of two or more methods of control (e. g. entomopathogens, parasites and predators, antifeedants, sex pheromones, sterilization etc.). On cotton plants the following organo-phosphorous insecticides may be used for control: Phosalone

(1.50 l/acre), wettablé chlorpyrifos (Dursban) 25 % (2 kg/acre), methamidophos (Monitor) (1 l/acre) and leptophos (Phosvel (2.25 l/acre).

On clover seedlings, the cotton leaf worm is treated either with spray applications of tetrachlorvinphos (2 kg/acre) or dusting with cotton dust (10–12 kg/acre). Tetrachlorvinphos 50 % (2 l/acre), Falxon 50 % (2 l/acre), Nolotran (106 l/acre) are also recommended for control of cotton leaf worm in other field crops including vegetables.

Literature

ABUL-NASR, S. (1956): Polyhedrosis-virus disease on the cotton leaf-worm *Prodenia litura* F. Bull. Soc. Ent. Egypte **40**, 321–332.

BISHARA, I. (1934): The Cotton Worm, Prodenia litura F., in Egypt. Bull. Soc. Entom. Egypte **18**, 288–420.

KAMAL, M. (1951): The Biological Control of the Cotton Leaf-Worm (*Prodenia litura* F.) in Egypt. Bull. Soc. Fouad 1er Ent. **35**, 221–270.

MOUSSA, A. M., M. A. ZAHER & F. KOTBY (1960): Abundance of the cotton leaf-worm *Prodenia litura* F. in relation to host plants. Bull. Soc. ent. Egypte **44**, 241–251.

NASR, E. A. N., M. A. MOUSSA & S. HASSAN (1960): Soil moisture in relation to pupation and moth emergence of the cotton leaf-worm *Prodenia litura* F. Bull. Soc. ent. Egypte **44**, 377–382.

PEARSON, E. O. (1958): The Insect Pests of Cotton in Tropical Africa. Empire Cotton Growing Corporation & Commonwealth Insitute of Entomology, London.

RIVNAY, E. (1962): Field Crop Pests in the Near East. Monographiae Biologicae, Dr. W. Junk, Den Haag.

SCHMUTTERER, H. (1969): Pests of Crops in Northeast and Central Africa. Gustav Fischer Verlag, Stuttgart & Portland.

TALHOUK, A.M.S. (1969): Insects and Mites Injurious to Crops in Middle Eastern Countries. Monogr. z. Angew. Entom. Paul Parey, Hamburg–Berlin.

WILLCOCKS, F. C. & S. BAHGAT (1937): The insect and related pests of Egypt. Vol **1**, Part 2, 792 pp., Cairo, Roy. Agric. Soc. Egypt.

Author: Mahmoud Hafez

Spodoptera litura (F.) (Fig. 188)

Common names: Tobacco caterpillar, Common cutworm; Asiatischer Baumwollwurm.

Geographical distribution: The insect has been reported from most of Asia including India, Burma, Ceylon, Thailand, Philippines, China, Japan, and Korea. It is distributed southward to Australia and throughout most of the Indian ocean. For a long time it has been confused with *S. littoralis* (see p. 500). CIE Map no 61 (revised).

Host plants: The insect is truly polyphagous and is reported to attack many species of crops. The important crops attacked are tobacco, rice, tomato, castor, cauliflower and lucerne. The insect has also been reported as a minor pest of potato, pepper, onion, egg-plant, water-melon, banana, okra, pigeon pea, Indian bean, lettuce, papaya, sweet potato, soybean, groundnut, mulberry, maize, turmeric, *Colocasia, Sesamum,* clover, *Eucalyptus, Citrus* etc. It has also been reported to occur on a number of weeds such as *Eclipta alba, Amaranthus spinosus, Portulaca quadrifida, Zinnia elegans,* and *Chenopodium amaranticolor.*

Symptoms: In India, the pest causes serious damage to tobacco, cauliflower, castor and lucerne. Tobacco and cauliflower leaves are fleshy and the young larvae nibble the leaf from the lower surface leaving the upper surface intact. In late instars they become distributed on other leaves in which they chew big holes. In crops like castor and lucerne, the early instars nibble holes in leaves and late larval instars defoliate the plants. The caterpillar also causes damage as a cutworm by cutting tender tobacco plants at ground level; it then hides in the soil near the plant during the day hours. In severe outbreaks the pest causes widespread defoliation of crops.

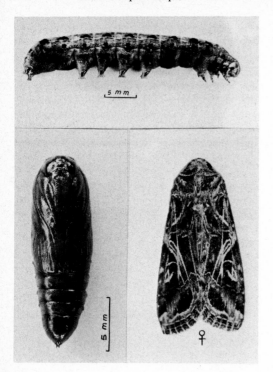

Fig. 188. Larva, pupa and adult moth of *Spodoptera litura* (phot. R. C. Patel)

Economic importance: In India, 3–17 % of young tobacco plants are damaged by this pest. When tobacco plants are infested with 2, 4 and 8 larvae per plant, the reduction in yield has been recorded as 23, 44 and 50 % respectively. In groundnut, the damage by this pest has resulted in 4 to 37 % loss of the crop. Leaf injury to tobacco in Sumatra has been estimated at 33 %. It is considered as a serious pest of mulberry in Taiwan and rice in the Philippines.

Morphology: The eggs are round and cream-yellow to greenish in colour, measuring 0.51 mm in diameter. The chorion is sculptured with ridges converging at the apex of the egg. The young larvae are green with black patches on each side of the first and last abdominal segments. In late instars, the larvae are dirty brown with five thin orange lines along the length of the body, two on each side and one in mid-dorsal position. Each segment has a black spot laterally and a triangular black patch in the dorsolateral position. These black spots and patches are very useful diagnostic criteria. The fully grown larvae are plump measuring 30 to 40 mm in length and 5 to 7 mm in diameter. The pupae are lustrous reddish brown. The adults measure 32 to 38 mm in wing span. In males, the forewings and thorax are brownish with five light brown strips, whereas in females these areas have narrow streaks of light brown scales. In general, the males are covered with brighter patches of light brown scales when compared to the females. The hind wings are membraneous white and have a margin with a brown border.

Life cycle: The eggs are laid in groups of 50 to 300 on the undersurface of leaves and hatch in 3 to 4 days. A female lays from 1,500–2,500 eggs in the adult life of about 8 days. In cauliflower and tobacco, the larvae in the first three instars feed on the same leaf and only move to adjacent leaves after completely eating the leaf away. In later instars, they become solitary and are distributed among adjacent plants. The larvae complete their development in 13–19 days and then enter the soil to prepare an earthen cell in which they pupate. The pupal period varies from 6–10 days depending upon the temperature. The pest breeds throughout the year, if the host is available. In India, three main generations, from June to September, are completed on tobacco, cauliflower and castor. Subsequently the insect continues to breed on tomatoes, lucerne and other host plants. In April and May, the pest is present very sporadically due to high temperatures and the lack of host plants.

Natural enemies: There is no cannibalism in this species during the early instars. In late instars however, if there is a shortage of food or a mixture of different instars, cannibalism is common. The larvae have been found to succumb to protozoan, virus, fungal, and bacterial diseases.

Several predators and ectoparasitic Hymenoptera have been recorded in various parts of Asia, but none of them has so far been used for biological control measures.

Control: During the early stages of infestation, when the larvae are feeding on leaves in masses, infested leaves should be collected and destroyed. Application of 0.5 % fentin hydroxide or 0.2 % triphenyl tin acetate or 0.2 % Brestanol can give 90 % protection from the pest. Among insecticides, phosphamidon 0.03 %, endosulfan 0.05 %, carbaryl 0.22 %, parathion-methyl 0.025 % and monocrotophos 0.04 % have been shown to be very effective. Phoxim 1 %, quinalphos (Bayrusil) 0.5 %, chlorpyrifos 0.5 %, chlordimeform 0.25 % and methomyl 0.25 % have shown 100 % ovicidal acitivity.

Literature

CHARI, M. S. & N. G. PATEL (1972): Efficacy of some newer insecticides against the tobacco leaf eating caterpillar, *Spodoptera litura* (Fab.) Indian J. Ent. **34** (3), 261–262.
PATEL, R. C., J. C. PATEL & J. K. PATEL (1973): Biology and mass breeding of the tobacco caterpillar, *Spodoptera litura* (F.). Israel J. Ent. **8**, 131–142.
RAO, R.S.N. & B. G. JOSHI (1973): Chemical control of *Prodenia litura* (F.) in flue cured virginia tobacco nurseries of Andhra Pradesh. Pesticides **7** (3), 20–21.
VERMA, J. P. & P. C. JAIN (1972): Efficacy of triphenyl tin acetate as a crop protectant for some lepidopterous pests. Indian J. Agric. Sci. **42** (6), 529–531.

Author: R. C. Patel

Trichoplusia ni (Hb.) (Fig. 189 and plate 45 c, d)

Common names: Cabbage looper; Amerikanische Gemüseeule; Falso gusano medidor.

Geographical distribution: *T. ni* has a very wide distribution in the tropics and subtropics of the New and Old world but also occurs in climatically favourable areas outside these regions (U.S.A., Mediterranean basin). CIE Map no 328.

Host plants: Cabbage, cole, collard, cauliflower, broccoli, tobacco, lettuce, beans, soybeans, cotton, tomato, spinach, melons, pea, parsnip, turnip, celery, cucumbers, kale, potatoes, mustard, radish, rutabago, sweet potatoes, lambsquarters (*Chenopodium*). Collards and cotton were preferred by ovipositing moths to broccoli, cauliflower or cabbage in northern Mississippi.

Symptoms: The larvae feed on the leaves of host plants riddling them with holes of irregular shape and size. On cabbage they eat into the heads. Parting the leaves large frass pellets can be found. The larvae remove considerable quantities of leaf tissue interfering with the plants' growth and marketability.

Economic importance: *T. ni* is throughout its range the most serious pest on cruciferous crops, and in Nicaragua on tobacco. On cotton in Nicaragua (in many respects representative for Central America) *T. ni* appears in mid to late season but seldomly reaches pest status. In late season its action, as other defoliators', can be beneficial: looper defoliation opens the thick lush cotton stands improving aeration and light penetration which lowers humidity, enhances boll maturation and attenuates boll rot. The defoliated crop can easier be hand-picked. Where harvest is mechanical and preceded by chemical defoliation, looper infestation may increase lint contamination. Damaged leaves are less affected by the chemical defoliant, stay on the plants and are stripped off together with the lint. In the U.S.A., *T. ni* is a secondary pest on cotton. On California cabbage it is a pest of summer and early autumn, and in Canada of late-season crucifers.

Fig. 189.   Cotton leaf, damaged by larvae of *Trichoplusia ni* (phot. H. Schmutterer)

Morphology: Eggs. greenish-white, round, deposited singly. Larvae. General color green, the back suffused with whitish. Thin white line along body sides, two white lines near the middle line of the back. 3 pairs of true legs and 3 pairs of prolegs. Body tapers to the head. Looping movement, body humped up in median region. Adult. Dark-brown moth with silvery spot resembling an "8" in the middle of each front wing.

Similarities to other pests: *T. ni* larvae are very similar in appearance to those of *Pseudoplusia includens*.

Life cycle: Eggs are deposited singly on the underside of host plant leaves, on cotton within the upper half of the plant. Five larval instars. Pupation occurs on a leaf often near the plant base or on a fallen leaf. The chrysalis is formed within a white silken cocoon. Developmental times vary with ambient temperatures; at 27 °C the following average numbers of days are required to complete the respective instars (laboratory data): L_1–3.5; L_2–5.5; L_3–6.9; L_4–8.6; L_5–10.9; prepupa–3.0; pupa–14.9; adult–21.4 days. Eggs hatch after 2–3 days.
Diapause has not been found in *T. ni*. In temperate zones larval activity continues at transitory subfreezing temperatures. 10–13 °C is the minimum average temperature for development. Flight and mating are curtailed below 16 °C.

Ecology: *T. ni* is a tropical/subtropical insect. Overwintering in cold regions is not successful. Where average winter temperatures are below 10 °C no adult activity occurs in winter, and populations do not reach significant levels until mid-summer. In zones of 10–16 °C avg. winter temperatures, adult activity is very sporadic, increases sharply in spring and continues until fall. In zones of 16 °C winter temperature adult activity is significant, and continuous reproduction and development occur throughout the year. Therefore *T. ni* overwinters in the U.S.A. only in southern states, and migration northward follows the advancing 16 °C temperature zone. *T. ni* is thus a late-season pest in colder northern or inland areas of the North American subcontinent. Larval populations peak in September on cabbage in southern California. In North Carolina 5 generations occur on collard, the 5th is small and heavily decimated by cold weather. On California cotton there are 3 distinct summer generations. Light trap records indicate the pest's phenology in Nicaragua: catches increase as of October and peak in January–February, then decline into April. There is very low *T. ni* incidence during May through September.

Natural enemies: *T. ni* is attacked by a wide array of natural enemies which have paramount importance in population regulation. Predators: *Chrysopa;* Coccinellidae, Carabidae, *Collops vittatus* (Coleoptera); *Orius, Geocoris, Nabis* spp., Reduviidae (Heteroptera); spiders and Gryllidae. Parasites: *Voria ruralis, Eucelatoria armigera* (Tachinidae); *Microplitis brassicae, Trichogramma* spp., *Chelonus texanus* (Braconidae); *Hyposoter exiguae* (Ichneumonidae); *Copidosoma truncatellum* (Encyrtidae); *Brachymeria ovata, Patrocloides montanus, Winthemia* sp.. Pathogens: Nuclear polyhedrosis virus (NPV) is often a primary mortality factor, especially in large larvae of late-season generations. The virus occurs naturally in the soil and on plants in most crop areas. Virus epizootics greatly reduce periodically *T. ni* populations, but often only at peak host densities when most of the damage to the crop is done.

Control:

Cultural practices. *T. ni* populations, like other Noctuids', tend to increase at new moon and to decline at full moon periods. Crop planting dates can be chosen so that the most susceptible crop stage falls as favourably as possible between two new-moon-induced peaks of oviposition and small-larvae activity (see also *Heliothis zea*).

Biological/integrated control. Natural enemies play the most important role in population regulation. *T. ni* infestations often erupt after use of broadly toxic insecticides which reduce the antagonist fauna. The pest, free of its enemies, resurges to damaging levels. Biological control therefore consists of promotion and replenishment of predators and parasites. Refrain as long as justifiable from use of broadspectrum materials; mass releases of *Trichogramma* (proven effective on cole crops) and *Chrysopa;* attract predators to fields by food sprays (see *Heliothis zea,* p. 486); provide food base for antagonists through inoculative releases of pests, e.g. *T. ni* eggs on cabbage prior to *Trichogramma* liberations.

Insecticide applications must be based on economic injury levels indicated by field scouting. For cabbage this level lies currently at 0.5 larva/plant, for cauliflower at 0.6–1.0 larva/plant in the U.S.A. Cotton in Nicaragua tolerates 20 % defoliation during critical fruit formation, and 50 % before and thereafter. When artificial control becomes unavoidable selective materials should be used. The high susceptibility of *T. ni* to NPV and *Bacillus thuringiensis* (Bt) preparations is of great advantage. They are more effective than chemical insecticides against medium and large larvae. On cabbage several foliar applications of 1.5 x 10^{12} polyhedra/ha, or soil treatments of 7.5 x 10^{12} polyhedra/ha give excellent control. So do Bt/HD–1 formulations, e. g. Thuricide, at 1.1, 2.2 or 4.5 x 10^9 International Units, Thuricide 90 TS at 2 l in 100 gal/acre, and Dipel at 1 lb/acre. The pathogens used alone or in combination with *Trichogramma* releases can make chemical control unnecessary. NPV and Bt can be applied right up to harvest (no residue problems). The virus can be collected in the field (diseased larvae) and applied during early stages of population increase to prevent major outbreaks: 10 larval equivalents (mature virus-killed larvae) per acre. Often the virus is self-perpetuating, and one application provides adequate population suppression for the remainder of the growing season.

Traps baited with blacklight (BL) and looper sex pheromone (looplure, cis-7-dodecen-1-ol-acetate) may be effective in suppression of the pest on smaller fields or on shade-grown tobacco. An efficient trap type (electric grid, screen cage or maze trap) must be employed and the right spacing ensured: 60–106 m for BL traps, not less than 244 m for lure traps. Phenylacetaldehyde 10 % in diethyl phthalate + looplure increases total catch. The lure must be protected against olar and BL radiation.

Chemical control. a) Insecticides. – *T. ni* is quite difficult to control chemically. Many insecticides are registered for use against this insect but frequently fail to give acceptable economic control. Methomyl (Lannate), naled, mevinphos, phosvel, methamidophos (Monitor), chlordimeform (may be phytotoxic) on cole crops. Endosulfan, toxaphene + methyl-parathion have sometimes failed in the U.S.A.. On cotton in Nicaragua, toxaphene-DDT (4–2) at 5.4–8.1 l/ha, or methomyl 160–240 g + methyl parathion 1.4 l/ha are recommended. Systemic disulfoton in tobacco as side dress and band treatment at and after transplanting, respectively, gives some control.

b) Prognosis. – Light traps with or without pheromone are effective survey tools for estimating generations and forecasting. However, factors other than local population densities may influence trap catches: time of day, rainfall, pheromone evaporation and dispersion, disease, lunar phase. Moon phase does not affect catches when BL traps are baited with pheromone.

Resistance. Resistance has developed in many areas toward a wide range of insecticides including DDT, parathion and other organophosphates, and carbaryl. Methomyl resistance is currently developing in the U.S.A.

Literature

DULMAGE, H. T., D. A. WOLFENBARGER, J. J. LUKEFAHR & J. A. CORREA (1971): Field tests with the HD-1 formulation of the gamma-endotoxin of *Bacillus thuringiensis* against the cabbage looper on cabbage. J. Econ. Ent. **64**, 1421–1422.

EHLER, L. E. (1972): Natural biological control of cabbage looper populations on cotton the San Joaquín Valley of California. Ph. D.-Dissertation, University of California, Berkeley, USA.

EHLER, L. E., K. G. EVELEENS & R. VAN DEN BOSCH (1973): An evaluation of some natural enemies of cabbage looper on cotton in California. Environm. Ent. **2**, 1009–1015.

FALCON, L. A. (1971): Microbial control as a tool in integrated control programs. In: HUFFAKER, C. B. (ed.); Biological Control. Plenum Press, New York, pp. 346–364.

FALCON, L. A. & R. DAXL (1973): Report to the government of Nicaragua on the integrated control of cotton pests NIC/70/002/AGP. Food and Agriculture Organization, Rome.

KISHABA, A. N., W. W. WOLF, H. H. TABA, A. F. HOWLAND & T. GIBSON (1970): Light and synthetic pheromone as attractants for male cabbage loopers. J. Econ. Ent. **64**, 1417–1420.

KILLENEN, R. G. & R. W. OST (1971): Pheromone-maze trap for cabbage looper moths. J. Econ. Ent. **64**, 310–311.

OATMAN, E. R. & G. R. PLATNER (1969): An ecological study on insect populations on cabbage in southern California. Hilgardia **40**, 1–40.

Author: R. Daxl

Other injurious Lepidoptera (Figs. 190–193):

Phyllocnistis citrella Staint., Citrus leaf miner (Citrusminiermotte). Occurs in the tropical regions of Asia and Africa (CIE Map no 274). Larvae mine in young leaves of *Citrus* spp.

Bucculatrix thurberiella Busck, Cotton leaf perforator (Baumwollzwergwickler) and related species attack leaves and flower buds of cotton in the southern parts of the USA, in tropical Central America and in Australia. Chemical control of caterpillars with trichlorphon, azinphos-ethyl and parathion.

Leucoptera spp., Coffee leaf miners (Kaffeeminiermotten). Members of this genus occur in various parts of the African tropics as important leaf pests of coffee. *L. meyricki* Ghesq. (East African coffee leaf miner, Ostafrikanische Kaffeeminiermotte) is at present the main coffee pest in Kenya, while *L. caffeina* Washb. (Central African coffee leaf miner, Zentralafrikanische Kaffeeminiermotte) produces epidemics particularly in the Kilimanjaro region. *L. coma* Ghesq. affects Robusta coffee in Central Africa (Zaire). Control: Spraying with parathion, fenitrothion and fenthion.

Prays spp. *P. citri* Mill. (Citrus flower moth, Citrusmotte) feeds on citrus flowers and on the fruit rind in the mediterranean region, in South and South East Asia and in Australia. *P. endocarpa* Meyr. (Citrus rind borer) feeds in tropical Asia (India, Indonesia) exclusively on the rind of the citrus fruit.

Scrobipalpa heliopa (Low.) (= *Gnorimoschema heliopa*), Tobacco stem borer, Eggplant budworm (Tabakstengelbohrer). Caterpillar feeds inside the stems of tobacco plants and in eggplant flowers in the eastern mediterranean region, in the Black Sea region, in Africa south of the Sahara, in South and South East Asia and in East Australia (CIE Map no 276).

Nephantis serinopa Meyr. Larvae feed in Sri Lanka, South India and Burma on the undersurface of coconut palm leaves (CIE Map no 211). Some wild and ornamental palm species serve as alternative host plants.

Acrocercops cramerella (Snell.), Javanese cocoa moth (Javanesische Kakaomotte) (Fig. 190), is found in South East Asia (Indonesia, Philippines, New Guinea). The larvae feed inside cocoa pods, which are traversed by their dark larval galleries. This renders the beans worthless, although these are not nibbled. Apart from cocoa, the moth also occurs on *Cola* sp., *Nephelium* sp. and some other plants. Control is difficult. By removing all the fruit, even the very smallest, after the main picking period, the life cycle of the pest can be interrupted, so that a renewed build-up of population in the cocoa plantations is very slow. Chemical control can be achieved with DDT and endrin, but a large number of spray applications are required.

Elasmopalpus lignosellus (Zell.), Lesser corn stalk borer (Kleiner Maisstengelbohrer). Occurs in North, Central and South America (CIE Map no 114). Caterpillars bore in the stems of maize and sugar cane and can also attack beans and other Leguminosae.

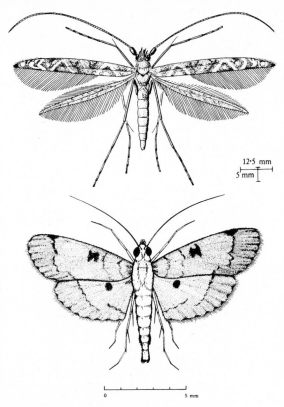

Fig. 190.   Adult moth of *Acrocercops cramerella* (after Entwistle, Pests of Cocoa, Longman, London)

12·5 mm
5 mm

0   5 mm

Fig. 191.   Adult moth of *Nacoleia octasema* (after PANS Manual no 1, Pest Control in Bananas, Crown Copyright 1971)

Eldana saccharina Wlk. occurs mainly in Africa, south of the Sahara (CIE Map no 291). The main host plants of the stem borer are maize and sorghum, but rice and sugar cane are also attacked.

Nacoleia octasema (Meyr.), Banana scab moth (Bananenschorfmotte) (Fig. 191). The gregarious caterpillars feed on young female flowers and scab-like scars are formed on the young fruit as a result. In addition, the inflorescences are soiled with frass and refuse. The pest also develops on Manila hemp, maize and some wild plants. It occurs in Indonesia, East Australia (Queensland), New Guinea, on the Fiji Islands and some other islands of the Western Pacific. A combination of DDT-gamma BHC is recommended for chemical control, which should be applied when inflorescences emerge from the leaf cover.

Nymphula depunctalis Gn., Rice caseworm (Reisblattzünsler) (CIE Map no 176). Occurs in tropical Africa, Asia and parts of Australia. Its larvae live in cases made of tips of rice leaves and can be very harmful on young rice plants.

Etiella zinckenella (Treitschke), Lima bean pod-borer. Widely distributed in the tropics, subtropics and in temperate zones (CIE Map no 105 rev.). Attacks legume pods, especially of lima bean, cowpea and sunn hemp.

Ostrinia nubilalis (Hb.) (= *Pyrausta nubilalis*), European corn borer (Maiszünsler). Attacks maize in Europe, North America, North Africa (Egypt), in the Near and Middle East and in Central America (Guatemala) (CIE Map no 11). In Central and East Asia, its role is taken on by the closely related species *O. furnacalis* (see p. 459).

Tryporyza innotata (Wlk.), White rice borer (Weißer Reisstengelbohrer) is a major pest of rice in Southern Asia (India), South East Asia and Australia (CIE Map no 253). The Pyralid is especially important in Indonesia, where it occurs in low lying regions up to 200 m above sea level. The caterpillar feeds like that of other stem borers in shoots and stems, destroying leaves and spikelets. The dry period is survived as diapause larva in the stubble or at the base of the plants. Control measures are the same as those recommendend for other rice stem borers (see p. 454).

Citripestis sagittiferella Moore, Moth borer. Larva feeds in Malaysia and Indonesia on the rind and in the fleshy part of the citrus fruit, particularly on grapefruit.

Cephanodes hylas (L.), Coffee hawk moth (Kaffeeschwärmer). Widely distributed in tropical and subtropical Africa and Asia and also found in Australia. Caterpillar attacks coffee leaves. Control: Application of DDT, carbaryl and endrin.

Manduca sexta (Joh.), American tobacco hornworm (Amerikanischer Tabakschwärmer). Widely distributed in America. Larvae feed on leaves of tomato, tobacco and other Solanaceae. Control: Thuricide (*Bacillus thuringiensis* preparation), azinphos-methyl, carbaryl, monocrotophos and other insecticides.

Parasa (= *Latoia*) spp. and **Thosea** spp., Stinging caterpillars, Nettle grubs. Various cultivated plants are attacked by several species belonging to these genera, among them *P. lepida* (Cram.) (South and South East Asia) and *P. vivida* (Wlk.) (Africa). *P. lepida* does considerable damage by feeding on the leaves of coconut palm and tea, *P. vivida* attacks coffee, while *T. cervina* Moore, *T. recta* Hmps. and *T. divergens* Moore sometimes occur as pests of tea in Southern Asia (India, Sri Lanka). The brightly coloured caterpillars also hinder cultivation procedures and picking, since contact with their stinging hairs produces a painful sensation on the skin. Pupation often occurs in groups, in solid, almost spherical cocoons on stems or branches of the host plants. Chemical control: Sprayings with parathion or gamma-BHC.

Amsacta moorei (Butl.). Caterpillars attack and defoliate in India young groundnut plants. Control: Trichlorphon, endrin or parathion.

Estigmene acrea (Drury), Salt-marsh caterpillar. In Central America and in the southern parts of the USA on various crops, including cotton and legumes.

Cryptophlebia leucotreta (Meyr.) (= *Argyroploce leucotreta*), False codling moth (Fig. 192). Occurs in South, East and West Africa. Caterpillar in fruit of citrus, guava, castor bean, okra, olive, cotton bolls and maize cobs. Control: Sprayings with parathion (citrus) or carbaryl, azinphos and endrin (cotton). Destruction of dropped fruit.

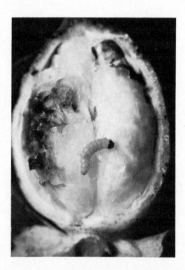

Fig. 192.   Larva of *Cryptophlebia leucotreta* in a cotton boll (phot. H. Schmutterer)

Fig. 193.   Cabbage showing serious damage by *Plutella xylostella* (phot. H. Schmutterer)

Cydia leucostoma (Meyr.), Tea flush worm (Teetriebspitzenwickler) (CIE Map no 104). Caterpillar destroys in South, Southeast and East Asia apical leaves of young tea shoots.

Homona coffearia (Nietn.), Tea tortrix (Teewickler). Occurs in Southern Asia (India, Sri Lanka), South East Asia and New Guinea. Larva affects tea, coffee and some deciduous trees by destruction of young leaves. Control: Biological control by *Macrocentrus homonae* (Braconidae). Sprayings with DDT (do not seem to affect *M. homonae* to any great extent).

Zeuzera coffeae Nietn., Red branch borer (Roter Kaffeebohrer). Caterpillars bore in branches and stems of cocoa, coffee, tea, citrus, kapok, teak and many other forest trees in South, South East and East Asia. Control: Cutting off and destroying affected branches and use of DDT or dieldrin.

Plutella xylostella (L.) (= *P. maculipennis)*, Diamondback moth (Kohlmotte, Kohlschabe) (Fig. 193). Occurs in tropical, subtropical and temperate climatic regions (CIE Map no 32) and attacks wild and cultivated crucifers. In many hot countries, it is one of the main cabbage pests. The greenish caterpillar first mines in the leaves and later goes on to fenestral and pitted feeding. Pupation takes place inside a cocoon near the feeding place on the leaves. Spray or dust applications of trichlorphon, azinphos, mevinphos, carbaryl etc. are effective.

Metisma plana Wlk. Caterpillars of this Psychid moth and of other related species attack leaves of oil palm in Malaysia.

Papilio spp. (*P. demodocus* Esp.: Africa, *P. memnon* L.: South and South East Asia, *P. thoas* L.: Tropical America, and other species) attack the leaves of *Citrus* spp..

Achaea spp., **Anomis** spp., **Calpe** sp., **Ophideres** (= *Othreis*) sp., **Sphingomorpha** spp., **Serrodes** spp. et al., Fruit piercing moths (Fruchtstechereulen). The adults of these Noctuid genera are distinguished by having a particularly well developed proboscis with a dentate tip. With this, they are able to pierce ripening fruit such as mango, citrus, grapes and many others. They are relatively rarely observed, as they have nocturnal habits. The damaged fruit often rots or drops prematurely, since the punctured region is easily infected with fungi or bacteria. Control measures to suppress the pests are difficult, since the caterpillars do not develop in the crops in which the adult does its damage. *Achaea* caterpillars for instance, live on castor bean and sweet potato, *Anomis* caterpillars on jute and kenaf.

Agrotis segetum (Schiff.), Dark moth (Wintersaateule). In tropical, subtropical and temperate zones of the Old World (Europe, Asia Minor, Africa). Caterpillars feed on the base of young plants ("cutworms") and on root crops in the soil.

Anomis sabulifera (Gn.) (Juteeule). Larvae attack leaves of jute on the Indian subcontinent. *A. flava* (F.) (= *Cosmophila flava*) is a cotton pest in Africa, Asia and Australia and a kenaf pest in Taiwan.

Heliothis spp.. *H. assulta* Gn. (Capegooseberry budworm) attacks tobacco, maize, tomato and other Solanaceae in tropical and subtropical regions of Africa, Asia and North Australia (CIE Map no 262). *H. punctigera* Wllgr. occurs in Australia (CIE Map no 263) on tobacco, cotton, lucerne, flax, sunflower and other crops.

Mythimna separata (Wlk.) (= *Pseualetia separata, Leucania separata*), Rice ear-cutting caterpillar (Asiatische Reiseule) (CIE Map no 230). The caterpillars of this Noctuid, which occurs in S., SE. and E. Asia as well as in Australia, are among the worst rice pests, especially in Asia (Bangladesh). They appear suddenly in large numbers ("army worms") and have nocturnal habits, so that their early developmental instars are not readily discovered. On rice plants, the ear is often cut off. Control measures include burning of stubble, ploughing up of fields after harvest, planting early ripening varieties and spraying with gamma-BHC or DDT. Bait (wheat bran + molasses + insecticide such as gamma-BHC or aldrin plus water) can also be used. The species is often confused with *M. unipuncta* (Haw.) which, together with other *Mythimna* spp. attacks cereals and fodder plants in Asia and Australia.

Spodoptera mauritia (Boisd.), Rice army worm, Rice swarming caterpillar (Reissaateule). In South and South East Asia and parts of Africa and North America (CIE Map no 162). Caterpillars feed mainly on young rice plants in seed beds or shortly after planting out, and destroy them within a short period. When a field has been stripped bare, they migrate in large numbers into adjoining fields to continue feeding at night. Chemical control by spraying with gamma-BHC, DDT, endrin or parathion. Baits containing gamma-BHC or aldrin are also effective.

Tiracola plagiata (Wlk.), Cocoa army worm (CIE Map no 303). Larvae feed in New Guinea on young cocoa leaves. Control by spraying with carbaryl, DDT or endrin.

H. Sch.

True flies; Zweiflügler; Mouches; Moscas

Order: Diptera

General features: The true flies fall into two major sub-groups, the graceful midges and the rather more coarsely structured plump flies. A feature common to the members of both groups is the possession of only one pair of normally developed wings. These are usually transparent forewings, while the hind wings are reduced to a drum-stick-like organ.

Only the larval stages of Diptera occur as plant pests. Grain is often damaged by midge larvae, e. g. gall midges on cereals, or galls may be induced by the enzymes in their saliva. The apodous and headless maggots of flies do damage on various plants by feeding inside fruit or shoot. Many species mine in leaves and stems.

Tropical plant pests of economic significance are particularly the gall midges (Cecidomyiidae) and among the flies the Muscidae and fruit flies (Tephritidae). The fruit fly female transmits bacteria with oviposition, which cause affected fruit to rot.

H. Sch.

Family: Cecidomyiidae

Contarinia sorghicola (Coq.) (Figs. 194–195)

Synonyms: *Contarinia andropoginis, C. palposa*

Common names: Sorghum midge; Amerikanische Hirsegallmücke; Cécidomyie du sorgho; Mosquita del sorgo.

Geographical distribution: Sorghum midge is native to the intertropical zone of Africa, although it was first discovered and described in Texas, U.S.A. in 1895 where it had been introduced on fodder sorghum, *Sorghum vulgare* var. *drummondii*. It is now spread in nearly thirty countries in the tropical, intertropical and warm temperate zones, having been helped to follow the areas of cultivation of this crop by the distribution of seeds. However, *C. sorghicola* causes damage only in the subtropical zones (Africa, South America, southern part of the U.S.A., India).

Host plants: Nearly all species and varieties of *Sorghum* have been recorded as hosts: *S. bicolor, S. caffrorum, S. caudatum, S. drummondii, S. durra, S. guineense, S. halepense, S. saccharatum, S. sudanense, S. verticilliflorum, S. vulgare.* There is some doubt as to whether *C. sorghicola* is able to develop on other Gramineae: *Triodia flava, Setaria glauca.*

Wild sorghums and those cultivated for fodder serve as primary or alternative hosts and are sources of infestation.

Symptoms: The glumes of attacked flowers retain the narrow and flat form which they have at flowering. In such flowers the seeds fail to develop; they remain small, malformed and enclosed between the glumes.

Attacked spikelets can be easily detected by pressing between finger and thumb, when any larvae or pupae will be squashed and revealed as droplets of red exudate from between the glumes.

Fig. 194. Egg-laying female of *Contarinia sorghicola* (phot. R. Coutin)

Fig. 195. Part of sorghum head showing few normally developed grains; all other grains have been destroyed by larvae of *C. sorghicola* (phot. R. Coutin)

In severe attacks the ears look either completely or partially dried out or sterile. Various piercing insects can give rise to similar abnormal development.

Economic importance: Sorghum midge is the chief pest of grain sorghum and is especially damaging to slow-maturing varieties with a long vegetative phase. Such varieties sometimes suffer a non-formation of more than half their seeds.

Morphology: 1. Within abnormal flowers. Upon separating the glumes, one or more larvae are seen in contact with aborted seeds whose size is only a third or fifth of healthy seeds of the same age. The larvae are 2 mm long, apodous, with a vestigial head and coloured orange or orange-red. Red pupae, about 2 mm long, with black wing and leg cases are to be found in the same location. 2. Behaviour of adults. Midges are 1.3–1.6 mm long, coloured reddish and black. During the morning they fly around panicles which are beginning to flower. Females visit the flowers, particularly in late morning, and insert their ovipositor between the glumes. Eggs are laid within the flowers.

Similarities to other pests: Seeds abort for various reasons: faulty fertilization, physiological or genetic failure, inclement weather during flowering such as persistant rain and dry winds. Also, and according to regions, other insects, particularly various species of bug, can cause seeds to abort: *Agonoscelis pubescens, Dysdercus völkeri, Mirperus jaculus, Riptortus* sp., *Calidea* sp. and various Miridae.
A related cecidomyiid, *C. sorghi*, exists on *Sorghum* and *Pennisetum* but is of negligible importance.

Life cycle and ecology: In the tropics and subtropics with the end of the rains and the return of the dry season larvae which have completed their growth do not pupate but weave brownish, parchment cocoons in contact with the invaded seeds. Within the cocoons the larvae pass the dry season in a state of diapause, and then quiescence, in which state they can remain for several years. In temperate zones the fall of temperature causes the cessation of pupation and an entry into diapause.

With the return of the rains and the wetting of old, unharvested seed heads in the fields and of the trash left from threshing, there is a staggered pupation of the larvae, the first adults appear 45–60 days later, when about 250–350 mm of rain has fallen.

Mating is brief and takes place soon after the adults appear. The females immediately lay their eggs in the sorghum flowers which are the first to open. The adults rarely live longer than a day, and so new midges visit the flowering panicles daily.

The period of a generation is about 15–20 days, and varying between regions there can be 4–7 generations. In the absence of any efficient and permanent regulation of population numbers by natural enemies, the midges are continuously present when the sorghum is at the heading stage. It is the entry of the larvae into diapause which stops the growth of the pest population. Slow-developing sorghum varieties usually suffer the most severe attacks.

Natural enemies: Two endoparasitic Chalcids (Hymenoptera), *Eupelmus popa* and *Tetrastichus diplosidis,* have been reported in nearly all areas where *C. sorghicola* occurs. A third species, *Pediobius pyrgo* may also be parasitic.

Among predators, the Anthocorid *Orius maxidentex* attacks adults and larvae, but it seems to be of limited and sporadic activity. Various spiders (*Thomisus* sp.) trap adult midges in their webs.

Control:

Cultural methods. Thorough destruction of old seed heads and the trash left from threshing removes the great majority of larvae in diapause and quiescence, and to this extent reduces the number of adults which produce the first generation.

A series of measures can be taken to avoid conditions which would encourage the multiplication and spread of the pest:–

Obtain pure varieties with coincident and short flowering periods.

Avoid varieties characterized by a staggered flowering, and those which frequently form secondary seed heads beneath the main panicle or on the slowest tillers.

Avoid growing varieties with staggered flowering in neighbouring fields.

Sow varieties that flower simultaneously. Alternatively, avoid sowing late-flowering varieties leeward of the prevailing wind in order to limit the dispersal of adult midges to those stands.

Rogue secondary host plants such as volunteer seedlings and regrowths.

Cut fodder sorghum before it flowers.

Resistant varieties. Several cases of resistance have been noted. In West Africa, varieties of the "Nunaba" type, derived from *Sorghum membranaceum,* have very long glumes which fail to separate at anthesis. These cleistogamous flowers impede the insertion of ovipositors by the females. Other resistance phenomens are not really true resistance characters, but are associated with the separation in time of the insects and the flowers of certain varieties.

Chemical control. Only in exceptional circumstances will there be a need to apply insecticides. The eggs, larvae and pupae are well protected by the floral parts and therefore difficult targets to reach. The adults can be destroyed, but with much difficulty because 1. they have a brief life and egg-laying takes place shortly after emergence and mating, and 2. the active population is renewed daily.

There are few contact insecticides capable of killing an insect in so short a time, and so those which have been tested have given only partial control. The majority have a very brief persistence. Those which have given satisfactory results, albeit of brief duration, are carbophenothion, disulfoton, endrin, parathion-methyl and phosalone.

Insecticides therefore offer a partial but inadequate solution and will be reserved for the protection of field trials and selection and multiplication plate, where the necessity to grow together varieties with differing vegetative cycles produces conditions which encourage multiplication of the pest.

Literature

BOWDEN, J. (1965): Sorghum midge, *Contarinia sorghicola* (COQ.) and other causes of grain sorghum loss in Ghana. Bull. Ent. Res. **56,** 169–189.

COUTIN, R. (1969): Récente extension mondiale et présence de la Cécidomyie du Sorgho, *Contarinia sorghicola* (COQ.), 1898, en France méridionale. Bull. Soc. Ent. Fr. **74**, 13–20.
COUTIN, R. (1970): Biologie de la Cécidomyie du Sorgho, *Contarinia* sorghicola (COQ.) et lutte chimique. Phyt. phytoph. **19**, 65–83.
COUTIN, R. & K. M. HARRIS (1974): Biologie de *Contarinia sorghi* (Harris) comb. nov. sur le mil au Sénégal (Dipt. Cecidomyiidae). Ann. Soc. Ent. Fr. **10**, 457–465.
HARRIS, K. M. (1969): The Sorghum-midge. World Crops **21** (3), 176–179.
HUDDLESTON, E. W. et al. (1972): Biology and Control of the Sorghum Midge. 1–2–3. J. econ. Ent. **65** (3), 796–799; 817–818; 851–855.
PASSLOW, T. (1965): Bionomics of Sorghum Midge, *Contarinia sorghicola* (COQ.) in Queensland, with particular reference to diapause. Queensland Jl. Agr. Anim. Sc. **22**, 149–167.
WISEMAN, B. R. & W. W. MC MILLIAN (1970): Preference of Sorghum midge among selected Sorghum lines, with notes on overwintering Midges and Parasite Emergence. Prod. Res. Rpt. 122 US. Dept. Agr. 8 pp.

Author: R. Coutin

Geromyia penniseti (Felt.) (Figs. 196–197)

Synonym: *Cecidomyia penniseti*

Common names: Millet grain midge; Kolbenhirsegallmücke; Cécidomyie du mil.

Geographical distribution: There is little doubt that like its host *Pennisetum typhoides* (bulrush millet, pearl millet), *G. penniseti* originated in Africa. However, it was discovered and described in India. This midge is now known 1. in several West African countries in the Sahel – Sudan dry savanna vegetation zones: Senegal, Mali (?), Upper Volta, Niger, Sudan and probably also in Ghana, Nigeria, Uganda and elsewhere; 2. in Madagascar, and 3. in southern India (Coimbatore).

Host plants: *G. penniseti* has been recorded on various species of *Pennisetum: P. typhoides, P. polystachyon, P. pedicellatum, P. alopecuros, P. cenchroides.*

Symptoms of damage and economic importance: Early and normal maturing varieties (the "souna" type in Senegal) suffer from partial to total losses of grain. The damage is less severe on late maturing varieties ("sanio" type) with a long vegetative phase. Empty pupal cases are found at the tips of the glumes.
Varieties of the "souna" type flower between mid-September and early October and give relatively poor yields. When attacked they suffer large reductions of crop, greater than 50 % and even reaching 90 % of the potential crop weight. These early varieties are valuable because they are grown to bridge the food gap before the main harvest.

Morphology: The adults have long legs, are coloured pale orange and measure about 2.5 mm. A full description of both sexes has been made following studies in Senegal. The orange larvae never weave their cocoons before entering diapause, which is in contrast to the behaviour of *Contarinia sorghicola* (sorghum midge).

Similarities to other pests: *Contarinia sorghi* normally develops within male flowers and is therefore of no economic importance.

Life cycle and ecology: The larvae pass the dry season in diapause, then in quiescence, within the flowers and in contact with attacked seeds. They pupate when there has been sufficient rain to wet the unharvested ears which remain in the fields.

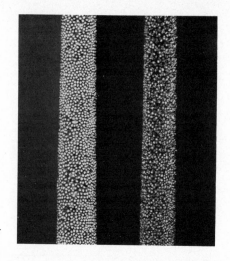

Fig. 196.   Ovipositing female of *Geromyia penniseti* (phot. R. Coutin)

Fig. 197.   Left: head of Pennisetum with normally developed grains; right: head with numerous grains attacked and destroyed by larvae of *G. penniseti* (phot. R. Coutin)

The appearance of the first adults coincides with the flowering of the earliest maturing varieties. The activity of the adults is strictly nocturnal; emergence always takes place at dusk, at about 7 p. m. Mating occurs without delay and the females lay eggs before midnight by inserting their ovipositor between two flowers and depositing eggs individually outside these flowers, on the subtending bristles or the glumes.

The female midges show a clear preference for spikes or parts of spikes which have reached the female phase of anthesis. The eggs hatch after 3 days and young larvae then enter the flowers when, with free stamens and separated glumes, the spikes are in the male phase. The larvae reach the ovaries which then stop development.

Larvae grow for 7–8 days and pupate for 2–3 days, and so four or five generations can appear and overlap in the rainy season. The population increases rapidly and can easily multiply to nearly fifty times its original size, but eventually the number is suddenly reduced by the combined effects of the larval diapause and natural enemies.

Natural enemies: Six species of parasitic Hymenoptera are known but not fully identified. Two are ectoparasites of the genus *Eupelmus,* and four are endoparasites belonging to *Tetrastichus* (2 species), *Platygaster,* and *Aphanogonus.* One species of *Tetrastichus* constitutes 85 % of the natural enemies. The main predator is the Anthocorid *Orius maxidentex.*

Control: The same general recommendations apply as for the protection of sorghum from *Contarinia sorghicola* (see p. 514). If possible, applications of insecticides should be avoided in view of the many very active natural enemies that play a decisive role in making tolerable the attacks of *G. penniseti* on late maturing varieties of bulrush millet.

Literature

COUTIN, R. & K. M. HARRIS (1968): The taxonomy, distribution, biology and economic importance of the millet grain midge, *Geromyia penniseti* (Felt.), gen.n., comb. n. (Dipt. Cecidomyiidae). Bull. ent. Res. **59**, 259–273.

COUTIN, R. & K. M. HARRIS (1974): Biologie de *Contarinia sorghi* (Harris) comb. nov. sur le mil au Sénégal (Dipt. Cecidomyiidae). Ann. Soc. Ent. Fr. **10**, 457–265.

Author: R. Coutin

Pachydiplosis (Orseolia) oryzae (Wood-Mason) (Plate 46 a)

Common names: Rice gall midge, Rice gall fly; Reisgallmücke.

Geographical distribution: Burma, Thailand, Vietnam, China, Indonesia, India, Sri Lanka, Sudan, Nigeria, Togo, Northern Cameroon. CIE Map no 171.

Host plants: *Oryza sativa, O. officinalis, Panicum stagninum, Paspalum scrobiculatum, Pennisetum centroides, Ischaemum ciliare, I. aristatum, Apluda mutica, Leersia hexandra, Imperata cylindrica, Echinochloa colonum, E. frumentacea, Paspalum* sp., and *Mnesithea laevis.*

Symptoms: Infestation of active buds or growing points of young rice plants by midge larvae alters the normal growth pattern resulting in the growing shoot becoming a hollow, tubular, elongated gall terminating in a highly reduced leaf lamina. The production of this gall signals the end of growth of the tiller involved. In addition to gall formation and tiller loss attack by the pest causes stunting of rice plants and stimulates tillering.

Economic importance: *P. oryzae* is a major pest of rice in most countries of Southern and Southeastern Asia and in some parts of Africa. Midge infestation of rice plants, up to the end of the period of productive tiller formation, causes considerable losses of rice yields in some cases ranging up to 100 % of the crop.

Morphology: Adult. *P. oryzae* is a minute, mosquito-like insect. The female is orange to orange-brown and the male considerably smaller and pale brown.
Egg. The freshly laid egg is elongate (0.44 x 0.125 mm), translucent and creamish brown with an orange tinge.
Larva. The minute first instar larva (0.50 x 0.127 mm) is translucent with a reduced head, minute antennae, an X-shaped eye spot and a sclerotized circular oral area. The body is 13-segmented and segments 12 and 13 have postero-laterally located spine-bearing tubercles. One pair of spines located on the last segment are characteristically elongated. The second instar larva resembles the first in every respect except that it is larger and minute spines are present only on segment 13. The third instar larva is considerably larger than the second and has a heavily chitinized, Y-shaped sternal spatula mid-ventrally between the second and third body segment.

Life cycle and ecology: *P. oryzae* lays its eggs singly or in small groups mainly on the undersides of the leaves but also a very few on the leaf sheaths of seedling rice. Freshly emerged females commence egg-laying on the evening if the first day as adults and it reaches a maximum in the first night. Females survive for about three to four days and continue laying eggs but only in very small numbers after the first day. One female lays up to 285 eggs but on average only about 175 eggs. Embryonic development is completed in about 72 hours and hatching commences on the third evening after oviposition and is completed by midnight. This timing of hatching is adaptive for larval survival because rice seedlings are wet with dew or guttation at this time and freshly hatched larvae need wet surfaces for movement to reach their feeding site at the growing point of the seedling.
The first instar larva moves rapidly over wet leaf surfaces aided by its posterior spines and by a slimy substance which covers its body. It then enters the plant under the outer leaf sheaths and progresses downwards and inwards under successive leaf sheaths to reach the main growing point or an axillary shoot apex. The larva never bores through plant tissue to reach the feeding sites. If the leaf surfaces are not wet the slimy substance covering the freshly hatched larva hardens into a creamish brittle substance which protects the larva until moisture becomes available. At the main shoot apex the larva is situated between the youngest leaf primordium and the growth cone with its head pointing downwards. Larvae take 6–12 hours to reach the growing points after hatching. After 3–4 days at the growing point the first instar larva moults into the second instar. This stage

lasts 3–4 days. At this time the gall cavity is about 2 mm long. By the end of the third larval instar, which lasts 6–7 days, the gall cavity has grown from about 2 mm to about 9 mm. The larva stops feeding and reverses its direction inside the gall cavity, using the sternal spatula for this movement.

The pupal stage lasts 6–7 days. As the end of that period approaches the gall primordium undergoes a spectacular elongation from about 9 mm to about 175 mm or more. For adult emergence the gall midge pupa wriggles up the hollow of the tubular gall with the aid of a series of adaptive spines located on its body, until it reaches the upper limit of this cavity. Here it bores a circular hole in the wall of the gall with its heavily chitinized cephalic horns and subocular spines, to permit the protrusion of the anterior part of the pupal body. The adult midge thereafter emerges from the pupa leaving behind the pupal exuvium protruding from the hole in the upper part of the gall. Gall formation normally occurs in young rice plants up to the early post-shooting stage. Meristematic tissue, even in the developing earhead, can occasionally be affected and galls can be produced, though very rarely, on this structure.

Adult midges mate, at night, soon after emergence and a female is known to mate but once. Males, which are extremely fragile, do not survive for more than one day but the female lives from 3–4 days.

All the larvae hatching on a single rice seedling move towards the main and axillary shoot apices. Frequently, therefore, more than one larva can be found at each of the shoot apices. Those which reach the terminal shoot apices develop normally with a maximum survival of three second instars, two third instars or one pupal stage.

Larvae which reach the axillary shoot apices remain dormant until the shoots start active growth. Under such conditions in inactive shoot apices larval dormancy has been found to last up to one month in the first instar, development proceeding normally thereafter. Aestivation and seasonal carryover of this pest may also be achieved by first instar larval dormancy in the inactive axillary buds of host plants.

Gall midge populations in Thailand and Sri Lanka gradually increase as the rice crop develops and reach a maximum as the maximum tillering phase approaches. This is to be expected because the larvae live on active growing points and the larger the number of tillers the larger the number of feeding sites for the larvae. It has been noted in Sri Lanka that, after the maximum tillering phase is reached, the population tapers off to very low levels because of parasitization by *Platygaster oryzae,* which can reach up to 85 %, and also because of a drop in the proportion of male midges as temperatures rise and humidity drops towards the end of the cropping season. From these observations it is apparent that the rice crop (a $4^{1}/_{2}$ month variety) is most vulnerable to gall midge attack and damage for the first 8 weeks of its life.

Natural enemies: Several hymenopterous parasites have been recorded from Asia and Africa, namely *Platygaster oryzae, P. diplosiae, P.* spp., *Neanastatus* sp., *Eupelmus* spp., *Norbanus* sp., *Anisopteromalus camerunus,* and *Tetrastichus pachydiplosiae.* In Sri Lanka the Carabid, *Casnoidea interstitialis* and the bug *Nabis capsiformis* are predators.

Control: The mechanical removal and destruction of galls, burning of rice stubble or of grasses on bunds and the use of light traps have proved ineffective. In Thailand delaying the time of transplanting of rice seedlings to August instead of July has resulted in less midge damage.

Biological control by parasite introductions could prove very fruitful for controlling the rice gall midge. Such attempts have not been made so far, however.

Resistant varieties of rice have been produced in many countries. Gall midge resistance genes from Ptb 18, Ptb 21, Siam 29, W 1263 etc. have been incorporated into modern commercial varieties such as IR 8, Bg 11–11 and Bg 34–8 etc. Some of these lines are highly resistant. Several biotypes of the rice gall midge have already been recorded from India so it remains to be seen how long resistance will stand up to the variability observed in this pest species.

Chemical control of the rice gall midge has given varying results. In Sri Lanka, insecticidal seed treatment with gamma-BHC has given protection to seedlings against midge attack for the first two weeks. Dipping seedlings prior to transplanting for 24 hours, using a wide range of organo-phosphate and carbamate insecticidal emulsions or suspensions diluted at 30 ppm, can give a complete kill of midge larvae. As soil-water treatments, the insecticides salithion, fensulfothion, diethchinalphion, chlorpyrifos, diazinon and cyanophos at 0.5 lbs active ingredient per acre have given excellent control of midge larvae.

In field control operations it has been repeatedly shown that soaking seedlings in a suitable insec-ticide such as diazinon, phenthoate, diethchinalphion, chlorpyrifos, fenitrothion etc. before transplanting followed by soil-water application of insecticides such as diethchinalphion, fenitro-thion, cyanophos, diazinon etc. at 2 lbs active ingredient per acre 4 weeks after transplanting, can give good control of the gall midge. This is consistent with the finding, that a $4^1/_2$-month rice crop is vulnerable to midge damage only in the first 8 weeks of growth.

Chemical treatments are however costly and laborious. The integrated use of introduced parasites and resistant rice varieties coupled with a minimal use of insecticides only where essential, offers the best potentialities for a cheap and simple method of control of this pest in the immediate futu-re.

Literature

FERNANDO, H. E. (1971): Ecological studies on rice gall midge in Ceylon. Proceedings of a Symposium on Rice Insects, 19–24 July 1971. Tropical Agricultural Research Center, Nishigahara, Japan, 291–308.

FERNANDO, H. E. (1972): Biology and laboratory culture of rice gall midge and studies on varietal resi-stance. International Rice Research Institute, 1972. Rice Breeding. Los Banos, Philippines. 343–351.

HUANG, C. K. (1957): Study of *Pachydiplosis oryzae* Wood-Mason in Fu-Chien Province. East China Sci. Agr. J. **6**, 293–304.

LI, C. S. & S. F. CHIU (1951): A study of the rice gall midge, *Pachydiplosis oryzae* (Wood-Mason). Agr. Res. Taiwan **2** (4), 1–13.

MODDER, W. W. D. & A. ALAGODA (1972): A comparison of the susceptibility of the rice varieties, IR 8 and Warangal 1263, to attack by the gall midge, *Pachydiplosis oryzae* (Wood-Mason) (Dipt., Cecido-myiidae). Bull. Ent. Res. **61**, 745–753.

PERERA, N. & H. E. FERNANDO (1970): Infestation of young rice plants by the rice gall midge, *Pachydi-plosis oryzae,* with special reference to shoot morphogenesis. Bull. Ent. Res. **59**, 605–613.

PONGPRASERT, S., K. KOVITVADHI, P. LEAUMSANG & B. R. JACKSON (1972): Progress in mass rearing, field testing and breeding for resistance to the rice gall midge in Thailand. International Rice Re-search Institute. 1972. Rice Breeding. Los Baños, Philippines, 367–371.

REDDY, D. B. (1967): The rice gall midge, *Pachydiplosis oryzae* (Wood-Mason). Proceedings of Sympo-sium on major insect pests of rice plant. Baltimore Md., Johns Hopkins Pr., 457–491.

SHASTRY, S. V. S., W. H. FREEMAN, D. V. SESHU, P. ISRAEL & J. K. ROY (1972): Host-plant resi-stance to rice gall midge. International Rice Research Institute. 1972. Rice Breeding, Los Baños, Philippi-nes, 353–365.

WICKREMASINGHE, N. (1969): Observations on the rice gall midge and on its effect on the rice plant. Int. Rice Com. Newsletter **18**, no 4, 27–32.

WONGSIRI, T., P. VUNGSILABUTR & T. HIDAKA (1971): Study on ecology of the rice gall midge in Thailand. Proceedings of a Symposium on Rice Insects, 19–24 July 1974. Tropical Agriculture Research Center, Nishigahara, Japan, 267–290.

Author: H. E. Fernando

Family: Agromyzidae

Ophiomyia phaseoli (Try.) (Figs. 198–199)

Synonym: *Melanagromyza phaseoli*

Common names: (Agromyzid) bean fly; Tropische Bohnenminierfliege; Mosca minadora del fri-jol.

Geographical distribution: Egypt, Sudan, Kenya, Uganda, Tanzania, Zaire, Malawi, Mauritius,

Rhodesia, Senegal, South Africa, Israel, Sri Lanka, India, China, Indonesia, Malaysia, Philippines, Singapore, Australia, and Pacific Islands. CIE Map no 130 (revised)..

Host plants: Streak bean *(Phaseolus vulgaris),* cowpea *(Vigna sinensis),* lima bean *(Phaseolus lunatus),* soy bean *(Soja hispida), Cajanus, Canavalia* and *Dolichos.*

Symptoms: Streak beans are the most susceptible host plants. The plants are liable to become infested during the seedling stage when the tender plants may be killed, or even throughout the plant's life. Infested plants are recognized by the presence of light coloured streaks on their leaf blades, which are the mines that harbour the insect larvae. Several small swellings, the sites of the insect's pupation, may be discovered along the plant stem down to the soil level or below (Fig. 199). Infested plants lose their vigour and their foliage becomes pale and shrivelled.

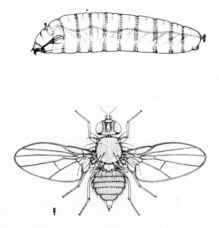

Fig. 198.   Larva (above) and adult fly of *Ophiomyia phaseoli* (drawing S. Abul-Nasr)

Fig. 199.   Swollen stems of bean plants, showing damage by larvae of *O. phaseoli* (phot. H. Schmutterer)

Economic importance: Infestation by this pest is considered to be a limiting factor in growing beans in those regions subject to severe infestation. Spring crops usually suffer less infestation than late summer crops in which infested plants may constitute over 70 % of the plant population. The yield is affected proportional to the level of infestation, since in severely infested plants, the pods are few, many are empty or their seeds are small.

Morphology: The bean fly is a very minute insect, body length of the female being about 2.2 mm and the male 1.9 mm. The general colour is shiny black except for the legs, antennae and wing veins which are light brown. The ocellar triangle is brilliantly shining-black, conspicuously long and narrow, extending beyond the lower orbits.
The maggot is creamy in colour and of the usual apodous form, in which the front end carrying the mouth parts is pointed and the posterior end is rather rounded or blunt.
The puparium measures 2.3 mm in length and 0.88 mm in width.

Similarities to other pests: Infestation by the pest is easily discovered by examining the leaves of host plants, especially beans, which show pale irregular lines of the larval mines. Other insects, e. g. leaf miners, cause the same symptoms on other host plants, but on bean only *O. phaseoli* is responsible.

Life cycle: The female fly lays its eggs mostly on the upper leaf surface and the hatching larva forms a short linear leaf mine. The maggot tunnels underneath the epidermis of the leaf until it reaches one of the veins which leads it to the midrib and then to the leaf stalk. The larval tunnels appear as narrow streaks, pale in colour with a silvery shade. The yellow granules of the larval frass can be seen inside the tunnel. The larva consumes the mesophyll tissue and the midrib of the leaf, leaving only the outer sheath. It then reaches the stem, or in older plants the petiole, which as a result becomes swollen. Numerous larvae may be found in one plant, and with a serious infestation, the stem turns brown, becomes swollen and breaks down; the plant then soon dies. The puparia remain inside the stem.

In a young infested plant, the maggots can push their way easily through the tender tissues, thus reaching the crown of the plant, at the soil surface, or the roots where they pupate. As the plant grows, its stem gets longer and its tissue harder and so the maggots are forced to pupate higher above the ground, particularly inside the fleshy joints, or even in the leaf stalks. There are 6–7 generations during the active season of the pest's infestation in Egypt. A spring generation may be extended to more than three weeks, but in later generations, the life cycle is shortened to less than two weeks.

Control:

1. In severely infested areas, beans should be grown at times when only mild levels of infestation are expected to occur, mostly in spring. A long period when the host plants are absent would limit drastically the build up of populations in successive generations.
2. After harvesting the pods, all plant residues should be burnt down to get rid of the harboured larvae and pupae that would carry over infestation to next season.
3. Chemical control. The use of phorate (Thimet) or disulfoton (Disyston) as seed dressings has proved effective in keeping the plants free from infestation for two to three weeks after emergence from seed. Endrin 19.5 % E. C. or carbaryl (Sevin) 85 % W. P., at a rate of $1^1/_2$ litre for the first and $1^1/_2$ kg for the second, per acre, have given very good control results. The first treatment should be applied when the seedlings have fully grown cotyledons, followed by three sprays at biweekly intervals. Spraying should be stopped before the flowers set pods.

Literature

SALAH ABUL-NASR & M. ASSEM (1966): The external morphology of the bean fly, *Melanagromyza phaseoli* (Tryon). Bull. Soc. ent. Egypte **50,** 61–69.
SALAH ABUL-NASR & M. ASSEM (1966): Some ecological aspects concerning the bean fly, *Melanagromyza phaseoli* (Tryon). Bull. Soc. ent. Egypte **50,** 163–172.
SALAH ABUL-NASR & M. ASSEM (1968): Chemical control of the bean fly, *Melanagromyza phaseoli* (Tryon). Bull. ent. Soc. Egypte, Econ. Ser. **11,** 151–159.
SALAH ABUL-NASR & M. ASSEM (1968): Studies on the biological processes of the bean fly, *Melanagromyza phaseoli* (Tryon). Bull. Soc. ent Egypte **52,** 283–295.
WALKER, P. T. (1961): Seed dressing for the control of the bean fly, *Melanagromyza phaseoli* Coq. in Tanganyika. Bull. Entom. Res. **50,** 781–793.

Author: S. Abul-Nasr

Family: Tephritidae (Trypetidae)

Anastrepha ludens (Lw.)

Common names: Mexican fruit fly; Mexikanische Fruchtfliege; Mouche mexicaine des fruits; Mosca mejicana de la fruta.

Geographical distribution: USA (Texas), Mexico and Central America (Guatemala, Costa Rica). (CIE Map no 89).

Host plants: *A. ludens* affects the fruit of *Citrus* species. Grapefruit is preferred, while lemon and bitter orange are not attacked. The highly polyphagous pest also develops in the fruit of mango, guava, pomegranate, avocado, fig, annona, *Spondias* sp., peach, pear, apple, quince, *Eugenia* sp., and of other wild and cultivated plants.

Symptoms: The damage done by the fruit-inhabiting larvae, is like that caused by *Ceratitis* and *Dacus* spp. (see p. 523 and 526). Necrotic lesions form on the peel in places of oviposition, and are often surrounded by a clear zone. Feeding activity destroys the fruit flesh, which is further rotted by bacteria introduced by the female fly on oviposition, leading to premature fruit drop.

Economic importance: *A. ludens* is one of the main citrus pests in Mexico and adjoining Central American countries. The fruit fly also does considerable damage on mango and other valuable tropical fruit.

Morphology: The Mexican fruit fly is about the size of the common housefly and basically of a yellowish brown colour. The thorax is traversed by lighter coloured longitudinal striations, with a dark brown spot at the centre of the hind portion of the median thoracic segment. Yellowish brown spots and stripes are present on the transparent wings. The stripe on the inside of the rear half of the wing resembles an inverted V, and is not joined with the other stripes on the wing. This feature distinguishes the fly from closely related *Anastrepha* spp.. The ovipositor of the female is remarkably long, slender and larger than the rest of the abdomen.

Similarities to other pests: Some other *Anastrepha* spp. are found in Mexico, in Central American regions and on the Caribbean Islands, whose mode of life is very similar to that of *A. ludens*. The most important species is *A. fraterculus* (see p. 532), which differs from *A. ludens* by having three sulphur yellow longitudinal stripes on the median thoracic segment and a stout ovipositor which is shorter than the rest of the body.

Life cycle and ecology: The female fly deposits several eggs at a time under the peel with her ovipositor, which is thrust forwards obliquely on oviposition. One female can produce about 800 eggs in the course of her life. The yellowish white larvae feed into the fruit flesh after hatching and remain inside the gradually rotting fruit until ready for pupation. They then bore out into the open and move into the soil, where they pupate in the uppermost layers. The damaged fruit has frequently dropped by that time. The period of development varies with temperature and type of food (affected kind of fruit) and takes from about 30 to 50 days.

Natural enemies: Various Hymenoptera are important parasites. In Mexico, *Diachasma (Opius) crawfordi* is considered to be the main larval parasite. Some predators pursue larvae and pupae in the soil. These natural enemies usually do not have the potency required to keep the damaging effects of the fruit fly below the economic threshold.

Control: Attempts have been made for some time, to control *A. ludens* by releasing sterilised males. At first, flies were used which had been sterilised with Tepa, but nowadays gamma irradiation is mostly used for sterilisation. By releasing sterilised males in the north western parts of Mexico and in the south of California, it has been possible to prevent the annual immigration of the pest into California to a large extent.

The flies are easily lured into traps containing cottonseed hydrolysate and borax. A considerable proportion of the population can be trapped in this way, so that the extent of the damage is much reduced. As with other fruit flies, it is advisable to control *A. ludens* by means of the important preventive measure of collecting and destroying dropped fruit several times a week. Destruction can take the form of deep burial.

Chemical control consists chiefly of repeated bait sprays with protein hydrolysate + insecticide (malathion, trichlorophon, diazinon, fenthion) + water. The flies are attracted by the protein hydrolysate and poisoned on nutrient intake.

Literature

BALOCK, J. W. & F. LOPEZ-D. (1969): Trapping for control of the Mexican fruit fly in mango and citrus groves. J. Econ. Ent. **62**, 53–56.
EBELING, W. (1959): Subtropical fruit pests. University of California, 436 pp.
SHAW, J. G., W. P. PATTON, M. SANCHEZ-R., L. M. SPISHAKOFF & B. C. REED (1966): Mexican fruit fly control. Calif. Citrogr. **51**, 209–214.
SHAW, J. G., F. LOPEZ-D. & D. L. CHAMBERS (1970): A review of research done with the Mexican fruit fly and the citrus blackfly in Mexico by the Entomology Research Division. Bull. ent. Soc. America **16**, 186–193.

Author: **H. Schmutterer**

Ceratitis capitata (Wied.) (Plate 46 c, d)

Common names: Mediterranean fruit fly; Mittelmeerfruchtfliege; Mouche de la Mediterranée; Mosca del mediterráneo, Mosca de la fruta.

Geographical distribution: All Mediterranean countries, Sudan, East and South Africa, West Africa, California, parts of Central America, South America, and Western Australia. CIE Map no 1.

Host plants: Fruits of peach, citrus, apricot, persimmon, pear, plum, apple and a number of tropical fruits.

Symptoms: On citrus fruit, egg-laying is marked by a circle in the rind, approximately 1 cm in diameter and whose colour becomes paler, or darker, than the rind around it depending on the host variety; the flesh beneath it rots. On other fruits, the egg-laying scar appears as a brownish circle on the fruit peel and the fruit flesh under it also rots.

Economic importance: A most serious pest of citrus and many fruits of subtropical, tropical, and warm temperate climates. Late citrus fruit varieties may be 100 % infested in some years. Certain peach varieties that mature in August–September may be up to 85 % infested, while 15–20 % of those maturing in July or September may be infested.

Morphology: The adult is 4–5 mm long with green eyes, a yellow head, brown antennae and thorax, and a brown abdomen with yellowish bands. The hyaline wings bear 4 transverse brownish bands.

Life-cycle and ecology: This pest is multi-voltine. Its threshold of development is around 12 °C while that of mating is around 16 °C. A preoviposition period of 2 to 4 days exists during which the newly emerged adults must feed on a proteinaceous source so that their internal genitalia develop. Copulation is followed by egg-laying. Females are provided with a sharp ovipositor which pierces the fruit skin. Several eggs (mostly 6–10) are deposited in a fruit at each time, and it is reported that a female may deposit a total of 300–400 eggs during her lifetime. The duration of the life-cycle is approximately 20 days at 27 °C, and about 65 days at 16 °C. The eggs are always contaminated with fruit-rotting, symbiotic micro-organisms in the fly. The ensuing maggots feed in and on the disintegrating flesh of the fruit. By the time the larvae complete their development, the infested fruit falls to the ground and the larvae leave it and bury themselves about 5–10 cm deep in the soil and pupate. The pupal period varies between 5 days in summer and 35 days in winter, after which the flies emerge from the soil. The adult is positively phototropic, and lays mostly in exposed fruits. Laying takes place in fruits at the time when their skin changes from green to yellow (a sign of ripening), but rarely when still green.

Natural enemies: Braconid wasps of the genus *Opius,* particularly *O. tryoni* and to a lesser extent *O. humilis* (not indigenous to the Palearctic Region).

Control: Attacked, fallen fruit should be destroyed (daily) before maggots leave it to pupate. Avoid planting varieties of fruit that serve as continuous hosts; e. g., early, medium, and late maturing peach or citrus varieties in the same orchard or locality.
Biological control in Hawaii by means of *Opius humilis* and *O. tryoni* has been found to be satisfactory. Release of laboratory-bred males of this fly, sterilized with X-rays or by the chemosterilant Apholate, were reported "effective" only in well secluded geographic areas.
Trichlorfon and fenthion are highly effective as cover sprays, or as baits mixed together with protein hydrolysates. Treatment in either case should be applied first when the fruit colour turns from greenish to yellowish, and then followed about ten days later with another application.

Literature

BACK, E. A., & C. E. PEMBERTON (1918): The Mediterranean Fruit Fly. U.S.D.A. Bull. 640.
HANNA, A. D. (1947). Studies on the Mediterranean Fruit Fly. Bull. Soc. Fouad 1er Ent. **31,** 251–285.
HANNA, A. D. (1948). Do. do. **32,** 175–202.
STEINER, L. F. (1955): Bait Spray for Fruit Fly Control. Agr. Chem. **10,** 32–34, 113–115.

Author: A. M. Talhouk

Dacus cucurbitae Coq.

Synonyms: *Batrocera cucurbitae, Chaetodacus cucurbitae*

Common names: Melon fruit fly; Tropische Melonenfliege; Mosca tropical del melón.

Geographical distribution: Northern India has been reported as the region of origin of this pest. Its occurrence has been reported from India, Burma, Philippines, Sri Lanka, Pakistan, Taiwan, Okinawa, Kenya, Mauritius, Guam, Japan, Hawaii, Australia, Java, USA (California) and Malaysia. CIE Map no 64.

Host plants: Besides cucurbitaceous vegetables, *D. cucurbitae* has been reported to attack bean, tomato, cowpea, guava, papaya, orange, mango, date palm, peach and green pepper. In India, 70 host plants of the fruit fly have been reported whilst 128 host plants have been reported from other countries.

Symptoms: Most of the damage results from oviposition behaviour of the fly and feeding activities of its larvae. The female punctures the fruit and lays eggs inside the epidermal layer. On hatching maggots feed on the pulp of the fruit which in turn becomes unfit for human consumption. Infestation of the fruit is usually followed by its decomposition due to invasion by secondary organisms. Besides oviposition inside fruits, eggs are also laid on flowers and even on stems. Formation of stem galls takes place as a result of fly infestation. The infested fruits become smaller and yellow in colour.

Economic importance: *D. cucurbitae* is one of the most serious pests of fruit and vegetables in temperate and tropical countries of the world. It is reported to cause enormous damage to pumpkin cucumber in the Hawaiian Islands and in Taiwan. In Hawaii, the loss due to fly injuries reaches as high as 75,000 dollars a year. In India more than 50 % of cucurbits are partially or wholly destroyed by fruit flies every year.

Morphology: The adult fruit fly is medium sized and yellow in colour. Lower front orbital bristles are present, vibrissae and ocelli absent. Spines are present on the middle tarsi. The wing is horny and flattened. Greenish brown patches are present on the apical margins of the wings. Black bands are present on the radio-medial veins and on the abdomen. Yellowish patches are present on the thorax. Ovipositor is three segmented, horny and skeletonized.

Similarities to other pests: There are various species of *Dacus* which infest fruits of tropical plants. They resemble each other in respect of body structure and colours. Most of the species are yellow or reddish yellow and more or less dark greyish black. The dorsal part of the thorax is frequently found to be blackish with yellow markings.

Life cycle: Eggs are laid by the female just under the skin of the fruit through its long, horny ovipositor. The number of eggs laid by one female ranges from 100–120. The eggs hatch within 2–3 days and the young maggots tunnel into the fruit and continue feeding on its pulp for about a fortnight. When the larvae are fully-grown they leave the fruits and fall to the ground where they burrow to a depth of 2.5–5 cm and pupate. The pupal stage lasts for 7–8 days. The duration of the life cycle varies between 23–34 days depending upon prevailing weather conditions. During November to December in Indian conditions the fruit fly overwinters in the adult stage under the leaves of guava or loquat. The period of greatest activity of the fly in the field has been observed to be during July and August. There are 8–10 generations each year.

Natural enemies: *D. cucurbitae* is attacked by a predaceous staphylinid beetle and two species of earwigs *(Anisolabis eleronome* and *Sphingolabis hawaiiensis)* in Hawaii. It is largely controlled by a chalcid parasite *(Spalangia hirta)* and a braconid parasite *(Opius fletcheri)* in Hawaii. The parasites *Opius fletcheri* and *Biosterus longicaudatus* have been found to parasitise the pest in Sri Lanka.

Control:
Sanitary methods. Collection and detruction of the infested fruits, stumps and rubbish after each fruit harvest is recommended to prevent new infestation. Burying the infested fruits under the soil to a depth of 2 to 3 feet or using them for compost making is also suggested.

Cultural practices. Ploughing and destruction of weeds constitutes an important measure of cultural control. A light ploughing after crop harvest is recommended in order to expose the pupae to the attacks of parasites or predators. Sowing of early or late varieties of cucurbits goes a long way to help escape pest injuries. Heavy irrigation of infested fields leads to destruction of the pupae.

Resistant crops. Crop resistance has been reported in the case of "Jaunpur jewel" variety of musk melon, "Improved long green" variety of cucumber, "Pilibhit padmani" of sponge gourd, "Soft green" of bitter gourd, "Smaller sugar" of pumpkin and "Sultan's long green" of bottle gourd in India.

Biological control. The braconid parasite *Opius fletcheri* has been successfully introduced and established in Hawaii and 50 % reduction in fruit fly population has been achieved. A similar level of success has been reported from the islands of Loocho and Mauritius. Complete eradication of the fruit fly in the island of Rota has been obtained by the release of sterilised males in combination with protein hydrolysate bait sprays.

Chemical control. Chemical control methods comprise two lines of approach viz. a) Insecticidal sprays; b) Bait sprays. In the former, the insecticides parathion (0.25 %), endrin (0.3 %) and dichlorvos are effective while in the latter, the bait sprays (2 lb. 50 % wettable malathion + 1 lb. protein hydrolysate dissolved in 100 gallons of water) at weekly intervals result an excellent control. A combination of methyl eugenol with parathion is also an effective bait trap.

Literature

LALL, B. S. & S. N. SINHA (1959): On the Biology of the melon fly *D. cucurbitae* Coq. Sci. & Cult. **25** (2), 159–161.
LALL, B. S. & S. N. SINHA (1960): A trap for the control of the melon fly *D. cucurbitae* Coq. c. f. Hort. Abs. **30** (4), 5428.

LALL, B. S. (1964): Entomology in India. Vegetable pests, pp. 187–211.
NARAYANAN, E. S. & H. N. BATRA (1960): Fruit flies and their control. I.C.A.R. Publication, Mono-
    graph, 68 pp.
NISHIDA, T. et al. (1957): Comparative effectiveness of malathion and malathion yest hydrolysate bait
    sprays for the control of Melon fly. J. econ. Ent. **50**, 680–684.

Author: B. S. Lall

Dacus dorsalis Hend. (Plate 47 a, b)

Synonyms: *Dacus ferrugineus* var. *mangiferae, Chaetodacus ferrugineus* (several varieties, see
Hardy, 1969), *Strumeta dorsalis*

Common names: Oriental fruit fly; Orientalische Fruchtfliege; Mouche de fruits asiatique; Mosca
oriental de la fruta.

Geographical distribution: CIE Map no 109. The following modifications are necessary to this
map: a) No longer in Mariana Is. b) It became established in San Diego, California, U.S.A. in
1974 and in Northern Australia in 1975. c) Present distribution: Pakistan, India, S. E. Asia, Philippines, Taiwan, Ryukyu Is., California and Northern Australia.

Host plants: Wide host range, mostly fleshy fruits. In Hawaii, it has been reared from more than
125 different kinds of fruits. Preferred hosts in Hawaii are: guava *(Psidium)*, mango *(Mangifera)*,
citrus *(Citrus, Murraya)*, banana *(Musa)*, papaya *(Carica)*, avocado *(Persea)*, peach *(Prunus)*,
coffee *(Coffea)*, and passion fruit *(Passiflora)*.

Symptoms: Females puncture the skin of fruits with their ovipositor and lay a batch of eggs about
6.0 mm below the surface. Malformation of developing fruits may occur or they may drop prematurely. Sap may ooze from the puncture and attract other insects to feed or oviposit in the wound.
Also various decay organisms may enter and cause discoloration and deterioration of the fruits.
After hatching the maggots feed on the fleshy parts and with associated microorganisms cause
breakdown of the parts of the fruits affected.

Economic importance: The oriental fruit fly not only causes direct damage to fruits but indirectly
is of great economic importance since strict quarantine regulations are imposed on the shipment
of fruits from countries where it occurs to countries where the fly is not present. The costs involved
in the treatment of fruits to meet quarantine regulations are expensive and have been a major factor in impeding the development and expansion of tropical fruit programs. Where the population
density of this fly is extremely high, such as was true in Hawaii in 1947–49, it may infest essentially
100 percent of favored host fruits.

Morphology: The adult is a clear winged fly with a wing span of 5.3–7.3 mm and a body length of
6.0–8.0 mm. Viewed from above, the over all color of the abdomen is basically light brown with
dark brown transverse bands and the thorax dark brown with conspicuous markings of yellow or
occasionally white. The white spindle-shaped eggs are 1.2 mm in length and 0.2 mm in width. The
young maggots are white and when fully-grown yellowish and about 10.0 mm in length.

Similarities to other pests: The immature stages of this species are similar and difficult to distinguish from other tephritid fruit flies, such as *Ceratitis capitata*. There are several species that belong to the *dorsalis* complex, the adults of which are undistinguishable on the basis of size and color pattern but can be distinguished through microscopic inspection of the ovipositor.

Life cycle: All stages, egg, larva, pupa and adult, occur throughout the year in warm areas. The lowest average temperature at which the immature stages can develop is about 14 °C and temperatures above 21 °C are necessary for the fly to attain sexual maturity without undue prolongation in the preoviposition period. At temperatures between 25–30 °C eggs hatched in 30–36 hours after deposition, most larvae fed for 7 days before becoming fully-grown and leaving the fruits or rearing media. Fully-grown larvae have the habit of curling up and subsequently springing in the air resulting in dispersal for a distance of 30 cm at a time. They entered the soil provided as a pupation media to a depth of 1–5 cm and transformed into puparia within a few hours. Emergence of adult flies occurred 10 days later. Females began laying eggs 5–7 days after emergence. Therefore, the life cycle, egg to egg, was about 25 days but may be considerably prolonged by lower temperatures.

Ecology: Adult flies move freely in and out of orchards and other host fruit areas. Marked flies have been recovered at least 50 kilometers from the point of release, both over land and water. Females may be commonly seen ovipositing in fruits but are seldom observed when fruits are not present. Apparently adult food and shelter are commonly obtained from non-host plants. Many flies have been observed on the foliage of panax *(Nothapanax)* and mokihana *(Pelea)*, the blossoms of honohono orchid *(Dendrobium)*, passion fruit *(Passiflora)* and shower trees *(Cassia)*, and extrafloral glands of passion fruit, wild euphorbia *(Euphorbia)* and castor bean *(Ricinus)*. Activity of this species is greater at elevations below 1000 feet than at higher elevations and also greater during the summer and fall than during the winter. Ovipositional attack is influenced by degree of maturity or ripeness of fruits. Flies oviposit more freely in young passion fruit fruits than older ones, in mature green than young or ripe guava fruits and more readily in ripe banana, papaya, citrus, and mango fruits than in younger ones.

Natural enemies: Several entomophagous arthropods and microorganisms are known to attack the oriental fruit fly. Among arthropods are general predators, such as ants, spiders, staphilinid beetles and earwigs, and a number of larval and puparial parasites. Parasites worthy of mention are: *Opius oophilus, O. longicaudatus, O. persulcatus, Dirhinus giffardii, Syntomosphyrum indicum, Spalangia philippinensis, Tetrastichus giffardianus,* and *T. dacicida*.

Control:
Sanitary method. Prompt disposal of unmarketable fruits from orchards is highly recommended to prevent attraction into and reproduction in them of flies.
Cultural practices. Bagging of fruits to protect them during development is practiced in many countries. Trapping of flies is also being practiced but there may be little or no control brought about by removal of a small portion of the adult population of an area.
Biological control. Introduced opiine parasites have been of appreciable value. In Hawaii they changed the status of the fly from that of epidemic conditions to tolerable levels within 2 years. Since 1957 *O. oophilus* has been the principal parasite involved in the regulation of the abundance of the fly at the general level reached more than 2 decades ago there.
Chemical control. Malathion used in combination with a bait, protein hydrolysate, has been recommended for field application to kill adult flies attracted to the mixture. Naled, together with a highly attractive lure, methyl eugenol, has been used experimentally in male annihilation programs with promising results under "island" situations where the male population was relatively low and confined. Integrated with this method of reducing the natural male population to prevent fertilization of the females present, mass releases of irradiated puparia, which produce sterile adults, have been used to further reduce fertilization, with the ultimate goal of eradication. This species was eradicated from Guam by using the sterile-insect-release technique.
Since conventional spraying of crops with present day insecticides does not kill the eggs and maggots inside the fruit, or the puparia in the soil, and is not effective in controlling the adults for reasons discussed above, spraying schemes have not been developed.
Treatments which meet quarantine requirements of importing countries have been developed for

certain fruits. These include fumigation with methyl bromide or ethylene dibromide, gamma irradiation, freezing, as well as other low and high temperature exposures which kill all eggs and maggots in the fruits.

Literature

BESS, H. A. & F. H. HARAMOTO (1961): Contributions to the biology and ecology of the oriental fruit fly, *Dacus dorsalis* Hendel (Diptera: Tephritidae), in Hawaii. Univ. of Hawaii, Hawaii Agric. Expt. Sta. Tech. Bull. 44, 30 pp.

HARAMOTO, F. H. & H. A. BESS (1970): Recent studies on the abundance of the oriental and Mediterranean fruit flies and the status of their parasites. Proc. Hawaiian Entomol. Soc. **20** (3), 551–566.

HARDY, D. E. (1969): Taxonomy and distribution of the oriental fruit fly and related species (Tephritidae-Diptera). Proc. Hawaiian Entomol. Soc. **20** (2), 395–428.

HARRIS, E. J., D. L. CHAMBERS, L. F. STEINER, D. C. KAMAKAHI & M. KOMURA (1971): Mortality of tephritids attracted to guava foliage treated with either malathion or naled plus protein-hydrolysate bait. J. Econ. Entomol. **64** (5), 1213–1216.

SEO, S. T., D. L. CHAMBERS, E. K. AKAMINE, M. KOMURA & C. Y. L. LEE (1972): Hot water-ethylene dibromide fumigation-refrigeration treatment for mangoes infested by oriental and Mediterranean fruit flies. J. Econ. Entomol. **65** (5), 1372–1374.

SEO, S. T., R. M. KOBAYASHI, D. L. CHAMBERS, A. M. DOLLAR & M. HANAOKA (1973): Hawaiian fruit flies in papaya, bell pepper, and eggplant: Quarantine treatment with gamma irradiation. J. Econ. Entomol. **66** (4), 937–939.

SEO, S. T., B. K. S. HU, M. KOMURA, C. Y. L. LEE & E. J. HARRIS (1974): *Dacus dorsalis:* Vapor heat treatment in papayas. J. Econ. Entomol. **67** (2), 240–242.

STEINER, L. F., W. G. HART, E. J. HARRIS, R. T. CUNNINGHAM, K. OHINATA & D. C. KAMAKAHI (1970): Eradication of the oriental fruit fly from the Mariana Islands by the methods of male annihilation and sterile insect release. J. Econ. Entomol. **63** (1), 131–135.

Authors: H. A. Bess and F. H. Haramoto

Dacus oleae (Gmel.) (Plate 47 d)

Common names: Olive fruit fly; Olivenfruchtfliege; Mouche de l'olive; Mosca del olivo.

Geographical distribution: All Mediterranean countries and Portugal. Reported also from limited areas of N. Pakistan, the Caucasus, Ethiopia and South Africa. CIE Map no 74.

Host plant: Olive tree (*Olea europaea*).

Symptoms: Green olive fruits show roundish violet to dark-blue areas of skin with a tiny hole in the center of each. The flesh under the affected area is soft and rotten. One whitish maggot (max. length 7 mm), with blunt posterior end and a pointed head, feeds in the fruit flesh.

Economic importance: The fruit of all olive varieties are susceptible to attacks by this fly. Large-fruiting and late-maturing varieties suffer great losses. In November–December, in the eastern Mediterranean, practically 100 % of the fruits of local varieties may get infested in those years with particularly early rainfall.

Morphology: The fly is approximately 5 mm long with a light yellow head and black eyes. Thorax black, covered with white pubescence and white stripes on mesothorax. Abdomen shows alternation of light and dark brown bands. Wings hyaline with brown veins and pterostigma. Maggot white, 6–7 mm long.

Similarities to other pests: No dipterous insect other than *Dacus oleae* is known to attack the fruits of olives.

Life cycle and ecology: The insect is multivoltine, and does not go into forced diapause. It passes the winter mostly in the pupal stage, or as the adult. It is reported that adults which emerge in April can survive until June and then lay their eggs. Egg-laying may stretch over six to eight weeks. Most eggs laid before mid-July are aborted. Late-emerging flies are therefore much more economically serious. A pre-oviposition period of 2–5 days exists during which the adults of both sexes feed and mature sexually. Their food consists of insect honeydew, nectar, and juices of olive fruit exuding from oviposition scars.
A female is capable of laying about 200 eggs in its whole adult life, which is about 3 weeks in summer. One egg is laid per fruit. The egg is deposited about 2 mm deep by the ovipositor in the flesh of the olive fruit. Incubation is 2–3 days under optimal conditions. High temperatures are detrimental to eggs. After hatching the maggots tunnel into the already disintegrating fruit flesh softened by symbiotic bacteria which have been introduced by the oviposition of the fly. The maggot tunnels galleries near the seed and causes the fruit to drop. The maggot then leaves the fruit and buries itself in the soil 5–10 cm deep where it pupates. The pupal period in summer is about one week followed by adult emergence from the soil. A complete generation in summer takes about 4–5 weeks, while in autumn it takes about 7–8 weeks.

Natural enemies: The most important parasite is *Opius concolor* (Braconidae). Other parasitic Hymenoptera are *Eupelmus urozonus, Eurytoma rosae* and *Pnigalio mediterraneus*.

Control:
Hygienic measures. In the oil presses, maggots leave wormy fruits and pupate on the walls of the storage room. These pupae should be scraped and killed, and windows closed with a wire screen to prevent the flies from reaching the olive groves.
Biological control. Breeding the braconid *Opius concolor* on maggots of *Ceratitis capitata* and releasing it in the groves in August has reduced infestation in a number of the Mediterranean islands, but apparently not adequately.
Chemical control. Dimethoate used as a cover or a bait spray has been effective when applied about 3 times during the season, beginning in early August, and repeated at a 3-weekly interval.

Literature

ARAMBOURG, Y. & R. PRALAVORI (1970): Survie ivernale de *Dacus oleae* Gmel. Ann. Zool. Ecol. anim., 659–662.
MELLIS, A. (1953): Nuove Osservazioni Sui Costumi Della Mosca Delle Olive *(Dacus oleae* Gmel.*)*. Nella Toscana Litoranea, Con Particolare Riferimento Agli Sfarfallamenti Invernali E Primaverili. Redia **38**, 1–84.
MONASTERO, S. & P. DELANOUE (1967): Première experimentation a grande echelle, de lutte biologique contre la Mouche de l'Olive *(Dacus oleae* Gmel.) au moyen d'*Opius concolor* Szepl. *siculus* Mon. en Sicile. Entomophaga **12**, 381–398.

Author: A. M. Talhouk

Family: Muscidae

Atherigona (varia) soccata Rond. (Plate 46 b)

Synonyms: *A. indica, A. acutipennis, A. indica* spp. *infuscata* and *A. excisa* (probably a misidentification)

Common names: Sorghum shoot fly, Central shoot fly; Hirseschößlingsfliege.

Geographical distribution: Most countries of Africa, Mediterranean area, Middle East and South-East Asia where sorghum is grown.

Host plants: *Cymbopogon citratus, Cynodon dactylon, Desmostachya bipinnata, Echinochloa frumentacea* (probably a misidentification), *Eleusine coracana, Panicum miliaceum, P. miliare, P. sumatrense, Pennisetum typhoides, Sorghum dochna, S. halepense, S. sudanense, S. vulgare, S. bicolor, S. purpureo-sericeum, S. verticilliforme, Triticum aestivum* (probably a misidentification), *Andropogon sorghum, A. s. saccharatum,* and *Brachiaria brizantha.*

Symptoms: The larvae destroy the growing point of young shoots and cause a typical dead heart effect which may be observed on seedlings of sorghum within 2–3 days after the attack. Sorghum is stimulated to tiller when attacked. Very young seedlings may dry up, especially during dry periods. However, plants attacked after they attain a height of about 35–40 cm (7–8 leaf stage) rarely have the main stem killed.

Economic importance: *A. (v.) soccata* is considered as an important pest of sorghum in parts of Africa and Asia. Heavy infestation results in destruction or retarded growth of young plants. Sorghum plants that have suffered from shootfly attack flower and ripe at very different times and vary considerably in height. For the latter reason, combined harvesting becomes difficult.

Morphology: Egg. The egg is white, sculptured, and elongated. It averages 1.3 mm long and 0.6 mm wide near the middle and is slightly tapered on each end.
Larva. The newly hatched larva is slightly shorter than the egg. It is white until about 2 days before pupation (longer if the insect enters a quiescent period), when it becomes yellow and gradually turns yellowish brown. The full grown larva averages 6.5 mm long and 0.8 mm in diameter and has 2 posterior black spiracle lobes.
Pupa. It is initially light brown but becomes darker with age. It averages 3.6 mm long and 1.2 mm in diameter and is slightly tapered at the posterior end where the 2 spiracle lobes are located, though they are flat to slightly concave on the anterior end.
Adult. The adult fly is in general about $^1/_2$ the size of the house fly, *Musca domestica,* but indiviudal flies are quite variable in size. Males are consistently smaller than the females. Females also differ from the males by having a darker marking on the posterior part of the abdomen.

Similarities to other pests: There are various other *Atherigona* spp. attacking shoots of cereals in Africa and Asia, and causing the same symptoms of damage as the larvae of *A. (v.) soccata.*

Life cycle and ecology: The eggs are normally deposited singly on the underside of the sorghum leaf, usually oriented parallel to the midrib. Hatching occurs within 2–5 days, average of 3.5 days, but these statistics may vary, depending upon the temperature and humidity. The first instar larva migrates from the oviposition site to the top side of the leaf and down the whorl of the plant until it reaches the growing apex. Many larvae, especially those infesting resistant cultivars, have been observed to die within the whorl of the plant before reaching this primary feeding site. Those that survive commence to feed at the growing point and pass through 3 instars. Some larvae remain quiescent for an extended period, which may be a period of diapause. The larval stage averages 13.0 days (13.0 is the average number of days for 50 % pupation) and has a range of 11.5 to 14.5 days. These figures will vary somewhat depending on environmental factors, particularly temperature.
The pupa is usually found within the stem of the sorghum seedling, but occasionally this stage is found in the soil near the surface at the base of the plant. An average of 10.4 days is required for the pupal stage, but this may be more or less depending upon the temperature.
Adults are active during the day or night but usually tend to stay in a sheltered area during the warmer part of the day. However, egg deposition apparently occurs about equally during the day or night. Egg deposition within a field is usually spotty unless there is an extremely heavy population of flies, probably because of a gregarious habit during oviposition.
A.(v.) soccata is attracted to meat meal, fish meal and ammonium sulfide. The latter has been used for making surveys and fish and meat meal have been used to induce heavy populations of flies in test plots, a technique used extensively in host plant resistance studies.

The duration of the adult life of this fly is varied and depends on the environment. In Uganda, the adult life cycle requires an average of 27 days.

Natural enemies: The following parasites and predators have been reported: *Tetrastichus nyemitawus, Aprostocetus* sp., *Callitula bipartitus, Trichogramma evanescens, Syrphophilus bizonaris, Phygadeuon* sp., gen. near *Alysia, Pachyneuron* sp., *Exoristobia* sp., *Camponotus* sp., and *Crematogaster castanea inversa.*

Control:
Cultural practices. In most areas where the sorghum shoot fly is a problem, damage on the first crop of the season can be greatly reduced (not effective for later crops) by early uniform planting. This practice was usual in the past where long-season, photosensitive sorghum cultivars were grown. (The practice also helped to reduce the damage done by the sorghum midge, *Contarinia sorghicola,* see p. 514). We now have higher yielding, short-season, non-photosensitive cultivars with some resistance to head mold but the insect problems have been magnified.

Resistance of crops. Host plant resistance appears to be the most effective approach to control of the sorghum shoot fly. Also, this method can easily be integrated into other control programs when resistant cultivars are available.

Two types of resistance of sorghum to this insect have been identified, so-called "recovery" and "primary" resistance. Recovery resistance is the ability of the sorghum plant to recover from an initial attack by producing tiller(s) which escape attack and will produce "respectable" head(s) that mature within 10–14 days of a plant of the same age that was not attacked. Primary resistance is the ability of the seedling to escape attack either by non-preference or by antibiosis.

The source of germ plasm for recovery resistance has been identified in Uganda from a beer variety, Namatera, and a grain variety, Serena. Several selections from various crosses of these with other materials (i. e. combine Kafir 60 and SB 79) have been made and seed has been distributed to East and West Africa, India, Israel and Thailand. Likewise, cultivars from India with primary resistance have been identified and distributed as noted. The cultivars with primary resistance are representatives of Durra and Cernum groups of sorghum, and are currently being tested in sorghum breeding programs at several research institutions. These cultivars are generally of undesirable types and require much improvement in yield, maturity, quality of grain, head type, photosensitivity and height.

Chemical control. Insecticides evaluated for control of sorghum shoot fly varied from a very high level to complete failure. In general, foliar applications are only partially successful or failures, because of the difficulty of having adequate amounts of insecticide at the right places on the plant at the right time.

Systemic insecticides, in contrast, can give excellent control, for example, phorate, disulfoton, and carbofuran. However, toxicity of these create too much of a hazard to the applicators for use in developing countries, and the cost of materials and application are usually prohibitive for the farmers. Nevertheless, these compounds may have a use in research plots in developing countries.

Literature

Control of Sorghum Shoot Fly. Proceedings of an International Symposium, Hyderabad, India. Nov. 1–3, 1971. Edited by Jotwani, M. G. and W. R. Young, published by Oxford and IBH Publishing Co., India.

Author: D. Barry

Other harmful Diptera (Fig. 200 and Plate 47 c):

Asphondylia sesami Felt, Sesame gall midge (Sesamgallmücke). In India and Africa (NE., E. and West Africa). Larvae convert fruit capsules into spherical galls.

Diopsis thoracica Westw., Stalk-eyed fly (Reisstielaugenfliege). The elongate, whitish maggots feed on the central shoots of young rice plants and cause a typical dead-heart effect. Serious damage has been reported in parts of tropical Africa (South and West Africa).

Anastrepha fraterculus (Wied.), the South American fruit fly (Südamerikanische Fruchtfliege), occurs in Mexico and in Central and South America (CIE Map no 88). The bionomics of this pest are much like those of *A. ludens* (see p. 521). It causes particularly severe damage on citrus and other fruit in some parts of Central America, in Bolivia, Brazil and in the Northern Argentine. Control measures as for *A. ludens,* also "bait sprays" and repeated treatment with ethion, dimethoat, or formothion. Good results were obtained in the Argentine with biological control measures, i. e. the liberation of laboratory-bred parasitic Hymenoptera. Other *Anastrepha* spp. are also fruit pests in South America and on the Caribbean Islands.

Fig. 200.   Egg-laying scar, caused by *Dacus* sp. on cucumber (phot. H. Schmutterer)

Dacus spp. *D. vertebratus* Bez. (= *D. frontalis*), *D. ciliatus* Lw. (Fig. 200 and plate 47 c) and some others occur in Africa and/or Asia mainly as fruit pests of cucurbitaceous plants. Their larvae destroy the fruit flesh, and in conjunction with bacterial activity, sweet melons, water melons and cucumbers are rotted. *D. zonatus* Saund. (CIE Map no 125) is a pest of mango, guava and other tropical fruit in Pakistan, India and Bangladesh, *D. tryoni* (Frogg.) (CIE Map no 110) in Australia and *D. tsuneonis* (Miy.) on citrus in China and Japan.

Myiopardalis pardalina (Big.), Baluchistan fruit fly (Vorderasiatische Melonenfliege). Attacks melon and other cultivated and wild Cucurbitaceae, and occurs in Western mediterranean and Black Sea regions, in Iran, Pakistan, India and West Africa (CIE Map no 124). Control with "bait sprays" of protein hydrolysate + sugar + insecticide (malathion, trichlorphon, parathion).

Carpolonchaea chalybea (Wied.) (= *Lonchaea chalybea*) (Cassavetriebspitzenfliege). This species is a major pest of cassava in Central and South America. Eggs are deposited by the female at the tip of shoots and the larvae penetrate into the shoots after hatching, where they develop. Affected shoots wilt and eventually die. Severe and repeated attack can kill the entire plant. Control measures include the cutting off and burning of affected shoots.

Atherigona spp.. Apart from *A.(varia)soccata* (see p. 529), several other species attack shoots of rice, millet, wheat, barley and maize in Africa and Asia. *A. oryzae* Mall., for instance, occurs mainly in South and South East Asia as an important pest of rice.

H. Sch.

Birds; Vögel; Oiseaux; Pájaros

Phylum: Aves

General features: Birds are well known for their habits and distinctive appearance (plumage). Their characteristic beak is used to pick up and break up the food. Birds which feed on grain like the Ploceidae (weaver birds and sparrows) can destroy large amounts of cereal grain with their exceedingly strong beak. Since these granivorous birds are often gregarious, i. e. appear in flocks, they can be serious pests in tropical and subtropical regions, especially on small grained cereal species like rice, millet and wheat. Cereal, peanut and other seed can also be dug up and picked off by birds such as crows, after it has been sown in the ground. Larger species of birds such as geese or ducks, can trample young rice plants underfoot fairly extensively. Still other birds, for instance pigeons and doves, do damage by feeding on thrashed cereal temporarily stored in the open. Finally there are birds which feed on fruit and do much damage by chopping into ripening mangoes, guavas, citrus fruit, dates and other soft fruit.

H. Sch.

Quelea quelea (L.) (Figs. 201–202 and plate 48 a)

Common names: Red-billed quelea, Sudan dioch, Red-billed weaver, Black-faced dioch; Blutschnabelweber; Mange-mil à bec rouge.

Geographical distribution: Throughout the semi-arid region of Africa south of the Sahara Desert. Total range exceeds 500,000 sq. km, but there is great regional variation in abundance. Highest densities are found in those areas where production of wild grass seeds is greatest e. g. river terraces, lacustrine plains and seasonal wetlands in low rainfall areas, where annual grasses predominate. There is everywhere great seasonal variation in numbers caused by the birds nomadic movements and regular seasonal migrations (see later). Also, annual variation in density can be very great, especially in regions of erratic rainfall. Following a succession of low rainfall years the density may fall to only a few percent of peak density. It will then recover in the course of a succession of wet years.

Host plants: The principle plant food comprises the seeds of wild grasses belonging to *Echinochloa, Panicum, Brachiaria, Pennisetum, Dactyloctenium, Digitaria, Oryza* and other genera. The seeds are obtained from the grass heads during a few weeks in the wet season, and from the surface of the ground throughout the rest of the year. Cultivated cereal seeds are taken from the ripening heads. (Queleas are rarely if ever implicated in losses of planted seed). Over the species whole range the cereal crops suffering damage in order of importance are bulrush millet *(Pennisetum)*, Guinea-corn *(Sorghum)*, rice, wheat, and finger millet *(Eleusine)*.

Fig. 201. Sorghum head, badly damaged by *Quelea quelea* (phot. H. Schmutterer)

Fig. 202. Nests of *Q. quelea* in an acacia tree (phot. H. Schmutterer)

Symptoms: Seeds removed from the ear at any stage from milky-stage until harvest. Generally the seeds are removed whole, but in the case of the larger *Sorghum* seeds these may be broken by the birds' beak. In the case of *Pennisetum* millet and *Sorghum,* damage is frequently concentrated on the top of each seed-head. Damage is generally very uneven within a field, being greatest in those areas adjoining thick cover provided by trees or bushes. The ground beneath attacked plants is often littered with seed husks and seeds accidentally dropped by the birds.

Although *Quelea* damage is distinguishable from rodent damage, it cannot be distinguished from that caused by a large number of other bird species. The only way to be sure that *Q. quelea* is the main culprit is to observe the fields in the early morning or late afternoon, when the birds are feeding, and identify the species feeding on the crop, preferably with binoculars. The presence of large numbers of *Q. quelea* in an area does not necessarily mean that the bird-damage seen in fields can be attributed to this species (see next section).

Economic importance: There is no reliable information on the value of crops lost over any large area or country. Damage is sporadic in time, uneven in distribution, and differs greatly in intensity from year to year in any place. The only generalization that can be made is that very serious damage, sometimes amounting to total crop loss over resticted areas, occurs in some parts of twenty African nations every year. Even in those countries where the overall average loss to *Quelea* is very small, the socio-economic consequences of heavy losses in certain areas are very serious. The sporadic nature of *Quelea* damage is due firstly to the highly mobile nature of *Quelea* flocks, secondly to the great variations in the pest's population size caused by climatic changes, and thirdly to the fact that Queleas seriously damage cultivated crops mainly when they are unable to obtain a sufficient supply of their natural food of wild grass seeds. This last factor means that the intensity of damage in an area is not necessarily related to the numbers of Queleas living there.

Morphology: Small (11–12 cm long) birds superficially like sparrows. In the dry season both sexes are brown in colour and very similar in general appearance to many other related species of weaver-birds. However, at close range the bright red colour of the beak distinguishes this species from all others in Africa of similar size. During the wet-season the males assume a distinctive breeding dress which is extremely variable, though all retain the red beak. Thus, while 80–90 % of individuals adopt a black or dark-brown mask on the sides of the head and chin, in the remaining 10–20 % it is white or pale buff. The rest of the head and the underparts change to some shade of buff, often suffused with pink. The female in breeding dress has the same general coloration as during the dry season, but the colour of the beak changes from red to yellow. Various subspecies are differentiated within the distribution range of this bird.

Similarities to other pests: Most of the other bird pests causing damage in African countries are very different in appearance from *Q. quelea.* For example, the many species of *Ploceus* are yellow or black. However, the closely related *Quelea erythrops* is very similar when in non-breeding dress, but the bill is black, not red, and in breeding plumage the males have a completely red head. Several species of Bishop-birds *Euplectes* spp. may also be confused with *Q. quelea,* especially when in non-breeding dress. However, although from a distance flocks of these birds resemble *Quelea* flocks, a close view will show that none of them have red bills.

Life cycle and ecology: Queleas breed only during the latter half of the wet season and occasionally the first few weeks of the ensueing dry season. They form enormous breeding colonies, often comprising millions of nests in dense vegetation such as *Acacia* groves, swamp grasses and papyrus. The roughly spherical nests, made by weaving grass strips together, are placed very close to one another. Breeding acitivites are usually closely synchronized throughout a colony. *Q. quelea* is monogamous and each pair produces 2–4 young in a brood, rarely more. The entire nesting period, from choosing the nest site to the abandonment of fully-grown young takes only six weeks. Several broods may be produced in the course of a single wet season, though the parents must usually move considerable distances between successive broods. By this means, each female Que-

lea may produce anything from two to fifteen young in a year depending on the climatic and other circumstances.

During the dry season Queleas concentrate in good feeding areas where they feed in flocks of hundreds or thousands. Each night many such flocks assemble in huge communal roosts situated in trees, bushes or tall grasses. At the end of the dry season, Queleas perform a definite migration the length of which varies according to locality. Thus in East Africa the flight may be up to 2,000 km., whereas in West Africa a different race of the species has a migration of only 500 km.

Natural enemies: A variety of falcons and hawks (notably the Chanting Goshawk *Melierax metabates,* Gabar Goshawk *Micronisus gabar* and Lanner falcon *Falco biarmicus*) prey on *Q. quelea,* but these predators are always in very small numbers compared with the density of the prey species and there is no indication that they, or the mammal predators which take some birds at night, play any important role in the natural control of the population size. *Q. quelea* is remarkably free for epizootic disease and parasites, both internal and external. Population regulation appears to be effected almost entirely through the supply of grass seeds. Also, a copious supply of insect food, mainly Acridid grasshoppers and caterpillars, is essential for successful breeding.

Control: At present, in many countries attempts are being made to reduce the size of the *Quelea* population by the destruction of roosts and colonies wherever they can be found. It is unlikely that such a strategy can ever be successful, and where great reductions have been claimed they have in fact coincided with the drought periods when the population would be expected to decline naturally anyway. In both southern and East Africa such declines have been temporary and have been followed by great resurgence in the population which could not be checked by continuing "control"measures. Recently a new strategy has been proposed by this author which involves the destruction of only those *Quelea* concentrations (communal roosts or breeding colonies) which are in or close to important areas of vulnerable crops, and only during the time of year when the crops are at a vulnerable stage. The advantages of this "immediate crop protection" strategy are: economy in men and materials, reduction in quantity of avicide used (and therefore in pollution and accidental destruction of wildlife), and better protection for the more threatened and valuable crop areas.

Methods used for destroying *Quelea* roosts and colonies vary greatly over the African Continent, but aerial application of fenthion (Queletox) in diesolene to the bird concentrations at dusk, is the most general. Parathion + diesolene are also used but is more dangerous. The relative advantage of fixed wing plane versus helicopter, and of different spraying techniques can only be judged in the light of local conditions which vary enormously within the continent. Accessible sites may be successfully treated with explosives, and provided they are small also, by ground spraying with a fenthion/water mixture.

No method of biological control is known and it seems unlikely that any will be found. Resistant varieties of crops have been tested but appear to be effective only when non-resistant varieties (which then receive increased attack) are grown nearby. Otherwise the so-called resistant varieties are consumed by the birds. In some areas damage may be avoided by cultural practices i. e. by planting so that the harvest coincides with a period when the birds have ample wild food, or when they are away on migration. The scope for such avoidance is limited, however, since in most regions the planting time is largely dictated by the timing of the rains.

Literature

CROOK, J. H. & P. WARD (1968): The *Quelea* problem in Africa. In: Murton, R. K. & Wright, E. N. (Eds.). The Problems of Birds as Pests. London, Academic Press.
MAGOR, J. I. & P. WARD (1972): Illustrated descriptions, distribution maps and bibliography of the species of *Quelea* (weaver-birds: Ploceidae). Trop. Pest Bull. **1.**
WARD, P. (1971): The migration patterns of *Quelea quelea* in Africa. Ibis **113**, 272–297.
WARD, P. (1973): A new strategy for the control of damage by Queleas. PANS **19**, 97–106.

Author: P. Ward

Other harmful birds:

Euplectes orix L., Dura bird. Attacks pennisetum and sorghum crops in African savannahs.
Ploceus spp.. Various species of this genus damage rice, sorghum and pennisetum, sometimes also maize in Africa and Asia. Some species in Africa defoliate coconut palms to build their nests in them.
Passer spp.. Attack millet crops, wheat and rice especially in and around inhabited areas in various parts of the tropics. Occasionally they also damage soft fruit.
Psittacula crameri Scop., Long-tailed parakeet. Widely distributed in tropical Africa and Asia (various subspecies). Feeds on milk-ripe millet grains.
Agelaius spp., Blackbirds. Do much damage on rice in the USA and in other parts of the American continent.
Sturnus vulgaris L., Starling (Star). Causes damage by feeding on olive fruits in Tunesia and elsewhere in North Africa.

H. Sch.

Rodents; Nagetiere; Rongeurs; Roedores

Class: Mammalia

Order: Rodentia

This important mammalian order is represented by many destructive rat and mouse species in tropical and subtropical regions. Rats in particular include a number of major pests, which gnaw at and on plants and plant portions with their large, chiselled incisors, which are situated far in the front of their jaws and isolated from the rest of the teeth. They can also be responsible for large losses in stores by soiling and feeding on stored products, especially cereal.

H. Sch.

Family: **Muridae** (Figs. 203–205 and plate 48 b, c, d)

Common names: Rats and mice; Ratten und Mäuse; Rats et souris; Ratones y ratas.
Important species/subspecies, their synonyms and geographical distribution: *Bandicota bengalensis* (Gray) – India, Sri Lanka, Nepal, Burma, Southern China, Taiwan, Malaysia, and Indonesia; *Rattus argentiventer* Robins. & Kloss *(= R. r. argentiventer, R. r. brevicaudatus)* – Philippines, Pacific Islands; *R. natalensis macrolepis* (Sund.) *(=Mastomys natalensis)* – Africa south of the Sahara, and Morocco; *R. norvegicus* (Berk.) – worldwide; *R. rattus rattus* (L.) – worldwide; *R. r. mindanensis* Mearns – Philippines; *Millardia meltada* (Gray) *(= Rattus meltada)* – India, Nepal, Sri Lanka; *Tatera indica cuvieri* (Waterh.) – India, Sri Lanka, China, Iran, Iraq, Tropical Africa etc.; *Holochilus sciureus* Wagn. – South America; *Mus musculus* L. – worldwide.

Crops/Stored products attacked: Rats and mice are generally herbivorous and versatile in feeding behaviour and choice of food. They damage practically all orchard trees (fruits), forest and field crops. Rats are very serious pests of paddy mainly by cutting tillers. Various subspecies of *R. rattus* have been responsible for serious damage to coconuts in Fiji Islands, Tahiti, Philippines, St. Lucia, South India, Gilbert and Ellis Islands and many other islands in the Pacific region. Rats feed even on snails, crabs, cream, meat, fish and its products as well as on popped, cooked and fried rice.

Symptoms: Rats and mice are well known as gnawing animals. They break up their food first by gnawing, scraping or nibbling at it with their front teeth. The incisor teeth are sharp, chisel-shaped cutting implements. They are marvellously adapted to their food and their way of eating it. Food cut up roughly by the incisor teeth is thus strained before it reaches the molar teeth, which crush and grind it. Rats eat tender portions of crops particularly at the growth and ripening stages when they are sweet and succulent. The typical gnawing marks of the incisors can often be seen on damaged fruits, stems etc. which facilitates the recognition of rat damage. In stores, rats and mice contaminate food and other materials with their droppings and their urine.

Economic importance: Rats and mice are major pests of field crops and in stores in many parts of the tropics and subtropics, especially in Asia. Their outbreaks have occurred in the Philippines, Indonesia, Sri Lanka, Malaysia, Taiwan, Vietnam, Fiji Islands, India, Sierra Leone, Sudan, Guayana, and Colombia. The average percentage loss of various crops in India are: Barley 5.4–12.4 %, wheat 2.9 %, groundnut 1.7–7.3 %, coconut trees and nuts 6.24–28.3 %, sorghum 17.43 %, paddy 5.7–16.7 %, pigeon pea 6.6 %, and sugarcane 5.29 %. Annual economic losses of the world's cereal production due to rat and mouse damage are over 20 million tons in the field and 33 million tons in stores. In India, nearly 11 million tons of all types of edible and non-edible crops are lost.
A single rat on an average consumes 10–15 g of flour (soaked wheat up to 30 g) and 10 ml of water within 24 hours, i. e. 30 rats will eat enough grain annually to feed a cow for one year. Rats act also as carriers and reservoirs of more than 50 human diseases.

Fig. 203.   Feeding holes of *Rattus rattus mindanensis* in coconuts (phot. H. Schmutterer)

Fig. 204.   Damage (numerous shoots cut) by *R. r. mindanensis* in a rice field (phot. H. Schmutterer)

Morphology (of selected species/subspecies): *B. bengalensis* (Mole rat, Lesser bandicoot). Body robust and large. Fur above dark brown, occasionally blackish, rarely pale brownish or almost reddish, below lighter or darker grey, rarely whitish or very dark grey. – *R. argentiventer* (Rice-field rat). Nose shorter than in *R. r. rattus.* Fur with a "pepper and salt" structure, belly uniformly silvery. Pawpads smooth, bullae large and incisive foramina long. – *R. exulans* (Polynesian rat). Body relatively small (size between a mouse and a rat). Fur greyish-brown or black above and brownish-grey beneath. Hind foots with lamellated pads (good climber). – *R. natalensis macrolepis* (Multimammate rat). Head and body about 12–14 cm long. Upperside of fur thick and soft, yellowish-brown to dark brown, underside greyish-white. Female with up to 12 pairs of teats in a continuous row. – *R. norvegicus* (Norway rat, Sewer rat, Wharf rat). Body larger and more robust than in Black rat. Tail stout and shorter than head and body. Fur softer than in *R. r. rattus,* grooved bristles more slender and in small number. Colour brown (or black), dark at the back and whitish brown or light brown beneath. – *R. r. rattus* (Black rat, Roof rat, House rat, Ship rat). Body slender and medium-sized. Ears large, naked and translucent, reaching or covering eyes when pressed forward. Tail slender, at least as long as, and often longer than head and body length. Fur slaty or black, in adults intermixed with many slender grooved bristles. – *Millardia meltada* (Soft-furred field rat). Body rather small in size. Fur dark brownish or greyish or paler grey above and pale below, feet whitish. – *T. i. cuvieri* (Indian gerbil, Antelope rat). Size of body about the same as in *R. r. rattus.* Eyes very large. Fur light brownish or sandy above and darker with a pale stripe on each side below. Tail with a terminal tuft of long dark hairs. Hind feet very long (adapted for jumping). – *M. musculus* (House mouse). Tail almost naked, generally longer than head and body length. Fur short and without spines. Colour dark to light brown, paler from below.

Life history and ecology: Rats and mice possess a remarkable capacity to adjust themselves to any environmental conditions. They are colour blind and clear vision is limited to a short distance. They have well developed senses of smell and taste, which help them in keeping them away from toxic substances. Rats possess exceptionally good hearing and can recognise sounds of higher frequency than an average human ear. They recognise their routes by dark greasy marks left by them in their runways, but they are very much afraid of new obstacles which they encounter. Rats are also good swimmers. The mole rat can swim 16 to 91 metres (average 81.6 metres) in five minutes and can remain floating in water for hours without becoming exhausted. They have been seen to submerge and rest on the bottom, making no movement. Rats can climb pipes, walls and trees and can jump a horizontal distance of about 8 feet or can drop from a height of more than 4 metres. Field rats dig their burrows inside dense, vigorous crops and house rats near sheltered places close to food stores. The number of openings in one field burrow varies from 2–42. Rats make chambers inside their burrows for various purposes. Some of them serve for breeding and are made comfortable with dried grasses, straw etc., while others are used for storing foods for future consumption. The depth of the burrow ranges from 0.3 to 1.5 metres. The maximum length of burrows has been found to be 40 metres. The burrows are generally long with many branches and openings and have loose soil, unconsumed food and droppings at the surface openings (Fig. 205).

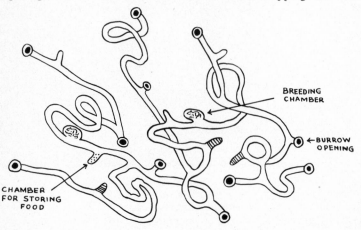

BREEDING CHAMBER

←BURROW OPENING

CHAMBER FOR STORING FOOD

Fig. 205. Burrow pattern of *Bandicota bengalensis* (drawing A. S. Srivastava)

R. r. rattus inhabits houses, warehouses, packing houses, seed stores, ships and sea ports. It is an excellent climber. *R. norvegicus* is essentially a water-loving and burrowing animal, found in drains and sewers. *M. musculus* inhabits houses, but sometimes gardens and fields near villages and towns. *B. bengalensis* feeds mostly on field crops, vegetables and fruits. Its burrows have usually more than one opening which are closed with a ball of hard clay or loose excavated soil during the daytime. They hoard grain and ears of cereal crops inside the burrows for future consumption. *T. i. cuvieri* makes its burrows on dry land in patches near fields, rivers and bunds, village sites, under bushes or along railway lines. *M. meltada* lives in cultivated fields and makes burrows both in fields and field bunds. This rat does not hoard food material.

Breeding in domestic rats starts after they become 3 to 4 months of age. The period of gestation lasts from 21 to 25 days. Fertility is at its maximum when the rats are from 100–300 days of age, then the number of young ones in a litter are above the average. The oestrus cycle is about 4 days. Both the males and females become sexually mature at about 50–60 days of age. The time required for parturition may take a few minutes or be prolonged for many hours. The life span is about 3 years.

With the peri-domestic or wild rats and particularly the Lesser bandicoot, the female comes into heat every 4 to 5 days and remains in this condition for 2 to 3 days. Breeding commonly takes place twice a year and coincides with the maturation of crops, i. e. in India, March and September to October and giving birth to from 8 to 10 young ones in each litter. Breeding takes place either in subterranean burrows or in dense plants (rice) or trees (coconuts). The latter has been observed in various subspecies of *R. rattus,* which are excellent climbers. However, the maximum number of young ones has been found to be 22. The life span of a rat in large populations is about 6 months.

Natural enemies: The natural enemies of rats are cats, terrier dogs, owls and other birds, mongooses, weasels, skunks, snakes and other reptiles.

Control:

Sanitary methods. In houses, along main roads and godowns, heaps of trash, garbage and sweepings should not be kept for a long period. Clean-up programmes should be enforced in rat-infested localities after which the rats are bound to be reduced in number. Stored materials should never be allowed to be piled on floors. Edible foods should be kept, whenever possible, in metal containers.

Rat proofing. Rodent proofing checks the movement of house rats and mice into or around the outside of a house or building. Rat proofing can be done by sealing all openings and covering the edges of doors, windows and other inlets with metal sheets. The metal sheet, 12" in height, should be inserted smoothly around all corners above the floor or ground level to prevent the rats climbing.

Trapping. Traps are ineffective in catching large numbers of rats, particularly in dwellings, and their use requires great skill and is time-consuming. They are recommended in small infestations where chemical control like poison bait or gassing are hazardous or impracticable. Various types of traps (pot, bamboo, bow and arrow, wire and snap traps) are employed in Asian countries.

Cultural practices. Heavy rains reduce rat populations by drowning the young ones. Similarly, artificial flooding of infested fields can act in the same way. Deep ploughing helps in exposing the rat burrows causing the adult rats to run away and the young ones to be picked up by birds or eaten by other animals.

Biological control. Villagers put sticks near the rat burrows in the field to act as resting places for owls which then catch the rats.

Chemical control. Because of the continuous migration of rats from infested neighbouring areas, chemical control operations are fully successful if they are carried out on an extensive area. Systematic and proper planning of rat control goes a long way in achieving maximum mortality of rats in different environmental conditions.

Baiting. Baits are prepared with various types of rodenticides which are mixed with ground cereals or pulses, cut portions of fruits, vegetables or meat. Crushed grains are soaked in water for a few hours and then mixed with a small quantity of vegetable oil like mustard, groundnut or linseed. Rodenticides generally used are 2 % zinc phosphide, 1–3 % naphthyl thiourea (Antu) or 0.5 % Norbormide (Raticate). The anticoagulants are Dicoumarol, Tomorin (Coumachlor), Fumarin (Coumafuryl), Pindone or Pival, Diphacine, Racumin, Rodafarin, or Ratafin but 0.025 % Warfarin is commonly employed. In the field, baits are offered to rats in bait stations of various types. Anti-rodent capsules have been found to be extremely useful, effective and convenient. Each capsule contains 295 mg of 2 % zinc phosphide in food and the capsule is treated externally with a mixture of glucose, mustard oil and saffron. The greatest advantage of anti-rodent capsules is that no bait shyness is developed; the rats are attracted to the capsule and then after eating, die outside.

Fumigation. A number of chemicals are used to fumigate burrows and kill the rats inside. Calcium cyanide (Cymag) at a rate of 6–10 g, or aluminium phosphide (Celphos) at a rate of 3 g per burrow are used. Other chemicals used are carbon monoxide, carbon dioxide, petrol, chloroform, methyl bromide, ethylene dibromide, EDCT mixture and dust of DDT and Antu in the burrows as well as in warehouses.

Integrated control. A new effective integrated technique has been evolved, developed and standardised in India, particularly for eradicating field rats in infested paddy, coconut, sugarcane, wheat and other fields.

Surveys or census of rats can accurately be carried out be multiplying the number of active rat burrows with the number of rats per burrow. The quantity and location of droppings will give an idea of the probable rat population.

Rat burrows should be prebaited with any kind of unpoisoned food or grain for two or more days so that the rats may become familiarised with the baits.

Poison baiting with 2 % zinc phosphide in the same food material together with a little vegetable oil may then be carried out for two to three days in the rat burrow openings. If there is any evidence of bait shyness, 0.025 % warfarin bait may be substituted particularly in very dense or unaccessible areas, where burrows cannot be located. Burrows which remain active may be fumigated for 2 to 3 days with HCN using calcium cyanide (Cymag). If the rats are then still alive, a mixture of chemosterilants viz., colchicine 1 part + furadantin 50 parts + wheat flour 20,000 parts is applied. 10 g of wheat flour containing this bait can be placed in a burrow opening and is sufficient for one rat. The bait will render the male or female rats completely sterile.

Resistance. Resistance has appeared to rodenticides, particularly Warfarin, in rat populations in Norway, Denmark, Netherlands, various parts of England, Guayana, U.S.A. and in other countries. In one area of India resistance of field rats to zinc phosphide has been detected.

Literature

CHITTY, D. (1954): Control of rats and mice. Vol 2. The Clarendon Press, Oxford, 307–632.
SCIENCE AND TECHNOLOGY SOCIETY, Kanpur (1971): International Symposium on 'Bionomics and Control of Rodents' held on 29. September–2. October, 1968. Proc. and Recommendations, Defence Research Laboratory (Materials) Kanpur (India). 1–185.
SRIVASTAVA, A. S. (1966): Rats and their control. Labdev Jour. Science and Technology 4 (4), 207–240. 21 figs.
SRIVASTAVA, A. S. (1966): Evolution, development and standardisation of a technique for the eradication of field rats. Proc. Indian Rodent Symposium, Calcutta, held on December 8–11, 1966. United States Agency for International Development, New Delhi, 283–290.
SRIVASTAVA, A. S. (1968): Rodent control for increased food production. Practical directions for rodent eradication campaign. Rotary Club (West) Kanpur, India. 1–152. 13 photographs, 6 figs. and 10 graphs.
SRIVASTAVA, A. S. (1974): A new integrated technique for rodent eradication "A breakthrough in protection technology" World Crops, London (Communication).
TAYLOR, K. D. (1972): The Rodent problem. Outlook on Agriculture. I.C.L. London 7 (2), 60–67.

Author: A. S. Srivastava

Other injurious mammals (Fig. 206):

Wild pigs (Suidae) or pigs run wild can do much damage to maize, root crops, groundnuts etc., in rain forests and woodlands of Africa and Asia. Where **monkeys** are common, they can also be destructive plant pests. Baboons (*Papio* spp.) damage groundnuts, maize (see Fig. 206) and other cereals in Africa and smaller monkeys (*Cercopithecus* spp.) also attack cereals and fruit. **Flying foxes** (Pteropidae), which are reckoned among the bats, have been found do damage young coconuts and fruit in Asia and Africa. **Ruminants, elephants** and other large mammals may occasionally damage crops.

H. Sch.

Fig. 206.   Maize cobs, damaged by baboons (phot. H. Schmutterer)

Weeds
in Tropical Crops

Edited by Werner Koch

In collaboration with: S. Behrendt, F. Bischof, M. Gühne, R. Hansen del Orbe, G. Jürgens, G. Linden, S. K. Mukherji, K. Petzoldt, E. Raddatz, C. E. Reyes

Introduction

Weeds are higher plants that do more harm than good. Therefore under certain circumstances, each plant species can be a weed although hardly any plant species is a weed as such. Weed control is thus the reduction of a plant population to a level where its usefulness is greater than the damage it could reasonably be expected to cause. The expenditure necessary for weed control must not exceed the expected short and long term losses. This approach pre-supposes a detailed knowledge of the damage caused by individual weed species in relation to their numbers.

The intensification of plant production and the increase in the application of herbicides requires a detailed knowledge of the life history and population dynamics of weed species as well as of the losses due to weeds and the possibilities of their control. In many tropical and subtropical countries, this knowledge is at an early stage of development. It is therefore not surprising that relatively little is known about the life history of many weed species of warmer regions. There is, however, an increasing amount of work being done to improve the present state of knowledge. The results of respective research work are published in various journals (for example PANS, Weed Research, Weed Science, Weed Abstracts) or presented at national and international congresses and printed in congress reports.

In spite of the above reservations concerning the present state of knowledge in the field of weed science in the tropics and subtropics, there exists a number of books written about weeds and weed control in these regions. A relevant review of those publications was carried out by Holm & Herberger (1971). The books quoted from their publication are, in general, not acknowledged in the following descriptions of individual weed species. The same applies for the general floras which are used when dealing with each weed species. Only in exceptional circumstances are they quoted in the list of references.

The descriptions of those weed species which have been dealt with by Hansen del Orbe and Jürgens are based to a large extent on results of their own work which has partially been published in 1973 (Jürgens et al.). Again this publication is usually not quoted in the list of references of the individual species described.

The following work centres around individual weed species of arable land, plantation crops and, to a lesser extent, of pasture-land. With the exception of some weed species of paddy rice, aquatic plant species have not been considered. Weed control in practice is mostly concerned with simultaneous control of several weed species. This aspect was largely taken into account by Kasasian (1971) in his book dealing with weed control in the tropics.

The decision which of the different common names should be chosen is often very difficult. For English common names, the "Composite List of Weeds" (Anonym. 1971) is referred to in many cases. No such lists were available in French and Spanish.

Literature

ANONYM (1971): Composite list of weeds. Weed Science **19**, 437–476.
HOLM, G. LEROY & J. HERBERGER (1971): World list of useful publications for the study of weeds and their control. PANS **17**, 119–132.
JÜRGENS, G., J. E. BAUTISTA & R. HANSEN del ORBE (1973): Control de malezas en la República Dominicana. Schriftenreihe BfE, No 10.
KASASIAN, L. (1971): Weed Control in the Tropics. London.

Family: Aizoaceae

Trianthema portulacastrum L. (Fig. 207 and plate 49 a, b, c)

Synonym: *T. monogyna* L.

Common names: black pigweed, horse purslane; –; poupier courant; verdolaga blanca.

Related species: *Portulaca oleracea* L. (Plate 49 a, b).

Geographical distribution: The species is widespread throughout the tropics.

Habitat: *Trianthema portulacastrum,* a plant of warm climates, predominantly invades annual crops such as cereals, legumes and cotton. On Hispaniola, the species is only important as a weed on light to medium soils of dry regions. In semi-humid regions it shows a marked increase in growth during the dry season. Salt-works and habitats close to the sea are also colonised.

Description: Prostrate or somewhat ascending plant with stems up to 1 m long (Fig. 207). Leaves opposite, petioled, round to oval, often purple coloured at margins, 1–5 cm long. Flowers light pink to white, 4–5 mm. Fruit a capsule with black seeds approximately 1 mm or more in diameter. *Portulaca oleracea* has smaller, sessile leaves and yellow flowers (Plate 49 a).

Development: This annual species reproduces exclusively by seeds. Storing the seeds at changing temperatures and varying air humidities had no significant influence on the percentage germination. However, 50 % of the seeds germinated less than 4 months after harvesting if grown in a dark room or in the dark in a greenhouse. The seeds germinated well at fluctuating temperatures of between 20–25 °C. Cotyledons oblong oval, about 15–25 mm long, 5–7 mm wide (Plate 49 b,

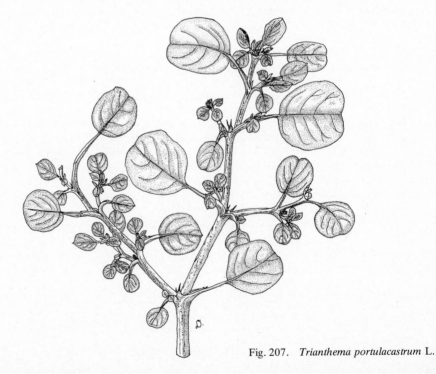

Fig. 207.   *Trianthema portulacastrum* L.

c). Cotyledons and primary leaves purple tinged on the lower surface. Onset of flowering about 4 weeks after emergence. During the following 2–3 months, continuous formation of flowers and fruits on the spreading plant.

Supplementary: It it reported from India that the weed is heavily attacked by the butterfly *Hymenia recurvalis* which can totally defoliate the plant. The species is a host plant for the virus of a mosaic disease of aubergines. *Trianthema portulacastrum* is listed as a poisonous plant because of its high oxalate content.

Control: All mechanical methods of crop cultivation which lead to the excision of the tap root can destroy the weed.
Chemical control can be carried out through soil treatments with simazine, atrazine, prometryne, DCPA, EPTC, pebulate, diuron, fluometuron, chlorbromuron, alachlor and nitrofen. Trifluralin, ametryne and various herbicide combinations are also recommended.

Literature

BAJPAI, N. R., B. L. PORWAL & D. K. MISRA (1969): A comparative study of new herbicides on *Cyperus rotundus* and *Trianthema portulacastrum*. Indian J. Weed Sci. **1**, 41–47.
CAMERON, D. G. (1971): Control of black pigweed *(Trianthema portulacastrum)* with trifluralin for pasture legume establishment. Qd. J. Agric. Anim. Sci. **28**, 217–226.
KHURANA, S. M. P. (1970): *Trianthema monogyna* and *Boerhavia diffusa;* unrecorded hosts of brinjal mosaic disease. Pl. Dis. Reptr. **54**, 437–438.
PANDE, Y. D. (1969): Observations on the biology of *Hymenia recurvalis* Fabricius *(Pyralidae: Lepidoptera)* as a defoliator of the serious kharif weeds in Rajasthan. Indian J. Sci. & Ind. (Sect. A) **3**, 107–108.
VAN RJIN, P. J. (1968): Ecological aspects of weed control in cotton in the Ord River valley, W. A. 1. Conditions affecting germination of weeds. Aust. J. Exp. Agric. Anim. Husb. **8**, 620–624.

Author: G. Jürgens

Family: Amaranthaceae

Amaranthus L. (Fig. 208, plates 49 d and 50 a–d)

Common names: amaranth, pigweed; Amarant, Fuchsschwanz; zepina; epinard; bledo.

Most important weed species: *A. dubius* Mart. ex Thell. (Syn: *A. tristis* F. & R., non L.), *A. hybridus* L., *A. retroflexus* L., *A. spinosus* L., *A. viridis* L. (Syn: *A. gracilis* Desf.).

Geographical distribution: Genus is widely distributed in warmer climates. Many among the more than 50 species have at least a regional importance as weeds.

Habitat: *Amaranthus* species invade fields and plantation crops in lowland as well as in higher, but still reasonably warm areas of the tropics and subtropics. Due to the numerous species and ecotypes present, one or more of the species can be found in every type of habitat. A detailed study of the ecological requirements of the more important genus members is still outstanding.
Three year long studies in the USA have shown that 4 weeks of competition from *Amaranthus* plants at a density of 12 plants per metre per row significantly reduced the yield of millet. Frequently, as few as one or two sturdy plants per square metre are strong competitors in low growing crops.

Description: Creeping to erect, glabrous or hairy plant. Leaves alternate, simple. Flowers in axillary clusters or in terminal ears or panicles. Flower formed in conjunction with subtending leaf,

Fig. 208.   *Amaranthus dubius* Mart. ex Thell.

small, plain, inconspicuous, white, crimson or green. Calyx consisting of 3–5 segments. Stamens 2–5, fruit costate, opening with a lid.

A. spinosus: erect plant with red stem and spines in leaf axil. Leaves oval to lanceolate. Stamens 5, seeds glossy, dark brown (Plate 49 d).

A. dubius: erect plant with green to pink stem. Leaves oval to rhomboid, stamens 5, seeds reddish black (Fig. 208, plate 50 a).

A. hybridus: erect, somewhat decumbent habit. Reddish coloured. Leaves oval to rhomboid. Seeds glossy black.

A. retroflexus: erect plant usually with pale green stem. Leaves rhomboid-ovate, Seeds glossy, black.

A. viridis: erect or ascending plant with great diversity of forms. Leaves rhomboid, notched at tip. Stamens 3, seeds black, not glossy.

Development: *Amaranthus* species are annual seed producing weeds. In vegetation hall experiments newly harvested mature seeds of *A. dubius, A. viridis* and *A. hybridus* showed considerably less dormancy than seeds of *A. spinosus.* Santelmann and Evetts (1971) confirmed that with no pre-treatment, seeds of *A. hybridus* germinated better than those of *A. spinosus.*

The cotyledons of *Amaranthus* plants are linear lanceolate to oval lanceolate, approximately 7–12 mm long, 1.5–2 mm wide in the case of *A. dubius* and *A. viridis,* smaller with *A. spinosus* and larger with *A. hybridus* (Plate 50 b, c, d).

Under favourable conditions, especially at high temperatures, *A. dubius* and *A. viridis* are able to flower about three to four weeks after emergence. There is a life span of several months. Of the five described species, *A. spinosus* is the most enduring. A heavy infestation with this species can result in the presence of 5 billion viable seeds per hectare (Schwerzel, 1970).

Supplementary: According to Kanodia and Gupta (1968), *A. hybridus, A. spinosus* and *A. viridis* are used in India as vegetables. *A. spinosus* is counted as a medicinal plant (Garcia, 1974).

Control: It is advisable to prevent competition from *Amaranthus* in all crops at an early stage. Young plants can be relatively easily destroyed by hoeing. In crops which give little ground shade further measures are necessary to remove subsequent weed infestations.

Amaranthus is more or less controlled by a number of pre- and post-emergence herbicides.

Literature

GARCIA, H. (1974): Flora Medicinal de Colombia. Vol 1. Bogotá.
KANODIA, K. C. & R. K. GUPTA (1968): Some useful and interesting supplementary food plants of the arid regions. J. Agric. trop. Bot. appl. **15,** 71–74.

NAVE, W. R. & L. M. WAX (1971): Effect of weeds on soybean yield and harvesting efficiency. Weed Sci. **19**, 533–535.

SANTELMANN, P. W. & C. EVETTS (1971): Germination and herbicide susceptibility of six pigweed species. Weed Sci. **19**, 51–54.

SCHWERZEL, P. J. (1970): Weed phenology and lifespan observations. PANS **16**, 511–515.

Author: R. Hansen del Orbe

Family: Capparaceae

Cleome viscosa L. (Fig. 209 and plate 51 a, b)

Synonym: *Polanisia viscosa* (L.) DC.

Common names: caia; Spinnenpflanze; –; jitomate, tabaquillo.

Related species: *C. gynandra* L. (Syn.: *Gynandropsis gynandra* (L.) Briq.), *C. monophylla* L., *C. rutidosperma* DC. (Syn.: *C. ciliata* Schuhmach.), *C. spinosa* Jacq.

Geographical distribution: *Cleome viscosa* and *C. gynandra* which originated in the Old World have now spread to the tropical zones of both hemispheres. *Cleome spinosa* occurs in the southern part of the United States as far as Latin America. *Cleome monophylla* has become a weed in Africa, *C. rutidosperma* in the Philippines and Jamaica.

Habitat: *Cleome viscosa* prefers light to medium soils. The species thrives during the wet period in semi-humid climates, but can also tolerate dry periods very well. On Hispaniola, the weed belongs to species that are dominant in irrigated crops (vegetables, legumes) of arid regions.

Description: An erect aromatic plant 50–120 cm in height, covered with dense, glandular hairs. Leaves 3–5 times pinnately dissected (Fig. 209). Leaflets are oval to elliptical, 2–7 cm long. Flowers solitary, axillary, born on long pedicels. Sepals yellow. The fruit is a pod up to 10 cm long. Seeds dark brown, transversely grooved, 1.4–1.6 mm in length. Although *C. viscosa* contains 8–30 stamens, the other species mentioned here have only 6 stamens. *Cleome monophylla* is further differentiated by its lanceolate leaves and pink or violet flowers. *Cleome rutidosperma* has white to light violet flowers. *Cleome gynandra* and *C. spinosa* are characterised by their white flowers – the latter having spines on its stem.

Fig. 209. *Cleome viscosa* L.

Development: *C. viscosa* is distinguished by rapid early growth. A high proportion of the viable seeds can germinate upon fruit dehiscence. Cotyledons oval shaped, 3–9 mm long, 2–7 mm wide (Plate 51 a, b). Primary leaves contain only three leaflets. The first flower buds appear 3–4 weeks after germination. The life cycle of this short lived species is only three months. On Hispaniola, with the onset of the cool season with shorter days, only plants of reduced height occur.

Control: Due to the rapid growth of *C. viscosa,* its control is necessary in many annual crops. Besides the normal hoeing, soil applied herbicides such as monolinuron, trifluralin, linuron, chlorbromuron, atrazine, prometryne, terbutryne, metribuzin, diuron and oxadiazon have proved successful. In contrast to these, alachlor and fluorodifen were inefficient. Some foliar-applied herbicides such as MCPA, 2,4-D and paraquat give satisfactory control also.

Literature

HASELWOOD, E. L. & G. G. MOTTER (1966): Handbook of Hawaiian weeds. Honolulu, Hawaii.
HEBBLETHWAITE, J. F. (1970): The performance of alachlor on some annual summer crops and weeds in South Africa. Proc. 10th Br. Weed Control Conf., 452–459.
JÜRGENS, G., J. E. BAUTISTA & R. HANSEN del ORBE (1973): Control de malezas en la República Dominicana. Schriftenreihe BfE, No 10.

Author: R. Hansen del Orbe

Family: Caesalpiniaceae

Cassia obtusifolia L. (Fig. 210 and plate 51 c)

Synonym: *C. tora* F. & R., non L.

Common names: sicklepod; Sennespflanze; pistache marron, sené; biche manso, bicho, brusca hembra.

Related species: The genus *Cassia* contains about 450 species of which a number can occur as weeds. Besides *C. obtusifolia,* other weeds of some importance are *C. tora* L. (Syn.: *Emelista tora* (L.) Britton & Rose), *C. occidentalis* L. (Syn.: *Ditremexa occidentalis* (L.) Britton & Rose) and *C. italica* (Mill.) Lam. (Syn.: *Senna italica* Mill., *C. obovata* Coll.).

Geographical distribution: With the exception of South East Asia, *C. obtusifolia* is distributed over the tropics of both hemispheres.

Habitat: The weed enjoys favourable growth conditions on medium to heavy soils. Results of observations on Hispaniola indicate a higher incidence of the weed during the seasonal rainfall in semi-arid regions; upland areas over 400 m are not colonised.
Cassia usually invades pasture-lands and perennial crops such as sugar cane. Singh et al. (1970) noted that following overgrazing, *C. tora* was able to displace cultivated grasses.
Cassia obtusifolia is a noxious weed in annual crops such as cotton and legumes.

Description: Shrub-like plant up to 1 m tall (Fig. 210). Stem almost glabrous. Leaflets normally in three pairs, 2–5 cm long, 1–3 cm wide. Flowers with short peduncles, occurring mostly in pairs in leaf axils, yellow to orange-yellow. Pods narrow, curved, about 10–20 cm long. Seeds light brown, glossy, 4–5 mm long.
Under natural conditions, *C. obtusifolia* and *C. tora* differ in their growth habits and exhibit differences even when grown in a uniform environment (Singh, 1968). *Cassia obtusifolia* has pedicels about 12–22 mm long and usually only one petiolar gland between the lower pair of leaflets. *Cas-*

Fig. 210. *Cassia obtusifolia* L.

sia tora on the other hand has a pedicel 5–11 mm long and two petiolar glands, one between the lower and the other between the middle leaflet pair.

Development: Annual seed-bearing weed with a slow developmental cycle. Under favourable habitat conditions it can flower and bear fruit throughout the year. The seed coats of both species are impermeable, but scarifying the coat will encourage germination (Singh, 1968). Seeds of *C. obtusifolia* can remain dormant for several years and germination can occur relatively deep within the soil (Buchanan & Hoveland, 1971). Germination is possible over a wide temperature, nutrient and pH range. Results of pot experiments in the Dominican Republic have shown that 30–35 % of the seeds can germinate immediately after maturity.

Cotyledons approximately circular, up to 2.5 cm in diameter. Primary leaves with only two leaflet pairs (Plate 51 c). Flowering begins 4–6 weeks after emergence. *Cassia tora* can produce a total of 595 seeds per plant (Hosamani et al., 1971).

Control: 2,4-D, 2,4-D/2,4,5-T, 2,4-D/picloram and dicamba can successfully control *Cassia* in pasture-lands.

Trifluralin or nitralin 0.6–1.1 kg/ha incorporated into the soil before weed emergence were unable to control *C. obtusifolia*. Fluometuron 1.6–2.2 kg/ha, however, is effective against this species. Cyanazine 1.1–4.5, atrazine 3.4, napropamide 4.5 and diphenamid 5.6 kg/ha have also proved to be effective. Alachlor only gives good results at a higher dosage of 4.5 kg/ha.

Effective post-emergence herbicides are paraquat 0.3, dinoseb 1.6, linuron 0.6–1.1, chlorbromuron 0.6, chloroxuron 1.6 and metribuzin 0.3–0.6 kg/ha. Alachlor in combination with 2.4-D or dinoseb can also be applied.

Literature

BUCHANAN, G. S. & E. R. BURNS (1971): Weed competition in cotton. 1. Sicklepod and tall morning-glory. Weed Sci. **19**, 576–679.

BUCHANAN, G. S. & C. S. HOVELAND (1971): Sicklepod – success story of a weed and how to control it in soybeans. Weeds Today **2**, 11–12

HOSAMANI, M. M., B. SHIVARAJ & C. B. KURDIKEI (1971): Seed production potentialities of common weeds of Dharwar. PANS **17**, 237–239.

SINGH, J. S. (1968): Comparison of growth performance and germination behaviour of seeds of *Cassia tora* L. and *Cassia obtusifolia* L. Trop. Ecol. **9**, 64–71.

SINGH, J. S. MUKHTAR, R. K. RANDEY & K. A. SHANKRANARAYAN (1970): Problems of grassland weeds and their control in India. Proc. 11th int. Grassld Congr., Surfers Paradise, Australia, 71–74.

Author: G. Jürgens

Family: Characeae

Chara zeylanica Willdelow

Related species: Several species of *Chara, Nitella* and some other genera are of importance.

Geographical distribution: In coastal West Bengal an area of about 0.4 million hectare is algae infested, comprising of low lying areas in the districts of 24-Parganas, Howrah, and Midnapore. In Spain and Italy also some paddy fields are algae infested but the algae do not belong to the *Chara* and *Nitella* genera.

In badly managed seedbeds and low lying areas algae like *Spirogyra, Vaucheria, Anabaena, Nostoc, Volvox, Cladophora* etc. are often found. Mostly these form surface-mats on the standing water when they come up after entangling gas bubbles and many form a sheet on the soil surface when the water dries up. Generally they do not cause much damage except in seedbeds where they are found to be controlled by the use of carbaryl insecticide on seedling rice.

Habitat: In some low land and ill-drained coastal areas of West Bengal and neighbouring regions, the period of August to October causes considerable damage to paddy crop. These algae find the soil and climate very favourable here as the soil and water are somewhat saline (1–4 millimhos/cm) and alkaline (pH 6.5–7.8). The humidity and air temperature are relatively high throughout the year and the land remains under water for about six months in the year. The algae thickly infest paddy fields which are mono-cropped and not tended properly.

The algae grow usually in water depths of 15–50 cm and do not thrive well in deeper or turbid water as it interferes with their carbon-assimilation. For the same reason cloudy and rainy days as well as sudden changes in water level are also detrimental to their growth. With the advent of the cooler weather and lowering of water level, the algae start sporulating and then drying up. The algae survive as resistant spores in pools or moist places during the dry period. Control measures are usually taken up during August and September.

Description: These algae grow as submerged plants up to a length of about 50 cm with false leaf-like structures, nodes and internodes and filamentous rhizoids by which they are fixed to the soil. These algae are characteristically encrusted with calcium carbonate crystals which make them a little brittle. The infested fields emit a garlic like odour.

The algal weeds twine round paddy plants so that it is difficult to walk in the field, they hamper tiller formation of paddy, interfere with interculture operation, compete for feed and make harvest difficult. The result is that paddy growth is reduced and plants become reddish yellow in colour and look sickly. The paddy panicles, when they emerge, are short and the grains are only partially filled. The average yield is depressed by 10–25 % with moderate algae infestation. From one hectare of such a field 5–8 tons of green algae can be easily collected.

Control: It is very difficult if not impossible to control these algae by mechanical or manual means. Besides causing injury to the paddy crop, mechanical or manual removal is never complete, resulting in a quick reinfestation. Draining out water from the field can reduce infestation but is not possible, as long as all fields are at the same level. Moreover, in Bengal water supply to bring back standing water is not assured even in the monsoon season. So far chemical control measure seems to be the only answer and it has to be repeated practically every year as resistant spores overwinter.

Effective are copper sulphate at 18 kg/ha or copper oxychloride (with 50 % copper content) at 9 kg/ha of infested paddy field with an average depth of 30 cm of water. They are dispensed in the field water either by spraying a suitable aqueous preparation or spreading a mixture of the chemical and soil by hand. Movement of the operator in the water mixes the chemical. In about 48 hours all the algae are fully killed and are trampled down in the soil and soon act as an organic manure for the paddy. The final concentration of the copper comes to about 2 ppm which is slightly toxic to fish. One application, however, is adequate. On an average under West Bengal conditions cost of this chemical control came to about $^1/_{15}$th of the value of the yield increase.

Triphenyl tin acetate is very effective and quick acting at the dose of 1 kg/ha Brestan-60 for a water level of 30 cm depth. Also effective are the herbicide nitrofen, Dithane Z-78, triphenyl tin chloride and disodium ethylene-bisdithiocarbamate (Dithane A-40). An interesting work (Mukherji, 1972) with pentachlorophenol (PCP) and sodium pentachlorophenate showed in this connection that not only are these compounds effective algicides at 4.75 kg/ha and 3.74 kg/ha respectively but also when pentachlorophenol is incorporated in infested soils 3 weeks before transplanting rice at 6.25 kg/ha prevented the appearance of *Chara* and *Nitella* for that season. However, as regards fish toxicity (for some fish is cultured in the paddy-field water in these areas) it was found that all chemicals except Brestan-60, Dithane Z-78 and Dithane A-40 at the recommended doses are toxic to the fish.

Literature

MUKHERJI. S. K. & S. K. ENGUPTA (1964): Control of algal weeds in paddy fields in West Bengal, India. FAO Plt. Prot. Bull. **12**: 120–130.
MUKHERJI, S. K. & B. K. RAY (1966): Algal weed flora of paddy of coastal West Bengal and their control by a new chemical. Z. Pflanzenkrankheiten **73**, 35–40.
MUKHERJI, S. K. (1970): Further studies on the chemical control of algal weeds in West Bengal. World Crops, **22**, 387–388.
MUKHERJI, S. K. (1972): Use of pentachlorophenol as an algicide in paddy fields in West Bengal. Weed Res. **12**, 389–390.

Author: Sudhakrishna Mukherji

Family: Commelinaceae

Commelina diffusa Burm. f. (Fig. 211 and plate 51 d)

Synonym: *C. longicaulis* Jacq.

Common names: spreading dayflower, water grass; –; Curage; canutillo, hierba de pollo, suelda consuelda, siempreviva.

Related species: *C. africana* L., *C. benghalensis* L., *C. communis* L., *C. elegans* Kunth.

Geographical distribution: The genus *Commelina* is comprised of more than a hundred species which are widespread in the tropics and subtropics of both hemispheres but which are mainly present in the Old World. Many of these species can occur as weeds. *Commelina diffusa* and *C. elegans* appear mainly in the American tropics while *C. africana, C. benghalensis* and *C. communis* are predominantly found in the Old World.

Habitat: *Commelina* species prefer humous or clayey soils which are constantly damp for at least part of the year. *Commelina diffusa* finds ideal growing conditions in coffee or cacao plantations, but also frequently occurs in other perennial crops such as bananas and sugar cane. The species is commonly found in irrigated rice without it ever reaching a high degree of cover. *Commelina diffusa* also occurs in the higher ranges of mountain areas where it predominantly invades annual crops. Nicholls and Plucknett (1973) found a close relationship between the distribution of *C. diffusa* and the soil pH.

Description: Creeping to ascending, usually very much branched plant (Fig. 211). Stem somewhat succulent, glabrous, rooting at the nodes. Leaves lanceolate, ovate, about 2–6 cm long,

1–2.5 cm wide. Inflorescences in spathes on axillary peduncles, spathe tapering to a point, open 1–2.5 cm long. Sepals blue. Fruit a three loculated capsule with 5 grey-black seeds. *Commelina elegans* (Plate 51 d) and *C. benghalensis* are distinguished from *C. diffusa* by their closed spathes. *Commelina africana* is characterised by its yellow flowers. *Commelina communis* has blue and larger flowers, more than 1 cm in diameter.

Development: *Commelina diffusa* may be classified as a perennial plant because of the continuous growth of its stolon system. With a simultaneous formation of side shoots, the shoot growth rate can amount to 12–18 cm/week. The species flowers and bears fruit the whole year through, but its development can be interrupted during the dry period. In lowland areas of Hispaniola it flowers predominantly in the cooler season.

As relatively few seeds are formed, vegetative reproduction is of greater importance. Dispersal can occur through the fragmentation of the stem. More than 50 % of the clones planted on the soil surface could produce new plants if given moist ground and moderate shade. Storage of the plant material at 22–28 °C and 65–85 % relative humidity over a three month period had no influence on its rate of regrowth. Even after more than 6 months of storage, parts of the clone could still sprout. There was less regrowth when the plants were planted within the soil, regrowth decreasing with increased depth of planting.

Supplementary: In Colombia, *Commelina* has been used as a cover plant against erosion in coffee plantations. Before being recommended as a companion crop, competitive conditions should however be examined. Other important aspects are its association with nematodes or diseases that affect *Commelina* species. The leaf blotch pathogen on rice *(Corticium sasakii)* was observed on *C. benghalensis* (Roy, 1973).

Control: The control of *Commelina* by mechanical means is difficult, for the plants cannot be completely removed from the infested area, and the severed fragments are viable for a long period

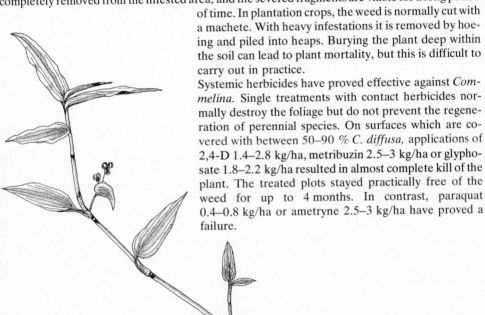

of time. In plantation crops, the weed is normally cut with a machete. With heavy infestations it is removed by hoeing and piled into heaps. Burying the plant deep within the soil can lead to plant mortality, but this is difficult to carry out in practice.

Systemic herbicides have proved effective against *Commelina*. Single treatments with contact herbicides normally destroy the foliage but do not prevent the regeneration of perennial species. On surfaces which are covered with between 50–90 % *C. diffusa*, applications of 2,4-D 1.4–2.8 kg/ha, metribuzin 2.5–3 kg/ha or glyphosate 1.8–2.2 kg/ha resulted in almost complete kill of the plant. The treated plots stayed practically free of the weed for up to 4 months. In contrast, paraquat 0.4–0.8 kg/ha or ametryne 2.5–3 kg/ha have proved a failure.

Fig. 211.   *Commelina diffusa Burm. f.*

Post-emergence treatments in rice have shown that the species cannot be controlled with propanil. Combinations with fluorodifen or fluorodifen on its own have proved better. Butachlor mixed with propanil was effective in post-emergence treatment against *C. diffusa,* whereas bentazon destroyed seedlings as well as flowering plants (Palmer, 1973).

Combinations of diuron, dalapon and 2,4-D applied at three monthly intervals as well as paraquat, dalapon and 2,4-D at 6 weekly intervals were effective against *C. elegans* in banana plantations. *Commelina benghalensis* in cotton was satisfactorily controlled by post-emergence treatments of noruron 5.6 kg/ha and fluometuron 2.4 kg/ha as well as by pre-sowing treatments with trifluralin 0.5–0.8 kg/ha followed by noruron 0.5 kg/ha and MSMA 1.5 kg/ha (de Almeida, 1970). The species was controlled by diuron, ametryne and linuron 1.6 kg/ha as well as prometryne 2.5 kg/ha.

Literature

ARISTEGUIETA, L. (1965): Notas sobre la Familia *Commelinaceae* en Venezuela. Bol. Acad. Cienc. Fis. Mat Nat. **25,** 94–142.
DE ALMEIDA, F. S. (1970): Herbicides in cotton – results of the trials carried out in Mozambique from 1963 to 1970. Proc. 10th Br. Weed Control Conf. 398–405.
EDMUNDS, J. E. (1971): Association of *Rotylenchus reniformis* with "Robusta" banana and *Commelina sp.* roots in the Windward Islands. Trop. Agric. Trinidad **48**, 55–61.
MATUDA, E. (1956): Las Commelinaceas del Estado de Mexico. Toluca, Mexico.
NICHOLLS, D. F. & D. L. PLUCKNETT (1973): Weed movement and distribution in a grazed tropical pasture. Proc. 4th Asian-Pacific Weed Sci. Soc. Conf., Rotorura, 94–104.
PALMER, R. D. (1973): Rice weed control in the Texas western belt. Proc. 26th An. Meet. Sthern Weed Sci. Soc., 146–154.
ROY, A. K. (1973): Natural occurrence of *Corticium sasakii* on some weeds. Current Sci. **42,** 842–843.

Author: G. Jürgens

Family: Compositae

Acanthospermum hispidum DC. (Fig. 212 and plate 52 a, b)

Common names: bristly sandbur, starbur, upright sandbur; –; dessalines; abrojo, cuajrilla, mala mujer.

Related species: *A. australe* (Loefl.) Kuntze, *A. humile* (Sw.) DC.

Geographical distribution: The genus *Acanthospermum* is a native of the American tropics. *Acanthospermum hispidum* is now widespread over the warmer regions of the world. *Acanthospermum australe* has also been introduced into parts of the Old World. In the West Indies, *A. humile* occurs more frequently than *A. hispidum* (Fig. 212, plate 52 a).

Habitat: The weed occurs near the equator at altitudes of up to 1300 m. Field crops and low grade types of pasture-land are invaded in East Africa (Ivens, 1968). It is one of the most important weeds of Rhodesia and can be found on all soil types (Thomas, 1970). *Acanthospermum* species are characteristic plants of arid regions.

Description: Erect growing, much branched plant, 20–60 cm tall (Fig. 212). Stem hispid. Leaves opposite, oval, hispid on both surfaces, up to 8 cm long, 4 cm wide. Leaf margins irregularly dentate to entire. Capitulum solitary, axillary, with 5–8 yellowish-green flowers. Achenes stellate with two strong terminal and numerous small prickly outgrowths. The very similar species *A. hispidum* and *A. humile* are distinguished from each other by their burs, the former with curved,

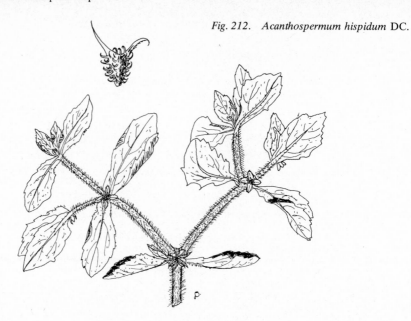

Fig. 212.   Acanthospermum hispidum DC.

hooked prickles over its whole surface, the latter with curved prickles only along the edges of the fruit.

Acanthospermum australe is a creeping plant with pedicelled leaves and capitula.

Development: *Acanthospermum* species are annual weeds whose seeds show a marked dormancy. After four years in the soil at a depth of 2.5 cm, 30 % of the seeds germinated. At a depth of 7.5 cm, 8 % of the seeds of *A. hispidum* were viable, while after five years, germination still continued at a steady rate (Anonym, 1971).

Seeds of *A. hispidum* collected immediately following physiological maturity had a germination count of less than 1 % over a three month period.

Cotyledons oblong, oval, about 9–11 mm long and 5–6 mm wide (Plate 52 b). About one month is required from emergence to flower bud formation. Development is possible throughout the whole year.

Hosamani et al. (1971) found that *A. hispidum* has a seed production of 455 per plant. Dispersal of the species is facilitated by the adhering quality of the burs.

Control: To avoid wool contamination by seeds of *Acanthospermum,* control measures in sheep pastures should be carried out before the weed flowers. Plants at early stages of growth are sensitive to 2,4-D and MCPA. Simazine 1–2 kg/ha, fluometuron 2.4 kg/ha, dichlobenil as a granulate 2.7 kg/ha, secbumeton 6.7–9 kg/ha, terbacil 2.2 kg/ha and diuron 0.8–1.6 kg/ha can be used in fields and plantation crops. Pebulate 5 kg/ha incorporated into the soil controlled *A. hispidum;* however trifluralin 0.8 or benfluralin 1.1 kg/ha did not. Alachlor 0.5–2 kg/ha and amiben 2–3 kg/ha were effective against *A. australe.*

Literature

ANÓNYM (1971): Weed biology. An. Rep., Henderson Res. Stn 1970–1971, 10–12.
HOSAMANI, M. M., B. SHIVARAJ & C. B. KURDIKERO (1971): Seed production potentialities of common weeds of Dharwar. PANS **17,** 237–239.
IVENS, G. W. (1968): East African weeds and their control. Nairobi, Kenia.
THOMAS, P. E. L. (1970): A survey of the weeds of arable lands in Rhodesia. Rhodesia agric. J. **67,** 34, 37.

Author: G. Jürgens

Ageratum conyzoides L. (Fig. 213 and plate 52 c, d)

Common names: goat weed, ageratum; Leberbalsam; baume; manrubio, chuva.

Related species: *A. houstonianum* Mill.

Geographical distribution: Both species, which are indigenous to the tropics of America, can now be found in most countries with tropical and subtropical climates.

Habitat: Besides tropical lowlands, mountain areas at high altitudes are also colonised; in the Caribbean up to about 1300 m, in East Africa up to 3000 m. The weed frequently occurs on medium to heavy soils in regions with high rainfall. Field crops (cereals, vegetables, cotton, legumes) and plantation crops (sugar cane, tea, coffee) are invaded. Late infestations with *Ageratum* can obstruct the burning down of sugar cane shortly before the harvest.

Description: Erect, branched, hairy plant, up to about 1 m tall (Fig. 213, plate 52 c). Leaves opposite, triangular or oval, about 2–8 cm long and 1.5–4 cm wide. Leaf margins crenate or serrate. Capitula in terminal compact corymbs. Flowers violet, blue or white. Achene pentagonal, black 1.5–2 mm, with pappus of about 2.5 mm.
Ageratum houstonianum is somewhat larger, with longer white hair, but otherwise a very similar species. The species can be distinguished by their involucral bracts which in *A. conyzoides* are oblong to oblong lanceolate and glabrous, in *A. houstonianum* linear lanceolate, with long acuminate tips, and hairy.

Development: Annual plants with a continuous development throughout the whole year. Morphologically mature seeds show a pronounced dormancy, with less than 1 % of freshly collected seeds germinating within three months. Cotyledons orbicular, somewhat wider than long, about 3–4 mm (Plate 52 d). The foliage leaf stage is passed through rather slowly. Onset of flowering about 8–9 weeks after emergence. Senescence is generally reached after 5 months.

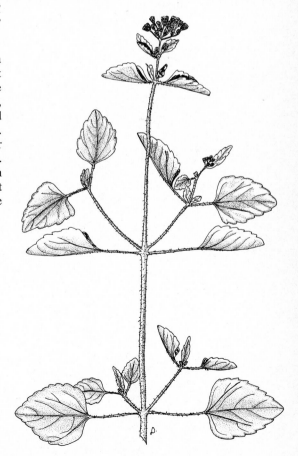

Fig. 213. *Ageratum conyzoides* L.

Control: *Ageratum conyzoides* is controlled in cereals and sugar cane with growth regulating herbicides such as 2,4-D, MCPA and 2,4,5-T. In sugar cane plantations, pre-emergence applications with diuron and ametryne are possible, the latter being also effective against emerged plants when applied at a higher dosage.

Ageratum houstonianum can be relatively well controlled with various soil applied herbicides such as linuron, diuron, chloroxuron, fluometuron, lenacil, propachlor, atrazine, atratone, desmetryne and prometryne. Various contact herbicides such as bipyridylium derivates and dinoseb give a rapid kill without any lasting effect.

Literature

AGARWALA, S. B. D. (1971): Weed control in tea in India. 3rd Conf. Asian-Pacific Weed Sci. Soc., Kuala Lumpur **13**, pp. 6.
CHRISTIE, G. A. (1971): The blue top weed problem in cane fields. Cane Grow. q. Bull. **34**, 78–83.
WETTASINGHE, D. T. & N. S. RAJENDRAM (1969): Evaluation of herbicides for weed control in mature tea. 1. Effects on the weed species. Tea. Q. **40**, 160–163.

Author: G. Jürgens

Bidens pilosa L. (Fig. 214 and plate 53 a, b)

Common names: common blackjack, hairy beggarstick, spanish needle; Zweizahn; aiguille; aceitilla, romerillo.

Related species: *B. cynapiifolia* H.B.K., *B. bipinnata* L.

Geographical distribution: *Bidens pilosa* is widely distributed over the tropical and subtropical areas of the world. *Bidens cynapiifolia* occurs in the West Indies, India, Hawaii and northern South America, *B. bipinnata* in South America, USA, India, China, Korea, Madagascar and the Philippines.

Habitat: Owing to the adaptation of individual sub-species to differing habitat conditions, there is an extensive spectrum of invaded crops. In subtropical regions, and in tropical upland areas, *B. pilosa* is one of the most important weeds in vegetable and other annual crops. In lowland and hilly land in the tropics, coffee and other plantation crops are predominantly invaded.

On Hispaniola, *B. pilosa* var. *dubia* (Fig. 214), which is an important weed there, prefers moist, shady upland places from 300–800 m, and fields or pastureland in upland valleys from 1000–1500 m. In contrast to this, *B. pilosa* var. *radiata* (Plate 53 a) prefers open terrain of lowland sites with permeable, gravelly soils.

Padmanabhan (1967–1968), recorded a heavy incidence of *B. pilosa* during the monsoon rainfall period. Areas with restricted drainage and temporarily flooded terrain are in general avoided.

Description: Erect, branched, herbaceous plant, 60–130 cm tall (Fig. 214). Stem four angled, variably hairy. Leaves opposite, simple or compound, divided into 3 to 5, rarely 7, oval or lanceolate oval leaflets, up to 8 cm long, 4 cm wide, but normally smaller and occasionally hairy. Achene linear, straight or nearly straight, 5–9 mm long with 2–3 bearded awns. Heads 6–10 mm in diameter. Flowers white or yellowish.

Bidens pilosa is divided into several varieties which are distinguished from each other by the presence or absence, as well as the size and colour of the ray florets.

Bidens cynapiifolia usually has a somewhat reflexed achene from 1.5–5 mm with 4–6 awns and leaves which are bipinnate. *Bidens bipinnata* has linear achenes, 2–4 mm with 3–4 awns. Leaves, pinnate or bipinnate.

Fig. 214. *Bidens pilosa* L.

Development: According to Valio et al. (1972), light promotes seed germination in *B. pilosa*. Under continuous fluorescent light, 80–90 % germination occurred. Germination was also induced by a short exposure to blue, green, red or far red light. Cold treatment and low concentrations of benzyl-adenine also gave a higher germination count.

With adequate moisture, the sub-species *dubia* can develop throughout the whole year. Even without any previous treatment, physiologically mature seeds are able to show more than 25 % germination. Cotyledons linear, 1.2–2.5 cm long (Plate 52 b). Primary leaves mostly simple. Foliage leaf development usually lasts five weeks, the plants start to die after a further 8 weeks. De Marinis (1973) found a reproductive capacity of 1205 seeds per plant. Distribution of the weed is promoted by the adhesiveness of the achenes.

Control: Owing to its large seed production combined with a rapid subsequent generation, *B. pilosa* can severely infest perennial crops especially after the soil has been cultivated. The species is however easily controlled by chemical methods.

In sugar cane and cereals, 2.4-D and MCPA can be employed. Other effective foliar applied herbicides in tree crops are paraquat, diquat and glyphosate. A combined application with soil applied herbicides is advisable for longer residual action.

Besides the above mentioned substances, the species can also be controlled with monuron 1.2, diuron 1.2–4.5, linuron 1–3, fluometuron 2.4, metobromuron 1, simazine 1.5, ametryne 1.6, metribuzin 1–2.5, terbacil 2–4, bromacil 3–4, alachlor 2.2 and propanil 3.6 kg/ha.

Literature

DE MARINIS, G. (1973): Note on the reproductive capacity of *Bidens pilosa*. Rev. Agric. **48,** 95–100.
PADMANABHAN, T. D. (1967/68): Weed flora in tea fields. Rep. United Planters Assoc. S. India, 22–25.
SHERF, E. E. & E. J. ALEXANDER (1965): N. Am. Flora II, 2, 1–190, New York Bot. Garden.
VALIO, I. F. M., S. L. KIRSZENZAFT & R. F. ROCHA (1972): Germination of achenes of *Bidens pilosa* L. 1. Effect of light of different wave lengths. New Phytologist **71,** 677–682.

Author: G. Jürgens

Eclipta alba (L.) Hussk. (Plate 53 c, d)

Synonym: *E. prostrata* (L.) L.

Common names: eclipta, false daisy; –; herbe à l'eau; yuyo, yerba de tajo, eclipta blanca.

Geographical distribution: The species is widespread over the warmer areas of the world.

Habitat: Heavy soils with a constant and abundant water supply are preferred. The species occurs in sugar cane, bananas, maize and vegetables. Dry and irrigated rice are among the most important crops to be invaded. Vegetational analyses in the Dominican Republic have shown that *E. alba* has a frequency of 67 % in the irrigated parts of the rice plots, with a mean degree of cover of 2 %. On the dams, the weed had an even higher frequency (75 %) giving 5 % cover.

Description: Mostly erect, often many branched plant, usually not more than 60 cm tall (Plate 53 c). Stem somewhat fleshy, and, as with the leaves, covered with short stiff hairs. Leaves sessile, elliptic-lanceolate about 4–10 cm long, 1–3 cm wide. Leaf margins toothed or entire. Heads white, mostly solitary, on peduncles up to 10 cm long, and surrounded by pointed sepals about 4 mm long. Fruit rugose, black, 2 mm long.

Development: Propagates exclusively by seeds some of which show no dormancy. Cotyledons oval, 4 mm long. Primary leaves oblong-oval (Plate 53 d). The weeds can develop on terrain that is continually covered with shallow water. The greatest proportion of the seedlings subsequently die. Those surviving are far weaker than seedlings growing on moist or temporarily flooded soils. Flowering stage begins approximately four weeks after emergence, the plant reaching maturity after a period of three to four months.

Control: Early control is necessary to prevent competition from this rapidly growing weed. Besides hand weeding and mechanical methods, the application of 2,4-D and MCPA in rice has proved successful. A complete kill can be obtained if the weeds are treated up to the flower-bud stage. The residual effect of a single application of these herbicides is too small to prevent subsequent weed infestations.

According to information from Columbia and the Philippines, the species cannot be controlled with propanil. This is in contrast to results obtained in America.

Somewhat contradictory data have been obtained concerning the control of the weed with soil applied herbicides. Atrazine 3 kg/ha, atrazine/linuron 1.5/0.75 kg/ha, butachlor 2–4.5 kg/ha, chloramben 2.3 kg/ha and terbutryne 2.4 kg/ha have all been mentioned as being successful. In Columbia, *E. alba* showed resistance to application of benthiokarb 3 and 6 kg/ha, nitrofen 5 kg/ha, butachlor 2 and 3 kg/ha as well as fluorodifen 5 kg/ha.

Herbicide combinations appear to be more reliable than an application of a single herbicide. Smith (1973) reports the successful application of these herbicide mixtures against emerged weeds: propanil/benthiokarb 3.3–4.5/3.3–4.5 kg/ha, propanil/butachlor 2.2–3.3/2.2–3.3 kg/ha as well as propanil/oxadiazon 2.2–3.3/0.8–1.4 kg/ha.

Literature

MADRID, M. T., F. L. PUNZALAN & R. T. LUBIGAN (1972): Some common weeds and their control. Laguna, Philippines.
SMITH, R. J. (1973): New herbicide treatments for weed control in rice. Rice J. **76**, 39–40.

Author: R. Hansen del Orbe

Mikania micrantha Kunth. (Fig. 215)

Common names: guaco, hempweed; Sommerefeu; liane Françoise; guaco, cepucillo.

Related species: From the more than 200 species of this genus, *M. micrantha* deserves most attention as a weed. Parker (1972) believes it is probably the most aggressive weed in South Asia, where it is erroneously labelled as *M. cordata* (Burm. f.) B. L. Robinson. *Mikania congesta* DC. is considered by some authors as a sub-species of *M. micrantha*.

Geographical distribution: This species is widespread in the tropics of America and has become naturalised in large areas of other tropical zones.

Habitat: *Mikania micrantha* readily colonises humid habitats and occurs in shady places as well as in open areas. The species is a noxious weed in young plantation crops which can be completely overgrown. It is also frequently found in pasture-land and occasionally on the banks of rice fields. The presence of *Mikania* is detrimental to the growth of young rubber plants due to its competition for water and nitrogen. The damage caused is further attributed to exudates which directly inhibit tree growth or suppress nitrification processes within the soil. The yield of oil palms was reduced when the *Mikania* species present had a ground cover of more than 45 %.

Description: Climbing and twining plant with slender stems, glabrous or sparsely hairy (Fig. 215). Leaves three lined, oval to oval hastate or cordate, normally 4–10 cm long and 2.5–6 cm wide. Corymb, axillary or terminal. Flowers white or greenish-white, aromatic. Involucre 3–4 mm. Corolla 2.5–3 mm. Achene 1.2–1.8 mm long.
Mikania micrantha var. *micrantha* has distinctly peduncled flowering heads whereas in var. *congesta*, peduncles are either missing or weakly formed. *Mikania cordata* is characterised by a considerably larger involucre 5–6 mm long.

Development: Perennial plant with limited life span. Reproduction and distribution by seeds. Spreading of individual plants through rapid stolon growth. After vigorous vegetative development, onset of reproductive phase with extensive seed production. Flowering and fruit formation on Hispaniola is mainly during the dry season from December to March.

Supplementary: The plant is used as a febrifuge against influenza and malaria.

Control: Young plants of *Mikania* are easily destroyed by mechanical methods or controlled with phenoxy-herbicides. Established plants are more difficult to remove by mechanical or chemical methods due to the rooting and partly lignified shoots. Compared with 2,4-D, higher dosages and repeated treatments with MCPA were needed to kill *Mikania*.

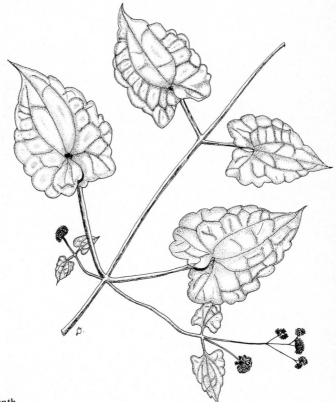

Fig. 215.   *Mikania micrantha* Kunth.

Single application of 0.28–0.56 kg/ha paraquat in 122 l water resulted in a 50 % regeneration after 2–3 weeks – making a further application necessary.

Experiments carried out in the Dominican Republic have shown that *M. micrantha* was hardly damaged by high levels of TCA or TCA/dalapon. Glyphosate caused a significant decrease in cover of the weed in the first month following application, but then a re-infestation occurred. Treatment with higher rates of bromacil, amitrole, 2,4,5-T or 2,4-D/picloram resulted in complete control of *M. micrantha*.

Literature

LOWE, J. S. (1971): The place of dinitrobutyl phenol in estate weed control. 3rd Conf. Asian-Pacific Weed Sci. Soc., Kuala Lumpur, **9**, pp. 6.

PARKER, C. (1972): The *Mikania* problem. PANS **18**, 312–315.

SETH, A. K. (1971): Control of *Mikania cordata* (Burm. f.) B. L. Robinson in plantation crops using paraquat. Weed Res. **11**, 77–88.

SOEPADIYO, M. & R. M. SOEWADJI (1973): The influence of cover crops on *Hevea*. I. The growth of cover crops. Bull. Balai Penelitian Perkebunan Medan **4**, 13–20.

WYCHERLEY, P. R. & M. M. CHANDAPILLAO (1969): Effects of cover plants. J. Rubb. Res. Inst. Malaya **21**, 140–157.

Author: G. Jürgens

Parthenium hysterophorus L. (Plate 54 a)

Common names: wormwood, whitehead; Mutterkraut; absinthe marron; yerba amarga.

Geographical distribution: The weed is widespread throughout the American tropics and subtropics and has furthermore been introduced into the Old World.

Habitat: Occurs in tropical lowlands as well as high mountain valleys. The species can be found in annual and perennial crops. On Hispaniola, it reaches its highest frequency on light to medium soils of irrigated and non irrigated arable lands in semi-arid regions. In India, the majority of the plants appear in the early part of the monsoon season.

Description: Aromatic, hairy, much branched and erect growing plant about 50–100 cm tall. Leaves alternate, pinnatifid, 8–12 cm long. Inflorescence a many branched panicle. Flowers white, in heads, about 4 mm in diameter. Fruit with two recurved awns, ovate, black, 2 mm long.

Development: Morphologically mature seeds taken from the plant, had a germination rate of about 20 % after 14 days in moist soil.

Cotyledons oval, petioled, about 4–5 mm long, 3–4 mm wide (Plate 54 a). The first foliage leaf is entire like the cotyledons, but in addition hairy. The following two leaves are sinuate, all further leaves pinnatifid. The weed needs about four weeks to reach the flowering stage. On Hispaniola, the mean life span can be said to be 4–5 months. Jayachandra (1971) reports that in India the plant continually produces flowers and fruit over a 6–8 month period. Dissemination carried out by wind and water, whereas road transport can account for long distance movement.

Supplementary: *Parthenium hysterophorus* is used as a febrifuge and a tonic. It contains parthenin which works as a sedative on the human nervous system. The plant can, however, harm the skin, and its pollen can cause allergies. According to Garciduenas et al. (1973), crude extracts, methanol fractions or parthenin found in *P. hysterophorus* inhibited the development of *Phaseolus vulgaris,* and especially influenced its germination and early development.

Control: 2,4-D and 2,4,5-T and pre-emergence treatments with linuron, metobromuron, chlorbromuron, terbutryne, fluorodifen and diphenamid have given satisfactory results.

Literature

GARCIDUENAS, M. R., X. A. DOMINGUEZ, J. FERNANDEZ & G. ALANIS (1972): New growth inhibitors from *Parthenium hysterophorus*. Rev. Latino Amer. Quimica **3**, 52–53.
JAYACHANDRA (1971): *Parthenium* weed in Myosore State and its control. Current Sci. **40**, 568–569.
KASASIAN, L. & J. SEEYVE (1968): Weedkillers for Caribbean Agriculture. Port-of-Spain, Trinidad.

Author: R. Hansen del Orbe

Xanthium pensylvanicum Wallr.

Synonym: *Xanthium canadense* Mill.

Common names: cocklebur, clotbur, sheepbur; Spitzklette; lampourde, glouteron; cadillo, abrojillo.

Related species: The taxonomy of the genus *Xanthium* L. is rather uncertain. However there are only a few species, all of which are noxious weeds of warmer zones and probably all are of American origin. Besides *X. pensylvanicum* the following four species are of importance as weeds: *X. chinense* Mill., *X. pungens* Wallr., *X. spinosum* L. (Syn.: *Acanthoxanthium spinosum* (L) Fourreau), *X. strumarium* L.

Geographical distribution: *Xanthium pensylvanicum* prefers warm and at times humid climates. As a weed therefore, its main areas of distribution lie in Central America, the Mississippi Delta, the South-Eastern states of the USA, Australia and South and South-East Europe.

Habitat: *Xanthium pensylvanicum* thrives on cultivated soils (sandy-loamy clay) as well as on fallow lands and poor pastures. The weed has especially become a problem in soya bean, but also in cotton and peanut fields. Moreover it frequently occurs in maize.

Description: Stem erect, branched above, normally bushy, grooved, rough, hairy and partly purple spotted. The plant usually up to 90 cm tall. The stem of *X. spinosum* has trifid yellow spines and is much branched.
Leaves alternate, oval or broadly cuneate, dentate or lobed margin, petioles as long as leaf blade, leaf axils without spines. Leaves rough on both surfaces, not tomentose. Leaves of *X. spinosum* oval to rhomboid, tometose underneath.
Male or female flowers unisexual, monoecious. The staminate flowers in short terminal peduncles, flowers fading soon after shedding of pollen. Involucre of staminate flowers subglobose with 7–12 separate bracts. Pistillate flowers in axillary clusters. Pistillate involucre ovoid, closed, hairy and spiny, bearing two pistillate flowers which develop into a hard woody fruit (bur). Flowering from August to October. Fruit oval to oblong, light brown, about 1–2 cm long, more or less hairy, with numerous hooked prickles 3–6 mm long.
Each fruit with two oblong seeds 1–1.5 cm long, flattened, and with a distinctly pointed apex, dark brown. Two seeds per fruit arranged as "upper" and "lower" seed. "Upper" seed larger and usually stays dormant longer. The "lower" seed with permeable seed coat, therefore germinating earlier.

Development: *Xanthium pensylvanicum* can usually germinate from a depth of up to 15 cm, but also from deeper levels when the soils are light and aerated. Depth of germination appears to depend on the clay content of the soil. The "lower" seeds frequently germinate in the spring following maturity. The "upper" seeds often stay viable in the soil for one or several years.
Xanthium pensylvanicum is a summer annual and a robust short day plant. The onset of the generative phase is dependent upon daylength. Given optimal daylength, it will flower even when the plant is only a few centimetres tall. It propagates exclusively by seeds.
Xanthium pensylvanicum forms a strong woody taproot which can reach deep into the soil.

Control: A complete control can be achieved by cultivation and cropping, as well as by chemical control measures. Early germinating crops which give extensive shade prevent the appearance of *Xanthium pensylvanicum* which is light dependent. Early sowing usually supports mechanical control methods. In Australia, biological control of *X. pensylvanicum* with a seed fly was unsuccessful. The introduction of a double furrow plough which placed the seeds at great depth within the soil was only partially successful.

Chemical control of *X. pensylvanicum* varies according to the crop. In maize, products based on triazines (atrazine), bentazon and phenoxy compounds (2,4-D) can be used. In soya bean, cotton and peanuts, use of products based on triazines, urea derivatives, dinoseb and bentazon is possible, depending on the crop and the method of application.

Literature

BALACH, G. M. & M. A. GANI (1969): The present status of biological control of *Xanthium (Compositae)*. PANS **15**, 154–159.

BEHRENDT, S. & J. LUDWIG (1972): *Xanthium pensylvanicum* Wallr., ein Problemunkraut im Sojabohnenanbau der USA. Berichte aus der Abteilung für Herbologie an der Universität Hohenheim, Heft 4, 13–21.

GARCKE, A. (1972): Illustrierte Flora. Verlag Paul Parey, Berlin–Hamburg, 23. Aufl.

SMITH, J. E. & A. W. COLE (1971): Selective chemical control of cocklebur in cottonseed. Weed Science **19**, 346–349.

WIDDER, D. (1923): Die Arten der Gattung *Xanthium*. Beiträge zu einer Monographie. Pepert. Spec. Nov. Beih. **20**, 1–222.

Author: S. Behrendt

Family: Convolvulaceae

Ipomoea congesta R. Br. (Plate 54 b, c)

Synonym: *I. indica* (Burm.) Merr., *I. insularis* Steud.

Common names: blue morning-glory; Sternwinde, Trichterwinde; –; batatilla lila.

Related species: The genus *Ipomoea* includes about 400 species of which some 40 have been described as weeds; among these: *I. aquatica* Forsk., *I. cairica* (L.) Sweet. (Syn.: *J palmata* Forsk.) *J cordofana* Choisy, *I. coscinosperma* Hochst. ex Choisy, *I. eriocarpa* R. Br., *I. hederacea* (L.) Jacq., *I. hirta* Mart & Gall, *I. nil* (L.) Roth. (Syn.: *I. hederacea* (non Jacq.) Brown & Massey), *I. pes-caprae* (L.) Roth., *I. pes-tigridis* L., *I. purpurea* (L.) Roth, *I. quinquefolia* Griseb., *I. tiliacea* (Willd.) Choisy.

Geographical distribution: *Ipomoea* species which are predominantly native to tropical America are today widespread throughout the tropics and subtropics of the Old and New World. In the tropics, the majority of the species colonise upland areas up to 1500 m, but are also present between 2000 and 3000 m.

Habitat: *Ipomoea* species are found in nearly all tropical crops, particularly in cotton, maize, sorghum, sugar cane, soya bean, peanuts and rice. Aquatic species and others that have become adapted to extremely moist habitats are also known.

Description: Prostrate to twining and climbing, mostly annual, partly also perennial plants. Flower bisexual, 5-merous; leaf entire, and then mostly cordate, lobed or partite to palmate; ciliate to tufted hairy. The annual species have deep penetrating tap roots. Some perennial species develop lateral roots or stolons which among other things contribute to vegetative reproduction. Rooting at the shoot nodes occurs frequently. The fruit capsule is nearly globular, widening at base and enveloped by a ridge. The other genera of the *Convolvulaceae* have no ridge and are not widened at base. The relatively large seeds are characterised by having one convex and two flattened sides.

Ipomoea congesta is an annual plant; stem prostrate or twining, cylindrical, hairy. Leaves three lobed, lobes acuminate, 10–14 cm long, 8–10 cm wide with grooved petioles, 7–20 cm, hairy, leaf margins darker in colour. Inflorescence of 2–5 axillary flowers, on pedicels, 3–5 cm. Flower tubular-campanulate, large, white at base, lilac towards margins. Calyx hairy. Fruit: globular capsule, glabrous, light brown in colour, with 4–6 seeds. Seeds similar in shape to an orange slice with two flattened and one convex sides, black, pubescent, with slight indentation on convex side.

Ipomoea tiliacea is also annual, stem prostrate or twining, angular, lilac coloured, weakly hairy. Leaves in two shapes: cordate with distinctly acuminate apex, or three-lobed with lobes deeply partite, 10–12 cm long, 6–8 cm wide, glabrous. Leaf margins deep violet in colour, petiole 6–8 cm long, cylindrical with groove-like depression, glabrous. Flower tubular-campanulate, small, light-violet. Calyx hairy. Fruit a globular capsule, glabrous, brown, with 4 seeds. Seeds speckled, light brown, with two flattened and one convex sides.

Development: The greater majority of the species complete their life cycles in 4–5 months. Few species are perennial (e. g. *I. cairica*, Plate 54 b). Vegetative reproduction is of minor importance. The seeds normally have a more or less pronounced period of dormancy, their readiness to germinate increasing noticeably after 8 weeks. In experiments with seeds of various ages the percentage germination was as follows:

	age of seeds in days						1000 seed weight in g
	10	22	30	45	60	240	
Ipomoea congesta	4	7	14	17	31	40	28
I. hederifolia	0	–	4	–	1	–	12
I. tiliacea	0	–	6	–	13	–	5

Seeds can emerge from depths of up to 15 cm. The cotyledons develop 4–6 days after sowing, the first foliage leaves appearing after 10 days (Plate 54 c). At this stage the tap root has already reached a considerable depth. Due to its large seed production, the species can rapidly build up a population. A production of 3340 seeds is reported for *I. cynanchifolia*. The seeds can often float and can be disseminated by sea currents.

Supplementary: Seeds of certain species are officinal, other species are used as fodder, ornamental plants and as food products. *Ipomoea batatas* Lamark is a widespread crop plant.

Control: Early and thorough cultivation, crop rotation and keeping farm machinery clean from seeds and plant parts are important cultural means of control. Hoeing by machine and by hand can be effective but might have to be carried out repeatedly. Biological control up until now has not been studied intensively; two unidentified larvae have been found that can destroy the seeds within the capsule.

No basic differences have become known concerning the sensitivity of annual species of *Ipomoea* (and only these are important in crops) to established herbicides. In experiments in Columbia, *I. hederacea, I. purpurea, I. tiliacea, I. quinquefolia, I. congesta* were equally sensitive to trifluralin, fluometuron and atrazine. The following table contains recommendations for herbicide applications based on the authors' own experience and from the extensive literature.

Control of *Ipomoea* spp. with herbicides in main crops of warmer countries

crop	type of application and herbicide		
	pre-sowing with incorporation	post-sowing	post-emergence***
cotton	trifluralin*	diuron	fluometuron*
maize	–	atrazine	atrazine, 2, 4-D
sugar cane	–	atrazine, atrazine/TCA/2, 4-D	2, 4-D
rice	–	–	2, 4-D
sorghum	–	atrazine	atrazine
soya bean	trifluralin*	linuron*	dinoseb, 2, 4-DB, chloroxuron
peanuts	trifluralin*/**	–	dinoseb, 2, 4-DB

*not always satisfactory,
**with restrictions in respect to soil and variety,
***in certain cases only treatment in rows tolerated, in which only the base of the crop plant is treated
 (sub foliage directed sprays)

Literature

BUCHANAN, G. A. & E. R. BURAS (1971): Weed competition in cotton. 1. Sicklepod and tall morning-glory. Weed Science, **19** (5), 576–9.
RADDATZ, E. & G. LINDEN (1972): Unkrautarten der Gattung *Ipomoea,* ihre Bedeutung in der Landwirtschaft warmer Klimate und die Möglichkeit künstlicher Aussaat zur Freilandprüfung von Herbiziden. Ber. Abt. Herbologie Univers. Hohenheim, Heft **4**, 23–35.
RADDATZ, E. & C. E. REYES (1972): El genero *Ipomoea*. Comalfi (Bogotá) 1972.
SCHWERZEL, P. I. (1967): Seed production of some common Rhodesian weeds. PANS (C) **13**, 215–17.

Authors: C. E. Reyes, E. Raddatz, G. Linden

Family: Cuscutaceae DUM. (frequently classified as *Convolvulaceae* Juss.)

Cuscuta campestris Yuncker (Plate 54 d)

Synonym: *C. arvensis* L.

Common names (for *Cuscuta*): dodder; Seide; cuscute; cabello de angel, cuerda de violín.

Related species: Especially worth mentioning from about 170 species are: *C. europaea* L., *C. suaveolens* Ser. (Syn: *C. racemosa* C.F.P. Martins), *C. cesatiana* Bertol.

Geographical distribution: *Cuscuta* is distributed throughout the temperate and warm regions of the whole world.

Habitat: *Cuscuta* species are without exception parasites which depend on suitable host plants for their growth. The individual species mostly prefer a few particular host plants on which they can achieve optimal growth, but they can also parasitise numerous other plants. *Cuscuta* is above all of major importance in vegetable and lucerne crops.

Description: The whitish to yellow to orange-red coloured filiform parasites twine round their hosts which can be grasses, herbs, shrubs and also trees, and penetrate them laterally with haustoria (Plate 54 d). The leaves are modified to minute scales. The floral clusters, which are furnished with prophylls, are white, reddish or yellowish and with few exceptions small and inconspicuous. The calyx is four or five lobed. The tubular bell-shaped corolla is three to five lobed, ten lobed in exceptional cases. The stamens are adnate to the corolla tube. The capsule is capsular or berry shaped and contains one to four seeds.

Development: *Cuscuta* reproduces by seeds and to a lesser extent by shoot fragments. Germination takes place on or just below the soil surface irrespective of whether a host plant is near or not. Through circular searching movements, the leafless seedling tries to come into contact with a host plant. Once it reaches a host, it twines around it and penetrates it with a haustorium. The development of the dodder is secured if the host enjoys favourable growth conditions. It then forms further haustoria and also attacks neighbouring plants. If the seedling does not encounter any host plant, it dies within a few days, as it is not self sufficient. Fragmented pieces of fully-grown dodder plants behave in the same way as seedlings. In contrast to most other parasitic plants, dodder plants only live on the above ground parts of the host plant.

Control: Species occurring in lucerne are disseminated with the seed of that crop, seed cleaning being therefore important. In infested areas, control is achieved by early mowing, grazing or spraying with diquat or paraquat. In one year old lucerne, dinoseb-acetate is applied as a post-emergence treatment; in older lucerne dichlobenil, chlorpropham and chlorthal; in beets cycloate is used as a pre-emergence treatment.
Biological control through insects is being examined, but up to now there is no practicable method available.

Literature

ANONYM (1973): Selected references to the biology and control of *Cuscuta* spp. A. R. C. Weed Research Organization, Annotated Bibliography No 51.
DAWSON, J. H. (1970): Dodder control in alfalfa with dichlobenil. Weed Science **18**, 225–230.
FEINBRUN, N. (1970): A taxonomic review of European *Cuscutae*. Israel J. Bot. **19**, 16–29.
KUIJT, J. (1969): The biology of parasitic flowering plants. Berkeley California.
NARIANI, T. K. & S. P. RAYCHAUDHURI (1970): Transmission of citrus tristeza virus by dodder, *Cuscuta reflexa* Roxb. Ann. of the Phytopathological Society of Japan **36**, 289–290.
WILSON, C. L. (1969): Use of plant pathogens in weed control. Ann. Rev. Phytopath. **7**, 411–434.

Author: F. Bischof

Family: Cyperaceae

Cyperus rotundus L. (Plate 55 a, b, c, d)

Common names: purple nutgrass, purple nutsedge; Nußgras, Nußsegge; coquito, chivasa totira.

Related species: The genus *Cyperus* includes around 600 species that are mainly distributed over the tropics and subtropics. Besides *C. rotundus, C. diffusus* Vahl, *C. esculentus* L., *C. iria* L. and *C. odoratus* L. (Syn.: *C. ferax* (L.) Rich.) are of special importance as weeds. A related species with importance as a weed is *Dichromena ciliata* Vahl (Syn.: *Rhynchospora nervosa* (Vahl) Boeck.).

Geographical distribution: *Cyperus rotundus* occurs throughout the warmer regions of all continents. In the USA, it is limited to those areas where temperatures rarely or never reach freezing point, in Japan to where the mean lowest air temperature is not below − 5 °C. In Iran, it is even found in those regions where the soils in winter are frozen for longer periods. *Cyperus rotundus* is found in nearly all horticultural and agricultural crops, but occurs particularly in cultivated fields and irrigated crops.

Cyperus esculentus penetrates somewhat further than *C. rotundus* into the Mediterranean region, the edge of the tropics as well as into continental areas, but apart from this has a similar distribution. *Dichromena ciliata* is common throughout the American tropics.

Habitat: *Cyperus rotundus* is highly adaptable to several types of soil. It occurs on light sandy as well as on heavy clay soils. It also has no particular soil moisture requirements and appears in very wet as well as in very dry habitats. However, pronounced phenotypic variations occur depending on the degree of soil moisture. The plant flourishes on moist soils, the tubers penetrating deep into the soil and staying mostly dormant. The leaves are dark green in colour. In dry habitats, the shoots remain stunted and the tubers are formed just below the soil surface. *Cyperus rotundus* reacts in a similar way to poor nitrogen supplies in the soil. Phosphorus and potassium appear to have no pronounced influence. On water-logged soils the majority of the tubers do not sprout. *Dichromena ciliata* is abundant in damp pastures and ditches.

Description: *Cyperus rotundus* is a perennial plant that forms underground rhizomes. Leaves arise in the form of a rosette from the basal thickening of the plant. It has a $^1/_3$ phyllotaxy. Flowering stem triangular, 20–60 cm long. Rhizomes are covered with cataphylls, are white at first, later black and wiry, and differentiate into tubers or aerial shoots. Tubers are mainly dark, oval to ovoid, 1–3 cm in diameter, containing starch and alkaloids, and have a bitter taste. Inflorescence is an anthela with 3–8 rays, each bearing 8–10 spikes. These possess 10–12 spikelets each with 10–50 tiny flowers. The fruit is a triangular achene. The roots are thin, fibrous and reach deep into the soil.
Cyperus esculentus (Plate 55 b) is larger than *C. rotundus* (Plate 55 a). Its flowering stem is 25–75 cm long, the foliage leaves are light green in colour and the same size or longer than the flowering stem. Tubers are formed at the end of the rhizomes, and are globular, light to dark brown. Freshly harvested tubers are dormant. *Cyperus odoratus* is also perennial but has no bulbs and rhizomes. It is 20–50 cm tall (Plate 55 c).
Cyperus iria is annual and is 10–50 cm tall. Umbels usually compound, 5–40 cm in diameter; bracts long, often overtopping the umbel.
Dichromena ciliata is perennial and 15–40 cm tall when in flower (Plate 55 d).

Development: Reproduction in *C. rotundus* is almost exclusively vegetative. The tubers sprout within the temperature range of 10–40 °C, the optimum lying between 30–35 °C. Because of apical dominance, only one shoot at a time reaches full development. As soon as the shoot penetrates the soil surface, its foliage leaves develop. Basal thickening occurs in the transition zone between the below and above ground parts of the shoot. From this thickening, 2–3 new rhizomes develop. After the rhizome has formed 6–8 nodes, its tip begins to thicken and either differentiates into a new shoot or a new tuber, so that chains of tubers arise, each tuber with six or more buds. Both can form rhizomes again so that eventually chains of rhizomes arise, each with tubers and leafy shoots. There is an increased formation of tubers and flowers with short days, and of leafy shoots with long days. Tuber and rhizome chains are subject to apical dominance.
Sexual reproduction plays a greater role in the development of *C. esculentus,* but apart from that its development is very similar to that of *C. rotundus.*

Supplementary: Several species of *Cyperus* were in former times used for many purposes: *C. esculentus, C. glomeratus, C. iwasakii, C. papyrus* L.

Control: The complete elimination of tubers which through apical dominance or other factors are dormant, is extremely difficult and time consuming. *Cyperus rotundus* is generally more resistant than *C. esculentus.*
Although several animals and micro-organisms feed on or parasitise *C. rotundus* and *C. esculentus,* no satisfactory method of biological control has yet been found. Intensive shading suppresses both species well, with *C. esculentus* reacting more strongly than *C. rotundus.* Shading can firstly

be achieved by densely growing crop plants as well as by mulching. Water-logging prevents the tubers from sprouting, but not the further growth of already emerged shoots. Deep soil cultivation during dry periods leads over the course of several years to a decisive or complete reduction of both species, as the tubers dry out very easily after being cut off from deep growing roots which formerly supplied the tubers with water. In climates with pronounced periods of drought, *Cyperus* is in general no problem as long as intensive and adequately deep soil cultivation is carried out. As in the past, herbicide applications have only limited success. The following herbicides are relatively effective in pre-emergence applications: thiol carbamates, dichlobenil, chlorothiamid, terbacil and bromacil. *Cyperus* is more or less sensitive to post-emergence treatments with 2,4-D and other phenoxy compounds, but their action is strongly dependent upon the plant's stage of development. Amitrole, arsenical herbicides and recently glyphosate in particular also work satisfactorily, but a decisive reduction in infestation can normally only be expected after several applications.

Literature

ANDREWS, F. W. (1940): The control of nut grass in the Sudan Gezira. Emp. J. Exp. Agric. **8**, 215–222.
GÜHNE, K. M. (1974): Knollenaustrieb, Entwicklung und Bekämpfung von *Cyperus rotundus* L. in Abhängigkeit von einigen ökologischen Faktoren. Dissertation Universität Hohenheim.
HAUSER, E. W. (1962): Development of purple nutsedge under field conditions. Weeds **10**, 315–321.
KASASIAN, L. (1971): Weed Control in the tropics. Leonard Hill, London.
RANADE, S. B. & W. BURNS (1925): The eradication of *Cyperus rotundus* L. (a study in pure and applied botany). India Dept. Agric. Mem. Bot. **13**, 99–192.
UEKI, K. (1969): Studies on the control of nutsedge. On the germination of a tuber. Proc. 2nd Asian Pacific Weed Control Interchange, 355–369.

Author: M. Gühne

Fimbristylis littoralis Gaudichaud (Fig. 216)

Common names: grass-like fimbristylis; –; barba de fraile, pajarillo, pelo mico.

Related species: The proper name for this rice weed of the genus *Fimbristylis,* which is today distributed over the whole world, is *F. littoralis* Gaudichaud. The majority of the reports concerning *F. miliacea* will in all likelihood refer to *F. littoralis,* as parts of the literature, especially from America, do not use the correct nomenclature. Related species are *F. miliacea* (L.) Vahl and *F. dichotoma* (L.) Vahl (Syn.: *F. annua* (All.) R. & S.).

Geographical distribution: *Fimbristylis littoralis, F. miliacea* and *F. dichotoma* can be found in nearly all tropical and subtropical areas.

Habitat: *Fimbristylis littoralis* is a characteristic species of moist, or temporarily flooded soils and finds its ideal growing conditions in paddy rice. According to investigations in the Philippines, 94 % of all seeds found in rice fields came from *F. "miliacea"*. In the Dominican Republic, the species is, in respect of frequency and degree of covering, the second most important weed in the irrigated parts of the plots, whereas the banks of the rice fields are not so heavily infested. In Surinam, the appearance of *F. "miliacea"* indicates insufficient water supply.
Fimbristylis dichotoma is more of a perennial species in the tropics, occurring in damp meadows and grasslands.

Description: Sedge, tufted, about 30–60 cm tall (Fig. 216). Stem weak, flattened at base, angular to apex, divergent above. Leaves soft, pliant, mostly shorter than the stem, about 1.5–2.5 mm wide. Bracts filiform. Inflorescence paniculate, with numerous nearly globular spikelets 2.5–4 mm long. Style trifid. Achene ovoid, scabrous, about 0.5 mm long. *Fimbristylis littoralis*

Fig. 216. *Fimbristylis littoralis*

and *F. miliacea* are distinguished from each other by their leaf shape, the former with bilaterally, the latter with dorsoventrally compressed leaves.

Fimbristylis dichotoma has a bifid style, ovoid to oblong spikelets, 5–8 mm, and ribbed achene, 0.8–1.2 mm long.

Development: *Fimbristylis littoralis* is an annual that reproduces exclusively by seeds. Its growth pattern is excellently adapted to that of the irrigated rice. Some of the achenes are able to germinate immediately after reaching physiological maturity. The early developmental stage is passed through relatively slowly. The period between emergence and the onset of flowering lasts approximately 6–8 weeks. Its life cycle is finished after about 4 months.

Control: Although *F. littoralis* is sensitive to a series of rice herbicides, the species is very difficult to suppress once it has infested an area. Due to its large seed production, the danger of plot reinfestation is always present.

The application of 2,4-D or MCPA alone or in combination with propanil up until shoot formation is most economical. The soil applied herbicides fluorodifen 3–4 kg/ha and butachlor 2.1–2.7 kg/ha have proved effective in the Dominican Republic. Furthermore, trifluralin and dichlobenil in granular form as well as various herbicide mixtures have been successful.

Literature

DIRVEN, J. G. P. (1970): Weed flora in fallow rice fields in Surinam. De Surinaamse Landbouw **18,** 47–63.
JIMÉNEZ, J. DE (1966): Catalogus Florae Domingensis. Supl. I. Arch. Bot. Biogeog. Ital. 39–43.
KOYAMA, T. (1961): Classification of the family *Cyperaceae* (1). – J. Fak. Sci. Univ. Tokyo, Section III, Botany **8,** 37–148.
VEGA, M. R. & J. M. SIERRA (1968): Population of weed seeds in a lowland rice field. Proc. 1st Philippine Weed Sci. Conf., 1–9.

Author: G. Jürgens

Family: Euphorbiaceae

Acalypha alopecuoridea Jacq. (Fig. 217)

Common names: copperleaf; Kupferblatt; petit pompon, derrière gouflé; cadillo de mazorca, hierba del cancer, rabo de zorra.

Related species: *A. australis* L., *A. indica* L., *A. ostryaefolia* Ridd., *A. segetalis* Müll. arg., *A. setosa* A. Rich., *A. virginica* L.

Geographical distribution: A series of weeds have been described within the genus *Acalypha* whose occurrence is mainly limited to certain regions of the tropics and subtropics. *Acalypha alopecuoridea* is distributed throughout the Caribbean, Central America and the northern part of South America.

Habitat: *Acalypha* species are weeds of arable fields and plantations. On Hispaniola, *A. alopecuoridea* frequently infests annual crops growing on light to medium soils, and is also found in perennial crops with moderate shading in upland areas up to 800 m. *Acalypha setosa* is a typical weed of coffee and cacao plantations.

Description: Hairy, erect, branching at the base, up to 60 cm tall (Fig. 217). Leaves alternate, long petioled, leaf-margin serrate, leaf triangular to rounded ovate, approximately cordate at base, acuminate, 3–7 cm long. Female flowers mainly in terminal spikes up to 5 cm long. Male flowers axillary, smaller. Fruit is a capsule approximately 1.5–2 mm long with reddish-brown to black seeds.

Development: The seeds can germinate immediately after becoming morphologically mature. Given adequate moisture, the weed can develop throughout the whole year. Cotyledons orbicular, 3–5 mm long, 4–6 mm wide. The foliage leaf stage is passed through in about three weeks. At the same time, branching occurs in the leaf axils. The life cycle is usually completed within three to four months.

Control: *Acalypha alopecuoridea* seldom reaches a high density in arable crops, and is easily eliminated by mechanical means. Pre-emergence treatments with alachlor 2.1, terbutryne 2.2–4, terbutryne/terbuthylazine 2.5, prometryne 0.8–1, linuron 1–1.5, nitrofen 3–4, fluorodifen 2.4 and trifluralin 0.9 kg/ha as well as trifluralin 0.9 kg/ha up to the first foliage leaf stage have proved effective. Besides the normal mechanical control methods against *Acalypha* in tree crops, control by foliar applied herbicides is possible. *Acalypha indica,* however, showed resistance to paraquat but is controlled at all stages with a mix-

Fig. 217. *Acalypha alopecuoridea* Jacq.

ture of paraquat and diuron (Gleadle and Thomas, 1971). Fluorodifen 4.8–5.9 kg/ha and oxadiazon 2.4–3.6 kg/ha also control this species (Hamdoun, 1970).

Early germinating *A. ostryaefolia* plants were successfully controlled with DNBP/MSMA 1.7–2.5/1.9 kg/ha + surfactant, followed by DNBP/diuron 1.7 or 2.5/0.4 kg/ha + surfactant. Pre-emergence treatments with propazine 1.8 and prometryne 3.9 kg/ha gave good control, but post-emergence treatments with prometryne 3.4 kg/ha + surfactant and atrazine 2.9 kg/ha and oil 9.3 l/ha were best. The species was also controlled with combinations of alachlor/dinoseb 2.2–3.4/0.8–3.4 kg/ha. Fluometuron brought good results against *A. segetalis* (De Almeida, 1969).

Literature

DE ALMEIDA, F. S. (1969): Study of herbicide combinations for the cotton plantations of the Limpopo alluviums. Agronomia Moçamb. **3**, 155–161.
GLEADLE, G. C. & W. D. THOMAS (1970): Weed control in Gezira cotton by mixtures of contact and residual herbicides. PANS **16**, 673–683.
HAMDOUN, A. M. (1970): Herbicides for weed control in groundnuts and their effect on subsequent crops. 4th E. Afr. Herbicide Conf. Arusha, pp. 13.

Author: G. Jürgens

Euphorbia heterophylla L. (Fig. 218, plates 56 a–d and 57 a)

Synonym: *E. geniculata* Ort., *Poinsettia heterophylla* Kl. & Garcke

Common names: milkweed, spurge (name of genus), painted euphorbia; Wolfsmilch (name of genus); poinsettia dézohomme; escoba lechosa, lechosito, yerba lechosa.

Related species: *E. glomifera* (Millsp.) L. C. Wheeler (Syn.: *E. hypericifolia* of F. & R., non L., *Chamaesyce hypericifolia* Millsp.), *E. hirta* L. (Syn.: *Ch. hirta* (L.) Millsp.), *E. hyssopifolia* L. (Syn.: *Ch. hyssopifolia* (L.) Small), *E. prostrata* Ait. (Syn.: *Ch. prostrata* (Ait.) Small), *Phyllanthus amarus* Schumach. & Thonn. (Syn.: *P. niruri* F. & R., non L.).

Geographical distribution: *Euphorbia heterophylla*, *E. hirta* and *E. prostrata* are distributed throughout the tropics and partially also in the subtropics. Other species of the genus are of more regional importance within the American tropics, such as *E. glomifera* and *E. hyssopifolia*. *Phyllanthus amarus* is distributed throughout the tropics.

Habitat: *Euphorbia* species are usually found in perennial crops such as sugar cane, fruit plantations and pasture-land. *Euphorbia heterophylla* and *E. glomifera* also frequently invade crops with a shorter vegetative growth period such as maize, legumes and vegetable crops. The species described here are found in the Caribbean region even in upland areas between 1200–1500 m, but are only important as weeds in the hot zone. On Hispaniola, *E. heterophylla* is a characteristic species of light to medium permeable soils in humid to semi-arid climates.
Phyllanthus amarus is common on waste places and penetrates into arable fields and plantations.

Description: Erect, sparsely hairy plant, containing a milky sap, approximately 30–80 cm tall (Fig. 218, plate 56 a, b). Leaves of variable shape and size, linear-lanceolate to oval, margins entire or irregularly toothed. Flowers in terminal clusters on main or side shoots. Dehiscent fruit with three carpels, 4-6mm in diameter. Seeds black, about 2mm long. Whereas *E.heterophylla* has

Fig. 218.   *Euphorbia heterophylla* L.

alternate leaves on the upper part of its shoot, the other species of the sub-genus *Chamaesyce* mentioned here have considerably smaller opposite leaves. *Euphorbia hirta* (Plate 56 c) is a creeping to ascending, densely hairy plant. *E. glomifera* (Plate 56 d) and *E. hyssopifolia* are more erect growing species with glabrous dehiscent fruits which are less than 1.4 mm and more than 1.6 mm long respectively. *Euphorbia prostrata* is a creeping plant with very small leaves and dehiscent fruits 1–1.4 mm in diameter with hairs along the edge of the fruit (Burch, 1966).

Phyllanthus amarus is an erect annual herb up to 25–30 cm high and light green in colour (Plate 57 a). Flowers greenish, very small, borne in the leaf axils. Fruit a small capsule.

Development: Seeds of the species described above show hardly any dormancy and reach a high percentage germination immediately following fruit dehiscence. In contrast to *Chamaesyce* species, seedlings of *E. heterophylla* are relatively large with reddish stems and oval cotyledons, 10–17 mm long, 5–7 mm wide. The primary leaves are entire and narrower than the succeeding leaves. Flowering begins about four weeks after emergence. *Euphorbia heterophylla* reaches an average age of 7–8 weeks. *Euphorbia glomifera* and *E. hyssopifolia* develop even faster and can already flower 8 days after germination.

Control: Post-emergence control of *E. heterophylla* in sugar cane can be carried out with atrazine 2.4–3.2, ametryne 2.4–3.2, cyanazine 1.5–2, metribuzine 1–1.4 or asulam 3.6 kg/ha in combination with 2.4-D. Foliar applications with ioxynil or paraquat can destroy the above ground parts of the plant but new shoots can subsequently develop at the plant base.

In papaya, pre-emergence treatments with trifluralin did not give a satisfactory control whereas applications of bromacil and terbacil 2.2 kg/ha as well as paraquat 0.6 kg/ha with diuron, linuron, atrazine, simazine or prometryne 3.4 kg/ha gave good results.

Atrazine or urea derivatives applied before or shortly after emergence (pre- or post-emergence) can be tentatively recommended to control *E. glomifera* and *E. hyssopifolia*.

There is no uniform information concerning possible methods of controlling *E. hirta*. As a low growing species similar to *E. prostrata,* it is usually of little importance in plantation crops.

Literature

BURCH, D. (1966): Two new species of *Chamaesyce (Euphorbiaceae),* new combinations and key to the Caribbean members of the genus. Ann. Missouri Bot. Gard. **53**, 375–376.
HAMMERTON, J. L. (1971): Weed control work in progress at the University of the West Indies. PANS **17**, 226–230.

Author: R. Hansen del Orbe

Family: Gramineae

Andropogon bicornis L. (Fig. 219)

Common names: West Indian foxtailgrass; Bartgras; z'herbe panache; barba de indio, cola de venado, pajón conojera.

Related species: *A. glomeratus* (Walt.) B.S.P., *A. virginicus* L., *A. pertusus* (L.) Willd. (Syn.: *Bothriochloa pertusa* (L.) A. Camus), *A. aristatus* Poir. (*A. annulatus* Hitchc., non Forsk.)

Geographical distribution: The occurrence of *A. bicornis, A. glomeratus* and *A. virginicus* is mainly limited to America, while *A. pertusus* and *A. aristatus,* which are indigenous to the Old World, are now widespread over the tropics.

Habitat: *Andropogon* species are treated as pasture weeds which frequently occur in neglected marginal lands. Because of their aggressiveness, they are a problem in sown forage grasses such as *Panicum maximum* Jacq. and *Cynodon plectostachyus* (K. Schum.) Pilg.
On the Virgin Islands, the frequently cultivated species *Digitaria decumbens* Stent. has proved to be an excellent replacement for *A. pertusus* (Oakes, 1968). In the Dominican Republic however, this forage grass is often displaced after several years by the less valuable *A. pertusus.*
Occasionally, *Andropogon* invades sugar cane and other plantation crops.
According to de Freitas et al. (1972), *A. bicornis* in Brazil occurs predominantly on acid and sandy soils.

Description: Grass which forms clumps, 1–2 m tall (Fig. 219). Culms robust, somewhat lignified at maturity. Leaves 2–6 mm wide, margins rough. Inflorescence of rather dense, feathery racemes, spikelets without awns. In contrast to *A. bicornis, A. glomeratus* and *A. virginicus* have awned spikelets, the former with a compact, clavate inflorescence, the latter with less densely grouped flowers. *A. pertusus* and *A. aristatus* are plants which are considerably lower in height.

Development: The propagation and dispersal of *Andropogon* species is predominantly carried out by seeds which have structures that assist in wind transport. Vegetative reproduction by rhizome plays an important role in *A. aristatus.* The early development of *A. bicornis* is a rather slow process, the first panicles appearing three months after emergence. Through the production of side shoots, perennial clumps of considerable size gradually develop. In the Caribbean area, *A. bicornis* can flower throughout the year, while other species

Fig. 219.   *Andropogon* bicornis L.

have a definite rhythm in which the reproductive phase starts at the beginning of the cool season with shorter day lengths.

Control: Up until now, control of the species in pasture-land has had to rely on mechanical methods such as removal by hoeing. Adjacent plots and edges of paths and ditches have to be included in control measures to prevent a further infestation by wind borne seeds. In uninfested areas, precaution must be taken to prevent the introduction of the weed.

In Columbia, post-emergence treatments with cacadylic acid 4 kg/ha, TCA 20 kg/ha, dalapon 8 kg/ha and the combination of DSMA/MSMA 4/2 + 2 kg/ha have proved ineffective against *A. bicornis* (Doll & Veloz, 1973). Paraquat and MSMA showed a good initial effect, but the plants recovered quickly. Glyphosate 1 or 2 kg/ha gave good control. In the Dominican Republic on the other hand, applications of glyphosate 3.3 kg/ha did not completely kill the established clumps.

Dalapon can be successfully used against *A. pertusus* in cacao and pepper plantations (Kasasian et al., 1968). EPTC and pebulate are effective against *A. annulatus* (Kar & Singh, 1966).

Literature

DE FREITAS, H. L. F., C. ARANHA & O. BACCHI (1972): Plantas invasoras de culturas no Estado Sao Paulo. Vol 1 Sao Paulo, Brasil.

DOLL, J. & A. VELOZ (1973): Control quimico de Rabo de zorro (*Andropogon bicornis*) y Guayacana (*Imperata contracta*). Res. V Semin. Comalfi, Bogotá, Colombia.

GOBERDHAN, L. C. (1971): *Andropogon annulatus* and *Ischaemum rugosum* – two new weeds of sugar cane in Trinidad. PANS **17**, 178–179.

KAR, K. & R. P. SINGH (1966): The use of Eptam and Tillam as weedicides in sugarcane fields. Indian Sug. **16**, 257–261.

KASASIAN, L., J. SEEYAVE & R. W. SMITH (1968): The effects of weeding and of several herbicides on the growth of young coconuts. PANS **14**, 375–379.

OAKES, A. J. (1968): Replacing hurricane grass in pastures of the dry tropics. Trop. Agric. Trin. **45**, 235–241.

Author: R. Hansen del Orbe

Avena sterilis L. **ssp. macrocarpa** (Moench) Briquet **var. maxima** Perez Lara (Plate 57 b, c)

Synonym: *Avena macrocarpa* Moench

Common names: winter wild oat, animated oats; Winterflughafer; avoine stérile; avena loca.

Related species: *Avena sterilis* L. ssp. *ludoviciana* (Dur.) Gill & Magne var. *psilathera* Thell. (Syn.: *Avena ludoviciana* Dur.), *Avena alba* Vahl var. *barbata* (Potter) Maire et Weiller (Syn.: *Avena barbata* Potter), *Avena fatua* L.

Geographical distribution: Weed species of the genus *Avena* cause problems mainly in the temperate (especially *A. fatua*) and moderately warm regions of both the Old and the New World. In the tropics they are found in higher elevations only.

Avena sterilis ssp. *macrocarpa* is the most serious annual grass weed in winter cereals in North Africa (e. g. Morocco, Algeria, Tunisia, Libya), Southern Spain, Italy, Lebanon, Turkey, and in Greece. In parts of these countries this weed causes a greater reduction in farm income than any other weed. *Avena s.* ssp. *macrocarpa* is found only occasionally in Northern Spain and in France. *Avena sterilis* ssp. *ludoviciana* thrives in all areas of the North-Mediterranean region particularly on less fertile soils. However, on better soils it is often associated with *A. s.* ssp. *macrocarpa*.

Avena alba var. *barbata* is considered as the most common wild oat species of the Mediterranean area by some scientists. It seems to be of little importance in well cultivated crops, however. *Avena fatua* occurs, if at all, as a sporadic plant in warmer areas.

Habitat: *Avena sterilis* ssp. *macrocarpa* is a subspecies which requires more fertile soils, and it is more common in valleys than on mountains. *Avena sterilis* ssp. *macrocarpa* (Plate 57 b) is most frequently found at the foot of mountains in areas of dependable rainfall. It also thrives in coastal areas. Generally this subspecies abounds on disturbed soils and is serious as a weed especially in cereal crops and in well cultivated orchards. It is found very frequently in many parts of North Africa where cereals have been grown intensively for a long time. It is not yet a serious problem in only recently irrigated areas of North-Africa. *Avena sterilis* ssp. *ludoviciana* is not adapted to the climate of North-Africa and occurs as a sporadic weed in poorly cultivated fields only.
Avena alba var. *barbata* is adapted to a wide range of habitats. It is ubiquitous as a weed of pastures and is found in ditches, along roadsides, excavations, and on construction sites. It is also common on dry rocky scrublands on hillsides as well as in irrigated areas.

Description: *Avena sterilis* is an annual species. Some of the morphological characteristics of the two subspecies mentioned are as follows (Plate 57 c):

| | *Avena sterilis* | |
	ssp. *macrocarpa*	ssp. *ludoviciana*
culms	80-200 cm, very robust	40-100 cm
florets	3-5	2 occasionally 3
glumes	30-50 cm	20-30 mm
lemmas	25-40 mm	20-25 mm

The uppermost florets sterile, glabrous, awnless; the two lower ones fertile, hairy and awned. Lemmas of fertile florets hard, densely hairy from the base to the middle, scabrous above and 2-parted at tip, with long awns (5–8 cm) attached below the middle, tightly twisted and bent at maturity. The lowermost floret has a broad, ovate abscission scar at base.
The lower floret is joined with the axis. When the axis of the mature spikelet breaks under the lower floret, all florets are shed together as one unit, leaving the empty glumes on the plant. *Avena alba* is a slender annual with flowering culms 40–80 cm high. All florets are awned, lemmas 2-parted at the tip into two fine awns, 5–12 mm long. All the florets fall separately at maturity.

Development: *Avena sterilis* sspp. have a shorter period of dormancy than other wild oat species. Larger seeds have a longer dormancy than smaller ones. *Avena sterilis* ssp. *ludoviciana* has a viability of about 3 years (*Avena fatua* about 5 years).
Wild oat seeds lying near the surface of the soil in autumn are exposed to weathering. Such seeds have a shorter period of dormancy than those ploughed or cultivated deeper into the soil. Germination of wild oat seeds lying on the surface is poor (by twisting the awns spikelets can move deeper into the soil). The seeds must be covered lightly to germinate well.
Seeds of wild oat can remain deep in the soil for several years without rotting; they will germinate and grow when conditions become favourable.
In North-Africa the first rainfall in autumn brings emergence and further rains during winter bring additional flushes of germination. Germination of *A. s.* ssp. *macrocarpa* is usually high in autumn when growing conditions are favourable.
Germination is possible from a depth of 15–25 cm. It is the larger seed which can emerge from greater depth.

Plate 49

a *Portulaca oleracea* L., flowering plant
b *Portulaca oleracea* L., young plants
c *Trianthema portulacastrum* L., young plants
d *Amaranthus spinosus* L.

Plate 50

a *Amaranthus dubius* Mart. ex Thell., inflorescence
b *Amaranthus dubius* Mart. ex Thell., young plant
c *Amaranthus viridis* L., seedling and young plants
d *Amaranthus hybridus* L., young plants

Plate 51

a *Cleome viscosa* L., young plant
b *Cleome gynandra* L., seedling and young plant
c *Cassia obtusifolia* L., seedlings
d *Commelina elegans* Kunth., inflorescence

Plate 52

a *Acanthospermum hispidum* DC., flowering plant
b *Acanthospermum hispidum* DC., young plant
c *Ageratum conyzoides* L., flowering plant
d *Ageratum conyzoides* L., young plant

Plate 53

a *Bidens pilosa* L. var. *radiata,* inflorescence
b *Bidens pilosa* L., young plants
c *Eclipta alba* (L.) Hassk., flowering plant
d *Eclipta alba* (L.) Hassk., young plants

Plate 54

a *Parthenium hysterophorus* L., young plants
b *Ipomoea cairica* (L.) Sweet., flowering plant
c *Ipomoea* spec., seedlings
d *Cuscuta* spec., flowering plant

Plate 55

a

b

c

d

a *Cyperus rotundus* L., inflorescence
b *Cyperus esculentus* L., inflorescence
c *Cyperus oderatus* L., inflorescence
d *Dichromena ciliata* Vahl., inflorescence

Plate 56

a *Euphorbia heterophylla* L., inflorescence
b *Euphorbia heterophylla* L., young plants
c *Euphorbia hirta* L., flowering plant
d *Euphorbia glomifera* (Millsp.) L. C. Wheeler, flowering plant

Plate 57

a *Phyllanthus amarus* Schumach. & Thonn., flowering and fruiting plant

c Spikelets of *Avena sterilis* L. ssp. *macrocarpa* (Moench) Briquet (left) and of *A. s.* ssp. *ludoviciana* (Dur.) Gill & Magne (right)

b *Avena sterilis* L. ssp. *macrocarpa* (Moench) Briquet, fruiting plants

d *Cynodon dactylon* (L.) Pers., flowering plant

Plate 58

a *Dactyloctenium aegyptium* (L.) Beauv., young plant
b *Digitaria sanguinalis* (L.) Scop., flowering plant
c *Echinochloa crus-galli* (L.) P. B., flowering plant
d *Echinochloa colonum* (L.) Link, inflorescence

Plate 59

a *Eleusine indica* (L.) Gaertn., young plant
b *Rottboellia exaltata* (L.) L. f., young plant
c *Setaria viridis* (L.) P. B., flowering plant
d *Sorghum halepense* (L.) Pers., flowering plant

Plate 60

a *Leonotis nepetifolia* (L.) Ait. f., flowering plant
b *Leonotis nepetifolia* (L.) Ait. f., young plant
c *Ammannia coccinea* Rottb., inflorescence
d *Ammannia coccinea* Rottb., young plant

Plate 61

a *Sida acuta* Burm. f., young plant
b *Sida rhombifolia* L., young plants
c *Ludwigia octovalvis* (Jacq.) Raven (left), *Ludwigia erecta* (L.) Hara (right), flowering plants
d *Ludwigia octovalvis* (Jacq.) Raven, young plant

Plate 62

a *Orobanche crenata* Forsk., flowering plant
b *Orobanche aegyptiaca* Pers., flowering plant
c *Argemone mexicana* L., flower
d *Argemone mexicana* L., young plants

Plate 63

a *Heteranthera reniformis* Ruiz & Pav., flowering plant
b *Monochoria vaginalis* (Burm. f.) Presl., inflorescence
c *Physalis angulata* L., flower and fruit with calyx
d *Physalis angulata* L., young plant

Plate 64

a *Kallstroemia maxima* (L.) Torr. & A. Gray, flowering plant
b *Kallstroemia maxima* (L.) Torr. & A. Gray, young plant
c *Tribulus cistoides* L., flowering plant
d *Tribulus terrestris* L., flowering and fruiting plant

Avena sterilis ssp. *macrocarpa* normally emerges in December/January, and quickly forms very vigorous plants with 2–3 leaves. Tillering is similar to that of winter wheat. Normally winter wheat and wild oat reach the same phenological stage at the end of their vegetative development. From this essential stage on, *A. s.* ssp. *macrocarpa* grows more quickly and dominates cereals after flowering, particularly during dry seasons in early summer.

Control: It is important to avoid infestation by using clean cereal seed, particularly on clean land. Where fallow is used on heavier soils, wild oat must be well controlled by offset discs and cultivators.

It is possible to control wild oat by following a good rotation particularly by addition of "cleanup" crops such as fodder crops (e. g. early harvested vetch-oats and clover) or row crops (e. g. horse beans, broad beans, peas, sugar beets). Winter barley is more competitive than winter wheat and should therefore be preferred to wheat in cases where cereals have to be grown on sites heavily infested with wild oats.

Hand weeding can be advisable on small farms, under extensive cropping conditions and especially on cereal multiplication fields. Wild oat is a good fodder and can be used for hay or silage. Burning of the stubble is not an effective means of controlling wild oat. However, there is a tendency for the dormancy to be broken. Deep ploughing in an attempt to bury seeds so deeply that they are not likely to germinate is also not effective. There is no possibility in timing of tillage operations in areas with light rainfall (e. g. North Africa).

Cereal crops: Cereal crops must obtain maximum benefit from the first rains and must be tilled as soon as possible in those areas.

There is no quick or easy way to eradicate wild oat from a field. But it seems possible by following a combination of suitable crop rotation, cultural practices and application of herbicides which effectively control wild oats.

In winter wheat the control of *A. s.* ssp. *macrocarpa* by post-emergence application of benzoylprop-ethyl gives good results with a sufficient safety margin for the wheat. In North Africa it can be applied in early spring when mechanical operations on the land are usually easier and the severity of the infestation can be clearly seen. The most favourable stage for application is the beginning of shooting up to the second node stage. The period when benzoylprop-ethyl can be applied successfully extends over two to three weeks, which is advantageous compared to some other wild oat herbicides. Benzoylprop-ethyl should not be mixed with 2,4-D and MCPA, and these herbicides should not be applied within ten days of benzoylprop-ethyl being sprayed. However mecoprop can be associated to benzoylprop-ethyl.

A very heavy and early infestation and the association with other grass weeds (e. g. *Phalaris* spp., *Lolium* spp.) may be controlled by early applications of chlortoluron, metoxuron, nitrofen or mixtures with these compounds. These herbicides must be applied post-emergence in the two to three leaf stage. The timing is very important. Tri-allate can be incorporated pre-sowing. A disadvantage of those pre- and early post-emergence herbicides is that those applications do not fully allow the farmer to see the extent of wild oat infestation before applying relatively expensive control measures. The critical time for early post-emergence applications is only up to ten days after emergence. Besides that, another flush of wild oat seedlings may appear after later rains. Incorporation is often very difficult on heavy soils after long hot and dry periods and the first rains must be waited for.

In winter barley wild oat control by herbicides is not so important because this crop is more competitive. Tri-allate can be incorporated pre-sowing.

Wild oat control in row crops such as sugar beets, cotton, beans is possible with pre-sowing incorporation of trifluralin or tri-allate.

Literature

GUILLEMENET, R. (1971): Les folles avoines dans la Vienne. Phytoma **23**, 24–27.
JORDAN, D., D. J. BOWLER & M. C. MOBERLY (1972): Suffix: a new herbicide for wild oat control in wheat. Span, **15**, 26–29.

LINDENBEIN, W. & B. RADEMACHER (1960): *Avena ludoviciana* Dur. Der Winterflughafer. Saatgutwirtschaft **7**, 191–193.

MALZEW, A. I. (1930): Wild and cultivated oat, Sectio Euavena Griseb. Suppl. 38, Bull. Appl Botany, Genetics and Plant Breeding, Leningrad.

POLLEHN, E. & H. SCHMIDT (1974): Ungrasprobleme im Getreidebau Tunesiens. Gesunde Pflanzen **26**, 134–137.

THURSTON, JOAN M. (1957): Morphological and physiological variation in wild oats (*Avena fatua* L. and *A. ludoviciana* Dur.) and in hybrids between wild and cultivated oats. J. Agric. Science **49**, 259–274.

Author: K. Petzoldt

Cenchrus echinatus L. (Fig. 220)

Common names: bur grass, southern sandbur; –; herbe rude; abrojo, cadillo.

Related species: *C. brownii* Roem. & Schult, *C. pauciflorus* Benth.

Geographical distribution: The three species are distributed over the warmer areas of America and have been introduced into parts of the Old World; for example *C. echinatus* into Australia and Africa, the islands of the Pacific and the Philippines (De Lisle, 1963).

Habitat: The species prefer sandy, stony soils and open ground. *Cenchrus echinatus* frequently occurs on fallow land, in newly sown forage grasses and is found in other crops which give poor soil cover or have become patchy. In South and Central America it infests maize, peanuts, cotton, sugar cane, citrus, coffee and bananas.

Description: Much tillering grass with ascending culms, 25–50 cm tall (Fig. 220). Culm often rooting at lower nodes. Leaf blades 15–25 cm long, 5–10 mm wide, hairy at base. Spikes often light purple in colour, about 4–7 mm long. Four spikelets joined to form globose spiny bur. At maturity, burs are easily released from the rachis, catch onto clothes and are thereby distributed. *Cenchrus brownii* can be distinguished from *C. echinatus* by its burs being more closely arranged on the spike which is a more uniform green colour. With *C. pauciflorus,* the ring of thin bristles at the base of the burs, a characteristic of the other two species, is missing.

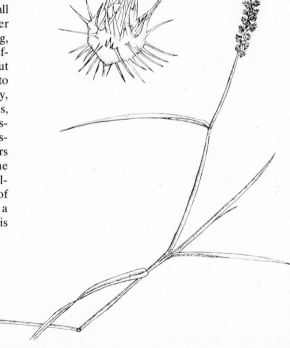

Fig. 220.   *Cenchrus echinatus* L.

Development: *Cenchrus echinatus* is probably a tetraploid arising from an original form, with a basic chromosome count of 17 (De Lisle, 1963). It reproduces sexually. Plants in the flowering phase can be found in the tropics at all times of the year. Although it is generally categorised as an annual, the species has to be classified as a perennial in the tropical zone. In greenhouse experiments on Hispaniola, the plants through the production of side culms, flowered and matured three times in nine months without dying. The seeds can germinate as soon as they have separated from the mother plant. 3–4 leaves are formed before the onset of tillering. Young plants have a characteristic deep reddish-brown colouring at the base. The formation of lateral shoots begins 10–12 days after emergence. With *C. echinatus,* spike formation begins after approximately four weeks, and the first fruits reach maturity after about 6 weeks. With moist conditions, germination can occur on the soil surface, with the radicle subsequently penetrating into the soil. Usually only 1 seedling develops per bur.

Supplementary: In the early developmental phase before the burs harden, *Cenchrus* species are considered as good forage grasses.

Control: In permanent pastures, grazing should take place at the beginning of spike formation to stop reproduction, and to make full use of the forage value of the grass.
Usually post-emergence treatments with dalapon 6 and 10 kg/ha, TCA 10 kg/ha, or MSMA/cacodylic acid 4 and 6 kg/ha effectively control *Cenchrus* for up to two months.
Cenchrus echinatus is well controlled by trifluralin 1 kg/ha, alachlor 0.9–2.6 kg/ha, linuron/propachlor 1/2 kg/ha, butylate 3.6, atrazine 2.5 kg/ha as well as fluometuron 2.4 kg/ha. However, pre-emergence treatments with pebulate 3.5 and 5 kg/ha, prometryne 1 and 1.5 kg/ha, MCPB 2 and 3 kg/ha as well as nitrofen 3.5 and 5 kg/ha did not give satisfactory results.
In sugar cane, asulam 3.6, ametryne 3–4 or ametryne/atrazine 3–4 kg/ha are recommended up to the second leaf stage against the weed.
In plantation crops, treatments with glyphosate 2.2 kg/ha resulted in the complete eradication of *C. brownii* plants.

Literature

DE LISLE, D. G. (1963): Taxonomy and distribution of the genus *Cenchrus.* Iowa ST. J. of Science **37,** 259–351.
HAVARD-DUCLOS, B. (1969): Las plantas forrajeras tropicales. Barcelona.
LANGE, A. H. (1968): Weeds in California fruit crops – a summary of problems and herbicide possibilities. Calif. Agric. **22,** 8–10.
LAROCHE, R. (1971): Nomenclature Polyglotte des plantes haitiennes et tropicales. Port-au-Prince, Haiti. 1971.

Author: G. Jürgens

Cynodon dactylon (L.) Pers. (Fig. 221 and plate 57 d)

Common names: bermuda grass, devil grass; Hundszahngrass; chiendent; hierba de bermuda, pasto bermuda, pasto argentina, grama dulce.

Geographical distribution: *Cynodon dactylon* which probably stems from Africa, is now widespread in the tropics and subtropics and has become naturalized in favourable habitats of the temperate zone.

Habitat: *Cynodon dactylon* thrives best on loam and clay soils but also occurs on sandy soils. It is fairly drought resistent but requires a minimum of 600–700 mm rainfall in the tropics. It invades irrigated areas of dry regions. The species has a certain salt tolerance. It is represented in nearly all

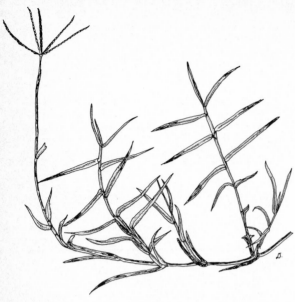

Fig. 221.   *Cynodon dactylon* (L.) Pers.

weed communities and is frequently dominant in plantation crops with moderate shade. Upland areas to 2000 m are colonised.

Description: Perennial grass with scaly rhizomes and stolons often covering the soil like a lawn (Fig. 221, plate 57 d). Culms 10–30 cm tall. Leaf blades on erect growing shoots up to 18 cm long, but usually considerably shorter. Inflorescence normally composed of 4–5 spikes all arising from the tip of the culm. Spikelets about 2 mm long.

Development: Reproduction either through rhizomes or stolons. Lateral shoots grow rapidly, irrespective of whether the soil is moist or flooded. It can achieve a growth rate of 50 cm or more per month due to its pattern of synchronised branching. Apart from vegetative reproduction, propagation by seeds also plays a role. In Nigeria, the best germination was obtained from seeds that had been collected at the end of the rainy season and the first month of the dry period. Emergence was strongly influenced not by the soil type, but by the water content of the soil. Fourteen days after emergence, the young plants had already began to form horizontally growing lateral shoots. Given favourable weather conditions, *C. dactylon* can flower and bear fruit the whole year through. For details of its biology and ecology see Horowitz (1971), Rochecouste (1962) and Thomas (1969).

Supplementary: *Cynodon dactylon* is used in many areas as a lawn or forage grass. Varieties with higher growth are especially suitable for fodder production. The grass is valued because of its drought resistance. The rhizomes can be used for medicinal purposes.

Control: During pronounced dry periods, the grass can be controlled by soil cultivation. This entails bringing the rhizomes to the soil surface and exposing them to dry weather for long periods of time. The rhizomes can also be destroyed by harrowing. An effective control can be achieved by the introduction of shade producing cover crops within a crop rotational system. In certain cases, the necessary mechanical and chemical methods must be combined with crop rotation (Gopal & Mani, 1968). As far as chemical control is concerned, applications of dalapon 4–8, TCA 60–100, terbacil 4.5–9, bromacil 4.5–9, amitrole 2.5, asulam 2.8–3.6 und glyphosate 2.3–4.5 kg/ha have been successful. Treatments have to be repeated if, and when, regrowth of the weed occurs.

Literature

GOPAL, R. & V. S. MANI (1968): Control of *Cyperus rotundus* and *Cynodon dactylon* by a combination of mechanical, chemical and cropping methods. Proc. 9th Br. Weed Control Conf., 809–813.
HOROWITZ, M. (1971): Development of *Cynodon dactylon*. Weed Research **12**, 207–220.
IDRIS, H. (1970): Chemical control of weeds in cotton in the Sudan Gezira. PANS **16**, 96–105.
ROCHECOUSTE, E. (1962): Studies on the biotypes of *Cynodon dactylon* (L.) Pers. I and II. Weed Research **2**, 1–23, 136–145.
THOMAS, P. E. L. (1969): Effects of desiccation and temperature on survival of *Cyperus esculentus* tubers and *Cynodon dactylon* rhizomes. – Weed Research **9**, 1–8.

Author: G. Jürgens

Dactyloctenium aegyptium (L.) Beauv. (Fig. 222 and plate 58 a)

Synonym: *D. aegyptiacum* Willd., *Eleusine aegyptiaca* Desf.

Common names: crowfoot grass; –; dactyloctenium d'Égypte; paja de palma, pata de gallina, yerba de Egipto.

Geographical distribution: The grass which originated from the tropics of the Old World is today widespread over the warmer areas of the world.

Habitat: *Dactyloctenium aegyptium* preferably colonises open land with sandy or gravelly soils, but can also be found on heavy soils. In some regions such as in India and Taiwan, it is one of the most important weeds of the summer season. On Hispaniola, it has been observed that it can develop under rather dry conditions. Havard-Duclos (1969) however, defined the weed as having little drought resistance. Annual and perennial crops which have become patchy, as well as lawns and meadows are invaded.

Description: Grass with prostrate or erect culms, rooting at lower nodes, up to 50 cm tall (Fig. 222). Leaves linear, hairy. Inflorescence of 1–5 spikes arranged digitately on the end of the culm, 1–5 cm long. Spikelets in two rows on one side of compressed rachis.

Development: Annual plant with a life span of several months (Plate 58 a). Mature seeds taken from the infructescence can germinate to a large extent without any preceding dormancy. Onset of tillering after the appearance of the fourth leaf. The formation of numerous side shoots leads to a mat-like soil covering. Onset of flowering about two months after emergence.

Supplementary: The fodder value has been described as very good, rather good, or even worthless.

Control: Applications of atrazine 1.6, atrazine/terbutryne 0.8/0.8, atrazine/simazine 1.2/0.8 or linuron 1 kg/ha kept maize free of *D. aegyptium* for more than nine weeks. Soil treatments with pebulate, EPTC, nitralin, trifluralin, DCPA, diuron, fluometuron, prometryne and nitrofen have also proved successful. Foliar applied propanil and paraquat are effective in controlling the grass weed.

Fig. 222. *Dactyloctenium aegyptium* (L.) Beauv.

Literature

HASELWOOD, E. L. & G. G. MOTTER (1966): Handbook of Hawaiian weeds. Honolulu, Hawaii.
HAVARD-DUCLOS, B. (1969): Las plantas forrajeras tropicales. Barcelona, 1969.
LEON, H. (1946): Flora de Cuba. Vol 1. La Habana, Cuba.

Author: G. Jürgens

Digitaria sanguinalis (L.) Scop. (Plate 58 b)

Synonym: *Panicum sanguinale* L.

Common names: crabgrass; Blut-Fingerhirse, Bluthirse, Blutfennich; digitaire sanguine; pendejuelo, pata de gallina.

Related species: *Digitaria ischaemum* (Schreb.) Mühlenb.

Geographical distribution: Almost cosmopolitan, probably not originally indigenous to Central Europe, chiefly in warmer and temperate zones of both hemispheres. Distribution of *D. ischaemum* somewhat similar to *D. sanguinalis* especially in maize and wine growing areas.

Habitat: *Digitaria sanguinalis* thrives on nitrogen-rich sand to moist loam soils. It is highly adaptable. *Digitaria ischaemum* is predominantly found on light, lime deficient, partly nutrient deficient and also nitrogen-rich soils. Both species prefer a warm climate with many hours of sunshine. Noxious weed in maize, root crops and vegetable fields as well as orchards and vineyards and in many crops of the subtropics and tropics. Likewise in ruderal places, railway embankments, neglected lawns and banks.
Digitaria ischaemum is mostly found regionally together with *D. sanguinalis* in the same habitat.

Description:

D. sanguinalis (Plate 58 b)

D. ischaemum

Growth habit and size: clump forming, 10–30 cm tall. Culm prostrate, branched at base, ascending from bent base. Smooth, glabrous, sparsely hairy at nodes.

Growth habit and size: clump forming about 5–50 cm. Culm usually much branched, smooth, glabrous, more delicate than that of *D. sanguinalis*.

Leaf: youngest leaf rolled.

Leaf: youngest leaf rolled.

Leaf blade: 3–10 (20) cm long, green, often purple, with silky hair, whitish-reddish midrib.

Leaf blade: 2–12 cm long, green, often purple, glabrous, sometimes sparsely hairy, somewhat rough at the base, with whitish-reddish midrib.

Leaf sheath: rather wide (the lower ones) with long ciliate hair.

Leaf sheath: glabrous, sometimes with tuft of hair at leaf base.

Ligule: 1–2 mm long, truncate, membranous, white.

Ligule: 1–2 mm long, truncate, membranous, white.

Auricle: absent.

Auricle: absent.

Inflorescence: false spikes, mostly 3–8, almost digitate but not originating from one point on the culm, erect.

Inflorescence: false spikes, mostly 3 or 2–4, which are close together, nearly digitate.

Spikelets: contain a single flower, about 3 mm long, oblong lanceolate, violet-tinged, lower glume very small, second glume about half as long as the spikelet, narrow, sparsely hairy.

Spikelets: contain a single flower, short, oval, pubescent, lower glume small, dark and transparent, the other as long as the lemma.

Development: *Digitaria sanguinalis* like *D. ischaemum* germinates in late spring and summer and needs warmth for germination. Freshly harvested seeds of both species are practically dormant. After-ripening through several months of storage increases the germination rate to 95–98 %. Both *D. sanguinalis* and *D. ischaemum* are annuals, propagation being exclusively by seeds.

Supplementary: *Digitaria sanguinalis* was already cultivated during the Middle Ages throughout Eastern Germany and Austria but is hardly ever cultivated nowadays. The hay is suitable as fodder.

Control: Mechanical control can be carried out by repeated hoeings and weedings as many bursts of germination often occur in temperate climates. Chemical control is possible (for details see *S. viridis*).

Literature

DUNN, St., G. R. GRUENDLING & A. S. THOMAS, JR. (1968): Effects of light quality on the life cycles of crabgrass and barnyardgrass. Weed Science, **16,** 58–60.
GARCKE, A. (1972): Illustrierte Flora. Verlag Paul Parey, Berlin–Hamburg, 23. Aufl.
GIANFAGNA, A. J. (1952): Some aspects of dormancy and germination of crabgrass seed, *Digitaria sanguinalis* Scop. NEWCC-Proc. 6, 321–326.

Author: S. Behrendt

Echinochloa crus-galli (L.) P. B. (Plate 58 c, d)

Synonym: *Panicum crus-galli* L.

Common names: cockspur, barnyardgrass; Hühner-Hirse, Dückergrass; panic pied-decoq; cerreig, pata de gallo, cola de caballo.

Related species: *Echinochloa colonum* (L.) Link (jungle rice), *E. crus-pavonis* (H.B.K.) Schult.

Geographical distribution: *Echinochloa crus-galli* occurs throughout the warm and temperate zones of the whole world. *Echinochloa colonum* and *E. crus-pavonis* however, are found especially in the tropical regions of both hemispheres.

Habitat: *Echinochloa crus-galli* occurs on dry to fresh, even silty (rice), warm, rich loamy sand, loam and clay soils. It thrives best on soils with an approximately neutral pH. *Echinochloa colonum* is found on nearly all types of soil, if sufficient moisture is available. On calcium rich soils, vegetative and sexual development are inhibited due to reduced seed viability and chlorosis.
Both species prefer warm habitats and are very adaptable, especially *E. crus-galli,* which can also be found in maritime regions of North Europe. *Echinochloa crus-galli* can be a disastrous weed in rice, maize, cotton, soya bean, lucerne, root crops and vegetable fields, as well as in orchards and vineyards. It is found in numerous crops of the subtropics, and at times also in the tropics. *Echinochloa colonum* and *E. crus-pavonis* are increasing as grass weeds mainly in tropical but also in subtropical crops, above all in rice but also in moist grasslands.

Description:

Echinochloa crus-galli (Plate 58 c)   *Echinochloa colonum* (Plate 58 d)

Growth habit and size: clump forming, up to 150 cm tall. Culm stout, often geniculately ascending at base. Young plants especially with tufted hair at nodes.

Growth habit and size: 15–60 cm tall. A distinction is made between a large and small sub-species. Culm prostrate to erect.

Leaf: youngest leaf rolled.

Leaf: youngest leaf rolled.

Leaf blade: up to 35 cm long, 0.5–1.5 cm wide, green to grey-green, often reddish, glabrous with white midrib. Young plants particularly with solitary hairs near leaf base.

Leaf blade: often flaccid, 3–6 mm wide, occasionally with purple coloured regions running transversely across the leaf veins.

Leaf sheath: glabrous, almost closed and often flattened.

Leaf sheath: glabrous almost closed and often flattened.

Ligule and auricle: absent.

Ligule and auricle: absent.

Inflorescence: is a paniculate or racemose false spike up to more than 10 mm long. Inflorescence often becoming denser at apical end.

Inflorescence: is a paniculate false spike, 5–15 cm long. Panicle with numerous branches, each 1–2 cm long, appressed or ascending, solitary or occasionally two of the same kind.

Spikelets: with single flower, green-violet, lower glumes about half as long as the spikelet, upper glume often with ± bristly hairs. Awned (up to 1 cm) and awnless forms occur.

Spikelets: about 3 mm long, almost without pedicels, acute, lemma weakly nerved, ± hispid. Awn is reduced to a short point.

One distinguishes *E. crus-galli* varieties as follows:
E. crus-galli forma *longiseta* (Trin.) Farw.
Spikelets with long awns. Caryopsis ovate, 2.5–3.5 mm long, tan to brown, convex surface striate.
E. crus-galli var. *mitis* (Pursh) Peterm.
Inflorescence denser at top, awns of spikelets reduced to points, awns < 3 mm. Leaf sheath pubescent.
E. crus-galli var. *zelaymis* (H.B.K.) Hitchc.
Inflorescence loose, spikelets awnless, ± hairy, occurring mostly in alkaline habitats.
E. crus-galli var. *frumentacea* (Roxb.) W. F. Wight
Inflorescence thick, but relatively loose, spikelets awnless, reddish-violet in colour, ± hairy.
Small and large forms have also been established for *E. colonum*.

Development: *Echinochloa crus-galli* needs warmth for germination. It has a marked dormancy of 3–4 months. Minimum soil temperature for germination is 13 °C, optimum at 20–30 °C. It can germinate in the soil up to a depth of 10 cm. Optimal germination at 70–90 % of water holding capacity. Seeds can also germinate under water. Seeds kept in dry storage are viable for up to 7 years. *Echinochloa crus-galli* and *Echinochloa colonum* are annuals. Given favourable soil and climatic conditions, they can form mature seeds about 42–64 days after germination.

Supplementary: *Echinochloa crus-galli* and *E. colonum* damage crop plants by competing for water, light and nutrients. An 80–90 % reduction in yield is possible in maize. Roots reach a depth of 1 m.

Control: Repeated hoeing and weeding is necessary above all in temperate climates, because the seeds can germinate at various times of the year. Chemical control is possible (see *S. viridis*).

Literature

BROD, G. (1968): Untersuchungen zur Biologie und Ökologie der Hühnerhirse, *Echinochloa crus-galli* L. Beauv. Weed Res. **8,** 115–127.
HITCHCOCK, A. S. (1935): Manual of the grasses of the United States. US Dept. Agr. Misc., Publ. no 200.
KACPERSKA-PALACZ, A. E., E. C. PUTALA & J. VENGRIS (1963): Developmental anatomy of barnyardgrass seedlings. Weeds, **11,** 311–316.
RAMAKRISHNAN, P. S. (1971): Ecology of *Echinochloa colonum* Link. Tropical Ecology **12,** 112–22.
VODERBERG, K. (1967): Zur Keimungsphysiologie von Hirsearten der Unkrautflora. Nachr.bl. für d. Dt. Pflanzenschutzdienst, **21,** 176–179.
VOGT, E. (1955): Ein Beitrag zur Keimfähigkeit der Samen der Hühnerhirse und des Ampfer-Knöterichs, besonders ihrer im Boden ruhenden Samen. Angewandte Botanik **29,** 26–32.

Author: S. Behrendt

Eleusine indica (L.) Gaertn. (Fig. 223 and plate 59 a)

Common names: crow's foot grass, goosegrass; –; pied de poule; pata de gallina, pato de ganso.

Related species: *E. africana* Kennedy O'Byrne, is today classified as a sub-species of *E. indica*.

Geographical distribution: *Eleusine indica* was originally indigenous to the Old World, but is today widespread throughout the tropics and subtropics, and is an especially noxious weed in tropical regions.

Habitat: *Eleusine indica* is represented in many weed communities of several annual and perennial crops. It has no particular soil preference. With adequate soil moisture, a heavy build up of the weed occurs in fields of humid regions and also in irrigated crops of arid regions. Continual or occasional flooding of the soil can considerably reduce its growth. The species reaches a high degree of covering on the dams of rice fields, but rarely invades the irrigated plots. On Hispaniola, the appearance of this species in coffee plantations was promoted by the introduction of mineral fertilisers and a reduction in the amount of shading. In Zambia, *E. indica* is a noxious weed of intensive farming, but not of shifting cultivation.

Description: Tufted grass about 30–90 cm tall (Fig. 223). Culm compressed, prostrate at base then ascending, much branched. Leaf margins partly ciliate, leaf blades 3–9 mm wide. Inflorescence composed of 4–15 spikes. Spikelets 4–5 mm, with 3–6 flowers, on one side of triangular rachis only. Seeds brownish-black, finely granular on surface. *Eleusine africana* has spikelets 6–7.5 mm long.

Development: Experiments in the Dominican Republic showed that the majority of seeds removed from the infructescence at maturity and planted in moist soils, had no dormancy. According to information from Rhodesia, *E. indica* still germinated at a relatively constant rate even after five years of storage, and a proportion of the seeds were still viable after being placed in the soil for four years at a depth of 22.5–30 cm.

The different developmental stages are rapidly passed through with adequate moisture (Plate 59 a). Six leaves are formed before the onset of tillering which begins about ten days after emergence. The first formed inflorescences are normally composed of four to five segments. The number of shoots, inflorescences, spread, and dry weight yield increase with light intensity. It has been calculated that the plants can produce about 4.5–5 billion seeds/ha. *Eleusine indica* has been clas-

Fig. 223. *Eleusine indica* (L.) Gaertn.

sified as an annual by some authors, but this description does not apply in the tropics. Following maturity and subsequent cutting, the plant can regenerate and flower and bear fruit repeatedly. Plants at all developmental stages can be found throughout the year.

Supplementary: *Eleusine indica* is also used as a forage grass, and gives high yields with adequate irrigation. The grass is a host plant for virus diseases of maize and rice.

Control: Because of its rapid growth, control of the weed is necessary until the closing of the crop canopy. The compact root system of *Eleusine* is difficult to eradicate by mechanical means. *Eleusine indica* is sensitive to a number of herbicides. Compounds from the carbamate group (asulam, pebulate, vernolate, butylate, benthiokarb), the anilines (nitralin, trifluralin, isopropanil, dibutalin) and the amides (alachlor, butachlor, propachlor, napropamide) that are predominantly effective against grasses are suitable for the control of *Eleusine* when used at recommended dosages. Pre-emergence treatments with most urea derivates (diuron, linuron, norea, metobromuron, fluometuron, chlorbromuron, methabenzthiazuron) give a good control. From the triazine series, simazine, terbutryne, atrazine, prometryne, cyanazine, ametryne and metribuzin have proved satisfactory. Contact herbicides such as propanil and paraquat should be applied before the onset of tillering, for the grass weed is rather resistant at its later developmental stages. In plantation crops, repeated applications of dalapon or dalapon, alternating with paraquat, can be recommended.

Literature

HAVARD-DUCLOS, B. (1968): Las plantas forrajeras tropicales. Barcelona.
HITCHCOCK, A. S. (1971): Manual of the grasses of the United States. Vol 1. New York.
HOLM, L. G. (1969): Weed problems in developing countries. Weed Sci. **17**, 113–118.

Author: G. Jürgens

Ischaemum rugosum Salisb. (Fig. 224)

Common names: wrinklegrass; –; –; caminadora, triguillo, yerba popa.

Related species: *Ischaemum afrum* (J. F. Gmel.) Dandy, comb. nov. (Syn.: *I. brachyatherum* (Hochst.) Fenzel ex Hack., *Andropogon afer* J. L. Gmel.)

Geographical distribution: The species has been introduced into America from the Old World, and has now spread throughout the tropics.

Habitat: *Ischaemum rugosum* is a characteristic species of moist and wet habitats. Owing to its respiratory root system it can also colonise areas that are permanently flooded with water. The species has become a noxious grass weed especially in dry and irrigated rice crops, but also in sugar cane and other field crops.

Description: Much branched grass about 50–100 cm tall, its roots sometimes aerial (Fig. 224). Culms ascending. Leaf sheath densely hairy, leaf blade with less hair, 1–2 cm wide. Before maturity, raceme firmly joined together as in a spike, but later separating into two parts beginning at the top, about 5–12 cm long. Spikelets 3–4 mm, awns about 15 mm long.

Development: In the Caribbean it follows a distinct growth pattern. The majority of the plants emerge in April and May and flower in the last 4 months of the year. A marked vegetative phase begins with the onset of tillering. Under favourable conditions, more than 200 inflorescence-bearing culms may be formed. The reproductive phase is probably initiated through the advent of shorter day lengths in early autumn. Besides the cycle described here, a considerable number of more weakly developed plants appear which flower from February to May.

Young plants are very similar in appearance to rice. *Ischaemum rugosum* however has ascending shoots and deep reddish brown to purple leaf sheaths. With rice, this colouring is only weakly developed, its tillering shoots having a more vertical growth habit.

Fig. 224. *Ischaemum rugosum* Salisb.

Control: In the case of transplanted rice, the dispersal of *I. rugosum* from seed bed to field should be avoided. With chemical control, propanil has given the best practical results. The treatment must be carried out when *Ischaemum* has developed 1–3 leaves. Later applications will not destroy the plant even if the dosages are increased. Applications at the 4 leaf stage (3.8 kg/ha) and at the flowering stage (5 kg/ha) resulted in a 40–50 % control.

Plants that have escaped control measures should be removed by hand to prevent seed production. Soil herbicides to be recommended are fluorodifen 2, benthiokarb 2–2.5 and butachlor 1–1.5 kg/ha. Trifluralin or dichlobenil 2 kg/ha and chloramben 1.5–2.5 kg/ha control the weed.

Literature

EVANS, W. F., A. R. COOKE & J. L. LAMPITT (1971): Amiben for weed control in transplanted rice. 3rd Conf. Asian-Pacific Weed Sci. Soc. Kuala Lumpur 25, pp. 7.

GOBERDHAN, L. C. (1971): *Andropogon annulatus* and *Ischaemum rugosum* – two new weeds of sugarcane in Trinidad. PANS **17**, 178–179.

JIMÉNEZ, J. DE (1963–1967): Catalogus Florae Domingensis, Supl. 1. Arch. Bot. Biogeog. Ital. 39–43.

KENNARD, C. P. (1973): Control of weeds in direct seeded rice with some of the newer herbicides. Intern. Rice Comm. Newsletter **22**, 15–21.

Author: R. Hansen del Orbe

Panicum dichotomiflorum Michx.

Synonym: *Panicum miliaceum* Walt.

Common names: fall panicum; Rispenhirse; panic dichatome; borona.

Related species: *Panicum texanum* Buckl.

Geographical distribution: *Panicum dichotomiflorum* occurs chiefly in countries with dry warm climates such as Italy, Spain and the USA (infrequent or missing in the North, North West and Texas) and in India.

Panicum texanum also occurs in areas with dry warm climates (North Carolina to Florida, Arizona, Oklahoma, New Mexico in the USA and in North Mexico).

Habitat: *Panicum dichotomiflorum* prefers moist habitats and can occur on fallow land as well as on good cultivated soils. In the USA, Canada and Italy, the weed is found especially in maize, sorghum, soya bean and rice fields.

Panicum texanum grows in prairies, open lands, chiefly on plains and by rivers. In Texas, it is a widespread grass weed of arable land.

Description:

Panicum dichotomiflorum	*Panicum texanum*
Growth habit and form: clump forming, up to 150 (200!) cm tall.	**Growth habit and form:** clump forming, up to 180 cm tall.
Culm: flattened, ascending or bent abruptly at base, then ascending, single or ± branching at the base or the nodes. Lower nodes distinctly enlarged.	**Culm:** erect or ascending, 5–150 cm, rarely up to 300 cm, pubescent especially below the nodes.
Leaf: youngest leaf rolled.	**Leaf:** youngest leaf rolled.

Leaf blade: 10–50 cm long, 3–20 mm wide, rough, sometimes sparsely hairy on upper surface, with white midrib. Blade somewhat attenuate at base.

Leaf sheath: round, hispid.

Ligule: substituted by dense ring of white hair, 1–2 mm long.

Auricle: absent.

Inflorescence: an axillary or terminal panicle (10–40 cm long), mostly enclosed by the sheath at the base. Main panicle branches are ascending, while secondary and tertiary branches are flaccid.

Spikelets: narrow, oval to oblong (2–3 mm) with two flowers, one of which is rudimentary. Spikelets mostly longer than their sharp-edged pedicels, mostly on one side of panicle branchlets. First glume is rounded, triangular, $^1/_4$ to $^1/_5$ as long as the second and the lemma. Lemma and palea are shiny, drop out of glumes with the seed.

Leaf blade: 8–20 cm long, 7–15 mm wide, pubescent.

Leaf sheath: pubescent.

Ligule: substituted by dense ring of white hair.

Auricle: absent.

Inflorescence: panicle (8–20 cm long), with short appressed branchlets, rachis pubescent, ± long hair.

Spikelets: 5–6 mm long, often dark, pubescent.

Development: *Panicum dichotomiflorum* is an annual grass, needing light and warmth for germination. The main germination time in the USA and Mediterranean area is late spring (May to August). Broad leaved weeds in a standing crop prevent the germination of *P. dichotomiflorum* through shading. With the removal of broad leaved weeds through 2,4-D and atrazine in maize, and through the breeding of short-stemmed maize varieties, ideal growth conditions were created for the weed. Yield losses in maize of up to 20 % and more have been noted. *Panicum dichotomiflorum* also thrives in flooded habitats and develops an extensive root system that similar to rice has a succession of permeable cells that allow oxygen transport.

Control: Because of the previously mentioned germination requirements, *P. dichotomiflorum* can be somewhat reduced by a crop rotation (potatoes or rape) that gives soil covering very early on.
Chemical control is possible through products based on the dinitroanilines (trifluralin, nitralin), acid anilides (alachlor) and thiocarbamates (butylate). Triazine preparations are usually not satisfactory.

Literature

CHANDLER, JAMES M. & R. W. SANTELMANN (1969): Growth characteristics and herbicide susceptibility of texas panicum. Weed Science **17**, 1969, 91–93.
CIALONE, J. C. & G. LASSITER (1968): The control of fall panicum (*Panicum dichotomiflorum*) with pre- and post-emergence applications of chemicals. Abstr. Meet. Weed Science Soc. America, 4.
HOVELAND, S. C. & A. G. BUCHANAN (1972): Flooding tolerance of fall-panicum and texas-panicum. Weed Science **20**, 1–3.

Author: S. Behrendt

Rottboellia exaltata (L.) L. f. (Fig. 225 and plate 59 b)

Synonym: *Manisuris exaltata* Kuntze

Common names: guinea-fowl grass, itchgrass; –; l'herbe Bette-Elise; caminadora, cebadilla.

Geographical distribution: *Rottboellia exaltata,* originating from tropical Asia, is today widespread in the warmer areas of the world.

Habitat: In Rhodesia, the species is considered to be one of the most important weeds on heavy soils (loamy sand to clay) while in the Dominican Republic it is frequently found on light soils. The grass weed occurs in Equatorial Africa at altitudes of up to 2000 m, but at the edge of the tropics it is limited to lowland areas. Some authors stress its preference for moist conditions or its increased growth during the wet periods of the year. On Hispaniola, areas with water-logged soils are avoided. Despite its preference for moist conditions, *R. exaltata* has a considerable drought resistance. The weed invades a large number of tropical crops; among others, maize, millet, dry rice, cotton, vegetables, sugar cane and fruit plantations. Investigations in Rhodesia showed that *Rottboellia* plants which germinated before maize reduced its yield to a greater extent than plants emerging at the same time. *Rottboellia* sown two weeks later than maize, did not affect its yield. Light competition was most important when the weed had reached or overtopped the height of the crop plant. The presence of *Rottboellia* did not reduce the amount of water available for maize in the middle and later phases of growth during drought periods.

Fig. 225. *Rottboellia exaltata* (L.) L. f.

Description: Tufted, erect growing grass, with robust culms up to 3 m tall (Fig. 225, plate 59 b). Leaf sheaths with bristly stinging hairs, leaf blades flat, rough. Inflorescences axillary, numerous, about 3–4 mm wide, decreasing in width above, 8–12 cm long. Spikelets sessile, 5–7 mm, falling off successively at maturity starting from the apex.

Development: Following investigations in Columbia and Rhodesia concerning the development of this plant, it can be concluded that a greater part of the husked seeds go through a phase of dormancy. However, 4–8 % of the fruits given adequate soil moisture, already germinated 3–4 days after separation from the mother plant. Dormancy can be broken by removing the husks, and is further influenced by storage, age, temperature and moisture. The husked seeds stay viable in the soil for up to 2–3 years. They can emerge from depths of 1–8 cm. Onset of tillering about 14 days after emergence, reaching an average of about 37 shoots per plant. At a high initial density of 1670 plants/m², plant numbers are considerably reduced through intra-specific competition. Onset of flowering after about 8 weeks, of senescence after 15 weeks. Up to 1180 inflorescences totalling 20600 fruits per plant have been counted, with a production of 200 million seeds giving a yield of 2000 kg/ha. Dissemination is carried out by water, machinery, seed material and animals.

Supplementary: *Rottboellia exaltata* is occasionally used as forage for horses and sheep, but the irritation caused by the hairs on mucous membranes will only allow it to be used for hay or silage. In Rhodesia, the species is infected by a series of diseases and attacked by nematodes *(Meloidogyne javanica, M. incognita* var. *acrita)*.

Control: Introduction through water and seed material has to be avoided in uninfested areas. If seeding of the weed is prevented, *R. exaltata* can be rapidly eliminated from areas as the seeds are only viable in the soil for relatively short periods of time. Zero and minimum cultivation systems can help in reducing the danger of field re-infestation, as the seeds are only superficially incorporated into the soils. It is as difficult as ever to control *R. exaltata* with herbicides, even though a number of herbicides are known to have a reasonably satisfactory action. From more than 30 herbicides tested in Columbia, only trifluralin 1.5 kg/ha gave a good control. Other products with a noticeable effect were bromacil, propanil, paraquat, DSMA, DCPA and norea/MSMA. In Zambia, trifluralin 0.3–1 kg/ha was also suitable, although some plants managed to survive the treatment. Besides trifluralin 1 kg/ha, nitrofen 2–3 and chlorthal 8 kg/ha are recommended in the Philippines as a pre-emergence treatment. In the Dominican Republic, oxadiazon 1.2 kg/ha gave a successful control of more than 90 %. Maize is frequently infested by *R. exaltata,* but no herbicides have been found that can adequately control the weed in that crop. Crop rotations with cotton, peanuts and soya bean are recommended, as these crops are resistant to herbicides from the aniline group. Trifluralin can be applied some weeks before sowing, and any surviving *Rottboellia* plants should be destroyed by harrowing immediately before sowing. This combined method ensures a good control of the grass weed and reduces the danger of residues which might damage the maize.

In bananas, glyphosate (2.2 kg/ha) treatments gave a sufficient kill of *Rottboellia* at the tillering to flowering stage. After 6 weeks, however, a considerable amount of regrowth had occurred. In sugar cane, young *Rottboellia* plants can be controlled with combinations of diuron or ametryne with 2.4-D or 2.4-D/ioxynil. Other recommended mixtures are asulam with 2,4-D/ioxynil and cyanazine with 2,4-D. In the Dominican Republic, the application of cyanacine/2,4-D 2.2/3.4 kg/ha during tillering completely killed the plant.

Literature

DE LA CURZ, R., H. FRANCO & G. RIVEROS (1972): Caracteristicas y control de la caminadora (*Rottboellia exaltata* L. f.). Res. IV Semin. COMALFI, Ibague, Colombia, 43–44.
MILLHOLLON, R. W. (1971): The status of Raoulgrass as a weed. Sug. Bull. **49,** 291–293.

THOMAS, P. E. L. (1970): A study of the biology of *Rottboellia exaltata* Linn. Proc. 10th Br. Weed Control Conf., 669–676.

Authors: G. Jürgens & R. Hansen del Orbe

Setaria viridis (L.) P. B. (Plate 59 c)

Synonym: *Panicum viride* L.

Common names: green bristle grass, green foxtail; Grüne Borstenhirse, Katzenschweif; sétaire verte; amoslio.

Related species: *Setaria faberii* Herrm. (Große Borstenhirse, giant foxtail), *Setaria lutescens* (Weig. ex Stuntz) Hubb. (Niedrige Borstenhirse, yellow foxtail), *Setaria verticillata* (Unbeständige Borstenhirse, bur bristle grass).

Geographical distribution: *Setaria viridis* occurs in almost the whole of Europe as well as Siberia, East Asia, North Africa, South and North America and Australia; virtually in all warmer temperate zones.
Setaria faberii is of chinese origin. The grass was probably introduced into the USA with the seeds of chinese millet. Today it is widely distributed throughout the North American Corn Belt.

Habitat: *Setaria viridis* loves warmth and flourishes in light, open and warm habitats.
It prefers highly nitrogenous, rich sand or sandy-loamy soils, but can also exist on lime deficient moist soils, roadside verges and waste places. It is highly adaptable to each particular habitat. *S. viridis* is a common weed in maize, soya bean, cotton, root crops, vegetables and sometimes in cereals as well as in vineyards and orchards. It is found mainly in crops which are given an abundant nitrogen supply, but can also exist on poorer soils. *Setaria faberii* has similar requirements in respect of climate and soils. Up until now it has been mainly found in North American maize and soya bean fields.

Description

Setaria viridis (Plate 59 c)

Setaria faberii

Growth habit and size: forms loose tufts and reaches a height of 5–50 cm (up to 80 cm given the most favourable conditions).

Growth habit and size: forms loose tufts and reaches a height up to 180 cm.

Culm: thin, branched at base and abruptly bent then ascending, glabrous, rough towards the top. Nodes often have reddish cross bands. The younger plant is grass green, later green to red.

Culm: stronger than *S. viridis,* branched at base, more or less erect to abruptly bent then ascending, not very stable.

Leaf: youngest leaf rolled.

Leaf: youngest leaf rolled.

Leaf blade: lanceolate, 3–30 cm long, with prominent white to light green, occasionally also reddish midrib. Glabrous on both surfaces, both surfaces ± rough. Leaf is green and distinctly keeled. Margin weakly serrate.

Leaf blade: ± short haired with white to light green midrib, upper side ± rough.

Leaf sheath: glabrous, smooth and flat, ciliate, overlapping at collar.

Leaf sheath: glabrous, terete to somewhat flattened, ciliate.

Ligule: absent, replaced by a ring of short fine hair fused at the base.

Auricles: absent.

Inflorescence: cylindrical, spikelike panicle (false spike) 2–15 cm long, 0.7–1 cm thick. Panicle branches not verticillate and have a short rachis covered with white hair. Panicle bears numerous sterile branchlets called bristles that overtop spikelet stalks and are set with fine teeth which are upwardly barbed, therefore not upwardly rough to the touch.
Spikelet with solitary flower, relatively small, 1.8–2.2 mm long, elliptical. Bristles are 5–10 mm long. Green to purplish brown. Bristles longer than the spikelets. Rachis completely covered. Lemmas punctate.

Ligule: absent, replaced by a ring of ± long hair.

Auricles: absent.

Inflorescence: whole plant distinctly larger, therefore a much larger conspicuously nodding inflorescence, a cylindrical spikelike panicle (false spike) up to 20 cm long, up to 2.3 cm thick. 3 or many green bristles, distinctly longer than the spikelets. Bristles not upwardly rough to the touch, lemma cross wrinkled. Rachis of spike normally completely covered.

Development: *Setaria viridis* is a summer annual that germinates in the warmth in late spring or early summer. It flowers from summer to early autumn.
The plant produces about 370 viable seeds per panicle and can therefore multiply at a fast rate.

Supplementary: *Setaria viridis* is sometimes cultivated as a forage grass in southern Europe, being readily eaten by sheep. In fields, *S. viridis* is becoming more of a troublesome weed. Its damaging effect on plants is caused by competition for light, water and nutrients.

Control: Mechanical control of *S. viridis* can be supported by liming as the plant is a calcifuge. For chemical control, preparations based on acid anilides (alachlor, propachlor), nitroanilines (trifluralin, nitralin, fluchloralin) and thiocarbamates (cycloate, butylate) are available. Triazine derivates do not always give satisfactory results.

Literature

OLIVER, L. R. & M. M. SCHREIBER (1971): Differential selectivity of herbicides on six *Setaria* Taxa. Weed Science, **19**, 428–431.
SCHREIBER, M. M. & L. R. OLIVER (1971): Two new varieties of *Setaria viridis*. Weed Science, **19**, 424–427.
STANWAY, V. (1971): Laboratory germination of giant foxtail, *Setaria faberii* Herrm., at different stages of maturity. Journal Paper no 7117 from the Missouri Agricultural Experiment Station.
HITCHCOCK, A. S. (1950): Manual of the grasses of the United States. USDA, Misc. Publication 200.

Author: S. Behrendt

Sorghum halepense (L.) Pers. (Plate 59 d)

Synonym: *Andropogon halepensis* Brot., *Holcus halepensis* L.

Common names: Johnsongrass; Wilde Mohrenhirse, Aleppohirse; sorgho d'Alep; canota.

Related species: *Sorghum vulgare* Pers. (Syn.: *Andropogon sorgum* Brot. var. eu.–*Sorgum* Aschers et Graebner represents the cultivated form of *S. halepense*).

Geographical distribution: Originally indigenous to the Mediterranean area. Now found in most countries of warmer zones, in both hemispheres.

Habitat: *Sorghum halepense* is highly adaptable. It is found as a ruderal on both rich loess-loam soils (Mississippi Delta) as well as on low nutrient soils. It is unimportant whether the climate is predominantly continental or subtropical and moist. *Sorghum halepense* can be a troublesome weed in many crops found in warmer climates, such as soya bean, maize, sugar beet, legumes, sugar cane and orchards. It competes strongly within a crop population for light, water and nutrients. A 40 % yield loss through *S. halepense* is not unusual.

Description:
Sorghum halepense (Plate 59 d) forms extensive rhizomes, occurs in tussocks, up to 2 m or more tall. Culms erect, smooth and relatively stout. Youngest leaves rolled, leaves alternate, numerous. Leaf blade 30–60 cm long, 1.5–3 cm wide, with distinct light coloured midrib, margins often denticulate, therefore rough. Upper side of leaf mostly pubescent or acutely punctate. Leaf light to dark green, with several sub-species turning a reddish colour in cooler weather. Leaf sheath smooth, somewhat flattened. Ligule white to light green, 5 mm long. Leaf bases hairy, depending on habitat. Auricles absent. Inflorescence an open 15–50 cm long panicle usually containing one sessile fertile spikelet combined with one or two pedicillate sterile spikelets. Sessile spikelets about 3.5–7 mm long, oval, hairy. Pedicillate spikelets lanceolate, nearly hairy with or without hairy pedicels. Awns short and twisted, normally dropping off quickly. Caryopsis up to 2.5 mm long, oval, reddish brown, marked with fine lines on its dorsal side. Each panicle carries 87–352 spikelets depending on the sub-species.

Development: Depending on soil temperature and moisture, the seeds of *S. halepense* start to germinate in the spring, and germination usually continues throughout the whole season. Seeds stay viable in the soil for many years. *Sorghum halepense* is a perennial and reproduces vegetatively (rhizomes) and sexually with up to 80 000 fruits per plant being counted during its growth period. Seedlings begin forming rhizomes 3–4 weeks after emergence. Seven-week old plants can form up to 2.4 m of rhizomes. In a further eight weeks, a plant can develop over 250 m of rhizome. 600–900 m per plant is not unusual. In loamy soils approximately 80 % of the rhizomes are found in the uppermost 7.5 cm of soil; while in sandy soils they can occur up to 12.5 cm below the soil surface. As a rule, *S. halepense* forms rhizomes three times during its vegetative growth period. The primary rhizomes overwinter and develop new shoots in the spring. When these have reached 25–75 cm in length, the secondary rhizome begins to form, and the original rhizome usually starts to die off. The secondary rhizomes generally develop vegetative shoots. In late summer, the growth of the above-ground part of the plant is suspended and the formation of tertiary rhizomes starts. These then overwinter and initiate further growth once more as primary rhizomes in the following spring.

Supplementary: *Sorghum halepense* is one of the most important weeds in the USA and also within its total area of distribution.
On the other hand, as a forage grass it supplies a nutrient-rich fodder. *Sorghum halepense* is undesirable in a crop rotation, as the fruits and rhizomes can survive to infest the following crop. It is not suitable for cultivation in permanent pastures either, as the trampling of animals weakens its reproductive capacity.

Control: Chemical control can be carried out on fallow land, railway embankments, roadside verges, slopes etc. with herbicides based on dalapon, TCA, DMSA, MSMA and bromacil.
On arable land, a combination of cultivation and cropping with mechanical and chemical control measures is most suitable. A high percentage emergence of the rhizome buds is aimed at to provide a sufficient number of application sites for mechanical and chemical control. This is achieved by fragmenting the rhizomes through soil cultivations (cultivation of early maturing crops) in

early autumn or before sowing. Following this, a chemical control can take place. Subsequent cultivation however is then limited as a certain waiting period must be taken into account. Besides overall treatments, spot treatments with preparations on the basis of MSMA, DSMA, dalapon and TCA are usual. These applications should be repeated at three to four-weekly intervals. Control is normally carried out at the 4 to 6 leaf stage as secondary rhizomes start developing at this time. Seedlings originating from seed can usually be controlled by pre-emergence herbicides based on the nitro analines (trifluralin, fluchloralin) and the thiocarbamates (cycloate, eptam).

Literature

ANONYM (1973): Selected references to the biology and control of *Sorghum halepense,* 1968–1972. A. R. C. Weed Research Organization Annotated Bibliography no 53.
LITTLE, E. C. S. (1973): A review of the literature on the distribution, characteristics and control of *Sorghum halepense* (L.) Pers. in temperate crops 1961–1970. A. R. C. Weed Research Organization, Annotated Bibliography no 65.
MCWHORTER, C. G. (1971): Growth and development of Johnsongrass ecotypes. Weed Science **19,** 141–147.
MCWHORTER, C. G. (1971): Control of Johnsongrass ecotypes. Weed Science **19,** 229–233.
MCWHORTER, C. G. (1972): Competition of Johnsongrass and Cocklebur with six soybean varieties. Weed Science **20,** 56–59.
MCWHORTER, C. G. (1972): Factors affecting Johnsongrass control. Weed Science **20,** 238–41.
MCWHORTER, C. G. (1972): Flooding for Johnsongrass control. Weed Scince **20,** 238–41.

Author: S. Behrendt

Sporobolus jaquemontii Kunth (Fig. 226)

Synonym: *S. indicus* Hitchc. non (L.) R. Br.

Common names: dropseed, smutgrass; Fallsame; z'herbe fine; espartillo, gramolote.

Related species: In the literature, the name *S. indicus* has often been used for the species *S. jaquemontii.* According to Clayton (1965) however, *S. indicus* (L.) R. Br. corresponds to *S. poiretii* (R. & S.) Hitchc.

Geographical distribution: *Sporobolus jaquemontii* is distributed over Africa, Central America, the Caribbean and northern South America. *Sporobolus indicus* occurs from the south of the USA to Argentina, as well as in tropical Asia. Other species have regional or local importance.

Habitat: *Sporobolus* species are predominantly pasture grass weeds, but occasionally invade plantation crops as well. In the tropics, *S. jaquemontii* colonises low-lying areas to a greater extent than *S. indicus.*

Description: Erect growing, clump-forming grass, normally 50–70 cm tall (Fig. 226). Culms very compact, wiry. Diameter of culm at base is 1–2 mm. Leaves glabrous, leaf blades flat to subinvoluted, 1.5–5 mm wide, tapering to a fine point. Panicles rather compact, but less dense than those of *S. indicus.* Spikelets 1.5–1.8 mm long. The species are distinguished from each other by their glumes. In *S. jaquemontii* the upper glume is obtuse, about 0.6 mm long, lower glume one fifth to one quarter as long as spikelet. In *S. indicus,* upper glume subacute, about 0.9 mm long, lower glume about one third of the spikelet in length.

Development: *Sporobolus jaquemontii* is a perennial grass which reproduces sexually. Germination of mature seeds taken from the mother plant is not inhibited on adequately moist soils. Tillering stage begins upon the formation of 5–6 leaves. The first panicle-bearing culms can already form 7–8 weeks after germination. With increasing age, the individual plant covers a greater area. It can become a dominant species if the cultivated forage grasses are overgrazed.

Supplementary: Before panicle formation, *S. jaquemontii* is a valuable forage grass. The tough culms however are either rejected by animals or only grazed at the tips. Later on, the leaves are also avoided, as the pasture animals can be injured by the wiry stubble of the culms.

Control: On uninfested areas, introduction with seed or plant material must be prevented. Control normally consists of hoeing or hacking. Chemical control can be carried out by treating the clumps with compounds that are effective against grasses, such as TCA, dalapon or glyphosate. Glyphosate has proved to be more effective than dalapon against *S. jaquemontii*. Triazines in combination with paraquat worked better than diuron against *S. indicus* in plantation crops.

Literature

CLAYTON, W. D. (1965): Studies in the Gramineae. VI. The *Sporobolus indicus* complex. Kew Bull. **19**, 287–296.
CURREY, W. L. & P. MISLEVY (1974): Smutgrass control in Florida. Down to Earth **29**, 6–9.
HONORE, E. N. (1970): Control of ratstail in pasture. Proc. 23rd N. Z. Weed Pest Control Conf., 66–68.
SMITH, J. E., A. W. COLE & V. H. WATSON (1973): Influence of smutgrass control on forage quality. Proc. 26th A. Meet. Sthern Weed Sci. Soc. 174.

Author: G. Jürgens

Fig. 226. *Sporobolus jaquemontii* Kunth; left spikelet: *S. jaquemontii*, right spikelet: *S. indicus*

Family: Labiatae

Leonotis nepetifolia (L.) Ait. f. (Fig. 227 and plate 60 a, b)

Synonym: *Phlomis nepetifolia* L.

Common names: bald bush, Christmas candlestick, lion's ear, lion's tail; –; pompon rouge, cordon de fraile; molinillo.

Related species: *Leucas martinicensis* (Jacq.) Ait. f.

Geographical distribution: *Leonotis nepetifolia* comes originally from the tropical areas of Africa, but like *Leucas martinicensis* it is now distributed over the whole tropics.

Habitat: Both species are weeds of fields and pasture-land. *Leonotis nepetifolia* appears in East Africa mostly in upland areas over 1000 m, but in the Caribbean its occurrence is mainly limited to lowland areas. The weed grows on all soil types (de Freitas et al., 1972).

Description: Erect plant approximately 1–2 m tall (Fig. 227, Plate 60 a). Stem four angled, often unbranched. Leaves opposite, except those uppermost, oval or deltoid-oval, 4–12 cm long. Leaf margins distinctly crenate. Inflorescence nearly globose, 3–6 cm in diameter. Flowers orange, very hairy. Calyx 10–14 mm at flowering stage, up to 25 mm at maturity. Perianth composed of one long upper lip and a shorter three lobed lower lip. Seeds black, 2–3 mm long. *Leucas martinicensis,* in contrast to *L. nepetifolia,* has white flowers with lips of equal length.

Development: In the West Indies, the majority of *Leonotis* plants flower in the last and first quarter of the year. Physiologically mature seeds collected in January can only germinate on a large scale after several months of warm and dry storage. Cotyledons broadly oval, up to 12 mm long, 10 mm wide (Plate 60 b). Primary leaves narrower than succeeding leaves. The plant requires 6–7 weeks from emergence to the flower bud stage, the life span amounting to about 3–4 months.

Supplementary: *Leonotis nepetifolia* is suspected of being poisonous to herbivores. In Brazil, the plant is used for ritual purposes (Fichte, 1973).

Fig. 227. *Leonotis nepetifolia* (L.) Ait. f.

Control: In the Dominican Republic, soil treatments with linuron 1.4, terbutryne 2.2 and alachlor 2.8 kg/ha gave satisfactory control for up to 10 weeks. According to experimental results obtained from Columbia, the species is probably also controlled by other herbicides such as diuron, atrazine, ametryne, terbacil and bromacil. *Leonotis nepetifolia* is sensitive in its early growth stages to applications of 2,4-D and MCPA.

Literature

DE FREITAS, L. F. H., C. ARANHA & O. BACCHI (1972): Plantas invasoras de culturas no Estado Sao Paulo. Sao Paulo, Brasil.

FICHTE, H. (1973): Abó. Anmerkungen zu den rituellen Pflanzen der afrobrasilianischen Religionsgruppe. Ethnomedizin **2**, 361–403.

GOODING, E. G. B., A. R. LOVELESS & G. R. PROCTOR (1963): Flora of Barbados. London.

LAGOS, E. & J. GOMEZ (1969): Control químico de malezas en caña de azúcar. Res. I Semin. COMALFI, Bogotá, Colombia, 44–45.

LAROCHE, R. (1971): Nomenclature Polyglotte des plantes haitiennes et tropicales. Port-au-Prince, Haiti.

Author: G. Jürgens

Family: Lythraceae

Ammannia coccinea Rottb. (Fig. 228 and plate 60 c, d)

Common names: purple ammannia; –; –; alfabegeta, palo de agua.

Related species: *Ammannia auriculata* Willd., *A. baccifera* L., *A. latifolia* L., *Rotala indica* (Willd.) Koehne, *R. ramosior* (L.) Koehne.

Geographical distribution: *Ammannia coccinea* is a weed in the tropics and subtropics of the New World, in Southern Europe, Eastern Asia, and the islands of the Pacific. *Ammannia auriculata* is widespread throughout tropical and subtropical regions, *A. baccifera* and *R. ramosior* in the tropical zone of the Americas. Other species of *Ammannia* and *Rotala* are of regional importance under warm and humid conditions.

Habitat: *Ammannia* and *Rotala* are mainly semi-aquatic plants of warm climates. In two years of field trials and laboratory tests, however, *A. coccinea* showed signs of adapting to Mediterranean conditions. The weeds of both genera are in general limited to rice crops. It has been observed that the growth of *R. indica* is promoted by an increasing water depth of up to 9 cm. *Ammannia coccinea* and *R. ramosior,* with a frequency of 69 and 73 % respectively, rank among the most common weeds of irrigated rice in the Dominican Republic.

Description: Erect growing, glabrous, herbaceous plant; about 40–80 cm tall (Fig. 228, left, plate 60 c). Shoot axis mostly branched with stems spongy at the base, four-edged above. Leaves sessile, opposite, lanceolate-linear, auricled at base, nearly amplexicaul, up to 10 cm long and 1 cm wide. Flowers solitary or in clusters of 2–5, sessile, axillary, pink to purple-violet. Fruit a globular capsule, 4–5 mm, purple at maturity. *Ammannia latifolia* is distinguished from *A. coccinea* by the absence of petals. *Ammannia baccifera* also has either very small petals or none at all, and smaller fruit capsules. Unlike the other species named here, *A. auriculata* has distinctly pedicelled flowers. *Rotala* (Fig. 228, right) species in contrast to *Ammannia* species have dehiscent fruits. Leaves narrowed at base, not auricled as with *A. coccinea*.

Development: *Ammannia coccinea* and *R. ramosior* are annual plants that can develop throughout the whole year in the tropics. Pot experiments have shown that seeds of both species will germinate in moist soils immediately upon physiological maturity. Covering the soil with water does not inhibit germination and growth.

Fig. 228. Left: *Ammannia coccinea* Rottb.
right: *Rotala ramosior* (L.) Koehne

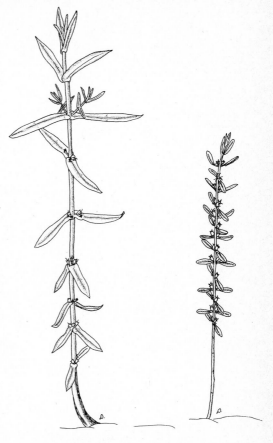

The seedlings are at first very small, but the cotyledons of *A. coccinea* reach a length of 1 cm. The primary leaves are not auricled, so that young *Ammannia* and *Rotala* plants are easily mistaken for each other (Plate 60 d). The life cycle of *A. coccinea* is completed after 4–5 months, while *R. ramosior* has a somewhat shorter life span.

Control: With mechanical methods of control, care must be taken to ensure that plants are completely removed from the plots, as severed pieces of stem can immediately form adventitious roots and grow again.

In Columbia, the herbicides butachlor, fluorodifen, propanil, 2,4-D, MCPA and 2,4,5-T are recommended against *A. coccinea*. Experiments in the Dominican Republic have shown that 2,4-D at high rates of application kills plants up to the flowering stage, whereas MCPA at the same rate of application is less effective.

The action of growth regulating herbicides is not likely to be sufficient at lower application rates as the plants are able to sprout again because of their exceptional regenerative ability. Late infestations with plants of both species can occur. *A. coccinea* can also be controlled with oxadiazon, mixtures of propanil with oryzalin, nitralin or butachlor whereas molinate, propanil and swep have not been sufficiently effective.

Literature

ARAI, M. (1969): Competition between rice plants and weeds. Proc. 1st Asian-Pacific Weed Control Interchange, Hawaii, 1967, 37–41.

KOEHNE, E. (1903): *Lythraceae*. In: A. Engler: Das Pflanzenreich IV, Heft 216, 1–326.

MUKHOPADHYAY, S. K. & S. BAG (1967): New herbicides for controlling weeds in upland rice. Indian J. Agron. **12**, 253–256.

NEGRE, R. & P. MAGHAMI (1968): On the biology of several annual weeds of French rice fields. Phyton. Horn **12**, 113–115.

Author: G. Jürgens

Family: Malvaceae

Sida acuta Burm. f. (Figs. 229, 230 and plate 61 a, b)

Synonym: *S. carpinifolia* L. f.

Common names: bromweed; Sammetpappel; balai; escoba.

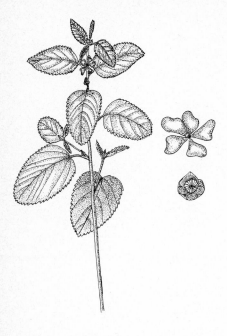

Fig. 229. *Sida acuta* Burm. f.

Related species: *S. cordifolia* L., *S. rhombifolia* L., *S. spinosa* L.

Geographical distribution: Several species of the genus *Sida* have been frequently listed as weeds for certain areas. The respective lists of weeds name four species for Taiwan, six species for the USA, six for East Africa, nine for the Dominican Republic, and eleven for the State of Sao Paulo, Brazil. The four species described here are widespread throughout the tropics and subtropics.

Habitat: Due to the large number of species, no uniform picture of ecological requirements can be obtained. They are mostly weeds of perennial crops such as pasture-land and plantations, as well as of annual crops with a longer growth cycle.
Sida acuta and *S. rhombifolia* prefer moist places in open or moderately shaded terrain. *Sida rhombifolia* appears to be more shade tolerant than *S. acuta;* it is a typical representative of weed communities in coffee plantations in the medium altitudes of upland regions. Both species occur on sandy as well as on loamy clay soils.

Fig . 230.   *Sida rhombifolia* L.

Under drier conditions, *S. cordifolia* and *S. spinosa* invade pasture-land and arable crops on light to medium soils, the latter species being, among other things, a noxious weed in cotton crops.

Description: Shrub-like, somewhat lignified plants, with varying degrees of hairiness. Leaves alternate, simple, linear to orbicular, serrate. Flowers normally yellow, axillary or terminal in racemes, spikes or capitula. *Sida acuta* (Fig. 229, Plate 61 a) 7–12 carpels; peduncles short, less than 1 cm long; leaves variable in shape and size. *Sida cordifolia* 7–12 carpels; leaves, calyx and stem with velvety hair, leaves ovate to approximately orbicular, cordate at base. *Sida rhombifolia* (Fig. 230, Plate 61 b) 7–14 carpels; leaves mostly rhomboid, peduncles more than 1 cm long. *Sida spinosa* 5 carpels; leaves relatively small and narrow, light grey-green in colour.

Development: The species of the genus *Sida* are mostly perennial weeds with a limited life span, propagation being carried out by seeds.
In Lousiana, USA, seeds of *S. rhombifolia* and *S. spinosa* need four to six weeks of after-ripening before noticeable germination occurs. The dormancy of both species could be broken by treating the seeds with water at 65 °C or sulphuric acid, but not through various light/dark treatments, freezing or treatments with alcohol, thio ureas, potassium nitrate, indole acetic acid, gibberellic acid or kinetin. In the Dominican Republic, seeds taken from *S. rhombifolia* plants growing in moist habitats, had a higher germination rate than those that matured under dry conditions. In Australia, seeds of *S. spinosa* reached a 50 % germination rate in the dark only after 12 months. The seeds germinated well at fluctuating temperatures of between 20–35 °C. In the Dominican Republic, germination experiments showed that there were considerable variations in the germination rates of freshly harvested material. According to species and origin, between 1 and 40 % of the seeds emerged within the first month after sowing. The onset of flowering in all four species occurred between five to six weeks after germination.

Supplementary: *Sida* is important as a host plant for virus and mycoplasma diseases of cotton.

Control: Several herbicides such as 2,4-D ester, 2,4-D/2,4,5-T ester, dicamba/2,4,5-T and picloram/2,4-D (spot treatment) are suitable for controlling *Sida* in pasture-land. Treatments should be carried out during the early stages of growth, but picloram/2,4-D can also kill adult plants of *S. acuta* and *S. rhombifolia*. In some instances, regrowth may occur after the application of these herbicides.
Following experiences in the Dominican Republic, *S. acuta* can be successfully controlled in sugar cane by treatments with cyanazine/2,4-D amine, ametryne/2,4-D amine or ioxynil/2,4-D ester. Diuron or fluometuron/paraquat, ametryne/2,4-D and diuron/2,4-D have proved effective against *S. cordifolia*.
In cotton, *S. spinosa* and probably other species of *Sida* can be controlled with fluometuron or prometryne. When using trifluralin or nitralin, additional post-emergence treatments are necessary, and these can be carried out with DNBP or MSMA.
In peanuts, pre-sowing applications of alachlor incorporated into the soil controlled *Sida*. Mixtures of alachlor with dinoseb applied as post-emergence treatments also gave a good control.
In soya bean, chlorbromuron and linuron as pre-emergence treatments as well as chlorbromuron, metribuzin and prometryne as post-emergence treatments were effective against *S. spinosa*. Young plants can be controlled with bentazon.
In coffee plantations, established *S. rhombifolia* plants were controlled more successfully by glyphosate or metribuzin than by ametryne or paraquat/diuron.

Literature

CONNEL, J. T., T. McCUTCHEN & L. S. JEFFERY (1973): Control of prickly sida in soybeans. Proc. 26th Ann. Meet Southern Weed Science Soc., 93.
IVY, H. W. & R. S. BAKER (1972): Prickly sida control and competition in cotton. Weed Science **20**, 137–139.

RIZK, T. Y., W. C. NORMAND & L. W. SLOANE (1969): Studies of *Sida* species in Louisiana. Proc. 22nd a. Meet. Sth. Weed Sci. Soc., 340.
VAN RIJN, P. J. (1968): Ecological aspects of weed control in cotton in the Ord River valley, W. A. 1. Conditions affecting germination of weeds. Aust. J. exp. Agric. Anim. Husb. **8**, 620–624.

Author: G. Jürgens

Family: Nyctaginaceae

Boerhavia erecta L. (Fig. 231)

Common names: erect spiderling; –; patagon; colombiana, hierba blanca, toston.

Related species: *B. diffusa* L. (Syn.: *B. paniculata* L. C. Rich.), *B. coccinea* Mill.

Geographical distribution: The species is spread over the tropical areas of America, occurs in West and East Africa, and has been detected in Malaya.

Habitat: *Boerhavia erecta* is a species of hot climates. At the edge of the tropics it is limited mainly to lowland areas up to 400 m above sea level, but occurs near the equator in areas up to about 1500 m. The species prefers light to medium soils of open terrain; shade is not well tolerated. The weed is found in annual, and occasionally in perennial crops.

Description: Erect growing plant up to 1 m tall (Fig. 231). Leaves opposite, lanceolate to ovate, tapering to a point or truncated at the tip. Cuneate, obtuse or cordate at the base, about 3–8 cm long. Petioles 2–4 cm long. Lower surface lighter in colour than upper surface, leaf margins crimson coloured. Corolla white or pink, 1.5–2 mm long. Inflorescence abundantly branched, overtopped by lateral shoots. Fruit glabrous, pentagonally shaped, 3–4 mm long. Each fruit has one light brown seed. *Boerhavia coccinea* and *B. diffusa* are distinguished from *B. erecta* by their corolla which is crimson coloured at the periphery. With the exception of *B. diffusa* L. var. *leiocarpa,* both species have hairy glandular fruit.

Development: Seed-bearing weed with a life span of approximately 3 months which flowers and fruits the whole year through. From pot experiments, it has been shown that a large proportion of the seeds are dormant after becoming physiologically mature. Seedlings with oval cotyledons 7 mm wide, 4 mm long, intensely crimson underneath following emergence. The first leaf pair develops 3–5 days after emergence. The flower bud stage is already reached after two weeks.

Fig. 231. *Boerhavia erecta* L.

Supplementary: Leon and Alain (1951) list *B. erecta* and *B. diffusa* among medicinal plants. The roots are supposed to be especially effective against a whole series of illnesses. *Boerhavia erecta* is used as pig fodder.

Control: *Boerhavia erecta* can be kept under control in the normal course of crop cultivation. In the Caribbean, applications of fluorodifen 2.5, chlorbromuron 1.2–1.5, metobromuron 1–2.2, linuron 1–3.4, fluometuron 1.5, terbutryne 1.2, and diphenamid 5 kg/ha have brought success. In contrast to this, alachlor 2.2, chloramben 1.9 and trifluralin 2.2–9 kg/ha have proved a failure. Combinations of paraquat with substituted ureas or triazines are recommended against plants that have already emerged.
Trifluralin followed by noruron 2.1, prometryne 1.2 or fluometuron 1.6 kg/ha as well as methazole 8, butachlor 3 or prometryne 1.5 kg/ha have had a good effect against *B. diffusa*.

Literature

ADAMS, C. D. (1970): Notes on Jamaican flowering plants II. Nomenclatural Changes and Additions in Nyctaginaceae. Mitt. Bot. München **8**, 111–121.
DE ALMEIDA, F. S. (1969): Chemical weeding in cotton crops in the Namapa Region. – Agronomia Moçamb. **3**, 163–168.
LAROCHE, R. (1971): Nomenclature Polyglotte des plantes haitiennes et tropicales. Port-au-Prince, Haiti.
LEON, H. & H. ALAIN (1951): Flora de Cuba. Vol. 2, La Habana, Cuba.

Author: R. Hansen del Orbe

Family: Onagraceae

Ludwigia octovalvis (Jacq.) Raven (Fig. 232 and plate 61 c, d)

Synonym: *Jussiaea suffructicosa* L.

Common names: water primrose; Heusenkraut; gironflée, herbe à pique; clavellina, clavelillo, yerba de hicotea, yerba de cigarro.

Related species: *L. erecta* (L.) Hara (Syn.: *J. erecta* L.), *L. hypssopifolia* (G. Don) Exell. (Syn.: *J. linifolia* Vahl).

Geographical distribution: The genus *Ludwigia* contains a whole number of species that have been described as weeds. The species mentioned here are widespread throughout the tropics.

Habitat: *Ludwigia* species are plants with similar habitat requirements; i. e. characteristically wet, boggy or occasionally flooded terrain. They can also be aquatic plants, as is the case with *L. peploides* (Kunth) Raven and *L. repens* J. R. Forst.
Ludwigia octovalvis is a frequent weed in paddy rice crops but can occasionally occur in other crops. The species is limited to hot climates.

Description: Erect, branched plant up to 2 m tall, with a lignified base (Fig. 232). Leaves alternate, sepals 4. 8–15 mm, petals 4, yellow, 1–2 cm long. Fruit is a cylindrical 8 ribbed capsule approximately 3–5 cm long. The typical form of this species is found in South East Asia and is more hairy than those plants of the New World which contain several known subspecies.
Ludwigia erecta (Plate 61 c, right) and *L. hyssopifolia* in contrast to *L. octovalvis* (Plate 61 c, left), have significantly smaller flowers, and smaller four angled fruit capsules.

Development: Cytological tests suggest that *L. octovalvis* has a basic chromosome number of n = 8 with a diploid form in India, a tetraploid form in America and a hexaploid form in Taiwan

Fig. 232. *Ludwigia octovalvis* (Jacq.) Raven

(Sheriff & Mahalakshmi, 1969). *Ludwigia octovalvis* is an annual plant that reproduces sexually. At least some of the seeds of var. *ligustrifolia* show no dormancy and will emerge immediately in damp or flooded soil. The cotyledons, which are at first very small and cuneiform shaped, reach 4–5 mm in length (Plate 61 d). The seedlings have red coloured stems. The plants grow slowly during the early vegetative growth stage. The first flowers appear 7–8 weeks after emergence, and there is a life span of several months.

Control: In rice areas receiving no herbicide application, the high growing plants are mostly weeded by hand.

Ludwigia (Jussiaea) species are frequently attacked by insects. In the Dominican Republic, the leaf eating *Disonycha eximia* Harold and *Systena basilis* J. Duval can practically destroy *L. erecta* (Marcano, 1974). In India, *Haltica caerulea* has proved successful in the biological control of *J. repens* (Sankaran et al., 1967). *Tilapia,* a species of fish, destroys the roots and stems of *J. repens* and *L. natans* (Lahser, 1967). *Ludwigia octovalvis* and *L. erecta* are easily controlled at an early growth stage with 2,4-D or MCPA. According to Madrid et al. (1972) butachlor, EPTC/MCPA, trifluralin/2,4-D-IPE, 2,4-D or MCPA in combination with propanil as well as nitrofen in combination with 2,4-D-IPE can be considered for the control of *L. octovalvis* in rice. In Columbia, 2,4-D, MCPA, 2,4,5-T, propanil, fluorodifen and butachlor are recommended against *L. hyssopifolia*. Trifluralin or dichlobenil in a granular form and diuron give good control against *Jussiaea* species.

Literature

JÜRGENS, G. & F. DURAN (1973): Las malezas en arroz de riego de la República Dominicana. Agro **1,** 25–31.
LAHSER, C. W. (1967): *Tilapia mossambica* as a fish for aquatic weed control. Prog. Fish Cult. **29,** 48–50.
MADRID, M. T., F. L. PUNZALAN & R. T. LUBIGAN (1972): Some common weeds and their control. Laguna, Philippines.
SANKARAN, T., D. SPRINATH & K. KRISHNA (1967): *Haltica caeruly* Olivier (Col.: *Halticidae*) as a possible agent of biological control of *Jussiaea repens*. Tech. Bull. Commonw. Inst. Biol. Contr. **8,** 117–137.
SHERIFF, A. & N. MAHALAKSHMI (1969): The caryotype of *Jussiaea suffructicosa* Linn. Curr. Sci. **38,** 23–24.
MARCANO, E. (1974): Personal communication about insects feeding on *Ludwigia*. Univ. Autonoma Santo Domingo, Rep. Dominicana.

Author: R. Hansen del Orbe

Family: Orobanchaceae

Orobanche crenata Forsk. (Plate 62 a, b)

Synonym: *O. speciosa* D. C., *O. pruinosa* Lapeyrouse, *O. segetum* Spruner, *O. klugei* Schmitz et Regel, *O. picta* Wilms, *O. pelargonii Caldesi*

Common names: scalloped broomrape; Schöne Sommerwurz; Orobanche blanc; –.

Related species: The genus *Orobanche* contains some 180 species whose systematic classification is not always certain. The following can be named as important weeds: *O. aegyptiaca* Pers., *O. cernua* Loefl. *O. eliator* Sutton (Syn.: *O. major* L.), *O. lutea* Baumg. (Syn.: *O. rubens* Wallr.), *O. minor* (Syn.: *O. apiculata* Wallr.), *O. muteli* Schultz, *O. ramosa* L. Sm. (Syn.: *Phelipaea ramosa* C.A.M., *Kopsia ramosa* (L.) Dumortier).

Geographical distribution: The genus *Orobanche* is distributed mainly throughout arid regions. Cold periods during the resting phase in zones with a continental climate do not adversely affect its appearance. *Orobanche* species are of greatest importance in the Mediterranean area and in the Near and Middle East. The individual species differ somewhat in their distribution areas and especially in their ability to colonise temperate zones (e. g. *O. minor, O. lutea, O. eliator* and *O. ramosa* are occasionally important as weeds in Central Europe as well).

Habitat: Species of the genus *Orobanche* are parasitic plants with a specific host range. In contrast to *Striga,* they predominantly attack dicotyledonous species. *Orobanche aegyptiaca* occurs among other things on various *Cucurbitaceae, Solanaceae, Leguminosae, Brassica* and *Gossypium*. *O. cernua* occurs on sunflowers, tobacco and tomatoes, *O. crenata* on numerous legumes, carrots and flax; *O. cumana, O. minor* and *O. muteli* occur on Leguminosae, *O. ramosa* on potatoes, tobacco, tomatoes, paprika, aubergines, hemp, safflower, sunflowers, lettuce, pyrethrum, carrots, celery, hops, mustard, cabbage, white clover, cotton, maize, melons.
Infestation and damage is usually greater on nutrient deficient soils. Fertilising with nitrogen frequently reduces the importance of *Orobanche*. There is some disagreement concerning the influence of soil acidity on its development, but as a rule, alkaline soils promote its occurrence. *Orobanche* cannot develop on wet or waterlogged soils.

Description: *Orobanche* is devoid of chlorophyll (Plate 62 a, b). Leaves are small, scale like, alternate. Two-lipped flowers from terminal racemes or spikes. Each flower contains 4 stamens and 1 style with 2–4 lobed stigma. Fruit is a capsule with many minute, mostly brown and reticulate seeds. *O. aegyptiaca* for example, has a weight of 9.8 mg per 1000 seed. Dispersal is carried out by wind and water. *O. crenata* can reach a size of 20–100 cm. The unbranched glandular-hairy stem is up to 2.5 cm thick. The flowers are arranged in a dense multiflorous spike, 15–70 cm long. Each flower arises from the axil of a glandular-hairy oval acuminate bract, usually as long as the flower. The two lateral sepals of the cleft calyx end in two long acuminate lobes which are about as long as the corolla tube. The corolla is bell-shaped, 20–25 mm long, white to yellow and reddish to violet with purple veins. The corolla tube is not distended in its lower part. The upper lip of the corolla is composed of two, and the lower of three rounded lobes, which are slightly sinous at the margins. The whole corolla is slightly curled. The stamens are glabrous, with the exception of individual hairs along seams, and are fused with the corolla tube at its base. Each plant produces about 40 000 seeds. The reticulate brown seeds are disseminated by wind and water. *O. aegyptiaca* is 15–40 cm tall with a long loose, multiflorous spike, 10–20 cm long. Each flower arises from the axil of one broad middle and two narrower lateral bracts which are about as long as the calyx. The latter in contrast to that of *O. crenata*, is not cleft; it is four-lobed, acute, the lobes being as long as the calyx tube. The bluish-violet to white petals are 20–30 mm long. The slightly curved corolla tube is somewhat distended in its lower part. The upper lip is two-lobed. The three spreading lobes of the lower lip are puberulent on the inside. The stamens are adnate to the distended lower part of the corolla. In contrast to *O. ramosa,* the anthers are covered with white woolly hair, and they adhere to each other through these.

Orobanche ramosa, like *O. aegyptiaca,* can be biennial or perennial and is 10–30 cm tall. The stem is puberulent, glandular-hairy, and branched. The scales like the stem are yellowish-violet. The flowers are arranged in a loose terminal spike. Each flower has an oval middle and two linear lateral bracts. The calyx is undivided, four lobed and shorter than the corolla tube. The petals are 10–18 mm long, with a curved corolla tube which is somewhat distended in its lower part. The violet to yellowish-violet flower is two-lipped, the upper lip being erect, two-lobed, the lower lip spreading, three-lobed. In contrast to *O. aegyptiaca,* the anthers are not hairy.

Development: The germinating ability of the seeds is usually low immediately after maturity. Furthermore, most *Orobanche* species prefer to, or will only germinate under the influence of root exudates. Under certain conditions, many of the species will have a proportion of their seeds germinating without exudates being present. With *O. crenata,* the seeds can germinate even at a distance of 10 mm from the host plant. The root however can only be parasitised from a distance of 2–3 mm. It is probable in the case of *O. ramosa,* that its increased occurrence on alkaline soils is due to root exudates being more rapidly inactivated under alkaline rather than acid conditions. Thus only those seeds will germinate which have a real chance of reaching the root. The optimal temperature for germination ranges from 20–25 °C for most species. The germ tube attaches itself to the host plant root with a haustoria and forms a small tubercle from which shoots and roots arise. The roots do not absorb nutrients from the soil but they can form further haustoria on other host plants. Available data suggest that the seeds have a life span of from less than two to at least twelve years.

Control: Control of *Orobanche* still presents difficulties. In paddy rice fields, the water logging of the soils can greatly reduce *Orobanche.* Fertilising, especially with nitrogen, can also considerably reduce infestations in the course of time. The practicability of growing trap plants is disputed and does not always give the expected degree of success. In some experiments, the placing of fragments of host plants into the soil brought about a remarkable reduction in the number of *Orobanche* seeds.

As far as the temperature requirements of the cultivated crop will allow, advancing the sowing or planting time to a cooler period, can substantially reduce or delay *Orobanche* infestations.

In Eastern Europe and the USSR, a *Fusarium* preparation is used for the biological control of *Orobanche.* Other fungi and the *Phytomyza* fly can also badly damage the parasite and are therefore promising agents of biological control.

By the time that *Orobanche* emerges, a considerable amount of damage has already been achieved, so that later attempts to eradicate it will only be partially successful. Regular hoeing and weeding prevents seed formation, and when consistently carried out over the course of several years can lead to a decisive reduction in the amount of infestation.

With various *Orobanche* species, differences in the variety-specific reactions within the host-parasite relationship have been observed, and this can be partly used to ease the *Orobanche* problem.

Sterilising the soil with chemical compounds is possible, but only economical in exceptional circumstances.

Numerous herbicides are more or less effective against *Orobanche,* but are often not sufficiently selective towards the cultivated plant. Directed spray with contact herbicides usually works well. Firm recommendations for herbicide application cannot, however, be given at the present time.

Literature

ANONYM (1974): Selected references on broomrape *(Orobanche* spp.) 1973–1974. A.R.C. Weed Research Organization Annotated Bibliography, no 77.
ANONYM (1973): Symposium on Parasitic Weeds. EWRC, Wageningen Netherlands.

BECK-MANNAGETTA, G. (1890): Monographie der Gattung *Orobanche*. Bibliotheca Botanica **19**, 1–275.
KASASIAN, L. (1971): Weed Control in the Tropics. Leonard Hill, London.

Author: F. Bischof

Family: Papaveraceae

Argemone mexicana L. (Fig. 233 and plate 62 c, d)

Common names: Mexican pricklepoppy, Mexican poppy, Mexican thistle, prickly poppy; Stachelmohn; chardon béni; cardo santo, chicolate.

Related species: *A. subfusiformis* G. B. Ownb.

Geographical distribution: Both species originate from Central America and are now naturalised in many warm areas of the world.

Habitat: Semi-arid regions are preferred. On Hispaniola, the weed appears especially during the cool dry season. Besides tropical lowlands, it also colonises upland mountain valleys. *Argemone* species are weeds of fields and pastures. *Argemone mexicana* is a late developing weed and frequently causes harvesting difficulties.

Description: Herbaceous plant, containing a yellow milky latex, 30–90 cm tall. Leaves alternate, sessile, pinnately lobed with spiny teeth at end of lobes, up to 25 cm long, 9 cm wide (Fig. 233). Perianth yellow, 2–8 cm in diameter (Plate 62 c). Fruit a prickly capsule, ovoid, 2.5–3.5 cm. Seeds round, black or dark grey, about 2 mm. Unlike *A. mexicana*, *A. subfusiformis* has light yellow or cream coloured flowers and oblong fruit capsules.

Development: In India and Hispaniola, *A. mexicana* can occur as a winter annual but has been observed growing throughout the year in other areas. Cotyledons linear, 1–2 mm wide and 2–3.5 cm long (Plate 62 d). The individual growth stages are passed through rather slowly. Plants in damp or shady areas show a longer growth period and mature more slowly than plants found in open and dry terrain. Seeds can be disseminated by wind, water and animals. It has been determined that each plant can produce 4015 seeds with a weight of 2.2 g/1000 seed.

Fig. 233. *Argemone mexicana* L.

Supplementary: After eating *A. mexicana,* domestic animals showed serious symptoms of poisoning. Its spines can contaminate wool and crops. According to Leon and Alain (1951), the plant can be used in various ways for medicinal purposes. It belongs to the ritual herbs of the Afrobrazilian religious community.

Control: *Argemone mexicana* can be controlled by growth regulating herbicides and paraquat. The success of 2,4-D and MCPA is dependent upon their time of application, which is recommended at time of emergence or until the plants are 5–7.5 cm tall.

From the range of soil applied herbicides, some triazine derivates, linuron, chlorbromuron, alachlor and nitralin have been effective against the weed.

Literature

ADAMS, C. D., K. MAGNUS & C. SEAFORTH (1963): Poisonous plants in Jamaica. Caribbean Affairs. no 2. Univ. West Indies.

FICHTE, H. (1973): Abó. Anmerkungen zu den rituellen Pflanzen der afrobrasilianischen Religionsgruppe. Ethnomedizin **2,** 361–403.

HENDERSON, M. & J. G. ANDERSON (1966): Common weeds in South Africa. Dep. Agric. Techn. Serv., South Africa.

HOSAMANI, M. M., B. SHIVARAJ & C. B. KURDIKERI (1971): Seed production potentialities of common weeds of Dharwar. PANS **17,** 237–239.

KAUL, M. L. H. (1968): Studies on *Argemone mexicana* Linn. 4. Phenology, dispersal and stomata. Proc. nat. Acad. Sci. India **39,** 121–128.

LEON, H. & H. ALAIN (1951): Flora de Cuba. Vol. 2, La Habana, Cuba.

Author: G. Jürgens

Family: Pontederiaceae

Heteranthera reniformis Ruiz. & Pav. (Fig. 234 and plate 63 a, b)

Common names: mudplantain; –; –; berillo, buche de gallina.

Related species: *Heteranthera limosa* (Sw.) Willd., *Monochoria vaginalis* (Burm. f.) Presl.

Geographical distribution: Both *Heteranthera* species occur from the south of the USA to Paraguay as well as on the Antilles (Cuba, Hispaniola and Jamaica). *Monochoria vaginalis* is widespread throughout South East Asia.

Habitat: The original habitats of the three species are muddy edges of rivers and ponds. They are characteristic weeds of paddy rice crops. Vegetation studies in the Dominican Republic have shown that *H. reniformis* is the species with the highest degree of covering in irrigated rice.

The low growing *H. reniformis* competes with rice for nutrients more than for light and space. Between the end of tillering up until flowering, the weed frequently covers the ground like a mat without essentially impairing the growth of the crop plant.

According to Lubigan and Vega (1971), an early and dense infestation of *M. vaginalis* reduced rice yields, but when the weed was planted 40 days after the rice, the yield was not affected. In experiments lasting for several years, it could be established that early competition from *H. limosa* also significantly reduced grain yields.

Description: Amphibious, aquatic plant with a creeping branched shoot system (Fig. 234, plate 63 a).

Leaves reniform, cordate at base, mostly 2–4 cm wide, with long petioles. Shoots and petioles soft, succulent. Inflorescences opposite to the spathe-like leaf sheath. Flowers 2–6 within the spathe. Perianth white, about 4 mm long.

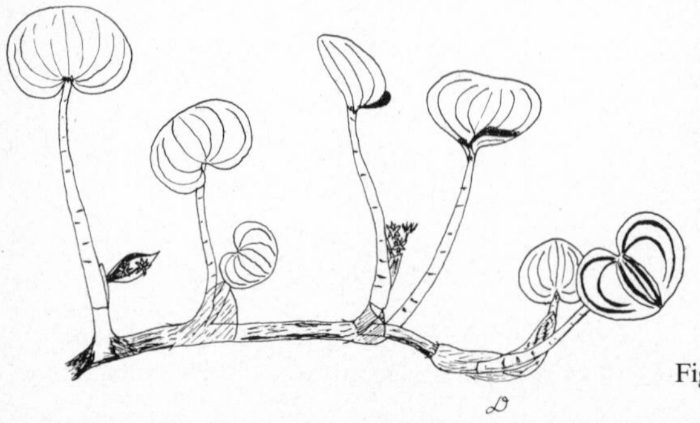

Fig. 234. *Heteranthera reniformis* Ruiz. & Pav.

Heteranthera limosa which occurs in the same area, has a tufted habit, leaves broadly oval to elliptical lanceolate, and rounded at base, flowers blue, solitary within the spathe. *Monochoria vaginalis* is a very similar blue flowering plant with acuminate leaves and multi-flowered spikes (Plate 63 b).

Development: Reproduction of the three species is mainly by seeds. Studies in the USA have shown that *H. limosa* is able to germinate within three days under anaerobic conditions. Light irradiations of between 630–680 nm effectively induce germination.

Seedlings of *H. reniformis* have lanceolate leaves, succeeding leaf shapes at first oblong oval, then cordate. Adult plants with reniform foliage leaves. The frequent dense covering of soils is due to the formation of emersed and submersed stolons. Onset of flowering about 4–5 weeks after emergence. Senescence normally occurs after the removal of water and drying off of soils at the rice harvest. Experiments have shown that the submersion of *M. vaginalis* at fruit set is advantageous to seed development.

Control: Repeated soil cultivation at one to three week intervals during the preparation of the seed bed has proved ineffective in controlling *Heteranthera,* while the flooding of plots over several weeks promoted the infestation.

Selective herbicides in rice from the phenoxy acid group such as 2,4-D, 2,4,5-T and MCPA are suitable for controlling *Heteranthera* and *Monochoria.* Propanil, on the other hand applied alone, rarely gives satisfactory results. Vega et al. (1971) report that *M. vaginalis* is a dominant weed on propanil treated plots in the Philippines. Similar observations exist for *H. reniformis* in the Dominican Republic. Therefore mixtures of this contact herbicides with other foliar and soil applied herbicides are recommended.

Post-emergence treatments with combinations of oxadiazon, oryzalin, nitralin, butachlor or benthiocarb are effective against *Heteranthera.* In experiments it was found that an infestation of *H. reniformis* was kept to a minimum by soil treatments with butachlor or dimethametryn/piperophos but not with fluorodifen.

Simazine at 1 ppm added to pond water kept treated areas in the south of the USA free from *H. reniformis* during the whole growth period. Fenuron, TCA, picloram and 2,4-D in granular form as well as paraquat and diquat failed to control the weed in flowing water.

Literature

GUPTA, S. R. (1968): Flowering process and curvature behaviour of the inflorescence in *Monochoria vaginalis* Presl. – Trop. Ecol. **9**, 234–238.
LUBIGAN, R. T. & M. R. VEGA (1971): The effect on yield of the competition of rice with *Echinochloa crus-galli* (L.) Beauv. and *Monochoria vaginalis* (Burm. f.) Presl. Phillipine Agric. **55**, 210–215.
SMITH, R. J. (1968): Weed competition in rice. Weed Sci. **16**, 252–255.
SMITH, R. J. & W. C. SHAW (1966): Weeds and their control in rice production. Agric. Handb. Agric. Res. Serv., Wash. **292**, pp. 64.
VEGA, M. R., E. C. PALLER & R. T. LUBIGAN (1971): The effect of continuous herbicide treatments on weed population and yield of lowland rice. Philippine Agric. **55**, 204–209.

Author G. Jürgens

Family: Portulacaceae

Portulaca oleracea L. (Fig. 235 and plate 49 a, b)

Common names: common purslane; Portulak; pourpier; verdolaga.

Geographical distribution: *Portulaca oleracea,* which probably originated from India, is today widespread throughout the tropics and subtropics. Under favourable climatic conditions, the species

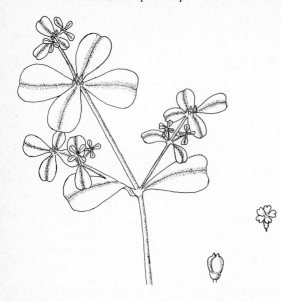

Fig. 235. *Portulaca oleracea* L.

even advances far into the temperate zones of Europe and America. Moderately warm higher areas of tropical mountainous country are also colonised.

Habitat: The common purslane grows best on soils well supplied with water and minerals. The most heavily infested crops are usually vegetables where strong competition can already occur within the first two weeks after emergence. Occasionally the species is also important in perennial crops.

Description: Much branched plant, glabrous apart from the leaf axils, with prostrate to ascending shoot system (Fig. 235, plate 49 a). Stem succulent and fleshy, sometimes reddish-brown in colour. Leaves opposite or alternate, obovate, 0.5–5 cm long, and 0.3–3 cm wide. Flowers solitary, axillary, or in clusters at shoot apices. Perianth yellow, about 8–9 mm in diameter. Sepals winged. Fruit a dehiscing capsule with numerous black seeds about 0.5 mm. The species tends to form ecotypes which are distinguished from each other by their growth form and colouring.

Development: *Portulaca oleracea* is an annual plant with a short life span. Reproduction is by seeds. On moist soils, reproduction by stem fragments has also been observed. Freshly harvested seeds usually show no dormancy. The optimum germination temperature is 20 °C, the minimum 12–13 °C. Experiments have shown that the highest rate of emergence occurred with the water supply at 70–85 % of field capacity. In the tropics, the foliage leaf stage is reached about four days after emergence (Plate 49 b). On developing the third leaf pair, the plant bends to one side and forms its first side shoot in the axils of the oldest true leaves. Onset of flowering about three weeks after emergence. Generally the plants have completed their life cycle after two months.
In Japan, *P. oleracea* can produce four generations between April and September.

Supplementary: The common purslane can be used as a salad or as spinach.

Control: Control in vegetable crops is carried out primarily by mechanical methods. In crops giving little shade, new seedlings can keep emerging following cultivation.
The majority of soil applied herbicides are active against common purslane. Herbicides such as linuron, metobromuron, chlorbromuron, methabenzthiazuron, simazine, atrazine, terbutryne, prometryne, cyanazine, trifluralin, nitralin, isopropanil, penoxalin, napropamide, alachlor, butylate, EPTC, chloramben, fluorodifen, nitrofen, methazole and oxadiazon have been successfully applied.
Foliar applied herbicides such as 2,4-D, MCPA, dinoseb, bentazon, paraquat and diquat can only satisfactorily eradicate *P. oleracea* at the earliest developmental stage.

Literature

HOPEN, H. J. (1972): Growth of common purslane as influencing control and importance as a weed. Weed Sci. **20**, 20–23.

LEGRAND, C. D. (1962): Las especies americanas de *Portulaca*. An. Museo Hist. Nat., Montevideo, Uruguay, **7**, Nr. 3.
NOGUCHI, K. & K. NAKAYAMA (1974): Studies on the ecological characteristics of common purslane. 2. Effects of air temperature on the growing period. Weed Res. Japan, no 18, 48–52.
NOGUCHI, K., K. NAKAYAMA & CH. D. BAN (1973): Studies on the ecological characteristics of common purslane. 1. On the germination of the seed and growth at early stage. Weed Res. Japan, no 15, 65–69.
SINGH, K. P. (1972): Effect of different photoperiods on growth and flowering in *Portulaca oleracea* L. Current Sci. **41**, 573–574.
VENGRIS, J. & M. STACEWICZ-SAPUNCAKIS (1971): Common purslane competition in table beets and snap beans. Weed Sci. **19**, 4–6.

Author: G. Jürgens

Family: Rubiaceae

Borreria laevis (Lam.) Griseb. (Fig. 236)

Synonym: *Spermacoce laevis* Lam.

Common names: buttonweed; –; couper colonne, herbe à macornet; botoncillo, garro morado, Juana la blanca, tostadita.

Related species: Other weeds are: *B. hispida* (L.) K. Schum., *B. latifolia* (Aubl.) K. Schum., *B. ocymoides* (Burm. f.) DC., *B. stricta* (L. f.) G. F. W. Meyer and *B. verticillata* (L.) G. F. W. Meyer. The species today known as *Borreria* were originally ascribed to the genus *Spermacoce*. *Diodia* L. and *Hemidiodia* K. Schum. are also similar in appearance.

Geographical distribution: The group of *Rubiaceae* described here are mostly indigenous to the warmer areas of America. Several species occur as weeds in the tropical regions of Asia and Africa.

Habitat: *Borreria laevis* is ecologically highly adaptive. The species colonises tropical lowland and hilly areas as well as temperate mountain zones and is found in climates ranging from semi-arid to very humid. It occurs in field and plantation crops as well as in pasture-land. The species frequently occurs within the plant community of coffee plantations.

Description: Erect or prostrate plant, glabrous or sparsely hairy, branched or unbranched, about 30–60 cm tall (Fig. 236). Leaves ovate, lanceolate or elliptic, opposite, nearly sessile, 2–6 cm long. Axillary or terminal clusters 8–14 mm, corollas white. Fruit a capsule, 2.5–3 mm.

Fig. 236. *Borreria laevis* (Lam.) Griseb.

Among the other species that occur in the same area, *B. ocymoides* is overall smaller with cymes 3–7 mm and fruit capsules 1–1.5 mm long. *Borreria latifolia* is a more robust plant with leaves up to 8 cm long. The formation of very short lateral shoots gives *B. verticillata* the impression of having a verticillate leaf arrangement. The inflorescence mostly terminal, up to 15 mm in diameter. The genera can be differentiated by the form of the fruit. *Borreria* and *Spermacoce* have dehiscent fruit. In the former both valves opening, in the latter one valve remaining closed. *Diodia* has two indehiscent cocci, *Hemidiodia* two cocci, which are dehiscent at the base.

Development: *Borreria laevis* is a rather persistent seed-bearing weed. No seasonal growth pattern has been observed. Mature seeds removed from the plant had a 15–20 % germination rate within four weeks. Cotyledons oval, about 3–5 mm long and 2.5–3 mm wide. The onset of flowering about 8–9 weeks after emergence. During the following months a continuous production of flowers and fruits.

Supplementary: According to Liogier (1974), *B. laevis* is valued as a medicinal plant and is administered against influenza and other illnesses. *Borreria verticillata* is listed as a poisonous plant due to the alkaloid content of its roots (Adams et al., 1963).

Control: In the course of crop tending in plantations, control is usually carried out by cutting with a machete or by the use of other hand implements. In both cases however, new weed growth is to be expected. Adult plants of *B. laevis* have proved to be resistant to applications of ametryne or paraquat/diuron. Glyphosate or metribuzin on the other hand, killed most of the plants. *B. hispida* and *B. ocymoides* are controlled by MSMA/2,4-D and either sodium chlorate or dalapon (Yogaratnam, 1971). Other herbicides that are effective against *Borreria* are linuron, diuron, fluometuron, neburon, atrazine, desmetryne, lenacil and dinoseb. It appears that some of the species are resistant to low dosages of paraquat and growth regulating herbicides.

Literature

ADAMS, C. D., K. MAGNUS & C. SEAFORTH (1963): Poisonous plants in Jamaica. Caribbean Affairs no 2, Jamaica.
LIOGIER, A. H. (1974): Diccionario botanico de nombres vulgares de la Española. Santo Domingo, Rep. Dominicana.
WETTASINGHE, D. T. & N. S. RAJENDRAM (1969): Evaluation of herbicides for weed control in mature tea. 1. Effects on the weed species. Tea Q. **40**, 160–163.
YOGARATNAM, N. (1971): Weed control under *Hevea* in Ceylon with herbicide mixtures based on MSMA. Qu. J. Rubber Res. Inst. Ceylon **48**, 168–181.

Author: G. Jürgens

Family: Scrophulariaceae

Striga asiatica (L.) Kuntze

Synonym: *S. lutea* Lour.; *S. hirsuta* Benth.

Common names: red witchweed; –; goutte de sang; hierba brujy.

Related species: *S. euphrasioides* Benth., *S. densiflora* Benth., *S. orobanchoides* Benth. (Syn.: *S. gesnerioides* Willd.), *S. hermonthica* (Del.) Benth.

Geographical distribution: Mainly spread throughout the tropics and subtropics of Asia and Africa. Only recently introduced into North America. It thus seems that the genus has not yet reached its final distribution limits.

Habitat: Occurs as a hemiparasite on maize, millet, sugar cane, rice, numerous non-cultivated grasses, sunflowers, tomatoes and some legumes. It preferably invades these host plants on poor sandy soils. A heavy infestation can lead to a complete yield loss. The various *Striga* species can parasitize a varying range of host plants. Host specific races have been found within the species, and variety specific reactions among cultivated crops.

Description: Erect plant, branched, 15–40 cm tall. Hemiparasite which through the use of haustoria can deprive the roots of the host plant of water, mineral substances, and, to a lesser extent, carbohydrates. The root system is therefore shallow and only weakly developed. The slender stem is four edged and densely covered with stiff hairs. The narrow sessile leaves are 1.5–3.5 cm long, opposite on the lower part of the plant, alternate above. The coarse leaves are covered with very strong hairs which arise from small tubercles. The numerous flowers are sessile. The two linear lanceolate bracts are about 5 mm long. The five lobed calyx has ten distinct ribs, as opposed to *S. euphrasioides* which has a calyx of 15 ribs. The flower itself is yellowish-white to scarlet. The slender perianth tube is approximately 1 cm long, is slightly refracted in its upper part which terminates in a round lobed two-lipped flower. The four stamens are fused to the perianth tube; ovary is superior. The fruit is an oblong capsule about 5 mm long which opens along two seams to release the numerous minute brown seeds. Each plant can produce up to 50,000 seeds, which are disseminated by wind and water.

Development: Reproduction is exclusively by seeds. The period between germination and emergence usually lasts one to two months; the time from emergence to flowering is a month. The stage from flowering to seed maturity then takes a further month. The seeds which after maturity may be dormant for up to 18 months, and which have a life span of between 5 and 20 years, germinate mainly under the influence of root exudations from particular plants. The seeds germinate better under the influence of light – optimal germination occurring at 30 °C. The 2–4 mm long germ tube which is produced by the tiny seed at germination, attaches itself through a haustorium to the host plant root and forms a nodule from which the shoots and roots arise. The green leaves can assimilate. Seed formation occurs with a 12–17 hr day.

Control: Although most of the damage to crops has already occurred before the hemiparasite has emerged, a post-emergence treatment is still worth-while, using methods that consist of hand weeding, hoeing or one or several applications of 2,4-D or MCPA. 2,3,6-TBA or fenac can be incorporated into the soil before sowing. Both treatments are occasionally combined with post-emergence treatments with 2,4-D. A comparatively high persistence and an often low crop tolerance requires that the herbicides are tested on a small scale before large scale applications are made. On small areas, soil sterilisation with methyl bromide is possible, but it is expensive. Experiments with dinitramin, prynachlor, trifluralin and several other herbicides gave promising results. Sometimes, however, specific application methods have to be employed.

Some success can be achieved through the cultivation of trap plants whose root exudates stimulate the germination of *Striga* seeds, but which are not themselves affected. Soya bean, pea, peanut, sunflower, flax, castor bean and cotton can be used as trap plants, depending upon the type of *Striga* species and the area. Frequently host plants are grown between two main crops, and are ploughed in before seeds of the hemiparasite can mature.

Literature

ANONYM (1973): Selected references to the biology and control of *Striga hermontheca* and other *Striga* species, 1966–1973. A. R. C. Weed Research Organization, Annotateal Bibliography no 50.

IVENS, G. W. (1971): East African Weeds and their Control. Oxford University Press, Nairobi.

KASASIAN, L. (1971): Weed Control in the Tropics. Leonard Hill, London.

PARKER, C. (1965): The *Striga* problem – a review. PANS (C) **11**, 99–111.

Author: F. Bischof

Family: Solanaceae

Physalis angulata L. (Fig. 237 and plate 63 c, d)

Common names: groundcherry, winter cherry, wild gooseberry; Judenkirsche; coqueret; topoto-ropo, tope-tope, vejigón, sacabuche.

Related species: Besides the commonly known *P. angulata,* other species of the genus have local or regional importance, such as *P. ixocarpa* Bret. ex Hornem in East Africa or *P. cordata* Mill. in the American tropics and subtropics.

Geographical distribution: *Physalis angulata* is distributed throughout the tropics and subtropics of the world.

Habitat: *Physalis* species are predominantly field weeds which can invade a large number of crops. *Physalis angulata* frequently occurs in maize, legumes and sugar cane plantations.
In Guinea, it is a common weed of rice fields with semi-hydromorphic soils on river terraces above flood level. On Hispaniola, *P. angulata* prefers moist but not flooded sites. No preference for any particular soil type has been observed.

Description: Much branched erect plant up to 1 m tall (Fig. 237). Stem hollow, angular, glabrous or sparsely hairy. Leaves alternate, ovate, broadly or narrowly cuneate at the base, sinuate-toothed at margin, up to 10 cm long, 7 cm wide. Calyx 4–7 mm long during flowering, enlarging at maturity and enclosing the fruit, 10 ribbed (Plate 63 c). Flowers dull yellow. Fruit a berry 10–12 mm in diameter.

Development: Seeds from well matured berries immediately show a high percentage germination on moist soils. Cotyledons oval, acuminate, about 5–6 mm long (Plate 63 d). Primary leaves almost entire. In a tropical climate the foliage leaf stage is passed through in about three weeks, the life cycle completed after 3–4 months. The plants, with some interruptions, flower the whole year through.

Fig. 237. *Physalis angulata* L.

Control: *Physalis* species are generally more conspicuous than important weeds, and can be easily controlled by normal mechanical methods. They show resistance however to a series of herbicides from the amide, aniline and carbamate groups. Treatments with 2,4-D and MCPA have also frequently proved ineffective. Applications of the above mentioned herbicides alone can lead to a heavy infestation of cultivated areas. Triazines and urea derivates are better suited for the control of *Physalis* species. In the Dominican Republic, *Physalis* species were effectively controlled by pre-emergence treatments with ametryne, terbutryne, metribuzin, linuron, diuron and alachlor. In sugar cane, mixtures of ametryne, diuron or asulam with 2,4-D or 2,4-D/ioxynil gave a satisfactory control.

Literature

HEBBLETHWAITE, J. F. (1970): The performance of alachlor on some annual summer crops and weeds in South Africa. Proc. 10th Br. Weed Control Conf., 452–459.

LIN, C. I. (1968): Weeds found on cultivated land in Taiwan. Vol 1 Taipei, Taiwan.

WATERFALL, U. T. (1967): *Physalis* in Mexico, Central America and the West Indies. Rhodora **69**, 82–120, 203–239, 319–329.

Author: G. Jürgens

Family: Zygophyllaceae

Kallstroemia maxima (L.) Torr. & A. Gray (Fig. 238 and plate 64 a–d)

Synonym: *Tribulus maximus* L.

Common names: police macca, caltrop; –; cresson courant, pourpier bátara; ábrojo.

Related species: *Kallstroemia pubescens* (G. Don) Dandy., *Tribulus cistoides* L., *T. terrestris* L.

Geographical distribution: Both *Kallstroemia* species and *T. cistoides* are indigenous to the tropical areas of America. *Kallstroemia pubescens* and *T. cistoides* are also found in parts of the Old World. *Tribulus terrestris* is a frequent weed in Africa, North America and some parts of Asia.

Habitat: *Kallstroemia maxima* is a species that has a high temperature requirement. According to Porter (1969), it colonises upland areas up to 1350 m. The plant grows best on light to medium, well nourished soils. It is an aggressive weed in low growing annual crops such as vegetables and hard seed legumes but is less important in perennial crops.
Tribulus cistoides and *T. terrestris* prefer dry, sandy areas, and invade field and pasture-land.

Fig. 238. *Kallstroemia maxima* (L.) Torr. & A. Gray

Description: Slightly hairy, creeping plants with branched shoots up to 1.5 m in length (Fig. 238, plate 64 a, b). Leaves are alternate or opposite, pinnately compound with 3–4 pairs of leaflets. The leaflets are of differing shapes between 0.5–2 cm in length. Flowers solitary, axillary on long peduncles. Sepals lanceolate, hairy. Flowers cream coloured. Fruits tuberculate, glabrous about 9–10 mm in length with 10 seeds which are brown when mature.

Kallstroemia pubescens is a closely related plant with light yellow flowers and hairy fruits.

In contrast to *Kallstroemia,* species of the genus *Tribulus* have spiny fruit and 6–8 leaflet pairs (Plate 64 c, d).

Development: Given sufficient moisture for germination, the species can flower and bear fruit throughout the whole year. Mature seeds with hard testas require at least 12 days in a moist soil however, before germination can occur. Cotyledons are oval shaped, 10–13 mm in length, 5–8 mm wide. Primary leaves with two pairs of leaflets. Branching occurs from the lowest leaf axil 10–12 days after emergence. During the following weeks, the extending plants are continuously and simultaneously producing buds, flowers and fruit. The plant generally has a life span of just under four months.

Supplementary: *Kallstroemia maxima* and *T. cistoides* are used as medicinal plants. *Tribulus terrestris* contains saponin which causes liver disease in pasture animals.

Control: Solitary plants of *K. maxima* often cover a large area and overgrow smaller plants, but they can be relatively easily controlled by mechanical means. Splitting the root collar results in the complete death of the plant.

Only some of the numerous herbicides tried against *K. maxima* have proved effective. 2,4-D, linuron, diuron, chlorbromuron, metobromuron, atrazine, terbutryne, metribuzin, fluorodifen, butilate and norea have given good results. Applications of simazine, benthiocarb, napropamide, nitralin, chloramben, alachlor and diphenamid have proved unsatisfactory.

Tribulus terrestris can be controlled with alachlor, chlorbromuron and 2,4,5-T and probably with most of the herbicides which are recommended against *Kallstroemia.*

Tribulus has been successfully controlled by the use of the stem borer *Microlarinus lypriformis.*

Literature

HSU, C. C., G. ODELL & T. WILLIAMS (1968): Characterization of the saponin fraction of *Tribulus terrestris.* Proc. Okla. Acad. Sci., **47,** 21–24.

LEON, H. & H. ALAIN (1969): Flora de Cuba. Vol 2. La Habana, Cuba 1951.

PORTER, D. M. (1969): The genus *Kallstroemia (Zygophyllaceae).* Contr. Gray Herb. Havard Univ. **198,** 41–153.

SEEYAVE, J. & L. KASASIAN (1969): Weed control in cereals in the West Indies. Proc. 2nd Asian-Pacific Weed Control Interchange, 292–301.

Author: G. Jürgens

List of books on diseases, pests and weeds in the tropics[1]

A. Plant diseases and pests

ANDRES CANARO, F. (1965): Enfermedades y plagas del Olivo. Ministerio de Agricultura, Madrid.

Anonymous (1968): An atlas of coffee pests and diseases. Coffee Board of Kenya.

BROWNE, F. G. (1968): Pests and diseases of forest plantation trees. Clarendon Press, Oxford.

BUYCKX, E. J. E. (ed.) (1962): Précis des maladies et des insectes nuisibles recontrés sur les plantes culti-vées au Congo, au Rwanda et au Burundi. INEAC, Bruxelles.

CHAPOT, H., & V. L. DELUCCHI (1964): Maladies troubles et revageurs des Agrumes au Maroc. Institut National de la Recherche Agronomique, Rabat.

CRAMER, H. H. (1967): Plant protection and world crop production. Pflanzenschutz-Nachrichten Bayer, **20** (1).

FEAKIN, SUSAN D. (ed.) (1967): Pest control in groundnuts. PANS Manual No 2. Centre for Overseas Research, London.

FEAKIN, SUSAN D. (ed.) (1970): Pest control in rice. PANS Manual No 3. Centre for Overseas Research, London.

FEAKIN, SUSAN D. (ed.) (1971): Pest control in bananas. PANS Manual No 1. Centre for Overseas Research, London.

FRÖHLICH, G., W. RODEWALD et al. (1970): Pests and diseases of tropical crops and their control. Pergamon Press, London.

HAINSWORTH, E. (1952): Tea pests and diseases and their control (with special reference to North East India). Heffer & Sons, Cambridge.

KASSEBEER et al. (1976): La défense des cultures en Afrique du Nord. Schriftenr. GTZ No **36**, Eschborn.

MERINO-RODRIGUEZ, M. (1966): Lexicon of plant pests and diseases. Elsevier Publishing Co., Amsterdam.

SCHMUTTERER, H. (1977): Plagas y enfermedades del algodón en Centroamerica. Schriftenr. GTZ No. **39**, Eschborn.

B. Plant diseases

ABEYGUNAWARDENA, D. V. W. (1969): Diseases of cultivated Plants. The Colombo Apothecaries' Co. Ltd., Colombo.

AINSWORTH, G. C. (1971): Dictionary of the fungi. 6th ed. Commonwealth Mycological Institute, Kew.

Anonymous (1971): Sweetpotato culture and diseases. Agriculture Handbook No **388.** Agricultural Research Service, US Dept. Agriculture.

Anonymous (1972): Le Palmier Dattier et sa fusariose vasculaire (Bayoud). Direction de la Recherche Agronomique Maroc et l'INRA, Rabat.

Anonymous (1973): A compendium of corn diseases. American Phytopathological Soc., St. Paul. Minn.

BOURIQUET, G. (1946): Les maladies des plantes cultivées à Madagascar. Lechevalier, Paris.

BOURIQUET, G., & J. P. BASSINO (1965): Les Urédinées de Madagascar. Lechevalier, Paris.

BOYCE, J. S. (1961): Forest pathology. 3rd ed. McGraw-Hill, New York, Toronto, London.

BROWN, A. G. P. (1969): A distribution list of the more important pathogens of economic plants, with particular reference to Africa. Commonwealth Mycological Institute, Kew.

CHEVAUGEON, J. (1956): Les maladies cryptogamiques du manioc en Afrique occidentale. Lechevalier, Paris.

CHUPP, C., & A. F. SHERF (1960): Vegetable diseases and their control. Ronald Press, New York.

---

[1] See also under literature of each chapter.

CMI (1968): Plant Pathologist's Pocketbook. Commonwealth Mycological Institute, Kew.

COOK, A. A. (1975): Diseases of subtropical fruits and nuts. Hafner Press, New York.

DICKSON, J. G. (1956): Diseases of field crops. 2nd ed. McGraw-Hill, New York. Also as TMH 2nd ed. Tata-McGraw-Hill Publ. Co., Bombay – New Delhi.

DOOLITTLE, S. P., A. L. TAYLOR & L. L. DANIELSON (1961): Tomato diseases and their control. Agric. Handb. US Dep. Agric. **203.**

EDGERTON, C. W. (1958): Sugarcane and its disease. 2nd ed. Baton Rouge, Louisiana State Univ. Press.

EVANS, E. (1968): Plant diseases and their chemical control. Blackwell, Oxford.

GRAHAM, K. J. (1971): Plant diseases of Fiji. Her Majesty's Stationary Office, London.

HILDEBRAND, E. M., & H. T. COOK (1959): Sweet potato diseases. Fmrs'Bull. US Dep. Agric. **1059.**

HILTON, R. N. (1959): Maladies of Hevea in Malaya. Rubber Research Institute, Kuala Lumpur.

HOLLIDAY, P., & W. P. MOWAT (1963): Foot rot of *Piper nigrum* L. Phytopathological Papers No 5. Commonwealth Mycological Institute, Kew.

HUGHES, C. G., E. V. ABBOTT & C. A. WISMER (eds.) (1964): Sugar-cane disease of the world. Vol. II, Elsevier Publishing Co., Amsterdam.

KLOTZ, L. J., & H. S. FAWCETT (1948): Color handbook of Citrus diseases. Univ. California Press, Berkeley.

KNORR, L. C. (1973): Citrus diseases and disorders. Univ. Florida Press, Gainesville.

LING, K. C. (1972): Rice virus diseases. International Rice Research Institute (IRRI), Los Baños.

LUCAS, G. B. (1975): Diseases of tobacco. 3rd ed. Biol. Consulting Associates, Raleigh N. C.

MARAMOROSCH, K. (1964): A survey of coconut diseases of unknown etiology. FAO Rome.

MARTIN, J. P., E. V. ABBOTT & C. G. HUGHES (1961): Sugar-cane diseases of the world. Vol. I (Vol. II s. Hughes). Elsevier Publishing Co., Amsterdam.

MEREDITH, D. S. (1970): Banana leaf spot disease (Sigatoka) caused by *Mycosphaerella musicola* Leach. Phytopathological Papers No 11. Commonwealth Mycological Institute, Kew.

MESSIAEN, C.-M., & R. LAFON (1963 & 1965): Les maladies des plantes maraichères (Diseases of market garden plants). Vol. I & II. Institut National Recherches Agronomique, Paris.

MILLER, P. R., & H. L. POLLARD (1976): Multilingual compendium of plant diseases. American Phytopathological Soc., St. Paul. Minn.

NOBLE, MARY, & M. J. RICHARDSON (1968): An annoted List of seedborne diseases. Phytopathological Papers No 1. Commonwealth Mycological Institute, Kew.

OU, S. H. (Techn. ed.) (1965): The rice blast disease. Johns Hopkins Press, Baltimore.

OU, S. H. (1972): Rice diseases. Commonwealth Mycological Institute, Kew.

RAMAKRISHNAN, T. S. (1963): Diseases of millets. Indian Council of Agricultural Research, New Delhi.

ROGER, L. (1951, 1953, 1954): Phytopathologie des pays chauds. Vol. I–III. Lechevalier, Paris.

SAFEEULA, K. M. (1976): Biology and control of the downy mildews of millet, Sorghum and finger millet. Manasagangothri, Mysore Univ., Mysore.

SARMAH, K. C. (1960): Diseases of Tea and associated crops in North-East India. Memor. Tocklai exp. Stn **26.**

SINCLAIR, J. B., & O. D. DHINGRA (1975): An annotated bibliography of soybean diseases. INTSOY Series Number 7, Coll. Agric. Univ. Illinois, Urbana-Champaign.

SINCLAIR, J. B., & M. C. SHURTLEFF (eds.) (1975): Compendium of soybean diseases. American. Phytopathological Soc., St. Paul. Minn.

SINGH, R. S. (1969): Plant diseases, 2nd ed. Oxford and IBH Publishing Co., Calcutta–Bombay–New Delhi.

SPRAGUE, H. B. (ed.) (1969): Hunger signs in crops. 3rd ed. David McKay Co., New York.

STOVER, R. H. (1972): Banana, Plantain and Abaca diseases. Commonwealth Mycological Institute, Kew.

TARR, S. A. J. (1951): Leaf curl disease of cotton. Commonwealth Mycological Institute, Kew.

TARR, S. A. J. (1962): Diseases of Sorghum, Sudan grass and broom corn. Commonwealth Mycological Institute, Kew.

THOMPSON, A., & G. LIM (1965): A laboratory manual of tropical mycology. Univ. Malaya Press, Kuala Lumpur.

THOROLD, C. A. (1975): Diseases of cocoa. Clarendon Press, Oxford.

TURNER, P. D. (1971): Micro-organisms associated with oil palms (*Elaeis guineensis* Jacqu.). Phytopathological Papers No 14. Commonwealth Mycological Institute, Kew.

TURNER, P. D., & R. A. BULL (1967): Diseases and disorders of the oilpalm in Malaysia. The Incorporated Society of Planters, Kuala Lumpur.

WALKER, J. C. (1952): Diseases of vegetable crops. McGraw-Hill, New York, Toronto and London.

WARDLAW, C. W. (1972): Banana diseases including plantains and abaca. 2nd ed. Longman, London.

WEBER, G. F. (1973): Bacterial and fungal diseases of plants in the tropics. Univ. Florida Press, Gainsville.

WELLMAN, F. L. (1972): Tropical American Plant disease (Neotropical Phytopathology Problems). The Scare Crow Press Inc., Metuchen N. J.

C. Pests

Anonymous (1966): The Locust Handbook. Anti-Locust Res. Centre, London.
Anonymous (1967): Coffee Pests and their Control. Coffee Res. Found., Ruiru, Kenya.
AVIDOV, Z., & I. HARPAZ (1969): Plant Pests of Israel. Israel Univ. Press, Jerusalem.
BAKER, E. W., & A. E. PRITCHARD (1960): The Tetranychoid Mites of Africa. Hilgardia **29**, 455–574.
BATEMANN, M. A. (1972): The Ecology of Fruit Flies. Ann. Rev. Ent. **17**, 493–518.
BODENHEIMER, F. S. (1951): Citrus Entomology in the Middle East. W. Junck, The Hague.
BOHLEN, E. (1973): Crop Pests in Tanzania and their Control. Verlag Paul Parey, Berlin und Hamburg.
CASWELL, G. H. (1962): Agricultural Entomology in the Tropics. E. Arnold, London.
COMMONWEALTH INSTITUTE OF ENTOMOLOGY (1951–1976): Distribution Maps of Pests, Ser. A (Agric.), nos 1–356.
CONWAY, G. R., & E. B. TAY (1969): Crop Pests in Sabah, Malaysia and their Control. St. Min. Agr. Fish., Sabah.
CRANHAM, J. E. (1966): Insect and Mite Pests of Tea in Ceylon and their Control. Tea Res. Inst. Ceylon.
CRANHAM, J. E. (1966): Tea Pests and their Control. Ann. Rev. Ent. **11**, 491–514.
DEBACH, P. (1964): Biological Control of Insect Pests and Weeds. Chapman & Hall, London.
DE PURY, J. M. S. (1968): Crop Pests of East Africa. Oxford Univ. Press, East Africa.
EBELING, W. (1959): Subtropical Fruit Pests. Univ. of Calif., Div. of Agric. Sci.
ENTWISTLE, P. F. (1972): Pests of Cocoa. Trop. Sci. Ser., Longman, London.
FENNAH, R. G. (1947): The Insect Pests of Food Crops in the Lesser Antilles. Dept. Agric. Antigua.
FORSYTH, J. (1966): Agricultural Insects of Ghana. Ghana Univ. Press.
GRIST, D. H., & R. J. A. W. LEVER (1969): Pests of Rice. Longmans, London.
HARRIS, W. V. (1969): Termites as Pests of Crops and Trees. Commonw. Inst. Ent., London.
HARRIS, W. V. (1971): Termites, their Recognition and Control. 2nd ed. Longmans, London.
HILL, D. S. (1975): Agricultural Insect Pests of the Tropics and their Control. Cambridge University Press, London–New York–Melbourne.
IRRI (1967): The Major Insect Pests of the Rice Plant. John Hopkins Press, Baltimore–Maryland.
KALSHOVEN, L. G. E. (1950/51): De plagen van de cultuurgewassen in Indonesie, vol. I. 'S-Gravenhage.
LAMB, K. P. (1974): Economic Entomology in the Tropics. Academic Press, London.
LAVABRE, E. M. (1961): Protection des cultures de caféiers, cacaoyers et autres plantes pérennes tropicales. Inst. Franc. Café Cacao, Paris.
LE PELLEY, R. H. (1968): Pests of Coffee. Trop. Sci. Ser., Longman, London.
LEPESME, P. (1947): Les insectes des palmiers. Paris.
LEVER, R. J. A. W. (1969): Pests of the Coconut Palm. FAO Agric. Stud. **77,** Rome.
LEWIS, T. (1973): Thrips, their Biology, Ecology and Economic Importance. Academic Press, London & New York.
LIBBY, J. L. (1968): Insect Pests of Nigerian Crops. Res. Bull. 269, Univ. of Wisconsin, Madison.
LONG, W. H., & S. D. HENSLEY (1972): Insect Pests of Sugarcane. Ann. Rev. Ent. **17**, 149–176.
MACKERRAS, I. M. (ed.) (1969): The Insect Pests of Australia. Melbourne Univ. Press.
MARIVONI, F. A. M. (1976): Insecticidas e seu emprego no combate as pragas. Tomo II (3.a edicao). Livraria Nobel S. A., São Paulo.
MUNRO, J. W. (1966): Pests of Stored Products. Hutchinson, London.
OSTMARK, H. E. (1974): Economic Insect Pests of Banana. Ann. Rev. Ent. **19,** 161–176.
PAINTER, R. H. (1968): Insect Resistance in Crop Plants. Univ. Press Kansas, Lawrence & London.
PATHAK, M. D. (1968): Ecology of Common Insect Pests of Rice. Ann. Rev. Ent. **13**, 257–294.
PEARSON, E. O. (1958): The Insect Pests of Cotton in Tropical Africa. London.
PEACHEY, J. E. (ed.) (1969): Nematodes of Tropical Crops. Commonw. Agric. Bureaux.
SCHMUTTERER, H. (1969): Pests of Crops in Northeast and Central Africa. Gustav Fischer Verlag, Stuttgart.
SINGH, J. P. (1970): Elements of Vegetable Pests. Vora & Co., Bombay.

SMART, G. C., & V. G. PERRY (eds.) (1968): Tropical Nematology. Univ. of Florida Press, Gainesville.
SPENCER, K. A. (1973): Agromyzidae (Diptera) of Economic Importance. W. Junck, The Hague.
TALHOUK, A. M. (1969): Insects and Mites Injourious to Crops in Middle Eastern Countries. Monogr. ang.
    Ent. no 21. Verlag Paul Parey, Hamburg und Berlin.
TAYLOR, D. P. (1976): Plant Nematology Problems in Tropical Africa. Helmin. Abst., Ser. B, **45**, 269–284.
WEBSTER, J. N. (1972): Economic Nematology. Acad. Press, New York & London.
WILLIAMS, J. R., et al. (1969): Pests of Sugar Cane. Elsevier, London & New York.
WYNIGER, R. (1962): Pests of Crops in Warm Climates and their Control. Verlag f. Recht u. Gesellschaft
    AG., Basel.
WOOD, B. J. (1968): Pests of Oil Palms in Malaysia and their Control. Inc. Soc. of Planters, Kuala Lumpur.

D. Weeds

ADAMS, C. D., L. KASASIAN & J. SEEYAVE (1970): Common weeds of the West Indies. University of
    the West Indies, St. Augustine, Trinidad.
Agricultural Research Service, U. S. D. A. (1970): Selected weeds of the United States. Agriculture Hand-
    book No 366, US Government Printing Office, Washington, D. C.
ALVA, A. S. (1973): Manual de las malezas de la Costa Norperuana. Universidad Nacional de Trujillo, Tru-
    jillo, Peru.
Anonymous (1968): Weeds found in cultivated land in Taiwan. Vol. 1 + 2. Dept. of Agronomy, College of
    Agriculture, National Taiwan University, Taipei, Taiwan, Republic of China.
Anonymous (1974): Herbicide handbook of the Weed Science Society of America. WSSA, 425 Illinois Buil-
    ding, 113 North Neil Street, Champaign, Illinois, USA.
ASHTON, F. M., & A. S. CRAFTS (1973): Mode of action of herbicides. John Wiley & Sons, New York,
    London, Sydney, Toronto.
CÁRDENAS, J., C. E. REYES & J. D. DOLL (1972): Tropical weeds – malezas tropicales. Vol. 1
    ICA/IPPC, Bogotà, Colombia, Corvallis, USA.
DELORIT, R. J. (1970): An illustrated taxonomy manual of weed seeds. Agronomy Publications River Falls,
    Wisc., USA.
EDGECOMBE, W. S. (1970): Weeds of Lebanon. 3rd ed. American University of Beirut, Beirut, Lebanon.
FRYER, J. D., & S. A. EVANS (eds.) (1968/70): Weed control handbook. Vol 1 5th, Vol 2 6th ed. Blackwell
    Scientific Publications, Oxford.
HASELWOOD, E. L., & G. G. MOTTER (1966): Handbook of Hawaiian weeds. Experiment Station, Ha-
    waiian Sugar Planters' Association, Honolulu, Hawaii.
HOLM, LEROY G., & J. HERBERGER (1971): World list of useful publications for the study of weeds and
    their control. PANS **17**, 119–132.
HOLM, LEROY G., D. L. PLUCKNETT, J. V. PANCHO & J. P. HERBERGER (1977): The world's
    worst weeds – distribution and biology. The University Press of Hawaii, Honolulu, Hawaii.
IVENS, G. W. (1971): East African weeds and their control. Oxford University Press, Nairobi.
KASAHARA, Y. (1970): Weeds of Japan illustrated – Seeds, seedlings and plants. Yokendo., Tokio.
KASASIAN, L. (1971): Weed control in the tropics. Leonard Hill, London.
KEARNEY, P. C., & D. D. KAUFMAN (eds.) (1975): Herbicides – Chemistry, degradation and mode of ac-
    tion. 2nd ed. Marcel Dekker, New York, Basel.
KLINGMAN, G. C., & F. M. ASHTON (1975): Weed Science: Principles and practices. John Willy & Sons,
    New York, London, Sydney, Toronto.
KOCH, W. (1970): Unkrautbekämpfung. Eugen Ulmer, Stuttgart.
KURTH, H. (1975): Chemische Unkrautbekämpfung. 4th ed. VEB Gustav Fischer, Jena.
TADULINGAM, C., G. VENKATANARAYANA, C. R. MUDALIAR & J. S. RAO (1955): A handbook
    of some South Indian weeds. Government Press, Madras.
VÉLEZ, J., & J. van OVERBEEK (1950): Plantas indeseables en los cultivos tropicales. Editorial Universi-
    taria, Rio Piedras, Puerto Rico.
WILD, H. (–): Common Rhodesian weeds. The Government Printer, Salisbury, Rhodesia.

Index of diseases by hosts[1]

Alfalfa (*Medicago sativa*)
Cucumber mosaic virus 37
Verticillium albo-atrum **229**

Annona (*Annona* spp.)
Fruit rot 83
Glomerella cingulata **119**
Phytophthora palmivora 83
Rosellinia necatrix 136
Seedling rot 83
White root rot 136

Areca palm (*Areca catechu*)
Fruit rot 83
Phytophthora palmivora 83

Arrowroot (*Maranta arundinacea*)
Black root rot 135
Rosellinia bunodes 135
Rosellinia pepo 135

Artichoke (*Cynara scolymus*)
Rosellinia necatrix 136
Sclerotinia sclerotiorum 138
White root rot 136

Avocado (*Persea gratissima*,
P. americana)
Anthracnose 227
Armillariella mellea 145
Armillariella root rot 77
Black root rot 135, 137
Blossom blight 61
Botryodiplodia theobromae 133
Botryosphaeria ribis 144
Canker 78
Cercospora blotch **192**
Cercospora purpurea **192**, 227
Cercospora spot **192**
Collar rot 78
Colletotrichum gloeosporioides 193
Crown rot 78
Damping-off 89
Diaporthe medusaea **108**
Dieback 61
Diplodia natalensis **133**
Dothiorella sp. 134
Fruit rot 89

Glomerella cingulata **119**
Gum exudation 61
Leaf blight 61, 89
Phellinus noxius 162
Phomopsis spp. 134
Phyllachora gratissima 144
Phytophthora cactorum 78
Phytophthora cinnamomi **76**
Phytophthora citricola 78
Phytophthora nicotianae var.
  parasitica 89
Phytophthora palmivora 78
Physalospora rhodina **133**
Phytophthora root rot **76**
Pseudomonas syringae 61
Rosellinia bunodes 135, 137
Rosellinia necatrix 136
Rosellinia pepo 137
Root rot 78, 89
Scab 227
Sphaceloma perseae 227
Stem canker 61, 89
Stem end rot **133**
Sunblotch virus 32
Surface rot 144
Tar spot 144
Verticillium albo-atrum 229
Verticillium spp. 77
White root rot 136

Banana incl. Abaca & Plantain (*Musa* spp.)
Abaca mosaic virus 34
Anthracnose **196**
Armillariella mellea 145
Black leaf streak **132**
Black root rot 135, 137
Botryodiplodia theobromae 188, 197
Bunchy top virus **5**
Cabbage top 5
Ceratocystis paradoxa 102, 197
Cercospora musae **129**
Chloridium musae 235
Cigar-end-rot 99, 234
Cladosporium musae 234
Colletotrichum musae 196
Cordana musae 235
Corynebacterium michiganense 59

Cucumber mosaic virus 8
Curly top 5
Deightoniella torulosa 235
Drechslera musae-sapientum 235
Erwinia carotovora 74
Freckles 236
Fruit spot 235
Fusarium oxysporum 203
Fusarium oxysporum f. sp. *cubense* **203**
Fusarium roseum 197
Fusarium spp. 59
Guignardia musae 236
Glomerella cingulata 119
Gloeosporium musarum 196
Haplobasidion musae 235
Large elliptical brown spot 234
Leaf blotch 235
Leaf speckle 235
Leaf spot **129**, 235
Macrophoma musae 236
Malayan leaf spot 235
Marasmius semiustus 161
Mycosphaerella fijiensis **132**
Mycosphaerella musicola **129**, 132
Panama disease **203**
Phyllostictina musarum 236
Pseudomonas solanacearum 58, 203
Post harvest decay **188**
Rosellinia bunodes 135
Rosellinia pepo 137
Roxana disease of Bananas 7
Rust 171
Stachylidium theobromae 234
Stem end rot 102
Stem rot 161
Strangles 5
Soft rot 74
Trachysphaeria fructigena 99
Uromyces musae 171
Uredo musae 171
Verticillium theobromae 234
Verticillium sp. 59
Wilt 59

Barley (*Hordeum sativum*)
Corticium sasakii 149

[1] Bold figures refer to specific chapters dealing with the pathogen or disease.

Index of pests by hostplants

General index

ACTA PHYTOMEDICA

Beihefte zur Phytopathologischen Zeitschrift

Supplements to Journal of Phytopathology

Herausgegeben von Prof. Dr. J. Colhoun, Manchester, Prof. Dr. H. Kern, Zürich, und Prof. Dr. Dr. h. c. H. Richter, Berlin.

Bisher sind folgende Hefte erschienen:

1: **Methodik der Analyse von Epidemien dargestellt am Apfelschorf**
[Venturia inaequalis (Cooke) Aderh.]

Von Dr. Spyros Analytis, Athen. 1973. 76 Seiten mit 19 Abbildungen und 29 Tabellen. Kartoniert DM 31,–

2: **Untersuchungen zur Thermotherapie von Steinobstvirosen**

Von Dr. Helmut Jacob, Gießen. 1974. 56 Seiten mit 15 Abbildungen und 7 Tabellen. Kartoniert DM 30,–

3: **Die Reaktionen der Pflanzen auf Wirkungen des photochemischen Smogs**

Von Tyge Claussen, Berlin. 1975. 132 Seiten mit 44 Abbildungen und 35 Tabellen. Kartoniert DM 39,60

4: **Translokation von ^{14}C-markiertem MCPA in verschiedenen Entwicklungsstadien mehrjähriger Unkräuter**

Von Priv.-Doz. Dr. Franz Müller, Stuttgart-Hohenheim. 1976. 160 Seiten mit 51 Abbildungen und 11 Tabellen. Kartoniert DM 44,–

5: **Mycoplasma-ähnliche Organismen als Krankheitserreger in Pflanzen**

Von Dr. Gisela Grunewald-Stöcker und Prof. Dr. Franz Nienhaus, beide Bonn. 1977. 112 Seiten mit 36 Abbildungen und 8 Tabellen. Kartoniert DM 44,–

Die Reihe wird fortgesetzt. Abonnenten der „Phytopathologischen Zeitschrift" erhalten auf die angegebenen Preise einen Nachlaß von 10 %.

Verlag Paul Parey
Berlin und Hamburg

Crop Pests in Tanzania and their Control

By Dr. EBERHARD BOHLEN, Agadir. 1973. 142 pages with 18 illustrations in the text and 252 colour photographs on 42 plates. Clothbound DM 64,–

The results of the five year study in Tanzania are applicable in regions of the same climates all over the world. The pests can be easily identified by 252 excellent colour photographs; they are being classified by their main characteristics in the first part of the book. Then, the main part deals with all species of pests attacking crops cultivated in Tanzania. Beneficial insects and pesticides in use are the subjects of the following chapters. Glossary, reference list and index are making the lot of practical information easily accessible to farmers, students, advisers and extension workers.

Handbuch der Pflanzenzüchtung
Handbook of Plant Breeding

Founded by THEODOR ROEMER and WILHELM RUDORF. Second completely revised edition in 6 volumes. In cooperation with many specialists and together with Prof. Dr. HUBERT KENDALL HAYES, USA, and Dr. ARNE MÜNTZING, Sweden, edited by Prof. Dr. Dr. h. c. HANS KAPPERT, Berlin, and Prof. Dr. WILHELM RUDORF. Contributions in German or English. 6 volumes. 1958–62. Clothbound. Special price for the complete work DM 1100,–

The volumes of the international standard work on the special breeding of cultivated plants in temperate climates are dealing with the following subjects: Vol. I: Fundamentals of Plant Breeding, Vol. II: Breeding of Grain Species, Vol. III: Breeding of Tubers and Root Crop Plants, Vol. IV: Breeding of Forage Plants, Vol. V: Breeding of Special Cultivated Plants, Vol. VI: Breeding of Legumes and Fruits, Viniculture and Silviculture. – They are also available as single volumes. More details on request.

Zeitschrift für Pflanzenzüchtung
Journal of Plant Breeding

Founded in 1913 by C. FRUWIRTH. Edited by a great number of international authorities. Managing editors: Prof. Dr. W. HORN, Hannover, and Prof. Dr. G. RÖBBELEN, Göttingen.
Mode of publication: 8 issues annually (= 2 volumes), 4 issues are forming a volume. Annual subscription DM 556,– plus postage (1977).
Publication languages: German, English or French. Each original paper with two summaries: German and English or French.
A supplement series "Fortschritte der Pflanzenzüchtung – Advances in Plant Breeding" is being published irregularly.

Phytopathologische Zeitschrift
Journal of Phytopathology

Founded in 1930 by E. SCHAFFNIT. In collaboration with leading authorities edited by Prof. Dr. J. COLHOUN, Manchester, Prof. Dr. H. KERN, Zürich, Prof. Dr. Dr. h. c. H. RICHTER, Berlin. Mode of publication: 12 issues annually (= 3 volumes), 4 issues are forming a volume. Annual subscription DM 699,– plus postage (1977).
Publication languages: German, English, Italian or French. Each original paper with two summaries: German and English.
A supplement series "Acta Phytomedica" is being published irregularly.

Verlag Paul Parey
Berlin und Hamburg